CRITICAL REVIEWS™

QUARTERLY JOURNALS

CRITICAL REVIEWS in ANALYTICAL CHEMISTRY
Edited by Louis Meites, Ph.D., Chairman, Department of Chemistry, Clarkson College of Technology. Associate Editor, Gunter Zweig, Ph.D., Director, Life Sciences Division, Syracuse University Research Corp. Assistant Editor: Irving Sunshine, Ph.D., Chief Toxicologist, Cuyahoga County Coroner's Office, Ohio.

CRITICAL REVIEWS in CLINICAL LABORATORY SCIENCES
Edited by John W. King, M.D., Ph.D., Director of Clinical Laboratories, Cleveland Clinic Foundation, and Willard R. Faulkner, Ph.D., Vanderbilt University Medical Center.

CRITICAL REVIEWS in ENVIRONMENTAL CONTROL
Edited by Richard G. Bond, M.P.S., Director of Environmental Health, University of Minnesota, and Conrad P. Straub, Director, Environmental Health Research and Training Center, University of Minnesota.

CRITICAL REVIEWS in FOOD TECHNOLOGY
Edited by Thomas E. Furia, Technical Development Manager, Industrial Chemicals Division, Geigy Chemical Corporation.

CRITICAL REVIEWS in RADIOLOGICAL SCIENCES
Edited by Yen Wang, M.D., D.Sc., Chairman, Department of Radiology, Homestead Hospital, Pittsburgh.

CRITICAL REVIEWS in SOLID STATE SCIENCES
Edited by Donald E. Schuele, Ph.D., and Richard Hoffman, Ph.D., both of the Department of Physics, Case Western Reserve University.

CRC HANDBOOK SERIES

Handbook of Chemistry and Physics, 50th edition

Standard Mathematical Tables, 17th edition

Handbook of tables for Mathematics, 3rd edition

Handbook of tables for Organic Compound Identification, 3rd edition

Handbook of tables for Probability and Statistics, 2nd edition

Handbook of Clinical Laboratory Data, 2nd edition

Manual for Clinical Laboratory Procedures, 2nd edition

Handbook of Laboratory Safety, 1st edition

Handbook of Food Additives, 1st edition

Handbook of Biochemistry, selected data for Molecular Biology, 1st edition

Handbook of Radioactive Nuclides, 1st edition

Handbook of Analytical Toxicology, 1st edition

*Handbook of tables for Applied Engineering Science, 1st edition

*Handbook of Lasers and Laser Applications, 1st edition

*Handbook of Chromatography, 1st edition

*Handbook of Properties of Engineering Materials, 1st edition

*Handbook of Environmental Pollution Control, 1st edition

*CRC-Fenaroli Handbook of Flavors, 1st edition

*Handbook of Laboratory Animal Care, 1st edition

*Currently in preparation

Standard Mathematical Tables

Tables

Seventeenth Edition

Editor-in-chief of Mathematics

SAMUEL M. SELBY, Ph.D. Sc.D.

Distinguished Professor Emeritus of Mathematics and formerly Chairman,
Mathematics Department, University of Akron.
Presently Chairman, Mathematics Department, Hiram College, Hiram, Ohio

THE CHEMICAL RUBBER CO.

18901 Cranwood Parkway, Cleveland, Ohio 44128

Preface

The 17th Edition of the *CRC Standard Mathematical Tables* takes full advantage of the reorganized, rewritten, and enhanced sections instituted in the 15th and 16th Editions. The popular reception accorded by users of these latter editions convinces The Chemical Rubber Co. that its policy of keeping reference materials updated is a "must" and will be continued.

The sections on mensuration, trigonometry, analytic geometry, curves and graphs, the algebra of sets, determinants and matrices, expanded sections on statistics, and the inclusion of the hexadecimal and decimal conversion tables continue to be the strengths of this new 17th Edition.

To meet the many requests of teaching personnel, it has been decided to bring back a Five-place Logarithmic Table with proportional parts. It is hoped that this additional table will increase classroom effectiveness. One of the real conrtibutions is the inclusion of a reorganized and expanded Table of Integrals. One Hundred and Fifty useful integral formulas have been added in the 17th Edition. The Editorial Staff is indebted to Mr. R. L. Pratt, a member of the Advisory Board, who undertook this project. Other improvements in format and style of presentation of facts should be observed throughout this edition.

As in the past, the Editor takes this means of expressing appreciation to members of the Advisory Board, who are listed in the forefront of this edition, for their continued cooperation. Constructive suggestions from interested users of this edition as well as preceding ones are important and are welcome at all times since they serve as a feed-back which continually assists and guides the publication efforts of The Chemical Rubber Co. It helps to maintain the high degree of accuracy that the *CRC Standard Mathematical Tables* has enjoyed for its many editions.

SAMUEL M. SELBY, *Editor-in-Chief, Mathematics*
ROBERT C. WEAST, *Editor-in-Chief*

CONTENTS

Units for a System of Measures as used Internationally

Quantity Measured	Unit	Abbreviation
Length	meter	m
Mass	kilogram	kg
Time	second	s
Electric current	ampere	A
Temperature	degree Kelvin	°K
Luminous intensity	candela	cd

Supplementary and Derived Units
From Base Units
as used Internationally

Supplementary Units

Plane angle	radian	rad
Solid angle	steradian	sr

Derived Units

Quantity	Unit	Abbreviation	
Area	square meter	m^2	
Volume	cubic meter	m^3	
Frequency	hertz	Hz	(s^{-1})
Density	kilogram per cubic meter	kg/m^3	
Velocity	meter per second	m/s	
Angular velocity	radian per second	rad/s	
Acceleration	meter per second squared	m/s^2	
Angular acceleration	radian per second squared	rad/s^2	
Force	newton	N	$(kg \cdot m/s^2)$
Pressure	newton per sq meter	N/m^2	
Kinematic viscosity	sq meter per second	m^2/s	
Dynamic viscosity	newton-second per sq meter	$N \cdot s/m^2$	
Work, energy, quantity of heat	joule	J	$(N \cdot m)$
Power	watt	W	(J/s)
Electric charge	coulomb	C	$(A \cdot s)$
Voltage, potential difference, electromotive force	volt	V	(W/A)
Electric field strength	volt per meter	V/m	
Electric resistance	ohm	Ω	(V/A)
Electric capacitance	farad	F	$(A \cdot s/V)$
Magnetic flux	weber	Wb	$(V \cdot s)$
Inductance	henry	H	$(V \cdot s/A)$
Magnetic flux density	tesla	T	(Wb/m^2)
Magnetic field strength	ampere per meter	A/m	
Magnetomotive force	ampere	A	
Luminous flux	lumen	lm	$(cd \cdot sr)$
Luminance	candela per sq meter	cd/m^2	
Illumination	lux	lx	(lm/m^2)

1

Units of Measure

METRIC CONVERSION TABLE
Linear, Weight

Inches	Centimeters	Centimeters	Inches
1	2.54	1	0.393701
2	5.08	2	0.787402
3	7.62	3	1.181103
4	10.16	4	1.574804
5	12.70	5	1.968505
6	15.24	6	2.362206
7	17.78	7	2.755907
8	20.32	8	3.149608
9	22.86	9	3.543309
Feet	Meters	Meters	Feet
1	0.3048	1	3.280840
2	0.6096	2	6.561680
3	0.9144	3	9.842520
4	1.2192	4	13.123360
5	1.5240	5	16.404200
6	1.8288	6	19.685040
7	2.1336	7	22.965880
8	2.4384	8	26.246720
9	2.7432	9	29.527560
Yards	Meters	Meters	Yards
1	0.9144	1	1.0936133
2	1.8288	2	2.1872266
3	2.7432	3	3.2808399
4	3.6576	4	4.3744532
5	4.5720	5	5.4680665
6	5.4864	6	6.5616798
7	6.4008	7	7.6552931
8	7.3152	8	8.7489064
9	8.2296	9	9.8425197
Miles (Statute)	Kilometers	Kilometers	Miles
1	1.609344	1	0.6213712
2	3.218688	2	1.2427424
3	4.828032	3	1.8641136
4	6.437376	4	2.4854848
5	8.046720	5	3.1068560
6	9.656064	6	3.7282272
7	11.265408	7	4.3495984
8	12.874752	8	4.9709696
9	14.484096	9	5.5923408
Pounds (av)	Kilograms	Kilograms	Pounds (av)
1	0.45359237	1	2.2046226
2	0.90718474	2	4.4092452
3	1.36077711	3	6.6138678
4	1.81436948	4	8.8184904
5	2.26796185	5	11.0231130
6	2.72155422	6	13.2277356
7	3.17514659	7	15.4323582
8	3.62873896	8	17.6369808
9	4.08233133	9	19.8416034

CONVERSION FACTORS
U. S. AND METRIC UNITS

Each unit in bold face type is followed by its equivalent in other units of the same quantity.

Acre—0.0015625 square mile (statute); 4.3560 × 10⁴ square feet; 0.40468564 hectare.

Bushel—(**U.S.**)—1.244456 cubic feet; 2150.42 cubic inches; 0.035239 cubic meter; 35.23808 liters.

Centimeter—0.0328084 foot; 0.393701 inch.

Circular Mil—7.853982 × 10⁻⁷ square inches; 5.067075 × 10⁻⁶ square centimeters.

Cubic Centimeter—0.061024 cubic inch; 0.270512 dram (U. S. fluid); 16.230664 minims (U. S.); 0.999972 milliliter.

Cubic Foot—0.803564 bushel (U. S.); 7.480520 gallons (U. S. liquid); 0.028317 cubic meter; 28.31605 liters.

Cubic Inch—16.387064 cubic centimeters.

Cubic Meter—35.314667 cubic feet; 264.17205 gallons (U. S. liquid).

Foot—0.3048 meter.

Gallon (**U. S. liquid**)—0.1336816 cubic foot; 0.832675 gallon (British); 231 cubic inches; 0.0037854 cubic meter; 3.785306 liters.

Grain—0.06479891 gram.

Gram—0.00220462 pound (avoirdupois); 0.035274 ounce (avoirdupois); 15.432358 grains.

Hectare—2.471054 acres; 1.07639 × 10⁵ square feet.

Inch—2.54 centimeters.

Kilogram—2.204623 pounds (avoirdupois).

Kilometer—0.621371 mile (statute).

Liter—0.264179 gallon (U. S. liquid); 0.0353157 cubic foot; 1.056718 quarts (U. S. liquid).

Meter—1.093613 yards; 3.280840 feet; 39.37008 inches.

Mile (statute)—1.609344 kilometers.

Ounce (U. S. fluid)—1.804688 cubic inches; 29.573730 cubic centimeters.

Ounce (avoirdupois)—28.349523 grams.

Ounce (apothecary or troy)—31.103486 grams.

Pint (U. S. liquid)—0.473163 liter; 473.17647 cubic centimeters.

Pound (avoirdupois)—0.453592 kilogram; 453.59237 grams.

Pound (apothecary or troy)—0.3732417 kilogram, 373.24172 grams.

Quart (U. S. dry)—1.10119 liters.

Quart (liquid)—0.946326 liter.

Radian—57.295779 degrees.

Rod—5.0292 meters.

Square Centimeter—0.155000 square inch.

Square Foot—0.09290304 square meter.

Square Inch—645.16 square millimeters.

Square Meter—10.763910 square feet.

Square Yard—0.836127 square meter.

Ton (short)—907.18474 kilograms.

Yard—0.9144 meter.

See Index for extensive Conversion Factors.

RECOMMENDED UNIT PREFIXES

Multiples and submultiples	Prefixes	Symbols
10^{12}	tera	T
10^{9}	giga	G
10^{6}	mega	M
10^{3}	kilo	k
10^{2}	hecto	h
10	deka	da
10^{-1}	deci	d
10^{-2}	centi	c
10^{-3}	milli	m
10^{-6}	micro	μ (greek mu)
10^{-9}	nano	n
10^{-12}	pico	p
10^{-15}	femto	f
10^{-18}	atto	a

DEFINED VALUES AND EQUIVALENTS

Meter .... **(m)**
1 650 763.73 wave lengths in vacuo of the unperturbed transition $2p_{10} - 5d_5$ in ^{86}Kr

Kilogram .... **(kg)**
mass of the international kilogram at Sèvres, France

Second .... **(s)**
1/31 556 925.974 7 of the tropical year at 12^{h} ET, 0 January 1900

Degree Kelvin .... **(°K)**
defined in the thermodynamic scale by assigning 273.16°K to the triple point of water (freezing point, 273.15°K = 0°C)

Unified atomic mass unit .... **(u)**
1/12 the mass of an atom of the ^{12}C nuclide

Mole .... **(mol)**
amount of substance containing the same number of atoms as 12 g of pure ^{12}C

Standard acceleration of free fall .... **(g_n)**
9.806 65 M s^{-2}, 980.665 cm s^{-2}

Normal atmospheric pressure .... **(atm)**
101 325 N m^{-2}, 1 013 250 dyn cm^{-2}

Thermochemical calorie .... **(cal_th)**
4.1840 J, 4.1840 $\times$ 10^7 erg

International Steam Table calorie .... **(cal_IT)**
4.1868 J, 4.1868 $\times$ 10^7 erg

Liter .... **(l)**
0.001 000 028 m^3, 1 000.028 cm^3 (recommended by CIPM, 1950)

0.001 m^3, 1000 cm^3 (recommended by GCWM 1964)

Inch .... **(in)**
0.0254 m, 2.54 cm

Pound (avdp) .... **(lb)**
0.453 592 37 kg, 453.592 37 g

The mass of the body is indicated by m.

Body	Axis	Moment of inertia
Uniform thin rod	Normal to the length, at one end	$m\dfrac{l^2}{3}$
Uniform thin rod	Normal to the length, at the center	$m\dfrac{l^2}{12}$
Thin rectangular sheet, sides a and b	Through the center parallel to b	$m\dfrac{a^2}{12}$
Thin rectangular sheet, sides a and b	Through the center perpendicular to the sheet	$m\dfrac{a^2 + b^2}{12}$
Thin circular sheet of radius r	Normal to the plate through the center	$m\dfrac{r^2}{2}$
Thin circular sheet of radius r	Along any diameter	$m\dfrac{r^2}{4}$
Thin circular ring. Radii r_1 and r_2	Through center normal to plane of ring	$m\dfrac{r_1^2 + r_2^2}{2}$
Thin circular ring. Radii r_1 and r_2	Any diameter	$m\dfrac{r_1^2 + r_2^2}{4}$
Rectangular parallelopiped, edges a, b, and c	Through center perpendicular to face ab, (parallel to edge c)	$m\dfrac{a^2 + b^2}{12}$
Sphere, radius r	Any diameter	$m\dfrac{2}{5}r^2$
Spherical shell, external radius, r_1, internal radius r_2	Any diameter	$m\dfrac{2}{5}\dfrac{(r_1^5 - r_2^5)}{(r_1^3 - r_2^3)}$
Spherical shell, very thin, mean radius, r	Any diameter	$m\dfrac{2}{3}r^2$
Right circular cylinder of radius r, length l	The longitudinal axis of the solid	$m\dfrac{r^2}{2}$
Right circular cylinder of radius r, length l	Transverse diameter	$m\left(\dfrac{r^2}{4} + \dfrac{l^2}{12}\right)$
Hollow circular cylinder, length l, radii r_1 and r_2	The longitudinal axis of the figure	$m\dfrac{(r_1^2 + r_2^2)}{2}$
Thin cylindrical shell, length l, mean radius, r	The longitudinal axis of the figure	mr^2
Hollow circular cylinder, length l, radii r_1 and r_2	Transverse diameter	$m\left[\dfrac{r_1^2 + r_2^2}{4} + \dfrac{l^2}{12}\right]$
Hollow circular cylinder, length l, very thin, mean radius	Transverse diameter	$m\left(\dfrac{r^2}{2} + \dfrac{l^2}{12}\right)$
Elliptic cylinder, length l, transverse semiaxes a and b	Longitudinal axis	$m\left(\dfrac{a^2 + b^2}{4}\right)$
Right cone, altitude h, radius of base r	Axis of the figure	$m\dfrac{3}{10}r^2$
Spheroid of revolution, equatorial radius r	Polar axis	$m\dfrac{2r^2}{5}$
Ellipsoid, axes $2a$, $2b$, $2c$	Axis $2a$	$m\dfrac{(b^2 + c^2)}{5}$

NUMBERS CONTAINING π

	Number	Logarithm		Number	Logarithm
π	3.1415 927	0.4971 499	$2\pi^2$	19.7392 088	1.2953 297
2π	6.2831 853	0.7981 799	$\pi/180$	0.0174 533	8.2418 774 − 10
3π	9.4247 780	0.9742 711	$180/\pi$	57.2957 795	1.7581 226
4π	12.5663 706	1.0992 099	$4\pi^2$	39.4784 176	1.5963 597
8π	25.1327 412	1.4002 399	$1/\pi^2$	0.1013 212	9.0057 003 − 10
$\pi/2$	1.5707 963	0.1961 199	$1/(2\pi^2)$	0.0506 606	8.7046 703 − 10
$\pi/3$	1.0471 976	0.0200 286	$1/(4\pi^2)$	0.0253 303	8.4036 403 − 10
$\pi/4$	0.7853 982	9.8950 899 − 10	$\sqrt{\pi}$	1.7724 539	0.2485 749
$\pi/6$	0.5235 988	9.7189 986 − 10	$\sqrt{\pi}/4$ or $\sqrt{\pi}/2$	0.8862 269	9.9475 449 − 10
$\pi/8$	0.3926 991	9.5940 599 − 10	$\sqrt{\pi/4}$	0.4431 135	9.6465 149 − 10
$2\pi/3$	2.0943 951	0.3210 586	$\sqrt{\pi/2}$	1.2533 141	0.0980 599
$4\pi/3$	4.1887 902	0.6220 886	$\sqrt{2/\pi}$	0.7978 846	9.9019 401 − 10
$1/\pi$	0.3183 099	9.5028 501 − 10	π^3	31.0062 767	1.4914 496
$2/\pi$	0.6366 198	9.8038 801 − 10	$\sqrt[3]{\pi}$	1.4645 919	0.1657 166
$4/\pi$	1.2732 395	0.1049 101	$1/\sqrt[3]{\pi}$	0.6827 841	9.8342 834 − 10
$1/(2\pi)$	0.1591 549	9.2018 201 − 10	$\sqrt[3]{\pi^2}$	2.1450 294	0.3314 332
$1/(4\pi)$	0.0795 775	8.9007 901 − 10	$1/\sqrt{\pi}$	0.5641 896	9.7514 251 − 10
$1/(6\pi)$	0.0530 516	8.7246 989 − 10	$1/\sqrt{2\pi}$	0.3989 423	9.6009 101 − 10
$1/(8\pi)$	0.0397 887	8.5997 601 − 10	$2/\sqrt{\pi}$	1.1283 792	0.0524 551
π^2	9.8696 044	0.9942 997			

MULTIPLES OF $\dfrac{\pi}{2}$

n	$n\dfrac{\pi}{2}$	n	$n\dfrac{\pi}{2}$	n	$n\dfrac{\pi}{2}$	n	$n\dfrac{\pi}{2}$
1	1.57079 63268	26	40.84070 44967	51	80.11061 26665	76	119.38052 08364
2	3.14159 26536	27	42.41150 08235	52	81.68140 89933	77	120.95131 71632
3	4.71238 89804	28	43.98229 71503	53	83.25220 53201	78	122.52211 34900
4	6.28318 53072	29	45.55309 34771	54	84.82300 16469	79	124.09290 98168
5	7.85398 16340	30	47.12388 98038	55	86.39379 79737	80	125.66370 61436
6	9.42477 79608	31	48.69468 61306	56	87.96459 43005	81	127.23450 24704
7	10.99557 42876	32	50.26548 24574	57	89.53539 06273	82	128.80529 87972
8	12.56637 06144	33	51.83627 87842	58	91.10618 69541	83	130.37609 51240
9	14.13716 69412	34	53.40707 51110	59	92.67698 32809	84	131.94689 14508
10	15.70796 32679	35	54.97787 14378	60	94.24777 96077	85	133.51768 77776
11	17.27875 95947	36	56.54866 77646	61	95.81857 59345	86	135.08848 41044
12	18.84955 59215	37	58.11946 40914	62	97.38937 22613	87	136.65928 04312
13	20.42035 22483	38	59.69026 04182	63	98.96016 85881	88	138.23007 67580
14	21.99114 85751	39	61.26105 67450	64	100.53096 49149	89	139.80087 30847
15	23.56194 49019	40	62.83185 30718	65	102.10176 12417	90	141.37166 94115
16	25.13274 12287	41	64.40264 93986	66	103.67255 75685	91	142.94246 57383
17	26.70353 75555	42	65.97344 57254	67	105.24335 38953	92	144.51326 20651
18	28.27433 38823	43	67.54424 20522	68	106.81415 02221	93	146.08405 83919
19	29.84513 02091	44	69.11503 83790	69	108.38494 65488	94	147.65485 47187
20	31.41592 65359	45	70.68583 47058	70	109.95574 28756	95	149.22565 10455
21	32.98672 28627	46	72.25663 10326	71	111.52653 92024	96	150.79644 73723
22	34.55751 91895	47	73.82742 73594	72	113.09733 55292	97	152.36724 36991
23	36.12831 55163	48	75.39822 36862	73	114.66813 18560	98	153.93804 00259
24	37.69911 18431	49	76.96902 00129	74	116.23892 81828	99	155.50883 63527
25	39.26990 81699	50	78.53981 63397	75	117.80972 45096	100	157.07963 26795

MISCELLANEOUS CONSTANTS

π CONSTANTS

$$\pi = 3.14159\ 26535\ 89793\ 23846\ 26433\ 83279\ 50288\ 41971\ 69399\ 37510$$
$$1/\pi = 0.31830\ 98861\ 83790\ 67153\ 77675\ 26745\ 02872\ 40689\ 19291\ 48091$$
$$\pi^2 = 9.86960\ 44010\ 89358\ 61883\ 44909\ 99876\ 15113\ 53136\ 99407\ 24079$$
$$\log_e \pi = 1.14472\ 98858\ 49400\ 17414\ 34273\ 51353\ 05871\ 16472\ 94812\ 91531$$
$$\log_{10} \pi = 0.49714\ 98726\ 94133\ 85435\ 12682\ 88290\ 89887\ 36516\ 78324\ 38044$$
$$\log_{10} \sqrt{2\pi} = 0.39908\ 99341\ 79057\ 52478\ 25035\ 91507\ 69595\ 02099\ 34102\ 92127$$

CONSTANTS INVOLVING e

$$e = 2.71828\ 18284\ 59045\ 23536\ 02874\ 71352\ 66249\ 77572\ 47093\ 69995$$
$$1/e = 0.36787\ 94411\ 71442\ 32159\ 55237\ 70161\ 46086\ 74458\ 11131\ 03176$$
$$e^2 = 7.38905\ 60989\ 30650\ 22723\ 04274\ 60575\ 00781\ 31803\ 15570\ 55184$$
$$M = \log_{10} e = 0.43429\ 44819\ 03251\ 82765\ 11289\ 18916\ 60508\ 22943\ 97005\ 80366$$
$$1/M = \log_e 10 = 2.30258\ 50929\ 94045\ 68401\ 79914\ 54684\ 36420\ 76011\ 01488\ 62877$$
$$\log_{10} M = 9.63778\ 43113\ 00536\ 78912\ 29674\ 98565 - 10$$

π^e AND e^π CONSTANTS

$$\pi^e = 22.45915\ 77183\ 61045\ 47342\ 71522$$
$$e^\pi = 23.14069\ 26327\ 79269\ 00572\ 90864$$
$$e^{-\pi} = 0.04321\ 39182\ 63772\ 24977\ 44177$$
$$e^{\frac{1}{2}\pi} = 4.81047\ 73809\ 65351\ 65547\ 30357$$
$$i^i = e^{-\frac{1}{2}\pi} = 0.20787\ 95763\ 50761\ 90854\ 69556$$

NUMERICAL CONSTANTS

$$\sqrt{2} = 1.41421\ 35623\ 73095\ 04880\ 16887\ 24209\ 69807\ 85696\ 71875\ 37694$$
$$\sqrt[3]{2} = 1.25992\ 10498\ 94873\ 16476\ 72106\ 07278\ 22835\ 05702\ 51464\ 70150$$
$$\log_e 2 = 0.69314\ 71805\ 59945\ 30941\ 72321\ 21458\ 17656\ 80755\ 00134\ 36025$$
$$\log_{10} 2 = 0.30102\ 99956\ 63981\ 19521\ 37388\ 94724\ 49302\ 67681\ 89881\ 46210$$
$$\sqrt{3} = 1.73205\ 08075\ 68877\ 29352\ 74463\ 41505\ 87236\ 69428\ 05253\ 81038$$
$$\sqrt[3]{3} = 1.44224\ 95703\ 07408\ 38232\ 16383\ 10780\ 10958\ 83918\ 69253\ 49935$$
$$\log_e 3 = 1.09861\ 22886\ 68109\ 69139\ 52452\ 36922\ 52570\ 46474\ 90557\ 82274$$
$$\log_{10} 3 = 0.47712\ 12547\ 19662\ 43729\ 50279\ 03255\ 11530\ 92001\ 28864\ 19069$$

OTHER CONSTANTS

$$\text{Euler's Constant } \gamma = 0.57721\ 56649\ 01532\ 86061$$
$$\log_e \gamma = -0.54953\ 93129\ 81644\ 82234$$
$$\text{Golden Ratio } \phi = 1.61803\ 39887\ 49894\ 84820\ 45868\ 34365\ 63811\ 77203\ 09180$$

MISCELLANEOUS CONSTANTS (Continued)

PHYSICAL CONSTANTS

Equatorial radius of the earth = 6378.388 km = 3963.34 miles (statute).
Polar radius of the earth, 6356.912 km = 3949.99 miles (statute).
1 degree of latitude at 40° = 69 miles.
1 international nautical mile = 1.15078 miles (statute) = 1852 m = 6076.115 ft.
Mean density of the earth = 5.522 g/cm^3 = 344.7 lb/ft^3.
Constant of gravitation, $(6.673 \pm 0.003) \times 10^{-8}$ cm^3/g × sec^2.
Acceleration due to gravity at sea level, latitude 45° = 980.621 cm/sec^2 = 32.1725 ft/sec^2.
Length of seconds pendulum at sea level, latitude 45° = 99.3574 cm = 39.1171 in.
1 knot (international) = 101.269 ft/min = 1.6878 ft/sec = 1.1508 miles (statute)/hr.
1 micron = 10^{-4} cm.
1 ångstrom = 10^{-8} cm.
Mass of hydrogen atom = $(1.67339 \pm 0.00031) \times 10^{-24}$ g.
Avogadro's number = $(6.02257 \pm 0.00009) \times 10^{23}$/g mole.
Planck's constant = $(6.62554 \pm 0.00015) \times 10^{-27}$ erg-sec.
Density of mercury at 0°C = 13.5955 g/ml.
Density of water at 3.98°C = 1.000000 g/ml.
Density, maximum, of water, at 3.98°C = 0.999973 g/cm^3.
Density of dry air at 0°C, 760 mm = 1.2929 g/liter.
Velocity of sound in dry air at 0°C = 331.36 m/sec = 1087.1 ft/sec.
Velocity of light in vacuum = $(2.997925 \pm 0.000002) \times 10^{10}$ cm/sec.
Heat of fusion of water 0°C = 79.71 cal/g.
Heat of vaporization of water 100°C = 539.55 cal/g.
Electrochemical equivalent of silver 0.001118 g/sec international amp.
Absolute wave length of red cadmium light in air at 15°C, 760 mm pressure = 6438.4696 A.
Wave length of orange-red line of krypton 86 = 6057.802 A.
Gas Constant = $(8.31432 \pm 0.00034) \times 10^7$ erg (g mole)$^{-1}$ deg^{-1}.

DECIMAL EQUIVALENTS OF COMMON FRACTIONS

		1/64	=	0.015 625				11/32	22/64	=	0.343 75						43/64	=	0.671 875
	1/32	2/64	=	.031 25					23/64	=	.359 375	11/16	22/32	44/64	=	.687 5
		3/64	=	.046 875	3/8	12/32	24/64	=	.375							45/64	=	.703 125
1/16	2/32	4/64	=	.062 5			25/64	=	.390 625		23/32	46/64	=	.718 75
		5/64	=	.078 125		13/32	26/64	=	.406 25							47/64	=	.734 375
	3/32	6/64	=	.093 75			27/64	=	.421 875	3/4	24/32	48/64	=	.75
		7/64	=	.109 375	7/16	14/32	28/64	=	.437 5							49/64	=	.765 625
1/8	4/32	8/64	=	.125			29/64	=	.453 125		25/32	50/64	=	.781 25
		9/64	=	.140 625		15/32	30/64	=	.468 75							51/64	=	.796 875
	5/32	10/64	=	.156 25			31/64	=	.484 375	13/16	26/32	52/64	=	.812 5
		11/64	=	.171 875	1/2	16/32	32/64	=	.50							53/64	=	.828 125
3/16	6/32	12/64	=	.187 5			33/64	=	.515 625		27/32	54/64	=	.843 75
		13/64	=	.203 125		17/32	34/64	=	.531 25							55/64	=	.859 375
	7/32	14/64	=	.218 75			35/64	=	.546 875	7/8	28/32	56/64	=	.875
		15/64	=	.234 375	9/16	18/32	36/64	=	.562 5							57/64	=	.890 625
1/4	8/32	16/64	=	.25			37/64	=	.578 125		29/32	58/64	=	.906 25
		17/64	=	.265 625		19/32	38/64	=	.593 75							59/64	=	.921 875
	9/32	18/64	=	.281 25			39/64	=	.609 375	15/16	30/32	60/64	=	.937 5
		19/64	=	.296 875	5/8	20/32	40/64	=	.625							61/64	=	.953 125
5/16	10/32	20/64	=	.312 5			41/64	=	.640 625		31/32	62/64	=	.968 75
		21/64	=	.328 125		21/32	42/64	=	.656 25							63/64	=	.984 375

MENSURATION FORMULAE

Dr. Howard Eves

TRIANGLES

In the following: K = area, r = radius of the inscribed circle, R = radius of the circumscribed circle.

Right Triangle

$A + B = C = 90°$
$c^2 = a^2 + b^2$ (*Pythagorean relation*)
$a = \sqrt{(c + b)(c - b)}$
$K = \frac{1}{2}ab$

$r = \dfrac{ab}{a + b + c}$, $\quad R = \frac{1}{2}c$

$h = \dfrac{ab}{c}$, $\quad m = \dfrac{b^2}{c}$, $\quad n = \dfrac{a^2}{c}$

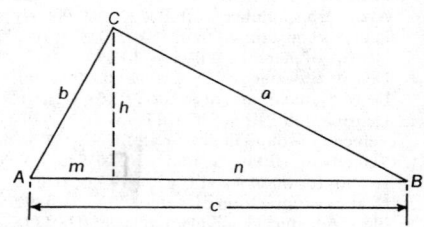

Equilateral Triangle

$A = B = C = 60°$
$K = \frac{1}{4}a^2\sqrt{3}$
$r = \frac{1}{6}a\sqrt{3}$, $\quad R = \frac{1}{3}a\sqrt{3}$
$h = \frac{1}{2}a\sqrt{3}$

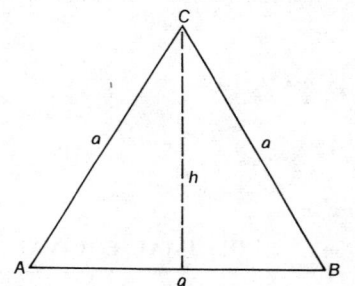

General Triangle

Let $s = \frac{1}{2}(a + b + c)$, h_c = length of altitude on side c, t_c = length of bisector of angle C, m_c = length of median to side c.

$A + B + C = 180°$
$c^2 = a^2 + b^2 - 2ab \cos C$

$\qquad$ (*law of cosines*)

$K = \frac{1}{2}h_c c = \frac{1}{2}ab \sin C$

$\quad = \dfrac{c^2 \sin A \sin B}{2 \sin C}$

$\quad = rs = \dfrac{abc}{4R}$

$\quad = \sqrt{s(s - a)(s - b)(s - c)}$ (*Heron's formula*)

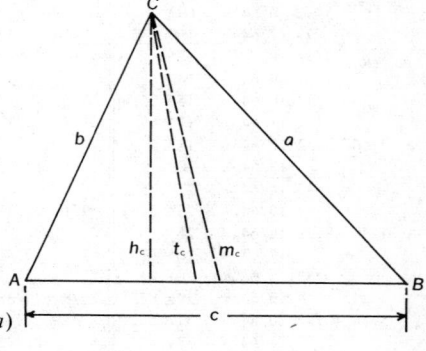

8

$$r = c \sin \frac{A}{2} \sin \frac{B}{2} \sec \frac{C}{2} = \frac{ab \sin C}{2s} = (s - c) \tan \frac{C}{2}$$

$$= \sqrt{\frac{(s - a)(s - b)(s - c)}{s}} = \frac{K}{s} = 4R \sin \frac{A}{2} \sin \frac{B}{2} \sin \frac{C}{2}$$

$$R = \frac{c}{2 \sin C} = \frac{abc}{4 \sqrt{s(s - a)(s - b)(s - c)}} = \frac{abc}{4K}$$

$$h_c = a \sin B = b \sin A = \frac{2K}{c}$$

$$t_c = \frac{2ab}{a + b} \cos \frac{C}{2} = \sqrt{ab \left\{ 1 - \frac{c^2}{(a + b)^2} \right\}}$$

$$m_c = \sqrt{\frac{a^2}{2} + \frac{b^2}{2} - \frac{c^2}{4}}$$

 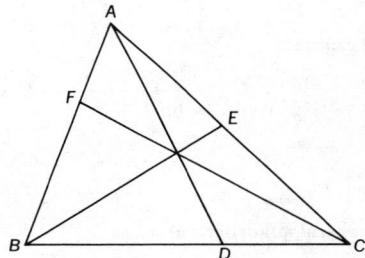

Menelaus' Theorem.   A necessary and sufficient condition for points *D, E, F* on the respective side lines *BC, CA, AB* of a triangle *ABC* to be collinear is that

$$BD \cdot CE \cdot AF = - DC \cdot EA \cdot FB,$$

where all segments in the formula are directed segments.

Ceva's Theorem.   A necessary and sufficient condition for *AD, BE, CF,* where *D, E, F* are points on the respective side lines *BC, CA, AB* of a triangle *ABC*, to be concurrent is that

$$BD \cdot CE \cdot AF = + DC \cdot EA \cdot FB,$$

where all segments in the formula are directed segments.

QUADRILATERALS

In the following: K = area, p and q are diagonals.

Rectangle

$$A = B = C = D = 90°$$
$$K = ab, \quad p = \sqrt{a^2 + b^2}$$

Parallelogram

$A = C$, $\quad B = D$, $\quad A + B = 180°$
$K = bh = ab \sin A = ab \sin B$
$h = a \sin A = a \sin B$
$p = \sqrt{a^2 + b^2 - 2ab \cos A}$
$q = \sqrt{a^2 + b^2 - 2ab \cos B} = \sqrt{a^2 + b^2 + 2ab \cos A}$

Rhombus

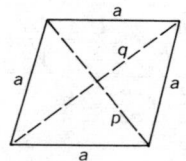

$p^2 + q^2 = 4a^2$
$K = \frac{1}{2}pq$

Trapezoid

$m = \frac{1}{2}(a + b)$
$K = \frac{1}{2}(a + b)h = mh$

General quadrilateral

Let $s = \frac{1}{2}(a + b + c + d)$.
$$
\begin{aligned}
K &= \tfrac{1}{2}pq \sin \theta \\
&= \tfrac{1}{4}(b^2 + d^2 - a^2 - c^2) \tan \theta \\
&= \tfrac{1}{4}\sqrt{4p^2q^2 - (b^2 + d^2 - a^2 - c^2)^2} \\
&\qquad \quad (Bretschneider's\ formula) \\
&= \sqrt{(s - a)(s - b)(s - c)(s - d) - abcd \cos^2\left(\frac{A + B}{2}\right)}
\end{aligned}
$$

Theorem. The diagonals of a quadrilateral with consecutive sides a, b, c, d are perpendicular if and only if $a^2 + c^2 = b^2 + d^2$.

Cyclic Quadrilateral

Let R = radius of the circumscribed circle.
$A + C = B + D = 180°$
$$
K = \sqrt{(s - a)(s - b)(s - c)(s - d)}
$$
$$(Brahmagupta's\ formula)$$
$$
= \frac{\sqrt{(ac + bd)(ad + bc)(ab + cd)}}{4R}
$$
$$
p = \sqrt{\frac{(ac + bd)(ab + cd)}{ad + bc}}, \quad q = \sqrt{\frac{(ac + bd)(ad + bc)}{ab + cd}}
$$
$$
R = \frac{1}{2}\sqrt{\frac{(ac + bd)(ad + bc)(ab + cd)}{(s - a)(s - b)(s - c)(s - d)}}, \quad \sin \theta = \frac{2K}{ac + bd}
$$

Ptolemy's Theorem. A convex quadrilateral with consecutive sides a, b, c, d and diagonals p and q is cyclic if and only if $ac + bd = pq$.

Cyclic-inscriptable Quadrilateral

Let r = radius of the inscribed circle, R = radius of the circumscribed circle, m = distance between the centers of the inscribed and the circumscribed circles.

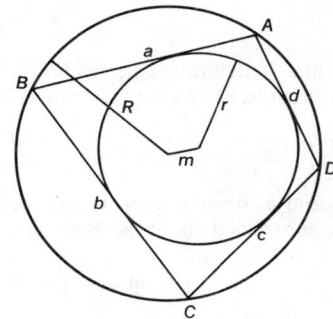

$$A + C = B + D = 180°$$
$$a + c = b + d$$
$$K = \sqrt{abcd}$$
$$\frac{1}{(R - m)^2} + \frac{1}{(R + m)^2} = \frac{1}{r^2}$$
$$r = \frac{\sqrt{abcd}}{s}$$
$$R = \tfrac{1}{2} \sqrt{\frac{(ac + bd)(ad + bc)(ab + cd)}{abcd}}$$

REGULAR POLYGONS

In the following: n = number of sides, s = length of each side, p = perimeter, θ = one of the vertex angles, r = radius of the inscribed circle, R = radius of the circumscribed circle, K = area.

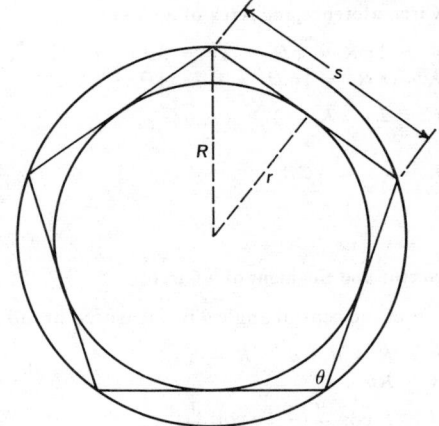

$$\theta = \left(\frac{n - 2}{n}\right) 180°$$
$$s = 2r \tan \frac{180°}{n} = 2R \sin \frac{180°}{n}$$
$$p = ns$$
$$K = \tfrac{1}{4} n s^2 \cot \frac{180°}{n}$$
$$= n r^2 \tan \frac{180°}{n}$$
$$= \tfrac{1}{2} n R^2 \sin \frac{360°}{n}$$
$$r = \tfrac{1}{2} s \cot \frac{180°}{n}, \quad R = \tfrac{1}{2} s \csc \frac{180°}{n}$$

Polygon	n	K	r	R
Triangle (equilateral)	3	$0.43301s^2$	$0.28867s$	$0.57735s$
Square	4	$1.00000s^2$	$0.50000s$	$0.70710s$
Pentagon	5	$1.72048s^2$	$0.68819s$	$0.85065s$
Hexagon	6	$2.59808s^2$	$0.86602s$	$1.00000s$
Heptagon	7	$3.63391s^2$	$1.0383s$	$1.1523s$
Octagon	8	$4.82843s^2$	$1.2071s$	$1.3065s$
Nonagon	9	$6.18182s^2$	$1.3737s$	$1.4619s$
Decagon	10	$7.69421s^2$	$1.5388s$	$1.6180s$
Undecagon	11	$9.36564s^2$	$1.7028s$	$1.7747s$
Dodecagon	12	$11.19615s^2$	$1.8660s$	$1.9318s$

If s_k denotes the side of a regular polygon of k sides inscribed in a circle of radius R, then

$$s_{2n} = \sqrt{2R^2 - R\sqrt{4R^2 - s_n^2}}.$$

If S_k denotes the side of a regular polygon of k sides circumscribed about a circle of radius r, then

$$S_{2n} = \frac{2rS_n}{2r + \sqrt{4r^2 + S_n^2}}$$

If p_k and P_k denote, respectively, the perimeters of regular polygons of k sides inscribed in and circumscribed about the same circle, then

$$P_{2n} = \frac{2p_n P_n}{p_n + P_n} \quad \text{and} \quad p_{2n} = \sqrt{p_n P_{2n}}.$$

If a_k and A_k denote, respectively, the areas of regular polygons of k sides inscribed in and circumscribed about the same circle, then

$$a_{2n} = \sqrt{a_n A_n} \quad \text{and} \quad A_{2n} = \frac{2a_{2n} A_n}{a_{2n} + A_n}.$$

CIRCLES

In the following: R = radius, D = diameter, C = circumference, K = area.

Circumference and Area of a Circle

$$C = 2\pi R = \pi D \qquad (\pi = 3.14159\cdots)$$
$$K = \pi R^2 = \tfrac{1}{4}\pi D^2 = 0.7854D^2$$
$$C = 2\sqrt{\pi K} = \frac{2K}{R}$$
$$K = \frac{C^2}{4\pi} = \tfrac{1}{2}CR$$

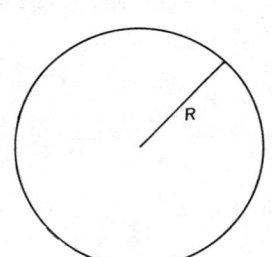

Sector and Segment of a Circle

Let the central angle θ be measured in radians ($\theta < \pi$).

$$h = R - d, \quad d = R - h$$
$$s = R\theta$$
$$d = R\cos\frac{\theta}{2} = \tfrac{1}{2}c\cot\frac{\theta}{2}$$
$$\quad = \tfrac{1}{2}\sqrt{4R^2 - c^2}$$
$$c = 2R\sin\frac{\theta}{2} = 2d\tan\frac{\theta}{2}$$
$$\quad = 2\sqrt{R^2 - d^2} = \sqrt{4h(2R - h)}$$
$$\theta = \frac{s}{R} = 2\,\mathrm{Cos}^{-1}\frac{d}{R} = 2\,\mathrm{Tan}^{-1}\frac{c}{2d} = 2\,\mathrm{Sin}^{-1}\frac{c}{2R}$$
$$K\,(\text{sector}) = \tfrac{1}{2}Rs = \tfrac{1}{2}R^2\theta$$
$$K\,(\text{segment}) = \tfrac{1}{2}R^2(\theta - \sin\theta) = \tfrac{1}{2}(Rs - cd) = R^2\,\mathrm{Cos}^{-1}\frac{d}{R} - d\sqrt{R^2 - d^2}$$
$$\quad = R^2\,\mathrm{Cos}^{-1}\frac{R - h}{R} - (R - h)\sqrt{2Rh - h^2}$$

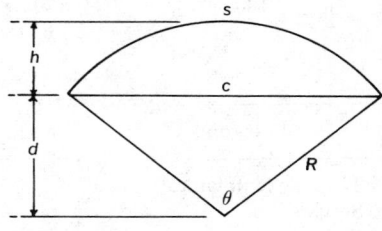

Sector of an Annulus

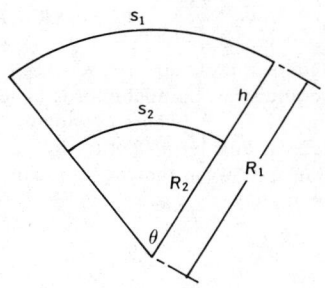

$$h = R_1 - R_2$$
$$K = \tfrac{1}{2}\theta(R_1 + R_2)(R_1 - R_2)$$
$$= \tfrac{1}{2}\theta h(R_1 + R_2)$$
$$= \tfrac{1}{2}h(s_1 + s_2)$$

CONIC SECTIONS

Ellipse

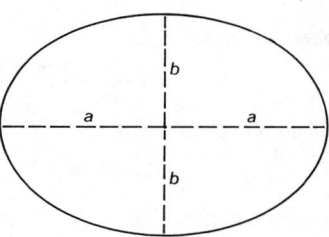

Let p = circumference, K = area

$$p = 2\pi \sqrt{\frac{a^2 + b^2}{2}} \quad \text{(approximately)}$$

$$= 4aE \quad \text{(exactly)} \quad \begin{array}{l}\text{See table of elliptic integral} \\ \text{for } E, \text{ using } k = \sqrt{a^2 - b^2}/a.\end{array}$$

$$K = \pi ab$$

Parabolic Segment

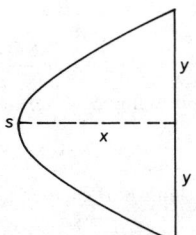

$$s = \sqrt{4x^2 + y^2} + \frac{y^2}{2x} \log_e\left[\frac{2x + \sqrt{4x^2 + y^2}}{y}\right]$$

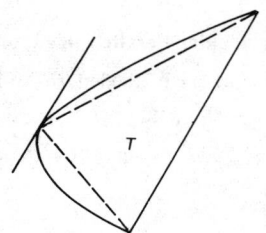

K (right segment) = $\tfrac{4}{3}xy$

K (oblique segment) = $\tfrac{4}{3}T$, where T is the area of the triangle with base along the chord of the segment and with opposite vertex at the point on the parabola at which the tangent to the parabola is parallel to the chord of the segment.

CAVALIERI'S THEOREM FOR THE PLANE

If two planar areas are included between a pair of parallel lines, and if the two segments cut off by the areas on any line parallel to the including lines are equal in length, then the two planar areas are equal.

PLANAR AREAS BY APPROXIMATION

Divide the planar area K into n strips by equidistant parallel chords of lengths $y_0, y_1, y_2, \ldots, y_n$ (where y_0 and/or y_n may be zero), and let h denote the common distance between the chords. Then, approximately:

Trapezoidal Rule

$$K = h(\tfrac{1}{2}y_0 + y_1 + y_2 + \cdots + y_{n-1} + \tfrac{1}{2}y_n)$$

Durand's Rule

$$K = h(\tfrac{4}{10}y_0 + \tfrac{11}{10}y_1 + y_2 + y_3 + \cdots + y_{n-2} + \tfrac{11}{10}y_{n-1} + \tfrac{4}{10}y_n)$$

Simpson's rule (*n* even)

$$K = \tfrac{1}{3}h(y_0 + 4y_1 + 2y_2 + 4y_3 + 2y_4 + \cdots + 2y_{n-2} + 4y_{n-1} + y_n)$$

Weddle's Rule ($n = 6$)

$$K = \tfrac{3}{10}h(y_0 + 5y_1 + y_2 + 6y_3 + y_4 + 5y_5 + y_6)$$

SOLIDS BOUNDED BY PLANES

In the following: S = lateral surface, T = total surface, V = volume.

Cube

Let a = length of each edge.

$$T = 6a^2, \quad \text{diagonal of face} = a\sqrt{2}$$
$$V = a^3, \quad \text{diagonal of cube} = a\sqrt{3}$$

Rectangular Parallelepiped (or box)

Let a, b, c be the lengths of its edges.

$$T = 2(ab + bc + ca), \quad V = abc$$
$$\text{diagonal} = \sqrt{a^2 + b^2 + c^2}$$

Prism

$$S = \text{(perimeter of right section)} \times \text{(lateral edge)}$$
$$V = \text{(area of right section)} \times \text{(lateral edge)}$$
$$= \text{(area of base)} \times \text{(altitude)}$$

Truncated Triangular Prism

$$V = \text{(area of right section)} \times \tfrac{1}{3}\text{(sum of the three lateral edges)}$$

Pyramid

S of regular pyramid = $\frac{1}{2}$ (perimeter of base) × (slant height)

$V = \frac{1}{3}$ (area of base) × (altitude)

Frustum of Pyramid

Let B_1 = area of lower base, B_2 = area of upper base, h = altitude.

S of regular figure = $\frac{1}{2}$ (sum of perimeters of bases) × (slant height)

$V = \frac{1}{3}h(B_1 + B_2 + \sqrt{B_1 B_2})$

Prismatoid

A *prismatoid* is a polyhedron having for bases two polygons in parallel planes, and for lateral faces triangles or trapezoids with one side lying in one base, and the opposite vertex or side lying in the other base, of the polyhedron. Let B_1 = area of lower base, M = area of midsection, B_2 = area of upper base, h = altitude.

$$V = \frac{1}{6}h(B_1 + 4M + B_2) \quad \text{(the } prismoidal\ formula)$$

Note: Since cubes, rectangular parallelepipeds, prisms, pyramids, and frustums of pyramids are all examples of prismatoids, the formula for the volume of a prismatoid subsumes most of the above volume formulae.

Regular Polyhedra

Let v = number of vertices, e = number of edges, f = number of faces, α = each dihedral angle, a = length of each edge, r = radius of the inscribed sphere, R = radius of the circumscribed sphere, A = area of each face, T = total area, V = volume.

$v - e + f = 2$ (the *Euler-Descartes formula*—actually holds for *any* convex polyhedron)

$$T = fA$$
$$V = \frac{1}{3}rfA = \frac{1}{3}rT$$

Name	Nature of Surface	T	V
Tetrahedron	4 equilateral triangles	$1.73205a^2$	$0.11785a^3$
Hexahedron (cube)	6 squares	$6.00000a^2$	$1.00000a^3$
Octahedron	8 equilateral triangles	$3.46410a^2$	$0.47140a^3$
Dodecahedron	12 regular pentagons	$20.64573a^2$	$7.66312a^3$
Icosahedron	20 equilateral triangles	$8.66025a^2$	$2.18170a^3$

Name	v	e	f	α	a	r
Tetrahedron	4	6	4	70° 32′	$1.633R$	$0.333R$
Hexahedron	8	12	6	90°	$1.155R$	$0.577R$
Octahedron	6	12	8	109° 28′	$1.414R$	$0.577R$
Dodecahedron	20	30	12	116° 34′	$0.714R$	$0.795R$
Icosahedron	12	30	20	138° 11′	$1.051R$	$0.795R$

Name	A	r	R	V
Tetrahedron	$\frac{1}{4}a^2\sqrt{3}$	$\frac{1}{12}a\sqrt{6}$	$\frac{1}{4}a\sqrt{6}$	$\frac{1}{12}a^3\sqrt{2}$
Hexahedron	a^2	$\frac{1}{2}a$	$\frac{1}{2}a\sqrt{3}$	a^3
Octahedron	$\frac{1}{4}a^2\sqrt{3}$	$\frac{1}{6}a\sqrt{6}$	$\frac{1}{2}a\sqrt{2}$	$\frac{1}{3}a^3\sqrt{2}$
Dodecahedron	$\frac{1}{4}a^2\sqrt{25 + 10\sqrt{5}}$	$\frac{1}{20}a\sqrt{250 + 110\sqrt{5}}$	$\frac{1}{4}a(\sqrt{15} + \sqrt{3})$	$\frac{1}{4}a^3(15 + 7\sqrt{5})$
Icosahedron	$\frac{1}{4}a^2\sqrt{3}$	$\frac{1}{12}a\sqrt{42 + 18\sqrt{5}}$	$\frac{1}{4}a\sqrt{10 + 2\sqrt{5}}$	$\frac{5}{12}a^3(3 + \sqrt{5})$

CYLINDERS AND CONES

In the following: B_1 = area of lower base, B_2 = area of upper base, h = altitude, S = lateral surface, T = total surface, V = volume.

Cylinder

S = (perimeter of right section) × (lateral edge)
V = (area of right section) × (lateral edge)

Right Circular Cylinder

Let R = radius of base.

$$S = 2\pi Rh, \quad T = 2\pi R(R + h), \quad V = \pi R^2 h$$

Cone

$$V = \tfrac{1}{3}B_1 h$$

Right Circular Cone

Let R = radius of base, s = slant height.

$$s = \sqrt{R^2 + h^2}$$
$$S = \pi Rs = \pi R\sqrt{R^2 + h^2}$$
$$T = \pi R(R + s) = \pi R(R + \sqrt{R^2 + h^2})$$
$$V = \tfrac{1}{3}\pi R^2 h$$

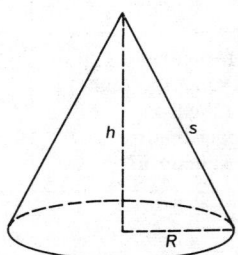

Frustum of Cone

$$V = \tfrac{1}{3}h(B_1 + B_2 + \sqrt{B_1 B_2})$$

Frustum of Right Circular Cone

Let R_1 = radius of lower base, R_2 = radius of upper base, s = slant height.

$$s = \sqrt{(R_1 - R_2)^2 + h^2}$$
$$S = \pi(R_1 + R_2)s$$
$$= \pi(R_1 + R_2)\sqrt{(R_1 - R_2)^2 + h^2}$$
$$T = \pi[R_1^2 + R_2^2 + (R_1 + R_2)s]$$
$$= \pi[R_1^2 + R_2^2 + (R_1 + R_2)\sqrt{(R_1 - R_2)^2 + h^2}]$$
$$V = \frac{1}{3}\pi h(R_1^2 + R_2^2 + R_1R_2)$$

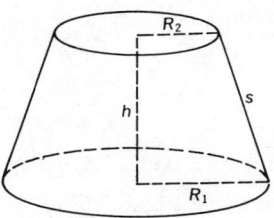

SPHERICAL FIGURES

In the following: R = radius of sphere, D = diameter of sphere, S = surface area, V = volume.

Sphere

$$D = 2R$$
$$S = 4\pi R^2 = \pi D^2 = 12.57R^2$$
$$V = \frac{4}{3}\pi R^3 = \frac{1}{6}\pi D^3 = 4.189R^3$$

Zone and Segment of One Base

$$S = 2\pi Rh = \pi Dh = \pi p^2$$
$$V = \frac{1}{3}\pi h^2(3R - h) = \frac{1}{6}\pi h(3a^2 + h^2)$$

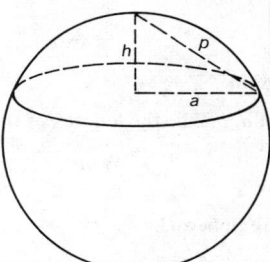

Zone and Segment of Two Bases

$$S = 2\pi Rh = \pi Dh$$
$$V = \frac{1}{6}\pi h(3a^2 + 3b^2 + h^2)$$

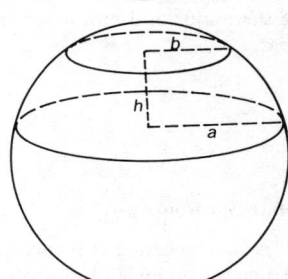

Lune

$$S = 2R^2\theta, \quad \theta \text{ in radians}$$

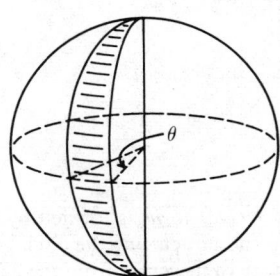

Spherical Sector

$$V = \tfrac{2}{3}\pi R^2 h = \tfrac{1}{6}\pi D^2 h$$

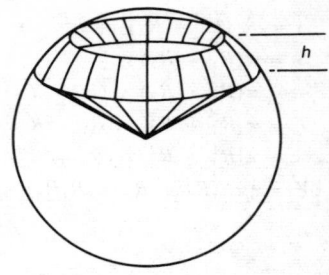

Spherical Triangle and Polygon

Let A, B, C be the angles, in radians, of the triangle; let θ = sum of angles, in radians, of a spherical polygon of n sides.

$$S = (A + B + C - \pi) R^2$$
$$S = [\theta - (n - 2)\pi] R^2$$

SPHEROIDS

Ellipsoid

Let a, b, c be the lengths of the semiaxes.

$$V = \tfrac{4}{3}\pi abc$$

Oblate Spheroid

An *oblate spheroid* is formed by the rotation of an ellipse about its minor axis. Let a and b be the major and minor semiaxes, respectively, and ϵ the eccentricity, of the revolving ellipse.

$$S = 2\pi a^2 + \pi \frac{b^2}{\epsilon} \log_e \frac{1 + \epsilon}{1 - \epsilon}$$
$$V = \tfrac{4}{3}\pi a^2 b$$

Prolate Spheroid

A *prolate spheroid* is formed by the rotation of an ellipse about its major axis. Let a and b be the major and minor semiaxes, respectively, and ϵ the eccentricity, of the revolving ellipse.

$$S = 2\pi b^2 + 2\pi \frac{ab}{\epsilon} \sin^{-1} \epsilon$$
$$V = \tfrac{4}{3}\pi ab^2$$

CIRCULAR TORUS

A *circular torus* is formed by the rotation of a circle about an axis in the plane of the circle and not cutting the circle. Let r be the radius of the revolving circle and let R be the distance of its center from the axis of rotation.

$$S = 4\pi^2 Rr$$
$$V = 2\pi^2 Rr^2$$

PAPPUS-GULDINUS THEOREMS

1. If a planar arc be revolved about an axis in its plane, but not cutting the arc, the area of the surface of revolution so formed is equal to the product of the length of the arc and the length of the path traced by the centroid of the arc.

2. If a planar area be revolved about an axis in its plane, but not intersecting the area, the volume of the solid of revolution so formed is equal to the product of the area and the length of the path traced by the centroid of the area.

CAVALIERI'S THEOREM FOR SPACE

If two solids are included between a pair of parallel planes, and if the two sections cut by them on any plane parallel to the including planes are equal in area, then the volumes of the solids are equal.

GENERAL PRISMATOID

A *general prismatoid* is a solid such that the area A_y of any section parallel to and distant y from a fixed plane can be expressed as a polynomial in y of degreee not higher than the third. That is,

$$A_y = ay^3 + by^2 + cy + d,$$

where a, b, c, d are constants which may be positive, zero, or negative. Let B_1 = area of lower base, M = area of midsection, B_2 = area of upper base, h = altitude.

$$V = \tfrac{1}{6}h(B_1 + 4M + B_2)$$

Note. All prismatoids, cylinders, cones, spheres, spheroids, and many other solids are general prismatoids.

CENTROIDS

If a geometrical figure possesses a center of symmetry, that point is the centroid of the figure.

If a geometrical figure possesses an axis of symmetry, the centroid of the figure lies on that axis.

Geometrical Figure	Location of Centroid
Perimeter of triangle	Center of the inscribed circle of the triangle whose vertices are the midpoints of the sides of the given triangle.
Arc of semicircle of radius R	Distance from diameter $= \dfrac{2R}{\pi}$
Arc of 2α radians of a circle of radius R	Distance from center of circle $= \dfrac{R \sin \alpha}{\alpha}$
Area of triangle	Intersection of the medians
Area of quadrilateral	Intersection of the diagonals of the parallelogram whose sides pass through adjacent trisection points of pairs of consecutive sides of the quadrilateral
Area of semicircle of radius R	Distance from diameter $= \dfrac{4R}{3\pi}$
Area of circular sector of radius R and central angle 2α radians	Distance from center of circle $= \dfrac{2R \sin \alpha}{3\alpha}$
Area of semiellipse of altitude h	Distance from base $= \dfrac{4h}{3\pi}$
Area of a quadrant of an ellipse of major and minor semiaxes a and b	Distance from minor axis $= \dfrac{4a}{3\pi}$, distance from major axis $= \dfrac{4b}{3\pi}$
Area of right parabolic segment of altitude h	Distance from base $= \frac{2}{5}h$
Lateral area of regular pyramid or right circular cone	Distance from base $= \frac{1}{3}h$
Area of hemisphere of radius R	Distance from base $= \frac{1}{2}R$
Volume of pyramid or cone	One fourth the way from the centroid of the base to the vertex of the pyramid or cone
Volume of frustum of pyramid or cone with d as the distance between the centroids of its bases and k as the ratio of similarity of the upper base to the lower base	On the line joining the centroids of the two bases at a distance from the centroid of the lower base $= \frac{1}{4}d\left(\dfrac{1 + 2k + 3k^2}{1 + k + k^2}\right)$
Volume of hemisphere of radius R	Distance from base $= \frac{3}{8}R$
Volume of revolution of altitude h obtained by revolving a semiellipse about its axis of symmetry	Distance from base $= \frac{3}{8}h$
Volume of paraboloid of revolution of altitude h	Distance from base $= \frac{1}{3}h$

RECIPROCALS, CIRCUMFERENCE AND AREA OF CIRCLES

As a matter of convenience, the values of $1000 \times (1/n)$ are given in the table. To obtain the actual value of the reciprocal, shift the decimal point three places to the left.

Circumferences and areas of circles are given for the values of n as the diameter.

n = dia	$1000\dfrac{1}{n}$	Circum-ference πn	Area $\dfrac{\pi n^2}{4}$	n = dia	$1000\dfrac{1}{n}$	Circum-ference πn	Area $\dfrac{\pi n^2}{4}$
0	∞	0.000000	.0000000	50	20.00000	157.0796	1963.495
1	1000.000	3.141593	.7853982	51	19.60784	160.2212	2042.821
2	500.0000	6.283185	3.141593	52	19.23077	163.3628	2123.717
3	333.3333	9.424778	7.068583	53	18.86792	166.5044	2206.183
4	250.0000	12.56637	12.56637	54	18.51852	169.6460	2290.221
5	200.0000	15.70796	19.63495	55	18.18182	172.7876	2375.829
6	166.6667	18.84956	28.27433	56	17.85714	175.9292	2463.009
7	142.8571	21.99115	38.48451	57	17.54386	179.0708	2551.759
8	125.0000	25.13274	50.26548	58	17.24138	182.2124	2642.079
9	111.1111	28.27433	63.61725	59	16.94915	185.3540	2733.971
10	100.0000	31.41593	78.53982	60	16.66667	188.4956	2827.433
11	90.90909	34.55752	95.03318	61	16.39344	191.6372	2922.467
12	83.33333	37.69911	113.0973	62	16.12903	194.7787	3019.071
13	76.92308	40.84070	132.7323	63	15.87302	197.9203	3117.245
14	71.42857	43.98230	153.9380	64	15.62500	201.0619	3216.991
15	66.66667	47.12389	176.7146	65	15.38462	204.2035	3318.307
16	62.50000	50.26548	201.0619	66	15.15152	207.3451	3421.194
17	58.82353	53.40708	226.9801	67	14.92537	210.4867	3525.652
18	55.55556	56.54867	254.4690	68	14.70588	213.6283	3631.681
19	52.63158	59.69026	283.5287	69	14.49275	216.7699	3739.281
20	50.00000	62.83185	314.1593	70	14.28571	219.9115	3848.451
21	47.61905	65.97345	346.3606	71	14.08451	223.0531	3959.192
22	45.45455	69.11504	380.1327	72	13.88889	226.1947	4071.504
23	43.47826	72.25663	415.4756	73	13.69863	229.3363	4185.387
24	41.66667	75.39822	452.3893	74	13.51351	232.4779	4300.840
25	40.00000	78.53982	490.8739	75	13.33333	235.6194	4417.865
26	38.46154	81.68141	530.9292	76	13.15789	238.7610	4536.460
27	37.03704	84.82300	572.5553	77	12.98701	241.9026	4656.626
28	35.71429	87.96459	615.7522	78	12.82051	245.0442	4778.362
29	υ4.48276	91.10619	660.5199	79	12.65823	248.1858	4901.670
30	33.33333	94.24778	706.8583	80	12.50000	251.3274	5026.548
31	32.25806	97.38937	754.7676	81	12.34568	254.4690	5152.997
32	31.25000	100.5310	804.2477	82	12.19512	257.6106	5281.017
33	30.30303	103.6726	855.2986	83	12.04819	260.7522	5410.608
34	29.41176	106.8142	907.9203	84	11.90476	263.8938	5541.769
35	28.57143	109.9557	962.1128	85	11.76471	267.0354	5674.502
36	27.77778	113.0973	1017.876	86	11.62791	270.1770	5808.805
37	27.02703	116.2389	1075.210	87	11.49425	273.3186	5944.679
38	26.31579	119.3805	1134.115	88	11.36364	276.4602	6082.123
39	25.64103	122.5221	1194.591	89	11.23596	279.6017	6221.139
40	25.00000	125.6637	1256.637	90	11.11111	282.7433	6361.725
41	24.39024	128.8053	1320.254	91	10.98901	285.8849	6503.882
42	23.80952	131.9469	1385.442	92	10.86957	289.0265	6647.610
43	23.25581	135.0885	1452.201	93	10.75269	292.1681	6792.909
44	22.72727	138.2301	1520.531	94	10.63830	295.3097	6939.778
45	22.22222	141.3717	1590.431	95	10.52632	298.4513	7088.218
46	21.73913	144.5133	1661.903	96	10.41667	301.5929	7238.229
47	21.27660	147.6549	1734.945	97	10.30928	304.7345	7389.811
48	20.83333	150.7964	1809.557	98	10.20408	307.8761	7542.964
49	20.40816	153.9380	1885.741	99	10.10101	311.0177	7697.687
50	20.00000	157.0796	1963.495	100	10.00000	314.1593	7853.982

RECIPROCALS, CIRCUMFERENCE AND AREA OF CIRCLES (Continued)

$n = $ dia	$1000\dfrac{1}{n}$	Circumference πn	Area $\dfrac{\pi n^2}{4}$	$n = $ dia	$1000\dfrac{1}{n}$	Circumference πn	Area $\dfrac{\pi n^2}{4}$
100	10.00000	314.1593	7853.982	**150**	6.666 667	471.2389	17671.46
101	9.900 990	317.3009	8011.847	151	6.622 517	474.3805	17907.86
102	9.803 922	320.4425	8171.282	152	6.578 947	477.5221	18145.84
103	9.708 738	323.5840	8332.289	153	6.535 948	480.6637	18385.39
104	9.615 385	326.7256	8494.867	154	6.493 506	483.8053	18626.50
105	9.523 810	329.8672	8659.015	155	6.451 613	486.9469	18869.19
106	9.433 962	333.0088	8824.734	156	6.410 256	490.0885	19113.45
107	9.345 794	336.1504	8992.024	157	6.369 427	493.2300	19359.28
108	9.259 259	339.2920	9160.884	158	6.329 114	496.3716	19606.68
109	9.174 312	342.4336	9331.316	159	6.289 308	499.5132	19855.65
110	9.090 909	345.5752	9503.318	**160**	6.250 000	502.6548	20106.19
111	9.009 009	348.7168	9676.891	161	6.211 180	505.7964	20358.31
112	8.928 571	351.8584	9852.035	162	6.172 840	508.9380	20611.99
113	8.849 558	355.0000	10028.75	163	6.134 969	512.0796	20867.24
114	8.771 930	358.1416	10207.03	164	6.097 561	515.2212	21124.07
115	8.695 652	361.2832	10386.89	165	6.060 606	518.3628	21382.46
116	8.620 690	364.4247	10568.32	166	6.024 096	521.5044	21642.43
117	8.547 009	367.5663	10751.32	167	5.988 024	524.6460	21903.97
118	8.474 576	370.7079	10935.88	168	5.952 381	527.7876	22167.08
119	8.403 361	373.8495	11122.02	169	5.917 160	530.9292	22431.76
120	8.333 333	376.9911	11309.73	**170**	5.882 353	534.0708	22698.01
121	8.264 463	380.1327	11499.01	171	5.847 953	537.2123	22965.83
122	8.196 721	383.2743	11689.87	172	5.813 953	540.3539	23235.22
123	8.130 081	386.4159	11882.29	173	5.780 347	543.4955	23506.18
124	8.064 516	389.5575	12076.28	174	5.747 126	546.6371	23778.71
125	8.000 000	392.6991	12271.85	175	5.714 286	549.7787	24052.82
126	7.936 508	395.8407	12468.98	176	5.681 818	552.9203	24328.49
127	7.874 016	398.9823	12667.69	177	5.649 718	556.0619	24605.74
128	7.812 500	402.1239	12867.96	178	5.617 978	559.2035	24884.56
129	7.751 938	405.2655	13069.81	179	5.586 592	562.3451	25164.94
130	7.692 308	408.4070	13273.23	**180**	5.555 556	565.4867	25446.90
131	7.633 588	411.5486	13478.22	181	5.524 862	568.6283	25730.43
132	7.575 758	414.6902	13684.78	182	5.494 505	571.7699	26015.53
133	7.518 797	417.8318	13892.91	183	5.464 481	574.9115	26302.20
134	7.462 687	420.9734	14102.61	184	5.434 783	578.0530	26590.44
135	7.407 407	424.1150	14313.88	185	5.405 405	581.1946	26880.25
136	7.352 941	427.2566	14526.72	186	5.376 344	584.3362	27171.63
137	7.299 270	430.3982	14741.14	187	5.347 594	587.4778	27464.59
138	7.246 377	433.5398	14957.12	188	5.319 149	590.6194	27759.11
139	7.194 245	436.6814	15174.68	189	5.291 005	593.7610	28055.21
140	7.142 857	439.8230	15393.80	**190**	5.263 158	596.9026	28352.87
141	7.092 199	442.9646	15614.50	191	5.235 602	600.0442	28652.11
142	7.042 254	446.1062	15836.77	192	5.208 333	603.1858	28952.92
143	6.993 007	449.2477	16060.61	193	5.181 347	606.3274	29255.30
144	6.944 444	452.3893	16286.02	194	5.154 639	609.4690	29559.25
145	6.896 552	455.5309	16513.00	195	5.128 205	612.6106	29864.77
146	6.849 315	458.6725	16741.55	196	5.102 041	615.7522	30171.86
147	6.802 721	461.8141	16971.67	197	5.076 142	618.8938	30480.52
148	6.756 757	464.9557	17203.36	198	5.050 505	622.0353	30790.75
149	6.711 409	468.0973	17436.62	199	5.025 126	625.1769	31102.55
150	6.666 667	471.2389	17671.46	**200**	5.000 000	628.3185	31415.93

RECIPROCALS, CIRCUMFERENCE AND AREA OF CIRCLES (Continued)

$n = $ dia	$1000\dfrac{1}{n}$	Circum-ference πn	Area $\dfrac{\pi n^2}{4}$	$n = $ dia	$1000\dfrac{1}{n}$	Circum-ference πn	Area $\dfrac{\pi n^2}{4}$
200	5.000 000	628.3185	31415.93	**250**	4.000 000	785.3982	49087.39
201	4.975 124	631.4601	31730.87	251	3.984 066	788.5398	49480.87
202	4.950 495	634.6017	32047.39	252	3.968 254	791.6813	49875.92
203	4.926 108	637.7433	32365.47	253	3.952 569	794.8229	50272.55
204	4.901 961	640.8849	32685.13	254	3.937 008	797.9645	50670.75
205	4.878 049	644.0265	33006.36	255	3.921 569	801.1061	51070.52
206	4.854 369	647.1681	33329.16	256	3.906 250	804.2477	51471.85
207	4.830 918	650.3097	33653.53	257	3.891 051	807.3893	51874.76
208	4.807 692	653.4513	33979.47	258	3.875 969	810.5309	52279.24
209	4.784 689	656.5929	34306.98	259	3.861 004	813.6725	52685.29
210	4.761 905	659.7345	34636.06	**260**	3.846 154	816.8141	53092.92
211	4.739 336	662.8760	34966.71	261	3.831 418	819.9557	53502.11
212	4.716 981	666.0176	35298.94	262	3.816 794	823.0973	53912.87
213	4.694 836	669.1592	35632.73	263	3.802 281	826.2389	54325.21
214	4.672 897	672.3008	35968.09	264	3.787 879	829.3805	54739.11
215	4.651 163	675.4424	36305.03	265	3.773 585	832.5221	55154.59
216	4.629 630	678.5840	36643.54	266	3.759 398	835.6636	55571.63
217	4.608 295	681.7256	36983.61	267	3.745 318	838.8052	55990.25
218	4.587 156	684.8672	37325.26	268	3.731 343	841.9468	56410.44
219	4.566 210	688.0088	37668.48	269	3.717 472	845.0884	56832.20
220	4.545 455	691.1504	38013.27	**270**	3.703 704	848.2300	57255.53
221	4.524 887	694.2920	38359.63	271	3.690 037	851.3716	57680.43
222	4.504 505	697.4336	38707.56	272	3.676 471	854.5132	58106.90
223	4.484 305	700.5752	39057.07	273	3.663 004	857.6548	58534.94
224	4.464 286	703.7168	39408.14	274	3.649 635	860.7964	58964.55
225	4.444 444	706.8583	39760.78	275	3.636 364	863.9380	59395.74
226	4.424 779	709.9999	40115.00	276	3.623 188	867.0796	59828.49
227	4.405 286	713.1415	40470.78	277	3.610 108	870.2212	60262.82
228	4.385 965	716.2831	40828.14	278	3.597 122	873.3628	60698.71
229	4.366 812	719.4247	41187.07	279	3.584 229	876.5044	61136.18
230	4.347 826	722.5663	41547.56	**280**	3.571 429	879.6459	61575.22
231	4.329 004	725.7079	41909.63	281	3.558 719	882.7875	62015.82
232	4.310 345	728.8495	42273.27	282	3.546 099	885.9291	62458.00
233	4.291 845	731.9911	42638.48	283	3.533 569	889.0707	62901.75
234	4.273 504	735.1327	43005.26	284	3.521 127	892.2123	63347.07
235	4.255 319	738.2743	43373.61	285	3.508 772	895.3539	63793.97
236	4.237 288	741.4159	43743.54	286	3.496 503	898.4955	64242.43
237	4.219 409	744.5575	44115.03	287	3.484 321	901.6371	64692.46
238	4.201 681	747.6991	44488.09	288	3.472 222	904.7787	65144.07
239	4.184 100	750.8406	44862.73	289	3.460 208	907.9203	65597.24
240	4.166 667	753.9822	45238.93	**290**	3.448 276	911.0619	66051.99
241	4.149 378	757.1238	45616.71	291	3.436 426	914.2035	66508.30
242	4.132 231	760.2654	45996.06	292	3.424 658	917.3451	66966.19
243	4.115 226	763.4070	46376.98	293	3.412 969	920.4866	67425.65
244	4.098 361	766.5486	46759.47	294	3.401 361	923.6282	67886.68
245	4.081 633	769.6902	47143.52	295	3.389 831	926.7698	68349.28
246	4.065 041	772.8318	47529.16	296	3.378 378	929.9114	68813.45
247	4.048 583	775.9734	47916.36	297	3.367 003	933.0530	69279.19
248	4.032 258	779.1150	48305.13	298	3.355 705	936.1946	69746.50
249	4.016 064	782.2566	48695.47	299	3.344 482	939.3362	70215.38
250	4.000 000	785.3982	49087.39	**300**	3.333 333	942.4778	70685.83

RECIPROCALS, CIRCUMFERENCE AND AREA OF CIRCLES (Continued)

n = dia	$1000\dfrac{1}{n}$	Circum- ference πn	Area $\dfrac{\pi n^2}{4}$	n = dia	$1000\dfrac{1}{n}$	Circum- ference πn	Area $\dfrac{\pi n^2}{4}$
300	3.333 333	942.4778	70685.83	**350**	2.857 143	1099.557	96211.28
301	3.322 259	945.6194	71157.86	351	2.849 003	1102.699	96761.84
302	3.311 258	948.7610	71631.45	352	2.840 909	1105.841	97313.97
303	3.300 330	951.9026	72106.62	353	2.832 861	1108.982	97867.68
304	3.289 474	955.0442	72583.36	354	2.824 859	1112.124	98422.96
305	3.278 689	958.1858	73061.66	355	2.816 901	1115.265	98979.80
306	3.267 974	961.3274	73541.54	356	2.808 989	1118.407	99538.22
307	3.257 329	964.4689	74022.99	357	2.801 120	1121.549	100 098.2
308	3.246 753	967.6105	74506.01	358	2.793 296	1124.690	100 659.8
309	3.236 246	970.7521	74990.60	359	2.785 515	1127.832	101 222.9
310	3.225 806	973.8937	75476.76	**360**	2.777 778	1130.973	101 787.6
311	3.215 434	977.0353	75964.50	361	2.770 083	1134.155	102 353.9
312	3.205 128	980.1769	76453.80	362	2.762 431	1137.257	102 921.7
313	3.194 888	983.3185	76944.67	363	2.754 821	1140.398	103 491.1
314	3.184 713	986.4601	77437.12	364	2.747 253	1143.540	104 062.1
315	3.174 603	989.6017	77931.13	365	2.739 726	1146.681	104 634.7
316	3.164 557	992.7433	78426.72	366	2.732 240	1149.823	105 208.8
317	3.154 574	995.8849	78923.88	367	2.724 796	1152.965	105 784.5
318	3.144 654	999.0265	79422.60	368	2.717 391	1156.106	106 361.8
319	3.134 796	1002.168	79922.90	369	2.710 027	1159.248	106 940.6
320	3.125 000	1005.310	80424.77	**370**	2.702 703	1162.389	107 521.0
321	3.115 265	1008.451	80928.21	371	2.695 418	1165.531	108 103.0
322	3.105 590	1011.593	81433.22	372	2.688 172	1168.672	108 686.5
323	3.095 975	1014.734	81939.80	373	2.680 965	1171.814	109 271.7
324	3.086 420	1017.876	82447.96	374	2.673 797	1174.956	109 858.4
325	3.076 923	1021.018	82957.68	375	2.666 667	1178.097	110 446.6
326	3.067 485	1024.159	83468.98	376	2.659 574	1181.239	111 036.5
327	3.058 104	1027.301	83981.84	377	2.652 520	1184.380	111 627.9
328	3.048 780	1030.442	84496.28	378	2.645 503	1187.522	112 220.8
329	3.039 514	1033.584	85012.28	379	2.638 522	1190.664	112 815.4
330	3.030 303	1036.726	85529.86	**380**	2.631 579	1193.805	113 411.5
331	3.021 148	1039.867	86049.01	381	2.624 672	1196.947	114 009.2
332	3.012 048	1043.009	86569.73	382	2.617 801	1200.088	114 608.4
333	3.003 003	1046.150	87092.02	383	2.610 966	1203.230	115 209.3
334	2.994 012	1049.292	87615.88	384	2.604 167	1206.372	115 811.7
335	2.985 075	1052.434	88141.31	385	2.597 403	1209.513	116 415.6
336	2.976 190	1055.575	88668.31	386	2.590 674	1212.655	117 021.2
337	2.967 359	1058.717	89196.88	387	2.583 979	1215.796	117 628.3
338	2.958 580	1061.858	89727.03	388	2.577 320	1218.938	118 237.0
339	2.949 853	1065.000	90258.74	389	2.570 694	1222.080	118 847.2
340	2.941 176	1068.142	90792.03	**390**	2.564 103	1225.221	119 459.1
341	2.932 551	1071.283	91326.88	391	2.557 545	1228.363	120 072.5
342	2.923 977	1074.425	91863.31	392	2.551 020	1231.504	120 687.4
343	2.915 452	1077.566	92401.31	393	2.544 529	1234.646	121 304.0
344	2.906 977	1080.708	92940.88	394	2.538 071	1237.788	121 922.1
345	2.898 551	1083.849	93482.02	395	2.531 646	1240.929	122 541.7
346	2.890 173	1086.991	94024.73	396	2.525 253	1244.071	123 163.0
347	2.881 844	1090.133	94569.01	397	2.518 892	1247.212	123 785.8
348	2.873 563	1093.274	95114.86	398	2.512 563	1250.354	124 410.2
349	2.865 330	1096.416	95662.28	399	2.506 266	1253.495	125 036.2
350	2.857 143	1099.557	96211.28	**400**	2.500 000	1256.637	125 663.7

RECIPROCALS, CIRCUMFERENCE AND AREA OF CIRCLES (Continued)

$n = $ dia	$1000\dfrac{1}{n}$	Circum-ference πn	Area $\dfrac{\pi n^2}{4}$	$n = $ dia	$1000\dfrac{1}{n}$	Circum-ference πn	Area $\dfrac{\pi n^2}{4}$
400	2.500 000	1256.637	125 663.7	**450**	2.222 222	1413.717	159 043.1
401	2.493 766	1259.779	126 292.8	451	2.217 295	1416.858	159 750.8
402	2.487 562	1262.920	126 923.5	452	2.212 389	1420.000	160 460.0
403	2.481 390	1266.062	127 555.7	453	2.207 506	1423.141	161 170.8
404	2.475 248	1269.203	128 189.5	454	2.202 643	1426.283	161 883.1
405	2.469 136	1272.345	128 824.9	455	2.197 802	1429.425	162 597.1
406	2.463 054	1275.487	129 461.9	456	2.192 982	1432.566	163 312.6
407	2.457 002	1278.628	130 100.4	457	2.188 184	1435.708	164 029.6
408	2.450 980	1281.770	130 740.5	458	2.183 406	1438.849	164 748.3
409	2.444 988	1284.911	131 382.2	459	2.178 649	1441.991	165 468.5
410	2.439 024	1288.053	132 025.4	**460**	2.173 913	1445.133	166 190.3
411	2.433 090	1291.195	132 670.2	461	2.169 197	1448.274	166 913.6
412	2.427 184	1294.336	133 316.6	462	2.164 502	1451.416	167 638.5
413	2.421 308	1297.478	133 964.6	463	2.159 827	1454.557	168 365.0
414	2.415 459	1300.619	134 614.1	464	2.155 172	1457.699	169 093.1
415	2.409 639	1303.761	135 265.2	465	2.150 538	1460.841	169 822.7
416	2.403 846	1306.903	135 917.9	466	2.145 923	1463.982	170 553.9
417	2.398 082	1310.044	136 572.1	467	2.141 328	1467.124	171 286.7
418	2.392 344	1313.186	137 227.9	468	2.136 752	1470.265	172 021.0
419	2.386 635	1316.327	137 885.3	469	2.132 196	1473.407	172 757.0
420	2.380 952	1319.469	138 544.2	**470**	2.127 660	1476.549	173 494.5
421	2.375 297	1322.611	139 204.8	471	2.123 142	1479.690	174 233.5
422	2.369 668	1325.752	139 866.8	472	2.118 644	1482.832	174 974.1
423	2.364 066	1328.894	140 530.5	473	2.114 165	1485.973	175 716.3
424	2.358 491	1332.035	141 195.7	474	2.109 705	1489.115	176 460.1
425	2.352 941	1335.177	141 862.5	475	2.105 263	1492.257	177 205.5
426	2.347 418	1338.318	142 530.9	476	2.100 840	1495.398	177 952.4
427	2.341 920	1341.460	143 200.9	477	2.096 436	1498.540	178 700.9
428	2.336 449	1344.602	143 872.4	478	2.092 050	1501.681	179 450.9
429	2.331 002	1347.743	144 545.5	479	2.087 683	1504.823	180 202.5
430	2.325 581	1350.885	145 220.1	**480**	2.083 333	1507.964	180 955.7
431	2.320 186	1354.026	145 896.3	481	2.079 002	1511.106	181 710.5
432	2.314 815	1357.168	146 574.1	482	2.074 689	1514.248	182 466.8
433	2.309 469	1360.310	147 253.5	483	2.070 393	1517.389	183 224.8
434	2.304 147	1363.451	147 934.5	484	2.066 116	1520.531	183 984.2
435	2.298 851	1366.593	148 617.0	485	2.061 856	1523.672	184 745.3
436	2.293 578	1369.734	149 301.0	486	2.057 613	1526.814	185 507.9
437	2.288 330	1372.876	149 986.7	487	2.053 388	1529.956	186 272.1
438	2.283 105	1376.018	150 673.9	488	2.049 180	1533.097	187 037.9
439	2.277 904	1379.159	151 362.7	489	2.044 990	1536.239	187 805.2
440	2.272 727	1382.301	152 053.1	**490**	2.040 816	1539.380	188 574.1
441	2.267 574	1385.442	152 745.0	491	2.036 660	1542.522	189 344.6
442	2.262 443	1388.584	153 438.5	492	2.032 520	1545.664	190 116.6
443	2.257 336	1391.726	154 133.6	493	2.028 398	1548.805	190 890.2
444	2.252 252	1394.867	154 830.3	494	2.024 291	1551.947	191 665.4
445	2.247 191	1398.009	155 528.5	495	2.020 202	1555.088	192 442.2
446	2.242 152	1401.150	156 228.3	496	2.016 129	1558.230	193 220.5
447	2.237 136	1404.292	156 929.6	497	2.012 072	1561.372	194 000.4
448	2.232 143	1407.434	157 632.6	498	2.008 032	1564.513	194 781.9
449	2.227 171	1410.575	158.337.1	499	2.004 008	1567.655	195 564.9
450	2.222 222	1413.717	159 043.1	**500**	2.000 000	1570.796	196 349.5

RECIPROCALS, CIRCUMFERENCE AND AREA OF CIRCLES (Continued)

$n=$ dia	$1000\dfrac{1}{n}$	Circum-ference πn	Area $\dfrac{\pi n^2}{4}$	$n=$ dia	$1000\dfrac{1}{n}$	Circum-ference πn	Area $\dfrac{\pi n^2}{4}$
500	2.000 000	1570.796	196 349.5	**550**	1.818 182	1727.876	237 582.9
501	1.996 008	1573.938	197 135.7	551	1.814 882	1731.018	238 447.7
502	1.992 032	1577.080	197 923.5	552	1.811 594	1734.159	239 314.0
503	1.988 072	1580.221	198 712.8	553	1.808 318	1737.301	240 181.8
504	1.984 127	1583.363	199 503.7	554	1.805 054	1740.442	241 051.3
505	1.980 198	1586.504	200 296.2	555	1.801 802	1743.584	241 922.3
506	1.976 285	1589.646	201 090.2	556	1.798 561	1746.726	242 794.8
507	1.972 387	1592.787	201 885.8	557	1.795 332	1749.867	243 669.0
508	1.968 504	1595.929	202 683.0	558	1.792 115	1753.009	244 544.7
509	1.964 637	1599.071	203 481.7	559	1.788 909	1756.150	245 422.0
510	1.960 784	1602.212	204 282.1	**560**	1.785 714	1759.292	246 300.9
511	1.956 947	1605.354	205 084.0	561	1.782 531	1762.433	247 181.3
512	1.953 125	1608.495	205 887.4	562	1.779 359	1765.575	248 063.3
513	1.949 318	1611.637	206 692.4	563	1.776 199	1768.717	248 946.9
514	1.945 525	1614.779	207 499.1	564	1.773 050	1771.858	249 832.0
515	1.941 748	1617.920	208 307.2	565	1.769 912	1775.000	250 718.7
516	1.937 984	1621.062	209 117.0	566	1.766 784	1778.141	251 607.0
517	1.934 236	1624.203	209 928.3	567	1.763 668	1781.283	252 496.9
518	1.930 502	1627.345	210 741.2	568	1.760 563	1784.425	253 388.3
519	1.926 782	1630.487	211 555.6	569	1.757 469	1787.566	254 281.3
520	1.923 077	1633.628	212 371.7	**570**	1.754 386	1790.708	255 175.9
521	1.919 386	1636.770	213 189.3	571	1.751 313	1793.849	256 072.0
522	1.915 709	1639.911	214 008.4	572	1.748 252	1796.991	256 969.7
523	1.912 046	1643.053	214 829.2	573	1.745 201	1800.133	257 869.0
524	1.908 397	1646.195	215 651.5	574	1.742 160	1803.274	258 769.8
525	1.904 762	1649.336	216 475.4	575	1.739 130	1806.416	259 672.3
526	1.901 141	1652.478	217 300.8	576	1.736 111	1809.557	260 576.3
527	1.897 533	1655.619	218 127.8	577	1.733 102	1812.699	261 481.8
528	1.893 939	1658.761	218 956.4	578	1.730 104	1815.841	262 389.0
529	1.890 359	1661.903	219 786.6	579	1.727 116	1818.982	263 297.7
530	1.886 792	1665.044	220 618.3	**580**	1.724 138	1822.124	264 207.9
531	1.883 239	1668.186	221 451.7	581	1.721 170	1825.265	265 119.8
532	1.879 699	1671.327	222 286.5	582	1.718 213	1828.407	266 033.2
533	1.876 173	1674.469	223 123.0	583	1.715 266	1831.549	266 948.2
534	1.872 659	1677.610	223 961.0	584	1.712 329	1834.690	267 864.8
535	1.869 159	1680.752	224 800.6	585	1.709 402	1837.832	268 782.9
536	1.865 672	1683.894	225 641.8	586	1.706 485	1840.973	269 702.6
537	1.862 197	1687.035	226 484.5	587	1.703 578	1844.115	270 623.9
538	1.858 736	1690.177	227 328.8	588	1.700 680	1847.256	271 546.7
539	1.855 288	1693.318	228 174.7	589	1.697 793	1850.398	272 471.1
540	1.851 852	1696.460	229 022.1	**590**	1.694 915	1853.540	273 397.1
541	1.848 429	1699.602	229 871.1	591	1.692 047	1856.681	274 324.7
542	1.845 018	1702.743	230 721.7	592	1.689 189	1859.823	275 253.8
543	1.841 621	1705.885	231 573.9	593	1.686 341	1862.964	276 184.5
544	1.838 235	1709.026	232 427.6	594	1.683 502	1866.106	277 116.7
545	1.834 862	1712.168	233 282.9	595	1.680 672	1869.248	278 050.6
546	1.831 502	1715.310	234 139.8	596	1.677 852	1872.389	278 986.0
547	1.828 154	1718.451	234 998.2	597	1.675 042	1875.531	279 923.0
548	1.824 818	1721.593	235 858.2	598	1.672 241	1878.672	280 861.5
549	1.821 494	1724.734	236 719.8	599	1.669 449	1881.814	281 801.6
550	1.818 182	1727.876	237.582.9	**600**	1.666 667	1884.956	282 743.3

RECIPROCALS, CIRCUMFERENCE AND AREA OF CIRCLES (Continued)

$n =$ dia	$1000\dfrac{1}{n}$	Circum-ference πn	Area $\dfrac{\pi n^2}{4}$	$n =$ dia	$1000\dfrac{1}{n}$	Circum-ference πn	Area $\dfrac{\pi n^2}{4}$
600	1.666 667	1884.956	282 743.3	**650**	1.538 462	2042.035	331 830.7
601	1.663 894	1888.097	283 686.6	651	1.536 098	2045.177	332 852.5
602	1.661 130	1891.239	284 631.4	652	1.533 742	2048.318	333 875.9
603	1.658 375	1894.380	285 577.8	653	1.531 394	2051.460	334 900.8
604	1.655 629	1897.522	286 525.8	654	1.529 052	2054.602	335 927.4
605	1.652 893	1900.664	287 475.4	655	1.526 718	2057.743	336 955.4
606	1.650 165	1903.805	288 426.5	656	1.524 390	2060.885	337 985.1
607	1.647 446	1906.947	289 379.2	657	1.522 070	2064.026	339 016.3
608	1.644 737	1910.088	290 333.4	658	1.519 757	2067.168	340 049.1
609	1.642 036	1913.230	291 289.3	659	1.517 451	2070.310	341 083.5
610	1.639 344	1916.372	292 246.7	**660**	1.515 152	· 2073.451	342 119.4
611	1.636 661	1919.513	293 205.6	661	1.512 859	2076.593	343 157.0
612	1.633 987	1922.655	294 166.2	662	1.510 574	2079.734	344 196.0
613	1.631 321	1925.796	295 128.3	663	1.508 296	2082.876	345 236.7
614	1.628 664	1928.938	296 092.0	664	1.506 024	2086.018	346 278.9
615	1.626 016	1932.079	297 057.2	665	1.503 759	2089.159	347 322.7
616	1.623 377	1935.221	298 024.0	666	1.501 502	2092.301	348 368.1
617	1.620 746	1938.363	298 992.4	667	1.499 250	2095.442	349 415.0
618	1.618 123	1941.504	299 962.4	668	1.497 006	2098.584	350 463.5
619	1.615 509	1944.646	300 933.9	669	1.494 768	2101.725	351 513.6
620	1.612 903	1947.787	301 907.1	**670**	1.492 537	2104.867	352 565.2
621	1.610 306	1950.929	302 881.7	671	1.490 313	2108.009	353 618.5
622	1.607 717	1954.071	303 858.0	672	1.488 095	2111.150	354 673.2
623	1.605 136	1957.212	304 835.8	673	1.485 884	2114.292	355 729.6
624	1.602 564	1960.354	305 815.2	674	1.483 680	2117.433	356 787.5
625	1.600 000	1963.495	306 796.2	675	1.481 481	2120.575	357 847.0
626	1.597 444	1966.637	307 778.7	676	1.479 290	2123.717	358 908.1
627	1.594 896	1969.779	308 762.8	677	1.477 105	2126.858	359 970.8
628	1.592 357	1972.920	309 748.5	678	1.474 926	2130.000	361 035.0
629	1.589 825	1976.062	310 735.7	679	1.472 754	2133.141	362 100.8
630	1.587 302	1979.203	311 724.5	**680**	1.470 588	2136.283	363 168.1
631	1.584 786	1982.345	312 714.9	681	1.468 429	2139.425	364 237.0
632	1.582 278	1985.487	313 706.9	682	1.466 276	2142.566	365 307.5
633	1.579 779	1988.628	314 700.4	683	1.464 129	2145.708	366 379.6
634	1.577 287	1991.770	315 695.5	684	1.461 988	2148.849	367 453.2
635	1.574 803	1994.911	316 692.2	685	1.459 854	2151.991	368 528.5
636	1.572 327	1998.053	317 690.4	686	1.457 726	2155.133	369 605.2
637	1.569 859	2001.195	318 690.2	687	1.455 604	2158.274	370 683.6
638	1.567 398	2004.336	319 691.6	688	1.453 488	2161.416	371 763.5
639	1.564 945	2007.478	320 694.6	689	1.451 379	2164.557	372 845.0
640	1.562 500	2010.619	321 699.1	**690**	1.449 275	2167.699	373 928.1
641	1.560 062	2013.761	322 705.2	691	1.447 178	2170.841	375 012.7
642	1.557 632	2016.902	323 712.8	692	1.445 087	2173.982	376 098.9
643	1.555 210	2020.044	324 722.1	693	1.443 001	2177.124	377 186.7
644	1.552 795	2023.186	325 732.9	694	1.440 922	2180.265	378 276.0
645	1.550 388	2026.327	326 745.3	695	1.438 849	2183.407	379 366.9
646	1.547 988	2029.469	327 759.2	696	1.436 782	2186.548	380 459.4
647	1.545 595	2032.610	328 774.7	697	1.434 720	2189.690	381 553.5
648	1.543 210	2035.752	329 791.8	698	1.432 665	2192.832	382 649.1
649	1.540 832	2038.894	330 810.5	699	1.430 615	2195.973	383 746.3
650	1.538 462	2042.035	331 830.7	**700**	1.428 571	2199.115	384 845.1

Numerical Tables

RECIPROCALS, CIRCUMFERENCE AND AREA OF CIRCLES (Continued)

n = dia	$1000\dfrac{1}{n}$	Circumference πn	Area $\dfrac{\pi n^2}{4}$	n = dia	$1000\dfrac{1}{n}$	Circumference πn	Area $\dfrac{\pi n^2}{4}$
700	1.428 571	2199.115	384 845.1	**750**	1.333 333	2356.194	441 786.5
701	1.426 534	2202.256	385 945.4	751	1.331 558	2359.336	442 965.3
702	1.424 501	2205.398	387 047.4	752	1.329 787	2362.478	444 145.8
703	1.422 475	2208 540	388 150.8	753	1.328 021	2365.619	445 327.8
704	1.420 455	2211.681	389 255.9	754	1.326 260	2368.761	446 511.4
705	1.418 440	2214.823	390 362.5	755	1.324 503	2371.902	447 696.6
706	1.416 431	2217.964	391 470.7	756	1.322 751	2375.044	448 883.3
707	1.414 427	2221.106	392 580.5	757	1.321 004	2378.186	450 071.6
708	1.412 429	2224.248	393 691.8	758	1.319 261	2381.327	451 261.5
709	1.410 437	2227.389	394 804.7	759	1.317 523	2384.469	452 453.0
710	1.408 451	2230.531	395 919.2	**760**	1.315 789	2387.610	453 646.0
711	1.406 470	2233.672	397 035.3	761	1.314 060	2390.752	454 840.6
712	1.404 494	2236.814	398 152.9	762	1.312 336	2393.894	456 036.7
713	1.402 525	2239.956	399 272.1	763	1.310 616	2397.035	457 234.5
714	1.400 560	2243.097	400 392.8	764	1.308 901	2400.177	458 433.8
715	1.398 601	2246.239	401 515.2	765	1.307 190	2403.318	459 634.6
716	1.396 648	2249.380	402 639.1	766	1.305 483	2406.460	460 837.1
717	1.394 700	2252.522	403 764.6	767	1.303 781	2409.602	462 041.1
718	1.392 758	2255.664	404 891.6	768	1.302 083	2412.743	463 246.7
719	1.390 821	2258.805	406 020.2	769	1.300 390	2415.885	464 453.8
720	1.388 889	2261.947	407 150.4	**770**	1.298 701	2419.026	465 662.6
721	1.386 963	2265.088	408 282.2	771	1.297 017	2422.168	466 872.9
722	1.385 042	2268.230	409 415.5	772	1.295 337	2425.310	468 084.7
723	1.383 126	2271.371	410 550.4	773	1.293 661	2428.451	469 298.2
724	1.381 215	2274.513	411 686.9	774	1.291 990	2431.593	470 513.2
725	1.379 310	2277.655	412 824.9	775	1.290 323	2434.734	471 729.8
726	1.377 410	2280.796	413 964.5	776	1.288 660	2437.876	472 947.9
727	1.375 516	2283.938	415 105.7	777	1.287 001	2441.017	474 167.6
728	1.373 626	2287.079	416 248.5	778	1.285 347	2444.159	475 388.9
729	1.371 742	2290.221	417 392.8	779	1.283 697	2447.301	476 611.8
730	1.369 863	2293.363	418 538.7	**780**	1.282 051	2450.442	477 836.2
731	1.367 989	2296.504	419 686.1	781	1.280 410	2453.584	479 062.2
732	1.366 120	2299.646	420 835.2	782	1.278 772	2456.725	480 289.8
733	1.364 256	2302.787	421 985.8	783	1.277 139	2459.867	481 519.0
734	1.362 398	2305.929	423 138.0	784	1.275 510	2463.009	482 749.7
735	1.360 544	2309.071	424 291.7	785	1.273 885	2466.150	483 982.0
736	1.358 696	2312.212	425 447.0	786	1.272 265	2469.292	485 215.8
737	1.356 852	2315.354	426 603.9	787	1.270 648	2472.433	486 451.3
738	1.355 014	2318.495	427 762.4	788	1.269 036	2475.575	487 688.3
739	1.353 180	2321.637	428 922.4	789	1.267 427	2478.717	488 926.9
740	1.351 351	2324.779	430 084.0	**790**	1.265 823	2481.858	490 167.0
741	1.349 528	2327.920	431 247.2	791	1.264 223	2485.000	491 408.7
742	1.347 709	2331.062	432 412.0	792	1.262 626	2488.141	492 652.0
743	1.345 895	2334.203	433 578.3	793	1.261 034	2491.283	493 896.8
744	1.344 086	2337.345	434 746.2	794	1.259 446	2494.425	495 143.3
745	1.342 282	2340.487	435 915.6	795	1.257 862	2497.566	496 391.3
746	1.340 483	2343.628	437 086.6	796	1.256 281	2500.708	497 640.8
747	1.338 688	2346.770	438 259.2	797	1.254 705	2503.849	498 892.0
748	1.336 898	2349.911	439 433.4	798	1.253 133	2506.991	500 144.7
749	1.335 113	2353.053	440 609.2	799	1.251 564	2510.133	501 399.0
750	1.333 333	2356.194	441 786.5	**800**	1.250 000	2513.274	502 654.8

RECIPROCALS, CIRCUMFERENCE AND AREA OF CIRCLES (Continued)

n = dia	$1000\dfrac{1}{n}$	Circumference πn	Area $\dfrac{\pi n^2}{4}$	n = dia	$1000\dfrac{1}{n}$	Circumference πn	Area $\dfrac{\pi n^2}{4}$
800	1.250 000	2513.274	502 654.8	**850**	1.176 471	2670.354	567 450.2
801	1.248 439	2516.416	503 912.2	851	1.175 088	2673.495	568 786.1
802	1.246 883	2519.557	505 171.2	852	1.173 709	2676.637	570 123.7
803	1.245 330	2522.699	506 431.8	853	1.172 333	2679.779	571 462.8
804	1.243 781	2525.840	507 693.9	854	1.170 960	2682.920	572 803.4
805	1.242 236	2528.982	508 957.6	855	1.169 591	2686.062	574 145.7
806	1.240 695	2532.124	510 222.9	856	1.168 224	2689.203	575 489.5
807	1.239 157	2535.265	511 489.8	857	1.166 861	2692.345	576 834.9
808	1.237 624	2538.407	512 758.2	858	1.165 501	2695.486	578 181.9
809	1.236 094	2541.548	514 028.2	859	1.164 144	2698.628	579 530.4
810	1.234 568	2544.690	515 299.7	**860**	1.162 791	2701.770	580 880.5
811	1.233 046	2547.832	516 572.9	861	1.161 440	2704.911	582 232.2
812	1.231 527	2550.973	517 847.6	862	1.160 093	2708.053	583 585.4
813	1.230 012	2554.115	519 123.8	863	1.158 749	2711.194	584 940.2
814	1.228 501	2557.256	520 401.7	864	1.157 407	2714.336	586 296.6
815	1.226 994	2560.398	521 681.1	865	1.156 069	2717.478	587 654.5
816	1.225 490	2563.540	522 962.1	866	1.154 734	2720.619	589 014.1
817	1.223 990	2566.681	524 244.6	867	1.153 403	2723.761	590 375.2
818	1.222 494	2569.823	525 528.8	868	1.152 074	2726.902	591 737.8
819	1.221 001	2572.964	526 814.5	869	1.150 748	2730.044	593 102.1
820	1.219 512	2576.106	528 101.7	**870**	1.149 425	2733.186	594 467.9
821	1.218 027	2579.248	529 390.6	871	1.148 106	2736.327	595 835.2
822	1.216 545	2582.389	530 681.0	872	1.146 789	2739.469	597 204.2
823	1.215 067	2585.531	531 973.0	873	1.145 475	2742.610	598 574.7
824	1.213 592	2588.672	533 266.5	874	1.144 165	2745.752	599 946.8
825	1.212 121	2591.814	534 561.6	875	1.142 857	2748.894	601 320.5
826	1.210 654	2594.956	535 858.3	876	1.141 553	2752.035	602 695.7
827	1.209 190	2598.097	537 156.6	877	1.140 251	2755.177	604 072.5
828	1.207 729	2601.239	538 456.4	878	1.138 952	2758.318	605 450.9
829	1.206 273	2604.380	539 757.8	879	1.137 656	2761.460	606 830.8
830	1.204 819	2607.522	541 060.8	**880**	1.136 364	2764.602	608 212.3
831	1.203 369	2610.663	542 365.3	881	1.135 074	2767.743	609 595.4
832	1.201 923	2613.805	543 671.5	882	1.133 787	2770.885	610 980.1
833	1.200 480	2616.947	544 979.1	883	1.132 503	2774.026	612 366.3
834	1.199 041	2620.088	546 288.4	884	1.131 222	2777.168	613 754.1
835	1.197 605	2623.230	547 599.2	885	1.129 944	2780.309	615 143.5
836	1.196 172	2626.371	548 911.6	886	1.128 668	2783.451	616 534.4
837	1.194 743	2629.513	550 225.6	887	1.127 396	2786.593	617 926.9
838	1.193 317	2632.655	551 541.1	888	1.126 126	2789.734	619 321.0
839	1.191 895	2635.796	552 858.3	889	1.124 859	2792.876	620 716.7
840	1.190 476	2638.938	554 176.9	**890**	1.123 596	2796.017	622 113.9
841	1.189 061	2642.079	555 497.2	891	1.122 334	2799.159	623 512.7
842	1.187 648	2645.221	556 819.0	892	1.121 076	2802.301	624 913.0
843	1.186 240	2648.363	558 142.4	893	1.119 821	2805.442	626 315.0
844	1.184 834	2651.504	559 467.4	894	1.118 568	2808.584	627 718.5
845	1.183 432	2654.646	560 793.9	895	1.117 318	2811.725	629 123.6
846	1.182 033	2657.787	562 122.0	896	1.116 071	2814.867	630 530.2
847	1.180 638	2660.929	563 451.7	897	1.114 827	2818.009	631 938.4
848	1.179 245	2664.071	564 783.0	898	1.113 586	2821.150	633 348.2
849	1.177 856	2667.212	566 115.8	899	1.112 347	2824.292	634 759.6
850	1.176 471	2670.354	567 450.2	**900**	1.111 111	2827.433	636 172.5

RECIPROCALS, CIRCUMFERENCE AND AREA OF CIRCLES (Continued)

n = dia	$1000\dfrac{1}{n}$	Circum-ference πn	Area $\dfrac{\pi n^2}{4}$	n = dia	$1000\dfrac{1}{n}$	Circum-ference πn	Area $\dfrac{\pi n^2}{4}$
900	1.111 111	2827.433	636 172.5	**950**	1.052 632	2984.513	708 821.8
901	1.109 878	2830.575	637 587.0	951	1.051 525	2987.655	710 314.9
902	1.108 647	2833.717	639 003.1	952	1.050 420	2990.796	711 809.5
903	1.107 420	2836.858	640 420.7	953	1.049 318	2993.938	713 305.7
904	1.106 195	2840.000	641 839.9	954	1.048 218	2997.079	714 803.4
905	1.104 972	2843.141	643 260.7	955	1.047 120	3000.221	716 302.8
906	1.103 753	2846.283	644 683.1	956	1.046 025	3003.363	717 803.7
907	1.102 536	2849.425	646 107.0	957	1.044 932	3006.504	719 306.1
908	1.101 322	2852.566	647 532.5	958	1.043 841	3009.646	720 810.2
909	1.100 110	2855.708	648 959.6	959	1.042 753	3012.787	722 315.8
910	1.098 901	2858.849	650 388.2	**960**	1.041 667	3015.929	723 822.9
911	1.097 695	2861.991	651 818.4	961	1.040 583	3019.071	725 331.7
912	1.096 491	2865.133	653 250.2	962	1.039 501	3022.212	726 842.0
913	1.095 290	2868.274	654 683.6	963	1.038 422	3025.354	728 353.9
914	1.094 092	2871.416	656 118.5	964	1.037 344	3028.495	729 867.4
915	1.092 896	2874.557	657 555.0	965	1.036 269	3031.637	731 382.4
916	1.091 703	2877.699	658 993.0	966	1.035 197	3034.779	732 899.0
917	1.090 513	2880.840	660 432.7	967	1.034 126	3037.920	734 417.2
918	1.089 325	2883.982	661 873.9	968	1.033 058	3041.062	735 936.9
919	1.088 139	2887.124	663 316.7	969	1.031 992	3044.203	737 458.2
920	1.086 957	2890.265	664 761.0	**970**	1.030 928	3047.345	738 981.1
921	1.085 776	2893.407	666 206.9	971	1.029 866	3050.486	740 505.6
922	1.084 599	2896.548	667 654.4	972	1.028 807	3053.628	742 031.6
923	1.083 424	2899.690	669 103.5	973	1.027 749	3056.770	743 559.2
924	1.082 251	2902.832	670 554.1	974	1.026 694	3059.911	745 088.4
925	1.081 081	2905.973	672 006.3	975	1.025 641	3063.053	746 619.1
926	1.079 914	2909.115	673 460.1	976	1.024 590	3066.194	748 151.4
927	1.078 749	2912.256	674 915.4	977	1.023 541	3069.336	749 685.3
928	1.077 586	2915.398	676 372.3	978	1.022 495	3072.478	751 220.8
929	1.076 426	2918.540	677 830.8	979	1.021 450	3075.619	752 757.8
930	1.075 269	2921.681	679 290.9	**980**	1.020 408	3078.761	754 296.4
931	1.074 114	2924.823	680 752.5	981	1.019 368	3081.902	755 836.6
932	1.072 961	2927.964	682 215.7	982	1.018 330	3085.044	757 378.3
933	1.071 811	2931.106	683 680.5	983	1.017 294	3088.186	758 921.6
934	1.070 664	2934.248	685 146.8	984	1.016 260	3091.327	760 466.5
935	1.069 519	2937.389	686 614.7	985	1.015 228	3094.469	762 012.9
936	1.068 376	2940.531	688 084.2	986	1.014 199	3097.610	763 561.0
937	1.067 236	2943.672	689 555.2	987	1.013 171	3100.752	765 110.5
938	1.066 098	2946.814	691 027.9	988	1.012 146	3103.894	766 661.7
939	1.064 963	2949.956	692 502.1	989	1.011 122	3107.035	768 214.4
940	1.063 830	2953.097	693 977.8	**990**	1.010 101	3110.177	769 768.7
941	1.062 699	2956.239	695 455.2	991	1.009 082	3113.318	771 324.6
942	1.061 571	2959.380	696 934.1	992	1.008 065	3116.460	772 882.1
943	1.060 445	2962.522	698 414.5	993	1.007 049	3119.602	774 441.1
944	1.059 322	2965.663	699 896.6	994	1.006 036	3122.743	776 001.7
945	1.058 201	2968.805	701 380.2	995	1.005 025	3125.885	777 563.8
946	1.057 082	2971.947	702 865.4	996	1.004 016	3129.026	779 127.5
947	1.055 966	2975.088	704 352.1	997	1.003 009	3132.168	780 692.8
948	1.054 852	2978.230	705 840.5	998	1.002 004	3135.309	782 259.7
949	1.053 741	2981.371	707 330.4	999	1.001 001	3138.451	783 828.2
950	1.052 632	2984.513	708 821.8	**1000**	1.000 000	3141.593	785 398.2

POWERS OF NUMBERS

This table contains the fourth through ninth power of the numbers from 1 to 100. Second and third powers will be found in a later table headed "Squares, Square Root, Cube and Cube Root."

The larger numbers are expressed exponentially to at least seven significant figures.

The approximate value written as a whole number may be obtained by shifting the decimal point to the right by the number of places indicated in the exponent of 10 shown at the head of each group of values. For example: the approximate value of 33^8 is found in the table as 14.064086×10^{11}. Written as a whole number it is 1 406 408 600 000.

POWERS OF NUMBERS

n	n^4	n^5	n^6	n^7	n^8	n^9
1	1	1	1	1	1	1
2	16	32	64	128	256	512
3	81	243	729	2187	6561	19683
4	256	1024	4096	16384	65536	262144
5	625	3125	15625	78125	390625	1953125
6	1296	7776	46656	279936	1679616	10077696
7	2401	16807	117649	823543	5764801	40353607
8	4096	32768	262144	2097152	16777216	134217728
9	6561	59049	531441	4782969	43046721	387420489
					$\times 10^8$	$\times 10^9$
10	10000	100000	1000000	10000000	1.000000	1.000000
11	14641	161051	1771561	19487171	2.143589	2.357948
12	20736	248832	2985984	35831808	4.299817	5.159780
13	28561	371293	4826809	62748517	8.157307	10.604499
14	38416	537824	7529536	105413504	14.757891	20.661047
15	50625	759375	11390625	170859375	25.628906	38.443359
16	65536	1048576	16777216	268435456	42.949673	68.719477
17	83521	1419857	24137569	410338673	69.757574	118.587876
18	104976	1889568	34012224	612220032	110.199606	198.359291
19	130321	2476099	47045881	893871739	169.835630	322.687697
				$\times 10^9$	$\times 10^{10}$	$\times 10^{11}$
20	160000	3200000	64000000	1.280000	2.560000	5.120000
21	194481	4084101	85766121	1.801089	3.782286	7.942800
22	234256	5153632	113379904	2.494358	5.487587	12.072692
23	279841	6436343	148035889	3.404825	7.831099	18.011527
24	331776	7962624	191102976	4.586471	11.007531	26.418075
25	390625	9765625	244140625	6.103516	15.258789	38.146973
26	456976	11881376	308915776	8.031810	20.882706	54.295037
27	531441	14348907	387420489	10.460353	28.242954	76.255975
28	614656	17210368	481890304	13.492929	37.780200	105.784559
29	707281	20511149	594823321	17.249876	50.024641	145.071460
			$\times 10^8$	$\times 10^{10}$	$\times 10^{11}$	$\times 10^{13}$
30	810000	24300000	7.290000	2.187000	6.561000	1.968300
31	923521	28629151	8.875037	2.751261	8.528910	2.643962
32	1048576	33554432	10.737418	3.435974	10.995116	3.518437
33	1185921	39135393	12.914680	4.261844	14.064086	4.641148
34	1336336	45435424	15.448044	5.252335	17.857939	6.071699
35	1500625	52521875	18.382656	6.433930	22.518754	7.881564
36	1679616	60466176	21.767823	7.836416	28.211099	10.155996
37	1874161	69343957	25.657264	9.493188	35.124795	12.996174
38	2085136	79235168	30.109364	11.441558	43.477921	16.521610
39	2313441	90224199	35.187438	13.723101	53.520093	20.872836
			$\times 10^9$	$\times 10^{10}$	$\times 10^{12}$	$\times 10^{14}$
40	2560000	102400000	4.096000	16.384000	6.553600	2.621440
41	2825761	115856201	4.750104	19.475427	7.984925	3.273819
42	3111696	130691232	5.489032	23.053933	9.682652	4.066714
43	3418801	147008443	6.321363	27.181861	11.688200	5.025926
44	3748096	164916224	7.256314	31.927781	14.048224	6.181218
45	4100625	184528125	8.303766	37.366945	16.815125	7.566806
46	4477456	205962976	9.474297	43.581766	20.047612	9.221902
47	4879681	229345007	10.779215	50.662312	23.811287	11.191305
48	5308416	254803968	12.230590	58.706834	28.179280	13.526055
49	5764801	282475249	13.841287	67.822307	33.232931	16.284136
50	6250000	312500000	15.625000	78.125000	39.062500	19.531250

POWERS OF NUMBERS (Continued)

n	n^4	n^5	n^6	n^7	n^8	n^9
			$\times 10^9$	$\times 10^{11}$	$\times 10^{13}$	$\times 10^{14}$
50	6250000	312500000	15.625000	7.812500	3.906250	19.531250
51	6765201	345025251	17.596288	8.974107	4.576794	23.341652
52	7311616	380204032	19.770610	10.280717	5.345973	27.799059
53	7890481	418195493	22.164361	11.747111	6.225969	32.997636
54	8503056	459165024	24.794911	13.389252	7.230196	39.043059
55	9150625	503284375	27.680641	15.224352	8.373394	46.053666
56	9834496	550731776	30.840979	17.270948	9.671731	54.161695
57	10556001	601692057	34.296447	19.548975	11.142916	63.514619
58	11316496	656356768	38.068693	22.079842	12.806308	74.276588
59	12117361	714924299	42.180534	24.886515	14.683044	86.629958
		$\times 10^8$	$\times 10^{10}$	$\times 10^{11}$	$\times 10^{13}$	$\times 10^{16}$
60	12960000	7.776000	4.665600	27.993600	16.796160	1.007770
61	13845841	8.445963	5.152037	31.427428	19.170731	1.169415
62	14776336	9.161328	5.680024	35.216146	21.834011	1.353709
63	15752961	9.924365	6.252350	39.389806	24.815578	1.563381
64	16777216	10.737418	6.871948	43.980465	28.147498	1.801440
65	17850625	11.602906	7.541889	49.022279	31.864481	2.071191
66	18974736	12.523326	8.265395	54.551607	36.004061	2.376268
67	20151121	13.501251	9.045838	60.607116	40.606768	2.720653
68	21381376	14.539336	9.886748	67.229888	45.716324	3.108710
69	22667121	15.640313	10.791816	74.463533	51.379837	3.545209
		$\times 10^8$	$\times 10^{10}$	$\times 10^{12}$	$\times 10^{14}$	$\times 10^{16}$
70	24010000	16.807000	11.764900	8.235430	5.764801	4.035361
71	25411681	18.042294	12.810028	9.095120	6.457535	4.584850
72	26873856	19.349176	13.931407	10.030613	7.222041	5.199870
73	28398241	20.730716	15.133423	11.047399	8.064601	5.887159
74	29986576	22.190066	16.420649	12.151280	8.991947	6.654041
75	31640625	23.730469	17.797852	13.348389	10.011292	7.508469
76	33362176	25.355254	19.269993	14.645195	11.130348	8.459064
77	35153041	27.067842	20.842238	16.048523	12.357363	9.515169
78	37015056	28.871744	22.519960	17.565569	13.701144	10.686892
79	38950081	30.770564	24.308746	19.203909	15.171088	11.985160
		$\times 10^8$	$\times 10^{10}$	$\times 10^{12}$	$\times 10^{14}$	$\times 10^{16}$
80	40960000	32.768000	26.214400	20.971520	16.777216	13.421773
81	43046721	34.867844	28.242954	22.876792	18.530202	15.009464
82	45212176	37.073984	30.400667	24.928547	20.441409	16.761955
83	47458321	39.390406	32.694037	27.136051	22.522922	18.694026
84	49787136	41.821194	35.129803	29.509035	24.787589	20.821575
85	52200625	44.370531	37.714952	32.057709	27.249053	23.161695
86	54700816	47.042702	40.456724	34.792782	29.921793	25.732742
87	57289761	49.842092	43.362620	37.725479	32.821167	28.554415
88	59969536	52.773192	46.440409	40.867560	35.963452	31.647838
89	62742241	55.840594	49.698129	44.231335	39.365888	35.035640
		$\times 10^9$	$\times 10^{11}$	$\times 10^{13}$	$\times 10^{15}$	$\times 10^{17}$
90	65610000	5.904900	5.314410	4.782969	4.304672	3.874205
91	68574961	6.240321	5.678693	5.167610	4.702525	4.279298
92	71639296	6.590815	6.063550	5.578466	5.132189	4.721614
93	74805201	6.956884	6.469902	6.017009	5.595818	5.204111
94	78074896	7.339040	6.898698	6.484776	6.095689	5.729948
95	81450625	7.737809	7.350919	6.983373	6.634204	6.302494
96	84934656	8.153727	7.827578	7.514475	7.213896	6.925340
97	88529281	8.587340	8.329720	8.079828	7.837434	7.602311
98	92236816	9.039208	8.858424	8.681255	8.507630	8.337478
99	96059601	9.509900	9.414801	9.320653	9.227447	9.135172
100	100000000	10.000000	10.000000	10.000000	10.000000	10.000000

POSITIVE POWERS OF TWO

n	2ⁿ				n	2ⁿ					
1	2				51	22517	99813	68524	8		
2	4				52	45035	99627	37049	6		
3	8				53	90071	99254	74099	2		
4	16				54	18014	39850	94819	84		
5	32				55	36028	79701	89639	68		
6	64				56	72057	59403	79279	36		
7	128				57	14411	51880	75855	872		
8	256				58	28823	03761	51711	744		
9	512				59	57646	07523	03423	488		
10	1024				60	11529	21504	60684	6976		
11	2048				61	23058	43009	21369	3952		
12	4096				62	46116	86018	42738	7904		
13	8192				63	92233	72036	85477	5808		
14	16384				64	18446	74407	37095	51616		
15	32768				65	36893	48814	74191	03232		
16	65536				66	73786	97629	48382	06464		
17	13107	2			67	14757	39525	89676	41292	8	
18	26214	4			68	29514	79051	79352	82585	6	
19	52428	8			69	59029	58103	58705	65171	2	
20	10485	76			70	11805	91620	71741	13034	24	
21	20971	52			71	23611	83241	43482	26068	48	
22	41943	04			72	47223	66482	86964	52136	96	
23	83886	08			73	94447	32965	73929	04273	92	
24	16777	216			74	18889	46593	14785	80854	784	
25	33554	432			75	37778	93186	29571	61709	568	
26	67108	864			76	75557	86372	59143	23419	136	
27	13421	7728			77	15111	57274	51828	64683	8272	
28	26843	5456			78	30223	14549	03657	29367	6544	
29	53687	0912			79	60446	29098	07314	58735	3088	
30	10737	41824			80	12089	25819	61462	91747	06176	
31	21474	83648			81	24178	51639	22925	83494	12352	
32	42949	67296			82	48357	03278	45851	66988	24704	
33	85899	34592			83	96714	06556	91703	33976	49408	
34	17179	86918	4		84	19342	81311	38340	66795	29881	6
35	34359	73836	8		85	38685	62622	76681	33590	59763	2
36	68719	47673	6		86	77371	25245	53362	67181	19526	4
37	13743	89534	72		87	15474	25049	10672	53436	23905	28
38	27487	79069	44		88	30948	50098	21345	06872	47810	56
39	54975	58138	88		89	61897	00196	42690	13744	95621	12
40	10995	11627	776		90	12379	40039	28538	02748	99124	224
41	21990	23255	552		91	24758	80078	57076	05497	98248	448
42	43980	46511	104		92	49517	60157	14152	10995	96496	896
43	87960	93022	208		93	99035	20314	28304	21991	92993	792
44	17592	18604	4416		94	19807	04062	85660	84398	38598	7584
45	35184	37208	8832		95	39614	08125	71321	68796	77197	5168
46	70368	74417	7664		96	79228	16251	42643	37593	54395	0336
47	14073	74883	55328		97	15845	63250	28528	67518	70879	00672
48	28147	49767	10656		98	31691	26500	57057	35037	41758	01344
49	56294	99534	21312		99	63382	53001	14114	70074	83516	02688
50	11258	99906	84262	4	100	12676	50600	22822	94014	96703	20537 6
					101	25353	01200	45645	88029	93406	41075 2

NEGATIVE POWERS OF TWO

n	2^{-n}							
0	1.0							
1	0.5							
2	0.25							
3	0.125							
4	0.0625							
5	0.03125							
6	0.01562	5						
7	0.00781	25						
8	0.00390	625						
9	0.00195	3125						
10	0.00097	65625						
11	0.00048	82812	5					
12	0.00024	41406	25					
13	0.00012	20703	125					
14	0.00006	10351	5625					
15	0.00003	05175	78125					
16	0.00001	52587	89062	5				
17	0.00000	76293	94531	25				
18	0.00000	38146	97265	625				
19	0.00000	19073	48632	8125				
20	0.00000	09536	74316	40625				
21	0.00000	04768	37158	20312	5			
22	0.00000	02384	18579	10156	25			
23	0.00000	01192	09289	55078	125			
24	0.00000	00596	04644	77539	0625			
25	0.00000	00298	02322	38769	53125			
26	0.00000	00149	01161	19384	76562	5		
27	0.00000	00074	50580	59692	38281	25		
28	0.00000	00037	25290	29846	19140	625		
29	0.00000	00018	62645	14923	09570	3125		
30	0.00000	00009	31322	57461	54785	15625		
31	0.00000	00004	65661	28730	77392	57812	5	
32	0.00000	00002	32830	64365	38696	28906	25	
33	0.00000	00001	16415	32182	69348	14453	125	
34	0.00000	00000	58207	66091	34674	07226	5625	
35	0.00000	00000	29103	83045	67337	03613	28125	
36	0.00000	00000	14551	91522	83668	51806	64062	5
37	0.00000	00000	07275	95761	41834	25903	32031	25
38	0.00000	00000	03637	97880	70917	12951	66015	625
39	0.00000	00000	01818	98940	35458	56475	83007	8125
40	0.00000	00000	00909	49470	17729	28237	91503	90625
41	0.00000	00000	00454	74735	08864	64118	95751	95312 5
42	0.00000	00000	00227	37367	54432	32059	47875	97656 25
43	0.00000	00000	00113	68683	77216	16029	73937	98828 125
44	0.00000	00000	00056	84341	88608	08014	86968	99414 0625
45	0.00000	00000	00028	42170	94304	04007	43484	49707 03125
46	0.00000	00000	00014	21085	47152	02003	71742	24853 51562 5
47	0.00000	00000	00007	10542	73576	01001	85871	12426 75781 25
48	0.00000	00000	00003	55271	36788	00500	92935	56213 37890 625
49	0.00000	00000	00001	77635	68394	00250	46467	78106 68945 3125
50	0.00000	00000	00000	88817	84197	00125	23233	89053 34472 65625

Numerical Tables

SUMS OF POWERS OF INTEGERS, $\displaystyle\sum_{k=1}^{n} k^m$

$(m = 1, 2, 3, 4); 1 \leq n \leq 40$

n	Σk	Σk^2	Σk^3	Σk^4
1	1	1	1	1
2	3	5	9	17
3	6	14	36	98
4	10	30	100	354
5	15	55	225	979
6	21	91	441	2275
7	28	140	784	4676
8	36	204	1296	8772
9	45	285	2025	15333
10	55	385	3025	25333
11	66	506	4356	39974
12	78	650	6084	60710
13	91	819	8281	89271
14	105	1015	11025	127687
15	120	1240	14400	178312
16	136	1496	18496	243848
17	153	1785	23409	327369
18	171	2109	29241	432345
19	190	2470	36100	562666
20	210	2870	44100	722666
21	231	3311	53361	917147
22	253	3795	64009	1151403
23	276	4324	76176	1431244
24	300	4900	90000	1763020
25	325	5525	105625	2153645
26	351	6201	123201	2610621
27	378	6930	142884	3142062
28	406	7714	164836	3756718
29	435	8555	189225	4463999
30	465	9455	216225	5273999
31	496	10416	246016	6197520
32	528	11440	278784	7246096
33	561	12529	314721	8432017
34	595	13685	354025	9768353
35	630	14910	396900	11268978
36	666	16206	443556	12948594
37	703	17575	494209	14822755
38	741	19019	549081	16907891
39	780	20540	608400	19221332
40	820	22140	672400	21781332

SUMS OF POWERS OF THE FIRST *n* INTEGERS

$$\sum_{k=1}^{n} k = 1 + 2 + 3 + \cdots + n = \frac{n(n+1)}{2}$$

$$\sum_{k=1}^{n} k^2 = 1^2 + 2^2 + 3^2 + \cdots + n^2 = \frac{n(n+1)(2n+1)}{6}$$

$$\sum_{k=1}^{n} k^3 = \frac{n^2(n+1)^2}{4}$$

$$\sum_{k=1}^{n} k^4 = \frac{n}{30}(n+1)(2n+1)(3n^2+3n-1).$$

$$\sum_{k=1}^{n} k^5 = \frac{n^2}{12}(n+1)^2(2n^2+2n-1).$$

$$\sum_{k=1}^{n} k^6 = \frac{n}{42}(n+1)(2n+1)(3n^4+6n^3-3n+1).$$

$$\sum_{k=1}^{n} k^7 = \frac{n^2}{24}(n+1)^2(3n^4+6n^3-n^2-4n+2).$$

$$\sum_{k=1}^{n} k^8 = \frac{n}{90}(n+1)(2n+1)(5n^6+15n^5+5n^4-15n^3-n^2+9n-3).$$

$$\sum_{k=1}^{n} k^9 = \frac{n^2}{20}(n+1)^2(2n^6+6n^5+n^4-8n^3+n^2+6n-3).$$

$$\sum_{k=1}^{n} k^{10} = \frac{n}{66}(n+1)(2n+1)(3n^8+12n^7+8n^6-18n^5$$
$$-10n^4+24n^3+2n^2-15n+5).$$

FACTORS AND PRIMES

The table presents the prime factors of *all* factorable numbers and the mantissas of the common logarithms of all prime numbers from 1 to 2000.

It should be noted that the third digit of the number is given at the top of the page and that the table runs across two facing pages. Thus, the factors of 258 are found, on the right hand page, on a line with 25 and under vertical column 8 to be $2 \cdot 3 \cdot 43$.

FACTORS AND PRIMES

If n is prime the mantissa of its common logarithm is given. If n is not prime its prime factors are given.

n	0	1	2	3	4
0	....		3010300	4771213	2^2
1	$2 \cdot 5$	0413927	$2^2 \cdot 3$	1139434	$2 \cdot 7$
2	$2^2 \cdot 5$	$3 \cdot 7$	$2 \cdot 11$	3617278	$2^3 \cdot 3$
3	$2 \cdot 3 \cdot 5$	4913617	2^5	$3 \cdot 11$	$2 \cdot 17$
4	$2^3 \cdot 5$	6127839	$2 \cdot 3 \cdot 7$	6334685	$2^2 \cdot 11$
5	$2 \cdot 5^2$	$3 \cdot 17$	$2^2 \cdot 13$	7242759	$2 \cdot 3^3$
6	$2^2 \cdot 3 \cdot 5$	7853298	$2 \cdot 31$	$3^2 \cdot 7$	2^6
7	$2 \cdot 5 \cdot 7$	8512583	$2^3 \cdot 3^2$	8633229	$2 \cdot 37$
8	$2^4 \cdot 5$	3^4	$2 \cdot 41$	9190781	$2^2 \cdot 3 \cdot 7$
9	$2 \cdot 3^2 \cdot 5$	$7 \cdot 13$	$2^2 \cdot 23$	$3 \cdot 31$	$2 \cdot 47$
10	$2^2 \cdot 5^2$	0043214	$2 \cdot 3 \cdot 17$	0128372	$2^3 \cdot 13$
11	$2 \cdot 5 \cdot 11$	$3 \cdot 37$	$2^4 \cdot 7$	0530784	$2 \cdot 3 \cdot 19$
12	$2^3 \cdot 3 \cdot 5$	11^2	$2 \cdot 61$	$3 \cdot 41$	$2^2 \cdot 31$
13	$2 \cdot 5 \cdot 13$	1172713	$2^2 \cdot 3 \cdot 11$	$7 \cdot 19$	$2 \cdot 67$
14	$2^2 \cdot 5 \cdot 7$	$3 \cdot 47$	$2 \cdot 71$	$11 \cdot 13$	$2^4 \cdot 3^2$
15	$2 \cdot 3 \cdot 5^2$	1789769	$2^3 \cdot 19$	$3^2 \cdot 17$	$2 \cdot 7 \cdot 11$
16	$2^5 \cdot 5$	$7 \cdot 23$	$2 \cdot 3^3$	2121876	$2^2 \cdot 41$
17	$2 \cdot 5 \cdot 17$	$3^2 \cdot 19$	$2^2 \cdot 43$	2380461	$2 \cdot 3 \cdot 29$
18	$2^2 \cdot 3^2 \cdot 5$	2576786	$2 \cdot 7 \cdot 13$	$3 \cdot 61$	$2^3 \cdot 23$
19	$2 \cdot 5 \cdot 19$	2810334	$2^6 \cdot 3$	2855573	$2 \cdot 97$
20	$2^3 \cdot 5^2$	$3 \cdot 67$	$2 \cdot 101$	$7 \cdot 29$	$2^2 \cdot 3 \cdot 17$
21	$2 \cdot 3 \cdot 5 \cdot 7$	3242825	$2^2 \cdot 53$	$3 \cdot 71$	$2 \cdot 107$
22	$2^2 \cdot 5 \cdot 11$	$13 \cdot 17$	$2 \cdot 3 \cdot 37$	3483049	$2^5 \cdot 7$
23	$2 \cdot 5 \cdot 23$	$3 \cdot 7 \cdot 11$	$2^3 \cdot 29$	3673559	$2 \cdot 3^2 \cdot 13$
24	$2^4 \cdot 3 \cdot 5$	3820170	$2 \cdot 11^2$	3^5	$2^2 \cdot 61$
25	$2 \cdot 5^3$	3996737	$2^2 \cdot 3^2 \cdot 7$	$11 \cdot 23$	$2 \cdot 127$
26	$2^2 \cdot 5 \cdot 13$	$3^2 \cdot 29$	$2 \cdot 131$	4199557	$2^3 \cdot 3 \cdot 11$
27	$2 \cdot 3^3 \cdot 5$	4329693	$2^4 \cdot 17$	$3 \cdot 7 \cdot 13$	$2 \cdot 137$
28	$2^3 \cdot 5 \cdot 7$	4487063	$2 \cdot 3 \cdot 47$	4517864	$2^2 \cdot 71$
29	$2 \cdot 5 \cdot 29$	$3 \cdot 97$	$2^2 \cdot 73$	4668676	$2 \cdot 3 \cdot 7^2$
30	$2^2 \cdot 3 \cdot 5^2$	$7 \cdot 43$	$2 \cdot 151$	$3 \cdot 101$	$2^4 \cdot 19$
31	$2 \cdot 5 \cdot 31$	4927604	$2^3 \cdot 3 \cdot 13$	4955443	$2 \cdot 157$
32	$2^6 \cdot 5$	$3 \cdot 107$	$2 \cdot 7 \cdot 23$	$17 \cdot 19$	$2^2 \cdot 3^4$
33	$2 \cdot 3 \cdot 5 \cdot 11$	5198280	$2^2 \cdot 83$	$3^2 \cdot 37$	$2 \cdot 167$
34	$2^2 \cdot 5 \cdot 17$	$11 \cdot 31$	$2 \cdot 3^2 \cdot 19$	7^3	$2^3 \cdot 43$
35	$2 \cdot 5^2 \cdot 7$	$3^3 \cdot 13$	$2^5 \cdot 11$	5477747	$2 \cdot 3 \cdot 59$
36	$2^3 \cdot 3^2 \cdot 5$	19^2	$2 \cdot 181$	$3 \cdot 11^2$	$2^2 \cdot 7 \cdot 13$
37	$2 \cdot 5 \cdot 37$	$7 \cdot 53$	$2^2 \cdot 3 \cdot 31$	5717088	$2 \cdot 11 \cdot 17$
38	$2^2 \cdot 5 \cdot 19$	$3 \cdot 127$	$2 \cdot 191$	5831988	$2^7 \cdot 3$
39	$2 \cdot 3 \cdot 5 \cdot 13$	$17 \cdot 23$	$2^3 \cdot 7^2$	$3 \cdot 131$	$2 \cdot 197$
40	$2^4 \cdot 5^2$	6031444	$2 \cdot 3 \cdot 67$	$13 \cdot 31$	$2^2 \cdot 101$
41	$2 \cdot 5 \cdot 41$	$3 \cdot 137$	$2^2 \cdot 103$	$7 \cdot 59$	$2 \cdot 3^2 \cdot 23$
42	$2^2 \cdot 3 \cdot 5 \cdot 7$	6242821	$2 \cdot 211$	$3^2 \cdot 47$	$2^3 \cdot 53$
43	$2 \cdot 5 \cdot 43$	6344773	$2^4 \cdot 3^3$	6364879	$2 \cdot 7 \cdot 31$
44	$2^3 \cdot 5 \cdot 11$	$3^2 \cdot 7^2$	$2 \cdot 13 \cdot 17$	6464037	$2^2 \cdot 3 \cdot 37$
45	$2 \cdot 3^2 \cdot 5^2$	$11 \cdot 41$	$2^2 \cdot 113$	$3 \cdot 151$	$2 \cdot 227$
46	$2^2 \cdot 5 \cdot 23$	6637009	$2 \cdot 3 \cdot 7 \cdot 11$	6655810	$2^4 \cdot 29$
47	$2 \cdot 5 \cdot 47$	$3 \cdot 157$	$2^3 \cdot 59$	$11 \cdot 43$	$2 \cdot 3 \cdot 79$
48	$2^5 \cdot 3 \cdot 5$	$13 \cdot 37$	$2 \cdot 241$	$3 \cdot 7 \cdot 23$	$2^2 \cdot 11^2$
49	$2 \cdot 5 \cdot 7^2$	6910815	$2^2 \cdot 3 \cdot 41$	$17 \cdot 29$	$2 \cdot 13 \cdot 19$
50	$2^2 \cdot 5^3$	$3 \cdot 167$	$2 \cdot 251$	7015680	$2^3 \cdot 3^2 \cdot 7$

FACTORS AND PRIMES (Continued)

n	5	6	7	8	9
0	6989700	$2 \cdot 3$	8450980	2^3	3^2
1	$3 \cdot 5$	2^4	2304489	$2 \cdot 3^2$	2787536
2	5^2	$2 \cdot 13$	3^3	$2^2 \cdot 7$	4623980
3	$5 \cdot 7$	$2^2 \cdot 3^2$	5682017	$2 \cdot 19$	$3 \cdot 13$
4	$3^2 \cdot 5$	$2 \cdot 23$	6720979	$2^4 \cdot 3$	7^2
5	$5 \cdot 11$	$2^3 \cdot 7$	$3 \cdot 19$	$2 \cdot 29$	7708520
6	$5 \cdot 13$	$2 \cdot 3 \cdot 11$	8260748	$2^2 \cdot 17$	$3 \cdot 23$
7	$3 \cdot 5^2$	$2^2 \cdot 19$	$7 \cdot 11$	$2 \cdot 3 \cdot 13$	8976271
8	$5 \cdot 17$	$2 \cdot 43$	$3 \cdot 29$	$2^3 \cdot 11$	9493900
9	$5 \cdot 19$	$2^5 \cdot 3$	9867717	$2 \cdot 7^2$	$3^2 \cdot 11$
10	$3 \cdot 5 \cdot 7$	$2 \cdot 53$	0293838	$2^2 \cdot 3^3$	0374265
11	$5 \cdot 23$	$2^2 \cdot 29$	$3^2 \cdot 13$	$2 \cdot 59$	$7 \cdot 17$
12	5^3	$2 \cdot 3^2 \cdot 7$	1038037	2^7	$3 \cdot 43$
13	$3^3 \cdot 5$	$2^3 \cdot 17$	1367206	$2 \cdot 3 \cdot 23$	1430148
14	$5 \cdot 29$	$2 \cdot 73$	$3 \cdot 7^2$	$2^2 \cdot 37$	1731863
15	$5 \cdot 31$	$2^2 \cdot 3 \cdot 13$	1958997	$2 \cdot 79$	$3 \cdot 53$
16	$3 \cdot 5 \cdot 11$	$2 \cdot 83$	2227165	$2^3 \cdot 3 \cdot 7$	13^2
17	$5^2 \cdot 7$	$2^4 \cdot 11$	$3 \cdot 59$	$2 \cdot 89$	2528530
18	$5 \cdot 37$	$2 \cdot 3 \cdot 31$	$11 \cdot 17$	$2^2 \cdot 47$	$3^3 \cdot 7$
19	$3 \cdot 5 \cdot 13$	$2^2 \cdot 7^2$	2944662	$2 \cdot 3^2 \cdot 11$	2988531
20	$5 \cdot 41$	$2 \cdot 103$	$3^2 \cdot 23$	$2^4 \cdot 13$	$11 \cdot 19$
21	$5 \cdot 43$	$2^3 \cdot 3^3$	$7 \cdot 31$	$2 \cdot 109$	$3 \cdot 73$
22	$3^2 \cdot 5^2$	$2 \cdot 113$	3560259	$2^2 \cdot 3 \cdot 19$	3598355
23	$5 \cdot 47$	$2^2 \cdot 59$	$3 \cdot 79$	$2 \cdot 7 \cdot 17$	3783979
24	$5 \cdot 7^2$	$2 \cdot 3 \cdot 41$	$13 \cdot 19$	$2^3 \cdot 31$	$3 \cdot 83$
25	$3 \cdot 5 \cdot 17$	2^8	4099331	$2 \cdot 3 \cdot 43$	$7 \cdot 37$
26	$5 \cdot 53$	$2 \cdot 7 \cdot 19$	$3 \cdot 89$	$2^2 \cdot 67$	4297523
27	$5^2 \cdot 11$	$2^2 \cdot 3 \cdot 23$	4424798	$2 \cdot 139$	$3^2 \cdot 31$
28	$3 \cdot 5 \cdot 19$	$2 \cdot 11 \cdot 13$	$7 \cdot 41$	$2^5 \cdot 3^2$	17^2
29	$5 \cdot 59$	$2^3 \cdot 37$	$3^3 \cdot 11$	$2 \cdot 149$	$13 \cdot 23$
30	$5 \cdot 61$	$2 \cdot 3^2 \cdot 17$	4871384	$2^2 \cdot 7 \cdot 11$	$3 \cdot 103$
31	$3^2 \cdot 5 \cdot 7$	$2^2 \cdot 79$	5010593	$2 \cdot 3 \cdot 53$	$11 \cdot 29$
32	$5^2 \cdot 13$	$2 \cdot 163$	$3 \cdot 109$	$2^3 \cdot 41$	$7 \cdot 47$
33	$5 \cdot 67$	$2^4 \cdot 3 \cdot 7$	5276299	$2 \cdot 13^2$	$3 \cdot 113$
34	$3 \cdot 5 \cdot 23$	$2 \cdot 173$	5403295	$2^2 \cdot 3 \cdot 29$	5428254
35	$5 \cdot 71$	$2^2 \cdot 89$	$3 \cdot 7 \cdot 17$	$2 \cdot 179$	5550944
36	$5 \cdot 73$	$2 \cdot 3 \cdot 61$	5646661	$2^4 \cdot 23$	$3^2 \cdot 41$
37	$3 \cdot 5^3$	$2^3 \cdot 47$	$13 \cdot 29$	$2 \cdot 3^3 \cdot 7$	5786392
38	$5 \cdot 7 \cdot 11$	$2 \cdot 193$	$3^2 \cdot 43$	$2^2 \cdot 97$	5899496
39	$5 \cdot 79$	$2^2 \cdot 3^2 \cdot 11$	5987905	$2 \cdot 199$	$3 \cdot 7 \cdot 19$
40	$3^4 \cdot 5$	$2 \cdot 7 \cdot 29$	$11 \cdot 37$	$2^3 \cdot 3 \cdot 17$	6117233
41	$5 \cdot 83$	$2^5 \cdot 13$	$3 \cdot 139$	$2 \cdot 11 \cdot 19$	6222140
42	$5^2 \cdot 17$	$2 \cdot 3 \cdot 71$	$7 \cdot 61$	$2^2 \cdot 107$	$3 \cdot 11 \cdot 13$
43	$3 \cdot 5 \cdot 29$	$2^2 \cdot 109$	$19 \cdot 23$	$2 \cdot 3 \cdot 73$	6424645
44	$5 \cdot 89$	$2 \cdot 223$	$3 \cdot 149$	$2^6 \cdot 7$	6522463
45	$5 \cdot 7 \cdot 13$	$2^3 \cdot 3 \cdot 19$	6599162	$2 \cdot 229$	$3^3 \cdot 17$
46	$3 \cdot 5 \cdot 31$	$2 \cdot 233$	6693169	$2^2 \cdot 3^2 \cdot 13$	$7 \cdot 67$
47	$5^2 \cdot 19$	$2^2 \cdot 7 \cdot 17$	$3^2 \cdot 53$	$2 \cdot 239$	6803355
48	$5 \cdot 97$	$2 \cdot 3^5$	6875290	$2^3 \cdot 61$	$3 \cdot 163$
49	$3^2 \cdot 5 \cdot 11$	$2^4 \cdot 31$	$7 \cdot 71$	$2 \cdot 3 \cdot 83$	6981005
50	$5 \cdot 101$	$2 \cdot 11 \cdot 23$	$3 \cdot 13^2$	$2^2 \cdot 127$	7067178

FACTORS AND PRIMES (Continued)

n	0	1	2	3	4
50	$2^2 \cdot 5^3$	$3 \cdot 167$	$2 \cdot 251$	7015680	$2^3 \cdot 3^2 \cdot 7$
51	$2 \cdot 3 \cdot 5 \cdot 17$	$7 \cdot 73$	2^9	$3^3 \cdot 19$	$2 \cdot 257$
52	$2^3 \cdot 5 \cdot 13$	7168377	$2 \cdot 3^2 \cdot 29$	7185017	$2^2 \cdot 131$
53	$2 \cdot 5 \cdot 53$	$3^2 \cdot 59$	$2^2 \cdot 7 \cdot 19$	$13 \cdot 41$	$2 \cdot 3 \cdot 89$
54	$2^2 \cdot 3^3 \cdot 5$	7331973	$2 \cdot 271$	$3 \cdot 181$	$2^5 \cdot 17$
55	$2 \cdot 5^2 \cdot 11$	$19 \cdot 29$	$2^3 \cdot 3 \cdot 23$	$7 \cdot 79$	$2 \cdot 277$
56	$2^4 \cdot 5 \cdot 7$	$3 \cdot 11 \cdot 17$	$2 \cdot 281$	7505084	$2^2 \cdot 3 \cdot 47$
57	$2 \cdot 3 \cdot 5 \cdot 19$	7566361	$2^2 \cdot 11 \cdot 13$	$3 \cdot 191$	$2 \cdot 7 \cdot 41$
58	$2^2 \cdot 5 \cdot 29$	$7 \cdot 83$	$2 \cdot 3 \cdot 97$	$11 \cdot 53$	$2^3 \cdot 73$
59	$2 \cdot 5 \cdot 59$	$3 \cdot 197$	$2^4 \cdot 37$	7730547	$2 \cdot 3^3 \cdot 11$
60	$2^3 \cdot 3 \cdot 5^2$	7788745	$2 \cdot 7 \cdot 43$	$3^2 \cdot 67$	$2^2 \cdot 151$
61	$2 \cdot 5 \cdot 61$	$13 \cdot 47$	$2^2 \cdot 3^2 \cdot 17$	7874605	$2 \cdot 307$
62	$2^2 \cdot 5 \cdot 31$	$3^3 \cdot 23$	$2 \cdot 311$	$7 \cdot 89$	$2^4 \cdot 3 \cdot 13$
63	$2 \cdot 3^2 \cdot 5 \cdot 7$	8000294	$2^3 \cdot 79$	$3 \cdot 211$	$2 \cdot 317$
64	$2^7 \cdot 5$	8068580	$2 \cdot 3 \cdot 107$	8082110	$2^2 \cdot 7 \cdot 23$
65	$2 \cdot 5^2 \cdot 13$	$3 \cdot 7 \cdot 31$	$2^2 \cdot 163$	8149132	$2 \cdot 3 \cdot 109$
66	$2^2 \cdot 3 \cdot 5 \cdot 11$	8202015	$2 \cdot 331$	$3 \cdot 13 \cdot 17$	$2^3 \cdot 83$
67	$2 \cdot 5 \cdot 67$	$11 \cdot 61$	$2^5 \cdot 3 \cdot 7$	8280151	$2 \cdot 337$
68	$2^3 \cdot 5 \cdot 17$	$3 \cdot 227$	$2 \cdot 11 \cdot 31$	8344207	$2^2 \cdot 3^2 \cdot 19$
69	$2 \cdot 3 \cdot 5 \cdot 23$	8394780	$2^2 \cdot 173$	$3^2 \cdot 7 \cdot 11$	$2 \cdot 347$
70	$2^2 \cdot 5^2 \cdot 7$	8457180	$2 \cdot 3^3 \cdot 13$	$19 \cdot 37$	$2^6 \cdot 11$
71	$2 \cdot 5 \cdot 71$	$3^2 \cdot 79$	$2^3 \cdot 89$	$23 \cdot 31$	$2 \cdot 3 \cdot 7 \cdot 17$
72	$2^4 \cdot 3^2 \cdot 5$	$7 \cdot 103$	$2 \cdot 19^2$	$3 \cdot 241$	$2^2 \cdot 181$
73	$2 \cdot 5 \cdot 73$	$17 \cdot 43$	$2^2 \cdot 3 \cdot 61$	8651040	$2 \cdot 367$
74	$2^2 \cdot 5 \cdot 37$	$3 \cdot 13 \cdot 19$	$2 \cdot 7 \cdot 53$	8709888	$2^3 \cdot 3 \cdot 31$
75	$2 \cdot 3 \cdot 5^3$	8756399	$2^4 \cdot 47$	$3 \cdot 251$	$2 \cdot 13 \cdot 29$
76	$2^3 \cdot 5 \cdot 19$	8813847	$2 \cdot 3 \cdot 127$	$7 \cdot 109$	$2^2 \cdot 191$
77	$2 \cdot 5 \cdot 7 \cdot 11$	$3 \cdot 257$	$2^2 \cdot 193$	8881795	$2 \cdot 3^2 \cdot 43$
78	$2^2 \cdot 3 \cdot 5 \cdot 13$	$11 \cdot 71$	$2 \cdot 17 \cdot 23$	$3^3 \cdot 29$	$2^4 \cdot 7^2$
79	$2 \cdot 5 \cdot 79$	$7 \cdot 113$	$2^3 \cdot 3^2 \cdot 11$	$13 \cdot 61$	$2 \cdot 397$
80	$2^5 \cdot 5^2$	$3^2 \cdot 89$	$2 \cdot 401$	$11 \cdot 73$	$2^2 \cdot 3 \cdot 67$
81	$2 \cdot 3^4 \cdot 5$	9090209	$2^2 \cdot 7 \cdot 29$	$3 \cdot 271$	$2 \cdot 11 \cdot 37$
82	$2^2 \cdot 5 \cdot 41$	9143432	$2 \cdot 3 \cdot 137$	9153998	$2^3 \cdot 103$
83	$2 \cdot 5 \cdot 83$	$3 \cdot 277$	$2^6 \cdot 13$	$7^2 \cdot 17$	$2 \cdot 3 \cdot 139$
84	$2^3 \cdot 3 \cdot 5 \cdot 7$	29^2	$2 \cdot 421$	$3 \cdot 281$	$2^2 \cdot 211$
85	$2 \cdot 5^2 \cdot 17$	$23 \cdot 37$	$2^2 \cdot 3 \cdot 71$	9309490	$2 \cdot 7 \cdot 61$
86	$2^2 \cdot 5 \cdot 43$	$3 \cdot 7 \cdot 41$	$2 \cdot 431$	9360108	$2^5 \cdot 3^3$
87	$2 \cdot 3 \cdot 5 \cdot 29$	$13 \cdot 67$	$2^3 \cdot 109$	$3^2 \cdot 97$	$2 \cdot 19 \cdot 23$
88	$2^4 \cdot 5 \cdot 11$	9449759	$2 \cdot 3^2 \cdot 7^2$	9459607	$2^2 \cdot 13 \cdot 17$
89	$2 \cdot 5 \cdot 89$	$3^4 \cdot 11$	$2^2 \cdot 223$	$19 \cdot 47$	$2 \cdot 3 \cdot 149$
90	$2^2 \cdot 3^2 \cdot 5^2$	$17 \cdot 53$	$2 \cdot 11 \cdot 41$	$3 \cdot 7 \cdot 43$	$2^3 \cdot 113$
91	$2 \cdot 5 \cdot 7 \cdot 13$	9595184	$2^4 \cdot 3 \cdot 19$	$11 \cdot 83$	$2 \cdot 457$
92	$2^3 \cdot 5 \cdot 23$	$3 \cdot 307$	$2 \cdot 461$	$13 \cdot 71$	$2^2 \cdot 3 \cdot 7 \cdot 11$
93	$2 \cdot 3 \cdot 5 \cdot 31$	$7^2 \cdot 19$	$2^2 \cdot 233$	$3 \cdot 311$	$2 \cdot 467$
94	$2^2 \cdot 5 \cdot 47$	9735896	$2 \cdot 3 \cdot 157$	$23 \cdot 41$	$2^4 \cdot 59$
95	$2 \cdot 5^2 \cdot 19$	$3 \cdot 317$	$2^3 \cdot 7 \cdot 17$	9790929	$2 \cdot 3^2 \cdot 53$
96	$2^6 \cdot 3 \cdot 5$	31^2	$2 \cdot 13 \cdot 37$	$3^2 \cdot 107$	$2^2 \cdot 241$
97	$2 \cdot 5 \cdot 97$	9872192	$2^2 \cdot 3^5$	$7 \cdot 139$	$2 \cdot 487$
98	$2^2 \cdot 5 \cdot 7^2$	$3^2 \cdot 109$	$2 \cdot 491$	9925535	$2^3 \cdot 3 \cdot 41$
99	$2 \cdot 3^2 \cdot 5 \cdot 11$	9960737	$2^5 \cdot 31$	$3 \cdot 331$	$2 \cdot 7 \cdot 71$
100	$2^3 \cdot 5^3$	$7 \cdot 11 \cdot 13$	$2 \cdot 3 \cdot 167$	$17 \cdot 59$	$2^2 \cdot 251$

FACTORS AND PRIMES (Continued)

n	5	6	7	8	9
50	$5 \cdot 101$	$2 \cdot 11 \cdot 23$	$3 \cdot 13^2$	$2^2 \cdot 127$	**7067178**
51	$5 \cdot 103$	$2^2 \cdot 3 \cdot 43$	$11 \cdot 47$	$2 \cdot 7 \cdot 37$	$3 \cdot 173$
52	$3 \cdot 5^2 \cdot 7$	$2 \cdot 263$	$17 \cdot 31$	$2^4 \cdot 3 \cdot 11$	23^2
53	$5 \cdot 107$	$2^3 \cdot 67$	$3 \cdot 179$	$2 \cdot 269$	$7^2 \cdot 11$
54	$5 \cdot 109$	$2 \cdot 3 \cdot 7 \cdot 13$	**7379873**	$2^2 \cdot 137$	$3^2 \cdot 61$
55	$3 \cdot 5 \cdot 37$	$2^2 \cdot 139$	**7458552**	$2 \cdot 3^2 \cdot 31$	$13 \cdot 43$
56	$5 \cdot 113$	$2 \cdot 283$	$3^4 \cdot 7$	$2^3 \cdot 71$	**7551123**
57	$5^2 \cdot 23$	$2^6 \cdot 3^2$	**7611758**	$2 \cdot 17^2$	$3 \cdot 193$
58	$3^2 \cdot 5 \cdot 13$	$2 \cdot 293$	**7686381**	$2^3 \cdot 3 \cdot 7^2$	$19 \cdot 31$
59	$5 \cdot 7 \cdot 17$	$2^2 \cdot 149$	$3 \cdot 199$	$2 \cdot 13 \cdot 23$	**7774268**
60	$5 \cdot 11^2$	$2 \cdot 3 \cdot 101$	**7831887**	$2^5 \cdot 19$	$3 \cdot 7 \cdot 29$
61	$3 \cdot 5 \cdot 41$	$2^3 \cdot 7 \cdot 11$	**7902852**	$2 \cdot 3 \cdot 103$	**7916906**
62	5^4	$2 \cdot 313$	$3 \cdot 11 \cdot 19$	$2^2 \cdot 157$	$17 \cdot 37$
63	$5 \cdot 127$	$2^2 \cdot 3 \cdot 53$	$7^2 \cdot 13$	$2 \cdot 11 \cdot 29$	$3^2 \cdot 71$
64	$3 \cdot 5 \cdot 43$	$2 \cdot 17 \cdot 19$	**8109043**	$2^3 \cdot 3^4$	$11 \cdot 59$
65	$5 \cdot 131$	$2^4 \cdot 41$	$3^2 \cdot 73$	$2 \cdot 7 \cdot 47$	**8188854**
66	$5 \cdot 7 \cdot 19$	$2 \cdot 3^2 \cdot 37$	$23 \cdot 29$	$2^2 \cdot 167$	$3 \cdot 223$
67	$3^3 \cdot 5^2$	$2^2 \cdot 13^2$	**8305887**	$2 \cdot 3 \cdot 113$	$7 \cdot 97$
68	$5 \cdot 137$	$2 \cdot 7^3$	$3 \cdot 229$	$2^4 \cdot 43$	$13 \cdot 53$
69	$5 \cdot 139$	$2^3 \cdot 3 \cdot 29$	$17 \cdot 41$	$2 \cdot 349$	$3 \cdot 233$
70	$3 \cdot 5 \cdot 47$	$2 \cdot 353$	$7 \cdot 101$	$2^2 \cdot 3 \cdot 59$	**8506462**
71	$5 \cdot 11 \cdot 13$	$2^2 \cdot 179$	$3 \cdot 239$	$2 \cdot 359$	**8567289**
72	$5^2 \cdot 29$	$2 \cdot 3 \cdot 11^2$	**8615344**	$2^3 \cdot 7 \cdot 13$	3^6
73	$3 \cdot 5 \cdot 7^2$	$2^5 \cdot 23$	$11 \cdot 67$	$2 \cdot 3^2 \cdot 41$	**8686444**
74	$5 \cdot 149$	$2 \cdot 373$	$3^2 \cdot 83$	$2^2 \cdot 11 \cdot 17$	$7 \cdot 107$
75	$5 \cdot 151$	$2^2 \cdot 3^3 \cdot 7$	**8790959**	$2 \cdot 379$	$3 \cdot 11 \cdot 23$
76	$3^2 \cdot 5 \cdot 17$	$2 \cdot 383$	$13 \cdot 59$	$2^8 \cdot 3$	**8859263**
77	$5^2 \cdot 31$	$2^3 \cdot 97$	$3 \cdot 7 \cdot 37$	$2 \cdot 389$	$19 \cdot 41$
78	$5 \cdot 157$	$2 \cdot 3 \cdot 131$	**8959747**	$2^2 \cdot 197$	$3 \cdot 263$
79	$3 \cdot 5 \cdot 53$	$2^2 \cdot 199$	**9014583**	$2 \cdot 3 \cdot 7 \cdot 19$	$17 \cdot 47$
80	$5 \cdot 7 \cdot 23$	$2 \cdot 13 \cdot 31$	$3 \cdot 269$	$2^3 \cdot 101$	**9079485**
81	$5 \cdot 163$	$2^4 \cdot 3 \cdot 17$	$19 \cdot 43$	$2 \cdot 409$	$3^2 \cdot 7 \cdot 13$
82	$3 \cdot 5^2 \cdot 11$	$2 \cdot 7 \cdot 59$	**9175055**	$2^2 \cdot 3^2 \cdot 23$	**9185545**
83	$5 \cdot 167$	$2^2 \cdot 11 \cdot 19$	$3^3 \cdot 31$	$2 \cdot 419$	**9237620**
84	$5 \cdot 13^2$	$2 \cdot 3^2 \cdot 47$	$7 \cdot 11^2$	$2^4 \cdot 53$	$3 \cdot 283$
85	$3^2 \cdot 5 \cdot 19$	$2^3 \cdot 107$	**9329808**	$2 \cdot 3 \cdot 11 \cdot 13$	**9339932**
86	$5 \cdot 173$	$2 \cdot 433$	$3 \cdot 17^2$	$2^2 \cdot 7 \cdot 31$	$11 \cdot 79$
87	$5^3 \cdot 7$	$2^2 \cdot 3 \cdot 73$	**9429996**	$2 \cdot 439$	$3 \cdot 293$
88	$3 \cdot 5 \cdot 59$	$2 \cdot 443$	**9479236**	$2^3 \cdot 3 \cdot 37$	$7 \cdot 127$
89	$5 \cdot 179$	$2^7 \cdot 7$	$3 \cdot 13 \cdot 23$	$2 \cdot 449$	$29 \cdot 31$
90	$5 \cdot 181$	$2 \cdot 3 \cdot 151$	**9576073**	$2^2 \cdot 227$	$3^2 \cdot 101$
91	$3 \cdot 5 \cdot 61$	$2^2 \cdot 229$	$7 \cdot 131$	$2 \cdot 3^2 \cdot 17$	**9633155**
92	$5^2 \cdot 37$	$2 \cdot 463$	$3^2 \cdot 103$	$2^5 \cdot 29$	**9680157**
93	$5 \cdot 11 \cdot 17$	$2^3 \cdot 3^2 \cdot 13$	**9717396**	$2 \cdot 7 \cdot 67$	$3 \cdot 313$
94	$3^3 \cdot 5 \cdot 7$	$2 \cdot 11 \cdot 43$	**9763500**	$2^2 \cdot 3 \cdot 79$	$13 \cdot 73$
95	$5 \cdot 191$	$2^2 \cdot 239$	$3 \cdot 11 \cdot 29$	$2 \cdot 479$	$7 \cdot 137$
96	$5 \cdot 193$	$2 \cdot 3 \cdot 7 \cdot 23$	**9854265**	$2^3 \cdot 11^2$	$3 \cdot 17 \cdot 19$
97	$3 \cdot 5^2 \cdot 13$	$2^4 \cdot 61$	**9898946**	$2 \cdot 3 \cdot 163$	$11 \cdot 89$
98	$5 \cdot 197$	$2 \cdot 17 \cdot 29$	$3 \cdot 7 \cdot 47$	$2^2 \cdot 13 \cdot 19$	$23 \cdot 43$
99	$5 \cdot 199$	$2^2 \cdot 3 \cdot 83$	**9986952**	$2 \cdot 499$	$3^3 \cdot 37$
100	$3 \cdot 5 \cdot 67$	$2 \cdot 503$	$19 \cdot 53$	$2^4 \cdot 3^2 \cdot 7$	**0038912**

Numerical Tables

FACTORS AND PRIMES (Continued)

n	0	1	2	3	4
100	$2^3 \cdot 5^3$	$7 \cdot 11 \cdot 13$	$2 \cdot 3 \cdot 167$	$17 \cdot 59$	$2^2 \cdot 251$
101	$2 \cdot 5 \cdot 101$	$3 \cdot 337$	$2^2 \cdot 11 \cdot 23$	**0056094**	$2 \cdot 3 \cdot 13^2$
102	$2^2 \cdot 3 \cdot 5 \cdot 17$	**0090257**	$2 \cdot 7 \cdot 73$	$3 \cdot 11 \cdot 31$	2^{10}
103	$2 \cdot 5 \cdot 103$	**0132587**	$2^3 \cdot 3 \cdot 43$	**0141003**	$2 \cdot 11 \cdot 47$
104	$2^4 \cdot 5 \cdot 13$	$3 \cdot 347$	$2 \cdot 521$	$7 \cdot 149$	$2^2 \cdot 3^2 \cdot 29$
105	$2 \cdot 3 \cdot 5^2 \cdot 7$	**0216027**	$2^2 \cdot 263$	$3^4 \cdot 13$	$2 \cdot 17 \cdot 31$
106	$2^2 \cdot 5 \cdot 53$	**0257154**	$2 \cdot 3^2 \cdot 59$	**0265333**	$2^3 \cdot 7 \cdot 19$
107	$2 \cdot 5 \cdot 107$	$3^2 \cdot 7 \cdot 17$	$2^4 \cdot 67$	$29 \cdot 37$	$2 \cdot 3 \cdot 179$
108	$2^3 \cdot 3^3 \cdot 5$	$23 \cdot 47$	$2 \cdot 541$	$3 \cdot 19^2$	$2^2 \cdot 271$
109	$2 \cdot 5 \cdot 109$	**0378248**	$2^2 \cdot 3 \cdot 7 \cdot 13$	**0386202**	$2 \cdot 547$
110	$2^2 \cdot 5^2 \cdot 11$	$3 \cdot 367$	$2 \cdot 19 \cdot 29$	**0425755**	$2^4 \cdot 3 \cdot 23$
111	$2 \cdot 3 \cdot 5 \cdot 37$	$11 \cdot 101$	$2^3 \cdot 139$	$3 \cdot 7 \cdot 53$	$2 \cdot 557$
112	$2^5 \cdot 5 \cdot 7$	$19 \cdot 59$	$2 \cdot 3 \cdot 11 \cdot 17$	**0503798**	$2^2 \cdot 281$
113	$2 \cdot 5 \cdot 113$	$3 \cdot 13 \cdot 29$	$2^2 \cdot 283$	$11 \cdot 103$	$2 \cdot 3^4 \cdot 7$
114	$2^2 \cdot 3 \cdot 5 \cdot 19$	$7 \cdot 163$	$2 \cdot 571$	$3^2 \cdot 127$	$2^3 \cdot 11 \cdot 13$
115	$2 \cdot 5^2 \cdot 23$	**0610753**	$2^7 \cdot 3^2$	**0618293**	$2 \cdot 577$
116	$2^3 \cdot 5 \cdot 29$	$3^3 \cdot 43$	$2 \cdot 7 \cdot 83$	**0655797**	$2^3 \cdot 3 \cdot 97$
117	$2 \cdot 3^2 \cdot 5 \cdot 13$	**0685569**	$2^2 \cdot 293$	$3 \cdot 17 \cdot 23$	$2 \cdot 587$
118	$2^2 \cdot 5 \cdot 59$	**0722499**	$2 \cdot 3 \cdot 197$	$7 \cdot 13^2$	$2^5 \cdot 37$
119	$2 \cdot 5 \cdot 7 \cdot 17$	$3 \cdot 397$	$2^3 \cdot 149$	**0766404**	$2 \cdot 3 \cdot 199$
120	$2^4 \cdot 3 \cdot 5^2$	**0795430**	$2 \cdot 601$	$3 \cdot 401$	$2^2 \cdot 7 \cdot 43$
121	$2 \cdot 5 \cdot 11^2$	$7 \cdot 173$	$2^2 \cdot 3 \cdot 101$	**0838608**	$2 \cdot 607$
122	$2^2 \cdot 5 \cdot 61$	$3 \cdot 11 \cdot 37$	$2 \cdot 13 \cdot 47$	**0874265**	$2^3 \cdot 3^2 \cdot 17$
123	$2 \cdot 3 \cdot 5 \cdot 41$	**0902581**	$2^4 \cdot 7 \cdot 11$	$3^2 \cdot 137$	$2 \cdot 617$
124	$2^3 \cdot 5 \cdot 31$	$17 \cdot 73$	$2 \cdot 3^3 \cdot 23$	$11 \cdot 113$	$2^2 \cdot 311$
125	$2 \cdot 5^4$	$3^2 \cdot 139$	$2^2 \cdot 313$	$7 \cdot 179$	$2 \cdot 3 \cdot 11 \cdot 19$
126	$2^2 \cdot 3^2 \cdot 5 \cdot 7$	$13 \cdot 97$	$2 \cdot 631$	$3 \cdot 421$	$2^4 \cdot 79$
127	$2 \cdot 5 \cdot 127$	$31 \cdot 41$	$2^3 \cdot 3 \cdot 53$	$19 \cdot 67$	$2 \cdot 7^2 \cdot 13$
128	$2^8 \cdot 5$	$3 \cdot 7 \cdot 61$	$2 \cdot 641$	**1082267**	$2^2 \cdot 3 \cdot 107$
129	$2 \cdot 3 \cdot 5 \cdot 43$	**1109262**	$2^2 \cdot 17 \cdot 19$	$3 \cdot 431$	$2 \cdot 647$
130	$2^2 \cdot 5^2 \cdot 13$	**1142773**	$2 \cdot 3 \cdot 7 \cdot 31$	**1149444**	$2^3 \cdot 163$
131	$2 \cdot 5 \cdot 131$	$3 \cdot 19 \cdot 23$	$2^5 \cdot 41$	$13 \cdot 101$	$2 \cdot 3^2 \cdot 73$
132	$2^3 \cdot 3 \cdot 5 \cdot 11$	**1209028**	$2 \cdot 661$	$3^3 \cdot 7^2$	$2^2 \cdot 331$
133	$2 \cdot 5 \cdot 7 \cdot 19$	11^3	$2^2 \cdot 3^2 \cdot 37$	$31 \cdot 43$	$2 \cdot 23 \cdot 29$
134	$2^2 \cdot 5 \cdot 67$	$3^2 \cdot 149$	$2 \cdot 11 \cdot 61$	$17 \cdot 79$	$2^6 \cdot 3 \cdot 7$
135	$2 \cdot 3^3 \cdot 5^2$	$7 \cdot 193$	$2^3 \cdot 13^2$	$3 \cdot 11 \cdot 41$	$2 \cdot 677$
136	$2^4 \cdot 5 \cdot 17$	**1338581**	$2 \cdot 3 \cdot 227$	$29 \cdot 47$	$2^2 \cdot 11 \cdot 31$
137	$2 \cdot 5 \cdot 137$	$3 \cdot 457$	$2^2 \cdot 7^3$	**1376705**	$2 \cdot 3 \cdot 229$
138	$2^2 \cdot 3 \cdot 5 \cdot 23$	**1401937**	$2 \cdot 691$	$3 \cdot 461$	$2^3 \cdot 173$
139	$2 \cdot 5 \cdot 139$	$13 \cdot 107$	$2^4 \cdot 3 \cdot 29$	$7 \cdot 199$	$2 \cdot 17 \cdot 41$
140	$2^3 \cdot 5^2 \cdot 7$	$3 \cdot 467$	$2 \cdot 701$	$23 \cdot 61$	$2^2 \cdot 3^3 \cdot 13$
141	$2 \cdot 3 \cdot 5 \cdot 47$	$17 \cdot 83$	$2^2 \cdot 353$	$3^2 \cdot 157$	$2 \cdot 7 \cdot 101$
142	$2^2 \cdot 5 \cdot 71$	$7^2 \cdot 29$	$2 \cdot 3^2 \cdot 79$	**1532049**	$2^4 \cdot 89$
143	$2 \cdot 5 \cdot 11 \cdot 13$	$3^3 \cdot 53$	$2^3 \cdot 179$	**1562462**	$2 \cdot 3 \cdot 239$
144	$2^5 \cdot 3^2 \cdot 5$	$11 \cdot 131$	$2 \cdot 7 \cdot 103$	$3 \cdot 13 \cdot 37$	$2^2 \cdot 19^2$
145	$2 \cdot 5^2 \cdot 29$	**1616674**	$2^2 \cdot 3 \cdot 11^2$	**1622656**	$2 \cdot 727$
146	$2^2 \cdot 5 \cdot 73$	$3 \cdot 487$	$2 \cdot 17 \cdot 43$	$7 \cdot 11 \cdot 19$	$2^3 \cdot 3 \cdot 61$
147	$2 \cdot 3 \cdot 5 \cdot 7^2$	**1676127**	$2^6 \cdot 23$	$3 \cdot 491$	$2 \cdot 11 \cdot 67$
148	$2^3 \cdot 5 \cdot 37$	**1705551**	$2 \cdot 3 \cdot 13 \cdot 19$	**1711412**	$2^2 \cdot 7 \cdot 53$
149	$2 \cdot 5 \cdot 149$	$3 \cdot 7 \cdot 71$	$2^2 \cdot 373$	**1740598**	$2 \cdot 3^2 \cdot 83$
150	$2^2 \cdot 3 \cdot 5^3$	$19 \cdot 79$	$2 \cdot 751$	$3^2 \cdot 167$	$2^5 \cdot 47$

FACTORS AND PRIMES (Continued)

n	5	6	7	8	9
100	$3 \cdot 5 \cdot 67$	$2 \cdot 503$	$19 \cdot 53$	$2^4 \cdot 3^2 \cdot 7$	**0038912**
101	$5 \cdot 7 \cdot 29$	$2^3 \cdot 127$	$3^2 \cdot 113$	$2 \cdot 509$	**0081742**
102	$5^2 \cdot 41$	$2 \cdot 3^3 \cdot 19$	$13 \cdot 79$	$2^2 \cdot 257$	$3 \cdot 7^3$
103	$3^2 \cdot 5 \cdot 23$	$2^2 \cdot 7 \cdot 37$	$17 \cdot 61$	$2 \cdot 3 \cdot 173$	**0166155**
104	$5 \cdot 11 \cdot 19$	$2 \cdot 523$	$3 \cdot 349$	$2^3 \cdot 131$	**0207755**
105	$5 \cdot 211$	$2^5 \cdot 3 \cdot 11$	$7 \cdot 151$	$2 \cdot 23^2$	$3 \cdot 353$
106	$3 \cdot 5 \cdot 71$	$2 \cdot 13 \cdot 41$	$11 \cdot 97$	$2^2 \cdot 3 \cdot 89$	**0289777**
107	$5^2 \cdot 43$	$2^2 \cdot 269$	$3 \cdot 359$	$2 \cdot 7^2 \cdot 11$	$13 \cdot 83$
108	$5 \cdot 7 \cdot 31$	$2 \cdot 3 \cdot 181$	**0362295**	$2^6 \cdot 17$	$3^2 \cdot 11^2$
109	$3 \cdot 5 \cdot 73$	$2^3 \cdot 137$	**0402066**	$2 \cdot 3^2 \cdot 61$	$7 \cdot 157$
110	$5 \cdot 13 \cdot 17$	$2 \cdot 7 \cdot 79$	$3^3 \cdot 41$	$2^2 \cdot 277$	**0449315**
111	$5 \cdot 223$	$2^2 \cdot 3^2 \cdot 31$	**0480532**	$2 \cdot 13 \cdot 43$	$3 \cdot 373$
112	$3^2 \cdot 5^3$	$2 \cdot 563$	$7^2 \cdot 23$	$2^3 \cdot 3 \cdot 47$	**0526939**
113	$5 \cdot 227$	$2^4 \cdot 71$	$3 \cdot 379$	$2 \cdot 569$	$17 \cdot 67$
114	$5 \cdot 229$	$2 \cdot 3 \cdot 191$	$31 \cdot 37$	$2^2 \cdot 7 \cdot 41$	$3 \cdot 383$
115	$3 \cdot 5 \cdot 7 \cdot 11$	$2^2 \cdot 17^2$	$13 \cdot 89$	$2 \cdot 3 \cdot 193$	$19 \cdot 61$
116	$5 \cdot 233$	$2 \cdot 11 \cdot 53$	$3 \cdot 389$	$2^4 \cdot 73$	$7 \cdot 167$
117	$5^2 \cdot 47$	$2^3 \cdot 3 \cdot 7^2$	$11 \cdot 107$	$2 \cdot 19 \cdot 31$	$3^2 \cdot 131$
118	$3 \cdot 5 \cdot 79$	$2 \cdot 593$	**0744507**	$2^2 \cdot 3^3 \cdot 11$	$29 \cdot 41$
119	$5 \cdot 239$	$2^3 \cdot 13 \cdot 23$	$3^2 \cdot 7 \cdot 19$	$2 \cdot 599$	$11 \cdot 109$
120	$5 \cdot 241$	$2 \cdot 3^2 \cdot 67$	$17 \cdot 71$	$2^3 \cdot 51$	$3 \cdot 13 \cdot 31$
121	$3^5 \cdot 5$	$2^6 \cdot 19$	**0852906**	$2 \cdot 3 \cdot 7 \cdot 29$	$23 \cdot 53$
122	$5^2 \cdot 7^2$	$2 \cdot 613$	$3 \cdot 409$	$2^2 \cdot 307$	**0895519**
123	$5 \cdot 13 \cdot 19$	$2^2 \cdot 3 \cdot 103$	**0923697**	$2 \cdot 619$	$3 \cdot 7 \cdot 59$
124	$3 \cdot 5 \cdot 83$	$2 \cdot 7 \cdot 89$	$29 \cdot 43$	$2^5 \cdot 3 \cdot 13$	**0965624**
125	$5 \cdot 251$	$2^3 \cdot 157$	$3 \cdot 419$	$2 \cdot 17 \cdot 37$	**1000257**
126	$5 \cdot 11 \cdot 23$	$2 \cdot 3 \cdot 211$	$7 \cdot 181$	$2^2 \cdot 317$	$3^3 \cdot 47$
127	$3 \cdot 5^2 \cdot 17$	$2^2 \cdot 11 \cdot 29$	**1061909**	$2 \cdot 3^2 \cdot 71$	**1068705**
128	$5 \cdot 257$	$2 \cdot 643$	$3^2 \cdot 11 \cdot 13$	$2^3 \cdot 7 \cdot 23$	**1102529**
129	$5 \cdot 7 \cdot 37$	$2^4 \cdot 3^4$	**1129400**	$2 \cdot 11 \cdot 59$	$3 \cdot 433$
130	$3^2 \cdot 5 \cdot 29$	$2 \cdot 653$	**1162756**	$2^2 \cdot 3 \cdot 109$	$7 \cdot 11 \cdot 17$
131	$5 \cdot 263$	$2^2 \cdot 7 \cdot 47$	$3 \cdot 439$	$2 \cdot 659$	**1202448**
132	$5^2 \cdot 53$	$2 \cdot 3 \cdot 13 \cdot 17$	**1228709**	$2^4 \cdot 83$	$3 \cdot 443$
133	$3 \cdot 5 \cdot 89$	$2^3 \cdot 167$	$7 \cdot 191$	$2 \cdot 3 \cdot 223$	$13 \cdot 103$
134	$5 \cdot 269$	$2 \cdot 673$	$3 \cdot 449$	$2^2 \cdot 337$	$19 \cdot 71$
135	$5 \cdot 271$	$2^2 \cdot 3 \cdot 113$	$23 \cdot 59$	$2 \cdot 7 \cdot 97$	$3^2 \cdot 151$
136	$3 \cdot 5 \cdot 7 \cdot 13$	$2 \cdot 683$	**1357685**	$2^3 \cdot 3^2 \cdot 19$	37^2
137	$5^3 \cdot 11$	$2^5 \cdot 43$	$3^4 \cdot 17$	$2 \cdot 13 \cdot 53$	$7 \cdot 197$
138	$5 \cdot 277$	$2 \cdot 3^2 \cdot 7 \cdot 11$	$19 \cdot 73$	$2^2 \cdot 347$	$3 \cdot 463$
139	$3^2 \cdot 5 \cdot 31$	$2^2 \cdot 349$	$11 \cdot 127$	$2 \cdot 3 \cdot 233$	**1458177**
140	$5 \cdot 281$	$2 \cdot 19 \cdot 37$	$3 \cdot 7 \cdot 67$	$2^7 \cdot 11$	**1489110**
141	$5 \cdot 283$	$2^3 \cdot 3 \cdot 59$	$13 \cdot 109$	$2 \cdot 709$	$3 \cdot 11 \cdot 43$
142	$3 \cdot 5^2 \cdot 19$	$2 \cdot 23 \cdot 31$	**1544240**	$2^2 \cdot 3 \cdot 7 \cdot 17$	**1550322**
143	$5 \cdot 7 \cdot 41$	$2^2 \cdot 359$	$3 \cdot 479$	$2 \cdot 719$	**1580608**
144	$5 \cdot 17^2$	$2 \cdot 3 \cdot 241$	**1604685**	$2^3 \cdot 181$	$3^2 \cdot 7 \cdot 23$
145	$3 \cdot 5 \cdot 97$	$2^4 \cdot 7 \cdot 13$	$31 \cdot 47$	$2 \cdot 3^6$	**1640553**
146	$5 \cdot 293$	$2 \cdot 733$	$3^2 \cdot 163$	$2^2 \cdot 367$	$13 \cdot 113$
147	$5^2 \cdot 59$	$2^2 \cdot 3^2 \cdot 41$	$7 \cdot 211$	$2 \cdot 739$	$3 \cdot 17 \cdot 29$
148	$3^3 \cdot 5 \cdot 11$	$2 \cdot 743$	**1723110**	$2^4 \cdot 3 \cdot 31$	**1728947**
149	$5 \cdot 13 \cdot 23$	$2^3 \cdot 11 \cdot 17$	$3 \cdot 499$	$2 \cdot 7 \cdot 107$	**1758016**
150	$5 \cdot 7 \cdot 43$	$2 \cdot 3 \cdot 251$	$11 \cdot 137$	$2^2 \cdot 13 \cdot 29$	$3 \cdot 503$

FACTORS AND PRIMES (Continued)

n	0	1	2	3	4
150	$2^2 \cdot 3 \cdot 5^3$	$19 \cdot 79$	$2 \cdot 751$	$3^2 \cdot 167$	$2^5 \cdot 47$
151	$2 \cdot 5 \cdot 151$	**1792645**	$2^3 \cdot 3^3 \cdot 7$	$17 \cdot 89$	$2 \cdot 757$
152	$2^4 \cdot 5 \cdot 19$	$3^2 \cdot 13^2$	$2 \cdot 761$	**1826999**	$2^2 \cdot 3 \cdot 127$
153	$2 \cdot 3^2 \cdot 5 \cdot 17$	**1849752**	$2^2 \cdot 383$	$3 \cdot 7 \cdot 73$	$2 \cdot 13 \cdot 59$
154	$2^2 \cdot 5 \cdot 7 \cdot 11$	$23 \cdot 67$	$2 \cdot 3 \cdot 257$	**1883659**	$2^3 \cdot 193$
155	$2 \cdot 5^2 \cdot 31$	$3 \cdot 11 \cdot 47$	$2^4 \cdot 97$	**1911715**	$2 \cdot 3 \cdot 7 \cdot 37$
156	$2^3 \cdot 3 \cdot 5 \cdot 13$	$7 \cdot 223$	$2 \cdot 11 \cdot 71$	$3 \cdot 521$	$2^2 \cdot 17 \cdot 23$
157	$2 \cdot 5 \cdot 157$	**1961762**	$2^3 \cdot 3 \cdot 131$	$11^2 \cdot 13$	$2 \cdot 787$
158	$2^2 \cdot 5 \cdot 79$	$3 \cdot 17 \cdot 31$	$2 \cdot 7 \cdot 113$	**1994809**	$2^4 \cdot 3^2 \cdot 11$
159	$2 \cdot 3 \cdot 5 \cdot 53$	$37 \cdot 43$	$2^3 \cdot 199$	$3^3 \cdot 59$	$2 \cdot 797$
160	$2^6 \cdot 5^2$	**2043913**	$2 \cdot 3^2 \cdot 89$	$7 \cdot 229$	$2^2 \cdot 401$
161	$2 \cdot 5 \cdot 7 \cdot 23$	$3^2 \cdot 179$	$2^2 \cdot 13 \cdot 31$	**2076344**	$2 \cdot 3 \cdot 269$
162	$2^2 \cdot 3^4 \cdot 5$	**2097830**	$2 \cdot 811$	$3 \cdot 541$	$2^3 \cdot 7 \cdot 29$
163	$2 \cdot 5 \cdot 163$	$7 \cdot 233$	$2^5 \cdot 3 \cdot 17$	$23 \cdot 71$	$2 \cdot 19 \cdot 43$
164	$2^3 \cdot 5 \cdot 41$	$3 \cdot 547$	$2 \cdot 821$	$31 \cdot 53$	$2^2 \cdot 3 \cdot 137$
165	$2 \cdot 3 \cdot 5^2 \cdot 11$	$13 \cdot 127$	$2^2 \cdot 7 \cdot 59$	$3 \cdot 19 \cdot 29$	$2 \cdot 827$
166	$2^2 \cdot 5 \cdot 83$	$11 \cdot 151$	$2 \cdot 3 \cdot 277$	**2208922**	$2^7 \cdot 13$
167	$2 \cdot 5 \cdot 167$	$3 \cdot 557$	$2^3 \cdot 11 \cdot 19$	$7 \cdot 239$	$2 \cdot 3^3 \cdot 31$
168	$2^4 \cdot 3 \cdot 5 \cdot 7$	41^2	$2 \cdot 29^2$	$3^2 \cdot 11 \cdot 17$	$2^2 \cdot 421$
169	$2 \cdot 5 \cdot 13^2$	$19 \cdot 89$	$2^2 \cdot 3^2 \cdot 47$	**2286570**	$2 \cdot 7 \cdot 11^2$
170	$2^2 \cdot 5^2 \cdot 17$	$3^5 \cdot 7$	$2 \cdot 23 \cdot 37$	$13 \cdot 131$	$2^3 \cdot 3 \cdot 71$
171	$2 \cdot 3^2 \cdot 5 \cdot 19$	$29 \cdot 59$	$2^4 \cdot 107$	$3 \cdot 571$	$2 \cdot 857$
172	$2^3 \cdot 5 \cdot 43$	**2357809**	$2 \cdot 3 \cdot 7 \cdot 41$	**2362853**	$2^2 \cdot 431$
173	$2 \cdot 5 \cdot 173$	$3 \cdot 577$	$2^2 \cdot 433$	**2387986**	$2 \cdot 3 \cdot 17^2$
174	$2^2 \cdot 3 \cdot 5 \cdot 29$	**2407988**	$2 \cdot 13 \cdot 67$	$3 \cdot 7 \cdot 83$	$2^4 \cdot 109$
175	$2 \cdot 5^3 \cdot 7$	$17 \cdot 103$	$2^3 \cdot 3 \cdot 73$	**2437819**	$2 \cdot 877$
176	$2^5 \cdot 5 \cdot 11$	$3 \cdot 587$	$2 \cdot 881$	$41 \cdot 43$	$2^2 \cdot 3^2 \cdot 7^2$
177	$2 \cdot 3 \cdot 5 \cdot 59$	$7 \cdot 11 \cdot 23$	$2^2 \cdot 443$	$3^2 \cdot 197$	$2 \cdot 887$
178	$2^2 \cdot 5 \cdot 89$	$13 \cdot 137$	$2 \cdot 3^4 \cdot 11$	**2511513**	$2^3 \cdot 223$
179	$2 \cdot 5 \cdot 179$	$3^2 \cdot 199$	$2^8 \cdot 7$	$11 \cdot 163$	$2 \cdot 3 \cdot 13 \cdot 23$
180	$2^3 \cdot 3^2 \cdot 5^2$	**2555137**	$2 \cdot 17 \cdot 53$	$3 \cdot 601$	$2^2 \cdot 11 \cdot 41$
181	$2 \cdot 5 \cdot 181$	**2579185**	$2^2 \cdot 3 \cdot 151$	$7^2 \cdot 37$	$2 \cdot 907$
182	$2^2 \cdot 5 \cdot 7 \cdot 13$	$3 \cdot 607$	$2 \cdot 911$	**2607867**	$2^5 \cdot 3 \cdot 19$
183	$2 \cdot 3 \cdot 5 \cdot 61$	**2626883**	$2^3 \cdot 229$	$3 \cdot 13 \cdot 47$	$2 \cdot 7 \cdot 131$
184	$2^4 \cdot 5 \cdot 23$	$7 \cdot 263$	$2 \cdot 3 \cdot 307$	$19 \cdot 97$	$2^2 \cdot 461$
185	$2 \cdot 5^2 \cdot 37$	$3 \cdot 617$	$2^2 \cdot 463$	$17 \cdot 109$	$2 \cdot 3^2 \cdot 103$
186	$2^2 \cdot 3 \cdot 5 \cdot 31$	**2697464**	$2 \cdot 7^2 \cdot 19$	$3^4 \cdot 23$	$2^3 \cdot 233$
187	$2 \cdot 5 \cdot 11 \cdot 17$	**2720738**	$2^4 \cdot 3^2 \cdot 13$	**2725378**	$2 \cdot 937$
188	$2^3 \cdot 5 \cdot 47$	$3^2 \cdot 11 \cdot 19$	$2 \cdot 941$	$7 \cdot 269$	$2^2 \cdot 3 \cdot 157$
189	$2 \cdot 3^3 \cdot 5 \cdot 7$	$31 \cdot 61$	$2^2 \cdot 11 \cdot 43$	$3 \cdot 631$	$2 \cdot 947$
190	$2^2 \cdot 5^2 \cdot 19$	**2789821**	$2 \cdot 3 \cdot 317$	$11 \cdot 173$	$2^4 \cdot 7 \cdot 17$
191	$2 \cdot 5 \cdot 191$	$3 \cdot 7^2 \cdot 13$	$2^3 \cdot 239$	**2817150**	$2 \cdot 3 \cdot 11 \cdot 29$
192	$2^7 \cdot 3 \cdot 5$	$17 \cdot 113$	$2 \cdot 31^2$	$3 \cdot 641$	$2^2 \cdot 13 \cdot 37$
193	$2 \cdot 5 \cdot 193$	**2857823**	$2^2 \cdot 3 \cdot 7 \cdot 23$	**2862319**	$2 \cdot 967$
194	$2^2 \cdot 5 \cdot 97$	$3 \cdot 647$	$2 \cdot 971$	$29 \cdot 67$	$2^3 \cdot 3^5$
195	$2 \cdot 3 \cdot 5^2 \cdot 13$	**2902573**	$2^5 \cdot 61$	$3^2 \cdot 7 \cdot 31$	$2 \cdot 977$
196	$2^3 \cdot 5 \cdot 7^2$	$37 \cdot 53$	$2 \cdot 3^2 \cdot 109$	$13 \cdot 151$	$2^2 \cdot 491$
197	$2 \cdot 5 \cdot 197$	$3^3 \cdot 73$	$2^2 \cdot 17 \cdot 29$	**2951271**	$2 \cdot 3 \cdot 7 \cdot 47$
198	$2^2 \cdot 3^2 \cdot 5 \cdot 11$	$7 \cdot 283$	$2 \cdot 991$	$3 \cdot 661$	$2^6 \cdot 31$
199	$2 \cdot 5 \cdot 199$	$11 \cdot 181$	$2^3 \cdot 3 \cdot 83$	**2995073**	$2 \cdot 997$
200	$2^4 \cdot 5^3$	$3 \cdot 23 \cdot 29$	$2 \cdot 7 \cdot 11 \cdot 13$	**3016809**	$2^2 \cdot 3 \cdot 167$

FACTORS AND PRIMES (Continued)

n	5	6	7	8	9
150	$5 \cdot 7 \cdot 43$	$2 \cdot 3 \cdot 251$	$11 \cdot 137$	$2^2 \cdot 13 \cdot 29$	$3 \cdot 503$
151	$3 \cdot 5 \cdot 101$	$2^2 \cdot 379$	$37 \cdot 41$	$2 \cdot 3 \cdot 11 \cdot 23$	$7^2 \cdot 31$
152	$5^2 \cdot 61$	$2 \cdot 7 \cdot 109$	$3 \cdot 509$	$2^3 \cdot 191$	$11 \cdot 139$
153	$5 \cdot 307$	$2^9 \cdot 3$	$29 \cdot 53$	$2 \cdot 769$	$3^4 \cdot 19$
154	$3 \cdot 5 \cdot 103$	$2 \cdot 773$	$7 \cdot 13 \cdot 17$	$2^2 \cdot 3^2 \cdot 43$	1900514
155	$5 \cdot 311$	$2^2 \cdot 389$	$3^2 \cdot 173$	$2 \cdot 19 \cdot 41$	1928461
156	$5 \cdot 313$	$2 \cdot 3^3 \cdot 29$	1950690	$2^5 \cdot 7^2$	$3 \cdot 523$
157	$3^2 \cdot 5^2 \cdot 7$	$2^3 \cdot 197$	$19 \cdot 83$	$2 \cdot 3 \cdot 263$	1983821
158	$5 \cdot 317$	$2 \cdot 13 \cdot 61$	$3 \cdot 23^2$	$2^2 \cdot 397$	$7 \cdot 227$
159	$5 \cdot 11 \cdot 29$	$2^2 \cdot 3 \cdot 7 \cdot 19$	2033049	$2 \cdot 17 \cdot 47$	$3 \cdot 13 \cdot 41$
160	$3 \cdot 5 \cdot 107$	$2 \cdot 11 \cdot 73$	2060159	$2^3 \cdot 3 \cdot 67$	2065560
161	$5 \cdot 17 \cdot 19$	$2^4 \cdot 101$	$3 \cdot 7^2 \cdot 11$	$2 \cdot 809$	2092468
162	$5^3 \cdot 13$	$2 \cdot 3 \cdot 271$	2113876	$2^2 \cdot 11 \cdot 37$	$3^2 \cdot 181$
163	$3 \cdot 5 \cdot 109$	$2^2 \cdot 409$	2140487	$2 \cdot 3^2 \cdot 7 \cdot 13$	$11 \cdot 149$
164	$5 \cdot 7 \cdot 47$	$2 \cdot 823$	$3^3 \cdot 61$	$2^4 \cdot 103$	$17 \cdot 97$
165	$5 \cdot 331$	$2^3 \cdot 3^2 \cdot 23$	2193225	$2 \cdot 829$	$3 \cdot 7 \cdot 79$
166	$3^2 \cdot 5 \cdot 37$	$2 \cdot 7^2 \cdot 17$	2219356	$2^2 \cdot 3 \cdot 139$	2224563
167	$5^2 \cdot 67$	$2^2 \cdot 419$	$3 \cdot 13 \cdot 43$	$2 \cdot 839$	$23 \cdot 73$
168	$5 \cdot 337$	$2 \cdot 3 \cdot 281$	$7 \cdot 241$	$2^3 \cdot 211$	$3 \cdot 563$
169	$3 \cdot 5 \cdot 113$	$2^5 \cdot 53$	2296818	$2 \cdot 3 \cdot 283$	2301934
170	$5 \cdot 11 \cdot 31$	$2 \cdot 853$	$3 \cdot 569$	$2^2 \cdot 7 \cdot 61$	2327421
171	$5 \cdot 7^3$	$2^2 \cdot 3 \cdot 11 \cdot 13$	$17 \cdot 101$	$2 \cdot 859$	$3^2 \cdot 191$
172	$3 \cdot 5^2 \cdot 23$	$2 \cdot 863$	$11 \cdot 157$	$2^6 \cdot 3^3$	$7 \cdot 13 \cdot 19$
173	$5 \cdot 347$	$2^3 \cdot 7 \cdot 31$	$3^2 \cdot 193$	$2 \cdot 11 \cdot 79$	$37 \cdot 47$
174	$5 \cdot 349$	$2 \cdot 3^2 \cdot 97$	2422929	$2^2 \cdot 19 \cdot 23$	$3 \cdot 11 \cdot 53$
175	$3^3 \cdot 5 \cdot 13$	$2^2 \cdot 439$	$7 \cdot 251$	$2 \cdot 3 \cdot 293$	2452658
176	$5 \cdot 353$	$2 \cdot 883$	$3 \cdot 19 \cdot 31$	$2^3 \cdot 13 \cdot 17$	$29 \cdot 61$
177	$5^2 \cdot 71$	$2^4 \cdot 3 \cdot 37$	2496874	$2 \cdot 7 \cdot 127$	$3 \cdot 593$
178	$3 \cdot 5 \cdot 7 \cdot 17$	$2 \cdot 19 \cdot 47$	2521246	$2^2 \cdot 3 \cdot 149$	2526103
179	$5 \cdot 359$	$2^2 \cdot 449$	$3 \cdot 599$	$2 \cdot 29 \cdot 31$	$7 \cdot 257$
180	$5 \cdot 19^2$	$2 \cdot 3 \cdot 7 \cdot 43$	$13 \cdot 139$	$2^4 \cdot 113$	$3^3 \cdot 67$
181	$3 \cdot 5 \cdot 11^2$	$2^3 \cdot 227$	$23 \cdot 79$	$2 \cdot 3^2 \cdot 101$	$17 \cdot 107$
182	$5^2 \cdot 73$	$2 \cdot 11 \cdot 83$	$3^2 \cdot 7 \cdot 29$	$2^2 \cdot 457$	$31 \cdot 59$
183	$5 \cdot 367$	$2^2 \cdot 3^3 \cdot 17$	$11 \cdot 167$	$2 \cdot 919$	$3 \cdot 613$
184	$3^2 \cdot 5 \cdot 41$	$2 \cdot 13 \cdot 71$	2664669	$2^3 \cdot 3 \cdot 7 \cdot 11$	43^2
185	$5 \cdot 7 \cdot 53$	$2^6 \cdot 29$	$3 \cdot 619$	$2 \cdot 929$	$11 \cdot 13^2$
186	$5 \cdot 373$	$2 \cdot 3 \cdot 311$	2711443	$2^2 \cdot 467$	$3 \cdot 7 \cdot 89$
187	$3 \cdot 5^4$	$2^2 \cdot 7 \cdot 67$	2734643	$2 \cdot 3 \cdot 313$	2739268
188	$5 \cdot 13 \cdot 29$	$2 \cdot 23 \cdot 41$	$3 \cdot 17 \cdot 37$	$2^5 \cdot 59$	2762320
189	$5 \cdot 379$	$2^3 \cdot 3 \cdot 79$	$7 \cdot 271$	$2 \cdot 13 \cdot 73$	$3^2 \cdot 211$
190	$3 \cdot 5 \cdot 127$	$2 \cdot 953$	2803507	$2^2 \cdot 3^2 \cdot 53$	$23 \cdot 83$
191	$5 \cdot 383$	$2^2 \cdot 479$	$3^3 \cdot 71$	$2 \cdot 7 \cdot 137$	$19 \cdot 101$
192	$5^2 \cdot 7 \cdot 11$	$2 \cdot 3^2 \cdot 107$	$41 \cdot 47$	$2^3 \cdot 241$	$3 \cdot 643$
193	$3^2 \cdot 5 \cdot 43$	$2^4 \cdot 11^2$	$13 \cdot 149$	$2 \cdot 3 \cdot 17 \cdot 19$	$7 \cdot 277$
194	$5 \cdot 389$	$2 \cdot 7 \cdot 139$	$3 \cdot 11 \cdot 59$	$2^2 \cdot 487$	2898118
195	$5 \cdot 17 \cdot 23$	$2^2 \cdot 3 \cdot 163$	$19 \cdot 103$	$2 \cdot 11 \cdot 89$	$3 \cdot 653$
196	$3 \cdot 5 \cdot 131$	$2 \cdot 983$	$7 \cdot 281$	$2^4 \cdot 3 \cdot 41$	$11 \cdot 179$
197	$5^2 \cdot 79$	$2^3 \cdot 13 \cdot 19$	$3 \cdot 659$	$2 \cdot 23 \cdot 43$	2964458
198	$5 \cdot 397$	$2 \cdot 3 \cdot 331$	2981979	$2^2 \cdot 7 \cdot 71$	$3^2 \cdot 13 \cdot 17$
199	$3 \cdot 5 \cdot 7 \cdot 19$	$2^2 \cdot 499$	3003781	$2 \cdot 3^3 \cdot 37$	3008128
200	$5 \cdot 401$	$2 \cdot 17 \cdot 59$	$3^2 \cdot 223$	$2^3 \cdot 251$	$7^2 \cdot 41$

EXTENDED TABLES OF FACTORS AND PRIMES

The following procedure makes possible the determination of a number between 2009 and 19,949 as being either prime, or if not, what its factors will be. It is herewith included with the kind permission of its author, Professor Leonard Caners.

The following symbols will be used:

N is the number whose factors, if any, are to be determined.

A is N with the last digit dropped. Thus if $N = 17,873$, $A = 1787$.

R is the range and is the integral part of the square root of N with its last two digits dropped. Thus R of $17,873 = 13$.

K is the key number and is found in the table below.

P_1 is a possible factor corresponding to K.

The twin series are given in the table for the sake of completeness but are not written down in actual practice.

There are two steps as outlined below.

Step I

N	K	P_1	Series	Procedure
Any number ending in 1, 3, 7, or 9, within limits stated above	$A - R$	$10R$ + last digit	$K + n$; $P_1 - 10n$ $n = 0, 1, \ldots, 2R + 1$	Beginning with K read table of Factors and Primes from left to right and look for corresponding possible factors

Step II

N ending in	K	P_1	Series	Procedure
1	$(A - 2) - 3R$	$10R + 7$	$K + 3n$; $P_1 - 10n$ $n = 0, 1, \ldots, 2R + 1$	Same as in Step I except that only every *third* entry in table of Factors and Primes is examined for corresponding possible factors
3	$A - 3R$	$10R + 1$	$n = 0, 1, \ldots, 2R + 1$	
7	$(A - 2) - 3R$	$10R + 9$	$n = 0, 1, \ldots, 2R + 1$	
9	$A - 3R$	$10R + 3$	$n = 0, 1, \ldots, 2R + 1$	

As an example consider 7519. Using tables on preceding pages proceed as follows:

Step I

From Table $N = 7519$; $A = 751$; $R = 8$, $K = 743$; $P_1 = 89$ and the series obtained:

743	89
744	79
745	69
746	59
—	—
751	9
752	1
753	11
—	—
760	81

EXTENDED TABLES OF FACTORS AND PRIMES (Continued)

Examining the Table of Factors and Primes beginning with 743 note whether 743 has 89 as a factor; whether 744 has 79 as a factor, etc. Then continue to read from left to right keeping in mind the possible factors 69, 59, . . . 81.

Since none are found one concludes that 7519 has no factors within the given range ending in 9 or 1.

Step II

From Table $K = 727$ and $P_1 = 83$; the series obtained is:

727	83
730	73
733	63
751	3
754	7
778	87

Proceed exactly as in Step I. Begin with 727 and note whether it has 83 as a factor. Thereafter examine every *third* entry for the remaining corresponding possible factors 73, 63 . . . 3, 7, . . . 87. Since 730 yields the factor 73 one concludes that 73 is the factor of 7519. By division $7519 = 73 \times 103$. Had no factor been found in either Step I or Step II the conclusion would be that the number under consideration was prime.

Proof for Step I

Let N end in 1. Then, if N has a factor ending in 1, write

$$(10a + 1)(10b + 1) = N = 10A + 1$$
$$10ab + a + b = A$$

or

$$b(10a + 1) = (A - a)$$

This proves that any factor $10a + 1$ of N is also a factor of $A - a$. Let $a = (R - n)$, then $(10a + 1)$ becomes $(10R + 1) - 10n$ and $(A - a)$ becomes $(A - R) + n$, i.e., $P_1 - 10n$ and $K + n$ respectively as given in the table. Since $P_1 - 10n$ becomes a number ending in 9 when $P_1 < 10n$, all possible factors ending in 9 are also provided for.

The proof for Step II is similar. For possible factors ending in 3 or 7 write

$$(10a + 7)(10b + 3) = N = 10A + 1.$$

By identical reasoning this results in $P_1 - 10n$ and $K + 3n$ respectively given in the table. This completes the proof for numbers ending in 1.

Identical reasoning establishes the key numbers and series for ending in 3, 7, or 9.

FACTORIALS, EXACT VALUES

n	n!	n	n!
1	1	11	399 16800
2	2	12	4790 01600
3	6	13	62270 20800
4	24	14	8 71782 91200
5	120	15	130 76743 68000
6	720	16	2092 27898 88000
7	5040	17	35568 74280 96000
8	40320	18	6 40237 37057 28000
9	3 62880	19	121 64510 04088 32000
10	36 28800	20	2432 90200 81766 40000

FACTORIALS AND THEIR COMMON LOGARITHMS

The product $n \times (n - 1) \times (n - 2) \times \cdots \times 1$ is called factorial n, expressed as $n!$ For example: *factorial* $5 = 5! = 5 \times 4 \times 3 \times 2 \times 1 = 120$. Factorials are very often met with in series. For purposes of computation in such cases the table giving the values of the factorials and of their logarithms for numbers from 1 to 100 is provided. The values of the factorials are expressed exponentially to 5 significant figures.

The following table gives the reciprocals of the factorials and their logarithms for numbers from 1 to 100.

Above is a short table giving the exact values of the factorials of the numbers from 1 to 20.

FACTORIALS AND THEIR COMMON LOGARITHMS

n	$n!$	$\log n!$	n	$n!$	$\log n!$
			50	3.0414×10^{64}	64.48307
1	1.0000	0.00000	51	1.5511×10^{66}	66.19065
2	2.0000	0.30103	52	8.0658×10^{67}	67.90665
3	6.0000	0.77815	53	4.2749×10^{69}	69.63092
4	2.4000×10	1.38021	54	2.3084×10^{71}	71.36332
5	1.2000×10^{2}	2.07918	55	1.2696×10^{73}	73.10368
6	7.2000×10^{2}	2.85733	56	7.1100×10^{74}	74.85187
7	5.0400×10^{3}	3.70243	57	4.0527×10^{76}	76.60774
8	4.0320×10^{4}	4.60552	58	2.3506×10^{78}	78.37117
9	3.6288×10^{5}	5.55976	59	1.3868×10^{80}	80.14202
10	3.6288×10^{6}	6.55976	60	8.3210×10^{81}	81.92017
11	3.9917×10^{7}	7.60116	61	5.0758×10^{83}	83.70550
12	4.7900×10^{8}	8.68034	62	3.1470×10^{85}	85.49790
13	6.2270×10^{9}	9.79428	63	1.9826×10^{87}	87.29724
14	8.7178×10^{10}	10.94041	64	1.2689×10^{89}	89.10342
15	1.3077×10^{12}	12.11650	65	8.2477×10^{90}	90.91633
16	2.0923×10^{13}	13.32062	66	5.4435×10^{92}	92.73587
17	3.5569×10^{14}	14.55107	67	3.6471×10^{94}	94.56195
18	6.4024×10^{15}	15.80634	68	2.4800×10^{96}	96.39446
19	1.2165×10^{17}	17.08509	69	1.7112×10^{98}	98.23331
20	2.4329×10^{18}	18.38612	70	1.1979×10^{100}	100.07841
21	5.1091×10^{19}	19.70834	71	8.5048×10^{101}	101.92966
22	1.1240×10^{21}	21.05077	72	6.1234×10^{103}	103.78700
23	2.5852×10^{22}	22.41249	73	4.4701×10^{105}	105.65032
24	6.2045×10^{23}	23.79271	74	3.3079×10^{107}	107.51955
25	1.5511×10^{25}	25.19065	75	2.4809×10^{109}	109.39461
26	4.0329×10^{26}	26.60562	76	1.8855×10^{111}	111.27543
27	1.0889×10^{28}	28.03698	77	1.4518×10^{113}	113.16192
28	3.0489×10^{29}	29.48414	78	1.1324×10^{115}	115.05401
29	8.8418×10^{30}	30.94654	79	8.9462×10^{116}	116.95164
30	2.6525×10^{32}	32.42366	80	7.1569×10^{118}	118.85473
31	8.2228×10^{33}	33.91502	81	5.7971×10^{120}	120.76321
32	2.6313×10^{35}	35.42017	82	4.7536×10^{122}	122.67703
33	8.6833×10^{36}	36.93869	83	3.9455×10^{124}	124.59610
34	2.9523×10^{38}	38.47016	84	3.3142×10^{126}	126.52038
35	1.0333×10^{40}	40.01423	85	2.8171×10^{128}	128.44980
36	3.7199×10^{41}	41.57054	86	2.4227×10^{130}	130.38430
37	1.3764×10^{43}	43.13874	87	2.1078×10^{132}	132.32382
38	5.2302×10^{44}	44.71852	88	1.8548×10^{134}	134.26830
39	2.0398×10^{46}	46.30959	89	1.6508×10^{136}	136.21769
40	8.1592×10^{47}	47.91165	90	1.4857×10^{138}	138.17194
41	3.3453×10^{49}	49.52443	91	1.3520×10^{140}	140.13098
42	1.4050×10^{51}	51.14768	92	1.2438×10^{142}	142.09477
43	6.0415×10^{52}	52.78115	93	1.1568×10^{144}	144.06325
44	2.6583×10^{54}	54.42460	94	1.0874×10^{146}	146.03638
45	1.1962×10^{56}	56.07781	95	1.0330×10^{148}	148.01410
46	5.5026×10^{57}	57.74057	96	9.9168×10^{149}	149.99637
47	2.5862×10^{59}	59.41267	97	9.6193×10^{151}	151.98314
48	1.2414×10^{61}	61.09391	98	9.4269×10^{153}	153.97437
49	6.0828×10^{62}	62.78410	99	9.3326×10^{155}	155.97000
50	3.0414×10^{64}	64.48307	100	9.3326×10^{157}	157.97000

$$n! = \left(\frac{n}{e}\right)^{n}\sqrt{2\pi n} + h; \; n = 1, 2, 3, \ldots \left[0 < \frac{h}{n!} < \frac{1}{12n}\right]$$

$$\lim_{n \to \infty} \frac{n!\, e^{n}}{n^{n+\frac{1}{2}}} = \sqrt{2\pi} \qquad \lim_{n \to \infty} \frac{(n!)^{\frac{1}{n}}}{n} = \frac{1}{e}$$

RECIPROCALS OF FACTORIALS AND THEIR COMMON LOGARITHMS

n	$1/n!$	$\log (1/n!)$	n	$1/n!$	$\log (1/n!)$
1	1.	.00000	51	$.64470 \times 10^{-66}$	$\overline{67}.80934$
2	0.5	$\overline{1}.69897$	52	$.12398 \times 10^{-67}$	$\overline{68}.09335$
3	.16667	$\overline{1}.22185$	53	$.23392 \times 10^{-69}$	$\overline{70}.36908$
*4	$.41667 \times 10^{-1}$	$\overline{2}.61979$	54	$.45282 \times 10^{-71}$	$\overline{72}.63668$
5	$.83333 \times 10^{-2}$	$\overline{3}.92082$	55	$.78765 \times 10^{-73}$	$\overline{74}.89632$
6	$.13889 \times 10^{-2}$	$\overline{3}.14267$	56	$.14065 \times 10^{-74}$	$\overline{75}.14813$
7	$.19841 \times 10^{-3}$	$\overline{4}.29757$	57	$.24675 \times 10^{-76}$	$\overline{77}.39226$
8	$.24802 \times 10^{-4}$	$\overline{5}.39448$	58	$.42542 \times 10^{-78}$	$\overline{79}.62883$
9	$.27557 \times 10^{-5}$	$\overline{6}.44024$	59	$.72108 \times 10^{-80}$	$\overline{81}.85798$
10	$.27557 \times 10^{-6}$	$\overline{7}.44024$	60	$.12018 \times 10^{-81}$	$\overline{82}.07983$
11	$.25052 \times 10^{-7}$	$\overline{8}.39884$	61	$.19701 \times 10^{-83}$	$\overline{84}.29450$
12	$.20877 \times 10^{-8}$	$\overline{9}.31966$	62	$.31776 \times 10^{-85}$	$\overline{86}.50210$
13	$.16059 \times 10^{-9}$	$\overline{10}.20572$	63	$.50439 \times 10^{-87}$	$\overline{88}.70276$
14	$.11471 \times 10^{-10}$	$\overline{11}.05959$	64	$.78808 \times 10^{-89}$	$\overline{90}.89658$
15	$.76472 \times 10^{-12}$	$\overline{13}.88350$	65	$.12125 \times 10^{-90}$	$\overline{91}.08367$
16	$.47795 \times 10^{-13}$	$\overline{14}.67938$	66	$.18371 \times 10^{-92}$	$\overline{93}.26413$
17	$.28115 \times 10^{-14}$	$\overline{15}.44893$	67	$.27419 \times 10^{-94}$	$\overline{95}.43805$
18	$.15619 \times 10^{-15}$	$\overline{16}.19365$	68	$.40323 \times 10^{-96}$	$\overline{97}.60554$
19	$.82206 \times 10^{-17}$	$\overline{18}.91491$	69	$.58439 \times 10^{-98}$	$\overline{99}.76668$
20	$.41103 \times 10^{-18}$	$\overline{19}.61388$	70	$.83479 \times 10^{-100}$	$\overline{101}.92159$
21	$.19573 \times 10^{-19}$	$\overline{20}.29165$	71	$.11758 \times 10^{-101}$	$\overline{102}.07034$
22	$.88968 \times 10^{-21}$	$\overline{22}.94923$	72	$.16331 \times 10^{-103}$	$\overline{104}.21300$
23	$.38682 \times 10^{-22}$	$\overline{23}.58751$	73	$.22371 \times 10^{-105}$	$\overline{106}.34968$
24	$.16117 \times 10^{-23}$	$\overline{24}.20728$	74	$.30231 \times 10^{-107}$	$\overline{108}.48045$
25	$.64470 \times 10^{-25}$	$\overline{26}.80935$	75	$.40308 \times 10^{-109}$	$\overline{110}.60538$
26	$.24796 \times 10^{-26}$	$\overline{27}.39438$	76	$.53036 \times 10^{-111}$	$\overline{112}.72457$
27	$.91836 \times 10^{-28}$	$\overline{29}.96302$	77	$.68880 \times 10^{-113}$	$\overline{114}.83808$
28	$.32799 \times 10^{-29}$	$\overline{30}.51586$	78	$.88308 \times 10^{-115}$	$\overline{116}.94599$
29	$.11310 \times 10^{-30}$	$\overline{31}.05346$	79	$.11178 \times 10^{-116}$	$\overline{117}.04836$
30	$.37644 \times 10^{-32}$	$\overline{33}.57634$	80	$.13973 \times 10^{-118}$	$\overline{119}.14527$
31	$.12161 \times 10^{-33}$	$\overline{34}.08498$	81	$.17250 \times 10^{-120}$	$\overline{121}.23679$
32	$.38004 \times 10^{-35}$	$\overline{36}.57983$	82	$.21037 \times 10^{-122}$	$\overline{123}.32297$
33	$.11516 \times 10^{-36}$	$\overline{37}.06131$	83	$.25345 \times 10^{-124}$	$\overline{125}.40390$
34	$.33872 \times 10^{-38}$	$\overline{39}.52984$	84	$.30173 \times 10^{-126}$	$\overline{127}.47962$
35	$.96775 \times 10^{-40}$	$\overline{41}.98577$	85	$.35497 \times 10^{-128}$	$\overline{129}.55020$
36	$.26882 \times 10^{-41}$	$\overline{42}.42946$	86	$.41276 \times 10^{-130}$	$\overline{131}.61570$
37	$.72653 \times 10^{-43}$	$\overline{44}.86126$	87	$.47443 \times 10^{-132}$	$\overline{133}.67618$
38	$.19120 \times 10^{-44}$	$\overline{45}.28148$	88	$.53914 \times 10^{-134}$	$\overline{135}.73170$
39	$.49024 \times 10^{-46}$	$\overline{47}.69041$	89	$.60577 \times 10^{-136}$	$\overline{137}.78231$
40	$.12256 \times 10^{-47}$	$\overline{48}.08835$	90	$.67308 \times 10^{-138}$	$\overline{139}.82806$
41	$.29893 \times 10^{-49}$	$\overline{50}.47557$	91	$.73964 \times 10^{-140}$	$\overline{141}.86902$
42	$.71174 \times 10^{-51}$	$\overline{52}.85232$	92	$.80399 \times 10^{-142}$	$\overline{143}.90523$
43	$.16552 \times 10^{-52}$	$\overline{53}.21885$	93	$.86445 \times 10^{-144}$	$\overline{145}.93675$
44	$.37618 \times 10^{-54}$	$\overline{55}.57540$	94	$.91962 \times 10^{-146}$	$\overline{147}.96362$
45	$.83598 \times 10^{-56}$	$\overline{57}.92219$	95	$.96805 \times 10^{-148}$	$\overline{149}.98590$
46	$.18173 \times 10^{-57}$	$\overline{58}.25943$	96	$.10084 \times 10^{-149}$	$\overline{150}.00363$
47	$.38667 \times 10^{-59}$	$\overline{60}.58733$	97	$.10396 \times 10^{-151}$	$\overline{152}.01686$
48	$.80554 \times 10^{-61}$	$\overline{62}.90609$	98	$.10608 \times 10^{-153}$	$\overline{154}.02563$
49	$.16440 \times 10^{-62}$	$\overline{63}.21590$	99	$.10715 \times 10^{-155}$	$\overline{156}.03000$
50	$.32880 \times 10^{-64}$	$\overline{65}.51693$	100	$.10715 \times 10^{-157}$	$\overline{158}.03000$

* For example $\log \dfrac{1}{4!} = \overline{2}.61979 = .61979 - 2 = 8.61979 - 10.$

POSITIONAL NOTATION

In our ordinary system of writing numbers, the value of any digit depends on its position in the number. The value of a digit in any position is ten times the value of the same digit one position to the right, or one-tenth the value of the same digit one position to the left. Thus, for example,

$$173.246 = 1 \times 10^2 + 7 \times 10^1 + 3 + 2 \times \frac{1}{10} + 4 \times \frac{1}{10^2} + 6 \times \frac{1}{10^3}.$$

There is no reason that a number other than 10 cannot be used as the *base*, or *radix*, of the number system. In fact, bases of 2, 8, and 16 are commonly used in working with digital computers. When the base used is not clear from the context, it is usually indicated as a parenthesized subscript. Thus

$$743_{(8)} = 7 \times 8^2 + 4 \times 8 + 3 = 7 \times 64 + 4 \times 8 + 3 = 448 + 32 + 3 = 483_{(10)}$$

$$1011.101_{(2)} = 1 \times 2^3 + 0 \times 2^2 + 1 \times 2 + 1 + 1 \times \tfrac{1}{2} + 0 \times \tfrac{1}{4} + 1 \times \tfrac{1}{8} = 11.625_{(10)}$$

CHANGE OF BASE

In this section, it is assumed that all calculations will be performed in base 10, since this is the only base in which most people can easily compute. However, there is no logical reason that some other base could not be used for the computations.

To convert a number from another base into base 10:

Simply write down the digits of the number, with each one multiplied by its appropriate positional value. Then perform the indicated computations in base 10, and write down the answer.

For examples, see the two examples in the previous section.

To convert a number from base 10 into another base:

The part of the number to the left of the point and the part to the right must be operated on separately. For the integer part (the part to the left of the point):

  a. Divide the number by the new base, getting an integer quotient and remainder.
  b. Write down the remainder as the last digit of the number in the new base.
  c. Using the quotient from the last division in place of the original number, repeat the above two steps until the quotient becomes zero.

For the fractional part (the part to the right of the point):

  a. Multiply the number by the new base.
  b. Write down the integral part of the product as the first digit of the fractional part in the new base.
  c. Using the fractional part of the last product in place of the original number, repeat the above two steps until the product becomes an integer, or until the desired number of places have been computed.

51

Examples:

These examples show a convenient method of arranging the computations.

1. Convert $103.118_{(10)}$ to base 8.

$$8 \ \underline{|103|} \ 7 \qquad\qquad\qquad\qquad .118$$
$$8 \ \ \underline{|12|} \ 4 \qquad\qquad\qquad\qquad \underline{\quad 8}$$
$$1 \qquad\qquad 147.074324\ldots \qquad .944$$
$$\underline{\quad 8}$$

The calculation of the fractional part could be carried out as far as desired. It is a non-terminating fraction which will eventually repeat itself.

$$7.552$$
$$\underline{\quad 8}$$
$$4.416$$
$$\underline{\quad 8}$$
$$3.328$$
$$\underline{\quad 8}$$
$$2.624$$
$$\underline{\quad 8}$$
$$103.118_{(10)} = 147.074324\ldots_{(8)} \qquad\qquad 4.992$$

The calculations may be further shortened by not writing down the multiplier and divisor at each step of the algorithm, as shown in the next example.

2. Convert $275.824_{(10)}$ to base 5.

$$5 \ \underline{|275|} \ 0 \qquad\qquad\qquad\qquad .824$$
$$\underline{|55|} \ 0 \qquad\qquad\qquad\qquad 4.120$$
$$\underline{|11|} \ 1 \qquad\qquad\qquad\qquad 0.600$$
$$2 \qquad\qquad\qquad\qquad 3.000$$

$$275.824_{(10)} = 2100.403_{(5)}$$

To convert from one base to another (neither of which is 10):

The easiest procedure is usually to convert first to base 10, and then to the desired base. However, there are two exceptions to this:

1. If computational facility is possessed in either of the bases, it may be used instead of base 10, and the appropriate one of the above methods applied.
2. If the two bases are different powers of the same number, the conversion may be done digit-by-digit to the base which is the common root of both bases, and then digit-by-digit back to the other base.

Example: Convert $127.653_{(8)}$ to base 16. (For base 16, the letters A–F are used for the digits $10_{(10)}-15_{(10)}$.)

The first step is to convert the number to base 2, simply by converting each digit to its binary equivalent:

$$127.653_{(8)} = 001 \ 010 \ 111 \cdot 110 \ 101 \ 011_{(2)}$$

Now by simply regrouping the binary number into groups of four binary digits, starting at the point, we convert to base 16:

$$127.653_{(16)} = 101 \ 0111 \cdot 1101 \ 0101 \ 1_{(2)} = 57.D58_{(16)}$$

$10^{\pm n}$ IN OCTAL SCALE

10^n	n	10^{-n}		10^n	n	10^{-n}
1	0	1.000 000 000 000 000		112 402 762 000	10	0.000 000 000 006 676
12	1	0.063 146 314 631 463		1 351 035 564 000	11	0.000 000 000 000 537
144	2	0.005 075 341 217 270		16 432 451 210 000	12	0.000 000 000 000 043
1 750	3	0.000 406 111 564 570		221 441 634 520 000	13	0.000 000 000 000 003
23 420	4	0.000 032 155 613 530		2 657 142 036 440 000	14	0.000 000 000 000 000
303 240	5	0.000 002 476 132 610		34 327 724 461 500 000	15	0.000 000 000 000 000
3 641 100	6	0.000 000 206 157 364		434 157 115 760 200 000	16	0.000 000 000 000 000
46 113 200	7	0.000 000 015 327 745		5 432 127 413 542 400 000	17	0.000 000 000 000 000
575 360 400	8	0.000 000 001 257 143		67 405 553 164 731 000 000	18	0.000 000 000 000 000
7 346 545 000	9	0.000 000 000 104 560				

2^n IN DECIMAL SCALE

n	2^n	n	2^n	n	2^n
0.001	1.00069 33874 62581	0.01	1.00695 55500 56719	0.1	1.07177 34625 36293
0.002	1.00138 72557 11335	0.02	1.01395 94797 90029	0.2	1.14869 83549 97035
0.003	1.00208 16050 79633	0.03	1.02101 21257 07193	0.3	1.23114 44133 44916
0.004	1.00277 64359 01078	0.04	1.02811 38266 56067	0.4	1.31950 79107 72894
0.005	1.00347 17485 09503	0.05	1.03526 49238 41377	0.5	1.41421 35623 73095
0.006	1.00416 75432 38973	0.06	1.04246 57608 41121	0.6	1.51571 65665 10398
0.007	1.00486 38204 23785	0.07	1.04971 66836 23067	0.7	1.62450 47927 12471
0.008	1.00556 05803 98468	0.08	1.05701 80405 61380	0.8	1.74110 11265 92248
0.009	1.00625 78234 97782	0.09	1.06437 01824 53360	0.9	1.86606 59830 73615

$n \log_{10} 2$, $n \log_2 10$ IN DECIMAL SCALE

n	$n \log_{10} 2$	$n \log_2 10$	n	$n \log_{10} 2$	$n \log_2 10$
1	0.30102 99957	3.32192 80949	6	1.80617 99740	19.93156 85693
2	0.60205 99913	6.64385 61898	7	2.10720 99696	23.25349 66642
3	0.90308 99870	9.96578 42847	8	2.40823 99653	26.57542 47591
4	1.20411 99827	13.28771 23795	9	2.70926 99610	29.89735 28540
5	1.50514 99783	16.60964 04744	10	3.01029 99566	33.21928 09489

ADDITION AND MULTIPLICATION TABLES

Addition   Multiplication

Binary Scale

$$0 + 0 = 0 \qquad\qquad 0 \times 0 = 0$$
$$0 + 1 = 1 + 0 = 1 \qquad 0 \times 1 = 1 \times 0 = 0$$
$$1 + 1 = 10 \qquad\qquad 1 \times 1 = 1$$

Octal Scale

Addition   Multiplication

0	01	02	03	04	05	06	07
1	02	03	04	05	06	07	10
2	03	04	05	06	07	10	11
3	04	05	06	07	10	11	12
4	05	06	07	10	11	12	13
5	06	07	10	11	12	13	14
6	07	10	11	12	13	14	15
7	10	11	12	13	14	15	16

1	02	03	04	05	06	07
2	04	06	10	12	14	16
3	06	11	14	17	22	25
4	10	14	20	24	30	34
5	12	17	24	31	36	43
6	14	22	30	36	44	52
7	16	25	34	43	52	61

MATHEMATICAL CONSTANTS IN OCTAL SCALE

$\pi = (3.11037\ 552421)_{(8)}$ $e = (2.55760\ 521305)_{(8)}$ $\gamma = (0.44742\ 147707)_{(8)}$

$\pi^{-1} = (0.24276\ 301556)_{(8)}$ $e^{-1} = (0.27426\ 530661)_{(8)}$ $\log_e \gamma = -(0.43127\ 233602)_{(8)}$

$\sqrt{\pi} = (1.61337\ 611067)_{(8)}$ $\sqrt{e} = (1.51411\ 230704)_{(8)}$ $\log_2 \gamma = -(0.62573\ 030645)_{(8)}$

$\log_e \pi = (1.11206\ 404435)_{(8)}$ $\log_{10} e = (0.33626\ 754251)_{(8)}$ $\sqrt{2} = (1.32404\ 746320)_{(8)}$

$\log_2 \pi = (1.51544\ 163223)_{(8)}$ $\log_2 e = (1.34252\ 166245)_{(8)}$ $\log_e 2 = (0.54271\ 027760)_{(8)}$

$\sqrt{10} = (3.12305\ 407267)_{(8)}$ $\log_2 10 = (3.24464\ 741136)_{(8)}$ $\log_e 10 = (2.23273\ 067355)_{(8)}$

OCTAL-DECIMAL INTEGER CONVERSION TABLE

	0	1	2	3	4	5	6	7
0000	0000	0001	0002	0003	0004	0005	0006	0007
0010	0008	0009	0010	0011	0012	0013	0014	0015
0020	0016	0017	0018	0019	0020	0021	0022	0023
0030	0024	0025	0026	0027	0028	0029	0030	0031
0040	0032	0033	0034	0035	0036	0037	0038	0039
0050	0040	0041	0042	0043	0044	0045	0046	0047
0060	0048	0049	0050	0051	0052	0053	0054	0055
0070	0056	0057	0058	0059	0060	0061	0062	0063
0100	0064	0065	0066	0067	0068	0069	0070	0071
0110	0072	0073	0074	0075	0076	0077	0078	0079
0120	0080	0081	0082	0083	0084	0085	0086	0087
0130	0088	0089	0090	0091	0092	0093	0094	0095
0140	0096	0097	0098	0099	0100	0101	0102	0103
0150	0104	0105	0106	0107	0108	0109	0110	0111
0160	0112	0113	0114	0115	0116	0117	0118	0119
0170	0120	0121	0122	0123	0124	0125	0126	0127
0200	0128	0129	0130	0131	0132	0133	0134	0135
0210	0136	0137	0138	0139	0140	0141	0142	0143
0220	0144	0145	0146	0147	0148	0149	0150	0151
0230	0152	0153	0154	0155	0156	0157	0158	0159
0240	0160	0161	0162	0163	0164	0165	0166	0167
0250	0168	0169	0170	0171	0172	0173	0174	0175
0260	0176	0177	0178	0179	0180	0181	0182	0183
0270	0184	0185	0186	0187	0188	0189	0190	0191
0300	0192	0193	0194	0195	0196	0197	0198	0199
0310	0200	0201	0202	0203	0204	0205	0206	0207
0320	0208	0209	0210	0211	0212	0213	0214	0215
0330	0216	0217	0218	0219	0220	0221	0222	0223
0340	0224	0225	0226	0227	0228	0229	0230	0231
0350	0232	0233	0234	0235	0236	0237	0238	0239
0360	0240	0241	0242	0243	0244	0245	0246	0247
0370	0248	0249	0250	0251	0252	0253	0254	0255

	0	1	2	3	4	5	6	7
0400	0256	0257	0258	0259	0260	0261	0262	0263
0410	0264	0265	0266	0267	0268	0269	0270	0271
0420	0272	0273	0274	0275	0276	0277	0278	0279
0430	0280	0281	0282	0283	0284	0285	0286	0287
0440	0288	0289	0290	0291	0292	0293	0294	0295
0450	0296	0297	0298	0299	0300	0301	0302	0303
0460	0304	0305	0306	0307	0308	0309	0310	0311
0470	0312	0313	0314	0315	0316	0317	0318	0319
0500	0320	0321	0322	0323	0324	0325	0326	0327
0510	0328	0329	0330	0331	0332	0333	0334	0335
0520	0336	0337	0338	0339	0340	0341	0342	0343
0530	0344	0345	0346	0347	0348	0349	0350	0351
0540	0352	0353	0354	0355	0356	0357	0358	0359
0550	0360	0361	0362	0363	0364	0365	0366	0367
0560	0368	0369	0370	0371	0372	0373	0374	0375
0570	0376	0377	0378	0379	0380	0381	0382	0383
0600	0384	0385	0386	0387	0388	0389	0390	0391
0610	0392	0393	0394	0395	0396	0397	0398	0399
0620	0400	0401	0402	0403	0404	0405	0406	0407
0630	0408	0409	0410	0411	0412	0413	0414	0415
0640	0416	0417	0418	0419	0420	0421	0422	0423
0650	0424	0425	0426	0427	0428	0429	0430	0431
0660	0432	0433	0434	0435	0436	0437	0438	0439
0670	0440	0441	0442	0443	0444	0445	0446	0447
0700	0448	0449	0450	0451	0452	0453	0454	0455
0710	0456	0457	0458	0459	0460	0461	0462	0463
0720	0464	0465	0466	0467	0468	0469	0470	0471
0730	0472	0473	0474	0475	0476	0477	0478	0479
0740	0480	0481	0482	0483	0484	0485	0486	0487
0750	0488	0489	0490	0491	0492	0493	0494	0495
0760	0496	0497	0498	0499	0500	0501	0502	0503
0770	0504	0505	0506	0507	0508	0509	0510	0511

0000	0000
to	to
0777	0511
(Octal)	(Decimal)

Octal	Decimal
10000-	4096
20000-	8192
30000-	12288
40000-	16384
50000-	20180
60000-	21576
70000-	28672

	0	1	2	3	4	5	6	7
1000	0512	0513	0514	0515	0516	0517	0518	0519
1010	0520	0521	0522	0523	0524	0525	0526	0527
1020	0528	0529	0530	0531	0532	0533	0534	0535
1030	0536	0537	0538	0539	0540	0541	0542	0543
1040	0544	0545	0546	0547	0548	0549	0550	0551
1050	0552	0553	0554	0555	0556	0557	0558	0559
1060	0560	0561	0562	0563	0564	0565	0566	0567
1070	0568	0569	0570	0571	0572	0573	0574	0575
1100	0576	0577	0578	0579	0580	0581	0582	0583
1110	0584	0585	0586	0587	0588	0589	0590	0591
1120	0592	0593	0594	0595	0596	0597	0598	0599
1130	0600	0601	0602	0603	0604	0605	0606	0607
1140	0608	0609	0610	0611	0612	0613	0614	0615
1150	0616	0617	0618	0619	0620	0621	0622	0623
1160	0624	0625	0626	0627	0628	0629	0630	0631
1170	0632	0633	0634	0635	0636	0637	0638	0639
1200	0640	0641	0642	0643	0644	0645	0646	0647
1210	0648	0649	0650	0651	0652	0653	0654	0655
1220	0656	0657	0658	0659	0660	0661	0662	0663
1230	0664	0665	0666	0667	0668	0669	0670	0671
1240	0672	0673	0674	0675	0676	0677	0678	0679
1250	0680	0681	0682	0683	0684	0685	0686	0687
1260	0688	0689	0690	0691	0692	0693	0694	0695
1270	0696	0697	0698	0699	0700	0701	0702	0703
1300	0704	0705	0706	0707	0708	0709	0710	0711
1310	0712	0713	0714	0715	0716	0717	0718	0719
1320	0720	0721	0722	0723	0724	0725	0726	0727
1330	0728	0729	0730	0731	0732	0733	0734	0735
1340	0736	0737	0738	0739	0740	0741	0742	0743
1350	0744	0745	0746	0747	0748	0749	0750	0751
1360	0752	0753	0754	0755	0756	0757	0758	0759
1370	0760	0761	0762	0763	0764	0765	0766	0767

	0	1	2	3	4	5	6	7
1400	0768	0769	0770	0771	0772	0773	0774	0775
1410	0776	0777	0778	0779	0780	0781	0782	0783
1420	0784	0785	0786	0787	0788	0789	0790	0791
1430	0792	0793	0794	0795	0796	0797	0798	0799
1440	0800	0801	0802	0803	0804	0805	0806	0807
1450	0808	0809	0810	0811	0812	0813	0814	0815
1460	0816	0817	0818	0819	0820	0821	0822	0823
1470	0824	0825	0826	0827	0828	0829	0830	0831
1500	0832	0833	0834	0835	0836	0837	0838	0839
1510	0840	0841	0842	0843	0844	0845	0846	0847
1520	0848	0849	0850	0851	0852	0853	0854	0855
1530	0856	0857	0858	0859	0860	0861	0862	0863
1540	0864	0865	0866	0867	0868	0869	0870	0871
1550	0872	0873	0874	0875	0876	0877	0878	0879
1560	0880	0881	0882	0883	0884	0885	0886	0887
1570	0888	0889	0890	0891	0892	0893	0894	0895
1600	0896	0897	0898	0899	0900	0901	0902	0903
1610	0904	0905	0906	0907	0908	0909	0910	0911
1620	0912	0913	0914	0915	0916	0917	0918	0919
1630	0920	0921	0922	0923	0924	0925	0926	0927
1640	0928	0929	0930	0931	0932	0933	0934	0935
1650	0936	0937	0938	0939	0940	0941	0942	0943
1660	0944	0945	0946	0947	0948	0949	0950	0951
1670	0952	0953	0954	0955	0956	0957	0958	0959
1700	0960	0961	0962	0963	0964	0965	0966	0967
1710	0968	0969	0970	0971	0972	0973	0974	0975
1720	0976	0977	0978	0979	0980	0981	0982	0983
1730	0984	0985	0986	0987	0988	0989	0990	0991
1740	0992	0993	0994	0995	0996	0997	0998	0999
1750	1000	1001	1002	1003	1004	1005	1006	1007
1760	1008	1009	1010	1011	1012	1013	1014	1015
1770	1016	1017	1018	1019	1020	1021	1022	1023

1000	0512
to	to
1777	1023
(Octal)	(Decimal)

OCTAL-DECIMAL INTEGER CONVERSION TABLE (Continued)

	0	1	2	3	4	5	6	7
2000	1024	1025	1026	1027	1028	1029	1030	1031
2010	1032	1033	1034	1035	1036	1037	1038	1039
2020	1040	1041	1042	1043	1044	1045	1046	1047
2030	1048	1049	1050	1051	1052	1053	1054	1055
2040	1056	1057	1058	1059	1060	1061	1062	1063
2050	1064	1065	1066	1067	1068	1069	1070	1071
2060	1072	1073	1074	1075	1076	1077	1078	1079
2070	1080	1081	1082	1083	1084	1085	1086	1087
2100	1088	1089	1090	1091	1092	1093	1094	1095
2110	1096	1097	1098	1099	1100	1101	1102	1103
2120	1104	1105	1106	1107	1108	1109	1110	1111
2130	1112	1113	1114	1115	1116	1117	1118	1119
2140	1120	1121	1122	1123	1124	1125	1126	1127
2150	1128	1129	1130	1131	1132	1133	1134	1135
2160	1136	1137	1138	1139	1140	1141	1142	1143
2170	1144	1145	1146	1147	1148	1149	1150	1151
2200	1152	1153	1154	1155	1156	1157	1158	1159
2210	1160	1161	1162	1163	1164	1165	1166	1167
2220	1168	1169	1170	1171	1172	1173	1174	1175
2230	1176	1177	1178	1179	1180	1181	1182	1183
2240	1184	1185	1186	1187	1188	1189	1190	1191
2250	1192	1193	1194	1195	1196	1197	1198	1199
2260	1200	1201	1202	1203	1204	1205	1206	1207
2270	1208	1209	1210	1211	1212	1213	1214	1215
2300	1216	1217	1218	1219	1220	1221	1222	1223
2310	1224	1225	1226	1227	1228	1229	1230	1231
2320	1232	1233	1234	1235	1236	1237	1238	1239
2330	1240	1241	1242	1243	1244	1245	1246	1247
2340	1248	1249	1250	1251	1252	1253	1254	1255
2350	1256	1257	1258	1259	1260	1261	1262	1263
2360	1264	1265	1266	1267	1268	1269	1270	1271
2370	1272	1273	1274	1275	1276	1277	1278	1279

	0	1	2	3	4	5	6	7
2400	1280	1281	1282	1283	1284	1285	1286	1287
2410	1288	1289	1290	1291	1292	1293	1294	1295
2420	1296	1297	1298	1299	1300	1301	1302	1303
2430	1304	1305	1306	1307	1308	1309	1310	1311
2440	1312	1313	1314	1315	1316	1317	1318	1319
2450	1320	1321	1322	1323	1324	1325	1326	1327
2460	1328	1329	1330	1331	1332	1333	1334	1335
2470	1336	1337	1338	1339	1340	1341	1342	1343
2500	1344	1345	1346	1347	1348	1349	1350	1351
2510	1352	1353	1354	1355	1356	1357	1358	1359
2520	1360	1361	1362	1363	1364	1365	1366	1367
2530	1368	1369	1370	1371	1372	1373	1374	1375
2540	1376	1377	1378	1379	1380	1381	1382	1383
2550	1384	1385	1386	1387	1388	1389	1390	1391
2560	1392	1393	1394	1395	1396	1397	1398	1399
2570	1400	1401	1402	1403	1404	1405	1406	1407
2600	1408	1409	1410	1411	1412	1413	1414	1415
2610	1416	1417	1418	1419	1420	1421	1422	1423
2620	1424	1425	1426	1427	1428	1429	1430	1431
2630	1432	1433	1434	1435	1436	1437	1438	1439
2640	1440	1441	1442	1443	1444	1445	1446	1447
2650	1448	1449	1450	1451	1452	1453	1454	1455
2660	1456	1457	1458	1459	1460	1461	1462	1463
2670	1464	1465	1466	1467	1468	1469	1470	1471
2700	1472	1473	1474	1475	1476	1477	1478	1479
2710	1480	1481	1482	1483	1484	1485	1486	1487
2720	1488	1489	1490	1491	1492	1493	1494	1495
2730	1496	1497	1498	1499	1500	1501	1502	1503
2740	1504	1505	1506	1507	1508	1509	1510	1511
2750	1512	1513	1514	1515	1516	1517	1518	1519
2760	1520	1521	1522	1523	1524	1525	1526	1527
2770	1528	1529	1530	1531	1532	1533	1534	1535

```
2000   |  1024
 to    |   to
2777   |  1535
(Octal)|(Decimal)

Octal   Decimal
10000-  4096
20000-  8192
30000-12288
40000-16384
50000-20480
60000-24576
70000-28672
```

```
3000   |  1536
 to    |   to
3777   |  2047
(Octal)|(Decimal)
```

	0	1	2	3	4	5	6	7
3000	1536	1537	1538	1539	1540	1541	1542	1543
3010	1544	1545	1546	1547	1548	1549	1550	1551
3020	1552	1553	1554	1555	1556	1557	1558	1559
3030	1560	1561	1562	1563	1564	1565	1566	1567
3040	1568	1569	1570	1571	1572	1573	1574	1575
3050	1576	1577	1578	1579	1580	1581	1582	1583
3060	1584	1585	1586	1587	1588	1589	1590	1591
3070	1592	1593	1594	1595	1596	1597	1598	1599
3100	1600	1601	1602	1603	1604	1605	1606	1607
3110	1608	1609	1610	1611	1612	1613	1614	1615
3120	1616	1617	1618	1619	1620	1621	1622	1623
3130	1624	1625	1626	1627	1628	1629	1630	1631
3140	1632	1633	1634	1635	1636	1637	1638	1639
3150	1640	1641	1642	1643	1644	1645	1646	1647
3160	1648	1649	1650	1651	1652	1653	1654	1655
3170	1656	1657	1658	1659	1660	1661	1662	1663
3200	1664	1665	1666	1667	1668	1669	1670	1671
3210	1672	1673	1674	1675	1676	1677	1678	1679
3220	1680	1681	1682	1683	1684	1685	1686	1687
3230	1688	1689	1690	1691	1692	1693	1694	1695
3240	1696	1697	1698	1699	1700	1701	1702	1703
3250	1704	1705	1706	1707	1708	1709	1710	1711
3260	1712	1713	1714	1715	1716	1717	1718	1719
3270	1720	1721	1722	1723	1724	1725	1726	1727
3300	1728	1729	1730	1731	1732	1733	1734	1735
3310	1736	1737	1738	1739	1740	1741	1742	1743
3320	1744	1745	1746	1747	1748	1749	1750	1751
3330	1752	1753	1754	1755	1756	1757	1758	1759
3340	1760	1761	1762	1763	1764	1765	1766	1767
3350	1768	1769	1770	1771	1772	1773	1774	1775
3360	1776	1777	1778	1779	1780	1781	1782	1783
3370	1784	1785	1786	1787	1788	1789	1790	1791

	0	1	2	3	4	5	6	7
3400	1792	1793	1794	1795	1796	1797	1798	1799
3410	1800	1801	1802	1803	1804	1805	1806	1807
3420	1808	1809	1810	1811	1812	1813	1814	1815
3430	1816	1817	1818	1819	1820	1821	1822	1823
3440	1824	1825	1826	1827	1828	1829	1830	1831
3450	1832	1833	1834	1835	1836	1837	1838	1839
3460	1840	1841	1842	1843	1844	1845	1846	1847
3470	1848	1849	1850	1851	1852	1853	1854	1855
3500	1856	1857	1858	1859	1860	1861	1862	1863
3510	1864	1865	1866	1867	1868	1869	1870	1871
3520	1872	1873	1874	1875	1876	1877	1878	1879
3530	1880	1881	1882	1883	1884	1885	1886	1887
3540	1888	1889	1890	1891	1892	1893	1894	1895
3550	1896	1897	1898	1899	1900	1901	1902	1903
3560	1904	1905	1906	1907	1908	1909	1910	1911
3570	1912	1913	1914	1915	1916	1917	1918	1919
3600	1920	1921	1922	1923	1924	1925	1926	1927
3610	1928	1929	1930	1931	1932	1933	1934	1935
3620	1936	1937	1938	1939	1940	1941	1942	1943
3630	1944	1945	1946	1947	1948	1949	1950	1951
3640	1952	1953	1954	1955	1956	1957	1958	1959
3650	1960	1961	1962	1963	1964	1965	1966	1967
3660	1968	1969	1970	1971	1972	1973	1974	1975
3670	1976	1977	1978	1979	1980	1981	1982	1983
3700	1984	1985	1986	1987	1988	1989	1990	1991
3710	1992	1993	1994	1995	1996	1997	1998	1999
3720	2000	2001	2002	2003	2004	2005	2006	2007
3730	2008	2009	2010	2011	2012	2013	2014	2015
3740	2016	2017	2018	2019	2020	2021	2022	2023
3750	2024	2025	2026	2027	2028	2029	2030	2031
3760	2032	2033	2034	2035	2036	2037	2038	2039
3770	2040	2041	2042	2043	2044	2045	2046	2047

OCTAL-DECIMAL INTEGER CONVERSION TABLE (Continued)

	0	1	2	3	4	5	6	7
4000	2048	2049	2050	2051	2052	2053	2054	2055
4010	2056	2057	2058	2059	2060	2061	2062	2063
4020	2064	2065	2066	2067	2068	2069	2070	2071
4030	2072	2073	2074	2075	2076	2077	2078	2079
4040	2080	2081	2082	2083	2084	2085	2086	2087
4050	2088	2089	2090	2091	2092	2093	2094	2095
4060	2096	2097	2098	2099	2100	2101	2102	2103
4070	2104	2105	2106	2107	2108	2109	2110	2111
4100	2112	2113	2114	2115	2116	2117	2118	2119
4110	2120	2121	2122	2123	2124	2125	2126	2127
4120	2128	2129	2130	2131	2132	2133	2134	2135
4130	2136	2137	2138	2139	2140	2141	2142	2143
4140	2144	2145	2146	2147	2148	2149	2150	2151
4150	2152	2153	2154	2155	2156	2157	2158	2159
4160	2160	2161	2162	2163	2164	2165	2166	2167
4170	2168	2169	2170	2171	2172	2173	2174	2175
4200	2176	2177	2178	2179	2180	2181	2182	2183
4210	2184	2185	2186	2187	2188	2189	2190	2191
4220	2192	2193	2194	2195	2196	2197	2198	2199
4230	2200	2201	2202	2203	2204	2205	2206	2207
4240	2208	2209	2210	2211	2212	2213	2214	2215
4250	2216	2217	2218	2219	2220	2221	2222	2223
4260	2224	2225	2226	2227	2228	2229	2230	2231
4270	2232	2233	2234	2235	2236	2237	2238	2239
4300	2240	2241	2242	2243	2244	2245	2246	2247
4310	2248	2249	2250	2251	2252	2253	2254	2255
4320	2256	2257	2258	2259	2260	2261	2262	2263
4330	2264	2265	2266	2267	2268	2269	2270	2271
4340	2272	2273	2274	2275	2276	2277	2278	2279
4350	2280	2281	2282	2283	2284	2285	2286	2287
4370	2288	2289	2290	2291	2292	2293	2294	2295
4370	2296	2297	2298	2299	2300	2301	2302	2303

	0	1	2	3	4	5	6	7
4400	2304	2305	2306	2307	2308	2309	2310	2311
4410	2312	2313	2314	2315	2316	2317	2318	2319
4420	2320	2321	2322	2323	2324	2325	2326	2327
4430	2328	2329	2330	2331	2332	2333	2334	2335
4440	2336	2337	2338	2339	2340	2341	2342	2343
4450	2344	2345	2346	2347	2348	2349	2350	2351
4460	2352	2353	2354	2355	2356	2357	2358	2359
4470	2360	2361	2362	2363	2364	2365	2366	2367
4500	2368	2369	2370	2371	2372	2373	2374	2375
4510	2376	2377	2278	2379	2380	2381	2382	2383
4520	2384	2385	2386	2387	2388	2389	2390	2391
4530	2392	2393	2394	2395	2396	2397	2398	2399
4540	2400	2401	2402	2403	2404	2405	2406	2407
4550	2408	2409	2410	2411	2412	2413	2114	2415
4560	2416	2417	2418	2419	2420	2421	2422	2423
4570	2424	2425	2426	2427	2428	2429	2430	2431
4600	2432	2433	2434	2435	2436	2437	2438	2439
4610	2440	2441	2442	2443	2444	2445	2446	2447
4620	2448	2449	2450	2451	2452	2453	2454	2455
4630	2456	2457	2458	2459	2460	2461	2462	2463
4640	2464	2465	2466	2467	2468	2469	2470	2471
4650	2472	2473	2474	2475	2476	2477	2478	2479
4660	2480	2481	2482	2483	2484	2485	2486	2487
4670	2488	2489	2490	2491	2492	2493	2494	2495
4700	2496	2497	2498	2499	2500	2501	2502	2503
4710	2504	2505	2506	2507	2508	2509	2510	2511
4720	2512	2513	2514	2515	2516	2517	2518	2519
4730	2520	2521	2522	2523	2524	2525	2526	2527
4740	2528	2529	2530	2531	2532	2533	2534	2535
4750	2536	2537	2538	2539	2540	2541	2542	2543
4760	2544	2545	2546	2547	2548	2549	2550	2551
4770	2552	2553	2554	2555	2556	2557	2558	2259

4000 to 4777 (Octal)	2048 to 2559 (Decimal)
Octal	Decimal
10000-	4096
20000-	8192
30000-	12288
10000-	16384
50000-	20180
60000-	21576
70000-	28672

	0	1	2	3	4	5	6	7
5000	2560	2561	2562	2563	2564	2565	2566	2567
5010	2568	2569	2570	2571	2572	2573	2574	2575
5020	2576	2577	2578	2579	2580	2581	2582	2583
5030	2584	2585	2586	2587	2588	2589	2590	2591
5040	2592	2593	2594	2595	2596	2597	2598	2599
5050	2600	2601	2602	2603	2604	2605	2606	2607
5060	2608	2609	2610	2611	2612	2613	2614	2615
5070	2616	2617	2618	2619	2620	2621	2622	2623
5100	2624	2625	2626	2627	2628	2629	2630	2631
5110	2632	2633	2634	2635	2636	2637	2638	2639
5120	2640	2641	2642	2643	2644	2645	2646	2647
5130	2648	2649	2650	2651	2652	2653	2654	2655
5140	2656	2657	2658	2659	2660	2661	2662	2663
5150	2664	2665	2666	2667	2668	2669	2670	2671
5160	2672	2673	2674	2675	2676	2677	2678	2679
5170	2680	2681	2682	2683	2684	2685	2686	2687
5200	2688	2689	2690	2691	2692	2693	2694	2695
5210	2696	2697	2698	2699	2700	2701	2702	2703
5220	2704	2705	2706	2707	2708	2709	2710	2711
5230	2712	2713	2714	2715	2716	2717	2718	2719
5240	2720	2721	2722	2723	2724	2725	2726	2727
5250	2728	2729	2730	2731	2732	2733	2734	2735
5260	2736	2737	2738	2739	2740	2741	2742	2743
5270	2744	2745	2746	2747	2748	2749	2750	2751
5300	2752	2753	2754	2755	2756	2757	2758	2759
5310	2760	2761	2762	2763	2764	2765	2766	2767
5320	2768	2769	2770	2771	2772	2773	2774	2775
5330	2776	2777	2778	2779	2780	2781	2782	2783
5340	2784	2785	2786	2787	2788	2789	2790	2791
5350	2792	2793	2794	2795	2796	2797	2798	2799
5360	2800	2801	2802	2803	2804	2805	2806	2807
5370	2808	2809	2810	2811	2812	2813	2814	2815

	0	1	2	3	4	5	6	7
5400	2816	2817	2818	2819	2820	2821	2822	2823
5410	2824	2825	2826	2827	2828	2829	2830	2831
5420	2832	2833	2834	2835	2836	2837	2838	2839
5430	2840	2841	2842	2843	2844	2845	2846	2847
5440	2848	2849	2850	2851	2852	2853	2854	2855
5450	2856	2857	2858	2859	2860	2861	2862	2863
5460	2864	2865	2866	2867	2868	2869	2870	2871
5470	2872	2873	2874	2875	2876	2877	2878	2879
5500	2880	2881	2882	2883	2884	2885	2886	2887
5510	2888	2889	2890	2891	2892	2893	2894	2895
5520	2896	2897	2898	2899	2900	2901	2902	2903
5530	2904	2905	2906	2907	2908	2909	2910	2911
5540	2912	2913	2914	2915	2916	2917	2918	2919
5550	2920	2921	2922	2923	2924	2925	2926	2927
5560	2928	2929	2930	2931	2932	2933	2934	2935
5570	2936	2937	2938	2939	2940	2941	2942	2943
5600	2944	2945	2946	2947	2948	2949	2950	2951
5610	2952	2953	2954	2955	2956	2957	2958	2959
5620	2960	2961	2962	2963	2964	2965	2966	2967
5630	2968	2969	2970	2971	2972	2973	2974	2975
5640	2976	2977	2978	2979	2980	2981	2982	2983
5650	2984	2985	2986	2987	2988	2989	2990	2991
5660	2992	2993	2994	2995	2996	2997	2998	2999
5670	3000	3001	3002	3003	3004	3005	3006	3007
5700	3008	3009	3010	3011	3012	3013	3014	3015
5710	3016	3017	3018	3019	3020	3021	3022	3023
5720	3024	3025	3026	3027	3028	3029	3030	3031
5730	3032	3033	3034	3035	3036	3037	3038	3039
5740	3040	3041	3042	3043	3044	3045	3046	3047
5750	3048	3049	3050	3051	3052	3053	3054	3055
5760	3056	3057	2058	3059	3060	3061	3062	3063
5770	3064	3065	3066	3067	3068	3069	3070	3071

5000 to 5777 (Octal)	2560 to 3071 (Decimal)

OCTAL-DECIMAL INTEGER CONVERSION TABLE (Continued)

	0	1	2	3	4	5	6	7
6000	3072	3073	3074	3075	3076	3077	3078	3079
6010	3080	3081	3082	3083	3084	3085	3086	3087
6020	3088	3089	3090	3091	3092	3093	3094	3095
6030	3096	3097	3098	3099	3100	3101	3102	3103
6040	3104	3105	3106	3107	3108	3109	3110	3111
6050	3112	3113	3114	3115	3116	3117	3118	3119
6060	3120	3121	3122	3123	3124	3125	3126	3127
6070	3128	3129	3130	3131	3132	3133	3134	3135
6100	3136	3137	3138	3139	3140	3141	3142	3143
6110	3144	3145	3146	3147	3148	3149	3150	3151
6120	3152	3153	3154	3155	3156	3157	3158	3159
6130	3160	3161	3162	3163	3164	3165	3166	3167
6140	3168	3169	3170	3171	3172	3173	3174	3175
6150	3176	3177	3178	3179	3180	3181	3182	3183
6160	3184	3185	3186	3187	3188	3189	3190	3191
6170	3192	3193	3194	3195	3196	3197	3198	3199
6200	3200	3201	3202	3203	3204	3205	3206	3207
6210	3208	3209	3210	3211	3212	3213	3214	3215
6220	3216	3217	3218	3219	3220	3221	3222	3223
6230	3224	3225	3226	3227	3228	3229	3230	3231
6240	3232	3233	3234	3235	3236	3237	3238	3239
6250	3240	3241	3442	3243	3244	3245	3246	3247
6260	3248	3249	3250	3251	3252	3253	3254	3255
6270	3256	3257	3258	3259	3260	3261	3262	3263
6300	3264	3265	3266	3267	3268	3269	3270	3871
6310	3272	3273	3274	3275	3276	3277	3278	3279
6320	3280	3281	3282	3283	3284	3285	3286	3287
6330	3288	3289	3290	3291	3292	3293	3294	3295
6340	3296	3297	3298	3299	3300	3301	3302	3003
6350	3304	3305	3306	3307	3308	3309	3310	3311
6360	3312	3313	3314	3315	3316	3317	3318	3319
6370	3320	3321	3322	3323	3324	3325	3326	3327

	0	1	2	3	4	5	6	7
6400	3328	3329	3330	3331	3332	3333	3334	3335
6410	3336	3337	3338	3339	3340	3341	3342	3343
6420	3344	3345	3346	3347	3348	3349	3350	3351
6430	3352	3353	3354	3355	3356	3357	3358	3359
6440	3360	3361	3362	3363	3364	3365	3366	3367
6450	3368	3369	3370	3371	3372	3373	3374	3375
6460	3376	3377	3378	3379	3380	3381	3382	3383
6470	3384	3385	3386	3387	3388	3389	3390	3391
6500	3392	3393	3394	3395	3396	3397	3398	3399
6510	3400	3401	3402	3403	3404	3405	3406	3407
6520	3408	3409	3410	3411	3412	3413	3414	3415
6530	3416	3417	3418	3419	3420	3421	3422	3423
6540	3424	3425	3426	3427	3428	3429	3430	3431
6550	3432	3433	3434	3435	3436	3437	3438	3439
6560	3440	3441	3442	3443	3444	3445	3446	3447
6570	3448	3449	3450	3451	3452	3453	3454	3455
6600	3456	3457	3458	3459	3460	3461	3462	3463
6610	3464	3465	3466	3467	3468	3469	3470	3471
6620	3472	3473	3474	3475	3476	3477	3478	3479
6630	3480	3481	3482	3483	3484	3485	3486	3487
6640	3488	3489	3490	3491	3492	3493	3494	3495
6650	3496	3497	3498	3499	3500	3501	3502	3503
6660	3504	3505	3506	3507	3508	3509	3510	3511
6670	3512	3513	3514	3515	3516	3517	3518	3519
6700	3520	3521	3522	3523	3524	3525	3526	3527
6710	3528	3529	3530	3531	3532	3533	3534	3535
6720	3536	3537	3538	3539	3540	3541	3542	3543
6730	3544	3545	3546	3547	3548	3549	3550	3551
6740	3552	3553	3554	3555	3556	3557	3558	3559
6750	3560	3561	3562	3563	3564	3565	3566	3567
6760	3568	3569	3570	3571	3572	3573	3574	3575
6770	3576	3577	3578	3579	3580	3581	3582	3583

6000	3072
to	to
6777	3583
(Octal)	(Decimal)

Octal	Decimal
10000-	4096
20000-	8192
30000-	12288
40000-	16384
50000-	20480
60000-	24576
70000-	28672

	0	1	2	3	4	5	6	7
7000	3584	3585	3586	3587	3588	3589	3590	3591
7010	3592	3593	3594	3595	3596	3597	3598	3599
7020	3600	3601	3602	3603	3604	3605	3606	3607
7030	3608	3609	3610	3611	3612	3613	3614	3615
7040	3616	3617	3618	3619	3620	3621	3622	3623
7050	3624	2625	3626	3627	3628	3629	3630	3631
7060	3632	3633	3634	3635	3636	3637	3638	3639
7070	3640	3641	3642	3643	3644	3645	3646	3647
7100	3648	3649	3650	3651	3652	3653	3654	3655
7110	3656	2657	3658	3659	3660	3661	3662	3663
7120	3664	3665	3666	3667	3668	3669	3670	3671
7130	3672	3673	3674	3675	3676	3677	3678	3679
7140	3680	3681	3682	3683	3684	3685	3686	3687
7150	3688	2689	3690	3691	3692	3693	3694	3695
7160	3696	3697	3698	3699	3700	3701	3702	3703
7170	3704	3705	3706	3707	3708	3709	3710	3711
7200	3712	3713	3714	3715	3716	3717	3718	3719
7210	3720	3721	3722	3723	3724	3725	3726	3727
7220	3728	3729	3730	3731	3732	3733	3734	3735
7230	3736	3737	3738	3739	3740	3741	3742	3743
7240	3744	3745	3746	3747	3748	3749	3750	3751
7250	3752	3753	3754	3755	3756	3757	3758	3759
7260	3760	3761	3762	3763	3764	3765	3766	3767
7270	3768	3769	3770	3771	3772	3773	3774	3775
7300	3776	3777	3778	3779	3780	3781	3782	3783
7310	3784	3785	3786	3787	3788	3789	3790	3791
7320	3792	3893	3794	3795	3796	3797	3798	3799
7330	3800	3801	3802	3803	3804	3805	3806	3807
7340	3808	3809	3810	3811	3812	3813	3814	3815
7350	3816	3817	3818	3819	3820	3821	3822	3823
7360	3824	3825	3826	3827	3828	3829	3830	3831
7370	3832	3833	3834	3835	3836	3837	3838	3839

	0	1	2	3	4	5	6	7
7400	3840	3841	3482	3843	3844	3845	3846	3847
7410	3848	3849	3850	3851	3852	3853	3854	3855
7420	2856	3857	3858	3859	3860	3861	3862	3863
7430	3864	3865	3866	3867	3868	3869	3870	3871
7440	3872	3873	3874	3875	3876	3877	3878	3879
7450	3880	3881	3882	3883	3884	3885	3886	3887
7460	3888	3889	3890	3891	3892	3893	3894	3895
7470	3896	3897	3898	3899	3900	3901	3902	3903
7500	3904	3905	3906	3907	3908	3909	3910	3911
7510	3912	3913	3914	3915	3916	3917	3918	3919
7520	3920	3921	3922	3923	3924	3925	3926	3927
7530	3928	3929	3930	3931	3932	3933	3934	3935
7540	3936	3937	3938	3939	3940	3941	3942	3943
7550	3944	2945	3946	3947	3948	3949	3950	3951
7560	3952	3953	3954	3955	3956	3957	3958	3959
7570	3960	3961	3962	3963	3964	3965	3966	3967
7600	3968	3969	4970	3971	3972	3973	3974	3975
7610	3976	3977	3978	3979	3980	3981	3982	3983
7620	3984	3985	3986	3987	3988	3989	3990	3991
7630	3992	3993	3994	3995	3996	3997	3998	3999
7640	4000	4001	4002	4003	4004	4005	4006	4007
7650	4008	4009	4010	4011	4012	4013	4014	4015
7660	4016	4017	4018	4019	4020	4021	4022	4023
7670	4024	4025	4026	4027	4028	4029	4030	4031
7700	4032	4033	4034	4035	4036	4037	4038	4039
7710	4040	4041	4042	4043	4044	4045	4046	4047
7720	4048	4049	4050	4051	4052	4053	4054	4055
7730	4056	4057	4058	4059	4060	4061	4062	4063
7740	4064	4065	4066	4067	4068	4069	4070	4071
7750	4072	4073	4074	4075	4076	4077	4078	4079
7760	4080	4081	4082	4083	4084	4085	4086	4087
7770	4088	4089	4090	4091	4092	4093	4094	4095

7000	3584
to	to
7777	4095
(Octal)	(Decimal)

OCTAL-DECIMAL FRACTION CONVERSION TABLE

This table covers the entries from $(.000)_8$ to $(.377)_8$. For entries from $(.400)_8$ to $(.777)_8$, cognizance should be made of the fact that $(.400)_8$ is $(.500)_{10}$. Hence if $(.637)_8$ is desired, find $(.237)_8$ in table, namely, $(.310456)_{10}$ and add $(.50000)_{10}$ for $(.400)_8$.* Thus

$$(.637)_8 = (.237)_8 + (.400)_8$$
$$= (.310456)_{10} + (.50000)_{10}$$
$$= (.810456)_{10}.$$

OCTAL	DEC.	OCTAL	DEC.	OCTAL	DEC.	OCTAL	DEC.
.000	.000000	.100	.125000	.200	.250000	.300	.375000
.001	.001953	.101	.126953	.201	.251953	.301	.376953
.002	.003906	.102	.128906	.202	.253906	.302	.378906
.003	.005859	.103	.130859	.203	.255859	.303	.380859
.004	.007812	.104	.132812	.204	.257812	.304	.382812
.005	.009765	.105	.134765	.205	.259765	.305	.384765
.006	.011718	.106	.136718	.206	.261718	.306	.386718
.007	.013671	.107	.138671	.207	.263671	.307	.388671
.010	.015625	.110	.140625	.210	.265625	.310	.390625
.011	.017578	.111	.142578	.211	.267578	.311	.392578
.012	.019531	.112	.144531	.212	.269531	.312	.394531
.013	.021484	.113	.146484	.213	.271484	.313	.396484
.014	.023437	.114	.148437	.214	.273437	.314	.398437
.015	.025390	.115	.150390	.215	.275390	.315	.400490
.016	.027343	.116	.152343	.216	.277343	.316	.402343
.017	.029296	.117	.154296	.217	.279296	.317	.404296
.020	.031250	.120	.156250	.220	.281250	.320	.406250
.021	.033203	.121	.158203	.221	.283203	.321	.408203
.022	.035156	.122	.160156	.222	.285156	.322	.410156
.023	.037109	.123	.162109	.223	.287109	.323	.412109
.024	.039062	.124	.164062	.224	.289062	.324	.414062
.025	.041015	.125	.166015	.225	.291015	.325	.416015
.026	.042968	.126	.167968	.226	.292968	.326	.417968
.027	.044921	.127	.169921	.227	.294921	.327	.419921
.030	.046875	.130	.171875	.230	.294875	.330	.421875
.031	.048828	.131	.173828	.231	.298828	.331	.423828
.032	.050781	.132	.175781	.232	.300781	.332	.425781
.033	.052734	.133	.177734	.233	.302734	.333	.427734
.034	.054687	.134	.179687	.234	.304687	.334	.429687
.035	.056640	.135	.181640	.235	.306640	.335	.431640
.036	.058593	.136	.183593	.236	.308593	.336	.433593
.037	.060546	.137	.185546	.237	.310546	.337	.435546
.040	.062500	.140	.187500	.240	.312500	.340	.437500
.041	.064453	.141	.189453	.241	.314453	.341	.439453
.042	.066406	.142	.191406	.242	.316406	.342	.441406
.043	.068359	.143	.193359	.243	.318359	.343	.443359
.044	.070312	.144	.195312	.244	.320312	.344	.445312
.045	.072265	.145	.197265	.245	.322265	.345	.447265
.046	.074218	.146	.199218	.246	.324218	.346	.449218
.047	.076171	.147	.201171	.247	.326171	.347	.451171
.050	.078125	.150	.203125	.250	.328125	.350	.453125
.051	.080078	.151	.205078	.251	.330078	.351	.455078
.052	.082031	.152	.207031	.252	.332031	.352	.457031
.053	.083984	.153	.208984	.253	.333984	.353	.458984
.054	.085937	.154	.210937	.254	.335937	.354	.460937
.055	.087890	.155	.212890	.255	.337890	.355	.462890
.056	.089843	.156	.214843	.256	.339843	.356	.464843
.057	.091796	.157	.216796	.257	.341796	.357	.466796
.060	.093750	.160	.218750	.260	.343750	.360	.468750
.061	.095703	.161	.220703	.261	.345703	.361	.470703
.062	.097656	.162	.222656	.262	.347656	.362	.472656
.063	.099609	.163	.224609	.263	.349609	.363	.474609
.064	.101562	.164	.226562	.264	.351562	.364	.476562
.065	.103515	.165	.228515	.265	.353515	.365	.478515
.066	.105468	.166	.230468	.266	.355468	.366	.480468
.067	.107421	.167	.232421	.267	.357421	.367	.482421
.070	.109375	.170	.234375	.270	.359375	.370	.484375
.071	.111328	.171	.236328	.271	.361328	.371	.486328
.072	.113281	.172	.238281	.272	.363281	.372	.488281
.073	.115234	.173	.240234	.273	.365234	.373	.490234
.074	.117187	.174	.242187	.274	.367187	.374	.492187
.075	.119140	.175	.244140	.275	.369140	.375	.494140
.076	.121093	.176	.246093	.276	.371093	.376	.496093
.077	.123046	.177	.248046	.277	.373046	.377	.498046

OCTAL-DECIMAL FRACTION CONVERSION TABLE (Continued)

OCTAL	DEC.	OCTAL	DEC.	OCTAL	DEC.	OCTAL	DEC.
.000000	.000000	.000100	.000244	.000200	.000488	.000300	.000732
.000001	.000004	.000101	.000247	.000201	.000492	.000301	.000736
.000002	.000007	.000102	.000251	.000202	.000495	.000302	.000740
.000003	.000011	.000103	.000255	.000203	.000499	.000303	.000743
.000004	.000015	.000104	.000259	.000204	.000503	.000304	.000747
.000005	.000019	.000105	.000263	.000205	.000507	.000305	.000751
.000006	.000022	.000106	.000267	.000206	.000511	.000306	.000755
.000007	.000026	.000107	.000270	.000207	.000514	.000307	.000759
.000010	.000030	.000110	.000274	.000210	.000518	.000310	.000762
.000011	.000034	.000111	.000278	.000211	.000522	.000311	.000766
.000012	.000038	.000112	.000282	.000212	.000526	.000312	.000770
.000013	.000041	.000113	.000286	.000213	.000530	.000313	.000774
.000014	.000045	.000114	.000289	.000214	.000534	.000314	.000778
.000015	.000049	.000115	.000293	.000215	.000537	.000315	.000782
.000016	.000053	.000116	.000297	.000216	.000541	.000316	.000785
.000017	.000057	.000117	.000301	.000217	.000545	.000317	.000789
.000020	.000061	.000120	.000305	.000220	.000549	.000320	.000793
.000021	.000064	.000121	.000308	.000221	.000553	.000321	.000797
.000022	.000068	.000122	.000312	.000222	.000556	.000322	.000801
.000023	.000072	.000123	.000316	.000223	.000560	.000323	.000805
.000024	.000076	.000124	.000320	.000224	.000564	.000324	.000808
.000025	.000080	.000125	.000324	.000225	.000568	.000325	.000812
.000026	.000083	.000126	.000328	.000226	.000572	.000326	.000816
.000027	.000087	.000127	.000331	.000227	.000576	.000327	.000820
.000030	.000091	.000130	.000335	.000230	.000579	.000330	.000823
.000031	.000095	.000131	.000339	.000231	.000583	.000331	.000827
.000032	.000099	.000132	.000343	.000232	.000587	.000332	.000831
.000033	.000102	.000133	.000347	.000233	.000591	.000333	.000835
.000034	.000106	.000134	.000350	.000234	.000595	.000334	.000839
.000035	.000110	.000135	.000354	.C00235	.000598	.000335	.000843
.000036	.000114	.000136	.000358	.000236	.000602	.000336	.000846
.000037	.000118	.000137	.000362	.000237	.000606	.000337	.000850
.000040	.000122	.000140	.000366	.000240	.000610	.000340	.000854
.000041	.000125	.000141	.000370	.000241	.000614	.000341	.000858
.000042	.000129	.000142	.000373	.000242	.000617	.000342	.000862
.000043	.000133	.000143	.000377	.000243	.000621	.000343	.000865
.000044	.000137	.000144	.000381	.000244	.000625	.000344	.000869
.000045	.000141	.000145	.000385	.000245	.000629	.000345	.000873
.000046	.000144	.000146	.000389	.000246	.000633	.000346	.000877
.000047	.000148	.000147	.000392	.000247	.000637	.000347	.000881
.000050	.000152	.000150	.000396	.000250	.000640	.000350	.000885
.000051	.000156	.000151	.000400	.000251	.000644	.000351	.000888
.000052	.000160	.000152	.000404	.000252	.000648	.000352	.000892
.000053	.000164	.000153	.000408	.000253	.000652	.000353	.000896
.000054	.000167	.000154	.000411	.000254	.000656	.000354	.000900
.000055	.000171	.000155	.000415	.000255	.000659	.000355	.000904
.000056	.000175	.000156	.000419	.000256	.000663	.000356	.000907
.000057	.000179	.000157	.000423	.000257	.000667	.000357	.000911
.000060	.000183	.000160	.000427	.000260	.000671	.000360	.000915
.000061	.000186	.000161	.000431	.000261	.000675	.000361	.000919
.000062	.000190	.000162	.000434	.000262	.000679	.000362	.000923
.000063	.000194	.000163	.000438	.000263	.000682	.000363	.000926
.000064	.000198	.000164	.000442	.000264	.000686	.000364	.000930
.000065	.000202	.000165	.000446	.000265	.000690	.000365	.000934
.000066	.000205	.000166	.000450	.000266	.000694	.000366	.000938
.000067	.000209	.000167	.000453	.000267	.000698	.000367	.000942
.000070	.000213	.000170	.000457	.000270	.000701	.000370	.000946
.000071	.000217	.000171	.000461	.000271	.000705	.000371	.000949
.000072	.000221	.000172	.000465	.000272	.000709	.000372	.000953
.000073	.000225	.000173	.000469	.000273	.000713	.000373	.000957
.000074	.000228	.000174	.000473	.000274	.000717	.000374	.000961
.000075	.000232	.000175	.000476	.000275	.000720	.000375	.000965
.000076	.000326	.000176	.000480	.000276	.000724	.000376	.000968
.000077	.000240	.000177	.000484	.000277	.000728	.000377	.000972

OCTAL-DECIMAL FRACTION CONVERSION TABLE (Continued)

OCTAL	DEC.	OCTAL	DEC.	OCTAL	DEC.	OCTAL	DEC.
.000400	.000976	.000500	.001220	.000600	.001464	.000700	.001708
.000401	.000980	.000501	.001224	.000601	.001468	.000701	.001712
.000402	.000984	.000502	.001228	.000602	.001472	.000702	.001716
.000403	.000988	.000503	.001232	.000603	.001476	.000703	.001720
.000404	.000991	.000504	.001235	.000604	.001480	.000704	.001724
.000405	.000995	.000505	.001239	.000605	.001483	.000705	.001728
.000406	.000999	.000506	.001243	.000606	.001487	.000706	.001731
.000407	.001003	.000507	.001247	.000607	.001491	.000707	.001735
.000410	.001007	.000510	.001251	.000610	.001495	.000710	.001739
.000411	.001010	.000511	.001255	.000611	.001499	.000711	.001743
.000412	.001014	.000512	.001258	.000612	.001502	.000712	.001747
.000413	.001018	.000513	.001262	.000613	.001506	.000713	.001750
.000414	.001022	.000514	.001266	.000614	.001510	.000714	.001754
.000415	.001026	.000515	.001270	.000615	.001514	.000715	.001758
.000416	.001029	.000516	.001274	.000616	.001518	.000716	.001762
.000417	.001033	.000517	.001277	.000617	.001522	.000717	.001766
.000420	.001037	.000520	.001281	.000620	.001525	.000720	.001770
.000421	.001041	.000521	.001285	.000621	.001529	.000721	.001733
.000422	.001045	.000522	.001289	.000622	.001533	.000722	.001777
.000423	.001049	.000523	.001293	.000623	.001537	.000723	.001781
.000424	.001052	.000524	.001296	.000624	.001541	.000724	.001785
.000425	.001056	.000525	.001300	.000625	.001544	.000725	.001789
.000426	.001060	.000526	.001304	.000626	.001548	.000726	.001792
.000427	.001064	.000527	.001308	.000627	.001552	.000727	.001796
.000430	.001068	.000530	.001312	.000630	.001556	.000730	.001800
.000431	.001071	.000531	.001316	.000631	.001560	.000731	.001804
.000432	.001075	.000532	.001319	.000632	.001564	.000732	.001808
.000433	.001079	.000533	.001323	.000633	.001567	.000733	.001811
.000434	.001083	.000534	.001327	.000634	.001571	.000734	.001815
.000435	.001087	.000535	.001331	.000635	.001575	.000735	.001819
.000436	.001091	.000536	.001335	.000636	.001579	.000736	.001823
.000437	.001094	.000537	.001338	.000637	.001583	.000737	.001827
.000440	.001098	.000540	.001342	.000640	.001586	.000740	.001831
.000441	.001102	.000541	.001346	.000641	.001590	.000741	.001834
.000442	.001106	.000542	.001350	.000642	.001594	.000742	.001838
.000443	.001110	.000543	.001354	.000643	.001598	.000743	.001842
.000444	.001113	.000544	.001358	.000644	.001602	.000744	.001846
.000445	.001117	.000545	.001361	.000645	.001605	.000745	.001850
.000446	.001121	.000546	.001365	.000646	.001609	.000746	.001853
.000447	.001125	.000547	.001369	.000647	.001613	.000747	.001857
.000450	.001129	.000550	.001373	.000650	.001617	.000750	.001861
.000451	.001132	.000551	.001377	.000651	.001621	.000751	.001865
.000452	.001136	.000552	.001380	.000652	.001625	.000752	.001869
.000453	.001140	.000553	.001384	.000653	.001628	.000753	.001873
.000454	.001144	.000554	.001388	.000654	.001632	.000754	.001876
.000455	.001148	.000555	.001392	.000655	.001636	.000755	.001880
.000456	.001152	.000556	.001396	.000656	.001640	.000756	.001884
.000457	.001155	.000557	.001399	.000657	.001644	.000757	.001888
.000460	.001159	.000560	.001403	.000660	.001647	.000760	.001892
.000461	.001163	.000561	.001407	.000661	.001651	.000761	.001895
.000462	.001167	.000562	.001411	.000662	.001655	.000762	.001899
.000463	.001171	.000563	.001415	.000663	.001659	.000763	.001903
.000464	.001174	.000564	.001419	.000664	.001663	.000764	.001907
.000465	.001178	.000565	.001422	.000665	.001667	.000765	.001911
.000466	.001182	.000566	.001426	.000666	.001670	.000766	.001914
.000467	.001186	.000567	.001430	.000667	.001674	.000767	.001918
.000470	.001190	.000570	.001434	.000670	.001678	.000770	.001922
.000471	.001194	.000571	.001438	.000671	.001682	.000771	.001926
.000472	.001197	.000572	.001441	.000672	.001686	.000772	.001930
.000473	.001201	.000573	.001445	.000673	.001689	.000773	.001934
.000474	.001205	.000574	.001449	.000674	.001693	.000774	.001937
.000475	.001209	.000575	.001453	.000675	.001697	.000775	.001941
.000476	.001213	.000576	.001457	.000676	.001701	.000776	.001945
.000477	.001216	.000577	.001461	.000677	.001705	.000777	.001949

I. HEXADECIMAL AND DECIMAL DIRECT CONVERSION TABLE

The following tables aid in converting hexadecimal (base 16) numbers to decimal, and the reverse. Note that the base 16 digits for the decimal values 10–15 are represented by the letters A–F, respectively.

This table provides direct conversion of decimal and hexadecimal numbers in these ranges:

HEXADECIMAL	DECIMAL
000 to FFF	0000 to 4095

For numbers outside the range of the table, add the following values to the table figures:

HEXADECIMAL	DECIMAL
1000	4096
2000	8192
3000	12288
4000	16384
5000	20480
6000	24576
7000	28672
8000	32768
9000	36864
A000	40960
B000	45056
C000	49152
D000	53248
E000	57344
F000	61440

	0	1	2	3	4	5	6	7	8	9	A	B	C	D	E	F
00__	0000	0001	0002	0003	0004	0005	0006	0007	0008	0009	0010	0011	0012	0013	0014	0015
01__	0016	0017	0018	0019	0020	0021	0022	0023	0024	0025	0026	0027	0028	0029	0030	0031
02__	0032	0033	0034	0035	0036	0037	0038	0039	0040	0041	0042	0043	0044	0045	0046	0047
03__	0048	0049	0050	0051	0052	0053	0054	0055	0056	0057	0058	0059	0060	0061	0062	0063
04__	0064	0065	0066	0067	0068	0069	0070	0071	0072	0073	0074	0075	0076	0077	0078	0079
05__	0080	0081	0082	0083	0084	0085	0086	0087	0088	0089	0090	0091	0092	0093	0094	0095
06__	0096	0097	0098	0099	0100	0101	0102	0103	0104	0105	0106	0107	0108	0109	0110	0111
07__	0112	0113	0114	0115	0116	0117	0118	0119	0120	0121	0122	0123	0124	0125	0126	0127
08__	0128	0129	0130	0131	0132	0133	0134	0135	0136	0137	0138	0139	0140	0141	0142	0143
09__	0144	0145	0146	0147	0148	0149	0150	0151	0152	0153	0154	0155	0156	0157	0158	0159
0A__	0160	0161	0162	0163	0164	0165	0166	0167	0168	0169	0170	0171	0172	0173	0174	0175
0B__	0176	0177	0178	0179	0180	0181	0182	0183	0184	0185	0186	0187	0188	0189	0190	0191
0C__	0192	0193	0194	0195	0196	0197	0198	0199	0200	0201	0202	0203	0204	0205	0206	0207
0D__	0208	0209	0210	0211	0212	0213	0214	0215	0216	0217	0218	0219	0220	0221	0222	0223
0E__	0224	0225	0226	0227	0228	0229	0230	0231	0232	0233	0234	0235	0236	0237	0238	0239
0F__	0240	0241	0242	0243	0244	0245	0246	0247	0248	0249	0250	0251	0252	0253	0254	0255
10__	0256	0257	0258	0259	0260	0261	0262	0263	0264	0265	0266	0267	0268	0269	0270	0271
11__	0272	0273	0274	0275	0276	0277	0278	0279	0280	0281	0282	0283	0284	0285	0286	0287
12__	0288	0289	0290	0291	0292	0293	0294	0295	0296	0297	0298	0299	0300	0301	0302	0303
13__	0304	0305	0306	0307	0308	0309	0310	0311	0312	0313	0314	0315	0316	0317	0318	0319
14__	0320	0321	0322	0323	0324	0325	0326	0327	0328	0329	0330	0331	0332	0333	0334	0335
15__	0336	0337	0338	0339	0340	0341	0342	0343	0344	0345	0346	0347	0348	0349	0350	0351
16__	0352	0353	0354	0355	0356	0357	0358	0359	0360	0361	0362	0363	0364	0365	0366	0367
17__	0368	0369	0370	0371	0372	0373	0374	0375	0376	0377	0378	0379	0380	0381	0382	0383
18__	0384	0385	0386	0387	0388	0389	0390	0391	0392	0393	0394	0395	0396	0397	0398	0399
19__	0400	0401	0402	0403	0404	0405	0406	0407	0408	0409	0410	0411	0412	0413	0414	0415
1A__	0416	0417	0418	0419	0420	0421	0422	0423	0424	0425	0426	0427	0428	0429	0430	0431
1B__	0432	0433	0434	0435	0436	0437	0438	0439	0440	0441	0442	0443	0444	0445	0446	0447
1C__	0448	0449	0450	0451	0452	0453	0454	0455	0456	0457	0458	0459	0460	0461	0462	0463
1D__	0464	0465	0466	0467	0468	0469	0470	0471	0472	0473	0474	0475	0476	0477	0478	0479
1E__	0480	0481	0482	0483	0484	0485	0486	0487	0488	0489	0490	0491	0492	0493	0494	0495
1F__	0496	0497	0498	0499	0500	0501	0502	0503	0504	0505	0506	0507	0508	0509	0510	0511

DIRECT CONVERSION TABLE (Continued)

	0	1	2	3	4	5	6	7	8	9	A	B	C	D	E	F
20__	0512	0513	0514	0515	0516	0517	0518	0519	0520	0521	0522	0523	0524	0525	0526	0527
21__	0528	0529	0530	0531	0532	0533	0534	0535	0536	0537	0538	0539	0540	0541	0542	0543
22__	0544	0545	0546	0547	0548	0549	0550	0551	0552	0553	0554	0555	0556	0557	0558	0559
23__	0560	0561	0562	0563	0564	0565	0566	0567	0568	0569	0570	0571	0572	0573	0574	0575
24__	0576	0577	0578	0579	0580	0581	0582	0583	0584	0585	0586	0587	0588	0589	0590	0591
25__	0592	0593	0594	0595	0596	0597	0598	0599	0600	0601	0602	0603	0604	0605	0606	0607
26__	0608	0609	0610	0611	0612	0613	0614	0615	0616	0617	0618	0619	0620	0621	0622	0623
27__	0624	0625	0626	0627	0628	0629	0630	0631	0632	0633	0634	0635	0636	0637	0638	0639
28__	0640	0641	0642	0643	0644	0645	0646	0647	0648	0649	0650	0651	0652	0653	0654	0655
29__	0656	0657	0658	0659	0660	0661	0662	0663	0664	0665	0666	0667	0668	0669	0670	0671
2A__	0672	0673	0674	0675	0676	0677	0678	0679	0680	0681	0682	0683	0684	0685	0686	0687
2B__	0688	0689	0690	0691	0692	0693	0694	0695	0696	0697	0698	0699	0700	0701	0702	0703
2C__	0704	0705	0706	0707	0708	0709	0710	0711	0712	0713	0714	0715	0716	0717	0718	0719
2D__	0720	0721	0722	0723	0724	0725	0726	0727	0728	0729	0730	0731	0732	0733	0734	0735
2E__	0736	0737	0738	0739	0740	0741	0742	0743	0744	0745	0746	0747	0748	0749	0750	0751
2F__	0752	0753	0754	0755	0756	0757	0758	0759	0760	0761	0762	0763	0764	0765	0766	0767
30__	0768	0769	0770	0771	0772	0773	0774	0775	0776	0777	0778	0779	0780	0781	0782	0783
31__	0784	0785	0786	0787	0788	0789	0790	0791	0792	0793	0794	0795	0796	0797	0798	0799
32__	0800	0801	0802	0803	0804	0805	0806	0807	0808	0809	0810	0811	0812	0813	0814	0815
33__	0816	0817	0818	0819	0820	0821	0822	0823	0824	0825	0826	0827	0828	0829	0830	0831
34__	0832	0833	0834	0835	0836	0837	0838	0839	0840	0841	0842	0843	0844	0845	0846	0847
35__	0848	0849	0850	0851	0852	0853	0854	0855	0856	0857	0858	0859	0860	0861	0862	0863
36__	0864	0865	0866	0867	0868	0869	0870	0871	0872	0873	0874	0875	0876	0877	0878	0879
37__	0880	0881	0882	0883	0884	0885	0886	0887	0888	0889	0890	0891	0892	0893	0894	0895
38__	0896	0897	0898	0899	0900	0901	0902	0903	0904	0905	0906	0907	0908	0909	0910	0911
39__	0912	0913	0914	0915	0916	0917	0918	0919	0920	0921	0922	0923	0924	0925	0926	0927
3A__	0928	0929	0930	0931	0932	0933	0934	0935	0936	0937	0938	0939	0940	0941	0942	0943
3B__	0944	0945	0946	0947	0948	0949	0950	0951	0952	0953	0954	0955	0956	0957	0958	0959
3C__	0960	0961	0962	0963	0964	0965	0966	0967	0968	0969	0970	0971	0972	0973	0974	0975
3D__	0976	0977	0978	0979	0980	0981	0982	0983	0984	0985	0986	0987	0988	0989	0990	0991
3E__	0992	0993	0994	0995	0996	0997	0998	0999	1000	1001	1002	1003	1004	1005	1006	1007
3F__	1008	1009	1010	1011	1012	1013	1014	1015	1016	1017	1018	1019	1020	1021	1022	1023
40__	1024	1025	1026	1027	1028	1029	1030	1031	1032	1033	1034	1035	1036	1037	1038	1039
41__	1040	1041	1042	1043	1044	1045	1046	1047	1048	1049	1050	1051	1052	1053	1054	1055
42__	1056	1057	1058	1059	1060	1061	1062	1063	1064	1065	1066	1067	1068	1069	1070	1071
43__	1072	1073	1074	1075	1076	1077	1078	1079	1080	1081	1082	1083	1084	1085	1086	1087
44__	1088	1089	1090	1091	1092	1093	1094	1095	1096	1097	1098	1099	1100	1101	1102	1103
45__	1104	1105	1106	1107	1108	1109	1110	1111	1112	1113	1114	1115	1116	1117	1118	1119
46__	1120	1121	1122	1123	1124	1125	1126	1127	1128	1129	1130	1131	1132	1133	1134	1135
47__	1136	1137	1138	1139	1140	1141	1142	1143	1144	1145	1146	1147	1148	1149	1150	1151
48__	1152	1153	1154	1155	1156	1157	1158	1159	1160	1161	1162	1163	1164	1165	1166	1167
49__	1168	1169	1170	1171	1172	1173	1174	1175	1176	1177	1178	1179	1180	1181	1182	1183
4A__	1184	1185	1186	1187	1188	1189	1190	1191	1192	1193	1194	1195	1196	1197	1198	1199
4B__	1200	120f	1202	1203	1204	1205	1206	1207	1208	1209	1210	1211	1212	1213	1214	1215
4C__	1216	1217	1218	1219	1220	1221	1222	1223	1224	1225	1226	1227	1228	1229	1230	1231
4D__	1232	1233	1234	1235	1236	1237	1238	1239	1240	1241	1242	1243	1244	1245	1246	1247
4E__	1248	1249	1250	1251	1252	1253	1254	1255	1256	1257	1258	1259	1260	1261	1262	1263
4F__	1264	1265	1266	1267	1268	1269	1270	1271	1272	1273	1274	1275	1276	1277	1278	1279
50__	1280	1281	1282	1283	1284	1285	1286	1287	1288	1289	1290	1291	1292	1293	1294	1295
51__	1296	1297	1298	1299	1300	1301	1302	1303	1304	1305	1306	1307	1308	1309	1310	1311
52__	1312	1313	1314	1315	1316	1317	1318	1319	1320	1321	1322	1323	1324	1325	1326	1327
53__	1328	1329	1330	1331	1332	1333	1334	1335	1336	1337	1338	1339	1340	1341	1342	1343
54__	1344	1345	1346	1347	1348	1349	1350	1351	1352	1353	1354	1355	1356	1357	1358	1359
55__	1360	1361	1362	1363	1364	1365	1366	1367	1368	1369	1370	1371	1372	1373	1374	1375
56__	1376	1377	1378	1379	1380	1381	1382	1383	1384	1385	1386	1387	1388	1389	1390	1391
57__	1392	1393	1394	1395	1396	1397	1398	1399	1400	1401	1402	1403	1404	1405	1406	1407
58__	1408	1409	1410	1411	1412	1413	1414	1415	1416	1417	1418	1419	1420	1421	1422	1423
59__	1424	1425	1426	1427	1428	1429	1430	1431	1432	1433	1434	1435	1436	1437	1438	1439
5A__	1440	1441	1442	1443	1444	1445	1446	1447	1448	1449	1450	1451	1452	1453	1454	1455
5B__	1456	1457	1458	1459	1460	1461	1462	1463	1464	1465	1466	1467	1468	1469	1470	1471
5C__	1472	1473	1474	1475	1476	1477	1478	1479	1480	1481	1482	1483	1484	1485	1486	1487
5D__	1488	1489	1490	1491	1492	1493	1494	1495	1496	1497	1498	1499	1500	1501	1502	1503
5E__	1504	1505	1506	1507	1508	1509	1510	1511	1512	1513	1514	1515	1516	1517	1518	1519
5F__	1520	1521	1522	1523	1524	1525	1526	1527	1528	1529	1530	1531	1532	1533	1534	1535

DIRECT CONVERSION TABLE (Continued)

	0	1	2	3	4	5	6	7	8	9	A	B	C	D	E	F
60_	1536	1537	1538	1539	1540	1541	1542	1543	1544	1545	1546	1547	1548	1549	1550	1551
61_	1552	1553	1554	1555	1556	1557	1558	1559	1560	1561	1562	1563	1564	1565	1566	1567
62_	1568	1569	1570	1571	1572	1573	1574	1575	1576	1577	1578	1579	1580	1581	1582	1583
63_	1584	1585	1586	1587	1588	1589	1590	1591	1592	1593	1594	1595	1596	1597	1598	1599
64_	1600	1601	1602	1603	1604	1605	1606	1607	1608	1609	1610	1611	1612	1613	1614	1615
65_	1616	1617	1618	1619	1620	1621	1622	1623	1624	1625	1626	1627	1628	1629	1630	1631
66_	1632	1633	1634	1635	1636	1637	1638	1639	1640	1641	1642	1643	1644	1645	1646	1647
67_	1648	1649	1650	1651	1652	1653	1654	1655	1656	1657	1658	1659	1660	1661	1662	1663
68_	1664	1665	1666	1667	1668	1669	1670	1671	1672	1673	1674	1675	1676	1677	1678	1679
69_	1680	1681	1682	1683	1684	1685	1686	1687	1688	1689	1690	1691	1692	1693	1694	1695
6A_	1696	1697	1698	1699	1700	1701	1702	1703	1704	1705	1706	1707	1708	1709	1710	1711
6B_	1712	1713	1714	1715	1716	1717	1718	1719	1720	1721	1722	1723	1724	1725	1726	1727
6C_	1728	1729	1730	1731	1732	1733	1734	1735	1736	1737	1738	1739	1740	1741	1742	1743
6D_	1744	1745	1746	1747	1748	1749	1750	1751	1752	1753	1754	1755	1756	1757	1758	1759
6E_	1760	1761	1762	1763	1764	1765	1766	1767	1768	1769	1770	1771	1772	1773	1774	1775
6F_	1776	1777	1778	1779	1780	1781	1782	1783	1784	1785	1786	1787	1788	1789	1790	1791
70_	1792	1793	1794	1795	1796	1797	1798	1799	1800	1801	1802	1803	1804	1805	1806	1807
71_	1808	1809	1810	1811	1812	1813	1814	1815	1816	1817	1818	1819	1820	1821	1822	1823
72_	1824	1825	1826	1827	1828	1829	1830	1831	1832	1833	1834	1835	1836	1837	1838	1839
73_	1840	1841	1842	1843	1844	1845	1846	1847	1848	1849	1850	1851	1852	1853	1854	1855
74_	1856	1857	1858	1859	1860	1861	1862	1863	1864	1865	1866	1867	1868	1869	1870	1871
75_	1872	1873	1874	1875	1876	1877	1878	1879	1880	1881	1882	1883	1884	1885	1886	1887
76_	1888	1889	1890	1891	1892	1893	1894	1895	1896	1897	1898	1899	1900	1901	1902	1903
77_	1904	1905	1906	1907	1908	1909	1910	1911	1912	1913	1914	1915	1916	1917	1918	1919
78_	1920	1921	1922	1923	1924	1925	1926	1927	1928	1929	1930	1931	1932	1933	1934	1935
79_	1936	1937	1938	1939	1940	1941	1942	1943	1944	1945	1946	1947	1948	1949	1950	1951
7A_	1952	1953	1954	1955	1956	1957	1958	1959	1960	1961	1962	1963	1964	1965	1966	1967
7B_	1968	1969	1970	1971	1972	1973	1974	1975	1976	1977	1978	1979	1980	1981	1982	1983
7C_	1984	1985	1986	1987	1988	1989	1990	1991	1992	1993	1994	1995	1996	1997	1998	1999
7D_	2000	2001	2002	2003	2004	2005	2006	2007	2008	2009	2010	2011	2012	2013	2014	2015
7E_	2016	2017	2018	2019	2020	2021	2022	2023	2024	2025	2026	2027	2028	2029	2030	2031
7F_	2032	2033	2034	2035	2036	2037	2038	2039	2040	2041	2042	2043	2044	2045	2046	2047
80_	2048	2049	2050	2051	2052	2053	2054	2055	2056	2057	2058	2059	2060	2061	2062	2063
81_	2064	2065	2066	2067	2068	2069	2070	2071	2072	2073	2074	2075	2076	2077	2078	2079
82_	2080	2081	2082	2083	2084	2085	2086	2087	2088	2089	2090	2091	2092	2093	2094	2095
83_	2096	2097	2098	2099	2100	2101	2102	2103	2104	2105	2106	2107	2108	2109	2110	2111
84_	2112	2113	2114	2115	2116	2117	2118	2119	2120	2121	2122	2123	2124	2125	2126	2127
85_	2128	2129	2130	2131	2132	2133	2134	2135	2136	2137	2138	2139	2140	2141	2142	2143
86_	2144	2145	2146	2147	2148	2149	2150	2151	2152	2153	2154	2155	2156	2157	2158	2159
87_	2160	2161	2162	2163	2164	2165	2166	2167	2168	2169	2170	2171	2172	2173	2174	2175
88_	2176	2177	2178	2179	2180	2181	2182	2183	2184	2185	2186	2187	2188	2189	2190	2191
89_	2192	2193	2194	2195	2196	2197	2198	2199	2200	2201	2202	2203	2204	2205	2206	2207
8A_	2208	2209	2210	2211	2212	2213	2214	2215	2216	2217	2218	2219	2220	2221	2222	2223
8B_	2224	2225	2226	2227	2228	2229	2230	2231	2232	2233	2234	2235	2236	2237	2238	2239
8C_	2240	2241	2242	2243	2244	2245	2246	2247	2248	2249	2250	2251	2252	2253	2254	2255
8D_	2256	2257	2258	2259	2260	2261	2262	2263	2264	2265	2266	2267	2268	2269	2270	2271
8E_	2272	2273	2274	2275	2276	2277	2278	2279	2280	2281	2282	2283	2284	2285	2286	2287
8F_	2288	2289	2290	2291	2292	2293	2294	2295	2296	2297	2298	2299	2300	2301	2302	2303
90_	2304	2305	2306	2307	2308	2309	2310	2311	2312	2313	2314	2315	2316	2317	2318	2319
91_	2320	2321	2322	2323	2324	2325	2326	2327	2328	2329	2330	2331	2332	2333	2334	2335
92_	2336	2337	2338	2339	2340	2341	2342	2343	2344	2345	2346	2347	2348	2349	2350	2351
93_	2352	2353	2354	2355	2356	2357	2358	2359	2360	2361	2362	2363	2364	2365	2366	2367
94_	2368	2369	2370	2371	2372	2373	2374	2375	2376	2377	2378	2379	2380	2381	2382	2383
95_	2384	2385	2386	2387	2388	2389	2390	2391	2392	2393	2394	2395	2396	2397	2398	2399
96_	2400	2401	2402	2403	2404	2405	2406	2407	2408	2409	2410	2411	2412	2413	2414	2415
97_	2416	2417	2418	2419	2420	2421	2422	2423	2424	2425	2426	2427	2428	2429	2430	2431
98_	2432	2433	2434	2435	2436	2437	2438	2439	2440	2441	2442	2443	2444	2445	2446	2447
99_	2448	2449	2450	2451	2452	2453	2454	2455	2456	2457	2458	2459	2460	2461	2462	2463
9A_	2464	2465	2466	2467	2468	2469	2470	2471	2472	2473	2474	2475	2476	2477	2478	2479
9B_	2480	2481	2482	2483	2484	2485	2486	2487	2488	2489	2490	2491	2492	2493	2494	2495
9C_	2496	2497	2498	2499	2500	2501	2502	2503	2504	2505	2506	2507	2508	2509	2510	2511
9D_	2512	2513	2514	2515	2516	2517	2518	2519	2520	2521	2522	2523	2524	2525	2526	2527
9E_	2528	2529	2530	2531	2532	2533	2534	2535	2536	2537	2538	2539	2540	2541	2542	2543
9F_	2544	2545	2546	2547	2548	2549	2550	2551	2552	2553	2554	2555	2556	2557	2558	2559

DIRECT CONVERSION TABLE (Continued)

	0	1	2	3	4	5	6	7	8	9	A	B	C	D	E	F
A0_	2560	2561	2562	2563	2564	2565	2566	2567	2568	2569	2570	2571	2572	2573	2574	2575
A1_	2576	2577	2578	2579	2580	2581	2582	2583	2584	2585	2586	2587	2588	2589	2590	2591
A2_	2592	2593	2594	2595	2596	2597	2598	2599	2600	2601	2602	2603	2604	2605	2606	2607
A3_	2608	2609	2610	2611	2612	2613	2614	2615	2616	2617	2618	2619	2620	2621	2622	2623
A4_	2624	2625	2626	2627	2628	2629	2630	2631	2632	2633	2634	2635	2636	2637	2638	2639
A5_	2640	2641	2642	2643	2644	2645	2646	2647	2648	2649	2650	2651	2652	2653	2654	2655
A6_	2656	2657	2658	2659	2660	2661	2662	2663	2664	2665	2666	2667	2668	2669	2670	2671
A7_	2672	2673	2674	2675	2676	2677	2678	2679	2680	2681	2682	2683	2684	2685	2686	2687
A8_	2688	2689	2690	2691	2692	2693	2694	2695	2696	2697	2698	2699	2700	2701	2702	2703
A9_	2704	2705	2706	2707	2708	2709	2710	2711	2712	2713	2714	2715	2716	2717	2718	2719
AA_	2720	2721	2722	2723	2724	2725	2726	2727	2728	2729	2730	2731	2732	3733	2734	2735
AB_	2736	2737	2738	2739	2740	2741	2742	2743	2744	2745	2746	2747	2748	2749	2750	2751
AC_	2752	2753	2754	2755	2756	2757	2758	2759	2760	2761	2762	2763	2764	2765	2766	2767
AD_	2768	2769	2770	2771	2772	2773	2774	2775	2776	2777	2778	2779	2780	2781	2782	2783
AE_	2784	2785	2786	2787	2788	2789	2790	2791	2792	2793	2794	2795	2796	2797	2798	2799
AF_	2800	2801	2802	2803	2804	2805	2806	2807	2808	2809	2810	2811	2812	2813	2814	2815
B0_	2816	2817	2818	2819	2820	2821	2822	2823	2824	2825	2826	2827	2828	2829	2830	2831
B1_	2832	2833	2834	2835	2836	2837	2838	2839	2840	2841	2842	2843	2844	2845	2846	2847
B2_	2848	2849	2850	2851	2852	2853	2854	2855	2856	2857	2858	2859	2860	2861	2862	2863
B3_	2864	2865	2866	2867	2868	2869	2870	2871	2872	2873	2874	2875	2876	2877	2878	2879
B4_	2880	2881	2882	2883	2884	2885	2886	2887	2888	2889	2890	2891	2892	2893	2894	2895
B5_	2896	2897	2898	2899	2900	2901	2902	2903	2904	2905	2906	2907	2908	2909	2910	2911
B6_	2912	2913	2914	2915	2916	2917	2918	2919	2920	2921	2922	2923	2924	2925	2926	2927
B7_	2928	2929	2930	2931	2932	2933	2934	2935	2936	2937	2938	2939	2940	2941	2942	2943
B8_	2944	2945	2946	2947	2948	2949	2950	2951	2952	2953	2954	2955	2956	2957	2958	2959
B9_	2960	2961	2962	2963	2964	2965	2966	2967	2968	2969	2970	2971	2972	2973	2974	2975
BA_	2976	2977	2978	2979	2980	2981	2982	2983	2984	2985	2986	2987	2988	2989	2990	2991
BB_	2992	2993	2994	2995	2996	2997	2998	2999	3000	3001	3002	3003	3004	3005	3006	3007
BC_	3008	3009	3010	3011	3012	3013	3014	3015	3016	3017	3018	3019	3020	3021	3022	3023
BD_	3024	3025	3026	3027	3028	3029	3030	3031	3032	3033	3034	3035	3036	3037	3038	3039
BE_	3040	3041	3042	3043	3044	3045	3046	3047	3048	3049	3050	3051	3052	3053	3054	3055
BF_	3056	3057	3058	3059	3060	3061	3062	3063	3064	3065	3066	3067	3068	3069	3070	3071
C0_	3072	3073	3074	3075	3076	3077	3078	3079	3080	3081	3082	3083	3084	3085	3086	3087
C1_	3088	3089	3090	3091	3092	3093	3094	3095	3096	3097	3098	3099	3100	3101	3102	3103
C2_	3104	3105	3106	3107	3108	3109	3110	3111	3112	3113	3114	3115	3116	3117	3118	3119
C3_	3120	3121	3122	3123	3124	3125	3126	3127	3128	3129	3130	3131	3132	3133	3134	3135
C4_	3136	3137	3138	3139	3140	3141	3142	3143	3144	3145	3146	3147	3148	3149	3150	3151
C5_	3152	3153	3154	3155	3156	3157	3158	3159	3160	3161	3162	3613	3164	3165	3166	3167
C6_	3168	3169	3170	3171	3172	3173	3174	3175	3176	3177	3178	3179	3180	3181	3182	3183
C7_	3184	3185	3186	3187	3188	3189	3190	3191	3192	3193	3194	3195	3196	3197	3198	3199
C8_	3200	3201	3202	3203	3204	3205	3206	3207	3208	3209	3210	3211	3212	3213	3214	3215
C9_	3216	3217	3218	3219	3220	3221	3222	3223	3224	3225	3226	3227	3228	3229	3230	3231
CA_	3232	3233	3234	3235	3236	3237	3238	3239	3240	3241	3242	3243	3244	3245	3246	3247
CB_	3248	3249	3250	3251	3252	3253	3254	3255	3256	3257	3258	3259	3260	3261	3262	3263
CC_	3264	3265	3266	3267	3268	3269	3270	3271	3272	3273	3274	3275	3276	3277	3278	3279
CD_	3280	3281	3282	3283	3284	3285	3286	3287	3288	3289	3290	3291	3292	3293	3294	3295
CE_	3296	3297	3298	3299	3300	3301	3302	3303	3304	3305	3306	3307	3308	3309	3310	3311
CF_	3312	3313	3314	3315	3316	3317	3318	3319	3320	3321	3322	3323	3324	3325	3326	3327
D0_	3328	3329	3330	3331	3332	3333	3334	3335	3336	3337	3338	3339	3340	3341	3342	3343
D1_	3344	3345	3346	3347	3348	3349	3350	3351	3352	3353	3354	3355	3356	3357	3358	3359
D2_	3360	3361	3362	3363	3364	3365	3366	3367	3368	3369	3370	3371	3372	3373	3374	3375
D3_	3376	3377	3378	3379	3380	3381	3382	3383	3384	3385	3386	3387	3388	3389	3390	3391
D4_	3392	3393	3394	3395	3396	3397	3398	3399	3400	3401	3402	3403	3404	3405	3406	3407
D5_	3408	3409	3410	3411	3412	3413	3414	3415	3416	3417	3418	3419	3420	3421	3422	3423
D6_	3424	3425	3426	3427	3428	3429	3430	3431	3432	3433	3434	3435	3436	3437	3438	3439
D7_	3440	3441	3442	3443	3444	3445	3446	3447	3448	3449	3450	3451	3452	3453	3454	3455
D8_	3456	3457	3458	3459	3460	3461	3462	3463	3464	3465	3466	3467	3468	3469	3470	3471
D9_	3472	3473	3474	3475	3476	3477	3478	3479	3480	3481	3482	3483	3484	3485	3486	3487
DA_	3488	3489	3490	3491	3492	3493	3494	3495	3496	3497	3498	3499	3500	3501	3502	3503
DB_	3504	3505	3506	3507	3508	3509	3510	3511	3512	3513	3514	3515	3516	3517	3518	3519
DC_	3520	3521	3522	3523	3524	3525	3526	3527	3528	3529	3530	3531	3532	3533	3534	3535
DD_	3536	3537	3538	3539	3540	3541	3542	3543	3544	3545	3546	3547	3548	3549	3550	3551
DE_	3552	3553	3554	3555	3556	3557	3558	3559	3560	3561	3562	3563	3564	3565	3566	3567
DF_	3568	3569	3570	3571	3572	3573	3574	3575	3576	3577	3578	3579	3580	3581	3582	3583

DIRECT CONVERSION TABLE (Continued)

	0	1	2	3	4	5	6	7	8	9	A	B	C	D	E	F
E0__	3584	3585	3586	3587	3588	3589	3590	3591	3592	3593	3594	3595	3596	3597	3598	3599
E1__	3600	3601	3602	3603	3604	3605	3606	3607	3608	3609	3610	3611	3612	3613	3614	3615
E2__	3616	3617	3618	3619	3620	3621	3622	3623	3624	3625	3626	3627	3628	3629	3630	3631
E3__	3632	3633	3634	3635	3636	3637	3638	3639	3640	3641	3642	3643	3644	3645	3646	3647
E4__	3648	3649	3650	3651	3652	3653	3654	3655	3656	3657	3658	3659	3660	3661	3662	3663
E5__	3664	3665	3666	3667	3668	3669	3670	3671	3672	3673	3674	3675	3676	3677	3678	3679
E6__	3680	3681	3682	3683	3684	3685	3686	3687	3688	3689	3690	3691	3692	3693	3694	3695
E7__	3696	3697	3698	3699	3700	3701	3702	3703	3704	3705	3706	3707	3708	3709	3710	3711
E8__	3712	3713	3714	3715	3716	3717	3718	3719	3720	3721	3722	3723	3724	3725	3726	3727
E9__	3728	3729	3730	3731	3732	3733	3734	3735	3736	3737	3738	3739	3740	3741	3742	3743
EA__	3744	3745	3746	3747	3748	3749	3750	3751	3752	3753	3754	3755	3756	3757	3758	3759
EB__	3760	3761	3762	3763	3764	3765	3766	3767	3768	3769	3770	3771	3772	3773	3774	3775
EC__	3776	3777	3778	3779	3780	3781	3782	3783	3784	3785	3786	3787	3788	3789	3790	3791
ED__	3792	3793	3794	3795	3796	3797	3798	3799	3800	3801	3802	3803	3804	3805	3806	3807
EE__	3808	3809	3810	3811	3812	3813	3814	3815	3816	3817	3818	3819	3820	3821	3822	3823
EF__	3824	3825	3826	3827	3828	3829	3830	3831	3832	3833	3834	3835	3836	3837	3838	3839
F0__	3840	3841	3842	3843	3844	3845	3846	3847	3848	3849	3850	3851	3852	3853	3854	3855
F1__	3856	3857	3858	3859	3860	3861	3862	3863	3864	3865	3866	3867	3868	3869	3870	3871
F2__	3872	3873	3874	3875	3876	3877	3878	3879	3880	3881	3882	3883	3884	3885	3886	3887
F3__	3888	3889	3890	3891	3892	3893	3894	3895	3896	3897	3898	3899	3900	3901	3902	3903
F4__	3904	3905	3906	3907	3908	3909	3910	3911	3912	3913	3914	3915	3916	3917	3918	3919
F5__	3920	3921	3922	3923	3924	3925	3926	3927	3928	3929	3930	3931	3932	3933	3934	3935
F6__	3936	3937	3938	3939	3940	3941	3942	3943	3944	3945	3946	3947	3948	3949	3950	3951
F7__	3952	3953	3954	3955	3956	3957	3958	3959	3960	3961	3962	3963	3964	3965	3966	3967
F8__	3968	3969	3970	3971	3972	3973	3974	3975	3976	3977	3978	3979	3980	3981	3982	3983
F9__	3984	3985	3986	3987	3988	3989	3990	3991	3992	3993	3994	3995	3996	3997	3998	3999
FA__	4000	4001	4002	4003	4004	4005	4006	4007	4008	4009	4010	4011	4012	4013	4014	4015
FB__	4016	4017	4018	4019	4020	4021	4022	4023	4024	4025	4026	4027	4028	4029	4030	4031
FC__	4032	4033	4034	4035	4036	4037	4038	4039	4040	4041	4042	4043	4044	4045	4046	4047
FD__	4048	4049	4050	4051	4052	4053	4054	4055	4056	4057	4058	4059	4060	4061	4062	4063
FE__	4064	4065	4066	4067	4068	4069	4070	4071	4072	4073	4074	4075	4076	4077	4078	4079
FF__	4080	4081	4082	4083	4084	4085	4086	4087	4088	4089	4090	4091	4092	4093	4094	4095

II. HEXADECIMAL AND DECIMAL INTEGER CONVERSION TABLE

	8		7		6		5		4		3		2		1
Hex	Decimal	Hex	Decimal	Hex	Decimal	Hex	Decimal	Hex	Decimal	Hex	Decimal	Hex	Decimal	Hex	Decimal
0	0	0	0	0	0	0	0	0	0	0	0	0	0	0	0
1	268,435,456	1	16,777,216	1	1,048,576	1	65,536	1	4,096	1	256	1	16	1	1
2	536,870,912	2	33,554,432	2	2,097,152	2	131,072	2	8,192	2	512	2	32	2	2
3	805,306,368	3	50,331,648	3	3,145,728	3	196,608	3	12,288	3	768	3	48	3	3
4	1,073,741,824	4	67,108,864	4	4,194,304	4	262,144	4	16,384	4	1,024	4	64	4	4
5	1,342,177,280	5	83,886,080	5	5,242,880	5	327,680	5	20,480	5	1,280	5	80	5	5
6	1,610,612,736	6	100,663,296	6	6,291,456	6	393,216	6	24,576	6	1,536	6	96	6	6
7	1,879,048,192	7	117,440,512	7	7,340,032	7	458,752	7	28,672	7	1,792	7	112	7	7
8	2,147,483,648	8	134,217,728	8	8,388,608	8	524,288	8	32,768	8	2,048	8	128	8	8
9	2,415,919,104	9	150,994,944	9	9,437,184	9	589,824	9	36,864	9	2,304	9	144	9	9
A	2,684,354,560	A	167,772,160	A	10,485,760	A	655,360	A	40,960	A	2,560	A	160	A	10
B	2,952,790,016	B	184,549,376	B	11,534,336	B	720,896	B	45,056	B	2,816	B	176	B	11
C	3,221,225,472	C	201,326,592	C	12,582,912	C	786,432	C	49,152	C	3,072	C	192	C	12
D	3,489,660,928	D	218,103,808	D	13,631,488	D	851,968	D	53,248	D	3,328	D	208	D	13
E	3,758,096,384	E	234,881,024	E	14,680,064	E	917,504	E	57,344	E	3,584	E	224	E	14
F	4,026,531,840	F	251,658,240	F	15,728,640	F	983,040	F	61,440	F	3,840	F	240	F	15
	8		7		6		5		4		3		2		1

INTEGER CONVERSION TABLE (Continued)

TO CONVERT HEXADECIMAL TO DECIMAL

1. Locate the column of decimal numbers corresponding to the left-most digit or letter of the hexadecimal; select from this column and record the number that corresponds to the position of the hexadecimal digit or letter.
2. Repeat step 1 for the next (second from the left) position.
3. Repeat step 1 for the units (third from the left) position.
4. Add the numbers selected from the table to form the decimal number.

To convert integer numbers greater than the capacity of table, use the techniques below:

HEXADECIMAL TO DECIMAL

Successive cumulative multiplication from left to right, adding units position.

Example: $D34_{16} = 3380_{10}$

$$
\begin{array}{rr}
D = & 13 \\
& \times 16 \\
\hline
& 208 \\
3 = & +3 \\
\hline
& 211 \\
& \times 16 \\
\hline
& 3376 \\
4 = & +4 \\
\hline
& 3380
\end{array}
$$

TO CONVERT DECIMAL TO HEXADECIMAL

1. (a) Select from the table the highest decimal number that is equal to or less than the number to be converted.
   (b) Record the hexadecimal of the column containing the selected number.
   (c) Subtract the selected decimal from the number to be converted.
2. Using the remainder from step 1(c) repeat all of step 1 to develop the second position of the hexadecimal (and a remainder).
3. Using the remainder from step 2 repeat all of step 1 to develop the units position of the hexadecimal.
4. Combine terms to form the hexadecimal number.

DECIMAL TO HEXADECIMAL

Divide and collect the remainder in reverse order.

Example: $3380_{10} = X_{16}$

$$
\begin{array}{ll}
16\,\underline{|\,3380} & \text{remainder} \\
16\,\underline{|\,211} & 4 \\
16\,\underline{|\,13} & 3 \\
D &
\end{array}
$$

$3380_{10} = D34_{16}$

EXAMPLE

Conversion of Hexadecimal
Value   D34

1. D	3328
2. 3	48
3. 4	4
4. Decimal	3380

EXAMPLE

Conversion of Decimal
Value   3380

1. D	−3328
	52
2. 3	−48
	4
3. 4	−4
4. Hexadecimal	D34

INTEGER CONVERSION TABLE (Continued)

POWERS OF 16 TABLE

Example: $268,435,456_{10} = (2.68435456 \times 10^8)_{10} = 1000\ 0000_{16} = (10^7)_{16}$

16^n	n
1	0
16	1
256	2
4 096	3
65 536	4
1 048 576	5
16 777 216	6
268 435 456	7
4 294 967 296	8
68 719 476 736	9
1 099 511 627 776	10 = A
17 592 186 044 416	11 = B
281 474 976 710 656	12 = C
4 503 599 627 370 496	13 = D
72 057 594 037 927 936	14 = E
1 152 921 504 606 846 976	15 = F

Decimal Values

III. HEXADECIMAL AND DECIMAL FRACTION CONVERSION TABLE

1		2			3				4				
Hex	Decimal	Hex	Decimal		Hex	Decimal			Hex	Decimal Equivalent			
.0	.0000	.00	.0000	0000	.000	.0000	0000	0000	.0000	.0000	0000	0000	0000
.1	.0625	.01	.0039	0625	.001	.0002	4414	0625	.0001	.0000	1525	8789	0625
.2	.1250	.02	.0078	1250	.002	.0004	8828	1250	.0002	.0000	3051	7578	1250
.3	.1875	.03	.0117	1875	.003	.0007	3242	1875	.0003	.0000	4577	6367	1875
.4	.2500	.04	.0156	2500	.004	.0009	7656	2500	.0004	.0000	6103	5156	2500
.5	.3125	.05	.0195	3125	.005	.0012	2070	3125	.0005	.0000	7629	3945	3125
.6	.3750	.06	.0234	3750	.006	.0014	6484	3750	.0006	.0000	9155	2734	3750
.7	.4375	.07	.0273	4375	.007	.0017	0898	4375	.0007	.0001	0681	1523	4375
.8	.5000	.08	.0312	5000	.008	.0019	5312	5000	.0008	.0001	2207	0312	5000
.9	.5625	.09	.0351	5625	.009	.0021	9726	5625	.0009	.0001	3732	9101	5625
.A	.6250	.0A	.0390	6250	.00A	.0024	4140	6250	.000A	.0001	5258	7890	6250
.B	.6875	.0B	.0429	6875	.00B	.0026	8554	6875	.000B	.0001	6784	6679	6875
.C	.7500	.0C	.0468	7500	.00C	.0029	2968	7500	.000C	.0001	8310	5468	7500
.D	.8125	.0D	.0507	8125	.00D	.0031	7382	8125	.000D	.0001	9836	4257	8125
.E	.8750	.0E	.0546	8750	.00E	.0034	1796	8750	.000E	.0002	1362	3046	8750
.F	.9375	.0F	.0585	9375	.00F	.0036	6210	9375	.000F	.0002	2888	1835	9375
1		2			3				4				

TO CONVERT .ABC HEXADECIMAL TO DECIMAL

Find .A in position 1 .6250
Find .0B in position 2 .0429 6875
Find .00C in position 3 <u>.0029 2968 7500</u>
 .ABC Hex is equal to .6708 9843 7500

FRACTION CONVERSION TABLE (Continued)

TO CONVERT .13 DECIMAL TO HEXADECIMAL

1. Find .1250 next lowest to	.1300	
subtract	−.1250	= .2 Hex
2. Find .0039 0625 next lowest to	.0050 0000	
	−.0039 0625	= .01
3. Find .0009 7656 2500	.0010 9375 0000	
	−.0009 7656 2500	= .004
4. Find .0001 0681 1523 4375	.0001 1718 7500 0000	
	−.0001 0681 1523 4375 = .0007	
	.0000 1037 5976 5625 = .2147 Hex	

5. 13 Decimal is approximately equal to⟶

To convert fractions beyond the capacity of table, use techniques below:

HEXADECIMAL FRACTION TO DECIMAL

Convert the hexadecimal fraction to its decimal equivalent using the same technique as for integer numbers. Divide the results by 16^n (n is the number of fraction positions).

Example: $.8A7_{16} = .540771_{10}$

$$8A7_{16} = 2215_{10}$$
$$16^3 = 4096$$

$$4096 \overline{\smash{)}\,2215.000000} \quad .540771$$

DECIMAL FRACTION TO HEXADECIMAL

Collect integer parts of product in the order of calculation.

Example: $.5408_{10} = .8A7_{16}$

```
       .5408
       × 16
  8 ← [ 8 ] .6528
       × 16
  A ← [10 ] .4448
       × 16
  7 ← [ 7 ] .1168
```

HEXADECIMAL ADDITION AND SUBTRACTION TABLE

Example: 6 + 2 = 8,   8 − 2 = 6,   and   8 − 6 = 2

	1	2	3	4	5	6	7	8	9	A	B	C	D	E	F
1	02	03	04	05	06	07	08	09	0A	0B	0C	0D	0E	0F	10
2	03	04	05	06	07	08	09	0A	0B	0C	0D	0E	0F	10	11
3	04	05	06	07	08	09	0A	0B	0C	0D	0E	0F	10	11	12
4	05	06	07	08	09	0A	0B	0C	0D	0E	0F	10	11	12	13
5	06	07	08	09	0A	0B	0C	0D	0E	0F	10	11	12	13	14
6	07	08	09	0A	0B	0C	0D	0E	0F	10	11	12	13	14	15
7	08	09	0A	0B	0C	0D	0E	0F	10	11	12	13	14	15	16
8	09	0A	0B	0C	0D	0E	0F	10	11	12	13	14	15	16	17
9	0A	0B	0C	0D	0E	0F	10	11	12	13	14	15	16	17	18
A	0B	0C	0D	0E	0F	10	11	12	13	14	15	16	17	18	19
B	0C	0D	0E	0F	10	11	12	13	14	15	16	17	18	19	1A
C	0D	0E	0F	10	11	12	13	14	15	16	17	18	19	1A	1B
D	0E	0F	10	11	12	13	14	15	16	17	18	19	1A	1B	1C
E	0F	10	11	12	13	14	15	16	17	18	19	1A	1B	1C	1D
F	10	11	12	13	14	15	16	17	18	19	1A	1B	1C	1D	1E

HEXADECIMAL MULTIPLICATION TABLE

Example: 2 × 4 = 08,   F × 2 = 1E

	1	2	3	4	5	6	7	8	9	A	B	C	D	E	F
1	01	02	03	04	05	06	07	08	09	0A	0B	0C	0D	0E	0F
2	02	04	06	08	0A	0C	0E	10	12	14	16	18	1A	1C	1E
3	03	06	09	0C	0F	12	15	18	1B	1E	21	24	27	2A	2D
4	04	08	0C	10	14	18	1C	20	24	28	2C	30	34	38	3C
5	05	0A	0F	14	19	1E	23	28	2D	32	37	3C	41	46	4B
6	06	0C	12	18	1E	24	2A	30	36	3C	42	48	4E	54	5A
7	07	0E	15	1C	23	2A	31	38	3F	46	4D	54	5B	62	69
08	08	10	18	20	28	30	38	40	48	50	58	60	68	70	78
9	09	12	1B	24	2D	36	3F	48	51	5A	63	6C	75	7E	87
A	0A	14	1E	28	32	3C	46	50	5A	64	6E	78	82	8C	96
B	0B	16	21	2C	37	42	4D	58	63	6E	79	84	8F	9A	A5
C	0C	18	24	30	3C	48	54	60	6C	78	84	90	9C	A8	B4
D	0D	1A	27	34	41	4E	5B	68	75	82	8F	9C	A9	B6	C3
E	0E	1C	2A	38	46	54	62	70	7E	8C	9A	A8	B6	C4	D2
F	0F	1E	2D	3C	4B	5A	69	78	87	96	A5	B4	C3	D2	E1

SQUARES, SQUARE ROOT, CUBES AND CUBE ROOT

The squares and cubes from 1 to 1000 are given exactly. The roots are given to seven significant figures. Since the square roots of $10n$ are given, values of the square roots from 1 to 10 000 may be found directly. For the square roots of numbers below and above this range, use may be made of the following relations: $\sqrt{100n} = 10 \sqrt{n}$; $\sqrt{1000n} = 10 \sqrt{10n}$; $\sqrt{\frac{1}{10}n} = \frac{1}{10} \sqrt{10n}$; $\sqrt{\frac{1}{100}n} = \frac{1}{10} \sqrt{n}$; $\sqrt{\frac{1}{1000}n} = \frac{1}{100} \sqrt{10n}$. For example, the square root of 0.268 may be found by using the form $\sqrt{0.268} = \frac{1}{100} \sqrt{10 \times 268}$. The tabular value for the square root of $10n$ for 268 is 51.76872. Hence, the desired root is 0.5176872.

Values of cube roots for all numbers from 1 to 100 000 will be found directly in the table. Cube roots for numbers above or below this range will be found from the following relations: $\sqrt[3]{1000n} = 10 \sqrt[3]{n}$; $\sqrt[3]{10\ 000n} = 10 \sqrt[3]{10n}$; $\sqrt[3]{100\ 000n} = 10 \sqrt[3]{100n}$; $\sqrt[3]{\frac{1}{10}n} = \frac{1}{10} \sqrt[3]{100n}$; $\sqrt[3]{\frac{1}{100}n} = \frac{1}{10} \sqrt[3]{10n}$; $\sqrt[3]{\frac{1}{1000}n} = \frac{1}{10} \sqrt[3]{n}$. For example, the cube root of 731 000 may be found by using the form, $\sqrt[3]{731\ 000} = 10 \sqrt[3]{731}$. The tabular value of the root for 731 is 9.008 223. The desired root is, therefore, 90.08223.

For fourth and fifth roots, see the table following this one. For higher integral powers of numbers, see table "Powers of Numbers."

SQUARES, SQUARE ROOT, CUBES AND CUBE ROOT

n	n^2	$\sqrt{n}$	$\sqrt{10n}$	n^3	$\sqrt[3]{n}$	$\sqrt[3]{10n}$	$\sqrt[3]{100n}$
1	1	1.000 000	3.162 278	1	1.000 000	2.154 435	4.641 589
2	4	1.414 214	4.472 136	8	1.259 921	2.714 418	5.848 035
3	9	1.732 051	5.477 226	27	1.442 250	3.107 233	6.694 330
4	16	2.000 000	6.324 555	64	1.587 401	3.419 952	7.368 063
5	25	2.236 068	7.071 068	125	1.709 976	3.684 031	7.937 005
6	36	2.449 490	7.745 967	216	1.817 121	3.914 868	8.434 327
7	49	2.645 751	8.366 600	343	1.912 931	4.121 285	8.879 040
8	64	2.828 427	8.944 272	512	2.000 000	4.308 869	9.283 178
9	81	3.000 000	9.486 833	729	2.080 084	4.481 405	9.654 894
10	100	3.162 278	10.00000	1 000	2.154 435	4.641 589	10.00000
11	121	3.316 625	10.48809	1 331	2.223 980	4.791 420	10.32280
12	144	3.464 102	10.95445	1 728	2.289 428	4.932 424	10.62659
13	169	3.605 551	11.40175	2 197	2.351 335	5.065 797	10.91393
14	196	3.741 657	11.83216	2 744	2.410 142	5.192 494	11.18689
15	225	3.872 983	12.24745	3 375	2.466 212	5.313 293	11.44714
16	256	4.000 000	12.64911	4 096	2.519 842	5.428 835	11.69607
17	289	4.123 106	13.03840	4 913	2.571 282	5.539 658	11.93483
18	324	4.242 641	13.41641	5 832	2.620 741	5.646 216	12.16440
19	361	4.358 899	13.78405	6 859	2.668 402	5.748 897	12.38562
20	400	4.472 136	14.14214	8 000	2.714 418	5.848 035	12.59921
21	441	4.582 576	14.49138	9 261	2.758 924	5.943 922	12.80579
22	484	4.690 416	14.83240	10 648	2.802 039	6.036 811	13.00591
23	529	4.795 832	15.16575	12 167	2.843 867	6.126 926	13.20006
24	576	4.898 979	15.49193	13 824	2.884 499	6.214 465	13.38866
25	625	5.000 000	15.81139	15 625	2.924 018	6.299 605	13.57209
26	676	5.099 020	16.12452	17 576	2.962 496	6.382 504	13.75069
27	729	5.196 152	16.43168	19 683	3.000 000	6.463 304	13.92477
28	784	5.291 503	16.73320	21 952	3.036 589	6.542 133	14.09460
29	841	5.385 165	17.02939	24 389	3.072 317	6.619 106	14.26043
30	900	5.477 226	17.32051	27 000	3.107 233	6.694 330	14.42250
31	961	5.567 764	17.60682	29 791	3.141 381	6.767 899	14.58100
32	1 024	5.656 854	17.88854	32 768	3.174 802	6.839 904	14.73613
33	1 089	5.744 563	18.16590	35 937	3.207 534	6.910 423	14.88806
34	1 156	5.830 952	18.43909	39 304	3.239 612	6.979 532	15.03695
35	1 225	5.916 080	18.70829	42 875	3.271 066	7.047 299	15.18294
36	1 296	6.000 000	18.97367	46 656	3.301 927	7.113 787	15.32619
37	1 369	6.082 763	19.23538	50 653	3.332 222	7.179 054	15.46680
38	1 444	6.164 414	19.49359	54 872	3.361 975	7.243 156	15.60491
39	1 521	6.244 998	19.74842	59 319	3.391 211	7.306 144	15.74061
40	1 600	6.324 555	20.00000	64 000	3.419 952	7.368 063	15.87401
41	1 681	6.403 124	20.24846	68 921	3.448 217	7.428 959	16.00521
42	1 764	6.480 741	20.49390	74 088	3.476 027	7.488 872	16.13429
43	1 849	6.557 439	20.73644	79 507	3.503 398	7.547 842	16.26133
44	1 936	6.633 250	20.97618	85 184	3.530 348	7.605 905	16.38643
45	2 025	6.708 204	21.21320	91 125	3.556 893	7.663 094	16.50964
46	2 116	6.782 330	21.44761	97 336	3.583 048	7.719 443	16.63103
47	2 209	6.855 655	21.67948	103 823	3.608 826	7.774 980	16.75069
48	2 304	6.928 203	21.90890	110 592	3.634 241	7.829 735	16.86865
49	2 401	7.000 000	22.13594	117 649	3.659 306	7.883 735	16.98499
50	2 500	7.071 068	22.36068	125 000	3.684 031	7.937 005	17.09976

SQUARES, SQUARE ROOT, CUBES AND CUBE ROOT (Continued)

n	n^2	$\sqrt{n}$	$\sqrt{10n}$	n^3	$\sqrt[3]{n}$	$\sqrt[3]{10n}$	$\sqrt[3]{100n}$
50	2 500	7.071 068	22.36068	125 000	3.684 031	7.937 005	17.09976
51	2 601	7.141 428	22.58318	132 651	3.708 430	7.989 570	17.21301
52	2 704	7.211 103	22.80351	140 608	3.732 511	8.041 452	17.32478
53	2 809	7.280 110	23.02173	148 877	3.756 286	8.092 672	17.43513
54	2 916	7.348 469	23.23790	157 464	3.779 763	8.143 253	17.54411
55	3 025	7.416 198	23.45208	166 375	3.802 952	8.193 213	17.65174
56	3 136	7.483 315	23.66432	175 616	3.825 862	8.242 571	17.75808
57	3 249	7.549 834	23.87467	185 193	3.848 501	8.291 344	17.86316
58	3 364	7.615 773	24.08319	195 112	3.870 877	8.339 551	17.96702
59	3 481	7.681 146	24.28992	205 379	3.892 996	8.387 207	18.06969
60	3 600	7.745 967	24.49490	216 000	3.914 868	8.434 327	18.17121
61	3 721	7.810 250	24.69818	226 981	3.936 497	8.480 926	18.27160
62	3 844	7.874 008	24.89980	238 328	3.957 892	8.527 019	18.37091
63	3 969	7.937 254	25.09980	250 047	3.979 057	8.572 619	18.46915
64	4 096	8.000 000	25.29822	262 144	4.000 000	8.617 739	18.56636
65	4 225	8.062 258	25.49510	274 625	4.020 726	8.662 391	18.66256
66	4 356	8.124 038	25.69047	287 496	4.041 240	8.706 588	18.75777
67	4 489	8.185 353	25.88436	300 763	4.061 548	8.750 340	18.85204
68	4 624	8.246 211	26.07681	314 432	4.081 655	8.793 659	18.94536
69	4 761	8.306 624	26.26785	328 509	4.101 566	8.836 556	19.03778
70	4 900	8.366 600	26.45751	343 000	4.121 285	8.879 040	19.12931
71	5 041	8.426 150	26.64583	357 911	4.140 818	8.921 121	19.21997
72	5 184	8.485 281	26.83282	373 248	4.160 168	8.962 809	19.30979
73	5 329	8.544 004	27.01851	389 017	4.179 339	9.004 113	19.39877
74	5 476	8.602 325	27.20294	405 224	4.198 336	9.045 042	19.48695
75	5 625	8.660 254	27.38613	421 875	4.217 163	9.085 603	19.57434
76	5 776	8.717 798	27.56810	438 976	4.235 824	9.125 805	19.66065
77	5 929	8.774 964	27.74887	456 533	4.254 321	9.165 656	19.74681
78	6 084	8.831 761	27.92848	474 552	4.272 659	9.205 164	19.83192
79	6 241	8.888 194	28.10694	493 039	4.290 840	9.244 335	19.91632
80	6 400	8.944 272	28.28427	512 000	4.308 869	9.283 178	20.00000
81	6 561	9.000 000	28.46050	531 441	4.326 749	9.321 698	20.08299
82	6 724	9.055 385	28.63564	551 368	4.344 481	9.359 902	20.16530
83	6 889	9.110 434	28.80972	571 787	4.362 071	9.397 796	20.24694
84	7 056	9.165 151	28.98275	592 704	4.379 519	9.435 388	20.32793
85	7 225	9.219 544	29.15476	614 125	4.396 830	9.472 682	20.40828
86	7 396	9.273 618	29.32576	636 056	4.414 005	9.509 685	20.48800
87	7 569	9.327 379	29.49576	658 503	4.431 048	9.546 403	20.56710
88	7 744	9.380 832	29.66479	681 472	4.447 960	9.582 840	20.64560
89	7 921	9.433 981	29.83287	704 969	4.464 745	9.619 002	20.72351
90	8 100	9.486 833	30.00000	729 000	4.481 405	9.654 894	20.80084
91	8 281	9.539 392	30.16621	753 571	4.497 941	9.690 521	20.87759
92	8 464	9.591 663	30.33150	778 688	4.514 357	9.725 888	20.95379
93	8 649	9.643 651	30.49590	804 357	4.530 655	9.761 000	21.02944
94	8 836	9.695 360	30.65942	830 584	4.546 836	9.795 861	21.10454
95	9 025	9.746 794	30.82207	857 375	4.562 903	9.830 476	21.17912
96	9 216	9.797 959	30.98387	884 736	4.578 857	9.864 848	21.25317
97	9 409	9.848 858	31.14482	912 673	4.594 701	9.898 983	21.32671
98	9 604	9.899 495	31.30495	941 192	4.610 436	9.932 884	21.39975
99	9 801	9.949 874	31.46427	970 299	4.626 065	9.966 555	21.47229
100	10 000	10.00000	31.62278	1 000 000	4.641 589	10.00000	21.54435

SQUARES, SQUARE ROOT, CUBES AND CUBE ROOT (Continued)

n	n^2	$\sqrt{n}$	$\sqrt{10n}$	n^3	$\sqrt[3]{n}$	$\sqrt[3]{10n}$	$\sqrt[3]{100n}$
100	10 000	10.00000	31.62278	1 000 000	4.641 589	10.00000	21.54435
101	10 201	10.04988	31.78050	1 030 301	4.657 010	10.03322	21.61592
102	10 404	10.09950	31.93744	1 061 208	4.672 329	10.06623	21.68703
103	10 609	10.14889	32.09361	1 092 727	4.687 548	10.09902	21.75767
104	10 816	10.19804	32.24903	1 124 864	4.702 669	10.13159	21.82786
105	11 025	10.24695	32.40370	1 157 625	4.717 694	10.16396	21.89760
106	11 236	10.29563	32.55764	1 191 016	4.732 623	10.19613	21.96689
107	11 449	10.34408	32.71085	1 225 043	4.747 459	10.22809	22.03575
108	11 664	10.39230	32.86335	1 259 712	4.762 203	10.25986	22.10419
109	11 881	10.44031	33.01515	1 295 029	4.776 856	10.29142	22.17220
110	12 100	10.48809	33.16625	1 331 000	4.791 420	10.32280	22.23980
111	12 321	10.53565	33.31666	1 367 631	4.805 896	10.35399	22.30699
112	12 544	10.58301	33.46640	1 404 928	4.820 285	10.38499	22.37378
113	12 769	10.63015	33.61547	1 442 897	4.834 588	10.41580	22.44017
114	12 996	10.67708	33.76389	1 481 544	4.848 808	10.44644	22.50617
115	13 225	10.72381	33.91165	1 520 875	4.862 944	10.47690	22.57179
116	13 456	10.77033	34.05877	1 560 896	4.876 999	10.50718	22.63702
117	13 689	10.81665	34.20526	1 601 613	4.890 973	10.53728	22.70189
118	13 924	10.86278	34.35113	1 643 032	4.904 868	10.56722	22.76638
119	14 161	10.90871	34.49638	1 685 159	4.918 685	10.59699	22.83051
120	14 400	10.95445	34.64102	1 728 000	4.932 424	10.62659	22.89428
121	14 641	11.00000	34.78505	1 771 561	4.946 087	10.65602	22.95770
122	14 884	11.04536	34.92850	1 815 848	4.959 676	10.68530	23.02078
123	15 129	11.09054	35.07136	1 860 867	4.973 190	10.71441	23.08350
124	15 376	11.13553	35.21363	1 906 624	4.986 631	10.74337	23.14589
125	15 625	11.18034	35.35534	1 953 125	5.000 000	10.77217	23.20794
126	15 876	11.22497	35.49648	2 000 376	5.013 298	10.80082	23.26967
127	16 129	11.26943	35.63706	2 048 383	5.026 526	10.82932	23.33107
128	16 384	11.31371	35.77709	2 097 152	5.039 684	10.85767	23.39214
129	16 641	11.35782	35.91657	2 146 689	5.052 774	10.88587	23.45290
130	16 900	11.40175	36.05551	2 197 000	5.065 797	10.91393	23.51335
131	17 161	11.44552	36.19392	2 248 091	5.078 753	10.94184	23.57348
132	17 424	11.48913	36.33180	2 299 968	5.091 643	10.96961	23.63332
133	17 689	11.53256	36.46917	2 352 637	5.104 469	10.99724	23.69285
134	17 956	11.57584	36.60601	2 406 104	5.117 230	11.02474	23.75208
135	18 225	11.61895	36.74235	2 460 375	5.129 928	11.05209	23.81102
136	18 496	11.66190	36.87818	2 515 456	5.142 563	11.07932	23.86966
137	18 769	11.70470	37.01351	2 571 353	5.155 137	11.10641	23.92803
138	19 044	11.74734	37.14835	2 628 072	5.167 649	11.13336	23.98610
139	19 321	11.78983	37.28270	2 685 619	5.180 101	11.16019	24.04390
140	19 600	11.83216	37.41657	2 744 000	5.192 494	11.18689	24.10142
141	19 881	11.87434	37.54997	2 803 221	5.204 828	11.21346	24.15867
142	20 164	11.91638	37.68289	2 863 288	5.217 103	11.23991	24.21565
143	20 449	11.95826	37.81534	2 924 207	5.229 322	11.26623	24.27236
144	20 736	12.00000	37.94733	2 985 984	5.241 483	11.29243	24.32881
145	21 025	12.04159	38.07887	3 048 625	5.253 588	11.31851	24.38499
146	21 316	12.08305	38.20995	3 112 136	5.265 637	11.34447	24.44092
147	21 609	12.12436	38.34058	3 176 523	5.277 632	11.37031	24.49660
148	21 904	12.16553	38.47077	3 241 792	5.289 572	11.39604	24.55202
149	22 201	12.20656	38.60052	3 307 949	5.301 459	11.42165	24.60719
150	22.500	12.24745	38.72983	3 375 000	5.313 293	11.44714	24.66212

SQUARES, SQUARE ROOT, CUBES AND CUBE ROOT (Continued)

n	n^2	$\sqrt{n}$	$\sqrt{10n}$	n^3	$\sqrt[3]{n}$	$\sqrt[3]{10n}$	$\sqrt[3]{100n}$
150	22 500	12.24745	38.72983	3 375 000	5.313 293	11.44714	24.66212
151	22 801	12.28821	38.85872	3 442 951	5.325 074	11.47252	24.71680
152	23 104	12.32883	38.98718	3 511 808	5.336 803	11.49779	24.77125
153	23 409	12.36932	39.11521	3 581 577	5.348 481	11.52295	24.82545
154	23 716	12.40967	39.24283	3 652 264	5.360 108	11.54800	24.87942
155	24 025	12.44990	39.37004	3 723 875	5.371 685	11.57295	24.93315
156	24 336	12.49000	39.49684	3 796 416	5.383 213	11.59778	24.98666
157	24 649	12.52996	39.62323	3 869 893	5.394 691	11.62251	25.03994
158	24 964	12.56981	39.74921	3 944 312	5.406 120	11.64713	25.09299
159	25 281	12.60952	39.87480	4 019 679	5.417 502	11.67165	25.14581
160	25 600	12.64911	40.00000	4 096 000	5.428 835	11.69607	25.19842
161	25 921	12.68858	40.12481	4 173 281	5.440 122	11.72039	25.25081
162	26 244	12.72792	40.24922	4 251 528	5.451 362	11.74460	25.30298
163	26 569	12.76715	40.37326	4 330 747	5.462 556	11.76872	25.35494
164	26 896	12.80625	40.49691	4 410 944	5.473 704	11.79274	25.40668
165	27 225	12.84523	40.62019	4 492 125	5.484 807	11.81666	25.45822
166	27 556	12.88410	40.74310	4 574 296	5.495 865	11.84048	25.50954
167	27 889	12.92285	40.86563	4 657 463	5.506 878	11.86421	25.56067
168	28 224	12.96148	40.98780	4 741 632	5.517 848	11.88784	25.61158
169	28 561	13.00000	41.10961	4 826 809	5.528 775	11.91138	25.66230
170	28 900	13.03840	41.23106	4 913 000	5.539 658	11.93483	25.71282
171	29 241	13.07670	41.35215	5 000 211	5.550 499	11.95819	25.76313
172	29 584	13.11488	41.47288	5 088 448	5.561 298	11.98145	25.81326
173	29 929	13.15295	41.59327	5 177 717	5.572 055	12.00463	25.86319
174	30 276	13.19091	41.71331	5 268 024	5.582 770	12.02771	25.91292
175	30 625	13.22876	41.83300	5 359 375	5.593 445	12.05071	25.96247
176	30 976	13.26650	41.95235	5 451 776	5.604 079	12.07362	26.01183
177	31 329	13.30413	42.07137	5 545 233	5.614 672	12.09645	26.06100
178	31 684	13.34166	42.19005	5 639 752	5.625 226	12.11918	26.10999
179	32 041	13.37909	42.30839	5 735 339	5.635 741	12.14184	26.15879
180	32 400	13.41641	42.42641	5 832 000	5.646 216	12.16440	26.20741
181	32 761	13.45362	42.54409	5 929 741	5.656 653	12.18689	26.25586
182	33 124	13.49074	42.66146	6 028 568	5.667 051	12.20929	26.30412
183	33 489	13.52775	42.77850	6 128 487	5.677 411	12.23161	26.35221
184	33 856	13.56466	42.89522	6 229 504	5.687 734	12.25385	26.40012
185	34 225	13.60147	43.01163	6 331 625	5.698 019	12.27601	26.44786
186	34 596	13.63818	43.12772	6 434 856	5.708 267	12.29809	26.49543
187	34 969	13.67479	43.24350	6 539 203	5.718 479	12.32009	26.54283
188	35 344	13.71131	43.35897	6 644 672	5.728 654	12.34201	26.59006
189	35 721	13.74773	43.47413	6 751 269	5.738 794	12.36386	26.63712
190	36 100	13.78405	43.58899	6 859 000	5.748 897	12.38562	26.68402
191	36 481	13.82027	43.70355	6 967 871	5.758 965	12.40731	26.73075
192	36 864	13.85641	43.81780	7 077 888	5.768 998	12.42893	26.77732
193	37 249	13.89244	43.93177	7 189 057	5.778 997	12.45047	26.82373
194	37 636	13.92839	44.04543	7 301 384	5.788 960	12.47194	26.86997
195	38 025	13.96424	44.15880	7 414 875	5.798 890	12.49333	26.91606
196	38 416	14.00000	44.27189	7 529 536	5.808 786	12.51465	26.96199
197	38 809	14.03567	44.38468	7 645 373	5.818 648	12.53590	27.00777
198	39 204	14.07125	44.49719	7 762 392	5.828 477	12.55707	27.05339
199	39 601	14.10674	44.60942	7 880 599	5.838 272	12.57818	27.09886
200	40 000	14.14214	44.72136	8 000 000	5.848 035	12.59921	27.14418

SQUARES, SQUARE ROOT, CUBES AND CUBE ROOT (Continued)

n	n^2	$\sqrt{n}$	$\sqrt{10n}$	n^3	$\sqrt[3]{n}$	$\sqrt[3]{10n}$	$\sqrt[3]{100n}$
200	40 000	14.14214	44.72136	8 000 000	5.848 035	12.59921	27.14418
201	40 401	14.17745	44.83302	8 120 601	5.857 766	12.62017	27.18934
202	40 804	14.21267	44.94441	8 242 408	5.867 464	12.64107	27.23436
203	41 209	14.24781	45.05552	8 365 427	5.877 131	12.66189	27.27922
204	41 616	14.28286	45.16636	8 489 664	5.886 765	12.68265	27.32394
205	42 025	14.31782	45.27693	8 615 125	5.896 369	12.70334	27.36852
206	42 436	14.35270	45.38722	8 741 816	5.905 941	12.72396	27.41295
207	42 849	14.38749	45.49725	8 869 743	5.915 482	12.74452	27.45723
208	43 264	14.42221	45.60702	8 998 912	5.924 992	12.76501	27.50138
209	43 681	14.45683	45.71652	9 129 329	5.934 472	12.78543	27.54538
210	44 100	14.49138	45.82576	9 261 000	5.943 922	12.80579	27.58924
211	44 521	14.52584	45.93474	9 393 931	5.953 342	12.82609	27.63296
212	44 944	14.56022	46.04346	9 528 128	5.962 732	12.84632	27.67655
213	45 369	14.59452	46.15192	9 663 597	5.972 093	12.86648	27.72000
214	45 796	14.62874	46.26013	9 800 344	5.981 424	12.88659	27.76331
215	46 225	14.66288	46.36809	9 938 375	5.990 726	12.90663	27.80649
216	46 656	14.69694	46.47580	10 077 696	6.000 000	12.92661	27.84953
217	47 089	14.73092	46.58326	10 218 313	6.009 245	12.94653	27.89244
218	47 524	14.76482	46.69047	10 360 232	6.018 462	12.96638	27.93522
219	47 961	14.79865	46.79744	10 503 459	6.027 650	12.98618	27.97787
220	48 400	14.83240	46.90416	10 648 000	6.036 811	13.00591	28.02039
221	48 841	14.86607	47.01064	10 793 861	6.045 944	13.02559	28.06278
222	49 284	14.89966	47.11688	10 941 048	6.055 049	13.04521	28.10505
223	49 729	14.93318	47.22288	11 089 567	6.064 127	13.06477	28.14718
224	50 176	14.96663	47.32864	11 239 424	6.073 178	13.08427	28.18919
225	50 625	15.00000	47.43416	11 390 625	6.082 202	13.10371	28.23108
226	51 076	15.03330	47.53946	11 543 176	6.091 199	13.12309	28.27284
227	51 529	15.06652	47.64452	11 697 083	6.100 170	13.14242	28.31448
228	51 984	15.09967	47.74935	11 852 352	6.109 115	13.16169	28.35600
229	52 441	15.13275	47.85394	12 008 989	6.118 033	13.18090	28.39739
230	52 900	15.16575	47.95832	12 167 000	6.126 926	13.20006	28.43867
231	53 361	15.19868	48.06246	12 326 391	6.135 792	13.21916	28.47983
232	53 824	15.23155	48.16638	12 487 168	6.144 634	13.23821	28.52086
233	54 289	15.26434	48.27007	12 649 337	6.153 449	13.25721	28.56178
234	54 756	15.29706	48.37355	12 812 904	6.162 240	13.27614	28.60259
235	55 225	15.32971	48.47680	12 977 875	6.171 006	13.29503	28.64327
236	55 696	15.36229	48.57983	13 144 256	6.179 747	13.31386	28.68384
237	56 169	15.39480	48.68265	13 312 053	6.188 463	13.33264	28.72430
238	56 644	15.42725	48.78524	13 481 272	6.197 154	13.35136	28.76464
239	57 121	15.45962	48.88763	13 651 919	6.205 822	13.37004	28.80487
240	57 600	15.49193	48.98979	13 824 000	6.214 465	13.38866	28.84499
241	58 081	15.52417	49.09175	13 997 521	6.223 084	13.40723	28.88500
242	58 564	15.55635	49.19350	14 172 488	6.231 680	13.42575	28.92489
243	59 049	15.58846	49.29503	14 348 907	6.240 251	13.44421	28.96468
244	59 536	15.62050	49.39636	14 526 784	6.248 800	13.46263	29.00436
245	60 025	15.65248	49.49747	14 706 125	6.257 325	13.48100	29.04393
246	60 516	15.68439	49.59839	14 886 936	6.265 827	13.49931	29.08339
247	61 009	15.71623	49.69909	15 069 223	6.274 305	13.51758	29.12275
248	61 504	15.74802	49.79960	15 252 992	6.282 761	13.53580	29.16199
249	62 001	15.77973	49.89990	15 438 249	6.291 195	13.55397	29.20114
250	62 500	15.81139	50.00000	15 625 000	6.299 605	13.57209	29.24018

SQUARES, SQUARE ROOT, CUBES AND CUBE ROOT (Continued)

n	n^2	$\sqrt{n}$	$\sqrt{10n}$	n^3	$\sqrt[3]{n}$	$\sqrt[3]{10n}$	$\sqrt[3]{100n}$
250	62 500	15.81139	50.00000	15 625 000	6.299 605	13.57209	29.24018
251	63 001	15.84298	50.09990	15 813 251	6.307 994	13.59016	29.27911
252	63 504	15.87451	50.19960	16 003 008	6.316 360	13.60818	29.31794
253	64 009	15.90597	50.29911	16 194 277	6.324 704	13.62616	29.35667
254	64 516	15.93738	50.39841	16 387 064	6.333 026	13.64409	29.39530
255	65 025	15.96872	50.49752	16 581 375	6.341 326	13.66197	29.43383
256	65 536	16.00000	50.59644	16 777 216	6.349 604	13.67981	29.47225
257	66 049	16.03122	50.69517	16 974 593	6.357 861	13.69760	29.51058
258	66 564	16.06238	50.79370	17 173 512	6.366 097	13.71534	29.54880
259	67 081	16.09348	50.89204	17 373 979	6.374 311	13.73304	29.58693
260	67 600	16.12452	50.99020	17 576 000	6.382 504	13.75069	29.62496
261	68 121	16.15549	51.08816	17 779 581	6.390 677	13.76830	29.66289
262	68 644	16.18641	51.18594	17 984 728	6.398 828	13.78586	29.70073
263	69 169	16.21727	51.28353	18 191 447	6.406 959	13.80337	29.73847
264	69 696	16.24808	51.38093	18 399 744	6.415 069	13.82085	29.77611
265	70 225	16.27882	51.47815	18 609 625	6.423 158	13.83828	29.81366
266	70 756	16.30951	51.57519	18 821 096	6.431 228	13.85566	29.85111
267	71 289	16.34013	51.67204	19 034 163	6.439 277	13.87300	29.88847
268	71 824	16.37071	51.76872	19 248 832	6.447 306	13.89030	29.92574
269	72 361	16.40122	51.86521	19 465 109	6.455 315	13.90755	29.96292
270	72 900	16.43168	51.96152	19 683 000	6.463 304	13.92477	30.00000
271	73 441	16.46208	52.05766	19 902 511	6.471 274	13.94194	30.03699
272	73 984	16.49242	52.15362	20 123 648	6.479 224	13.95906	30.07389
273	74 529	16.52271	52.24940	20 346 417	6.487 154	13.97615	30.11070
274	75 076	16.55295	52.34501	20 570 824	6.495 065	13.99319	30.14742
275	75 625	16.58312	52.44044	20 796 875	6.502 957	14.01020	30.18405
276	76 176	16.61325	52.53570	21 024 576	6.510 830	14.02716	30.22060
277	76 729	16.64332	52.63079	21 253 933	6.518 684	14.04408	30.25705
278	77 284	16.67333	52.72571	21 484 952	6.526 519	14.06096	30.29342
279	77 841	16.70329	52.82045	21 717 639	6.534 335	14.07780	30.32970
280	78 400	16.73320	52.91503	21 952 000	6.542 133	14.09460	30.36589
281	78 961	16.76305	53.00943	22 188 041	6.549 912	14.11136	30.40200
282	79 524	16.79286	53.10367	22 425 768	6.557 672	14.12808	30.43802
283	80 089	16.82260	53.19774	22 665 187	6.565 414	14.14476	30.47395
284	80 656	16.85230	53.29165	22 906 304	6.573 138	14.16140	30.50981
285	81 225	16.88194	53.38539	23 149 125	6.580 844	14.17800	30.54557
286	81 796	16.91153	53.47897	23 393 656	6.588 532	14.19456	30.58126
287	82 369	16.94107	53.57238	23 639 903	6.596 202	14.21109	30.61686
288	82 944	16.97056	53.66563	23 887 872	6.603 854	14.22757	30.65238
289	83 521	17.00000	53.75872	24 137 569	6.611 489	14.24402	30.68781
290	84 100	17.02939	53.85165	24 389 000	6.619 106	14.26043	30.72317
291	84 681	17.05872	53.94442	24 642 171	6.626 705	14.27680	30.75844
292	85 264	17.08801	54.03702	24 897 088	6.634 287	14.29314	30.79363
293	85 849	17.11724	54.12947	25 153 757	6.641 852	14.30944	30.82875
294	86 436	17.14643	54.22177	25 412 184	6.649 400	14.32570	30.86378
295	87 025	17.17556	54.31390	25 672 375	6.656 930	14.34192	30.89873
296	87 616	17.20465	54.40588	25 934 336	6.664 444	14.35811	30.93361
297	88 209	17.23369	54.49771	26 198 073	6.671 940	14.37426	30.96840
298	88 804	17.26268	54.58938	26 463 592	6.679 420	14.39037	31.00312
299	89 401	17.29162	54.68089	26 730 899	6.686 883	14.40645	31.03776
300	90 000	17.32051	54.77226	27 000 000	6.694 330	14.42250	31.07233

SQUARES, SQUARE ROOT, CUBES AND CUBE ROOT (Continued)

n	n^2	$\sqrt{n}$	$\sqrt{10n}$	n^3	$\sqrt[3]{n}$	$\sqrt[3]{10n}$	$\sqrt[3]{100n}$
300	90 000	17.32051	54.77226	27 000 000	6.694 330	14.42250	31.07233
301	90 601	17.34935	54.86347	27 270 901	6.701 759	14.43850	31.10681
302	91 204	17.37815	54.95453	27 543 608	6.709 173	14.45447	31.14122
303	91 809	17.40690	55.04544	27 818 127	6.716 570	14.47041	31.17556
304	92 416	17.43560	55.13620	28 094 464	6.723 951	14.48631	31.20982
305	93 025	17.46425	55.22681	28 372 625	6.731 315	14.50218	31.24400
306	93 636	17.49286	55.31727	28 652 616	6.738 664	14.51801	31.27811
307	94 249	17.52142	55.40758	28 934 443	6.745 997	14.53381	31.31214
308	94 864	17.54993	55.49775	29 218 112	6.753 313	14.54957	31.34610
309	95 481	17.57840	55.58777	29 503 629	6.760 614	14.56530	31.37999
310	96 100	17.60682	55.67764	29 791 000	6.767 899	14.58100	31.41381
311	96 721	17.63519	55.76737	30 080 231	6.775 169	14.59666	31.44755
312	97 344	17.66352	55.85696	30 371 328	6.782 423	14.61229	31.48122
313	97 969	17.69181	55.94640	30 664 297	6.789 661	14.62788	31.51482
314	98 596	17.72005	56.03570	30 959 144	6.796 884	14.64344	31.54834
315	99 225	17.74824	56.12486	31 255 875	6.804 092	14.65897	31.58180
316	99 856	17.77639	56.21388	31 554 496	6.811 285	14.67447	31.61518
317	100 489	17.80449	56.30275	31 855 013	6.818 462	14.68993	31.64850
318	101 124	17.83255	56.39149	32 157 432	6.825 624	14.70536	31.68174
319	101 761	17.86057	56.48008	32 461 759	6.832 771	14.72076	31.71492
320	102 400	17.88854	56.56854	32 768 000	6.839 904	14.73613	31.74802
321	103 041	17.91647	56.65686	33 076 161	6.847 021	14.75146	31.78106
322	103 684	17.94436	56.74504	33 386 248	6.854 124	14.76676	31.81403
323	104 329	17.97220	56.83309	33 698 267	6.861 212	14.78203	31.84693
324	104 976	18.00000	56.92100	34 012 224	6.868 285	14.79727	31.87976
325	105 625	18.02776	57.00877	34 328 125	6.875 344	14.81248	31.91252
326	106 276	18.05547	57.09641	34 645 976	6.882 389	14.82766	31.94522
327	106 929	18.08314	57.18391	34 965 783	6.889 419	14.84280	31.97785
328	107 584	18.11077	57.27128	35 287 552	6.896 434	14.85792	32.01041
329	108 241	18.13836	57.35852	35 611 289	6.903 436	14.87300	32.04291
330	108 900	18.16590	57.44563	35 937 000	6.910 423	14.88806	32.07534
331	109 561	18.19341	57.53260	36 264 691	6.917 396	14.90308	32.10771
332	110 224	18.22087	57.61944	36 594 368	6.924 356	14.91807	32.14001
333	110 889	18.24829	57.70615	36 926 037	6.931 301	14.93303	32.17225
334	111 556	18.27567	57.79273	37 259 704	6.938 232	14.94797	32.20442
335	112 225	18.30301	57.87918	37 595 375	6.945 150	14.96287	32.23653
336	112 896	18.33030	57.96551	37 933 056	6.952 053	14.97774	32.26857
337	113 569	18.35756	58.05170	38 272 753	6.958 943	14.99259	32.30055
338	114 244	18.38478	58.13777	38 614 472	6.965 820	15.00740	32.33247
339	114 921	18.41195	58.22371	38 958 219	6.972 683	15.02219	32.36433
340	115 600	18.43909	58.30952	39 304 000	6.979 532	15.03695	32.39612
341	116 281	18.46619	58.39521	39 651 821	6.986 368	15.05167	32.42785
342	116 964	18.49324	58.48077	40 001 688	6.993 191	15.06637	32.45952
343	117 649	18.52026	58.56620	40 353 607	7.000 000	15.08104	32.49112
344	118 336	18.54724	58.65151	40 707 584	7.006 796	15.09568	32.52267
345	119 025	18.57418	58.73670	41 063 625	7.013 579	15.11030	32.55415
346	119 716	18.60108	58.82176	41 421 736	7.020 349	15.12488	32.58557
347	120 409	18.62794	58.90671	41 781 923	7.027 106	15.13944	32.61694
348	121 104	18.65476	58.99152	42 144 192	7.033 850	15.15397	32.64824
349	121 801	18.68154	59.07622	42 508 549	7.040 581	15.16847	32.67948
350	122 500	18.70829	59.16080	42 875 000	7.047 299	15.18294	32.71066

SQUARES, SQUARE ROOT, CUBES AND CUBE ROOT (Continued)

n	n^2	$\sqrt{n}$	$\sqrt{10n}$	n^3	$\sqrt[3]{n}$	$\sqrt[3]{10n}$	$\sqrt[3]{100n}$
350	122 500	18.70829	59.16080	42 875 000	7.047 299	15.18294	32.71066
351	123 201	18.73499	59.24525	43 243 551	7.054 004	15.19739	32.74179
352	123 904	18.76166	59.32959	43 614 208	7.060 697	15.21181	32.77285
353	124 609	18.78829	59.41380	43 986 977	7.067 377	15.22620	32.80386
354	125 316	18.81489	59.49790	44 361 864	7.074 044	15.24057	32.83480
355	126 025	18.84144	59.58188	44 738 875	7.080 699	15.25490	32.86569
356	126 736	18.86796	59.66574	45 118 016	7.087 341	15.26921	32.89652
357	127 449	18.89444	59.74948	45 499 293	7.093 971	15.28350	32.92730
358	128 164	18.92089	59.83310	45 882 712	7.100 588	15.29775	32.95801
359	128 881	18.94730	59.91661	46 268 279	7.107 194	15.31198	32.98867
360	129 600	18.97367	60.00000	46 656 000	7.113 787	15.32619	33.01927
361	130 321	19.00000	60.08328	47 045 881	7.120 367	15.34037	33.04982
362	131 044	19.02630	60.16644	47 437 928	7.126 936	15.35452	33.08031
363	131 769	19.05256	60.24948	47 832 147	7.133 492	15.36864	33.11074
364	132 496	19.07878	60.33241	48 228 544	7.140 037	15.38274	33.14112
365	133 225	19.10497	60.41523	48 627 125	7.146 569	15.39682	33.17144
366	133 956	19.13113	60.49793	49 027 896	7.153 090	15.41087	33.20170
367	134 689	19.15724	60.58052	49 430 863	7.159 599	15.42489	33.23191
368	135 424	19.18333	60.66300	49 836 032	7.166 096	15.43889	33.26207
369	136 161	19.20937	60.74537	50 243 409	7.172 581	15.45286	33.29217
370	136 900	19.23538	60.82763	50 653 000	7.179 054	15.46680	33.32222
371	137 641	19.26136	60.90977	51 064 811	7.185 516	15.48073	33.35221
372	138 384	19.28730	60.99180	51 478 848	7.191 966	15.49462	33.38215
373	139 129	19.31321	61.07373	51 895 117	7.198 405	15.50849	33.41204
374	139 876	19.33908	61.15554	52 313 624	7.204 832	15.52234	33.44187
375	140 625	19.36492	61.23724	52 734 375	7.211 248	15.53616	33.47165
376	141 376	19.39072	61.31884	53 157 376	7.217 652	15.54996	33.50137
377	142 129	19.41649	61.40033	53 582 633	7.224 045	15.56373	33.53105
378	142 884	19.44222	61.48170	54 010 152	7.230 427	15.57748	33.56067
379	143 641	19.46792	61.56298	54 439 939	7.236 797	15.59121	33.59024
380	144 400	19.49359	61.64414	54 872 000	7.243 156	15.60491	33.61975
381	145 161	19.51922	61.72520	55 306 341	7.249 505	15.61858	33.64922
382	145 924	19.54482	61.80615	55 742 968	7.255 842	15.63224	33.67863
383	146 689	19.57039	61.88699	56 181 887	7.262 167	15.64587	33.70800
384	147 456	19.59592	61.96773	56 623 104	7.268 482	15.65947	33.73731
385	148 225	19.62142	62.04837	57 066 625	7.274 786	15.67305	33.76657
386	148 996	19.64688	62.12890	57 512 456	7.281 079	15.68661	33.79578
387	149 769	19.67232	62.20932	57 960 603	7.287 362	15.70014	33.82494
388	150 544	19.69772	62.28965	58 411 072	7.293 633	15.71366	33.85405
389	151 321	19.72308	62.36986	58 863 869	7.299 894	15.72714	33.88310
390	152 100	19.74842	62.44998	59 319 000	7.306 144	15.74061	33.91211
391	152 881	19.77372	62.52999	59 776 471	7.312 383	15.75405	33.94107
392	153 664	19.79899	62.60990	60 236 288	7.318 611	15.76747	33.96999
393	154 449	19.82423	62.68971	60 698 457	7.324 829	15.78087	33.99885
394	155 236	19.84943	62.76942	61 162 984	7.331 037	15.79424	34.02766
395	156 025	19.87461	62.84903	61 629 875	7.337 234	15.80759	34.05642
396	156 816	19.89975	62.92853	62 099 136	7.343 420	15.82092	34.08514
397	157 609	19.92486	63.00794	62 570 773	7.349 597	15.83423	34.11381
398	158 404	19.94994	63.08724	63 044 792	7.355 762	15.84751	34.14242
399	159 201	19.97498	63.16645	63 521 199	7.361 918	15.86077	34.17100
400	160 000	20.00000	63.24555	64 000 000	7.368 063	15.87401	34.19952

SQUARES, SQUARE ROOT, CUBES AND CUBE ROOT (Continued)

n	n^2	$\sqrt{n}$	$\sqrt{10n}$	n^3	$\sqrt[3]{n}$	$\sqrt[3]{10n}$	$\sqrt[3]{100n}$
400	160 000	20.00000	63.24555	64 000 000	7.368 063	15.87401	34.19952
401	160 801	20.02498	63.32456	64 481 201	7.374 198	15.88723	34.22799
402	161 604	20.04994	63.40347	64 964 808	7.380 323	15.90042	34.25642
403	162 409	20.07486	63.48228	65 450 827	7.386 437	15.91360	34.28480
404	163 216	20.09975	63.56099	65 939 264	7.392 542	15.92675	34.31314
405	164 025	20.12461	63.63961	66 430 125	7.398 636	15.93988	34.34143
406	164 836	20.14944	63.71813	66 923 416	7.404 721	15.95299	34.36967
407	165 649	20.17424	63.79655	67 419 143	7.410 795	15.96607	34.39786
408	166 464	20.19901	63.87488	67 917 312	7.416 860	15.97914	34.42601
409	167 281	20.22375	63.95311	68 417 929	7.422 914	15.99218	34.45412
410	168 100	20.24846	64.03124	68 921 000	7.428 959	16.00521	34.48217
411	168 921	20.27313	64.10928	69 426 531	7.434 994	16.01821	34.51018
412	169 744	20.29778	64.18723	69 934 528	7.441 019	16.03119	34.53815
413	170 569	20.32240	64.26508	70 444 997	7.447 034	16.04415	34.56607
414	171 396	20.34699	64.34283	70 957 944	7.453 040	16.05709	34.59395
415	172 225	20.37155	64.42049	71 473 375	7.459 036	16.07001	34.62178
416	173 056	20.39608	64.49806	71 991 296	7.465 022	16.08290	34.64956
417	173 889	20.42058	64.57554	72 511 713	7.470 999	16.09578	34.67731
418	174 724	20.44505	64.65292	73 034 632	7.476 966	16.10864	34.70500
419	175 561	20.46949	64.73021	73 560 059	7.482 924	16.12147	34.73266
420	176 400	20.49390	64.80741	74 088 000	7.488 872	16.13429	34.76027
421	177 241	20.51828	64.88451	74 618 461	7.494 811	16.14708	34.78783
422	178 084	20.54264	64.96153	75 151 448	7.500 741	16.15986	34.81535
423	178 929	20.56696	65.03845	75 686 967	7.506 661	16.17261	34.84283
424	179 776	20.59126	65.11528	76 225 024	7.512 572	16.18534	34.87027
425	180 625	20.61553	65.19202	76 765 625	7.518 473	16.19806	34.89766
426	181 476	20.63977	65.26868	77 308 776	7.524 365	16.21075	34.92501
427	182 329	20.66398	65.34524	77 854 483	7.530 248	16.22343	34.95232
428	183 184	20.68816	65.42171	78 402 752	7.536 122	16.23608	34.97958
429	184 041	20.71232	65.49809	78 953 589	7.541 987	16.24872	35.00680
430	184 900	20.73644	65.57439	79 507 000	7.547 842	16.26133	35.03398
431	185 761	20.76054	65.65059	80 062 991	7.553 689	16.27393	35.06112
432	186 624	20.78461	65.72671	80 621 568	7.559 526	16.28651	35.08821
433	187 489	20.80865	65.80274	81 182 737	7.565 355	16.29906	35.11527
434	188 356	20.83267	65.87868	81 746 504	7.571 174	16.31160	35.14228
435	189 225	20.85665	65.95453	82 312 875	7.576 985	16.32412	35.16925
436	190 096	20.88061	66.03030	82 881 856	7.582 787	16.33662	35.19618
437	190 969	20.90454	66.10598	83 453 453	7.588 579	16.34910	35.22307
438	191 844	20.92845	66.18157	84 027 672	7.594 363	16.36156	35.24991
439	192 721	20.95233	66.25708	84 604 519	7.600 139	16.37400	35.27672
440	193 600	20.97618	66.33250	85 184 000	7.605 905	16.38643	35.30348
441	194 481	21.00000	66.40783	85 766 121	7.611 663	16.39883	35.33021
442	195 364	21.02380	66.48308	86 350 888	7.617 412	16.41122	35.35689
443	196 249	21.04757	66.55825	86 938 307	7.623 152	16.42358	35.38354
444	197 136	21.07131	66.63332	87 528 384	7.628 884	16.43593	35.41014
445	198 025	21.09502	66.70832	88 121 125	7.634 607	16.44826	35.43671
446	198 916	21.11871	66.78323	88 716 536	7.640 321	16.46057	35.46323
447	199 809	21.14237	66.85806	89 314 623	7.646 027	16.47287	35.48971
448	200 704	21.16601	66.93280	89 915 392	7.651 725	16.48514	35.51616
449	201 601	21.18962	67.00746	90 518 849	7.657 414	16.49740	35.54257
450	202 500	21.21320	67.08204	91 125 000	7.663 094	16.50964	35.56893

SQUARES, SQUARE ROOT, CUBES AND CUBE ROOT (Continued)

n	n^2	$\sqrt{n}$	$\sqrt{10n}$	n^3	$\sqrt[3]{n}$	$\sqrt[3]{10n}$	$\sqrt[3]{100n}$
450	202 500	21.21320	67.08204	91 125 000	7.663 094	16.50964	35.56893
451	203 401	21.23676	67.15653	91 733 851	7.668 766	16.52186	35.59526
452	204 304	21.26029	67.23095	92 345 408	7.674 430	16.53406	35.62155
453	205 209	21.28380	67.30527	92 959 677	7.680 086	16.54624	35.64780
454	206 116	21.30728	67.37952	93 576 664	7.685 733	16.55841	35.67401
455	207 025	21.33073	67.45369	94 196 375	7.691 372	16.57056	35.70018
456	207 936	21.35416	67.52777	94 818 816	7.697 002	16.58269	35.72632
457	208 849	21.37756	67.60178	95 443 993	7.702 625	16.59480	35.75242
458	209 764	21.40093	67.67570	96 071 912	7.708 239	16.60690	35.77848
459	210 681	21.42429	67.74954	96 702 579	7.713 845	16.61897	35.80450
460	211 600	21.44761	67.82330	97 336 000	7.719 443	16.63103	35.83048
461	212 521	21.47091	67.89698	97 972 181	7.725 032	16.64308	35.85642
462	213 444	21.49419	67.97058	98 611 128	7.730 614	16.65510	35.88233
463	214 369	21.51743	68.04410	99 252 847	7.736 188	16.66711	35.90820
464	215 296	21.54066	68.11755	99 897 344	7.741 753	16.67910	35.93404
465	216 225	21.56386	68.19091	100 544 625	7.747 311	16.69108	35.95983
466	217 156	21.58703	68.26419	101 194 696	7.752 861	16.70303	35.98559
467	218 089	21.61018	68.33740	101 847 563	7.758 402	16.71497	36.01131
468	219 024	21.63331	68.41053	102 503 232	7.763 936	16.72689	36.03700
469	219 961	21.65641	68.48357	103 161 709	7.769 462	16.73880	36.06265
470	220 900	21.67948	68.55655	103 823 000	7.774 980	16.75069	36.08826
471	221 841	21.70253	68.62944	104 487 111	7.780 490	16.76256	36.11384
472	222 784	21.72556	68.70226	105 154 048	7.785 993	16.77441	36.13938
473	223 729	21.74856	68.77500	105 823 817	7.791 488	16.78625	36.16488
474	224 676	21.77154	68.84766	106 496 424	7.796 975	16.79807	36.19035
475	225 625	21.79449	68.92024	107 171 875	7.802 454	16.80988	36.21578
476	226 576	21.81742	68.99275	107 850 176	7.807 925	16.82167	36.24118
477	227 529	21.84033	69.06519	108 531 333	7.813 389	16.83344	36.26654
478	228 484	21.86321	69.13754	109 215 352	7.818 846	16.84519	36.29187
479	229 441	21.88607	69.20983	109 902 239	7.824 294	16.85693	36.31716
480	230 400	21.90890	69.28203	110 592 000	7.829 735	16.86865	36.34241
481	231 361	21.93171	69.35416	111 284 641	7.835 169	16.88036	36.36763
482	232 324	21.95450	69.42622	111 980 168	7.840 595	16.89205	36.39282
483	233 289	21.97726	69.49820	112 678 587	7.846 013	16.90372	36.41797
484	234 256	22.00000	69.57011	113 379 904	7.851 424	16.91538	36.44308
485	235 225	22.02272	69.64194	114 084 125	7.856 828	16.92702	36.46817
486	236 196	22.04541	69.71370	114 791 256	7.862 224	16.93865	36.49321
487	237 169	22.06808	69.78539	115 501 303	7.867 613	16.95026	36.51822
488	238 144	22.09072	69.85700	116 214 272	7.872 994	16.96185	36.54320
489	239 121	22.11334	69.92853	116 930 169	7.878 368	16.97343	36.56815
490	240 100	22.13594	70.00000	117 649 000	7.883 735	16.98499	36.59306
491	241 081	22.15852	70.07139	118 370 771	7.889 095	16.99654	36.61793
492	242 064	22.18107	70.14271	119 095 488	7.894 447	17.00807	36.64278
493	243 049	22.20360	70.21396	119 823 157	7.899 792	17.01959	36.66758
494	244 036	22.22611	70.28513	120 553 784	7.905 129	17.03108	36.69236
495	245 025	22.24860	70.35624	121 287 375	7.910 460	17.04257	36.71710
496	246 016	22.27106	70.42727	122 023 936	7.915 783	17.05404	36.74181
497	247 009	22.29350	70.49823	122 763 473	7.921 099	17.06549	36.76649
498	248 004	22.31591	70.56912	123 505 992	7.926 408	17.07693	36.79113
499	249 001	22.33831	70.63993	124 251 499	7.931 710	17.08835	36.81574
500	250 000	22.36068	70.71068	125 000 000	7.937 005	17.09976	36.84031

SQUARES, SQUARE ROOT, CUBES AND CUBE ROOT (Continued)

n	n²	√n	√10n	n³	∛n	∛10n	∛100n
500	250 000	22.36068	70.71068	125 000 000	7.937 005	17.09976	36.84031
501	251 001	22.38303	70.78135	125 751 501	7.942 293	17.11115	36.86486
502	252 004	22.40536	70.85196	126 506 008	7.947 574	17.12253	36.88937
503	253 009	22.42766	70.92249	127 263 527	7.952 848	17.13389	36.91385
504	254 016	22.44994	70.99296	128 024 064	7.958 114	17.14524	36.93830
505	255 025	22.47221	71.06335	128 787 625	7.963 374	17.15657	36.96271
506	256 036	22.49444	71.13368	129 554 216	7.968 627	17.16789	36.98709
507	257 049	22.51666	71.20393	130 323 843	7.973 873	17.17919	37.01144
508	258 064	22.53886	71.27412	131 096 512	7.979 112	17.19048	37.03576
509	259 081	22.56103	71.34424	131 872 229	7.984 344	17.20175	37.06004
510	260 100	22.58318	71.41428	132 651 000	7.989 570	17.21301	37.08430
511	261 121	22.60531	71.48426	133 432 831	7.994 788	17.22425	37.10852
512	262 144	22.62742	71.55418	134 217 728	8.000 000	17.23548	37.13271
513	263 169	22.64950	71.62402	135 005 697	8.005 205	17.24669	37.15687
514	264 196	22.67157	71.69379	135 796 744	8.010 403	17.25789	37.18100
515	265 225	22.69361	71.76350	136 590 875	8.015 595	17.26908	37.20509
516	266 256	22.71563	71.83314	137 388 096	8.020 779	17.28025	37.22916
517	267 289	22.73763	71.90271	138 188 413	8.025 957	17.29140	37.25319
518	268 324	22.75961	71.97222	138 991 832	8.031 129	17.30254	37.27720
519	269 361	22.78157	72.04165	139 798 359	8.036 293	17.31367	37.30117
520	270 400	22.80351	72.11103	140 608 000	8.041 452	17.32478	37.32511
521	271 441	22.82542	72.18033	141 420 761	8.046 603	17.33588	37.34902
522	272 484	22.84732	72.24957	142 236 648	8.051 748	17.34696	37.37290
523	273 529	22.86919	72.31874	143 055 667	8.056 886	17.35804	37.39675
524	274 576	22.89105	72.38784	143 877 824	8.062 018	17.36909	37.42057
525	275 625	22.91288	72.45688	144 703 125	8.067 143	17.38013	37.44436
526	276 676	22.93469	72.52586	145 531 576	8.072 262	17.39116	37.46812
527	277 729	22.95648	72.59477	146 363 183	8.077 374	17.40218	37.49185
528	278 784	22.97825	72.66361	147 197 952	8.082 480	17.41318	37.51555
529	279 841	23.00000	72.73239	148 035 889	8.087 579	17.42416	37.53922
530	280 900	23.02173	72.80110	148 877 000	8.092 672	17.43513	37.56286
531	281 961	23.04344	72.86975	149 721 291	8.097 759	17.44609	37.58647
532	283 024	23.06513	72.93833	150 568 768	8.102 839	17.45704	37.61005
533	284 089	23.08679	73.00685	151 419 437	8.107 913	17.46797	37.63360
534	285 156	23.10844	73.07530	152 273 304	8.112 980	17.47889	37.65712
535	286 225	23.13007	73.14369	153 130 375	8.118 041	17.48979	37.68061
536	287 296	23.15167	73.21202	153 990 656	8.123 096	17.50068	37.70407
537	288 369	23.17326	73.28028	154 854 153	8.128 145	17.51156	37.72751
538	289 444	23.19483	73.34848	155 720 872	8.133 187	17.52242	37.75091
539	290 521	23.21637	73.41662	156 590 819	8.138 223	17.53327	37.77429
540	291 600	23.23790	73.48469	157 464 000	8.143 253	17.54411	37.79763
541	292 681	23.25941	73.55270	158 340 421	8.148 276	17.55493	37.82095
542	293 764	23.28089	73.62065	159 220 088	8.153 294	17.56574	37.84424
543	294 849	23.30236	73.68853	160 103 007	8.158 305	17.57654	37.86750
544	295 936	23.32381	73.75636	160 989 184	8.163 310	17.58732	37.89073
545	297 025	23.34524	73.82412	161 878 625	8.168 309	17.59809	37.91393
546	298 116	23.36664	73.89181	162 771 336	8.173 302	17.60885	37.93711
547	299 209	23.38803	73.95945	163 667 323	8.178 289	17.61959	37.96025
548	300 304	23.40940	74.02702	164 566 592	8.183 269	17.63032	37.98337
549	301 401	23.43075	74.09453	165 469 149	8.188 244	17.64104	38.00646
550	302 500	23.45208	74.16198	166 375 000	8.193 213	17.65174	38.02952

SQUARES, SQUARE ROOT, CUBES AND CUBE ROOT (Continued)

n	n^2	$\sqrt{n}$	$\sqrt{10n}$	n^3	$\sqrt[3]{n}$	$\sqrt[3]{10n}$	$\sqrt[3]{100n}$
550	302 500	23.45208	74.16198	166 375 000	8.193 213	17.65174	38.02952
551	303 601	23.47339	74.22937	167 284 151	8.198 175	17.66243	38.05256
552	304 704	23.49468	74.29670	168 196 608	8.203 132	17.67311	38.07557
553	305 809	23.51595	74.36397	169 112 377	8.208 082	17.68378	38.09854
554	306 916	23.53720	74.43118	170 031 464	8.213 027	17.69443	38.12149
555	308 025	23.55844	74.49832	170 953 875	8.217 966	17.70507	38.14442
556	309 136	23.57965	74.56541	171 879 616	8.222 899	17.71570	38.16731
557	310 249	23.60085	74.63243	172 808 693	8.227 825	17.72631	38.19018
558	311 364	23.62202	74.69940	173 741 112	8.232 746	17.73691	38.21302
559	312 481	23.64318	74.76630	174 676 879	8.237 661	17.74750	38.23584
560	313 600	23.66432	74.83315	175 616 000	8.242 571	17.75808	38.25862
561	314 721	23.68544	74.89993	176 558 481	8.247 474	17.76864	38.28138
562	315 844	23.70654	74.96666	177 504 328	8.252 372	17.77920	38.30412
563	316 969	23.72762	75.03333	178 453 547	8.257 263	17.78973	38.32682
564	318 096	23.74868	75.09993	179 406 144	8.262 149	17.80026	38.34950
565	319 225	23.76973	75.16648	180 362 029	8.267 029	17.81077	38.37215
566	320 356	23.79075	75.23297	181 321 496	8.271 904	17.82128	38.39478
567	321 489	23.81176	75.29940	182 284 263	8.276 773	17.83177	38.41737
568	322 624	23.83275	75.36577	183 250 432	8.281 635	17.84224	38.43995
569	323 761	23.85372	75.43209	184 220 009	8.286 493	17.85271	38.46249
570	324 900	23.87467	75.49834	185 193 000	8.291 344	17.86316	38.48501
571	326 041	23.89561	75.56454	186 169 411	8.296 190	17.87360	38.50750
572	327 184	23.91652	75.63068	187 149 248	8.301 031	17.88403	38.52997
573	328 329	23.93742	75.69676	188 132 517	8.305 865	17.89444	38.55241
574	329 476	23.95830	75.76279	189 119 224	8.310 694	17.90485	38.57482
575	330 625	23.97916	75.82875	190 109 375	8.315 517	17.91524	38.59721
576	331 776	24.00000	75.89466	191 102 976	8.320 335	17.92562	38.61958
577	332 929	24.02082	75.96052	192 100 033	8.325 148	17.93599	38.64191
578	334 084	24.04163	76.02631	193 100 552	8.329 954	17.94634	38.66422
579	335 241	24.06242	76.09205	194 104 539	8.334 755	17.95669	38.68651
580	336 400	24.08319	76.15773	195 112 000	8.339 551	17.96702	38.70877
581	337 561	24.10394	76.22336	196 122 941	8.344 341	17.97734	38.73100
582	338 724	24.12468	76.28892	197 137 368	8.349 126	17.98765	38.75321
583	339 889	24.14539	76.35444	198 155 287	8.353 905	17.99794	38.77539
584	341 056	24.16609	76.41989	199 176 704	8.358 678	18.00823	38.79755
585	342 225	24.18677	76.48529	200 201 625	8.363 447	18.01850	38.81968
586	343 396	24.20744	76.55064	201 230 056	8.368 209	18.02876	38.84179
587	344 569	24.22808	76.61593	202 262 003	8.372 967	18.03901	38.86387
588	345 744	24.24871	76.68116	203 297 472	8.377 719	18.04925	38.88593
589	346 921	24.26932	76.74634	204 336 469	8.382 465	18.05947	38.90796
590	348 100	24.28992	76.81146	205 379 000	8.387 207	18.06969	38.92996
591	349 281	24.31049	76.87652	206 425 071	8.391 942	18.07989	38.95195
592	350 464	24.33105	76.94154	207 474 688	8.396 673	18.09008	38.97390
593	351 649	24.35159	77.00649	208 527 857	8.401 398	18.10026	38.99584
594	352 836	24.37212	77.07140	209 584 584	8.406 118	18.11043	39.01774
595	354 025	24.39262	77.13624	210 644 875	8.410 833	18.12059	39.03963
596	355 216	24.41311	77.20104	211 708 736	8.415 542	18.13074	39.06149
597	356 409	24.43358	77.26578	212 776 173	8.420 246	18.14087	39.08332
598	357 604	24.45404	77.33046	213 847 192	8.424 945	18.15099	39.10513
599	358 801	24.47448	77.39509	214 921 799	8.429 638	18.16111	39.12692
600	360 000	24.49490	77.45967	216 000 000	8.434 327	18.17121	39.14868

SQUARES, SQUARE ROOT, CUBES AND CUBE ROOT (Continued)

n	n²	√n	√10n	n³	∛n	∛10n	∛100n
600	360 000	24.49490	77.45967	216 000 000	8.434 327	18.17121	39.14868
601	361 201	24.51530	77.52419	217 081 801	8.439 010	18.18130	39.17041
602	362 404	24.53569	77.58866	218 167 208	8.443 688	18.19137	39.19213
603	363 609	24.55606	77.65307	219 256 227	8.448 361	18.20144	39.21382
604	364 816	24.57641	77.71744	220 348 864	8.453 028	18.21150	39.23548
605	366 025	24.59675	77.78175	221 445 125	8.457 691	18.22154	39.25712
606	367 236	24.61707	77.84600	222 545 016	8.462 348	18.23158	39.27874
607	368 449	24.63737	77.91020	223 648 543	8.467 000	18.24160	39.30033
608	369 664	24.65766	77.97435	224 755 712	8.471 647	18.25161	39.32190
609	370 881	24.67793	78.03845	225 866 529	8.476 289	18.26161	39.34345
610	372 100	24.69818	78.10250	226 981 000	8.480 926	18.27160	39.36497
611	373 321	24.71841	78.16649	228 099 131	8.485 558	18.28158	39.38647
612	374 544	24.73863	78.23043	229 220 928	8.490 185	18.29155	39.40795
613	375 769	24.75884	78.29432	230 346 397	8.494 807	18.30151	39.42940
614	376 996	24.77902	78.35815	231 475 544	8.499 423	18.31145	39.45083
615	378 225	24.79919	78.42194	232 608 375	8.504 035	18.32139	39.47223
616	379 456	24.81935	78.48567	233 744 896	8.508 642	18.33131	39.49362
617	380 689	24.83948	78.54935	234 885 113	8.513 243	18.34123	39.51498
618	381 924	24.85961	78.61298	236 029 032	8.517 840	18.35113	39.53631
619	383 161	24.87971	78.67655	237 176 659	8.522 432	18.36102	39.55763
620	384 400	24.89980	78.74008	238 328 000	8.527 019	18.37091	39.57892
621	385 641	24.91987	78.80355	239 483 061	8.531 601	18.38078	39.60018
622	386 884	24.93993	78.86698	240 641 848	8.536 178	18.39064	39.62143
623	388 129	24.95997	78.93035	241 804 367	8.540 750	18.40049	39.64265
624	389 376	24.97999	78.99367	242 970 624	8.545 317	18.41033	39.66385
625	390 625	25.00000	79.05694	244 140 625	8.549 880	18.42016	39.68503
626	391 876	25.01999	79.12016	245 314 376	8.554 437	18.42998	39.70618
627	393 129	25.03997	79.18333	246 491 883	8.558 990	18.43978	39.72731
628	394 384	25.05993	79.24645	247 673 152	8.563 538	18.44958	39.74842
629	395 641	25.07987	79.30952	248 858 189	8.568 081	18.45937	39.76951
630	396 900	25.09980	79.37254	250 047 000	8.572 619	18.46915	39.79057
631	398 161	25.11971	79.43551	251 239 591	8.577 152	18.47891	39.81161
632	399 424	25.13961	79.49843	252 435 968	8.581 681	18.48867	39.83263
633	400 689	25.15949	79.56130	253 636 137	8.586 205	18.49842	39.85363
634	401 956	25.17936	79.62412	254 840 104	8.590 724	18.50815	39.87461
635	403 225	25.19921	79.68689	256 047 875	8.595 238	18.51788	39.89556
636	404 496	25.21904	79.74961	257 259 456	8.599 748	18.52759	39.91649
637	405 769	25.23886	79.81228	258 474 853	8.604 252	18.53730	39.93740
638	407 044	25.25866	79.87490	259 694 072	8.608 753	18.54700	39.95829
639	408 321	25.27845	79.93748	260 917 119	8.613 248	18.55668	39.97916
640	409 600	25.29822	80.00000	262 144 000	8.617 739	18.56636	40.00000
641	410 881	25.31798	80.06248	263 374 721	8.622 225	18.57602	40.02082
642	412 164	25.33772	80.12490	264 609 288	8.626 706	18.58568	40.04162
643	413 449	25.35744	80.18728	265 847 707	8.631 183	18.59532	40.06240
644	414 736	25 37716	80.24961	267 089 984	8.635 655	18.60495	40.08316
645	416 025	25.39685	80.31189	268 336 125	8.640 123	18.61458	40.10390
646	417 316	25.41653	80.37413	269 586 136	8.644 585	18.62419	40.12461
647	418 609	25.43619	80.43631	270 840 023	8.649 044	18.63380	40.14530
648	419 904	25.45584	80.49845	272 097 792	8.653 497	18.64340	40.16598
649	421 201	25.47548	80.56054	273 359 449	8.657 947	18.65298	40.18663
650	422 500	25.49510	80.62258	274 625 000	8.662 391	18.66256	40.20726

SQUARES, SQUARE ROOT, CUBES AND CUBE ROOT (Continued)

n	n^2	$\sqrt{n}$	$\sqrt{10n}$	n^3	$\sqrt[3]{n}$	$\sqrt[3]{10n}$	$\sqrt[3]{100n}$
650	422 500	25 49510	80.62258	274 625 000	8.662 391	18.66256	40.20726
651	423 801	25.51470	80.68457	275 894 451	8.666 831	18.67212	40.22787
652	425 104	25.53429	80.74652	277 167 808	8.671 266	18.68168	40.24845
653	426 409	25.55386	80.80842	278 445 077	8.675 697	18.69122	40.26902
654	427 716	25.57342	80.87027	279 726 264	8.680 124	18.70076	40.28957
655	429 025	25 59297	80.93207	281 011 375	8.684 546	18.71029	40.31009
656	430 336	25.61250	80.99383	282 300 416	8.688 963	18.71980	40.33059
657	431 649	25.63201	81.05554	283 593 393	8.693 376	18.72931	40.35108
658	432 964	25.65151	81.11720	284 890 312	8.697 784	18.73881	40.37154
659	434 281	25.67100	81.17881	286 191 179	8.702 188	18.74830	40.39198
660	435 600	25.69047	81.24038	287 496 000	8.706 588	18.75777	40.41240
661	436 921	25.70992	81.30191	288 804 781	8.710 983	18.76724	40.43280
662	438 244	25.72936	81.36338	290 117 528	8.715 373	18.77670	40.45318
663	439 569	25.74879	81.42481	291 434 247	8.719 760	18.78615	40.47354
664	440 896	25.76820	81.48620	292 754 944	8.724 141	18.79559	40.49388
665	442 225	25.78759	81.54753	294 079 625	8.728 519	18.80502	40.51420
666	443 556	25.80698	81.60882	295 408 296	8.732 892	18.81444	40.53449
667	444 889	25.82634	81.67007	296 740 963	8.737 260	18.82386	40.55477
668	446 224	25.84570	81.73127	298 077 632	8.741 625	18.83326	40.57503
669	447 561	25.86503	81.79242	299 418 309	8.745 985	18.84265	40.59526
670	448 900	25.88436	81.85353	300 763 000	8.750 340	18.85204	40.61548
671	450 241	25.90367	81.91459	302 111 711	8.754 691	18.86141	40.63568
672	451 584	25.92296	81.97561	303 464 448	8.759 038	18.87078	40.65585
673	452 929	25.94224	82.03658	304 821 217	8.763 381	18.88013	40.67601
674	454 276	25.96151	82.09750	306 182 024	8.767 719	18.88948	40.69615
675	455 625	25.98076	82.15838	307 546 875	8.772 053	18.89882	40.71626
676	456 976	26.00000	82.21922	308 915 776	8.776 383	18.90814	40.73636
677	458 329	26.01922	82.28001	310 288 733	8.780 708	18.91746	40.75644
678	459 684	26.03843	82.34076	311 665 752	8.785 030	18.92677	40.77650
679	461 041	26.05763	82.40146	313 046 839	8.789 347	18.93607	40.79653
680	462 400	26.07681	82.46211	314 432 000	8.793 659	18.94536	40.81655
681	463 761	26.09598	82.52272	315 821 241	8.797 968	18.95465	40.83655
682	465 124	26.11513	82.58329	317 214 568	8.802 272	18.96392	40.85653
683	466 489	26.13427	82.64381	318 611 987	8.806 572	18.97318	40.87649
684	467 856	26.15339	82.70429	320 013 504	8.810 868	18.98244	40.89643
685	469 225	26.17250	82.76473	321 419 125	8.815 160	18.99169	40.91635
686	470 596	26.19160	82.82512	322 828 856	8.819 447	19.00092	40.93625
687	471 969	26.21068	82.88546	324 242 703	8.823 731	19.01015	40.95613
688	473 344	26.22975	82.94577	325 660 672	8.828 010	19.01937	40.97599
689	474 721	26.24881	83.00602	327 082 769	8.832 285	19.02858	40.99584
690	476 100	26.26785	83.06624	328 509 000	8.836 556	19.03778	41.01566
691	477 481	26.28688	83.12641	329 939 371	8.840 823	19.04698	41.03546
692	478 864	26.30589	83.18654	331 373 888	8.845 085	19.05616	41.05525
693	480 249	26.32489	83.24662	332 812 557	8.849 344	19.06533	41.07502
694	481 636	26.34388	83.30666	334 255 384	8.853 599	19.07450	41.09476
695	483 025	26.36285	83.36666	335 702 375	8.857 849	19.08366	41.11449
696	484 416	26.38181	83.42661	337 153 536	8.862 095	19.09281	41.13420
697	485 809	26.40076	83.48653	338 608 873	8.866 338	19.10195	41.15389
698	487 204	26.41969	83.54639	340 068 392	8.870 576	19.11108	41.17357
699	488 601	26.43861	83.60622	341 532 099	8.874 810	19.12020	41.19322
700	490 000	26.45751	83.66600	343 000 000	8.879 040	19.12931	41.21285

SQUARES, SQUARE ROOT, CUBES AND CUBE ROOT (Continued)

n	n^2	$\sqrt{n}$	$\sqrt{10n}$	n^3	$\sqrt[3]{n}$	$\sqrt[3]{10n}$	$\sqrt[3]{100n}$
700	490 000	26.45751	83.66600	343 000 000	8.879 040	19.12931	41.21285
701	491 401	26.47640	83.72574	344 472 101	8.883 266	19.13842	41.23247
702	492 804	26.49528	83.78544	345 948 408	8.887 488	19.14751	41.25207
703	494 209	26.51415	83.84510	347 428 927	8.891 706	19.15660	41.27164
704	495 616	26.53300	83.90471	348 913 664	8.895 920	19.16568	41.29120
705	497 025	26.55184	83.96428	350 402 625	8.900 130	19.17475	41.31075
706	498 436	26.57066	84.02381	351 895 816	8.904 337	19.18381	41.33027
707	499 849	26.58947	84.08329	353 393 243	8.908 539	19.19286	41.34977
708	501 264	26.60827	84.14274	354 894 912	8.912 737	19.20191	41.36926
709	502 681	26.62705	84.20214	356 400 829	8.916 931	19.21095	41.38873
710	504 100	26.64583	84.26150	357 911 000	8.921 121	19.21997	41.40818
711	505 521	26.66458	84.32082	359 425 431	8.925 308	19.22899	41.42761
712	506 944	26.68333	84.38009	360 944 128	8.929 490	19.23800	41.44702
713	508 369	26.70206	84.43933	362 467 097	8.933 669	19.24701	41.46642
714	509 796	26.72078	84.49852	363 994 344	8.937 843	19.25600	41.48579
715	511 225	26.73948	84.55767	365 525 875	8.942 014	19.26499	41.50515
716	512 656	26.75818	84.61678	367 061 696	8.946 181	19.27396	41.52449
717	514 089	26.77686	84.67585	368 601 813	8.950 344	19.28293	41.54382
718	515 524	26.79552	84.73488	370 146 232	8.954 503	19.29189	41.56312
719	516 961	26.81418	84.79387	371 694 959	8.958 658	19.30084	41.58241
720	518 400	26.83282	84.85281	373 248 000	8.962 809	19.30979	41.60168
721	519 841	26.85144	84.91172	374 805 361	8.966 957	19.31872	41.62093
722	521 284	26.87006	84.97058	376 367 048	8.971 101	19.32765	41.64016
723	522 729	26.88866	85.02941	377 933 067	8.975 241	19.33657	41.65938
724	524 176	26.90725	85.08819	379 503 424	8.979 377	19.34548	41.67857
725	525 625	26.92582	85.14693	381 078 125	8.983 509	19.35438	41.69775
726	527 076	26.94439	85.20563	382 657 176	8.987 637	19.36328	41.71692
727	528 529	26.96294	85.26429	384 240 583	8.991 762	19.37216	41.73606
728	529 984	26.98148	85.32292	385 828 352	8.995 883	19.38104	41.75519
729	531 441	27.00000	85.38150	387 420 489	9.000 000	19.38991	41.77430
730	532 900	27.01851	85.44004	389 017 000	9.004 113	19.39877	41.79339
731	534 361	27.03701	85.49854	390 617 891	9.008 223	19.40763	41.81247
732	535 824	27.05550	85.55700	392 223 168	9.012 329	19.41647	41.83152
733	537 289	27.07397	85.61542	393 832 837	9.016 431	19.42531	41.85056
734	538 756	27.09243	85.67380	395 446 904	9.020 529	19.43414	41.86959
735	540 225	27.11088	85.73214	397 065 375	9.024 624	19.44296	41.88859
736	541 696	27.12932	85.79044	398 688 256	9.028 715	19.45178	41.90758
737	543 169	27.14774	85.84870	400 315 553	9.032 802	19.46058	41.92655
738	544 644	27.16616	85.90693	401 947 272	9.036 886	19.46938	41.94551
739	546 121	27.18455	85.96511	403 583 419	9.040 966	19.47817	41.96444
740	547 600	27.20294	86.02325	405 224 000	9.045 042	19.48695	41.98336
741	549 081	27.22132	86.08136	406 869 021	9.049 114	19.49573	42.00227
742	550 564	27.23968	86.13942	408 518 488	9.053 183	19.50449	42.02115
743	552 049	27.25803	86.19745	410 172 407	9.057 248	19.51325	42.04002
744	553 536	27.27636	86.25543	411 830 784	9.061 310	19.52200	42.05887
745	555 025	27.29469	86.31338	413 493 625	9.065 368	19.53074	42.07771
746	556 516	27.31300	86.37129	415 160 936	9.069 422	19.53948	42.09653
747	558 009	27.33130	86.42916	416 832 723	9.073 473	19.54820	42.11533
748	559 504	27.34959	86.48699	418 508 992	9.077 520	19.55692	42.13411
749	561 001	27.36786	86.54479	420 189 749	9.081 563	19.56563	42.15288
750	562 500	27.38613	86.60254	421 875 000	9.085 603	19.57434	42.17163

SQUARES, SQUARE ROOT, CUBES AND CUBE ROOT (Continued)

n	n^2	$\sqrt{n}$	$\sqrt{10n}$	n^2	$\sqrt[3]{n}$	$\sqrt[3]{10n}$	$\sqrt[3]{100n}$
750	562 500	27.38613	86.60254	421 875 000	9.085 603	19.57434	42.17163
751	564 001	27.40438	86.66026	423 564 751	9.089 639	19.58303	42.19037
752	565 504	27.42262	86.71793	425 259 008	9.093 672	19.59172	42.20909
753	567 009	27.44085	86.77557	426 957 777	9.097 701	19.60040	42.22779
754	568 516	27.45906	86.83317	428 661 064	9.101 727	19.60908	42.24647
755	570 025	27.47726	86.89074	430 368 875	9.105 748	19.61774	42.26514
756	571 536	27.49545	86.94826	432 081 216	9.109 767	19.62640	42.28379
757	573 049	27.51363	87.00575	433 798 093	9.113 782	19.63505	42.30243
758	574 564	27.53180	87.06320	435 519 512	9.117 793	19.64369	42.32105
759	576 081	27.54995	87.12061	437 245 479	9.121 801	19.65232	42.33965
760	577 600	27.56810	87.17798	438 976 000	9.125 805	19.66095	42.35824
761	579 121	27.58623	87.23531	440 711 081	9.129 806	19.66957	42.37681
762	580 644	27.60435	87.29261	442 450 728	9.133 803	19.67818	42.39536
763	582 169	27.62245	87.34987	444 194 947	9.137 797	19.68679	42.41390
764	583 696	27.64055	87.40709	445 943 744	9.141 787	19.69538	42.43242
765	585 225	27.65863	87.46428	447 697 125	9.145 774	19.70397	42.45092
766	586 756	27.67671	87.52143	449 455 096	9.149 758	19.71256	42.46941
767	588 289	27.69476	87.57854	451 217 663	9.153 738	19.72113	42.48789
768	589 824	27.71281	87.63561	452 984 832	9.157 714	19.72970	42.50634
769	591 361	27.73085	87.69265	454 756 609	9.161 687	19.73826	42.52478
770	592 900	27.74887	87.74964	456 533 000	9.165 656	19.74681	42.54321
771	594 441	27.76689	87.80661	458 314 011	9.169 623	19.75535	42.56162
772	595 984	27.78489	87.86353	460 099 648	9.173 585	19.76389	42.58001
773	597 529	27.80288	87.92042	461 889 917	9.177 544	19.77242	42.59839
774	599 076	27.82086	87.97727	463 684 824	9.181 500	19.78094	42.61675
775	600 625	27.83882	88.03408	465 484 375	9.185 453	19.78946	42.63509
776	602 176	27.85678	88.09086	467 288 576	9.189 402	19.79797	42.65342
777	603 729	27.87472	88.14760	469 097 433	9.193 347	19.80647	42.67174
778	605 284	27.89265	88.20431	470 910 952	9.197 290	19.81496	42.69004
779	606 841	27.91057	88.26098	472 729 139	9.201 229	19.82345	42.70832
780	608 400	27.92848	88.31761	474 552 000	9.205 164	19.83192	42.72659
781	609 961	27.94638	88.37420	476 379 541	9.209 096	19.84040	42.74484
782	611 524	27.96426	88.43076	478 211 768	9.213 025	19.84886	42.76307
783	613 089	27.98214	88.48729	480 048 687	9.216 950	19.85732	42.78129
784	614 656	28.00000	88.54377	481 890 304	9.220 873	19.86577	42.79950
785	616 225	28.01785	88.60023	483 736 625	9.224 791	19.87421	42.81769
786	617 796	28.03569	88.65664	485 587 656	9.228 707	19.88265	42.83586
787	619 369	28.05352	88.71302	487 443 403	9.232 619	19.89107	42.85402
788	620 944	28.07134	88.76936	489 303 872	9.236 528	19.89950	42.87216
789	622 521	28.08914	88.82567	491 169 069	9.240 433	19.90791	42.89029
790	624 100	28.10694	88.88194	493 039 000	9.244 335	19.91632	42.90840
791	625 681	28.12472	88.93818	494 913 671	9.248 234	19.92472	42.92650
792	627 264	28.14249	88.99438	496 793 088	9.252 130	19.93311	42.94458
793	628 849	28.16026	89.05055	498 677 257	9.256 022	19.94150	42.96265
794	630 436	28.17801	89.10668	500 566 184	9.259 911	19.94987	42.98070
795	632 025	28.19574	89.16277	502 459 875	9.263 797	19.95825	42.99874
796	633 616	28.21347	89.21883	504 358 336	9.267 680	19.96661	43.01676
797	635 209	28.23119	89.27486	506 261 573	9.271 559	19.97497	43.03477
798	636 804	28.24889	89.33085	508 169 592	9.275 435	19.98332	43.05276
799	638 401	28.26659	89.38680	510 082 399	9.279 308	19.99166	43.07073
800	640 000	28.28427	89.44272	512 000 000	9.283 178	20.00000	43.08869

SQUARES, SQUARE ROOT, CUBES AND CUBE ROOT (Continued)

n	n^2	$\sqrt{n}$	$\sqrt{10n}$	n^3	$\sqrt[3]{n}$	$\sqrt[3]{10n}$	$\sqrt[3]{100n}$
800	640 000	28.28427	89.44272	512 000 000	9.283 178	20.00000	43.08869
801	641 601	28.30194	89.49860	513 922 401	9.287 044	20.00833	43.10664
802	643 204	28.31960	89.55445	515 849 608	9.290 907	20.01665	43.12457
803	644 809	28.33725	89.61027	517 781 627	9.294 767	20.02497	43.14249
804	646 416	28.35489	89.66605	519 718 464	9.298 624	20.03328	43.16039
805	648 025	28.37252	89.72179	521 660 125	9.302 477	20.04158	43.17828
806	649 636	28.39014	89.77750	523 606 616	9.306 328	20.04988	43.19615
807	651 249	28.40775	89.83318	525 557 943	9.310 175	20.05816	43.21400
808	652 864	28.42534	89.88882	527 514 112	9.314 019	20.06645	43.23185
809	654 481	28.44293	89.94443	529 475 129	9.317 860	20.07472	43.24967
810	656 100	28.46050	90.00000	531 441 000	9.321 698	20.08299	43.26749
811	657 721	28.47806	90.05554	533 411 731	9.325 532	20.09125	43.28529
812	659 344	28.49561	90.11104	535 387 328	9.329 363	20.09950	43.30307
813	660 969	28.51315	90.16651	537 367 797	9.333 192	20.10775	43.32084
814	662 596	28.53069	90.22195	539 353 144	9.337 017	20.11599	43.33859
815	664 225	28.54820	90.27735	541 343 375	9.340 839	20.12423	43.35633
816	665 856	28.56571	90.33272	543 338 496	9.344 657	20.13245	43.37406
817	667 489	28.58321	90.38805	545 338 513	9.348 473	20.14067	43.39177
818	669 124	28.60070	90.44335	547 343 432	9.352 286	20.14889	43.40947
819	670 761	28.61818	90.49862	549 353 259	9.356 095	20.15710	43.42715
820	672 400	28.63564	90.55385	551 368 000	9.359 902	20.16530	43.44481
821	674 041	28.65310	90.60905	553 387 661	9.363 705	20.17349	43.46247
822	675 684	28.67054	90.66422	555 412 248	9.367 505	20.18168	43.48011
823	677 329	28.68798	90.71935	557 441 767	9.371 302	20.18986	43.49773
824	678 976	28.70540	90.77445	559 476 224	9.375 096	20.19803	43.51534
825	680 625	28.72281	90.82951	561 515 625	9.378 887	20.20620	43.53294
826	682 276	28.74022	90.88454	563 559 976	9.382 675	20.21436	43.55052
827	683 929	28.75761	90.93954	565 609 283	9.386 460	20.22252	43.56809
828	685 584	28.77499	90.99451	567 663 552	9.390 242	20.23066	43.58564
829	687 241	28.79236	91.04944	569 722 789	9.394 021	20.23880	43.60318
830	688 900	28.80972	91.10434	571 787 000	9.397 796	20.24694	43.62071
831	690 561	28.82707	91.15920	573 856 191	9.401 569	20.25507	43.63822
832	692 224	28.84441	91.21403	575 930 368	9.405 339	20.26319	43.65572
833	693 889	28.86174	91.26883	578 009 537	9.409 105	20.27130	43.67320
834	695 556	28.87906	91.32360	580 093 704	9.412 869	20.27941	43.69067
835	697 225	28.89637	91.37833	582 182 875	9.416 630	20.28751	43.70812
836	698 896	28.91366	91.43304	584 277 056	9.420 387	20.29561	43.72556
837	700 569	28.93095	91.48770	586 376 253	9.424 142	20.30370	43.74299
838	702 244	28.94823	91.54234	588 480 472	9.427 894	20.31178	43.76041
839	703 921	28.96550	91.59694	590 589 719	9.431 642	20.31986	43.77781
840	705 600	28.98275	91.65151	592 704 000	9.435 388	20.32793	43.79519
841	707 281	29.00000	91.70605	594 823 321	9.439 131	29.33599	43.81256
842	708 964	29.01724	91.76056	596 947 688	9.442 870	20.34405	43.82992
843	710 649	29.03446	91.81503	599 077 107	9.446 607	20.35210	43.84727
844	712 336	29.05168	91.86947	601 211 584	9.450 341	20.36014	43.86460
845	714 025	29.06888	91.92388	603 351 125	9.454 072	20.36818	43.88191
846	715 716	29.08608	91.97826	605 495 736	9.457 800	20.37621	43.89922
847	717 409	29.10326	92.03260	607 645 423	9.461 525	20.38424	43.91651
848	719 104	29.12044	92.08692	609 800 192	9.465 247	20.39226	43.93378
849	720 801	29.13760	92.14120	611 960 049	9.468 966	20.40027	43.95105
850	722 500	29.15476	92.19544	614 125 000	9.472 682	20.40828	43.96830

SQUARES, SQUARE ROOT, CUBES AND CUBE ROOT (Continued)

n	n^2	$\sqrt{n}$	$\sqrt{10n}$	n^3	$\sqrt[3]{n}$	$\sqrt[3]{10n}$	$\sqrt[3]{100n}$
850	722 500	29.15476	92.19544	614 125 000	9.472 682	20.40828	43.96830
851	724 201	29.17190	92.24966	616 295 051	9.476 396	20.41628	43.98553
852	725 904	29.18904	92.30385	618 470 208	9.480 106	20.42427	44.00275
853	727 609	29.20616	92.35800	620 650 477	9.483 814	20.43226	44.01996
854	729 316	29.22328	92.41212	622 835 864	9.487 518	20.44024	44.03716
855	731 025	29.24038	92.46621	625 026 375	9.491 220	20.44821	44.05434
856	732 736	29.25748	92.52027	627 222 016	9.494 919	20.45618	44.07151
857	734 449	29.27456	92.57429	629 422 793	9.498 615	20.46415	44.08866
858	736 164	29.29164	92.62829	631 628 712	9.502 308	20.47210	44.10581
859	737 881	29.30870	92.68225	633 839 779	9.505 998	20.48005	44.12293
860	739 600	29.32576	92.73618	636 056 000	9.509 685	20.48800	44.14005
861	741 321	29.34280	92.79009	638 277 381	9.513 370	20.49593	44.15715
862	743 044	29.35984	92.84396	640 503 928	9.517 052	20.50387	44.17424
863	744 769	29.37686	92.89779	642 735 647	9.520 730	20.51179	44.19132
864	746 496	29.39388	92.95160	644 972 544	9.524 406	20.51971	44.20838
865	748 225	29.41088	93.00538	647 214 625	9.528 079	20.52762	44.22543
866	749 956	29.42788	93.05912	649 461 896	9.531 750	20.53553	44.24246
867	751 689	29.44486	93.11283	651 714 363	9.535 417	20.54343	44.25949
868	753 424	29.46184	93.16652	653 972 032	9.539 082	20.55133	44.27650
869	755 161	29.47881	93.22017	656 234 909	9.542 744	20.55922	44.29349
870	756 900	29.49576	93.27379	658 503 000	9.546 403	20.56710	44.31048
871	758 641	29.51271	93.32738	660 776 311	9.550 059	20.57498	44.32745
872	760 384	29.52965	93.38094	663 054 848	9.553 712	20.58285	44.34440
873	762 129	29.54657	93.43447	665 338 617	9.557 363	20.59071	44.36135
874	763 876	29.56349	93.48797	667 627 624	9.561 011	20.59857	44.37828
875	765 625	29.58040	93.54143	669 921 875	9.564 656	20.60643	44.39520
876	767 376	29.59730	93.59487	672 221 376	9.568 298	20.61427	44.41211
877	769 129	29.61419	93.64828	674 526 133	9.571 938	20.62211	44.42900
878	770 884	29.63106	93.70165	676 836 152	9.575 574	20.62995	44.44588
879	772 641	29.64793	93.75500	679 151 439	9.579 208	20.63778	44.46275
880	774 400	29.66479	93.80832	681 472 000	9.582 840	20.64560	44.47960
881	776 161	29.68164	93.86160	683 797 841	9.586 468	20.65342	44.49644
882	777 924	29.69848	93.91486	686 128 968	9.590 094	20.66123	·44.51327
883	779 689	29.71532	93.96808	688 465 387	9.593 717	20.66904	44.53009
884	781 456	29.73214	94.02127	690 807 104	9.597 337	20.67684	44.54689
885	783 225	29.74895	94.07444	693 154 125	9.600 955	20.68463	44.56368
886	784 996	29.76575	94.12757	695 506 456	9.604 570	20.69242	44.58046
887	786 769	29.78255	94.18068	697 864 103	9.608 182	20.70020	44.59723
888	788 544	29.79933	94.23375	700 227 072	9.611 791	20.70798	44.61398
889	790 321	29.81610	94.28680	702 595 369	9.615 398	20.71575	44.63072
890	792 100	29.83287	94.33981	⁄04 969 000	9.619 002	20.72351	44.64745
891	793 881	29.84962	94.39280	707 347 971	9.622 603	20.73127	44.66417
892	795 664	29.86637	94.44575	709 732 288	9.626 202	20.73902	44.68087
893	797 449	29.88311	94.49868	712 121 957	9.629 797	20.74677	44.69756
894	799 236	29.89983	94.55157	714 516 984	9.633 391	20.75451	44.71424
895	801 025	29.91655	94.60444	716 917 375	9.636 981	20.76225	44.73090
896	802 816	29.93326	94.65728	719 323 136	9.640 569	20.76998	44.74756
897	804 609	29.94996	94.71008	721 734 273	9.644 154	20.77770	44.76420
898	806 404	29.96665	94.76286	724 150 792	9.647 737	20.78542	44.78083
899	808 201	29.98333	94.81561	726 572 699	9.651 317	20.79313	44.79744
900	810 000	30.00000	94.86833	729 000 000	9.654 894	20.80084	44.81405

SQUARES, SQUARE ROOT, CUBES AND CUBE ROOT (Continued)

n	n^2	$\sqrt{n}$	$\sqrt{10n}$	n^3	$\sqrt[3]{n}$	$\sqrt[3]{10n}$	$\sqrt[3]{100n}$
900	810 000	30.00000	94.86833	729 000 000	9.654 894	20.80084	44.81405
901	811 801	30.01666	94.92102	731 432 701	9.658 468	20.80854	44.83064
902	813 604	30.03331	94.97368	733 870 808	9.662 040	20.81623	44.84722
903	815 409	30.04996	95.02631	736 314 327	9.665 610	20.82392	44.86379
904	817 216	30.06659	95.07891	738 763 264	9.669 176	20.83161	44.88034
905	819 025	30.08322	95.13149	741 217 625	9.672 740	20.83929	44.89688
906	820 836	30.09983	95.18403	743 677 416	9.676 302	20.84696	44.91341
907	822 649	30.11644	95.23655	746 142 643	9.679 860	20.85463	44.92993
908	824 464	30.13304	95.28903	748 613 312	9.683 417	20.86229	44.94644
909	826 281	30.14963	95.34149	751 089 429	9.686 970	20.86994	44.96293
910	828 100	30.16621	95.39392	753 571 000	9.690 521	20.87759	44.97941
911	829 921	30.18278	95.44632	756 058 031	9.694 069	20.88524	44.99588
912	831 744	30.19934	95.49869	758 550 528	9.697 615	20.89288	45.01234
913	833 569	30.21589	95.55103	761 048 497	9.701 158	20.90051	45.02879
914	835 396	30.23243	95.60335	763 551 944	9.704 699	20.90814	45.04522
915	837 225	30.24897	95.65563	766 060 875	9.708 237	20.91576	45.06164
916	839 056	30.26549	95.70789	768 575 296	9.711 772	20.92338	45.07805
917	840 889	30.28201	95.76012	771 095 213	9.715 305	20.93099	45.09445
918	842 724	30.29851	95.81232	773 620 632	9.718 835	20.93860	45.11084
919	844 561	30.31501	95.86449	776 151 559	9.722 363	20.94620	45.12721
920	846 400	30.33150	95.91663	778 688 000	9.725 888	20.95379	45.14357
921	848 241	30.34798	95.96874	781 229 961	9.729 411	20.96138	45.15992
922	850 084	30.36445	96.02083	783 777 448	9.732 931	20.96896	45.17626
923	851 929	30.38092	96.07289	786 330 467	9.736 448	20.97654	45.19259
924	853 776	30.39737	96.12492	788 889 024	9.739 963	20.98411	45.20891
925	855 625	30.41381	96.17692	791 453 125	9.743 476	20.99168	45.22521
926	857 476	30.43025	96.22889	794 022 776	9.746 986	20.99924	45.24150
927	859 329	30.44667	96.28084	796 597 983	9.750 493	21.00680	45.25778
928	861 184	30.46309	96.33276	799 178 752	9.753 998	21.01435	45.27405
929	863 041	30.47950	96.38465	801 765 089	9.757 500	21.02190	45.29030
930	864 900	30.49590	96.43651	804 357 000	9.761 000	21.02944	45.30655
931	866 761	30.51229	96.48834	806 954 491	9.764 497	21.03697	45.32278
932	868 624	30.52868	96.54015	809 557 568	9.767 992	21.04450	45.33900
933	870 489	30.54505	96.59193	812 166 237	9.771 485	21.05203	45.35521
934	872 356	30.56141	96.64368	814 780 504	9.774 974	21.05954	45.37141
935	874 225	30.57777	96.69540	817 400 375	9.778 462	21.06706	45.38760
936	876 096	30.59412	96.74709	820 025 856	9.781 946	21.07456	45.40377
937	877 969	30.61046	96.79876	822 656 953	9.785 429	21.08207	45.41994
938	879 844	30.62679	96.85040	825 293 672	9.788 909	21.08956	45.43609
939	881 721	30.64311	96.90201	827 936 019	9.792 386	21.09706	45.45223
940	883 600	30.65942	96.95360	830 584 000	9.795 861	21.10454	45.46836
941	885 481	30.67572	97.00515	833 237 621	9.799 334	21.11202	45.48448
942	887 364	30.69202	97.05668	835 896 888	9.802 804	21.11950	45.50058
943	889 249	30.70831	97.10819	838 561 807	9.806 271	21.12697	45.51668
944	891 136	30.72458	97.15966	841 232 384	9.809 736	21.13444	45.53276
945	893 025	30.74085	97.21111	843 908 625	9.813 199	21.14190	45.54883
946	894 916	30.75711	97.26253	846 590 536	9.816 659	21.14935	45.56490
947	896 809	30.77337	97.31393	849 278 123	9.820 117	21.15680	45.58095
948	898.704	30.78961	97.36529	851 971 392	9.823 572	21.16424	45.59698
949	900 601	30.80584	97.41663	854 670 349	9.827 025	21.17168	45.61301
950	902 500	30.82207	97.46794	857 375 000	9.830 476	21.17912	45.62903

SQUARES, SQUARE ROOT, CUBES AND CUBE ROOT (Continued)

n	n^2	$\sqrt{n}$	$\sqrt{10n}$	n^3	$\sqrt[3]{n}$	$\sqrt[3]{10n}$	$\sqrt[3]{100n}$
950	902 500	30.82207	97.46794	857 375 000	9.830 476	21.17912	45.62903
951	904 401	30.83829	97.51923	860 085 351	9.833 924	21.18655	45.64503
952	906 304	30.85450	97.57049	862 801 408	9.837 369	21.19397	45.66102
953	908 209	30.87070	97.62172	865 523 177	9.840 813	21.20139	45.67701
954	910 116	30.88689	97.67292	868 250 664	9.844 254	21.20880	45.69298
955	912 025	30.90307	97.72410	870 983 875	9.847 692	21.21621	45.70894
956	913 936	30.91925	97.77525	873 722 816	9.851 128	21.22361	45.72489
957	915 849	30.93542	97.82638	876 467 493	9.854 562	21.23101	45.74082
958	917 764	30.95158	97.87747	879 217 912	9.857 993	21.23840	45.75675
959	919 681	30.96773	97.92855	881 974 079	9.861 422	21.24579	45.77267
960	921 600	30.98387	97.97959	884 736 000	9.864 848	21.25317	45.78857
961	923 521	31.00000	98.03061	887 503 681	9.868 272	21.26055	45.80446
962	925 444	31.01612	98.08160	890 277 128	9.871 694	21.26792	45.82035
963	927 369	31.03224	98.13256	893 056 347	9.875 113	21.27529	45.83622
964	929 296	31.04835	98.18350	895 841 344	9.878 530	21.28265	45.85208
965	931 225	31.06445	98.23441	898 632 125	9.881 945	21.29001	45.86793
966	933 156	31.08054	98.28530	901 428 696	9.885 357	21.29736	45.88376
967	935 089	31.09662	98.33616	904 231 063	9.888 767	21.30470	45.89959
968	937 024	31.11270	98.38699	907 039 232	9.892 175	21.31204	45.91541
969	938 961	31.12876	98.43780	909 853 209	9.895 580	21.31938	45.93121
970	940 900	31.14482	98.48858	912 673 000	9.898 983	21.32671	45.94701
971	942 841	31.16087	98.53933	915 498 611	9.902 384	21.33404	45.96279
972	944 784	31.17691	98.59006	918 330 048	9.905 782	21.34136	45.97857
973	946 729	31.19295	98.64076	921 167 317	9.909 178	21.34868	45.99433
974	948 676	31.20897	98.69144	924 010 424	9.912 571	21.35599	46.01008
975	950 625	31.22499	98.74209	926 859 375	9.915 962	21.36329	46.02582
976	952 576	31.24100	98.79271	929 714 176	9.919 351	21.37059	46.04155
977	954 529	31.25700	98.84331	932 574 833	9.922 738	21.37789	46.05727
978	956 484	31.27299	98.89388	935 441 352	9.926 122	21.38518	46.07298
979	958 441	31.28898	98.94443	938 313 739	9.929 504	21.39247	46.08868
980	960 400	31.30495	98.99495	941 192 000	9.932 884	21.39975	46.10436
981	962 361	31.32092	99.04544	944 076 141	9.936 261	21.40703	46.12004
982	964 324	31.33688	99.09591	946 966 168	9.939 636	21.41430	46.13571
983	966 289	31.35283	99.14636	949 862 087	9.943 009	21.42156	46.15136
984	968 256	31.36877	99.19677	952 763 904	9.946 380	21.42883	46.16700
985	970 225	31.38471	99.24717	955 671 625	9.949 748	21.43608	46.18264
986	972 196	31.40064	99.29753	958 585 256	9.953 114	21.44333	46.19826
987	974 169	31.41656	99.34787	961 504 803	9.956 478	21.45058	46.21387
988	976 144	31.43247	99.39819	964 430 272	9.959 839	21.45782	46.22948
989	978 121	31.44837	99.44848	967 361 669	9.963 198	21.46506	46.24507
990	980 100	31.46427	99.49874	970 299 000	9.966 555	21.47229	46.26065
991	982 081	31.48015	99.54898	973 242 271	9.969 910	21.47952	46.27622
992	984 064	31.49603	99.59920	976 191 488	9.973 262	21.48674	46.29178
993	986 049	31.51190	99.64939	979 146 657	9.976 612	21.49396	46.30733
994	988 036	31.52777	99.69955	982 107 784	9.979 960	21.50117	46.32287
995	990 025	31.54362	99.74969	985 074 875	9.983 305	21.50838	46.33840
996	992 016	31.55947	99.79980	988 047 936	9.986 649	21.51558	46.35392
997	994 009	31.57531	99.84989	991 026 973	9.989 990	21.52278	46.36943
998	996 004	31.59114	99.89995	994 011 992	9.993 329	21.52997	46.38492
999	998 001	31.60696	99.94999	997 002 999	9.996 666	21.53716	46.40041
1000	1 000 000	31.62278	100.00000	1 000 000.000	10.000 000	21.54435	46.41589

FOURTH AND FIFTH ROOTS

This table is given as a supplement to the previous table. It contains the fourth and fifth roots of the numbers from 1 to 1000, accurate to seven significant digits.

FOURTH AND FIFTH ROOTS

n	$\sqrt[4]{n}$	$\sqrt[5]{n}$	n	$\sqrt[4]{n}$	$\sqrt[5]{n}$
1	1.0000 00	1.0000 00	51	2.6723 45	2.1954 02
2	1.1892 07	1.1486 98	52	2.6853 50	2.2039 45
3	1.3160 74	1.2457 31	53	2.6981 68	2.2123 57
4	1.4142 14	1.3195 08	54	2.7108 06	2.2206 43
5	1.4953 49	1.3797 30	55	2.7232 70	2.2288 07
6	1.5650 85	1.4309 69	56	2.7355 65	2.2368 54
7	1.6265 77	1.4757 73	57	2.7476 96	2.2447 86
8	1.6817 93	1.5157 17	58	2.7596 69	2.2526 08
9	1.7320 51	1.5518 46	59	2.7714 88	2.2603 22
10	1.7782 79	1.5848 93	60	2.7831 58	2.2679 33
11	1.8211 60	1.6153 94	61	2.7946 82	2.2754 43
12	1.8612 10	1.6437 52	62	2.8060 66	2.2828 55
13	1.8988 29	1.6702 78	63	2.8173 13	2.2901 72
14	1.9343 36	1.6952 18	64	2.8284 27	2.2973 97
15	1.9679 90	1.7187 72	65	2.8394 12	2.3045 32
16	2.0000 00	1.7411 01	66	2.8502 70	2.3115 79
17	2.0305 43	1.7623 40	67	2.8610 06	2.3185 42
18	2.0597 67	1.7826 02	68	2.8716 22	2.3254 22
19	2.0877 98	1.8019 83	69	2.8821 21	2.3322 22
20	2.1147 43	1.8205 64	70	2.8925 08	2.3389 43
21	2.1406 95	1.8384 16	71	2.9027 83	2.3455 87
22	2.1657 37	1.8556 01	72	2.9129 51	2.3521 58
23	2.1899 39	1.8721 71	73	2.9230 13	2.3586 56
24	2.2133 64	1.8881 75	74	2.9329 72	2.3650 83
25	2.2360 68	1.9036 54	75	2.9428 31	2.3714 41
26	2.2581 01	1.9186 45	76	2.9525 92	2.3777 31
27	2.2795 07	1.9331 82	77	2.9622 57	2.3839 56
28	2.3003 27	1.9472 94	78	2.9718 28	2.3901 16
29	2.3205 96	1.9610 09	79	2.9813 08	2.3962 13
30	2.3403 47	1.9743 50	80	2.9906 98	2.4022 49
31	2.3596 11	1.9873 41	81	3.0000 00	2.4082 25
32	2.3784 14	2.0000 00	82	3.0092 17	2.4141 42
33	2.3967 82	2.0123 47	83	3.0183 49	2.4200 01
34	2.4147 36	2.0243 97	84	3.0274 00	2.4258 05
35	2.4322 99	2.0361 68	85	3.0363 70	2.4315 53
36	2.4494 90	2.0476 73	86	3.0452 62	2.4372 48
37	2.4663 26	2.0589 24	87	3.0540 76	2.4428 90
38	2.4828 24	2.0699 35	88	3.0628 14	2.4484 80
39	2.4989 99	2.0807 17	89	3.0714 79	2.4540 19
40	2.5148 67	2.0912 79	90	3.0800 70	2.4595 09
41	2.5304 40	2.1016 32	91	3.0885 91	2.4649 51
42	2.5457 30	2.1117 86	92	3.0970 41	2.4703 45
43	2.5607 50	2.1217 47	93	3.1054 23	2.4756 92
44	2.5755 10	2.1315 26	94	3.1137 37	2.4809 93
45	2.5900 20	2.1411 27	95	3.1219 86	2.4862 50
46	2.6042 91	2.1505 60	96	3.1301 69	2.4914 62
47	2.6183 30	2.1598 30	97	3.1382 89	2.4966 31
48	2.6321 48	2.1689 44	98	3.1463 46	2.5017 58
49	2.6457 51	2.1779 06	99	3.1543 42	2.5068 42
50	2.6591 48	2.1867 24	100	3.1622 78	2.5118 86

FOURTH AND FIFTH ROOTS (Continued)

n	$\sqrt[4]{n}$	$\sqrt[5]{n}$	n	$\sqrt[4]{n}$	$\sqrt[5]{n}$
101	3.1701 54	2.5168 90	151	3.5054 54	2.7276 92
102	3.1779 72	2.5218 55	152	3.5112 43	2.7312 96
103	3.1857 33	2.5267 80	153	3.5170 04	2.7348 80
104	3.1934 37	2.5316 68	154	3.5227 37	2.7384 46
105	3.2010 86	2.5365 17	155	3.5284 42	2.7419 93
106	3.2086 80	2.5413 31	156	3.5341 19	2.7455 22
107	3.2162 21	2.5461 08	157	3.5397 69	2.7490 33
108	3.2237 10	2.5508 49	158	3.5453 92	2.7525 26
109	3.2311 46	2.5555 55	159	3.5509 89	2.7560 01
110	3.2385 32	2.5602 27	160	3.5565 59	2.7594 59
111	3.2458 67	2.5648 65	161	3.5621 03	2.7629 00
112	3.2531 53	2.5694 70	162	3.5676 21	2.7663 24
113	3.2603 90	2.5740 42	163	3.5731 14	2.7697 31
114	3.2675 80	2.5785 82	164	3.5785 82	2.7731 21
115	3.2747 22	2.5830 90	165	3.5840 25	2.7764 94
116	3.2818 18	2.5875 67	166	3.5894 43	2.7798 52
117	3.2888 68	2.5920 13	167	3.5948 36	2.7831 93
118	3.2958 73	2.5964 29	168	3.6002 06	2.7865 18
119	3.3028 34	2.6008 15	169	3.6055 51	2.7898 27
120	3.3097 51	2.6051 71	170	3.6108 73	2.7931 21
121	3.3166 25	2.6094 99	171	3.6161 72	2.7964 00
122	3.3234 56	2.6137 98	172	3.6214 47	2.7996 63
123	3.3302 46	2.6180 69	173	3.6266 99	2.8029 10
124	3.3369 94	2.6223 12	174	3.6319 29	2.8061 43
125	3.3437 02	2.6265 28	175	3.6371 36	2.8093 61
126	3.3503 69	2.6307 17	176	3.6423 21	2.8125 65
127	3.3569 97	2.6348 79	177	3.6474 83	2.8157 54
128	3.3635 86	2.6390 16	178	3.6526 24	2.8189 28
129	3.3701 36	2.6431 26	179	3.6577 44	2.8220 88
130	3.3766 48	2.6472 12	180	3.6628 42	2.8252 35
131	3.3831 23	2.6512 72	181	3.6679 18	2.8283 67
132	3.3895 61	2.6553 07	182	3.6729 74	2.8314 85
133	3.3959 61	2.6593 18	183	3.6780 09	2.8345 90
134	3.4023 28	2.6633 05	184	3.6830 23	2.8376 81
135	3.4086 58	2.6672 69	185	3.6880 17	2.8407 59
136	3.4149 53	2.6712 08	186	3.6929 91	2.8438 23
137	3.4212 13	2.6751 25	187	3.6979 45	2.8468 74
138	3.4274 39	2.6790 19	188	3.7028 79	2.8499 13
139	3.4336 32	2.6828 91	189	3.7077 93	2.8529 38
140	3.4397 91	2.6867 40	190	3.7126 88	2.8559 51
141	3.4459 17	2.6905 67	191	3.7175 63	2.8589 51
142	3.4520 10	2.6943 72	192	3.7224 19	2.8619 38
143	3.4580 72	2.6981 57	193	3.7272 57	2.8649 13
144	3.4641 02	2.7019 20	194	3.7320 76	2.8678 76
145	3.4701 00	2.7056 62	195	3.7368 76	2.8708 26
146	3.4760 68	2.7093 84	196	3.7416 57	2.8737 65
147	3.4820 05	2.7130 85	197	3.7464 21	2.8766 91
148	3.4879 11	2.7167 67	198	3.7511 66	2.8796 06
149	3.4937 88	2.7204 28	199	3.7558 93	2.8825 09
150	3.4996 36	2.7240 67	200	3.7606 03	2.8854 00

FOURTH AND FIFTH ROOTS (Continued)

n	$\sqrt[4]{n}$	$\sqrt[5]{n}$	n	$\sqrt[4]{n}$	$\sqrt[5]{n}$
201	3.7652 95	2.8882 79	251	3.9803 24	3.0194 98
202	3.7699 70	2.8911 48	252	3.9842 83	3.0219 00
203	3.7746 27	2.8940 05	253	3.9882 29	3.0242 95
204	3.7792 67	2.8968 50	254	3.9921 65	3.0266 82
205	3.7838 90	2.8996 85	255	3.9960 88	3.0290 61
206	3.7884 96	2.9025 08	256	4.0000 00	3.0314 33
207	3.7930 85	2.9053 21	257	4.0039 01	3.0337 98
208	3.7976 50	2.9081 22	258	4.0077 90	3.0361 55
209	3.8022 14	2.9109 13	259	4.0116 68	3.0385 05
210	3.8067 54	2.9136 93	260	4.0155 34	3.0408 48
211	3.8112 78	2.9164 63	261	4.0193 90	3.0431 83
212	3.8157 86	2.9192 22	262	4.0232 34	3.0455 12
213	3.8202 77	2.9219 71	263	4.0270 68	3.0478 33
214	3.8247 53	2.9247 10	264	4.0308 90	3.0501 47
215	3.8292 14	2.9274 38	265	4.0347 02	3.0524 54
216	3.8336 59	2.9301 56	266	4.0385 03	3.0547 55
217	3.8380 88	2.9328 64	267	4.0422 93	3.0570 48
218	3.8425 02	2.9355 62	268	4.0460 73	3.0593 34
219	3.8469 01	2.9382 50	269	4.0498 42	3.0616 14
220	3.8512 85	2.9409 29	270	4.0536 00	3.0638 87
221	3.8556 54	2.9435 98	271	4.0573 49	3.0661 53
222	3.8600 08	2.9462 57	272	4.0610 86	3.0684 13
223	3.8643 48	2.9489 06	273	4.0648 14	3.0706 66
224	3.8686 73	2.9515 46	274	4.0685 31	3.0729 12
225	3.8729 83	2.9541 77	275	4.0722 38	3.0751 52
226	3.8772 80	2.9567 98	276	4.0759 35	3.0773 85
227	3.8815 61	2.9594 10	277	4.0796 22	3.0796 12
228	3.8858 29	2.9620 13	278	4.0832 99	3.0818 32
229	3.8900 83	2.9646 07	279	4.0869 66	3.0840 46
230	3.8943 23	2.9671 91	280	4.0906 23	3.0862 54
231	3.8985 49	2.9697 67	281	4.0942 71	3.0884 55
232	3.9027 61	2.9723 34	282	4.0979 09	3.0906 50
233	3.9069 60	2.9748 92	283	4.1015 37	3.0928 39
234	3.9111 45	2.9774 41	284	4.1051 55	3.0950 21
235	3.9153 17	2.9799 82	285	4.1087 64	3.0971 98
236	3.9194 76	2.9825 13	286	4.1123 64	3.0993 68
237	3.9236 21	2.9850 37	287	4.1159 54	3.1015 33
238	3.9277 54	2.9875 51	288	4.1195 34	3.1036 91
239	3.9318 73	2.9900 58	289	4.1231 06	3.1058 44
240	3.9359 79	2.9925 56	290	4.1266 68	3.1079 90
241	3.9400 73	2.9950 45	291	4.1302 21	3.1101 30
242	3.9441 54	2.9975 27	292	4.1337 64	3.1122 65
243	3.9482 22	3.0000 00	293	4.1372 99	3.1143 94
244	3.9522 78	3.0024 65	294	4.1408 25	3.1165 17
245	3.9563 21	3.0049 22	295	4.1443 41	3.1186 34
246	3.9603 52	3.0073 71	296	4.1478 49	3.1207 45
247	3.9643 71	3.0098 12	297	4.1513 48	3.1228 51
248	3.9683 77	3.0122 45	298	4.1548 38	3.1249 51
249	3.9723 71	3.0146 71	299	4.1583 19	3.1270 46
250	3.9763 54	3.0170 88	300	4.1617 91	3.1291 35

FOURTH AND FIFTH ROOTS (Continued)

n	$\sqrt[4]{n}$	$\sqrt[5]{n}$	n	$\sqrt[4]{n}$	$\sqrt[5]{n}$
301	4.1652 55	3.1312 18	351	4.3283 94	3.2289 51
302	4.1687 10	3.1332 96	352	4.3314 74	3.2307 89
303	4.1721 57	3.1353 68	353	4.3345 47	3.2326 22
304	4.1755 95	3.1374 35	354	4.3376 13	3.2344 52
305	4.1790 25	3.1394 96	355	4.3406 73	3.2362 77
306	4.1824 46	3.1415 52	356	4.3437 27	3.2380 98
307	4.1858 59	3.1436 03	357	4.3467 74	3.2399 15
308	4.1892 64	3.1456 48	358	4.3498 15	3.2417 28
309	4.1926 60	3.1476 88	359	4.3528 49	3.2435 37
310	4.1960 48	3.1497 23	360	4.3558 77	3.2453 42
311	4.1994 28	3.1517 52	361	4.3588 99	3.2471 43
312	4.2027 99	3.1537 77	362	4.3619 14	3.2489 40
313	4.2061 63	3.1557 96	363	4.3649 24	3.2507 33
314	4.2095 18	3.1578 10	364	4.3679 27	3.2525 22
315	4.2128 66	3.1598 18	365	4.3709 24	3.2543 07
316	4.2162 06	3.1618 22	366	4.3739 14	3.2560 89
317	4.2195 37	3.1638 21	367	4.3768 99	3.2578 66
318	4.2228 61	3.1658 14	368	4.3798 77	3.2596 39
319	4.2261 77	3.1678 03	369	4.3828 50	3.2614 09
320	4.2294 85	3.1697 86	370	4.3858 16	3.2631 75
321	4.2327 85	3.1717 65	371	4.3887 77	3.2649 37
322	4.2360 78	3.1737 39	372	4.3917 31	3.2666 95
323	4.2393 63	3.1757 08	373	4.3946 80	3.2684 49
324	4.2426 41	3.1776 72	374	4.3976 22	3.2702 00
325	4.2459 11	3.1796 31	375	4.4005 59	3.2719 47
326	4.2491 73	3.1815 85	376	4.4034 89	3.2736 90
327	4.2524 28	3.1835 34	377	4.4064 14	3.2754 30
328	4.2556 75	3.1854 79	378	4.4093 34	3.2771 65
329	4.2589 15	3.1874 19	379	4.4122 47	3.2788 98
330	4.2621 48	3.1893 54	380	4.4151 54	3.2806 26
331	4.2653 73	3.1912 85	381	4.4180 56	3.2823 51
332	4.2685 91	3.1932 11	382	4.4209 52	3.2840 72
333	4.2718 01	3.1951 32	383	4.4238 43	3.2857 90
334	4.2750 05	3.1970 49	384	4.4267 28	3.2875 04
335	4.2782 01	3.1989 61	385	4.4296 07	3.2892 14
336	4.2813 90	3.2008 69	386	4.4324 80	3.2909 21
337	4.2845 72	3.2027 72	387	4.4353 48	3.2926 24
338	4.2877 47	3.2046 70	388	4.4382 11	3.2943 24
339	4.2909 15	3.2065 64	389	4.4410 68	3.2960 21
340	4.2940 76	3.2084 54	390	4.4439 19	3.2977 13
341	4.2972 30	3.2103 39	391	4.4467 65	3.2994 03
342	4.3003 77	3.2122 20	392	4.4496 06	3.3010 89
343	4.3035 17	3.2140 96	393	4.4524 41	3.3027 71
344	4.3066 50	3.2159 68	394	4.4552 70	3.3044 50
345	4.3097 77	3.2178 35	395	4.4580 95	3.3061 26
346	4.3128 96	3.2196 99	396	4.4609 13	3.3077 98
347	4.3160 09	3.2215 58	397	4.4637 27	3.3094 67
348	4.3191 15	3.2234 12	398	4.4665 35	3.3111 33
349	4.3222 15	3.2252 63	309	4.4693 38	3.3127 95
350	4.3253 08	3.2271 09	400	4.4721 36	3.3144 54

FOURTH AND FIFTH ROOTS (Continued)

n	$\sqrt[4]{n}$	$\sqrt[5]{n}$	n	$\sqrt[4]{n}$	$\sqrt[5]{n}$
401	4.4777 16	3.3161 10	451	4.6083 36	3.3949 65
402	4.4749 28	3.3177 62	452	4.6108 88	3.3964 69
403	4.4804 98	3.3194 11	453	4.6134 37	3.3979 71
404	4.4832 75	3.3210 57	454	4.6159 80	3.3994 70
405	4.4860 46	3.3226 99	455	4.6185 20	3.4009 66
406	4.4888 13	3.3243 38	456	4.6210 56	3.4024 60
407	4.4915 74	3.3259 74	457	4.6235 87	3.4039 51
408	4.4943 31	3.3276 07	458	4.6261 14	3.4054 35
409	4.4970 82	3.3292 37	459	4.6286 38	3.4069 29
410	4.4998 29	3.3308 63	460	4.6311 57	3.4084 08
411	4.5025 70	3.3324 86	461	4.6336 71	3.4098 89
412	4.5053 06	3.3341 06	462	4.6361 82	3.4113 67
413	4.5080 37	3.3357 23	463	4.6386 89	3.4128 42
414	4.5107 64	3.3373 37	464	4.6411 92	3.4143 15
415	4.5134 85	3.3389 48	465	4.6436 90	3.4157 86
416	4.5162 02	3.3405 55	466	4.6461 85	3.4172 53
417	4.5189 13	3.3421 60	467	4.6486 75	3.4187 19
418	4.5216 20	3.3437 61	468	4.6511 62	3.4201 82
419	4.5243 22	3.3453 60	469	4.6536 45	3.4216 42
420	4.5270 19	3.3469 55	470	4.6561 23	3.4230 89
421	4.5297 11	3.3485 47	471	4.6585 98	3.4245 55
422	4.5323 99	3.3501 36	472	4.6610 69	3.4260 08
423	4.5350 81	3.3517 23	473	4.6635 35	3.4274 59
424	4.5377 59	3.3533 06	474	4.6659 98	3.4289 07
425	4.5404 33	3.3548 86	475	4.6684 57	3.4303 52
426	4.5431 01	3.3564 63	476	4.6709 13	3.4317 95
427	4.5457 65	3.3580 38	477	4.6733 64	3.4332 36
428	4.5484 24	3.3596 09	478	4.6758 11	3.4346 74
429	4.5510 78	3.3611 78	479	4.6782 55	3.4361 10
430	4.5537 28	3.3627 43	480	4.6806 95	3.4375 44
431	4.5563 74	3.3643 06	481	4.6831 31	3.4389 75
432	4.5590 14	3.3658 65	482	4.6855 63	3.4404 04
433	4.5616 50	3.3674 22	483	4.6879 91	3.4418 30
434	4.5642 82	3.3689 76	484	4.6904 16	3.4432 54
435	4.5669 09	3.3705 27	485	4.6928 37	3.4446 76
436	4.5695 31	3.3720 76	486	4.6952 54	3.4460 95
437	4.5721 49	3.3736 21	487	4.6976 67	3.4475 12
438	4.5747 62	3.3751 64	488	4.7000 77	3.4489 27
439	4.5773 71	3.3767 03	489	4.7024 83	3.4503 39
440	4.5799 76	3.3782 40	490	4.7048 85	3.4517 49
441	4.5825 76	3.3797 74	491	4.7072 84	3.4531 57
442	4.5851 71	3.3813 06	492	4.7096 77	3.4545 62
443	4.5877 63	3.3828 34	493	4.7120 70	3.4559 65
444	4.5903 49	3.3843 60	494	4.7144 58	3.4573 66
445	4.5929 32	3.3858 83	495	4.7168 42	3.4587 65
446	4.5955 10	3.3874 04	496	4.7192 22	3.4601 61
447	4.5980 84	3.3889 21	497	4.7215 99	3.4615 55
448	4.6006 53	3.3904 36	498	4.7239 72	3.4629 47
449	4.6032 18	3.3919 49	499	4.7263 42	3.4643 37
450	4.6057 79	3.3934 58	500	4.7287 08	3.4657 24

FOURTH AND FIFTH ROOTS (Continued)

n	$\sqrt[4]{n}$	$\sqrt[5]{n}$	n	$\sqrt[4]{n}$	$\sqrt[5]{n}$
501	4.7310 71	3.4671 09	551	4.8449 34	3.5337 05
502	4.7334 30	3.4684 92	552	4.8471 31	3.5349 87
503	4.7357 85	3.4698 73	553	4.8493 25	3.5362 67
504	4.7381 37	3.4712 52	554	4.8515 16	3.5375 45
505	4.7404 86	3.4726 28	525	4.8537 04	3.5388 21
506	4.7428 31	3.4740 02	556	4.8558 88	3.5400 95
507	4.7451 72	3.4753 74	557	4.8580 70	3.5413 68
508	4.7475 10	3.4767 44	558	4.8602 49	3.5426 39
509	4.7498 45	3.4781 12	559	4.8624 25	3.5439 07
510	4.7521 76	3.4794 78	560	4.8645 99	3.5451 74
511	4.7545 04	3.4808 41	561	4.8667 69	3.5464 40
512	4.7568 28	3.4822 02	562	4.8689 36	3.5477 03
513	4.7591 49	3.4835 61	563	4.8711 01	3.5489 65
514	4.7614 67	3.4849 18	564	4.8732 62	3.5502 25
515	4.7637 81	3.4862 73	565	4.8754 21	3.5514 83
516	4.7660 92	3.4876 26	566	4.8775 77	3.5527 39
517	4.7684 00	3.4889 77	567	4.8797 30	3.5539 93
518	4.7707 04	3.4903 26	568	4.8818 80	3.5552 46
519	4.7730 04	3.4916 72	569	4.8840 27	3.5564 97
520	4.7753 02	3.4930 17	570	4.8861 72	3.5577 46
521	4.7775 96	3.4943 59	571	4.8883 13	3.5589 94
522	4.7798 87	3.4957 00	572	4.8904 52	3.5602 39
523	4.7844 59	3.4970 38	573	4.8925 88	3.5614 83
524	4.7821 75	3.4983 74	574	4.8947 21	3.5627 26
525	4.7867 40	3.4997 08	575	4.8968 52	3.5639 66
526	4.7890 18	3.5010 41	576	4.8989 79	3.5664 42
527	4.7912 92	3.5023 71	577	4.9011 04	3.5652 05
528	4.7935 63	3.5036 99	578	4.9032 27	3.5676 77
529	4.7958 32	3.5050 25	579	4.9053 46	3.5689 11
530	4.7980 96	3.5063 49	580	4.9074 63	3.5701 43
531	4.8003 58	3.5076 71	581	4.9095 77	3.5713 73
532	4.8026 16	3.5089 92	582	4.9116 88	3.5726 02
533	4.8048 72	3.5103 10	583	4.9137 96	3.5738 29
534	4.8071 24	3.5116 26	584	4.9159 02	3.5750 54
535	4.8093 73	3.5129 40	585	4.9180 05	3.5762 77
536	4.8116 19	3.5142 52	586	4.9201 05	3.5774 99
537	4.8138 61	3.5155 63	587	4.9222 03	3.5787 19
538	4.8161 01	3.5168 71	588	4.9242 98	3.5799 38
539	4.8183 37	3.5181 78	589	4.9263 90	3.5811 55
540	4.8205 71	3.5194 82	590	4.9284 80	3.5823 70
541	4.8228 01	3.5207 85	591	4.9305 67	3.5835 83
542	4.8250 28	3.5220 85	592	4.9326 51	3.5847 95
543	4.8272 52	3.5233 84	593	4.9347 33	3.5860 05
544	4.8294 73	3.5246 81	594	4.9368 12	3.5872 14
545	4.8316 91	3.5259 76	595	4.9388 89	3.5884 21
546	4.8339 06	3.5272 69	596	4.9409 63	3.5896 26
547	4.8361 17	3.5285 60	597	4.9430 34	3.5908 30
548	4.8383 26	3.5298 49	598	4.9451 02	3.5920 32
549	4.8405 32	3.5311 36	599	4.9471 69	3.5932 33
550	4.8427 35	3.5324 22	600	4.9492 32	3.5944 32

FOURTH AND FIFTH ROOTS (Continued)

n	$\sqrt[4]{n}$	$\sqrt[5]{n}$	n	$\sqrt[4]{n}$	$\sqrt[5]{n}$
601	4.9512 93	3.5956 29	651	5.0512 08	3.6535 60
602	4.9533 51	3.5968 29	652	5.0531 47	3.6546 81
603	4.9554 07	3.5980 19	653	5.0550 83	3.6558 02
604	4.9574 60	3.5992 12	654	5.0570 17	3.6569 21
605	4.9595 11	3.6004 03	655	5.0589 49	3.6580 38
606	4.9615 59	3.6015 92	656	5.0608 79	3.6591 55
607	4.9636 05	3.6027 80	657	5.0628 07	3.6602 70
608	4.9656 48	3.6039 66	658	5.0647 32	3.6613 83
609	4.9676 88	3.6051 51	659	5.0666 55	3.6624 95
610	4.9697 26	3.6063 34	660	5.0685 76	3.6636 06
611	4.9717 62	3.6075 16	661	5.0704 95	3.6647 16
612	4.9737 95	3.6086 96	662	5.0724 12	3.6658 24
613	4.9758 25	3.6098 74	663	5.0743 26	3.6669 31
614	4.9778 53	3.6110 51	664	5.0762 39	3.6680 36
615	4.9798 79	3.6122 27	665	5.0781 49	3.6691 40
616	4.9819 02	3.6134 01	666	5.0800 57	3.6702 43
617	4.9839 23	3.6145 73	667	5.0819 63	3.6713 45
618	4.9859 41	3.6157 44	668	5.0838 66	3.6724 45
619	4.9879 57	3.6169 14	669	5.0857 68	3.6735 44
620	4.9899 70	3.6180 81	670	5.0876 67	3.6746 41
621	4.9919 81	3.6192 48	671	5.0895 65	3.6757 38
622	4.9939 89	3.6204 13	672	5.0914 60	3.6768 33
623	4.9959 95	3.6215 76	673	5.0933 53	3.6779 26
624	4.9979 99	3.6227 38	674	5.0952 44	3.6790 19
625	5.0000 00	3.6238 98	675	5.0971 33	3.6801 10
626	5.0019 99	3.6250 57	676	5.0990 20	3.6811 99
627	5.0039 95	3.6262 15	677	5.1009 04	3.6822 88
628	5.0059 89	3.6273 71	678	5.1027 87	3.6833 75
629	5.0079 81	3.6285 25	679	5.1046 67	3.6844 61
630	5.0099 70	3.6296 78	680	5.1065 46	3.6855 46
631	5.0119 57	3.6308 30	681	5.1084 22	3.6866 29
632	5.0139 42	3.6319 80	682	5.1102 96	3.6877 11
633	5.0159 24	3.6331 28	683	5.1121 69	3.6887 92
634	5.0179 04	3.6342 76	684	5.1140 39	3.6898 71
635	5.0198 81	3.6354 21	685	5.1159 07	3.6909 50
636	5.0218 56	3.6365 66	686	5.1177 73	3.6920 27
637	5.0238 29	3.6377 08	687	5.1196 37	3.6931 02
638	5.0258 00	3.6388 50	688	5.1214 99	3.6941 77
639	5.0277 68	3.6399 90	689	5.1233 59	3.6952 50
640	5.0297 34	3.6411 28	690	5.1252 17	3.6963 22
641	5.0316 97	3.6422 66	691	5.1270 73	3.6973 93
642	5.0336 59	3.6434 01	692	5.1289 27	3.6984 62
643	5.0356 18	3.6445 36	693	5.1307 79	3.6995 31
644	5.0375 74	3.6456 68	694	5.1326 29	3.7005 98
645	5.0395 29	3.6468 00	695	5.1344 77	3.7016 64
646	5.0414 81	3.6479 30	696	5.1363 23	3.7027 28
647	5.0434 31	3.6490 59	697	5.1381 67	3.7037 92
648	5.0453 78	3.6501 86	698	5.1400 09	3.7048 54
649	5.0473 24	3.6513 12	699	5.1418 49	3.7059 15
650	5.0492 67	3.6524 36	700	5.1436 87	3.7069 75

FOURTH AND FIFTH ROOTS (Continued)

n	$\sqrt[4]{n}$	$\sqrt[5]{n}$	n	$\sqrt[4]{n}$	$\sqrt[5]{n}$
701	5.1455 23	3.7080 33	751	5.2349 19	3.7594 82
702	5.1473 57	3.7090 90	752	5.2366 61	3.7604 82
703	5.1491 89	3.7101 47	753	5.2384 01	3.7614 82
704	5.1510 19	3.7112 01	754	5.2401 39	3.7624 81
705	5.1528 47	3.7122 55	755	5.2418 76	3.7634 78
706	5.1546 74	3.7133 08	756	5.2436 11	3.7644 74
707	5.1564 98	3.7143 59	757	5.2453 44	3.7654 70
708	5.1583 20	3.7154 09	758	5.2470 75	3.7664 64
709	5.1601 41	3.7164 58	759	5.2488 05	3.7674 57
710	5.1619 59	3.7175 06	760	5.2505 33	3.7684 50
711	5.1637 76	3.7185 53	761	5.2522 59	3.7694 41
712	5.1655 91	3.7195 98	762	5.2539 84	3.7704 31
713	5.1674 04	3.7206 42	763	5.2557 07	3.7714 20
714	5.1692 14	3.7216 85	764	5.2574 28	3.7724 08
715	5.1710 23	3.7227 27	765	5.2591 48	3.7733 95
716	5.1728 31	3.7237 68	766	5.2608 65	3.7743 81
717	5.1746 36	3.7248 07	767	5.2625 82	3.7753 66
718	5.1764 39	3.7258 46	768	5.2642 96	3.7763 50
719	5.1782 41	3.7268 83	769	5.2660 09	3.7773 33
720	5.1800 40	3.7279 19	770	5.2677 20	3.7783 15
721	5.1818 38	3.7289 54	771	5.2694 29	3.7792 96
722	5.1836 34	3.7299 88	772	5.2711 37	3.7802 76
723	5.1854 28	3.7310 21	773	5.2728 43	3.7812 54
724	5.1872 20	3.7320 52	774	5.2745 48	3.7822 32
725	5.1890 10	3.7330 83	775	5.2762 51	3.7832 09
726	5.1907 98	3.7341 12	776	5.2779 52	3.7841 85
727	5.1925 85	3.7351 40	777	5.2796 51	3.7851 60
728	5.1943 70	3.7361 67	778	5.2813 49	3.7861 33
729	5.1961 52	3.7371 93	779	5.2830 46	3.7871 06
730	5.1979 33	3.7382 18	780	5.2847 40	3.7880 78
731	5.1997 13	3.7392 41	781	5.2864 33	3.7890 49
732	5.2014 90	3.7402 64	782	5.2881 25	3.7900 19
733	5.2032 66	3.7412 85	783	5.2898 14	3.7909 88
734	5.2050 39	3.7423 05	784	5.2915 03	3.7919 55
735	5.2068 11	3.7433 24	785	5.2931 89	3.7929 22
736	5.2085 81	3.7443 42	786	5.2948 74	3.7938 88
737	5.2103 50	3.7453 59	787	5.2965 57	3.7948 53
738	5.2121 16	3.7463 75	788	5.2982 39	3.7958 17
739	5.2138 81	3.7473 90	789	5.2999 19	3.7967 80
740	5.2156 44	3.7484 04	790	5.3015 98	3.7977 42
741	5.2174 05	3.7494 16	791	5.3032 75	3.7987 03
742	5.2191 64	3.7504 28	792	5.3049 50	3.7996 63
743	5.2209 22	3.7514 38	793	5.3066 24	3.8006 22
744	5.2226 78	3.7524 47	794	5.3082 96	3.8015 80
745	5.2244 32	3.7534 55	795	5.3099 67	3.8025 37
746	5.2261 84	3.7544 62	796	5.3116 36	3.8034 93
747	5.2279 35	3.7554 68	797	5.3133 03	3.8044 48
748	5.2296 83	3.7564 73	798	5.3149 69	3.8054 02
749	5.2314 30	3.7574 77	799	5.3166 33	3.8063 56
750	5.2331 76	3.7584 80	800	5.3182 96	3.8073 08

FOURTH AND FIFTH ROOTS (Continued)

n	$\sqrt[4]{n}$	$\sqrt[5]{n}$	n	$\sqrt[4]{n}$	$\sqrt[5]{n}$
801	5.3199 57	3.8082 59	851	5.4011 02	3.8546 59
802	5.3216 17	3.8092 10	852	5.4026 88	3.8555 64
803	5.3232 75	3.8101 59	853	5.4042 73	3.8564 69
804	5.3249 31	3.8111 08	854	5.4058 56	3.8573 72
805	5.3265 86	3.8120 55	855	5.4074 38	3.8582 75
806	5.3282 40	3.8130 02	856	5.4090 18	3.8591 77
807	5.3298 91	3.8139 47	857	5.4105 97	3.8600 79
808	5.3315 42	3.8148 92	858	5.4121 75	3.8609 79
809	5.3331 97	3.8158 36	859	5.4137 51	3.8618 79
810	5.3348 38	3.8167 79	860	5.4153 26	3.8627 77
811	5.3364 84	3.8177 21	861	5.4169 00	3.8636 75
812	5.3381 28	3.8186 62	862	5.4184 72	3.8645 72
813	5.3397 71	3.8196 02	863	5.4200 43	3.8654 69
814	5.3414 12	3.8205 41	864	5.4216 12	3.8663 64
815	5.3430 52	3.8214 79	865	5.4231 80	3.8672 59
816	5.3446 90	3.8224 17	866	5.4247 47	3.8681 52
817	5.3463 27	3.8233 53	867	5.4263 12	3.8690 45
818	5.3479 62	3.8242 89	868	5.4278 76	3.8699 37
819	5.3495 96	3.8252 23	869	5.4294 39	3.8708 29
820	5.3512 28	3.8261 57	870	5.4310 00	3.8717 19
821	5.3528 59	3.8270 90	871	5.4325 60	3.8726 09
822	5.3544 88	3.8280 21	872	5.4341 19	3.8734 98
823	5.3561 16	3.8289 52	873	5.4356 76	3.8743 86
824	5.3577 42	3.8298 82	874	5.4372 32	3.8752 73
825	5.3593 67	3.8308 12	875	5.4387 87	3.8761 59
826	5.3609 90	3.8317 40	876	5.4403 40	3.8770 45
827	5.3626 12	3.8326 67	877	5.4418 92	3.8779 30
828	5.3642 32	3.8335 94	878	5.4434 42	3.8788 14
829	5.3658 51	3.8345 19	879	5.4449 92	3.8796 97
830	5.3674 69	3.8354 44	880	5.4465 40	3.8805 79
831	5.3690 85	3.8363 68	881	5.4480 86	3.8814 61
832	5.3706 99	3.8372 90	882	5.4496 32	3.8823 41
833	5.3723 12	3.8382 12	833	5.4511 76	3.8832 21
834	5.3739 24	3.8391 33	884	5.4527 18	3.8841 00
835	5.3755 34	3.8400 54	885	5.4542 60	3.8849 79
836	5.3771 43	3.8409 73	886	5.4558 00	3.8858 56
837	5.3787 50	3.8418 91	887	5.4573 39	3.8867 33
838	5.3803 56	3.8428 09	888	5.4588 76	3.8876 09
839	5.3819 60	3.8437 26	889	5.4604 12	3.8884 84
840	5.3835 63	3.8446 42	890	5.4619 47	3.8893 59
841	5.3851 65	3.8455 57	891	5.4634 81	3.8902 32
842	5.3867 65	3.8464 71	892	5.4650 13	3.8911 05
843	5.3883 64	3.8473 84	893	5.4665 44	3.8919 77
844	5.3899 61	3.8482 96	894	5.4680 74	3.8928 49
845	5.3915 57	3.8492 08	895	5.4696 02	3.8937 19
846	5.3931 51	3.8501 18	896	5.4711 30	3.8945 89
847	5.3947 44	3.8510 28	897	5.4726 56	3.8954 58
848	5.3963 36	3.8519 37	898	5.4741 80	3.8963 26
849	5.3979 26	3.8528 45	899	5.4757 03	3.8971 93
850	5.3995 15	3.8537 52	900	5.4772 26	3.8980 60

FOURTH AND FIFTH ROOTS (Continued)

n	$\sqrt[4]{n}$	$\sqrt[5]{n}$	n	$\sqrt[4]{n}$	$\sqrt[5]{n}$
901	5.4787 46	3.8989 26	951	5.5532 23	3.9412 69
902	5.4802 66	3.8997 91	952	5.5546 82	3.9420 98
903	5.4817 84	3.9006 55	953	5.5561 41	3.9429 26
904	5.4833 01	3.9015 19	954	5.5575 98	3.9437 53
905	5.4848 17	3.9023 81	955	5.5590 53	3.9445 79
906	5.4863 32	3.9032 43	956	5.5605 08	3.9454 05
907	5.4878 45	3.9041 05	957	5.5619 62	3.9462 30
908	5.4893 57	3.9049 65	958	5.5634 14	3.9470 54
909	5.4908 68	3.9058 25	959	5.5648 65	3.9478 78
910	5.4923 77	3.9066 84	960	5.5663 15	3.9487 01
911	5.4938 85	3.9075 42	961	5.5677 64	3.9495 23
912	5.4953 92	3.9084 00	962	5.5692 12	3.9503 45
913	5.4968 98	3.9092 56	963	5.5706 59	3.9511 66
914	5.4984 03	3.9101 12	964	5.5721 05	3.9519 86
915	5.4999 06	3.9109 68	965	5.5735 49	3.9528 06
916	5.5014 08	3.9118 22	966	5.5749 92	3.9536 25
917	5.5029 09	3.9126 76	967	5.5764 35	3.9544 43
918	5.5044 09	3.9135 29	968	5.5778 76	3.9552 60
919	5.5059 07	3.9143 81	969	5.5793 16	3.9560 77
920	5.5074 04	3.9152 33	970	5.5807 55	3.9568 93
921	5.5089 00	3.9160 83	971	5.5821 92	3.9577 09
922	5.5103 95	3.9169 33	972	5.5836 29	3.9585 24
923	5.5118 89	3.9177 83	973	5.5850 65	3.9593 38
924	5.5133 81	3.9186 31	974	5.5864 99	3.9601 51
925	5.5148 72	3.9194 79	975	5.5879 33	3.9609 64
926	5.5163 62	3.9203 26	976	5.5893 65	3.9617 76
927	5.5178 51	3.9211 72	977	5.5907 96	3.9625 88
928	5.5193 38	3.9220 18	978	5.5922 26	3.9633 99
929	5.5208 24	3.9228 63	979	5.5936 55	3.9642 09
930	5.5223 09	3.9237 07	980	5.5950 83	3.9650 18
931	5.5237 93	3.9245 51	981	5.5965 10	3.9658 27
932	5.5252 76	3.9253 93	982	5.5979 35	3.9666 36
933	5.5267 58	3.9262 35	983	5.5993 60	3.9674 43
934	5.5282 38	3.9270 77	984	5.6007 83	3.9682 50
935	5.5297 17	3.9279 17	985	5.6022 06	3.9690 56
936	5.5311 95	3.9287 57	986	5.6036 27	3.9698 62
937	5.5326 72	3.9295 96	987	5.6050 47	3.9706 67
938	5.5341 47	3.9304 35	988	5.6064 67	3.9714 71
939	5.5356 22	3.9312 72	989	5.6078 85	3.9722 75
940	5.5370 95	3.9321 09	990	5.6093 02	3.9730 78
941	5.5385 67	3.9329 45	991	5.6107 18	3.9738 80
942	5.5400 38	3.9337 81	992	5.6121 33	3.9746 82
943	5.5415 07	3.9346 16	993	5.6135 46	3.9754 83
944	5.5429 76	3.9354 50	994	5.6149 59	3.9762 83
945	5.5444 43	3.9362 83	995	5.6163 71	3.9770 83
946	5.5459 10	3.9371 16	996	5.6177 81	3.9778 82
947	5.5473 75	3.9379 48	997	5.6191 91	3.9786 80
948	5.5488 38	3.9387 79	998	5.6205 99	3.9794 78
949	5.5503 01	3.9396 10	999	5.6220 07	3.9802 75
950	5.5517 63	3.9404 40	1000		

FACTORS AND EXPANSIONS

$(a \pm b)^2 = a^2 \pm 2ab + b^2.$

$(a \pm b)^3 = a^3 \pm 3a^2b + 3ab^2 \pm b^3.$

$(a \pm b)^4 = a^4 \pm 4a^3b + 6a^2b^2 \pm 4ab^3 + b^4.$

$a^2 - b^2 = (a - b)(a + b).$

$a^2 + b^2 = (a + b\sqrt{-1})(a - b\sqrt{-1}).$

$a^3 - b^3 = (a - b)(a^2 + ab + b^2).$

$a^3 + b^3 = (a + b)(a^2 - ab + b^2).$

$a^4 + b^4 = (a^2 + ab\sqrt{2} + b^2)(a^2 - ab\sqrt{2} + b^2).$

$a^n - b^n = (a - b)(a^{n-1} + a^{n-2}b + \ldots + b^{n-1}).$

$a^n - b^n = (a + b)(a^{n-1} - a^{n-2}b + \ldots - b^{n-1}),$
$$\text{for even values of } \textbf{\textit{n}}.$$

$a^n + b^n = (a + b)(a^{n-1} - a^{n-2}b + \ldots + b^{n-1}),$
$$\text{for odd values of } \textbf{\textit{n}}.$$

$a^4 + a^2b^2 + b^4 = (a^2 + ab + b^2)(a^2 - ab + b^2).$

$(a + b + c)^2 = a^2 + b^2 + c^2 + 2ab + 2ac + 2bc.$

$(a + b + c)^3 = a^3 + b^3 + c^3 + 3a^2(b + c) + 3b^2(a + c) +$
$$3c^2(a + b) + 6abc.$$

$(a + b + c + d + \ldots)^2 = a^2 + b^2 + c^2 + d^2 + \ldots +$
$$2a(b + c + d + \ldots) + 2b(c + d + \ldots) + 2c(d + \ldots) + \ldots$$

See also under Series.

POWERS AND ROOTS

$a^x \times a^y = a^{(x+y)}.$ $a^0 = 1 \text{ [if } a \neq 0]$ $(ab)^x = a^x b^x.$

$\dfrac{a^x}{a^y} = a^{(x-y)}.$ $a^{-x} = \dfrac{1}{a^x}.$ $\left(\dfrac{a}{b}\right)^x = \dfrac{a^x}{b^x}.$

$(a^x)^y = a^{xy}.$ $a^{\frac{1}{x}} = \sqrt[x]{a}.$ $\sqrt[x]{ab} = \sqrt[x]{a}\,\sqrt[x]{b}.$

$\sqrt[x]{\sqrt[y]{a}} = \sqrt[xy]{a}.$ $a^{\frac{x}{y}} = \sqrt[y]{a^x}.$ $\sqrt[x]{\dfrac{a}{b}} = \dfrac{\sqrt[x]{a}}{\sqrt[x]{b}}.$

PROPORTION

If $\dfrac{a}{b} = \dfrac{c}{d},$ then $\dfrac{a + b}{b} = \dfrac{c + d}{d},$

$\dfrac{a - b}{b} = \dfrac{c - d}{d},$ $\dfrac{a - b}{a + b} = \dfrac{c - d}{c + d}.$

*ARITHMETIC PROGRESSION

An arithmetic progression is a sequence of numbers such that each number differs from the previous number by a constant amount, called the *common difference*.

If a_1 is the first term; a_n the nth term; d the common difference; n the number of terms; and s_n the sum of n terms—

$$a_n = a_1 + (n - 1)d, \quad s_n = \frac{n}{2}[a_1 + a_n].$$

$$s_n = \frac{n}{2}[2a_1 + (n - 1)d].$$

The arithmetic mean between a and b is given by $\frac{a + b}{2}$.

*GEOMETRIC PROGRESSION

A geometric progression is a sequence of numbers such that each number bears a constant ratio, called the *common ratio*, to the previous number.

If a_1 is the first term; a_n the nth term; r thhe common ratio; n the number of terms; and s_n the sum of n terms

$$a_n = a_1 r^{n-1}; \; s_n = a_1 \frac{1^{\bullet} - r^n}{1 - r}$$

$$= a_1 \frac{r^n - 1}{r - 1}, \quad r \neq 1.$$

$$= \frac{a_1 - ra_n}{1 - r}$$

$$= \frac{ra_n - a_1}{r - 1}$$

If $|r| < 1$, then the sum of an infinite geometrical progression converges to the limiting value

$$\frac{a_1}{1 - r}, \quad \left[s_\infty = \lim_{n \to \infty} \frac{a_1(1 - r^n)}{1 - r} = \frac{a_1}{1 - r} \right]$$

The geometric mean between a and b is given by $\sqrt{ab}$.

*It is customary to represent a_n by l in a finite progression and refer to it as the last term.

HARMONIC PROGRESSION

A sequence of numbers whose reciprocals form an arithmetic progression is called an harmonic progression. Thus

$$\frac{1}{a_1}, \; \frac{1}{a_1 + d}, \; \frac{1}{a_1 + 2d}, \dots, \frac{1}{a_1 + (n - 1)d}, \dots,$$

where

$$\frac{1}{a_n} = \frac{1}{a_1 + (n - 1)d}$$

forms an harmonic progression. The harmonic mean between a and b is given by $\frac{2ab}{a + b}$.

If A, G, H respectively represent the arithmetic mean, geometric mean, and harmonic mean between a and b, then $G^2 = AH$.

FACTORIALS

$$\underline{/n} = n! = e^{-n} n^n \sqrt{2\pi n}, \quad \text{approximately.}$$

PERMUTATIONS

If $M = {}_nP_r = P_{n:r}$ denotes the number of permutations of n distinct things taken r at a time,—

$$M = n(n - 1)(n - 2)\cdots(n - r + 1) = \frac{n!}{(n - r)!}$$

COMBINATIONS

If $M = {}_nC_r = C_{n:r} = \binom{n}{r}$ denotes the number of combinations of n distinct things taken r at a time,—

$$M = \frac{n(n - 1)(n - 2)\cdots(n - r + 1)}{r!} = \frac{n!}{r!(n - r)!}$$

By definition $\binom{n}{0} = 1$

QUADRATIC EQUATIONS

Any quadratic equation may be reduced to the form,—

$$ax^2 + bx + c = 0.$$

Then

$$x = \frac{-b \pm \sqrt{b^2 - 4ac}}{2a}.$$

If a, b, and c are real then:
If $b^2 - 4ac$ is positive, the roots are real and unequal;
If $b^2 - 4ac$ is zero, the roots are real and equal;
If $b^2 - 4ac$ is negative, the roots are imaginary and unequal.

CUBIC EQUATIONS

A cubic equation, $y^3 + py^2 + qy + r = 0$ may be reduced to the form,—

$$x^3 + ax + b = 0$$

by substituting for y the value, $x - \dfrac{p}{3}$. Here

$$a = \tfrac{1}{3}(3q - p^2) \text{ and } b = \tfrac{1}{27}(2p^3 - 9pq + 27r).$$

For solution let,—

$$A = \sqrt[3]{-\frac{b}{2} + \sqrt{\frac{b^2}{4} + \frac{a^3}{27}}}, \qquad B = \sqrt[3]{-\frac{b}{2} - \sqrt{\frac{b^2}{4} + \frac{a^3}{27}}},$$

then the values of x will be given by,

$$x = A + B, \quad -\frac{A + B}{2} + \frac{A - B}{2}\sqrt{-3}, \quad -\frac{A + B}{2} - \frac{A - B}{2}\sqrt{-3}.$$

If p, q, r are real, then:

If $\dfrac{b^2}{4} + \dfrac{a^3}{27} > 0,$ there will be one real root and two conjugate imaginary roots;

If $\dfrac{b^2}{4} + \dfrac{a^3}{27} = 0,$ there will be three real roots of which at least two are equal;

If $\dfrac{b^2}{4} + \dfrac{a^3}{27} < 0,$ there will be three real and unequal roots.

Trignometric Solution of the Cubic Equation

The form $x^3 + ax + b = 0$ with $ab \neq 0$ can always be solved by transforming it to the trignometric identity

$$4 \cos^3 \theta - 3 \cos \theta - \cos(3\theta) \equiv 0.$$

Let $x = m \cos \theta$, then

$$x^3 + ax + b \equiv m^3 \cos^3 \theta + am \cos \theta + b \equiv 4 \cos^3 \theta - 3 \cos \theta - \cos(3\theta) \equiv 0.$$

Hence

$$\frac{4}{m^3} = -\frac{3}{am} = \frac{-\cos(3\theta)}{b},$$

from which follows that

$$m = 2\sqrt{-\frac{a}{3}}, \quad \cos(3\theta) = \frac{3b}{am}.$$

Any solution θ_1 which satisfies $\cos(3\theta) = \dfrac{3b}{am}$, will also have the solutions

$$\theta_1 + \frac{2\pi}{3} \quad \text{and} \quad \theta_1 + \frac{4\pi}{3}.$$

The roots of the cubic $x^3 + ax + b = 0$ are

$$2\sqrt{-\frac{a}{3}} \cos \theta_1, \quad 2\sqrt{-\frac{a}{3}} \cos\left(\theta_1 + \frac{2\pi}{3}\right), \quad 2\sqrt{-\frac{a}{3}} \cos\left(\theta_1 + \frac{4\pi}{3}\right).$$

Example where hyperbolic functions are necessary for solution with latter procedure

The roots of the equation $x^3 - x + 2 = 0$ may be found as follows:

Here

$$a = -1, \quad b = 2, \quad m = 2\sqrt{\tfrac{1}{3}} = 1.155$$

$$\cos(3\theta) = \frac{6}{-1.155} = -5.196$$

$$\cos(3\theta) = -\cos(3\theta - \pi) = -\cosh[i(3\theta - \pi)] = -5.196.$$

Using hyperbolic function tables for cosh $[i(3\theta - \pi)] = 5.196$, it is found that

$$i(3\theta - \pi) = 2.332.$$

Thus

$$3\theta - \pi = -i(2.332).$$
$$3\theta = \pi - i(2.332)$$
$$\theta_1 = \frac{\pi}{3} - i(0.777)$$
$$\theta_1 + \frac{2\pi}{3} = \pi - i(0.777)$$
$$\theta_1 + \frac{4\pi}{3} = \frac{5\pi}{3} - i(0.777)$$

$$\cos\theta_1 = \cos\left[\frac{\pi}{3} - i(0.777)\right]$$
$$= \left(\cos\frac{\pi}{3}\right)[\cos i(0.777)] + \left(\sin\frac{\pi}{3}\right)[\sin i(0.777)]$$
$$= \left(\cos\frac{\pi}{3}\right)(\cosh 0.777) + i\left(\sin\frac{\pi}{3}\right)(\sinh 0.777)$$
$$= (0.5)(1.317) + i(0.866)(0.858) = 0.659 + i(0.743).$$

Note that

$$\cos\mu = \cosh(i\mu) \quad \text{and} \quad \sin\mu = -i\sinh(i\mu).$$

Similarly

$$\cos\left(\theta_1 + \frac{2\pi}{3}\right) = \cos[\pi - i(0.777)]$$
$$= (\cos\pi)(\cosh 0.777) + i(\sin\pi)(\sinh 0.777)$$
$$= -1.317,$$

and

$$\cos\left(\theta_1 + \frac{4\pi}{3}\right) = \cos\left[\frac{5\pi}{3} - i(0.777)\right]$$
$$= \left(\cos\frac{5\pi}{3}\right)(\cosh 0.777) + i\left(\sin\frac{5\pi}{3}\right)(\sinh 0.777)$$
$$= (0.5)(1.317) - i(0.866)(0.858) = 0.659 - i(0.743).$$

The required roots are

$$1.155[0.659 + i(0.743)] = 0.760 + i(0.858)$$
$$(1.155)(-1.317) = -1.520$$
$$(1.155)[0.659 - i(0.743)] = 0.760 - i(0.858).$$

QUARTIC EQUATION

A quartic equation,

$$x^4 + ax^3 + bx^2 + cx + d = 0,$$

has the *resolvent cubic equation*

$$y^3 - by^2 + (ac - 4d)y - a^2d + 4bd - c^2 = 0.$$

Let y be any root of this equation, and

$$R = \sqrt{\frac{a^2}{4} - b + y}.$$

If $R \neq 0$, then let

$$D = \sqrt{\frac{3a^2}{4} - R^2 - 2b + \frac{4ab - 8c - a^3}{4R}}$$

and

$$E = \sqrt{\frac{3a^2}{4} - R^2 - 2b - \frac{4ab - 8c - a^3}{4R}}.$$

If $R = 0$, then let

$$D = \sqrt{\frac{3a^2}{4} - 2b + 2\sqrt{y^2 - 4d}}$$

and

$$E = \sqrt{\frac{3a^2}{4} - 2b - 2\sqrt{y^2 - 4d}}.$$

Then the four roots of the original equation are given by

$$x = -\frac{a}{4} + \frac{R}{2} \pm \frac{D}{2}$$

and

$$x = -\frac{a}{4} - \frac{R}{2} \pm \frac{E}{2}.$$

PARTIAL FRACTIONS

This section applies only to rational algebraic fractions with numerator of lower degree than the denominator. Improper fractions can be reduced to proper fractions by long division.

Every fraction may be expressed as the sum of component fractions whose denominators are factors of the denominator of the original fraction.

Let $N(x)$ = numerator, a polynomial of the form

$$n_0 + n_1x + n_2x^2 + \cdots + n_ix^i$$

I. *Non-repeated Linear Factors*

$$\frac{N(x)}{(x - a)G(x)} = \frac{A}{x - a} + \frac{F(x)}{G(x)}$$

$$A = \left[\frac{N(x)}{G(x)}\right]_{x = a}$$

$F(x)$ determined by methods discussed in the following sections.

Example:

$$\frac{x^2 + 3}{x(x - 2)(x^2 + 2x + 4)} = \frac{A}{x} + \frac{B}{x - 2} + \frac{F(x)}{x^2 + 2x + 4}$$

$$A = \left[\frac{x^2 + 3}{(x - 2)(x^2 + 2x + 4)}\right]_{x=0} = -\frac{3}{8}$$

$$B = \left[\frac{x^2 + 3}{x(x^2 + 2x + 4)}\right]_{x=2} = \frac{4 + 3}{2(4 + 4 + 4)} = \frac{7}{24}$$

II. *Repeated Linear Factors*

$$\frac{N(x)}{x^m G(x)} = \frac{A_0}{x^m} + \frac{A_1}{x^{m-1}} + \cdots + \frac{A_{m-1}}{x} + \frac{F(x)}{G(x)}$$

$$F(x) = f_0 + f_1 x + f_2 x^2 + \cdots, \quad G(x) = g_0 + g_1 x + g_2 x^2 + \cdots$$

$$A_0 = \frac{n_0}{g_0}, \quad A_1 = \frac{n_1 - A_0 g_1}{g_0}, \quad A_2 = \frac{n_2 - A_0 g_2 - A_1 g_1}{g_0}$$

General term:

$$A_k = \frac{1}{g_0}\left[n_k - \sum_{i=0}^{k-1} A_i g_{k-i}\right]$$

$$*m = 1 \begin{cases} f_0 = n_1 - A_0 g_1 \\ f_1 = n_2 - A_0 g_2 \\ f_j = n_{j+1} - A_0 g_{j+1} \end{cases}$$

$$m = 2 \begin{cases} f_0 = n_2 - A_0 g_2 - A_1 g_1 \\ f_1 = n_3 - A_0 g_3 - A_1 g_2 \\ f_j = n_{j+2} - [A_0 g_{j+2} + A_1 g_{j+1}] \end{cases}$$

$$m = 3 \begin{cases} f_0 = n_3 - A_0 g_3 - A_1 g_2 - A_2 g_1 \\ f_1 = n_3 - A_0 g_4 - A_1 g_3 - A_2 g_2 \\ f_j = n_{j+3} - [A_0 g_{j+3} + A_1 g_{j+2} + A_2 g_{j+1}] \end{cases}$$

$$\text{any } m: \ f_j = n_{m+j} - \sum_{i=0}^{m-1} A_i g_{m+j-i}$$

Example:

$$\frac{x^2 + 1}{x^3(x^2 - 3x + 6)} = \frac{A_0}{x^3} + \frac{A_1}{x^2} + \frac{A_2}{x} + \frac{f_1 x + f_0}{x^2 - 3x + 6}$$

$$A_0 = \frac{1}{6}, \quad A_1 = \frac{0 - (\frac{1}{6})(-3)}{6} = \frac{1}{12},$$

$$A_2 = \frac{1 - (\frac{1}{6})(1) - (\frac{1}{12})(-3)}{6} = \frac{13}{72},$$

$$m = 3 \begin{cases} f_0 = 0 - \frac{1}{6}(0) + \frac{1}{12}(1) - \frac{13}{72}(-3) = \frac{11}{24} \\ f_1 = 0 - \frac{1}{6}(0) - \frac{1}{12}(0) - \frac{13}{72}(1) = -\frac{13}{72} \end{cases}$$

*Note: If $G(x)$ contains linear factors, $F(x)$ may be determined by previous section I.

III. *Repeated Linear Factors*

$$\frac{N(x)}{(x-a)^m G(x)} = \frac{A_0}{(x-a)^m} + \frac{A_1}{(x-a)^{m-1}} + \cdots + \frac{A_{m-1}}{(x-a)} + \frac{F(x)}{G(x)}$$

Change to form $\dfrac{N'(y)}{y^m G'(y)}$ by substitution of $x = y + a$. Resolve into partial fractions in terms of y as described in Section II. Then express in terms of x by substitution $y = x - a$.

Example:

$$\frac{x-3}{(x-2)^2(x^2+x+1)}.$$

Let $x - 2 = y$, $\quad x = y + 2$

$$\frac{(y+2)-3}{y^2[(y+2)^2+(y+2)+1]} = \frac{y-1}{y^2(y^2+5y+7)} = \frac{A_0}{y^2} + \frac{A_1}{y} + \frac{f_1 y + f_0}{y^2+5y+7}$$

$$A_0 = -\frac{1}{7}, \quad A_1 = \frac{1-(-\frac{1}{7})(5)}{7} = \frac{12}{49},$$

$$m = 2 \begin{cases} f_0 = 0 - (-\frac{1}{7})(1) - (\frac{12}{49})(5) = -\frac{53}{49} \\ f_1 = 0 - (-\frac{1}{7})(0) - (\frac{12}{49})(1) = -\frac{12}{49} \end{cases}$$

$$\therefore \frac{y-1}{y^2(y^2+5y+7)} = \frac{-\frac{1}{7}}{y^2} + \frac{\frac{12}{49}}{y} + \frac{-\frac{12}{49}y - \frac{53}{49}}{y^2+5y+7}$$

Let $y = x - 2$, then

$$\frac{x-3}{(x-2)^2(x^2+x+1)} = \frac{-\frac{1}{7}}{(x-2)^2} + \frac{\frac{12}{35}}{(x-2)} + \frac{-\frac{12}{49}(x-2) - \frac{53}{49}}{x^2+x+1}$$

$$= -\frac{1}{7(x-2)^2} + \frac{12}{35(x-2)} + \frac{-12x-29}{49(x^2+x+1)}$$

IV. *Repeated Linear Factors*

Alternative method of determining coefficients:

$$\frac{N(x)}{(x-a)^m G(x)} = \frac{A_0}{(x-a)^m} + \cdots + \frac{A_k}{(x-a)^{m-k}} + \cdots + \frac{A_{m-1}}{x-a} + \frac{F(x)}{G(x)}$$

$$A_k = \frac{1}{k!}\left\{D_x^k\left[\frac{N(x)}{G(x)}\right]\right\}_{x=a}$$

where D_x^k is the differentiating operator, and the derivative of zero order is defined as:

$$D_x^0 u = u.$$

V. *Factors of Higher Degree*

Factors of higher degree have the corresponding numerators indicated.

$$\frac{N(x)}{(x^2+h_1x+h_0)G(x)} = \frac{a_1x+a_0}{x^2+h_1x+h_0} + \frac{F(x)}{G(x)}$$

$$\frac{N(x)}{(x^2 + h_1 x + h_0)^2 G(x)} = \frac{a_1 x + a_0}{(x^2 + h_1 x + h_0)^2} + \frac{b_1 x + b_0}{(x^2 + h_1 x + h_0)} + \frac{F(x)}{G(x)}$$

$$\frac{N(x)}{(x^3 + h_2 x^2 + h_1 x + h_0) G(x)} = \frac{a_2 x^2 + a_1 x + a_0}{x^3 + h_2 x^2 + h_1 x + h_0} + \frac{F(x)}{G(x)}$$

etc.

Problems of this type are determined first by solving for the coefficients due to linear factors as shown above, and then determining the remaining coefficients by the general methods given below.

VI. *General Methods for Evaluating Coefficients*

1.
$$\frac{N(x)}{D(x)} = \frac{N(x)}{G(x) H(x) L(x)} = \frac{A(x)}{G(x)} + \frac{B(x)}{H(x)} + \frac{C(x)}{L(x)} + \cdots$$

Multiply both sides of equation by $D(x)$ to clear fractions. Then collect terms, equate like powers of x, and solve the resulting simultaneous equations for the unknown coefficients.

2. Clear fractions as above. Then let x assume certain convenient values ($x = 1, 0, -1, \ldots$). Solve the resulting equations for the unknown coefficients.

3.
$$\frac{N(x)}{G(x) H(x)} = \frac{A(x)}{G(x)} + \frac{B(x)}{H(x)}$$

Then

$$\frac{N(x)}{G(x) H(x)} - \frac{A(x)}{G(x)} = \frac{B(x)}{H(x)}$$

If $A(x)$ can be determined, such as by Method I, then $B(x)$ can be found as above.

BASIC CONCEPTS IN ALGEBRA

Dr. W. E. Deskins

I. ALGEBRA OF SETS

1. Intuitively a set is a collection of objects called the elements of the set. Set and set membership are generally accepted as basic, undefined terms used to define and construct mathematical systems.

   The notation $a \in A$ indicates that a is an element of the set A. The notation $a \notin A$ means that a is not a member of A.

   A set is sometimes specified by listing its elements within a set of braces: $\{a\}$ is the set containing only the element a.

2. Set A is a subset of set B provided $a \in A$ implies $a \in B$. This is denoted by $A \subseteq B$. Every set has as a subset the empty or null set, denoted by ϕ, which has no elements.

3. Set A equals set B, written $A = B$, if and only if $A \subseteq B$ and $B \subseteq A$. A is a proper subset of B, sometimes indicated by $A \subset B$, if and only if $A \subseteq B$ and $A \neq B$; then B has at least one element which does not belong to A.

4. The Cartesian product of sets A and B, denoted by $A \times B$, is the set of all ordered pairs (a, b) where $a \in A$ and $b \in B$. A subset R of $A \times A$ is a binary relation on A, and this is an equivalence relation on A provided (i) $(a, a) \in R$ for every $a \in A$, (ii) $(a, b) \in R$ implies $(b, a) \in R$, and (iii) $(a, b) \in R$ and $(b, c) \in R$ imply $(a, c) \in R$. Ordinary equality of numbers, equality of sets, and congruence of plane figures are examples of equivalence relations.

5. A subset F of $A \times B$ is a *function* from A to B provided each element of A appears exactly once as the first element of a pair in F. A function F from A to B is *onto* provided each element of B appears at least once as the second element of a pair in F. It is *one-to-one* provided each element of B appears at most once as the second element of a pair in F. A function from $A \times A$ to A is a *binary operation* on A. Addition and multiplication of ordinary numbers are examples of binary operations.

6. If consideration is restricted to elements and subsets of a particular set I, then I is the universal set.

7. Common binary operations on subsets of I are: $A \cup B$, the union or join of sets A and B, is the set of all elements of I which belong to either A or B or both A and B.

   $A \cap B$, the intersection or meet of sets A and B, is the set of all elements of I which belong to both A and B.

   $A \setminus B$, the difference of sets A and B, is the set of elements of I which belong to A but not B.

   The difference $I \setminus A$ is denoted by A' and called the complement of A (relative to I). Except in dealing with the concept of complementation the use of a universal set is not essential to the above ideas.

8. Some theorems basic to the Algebra of Sets:

   Let A, B, and C be arbitrary subsets of a universal set I.

   (a) (Commutativity) $A \cup B = B \cup A$ and $A \cap B = B \cap A$.

   (b) (Associativity) $(A \cup B) \cup C = A \cup (B \cup C)$ and
   $(A \cap B) \cap C = A \cap (B \cap C)$.

(c) (Distributivity) $A \cap (B \cup C) = (A \cap B) \cup (A \cap C)$ and
$$A \cup (B \cap C) = (A \cup B) \cap (A \cup C).$$

(d) (Idempotency) $A \cup A = A \cap A = A$.

(e) Properties of I and ϕ: $A \cap I = A \cup \phi = A$,
$$A \cup I = I, \text{ and}$$
$$A \cap \phi = \phi.$$

(f) $(A \cap B) \cup (A \backslash B) = A$.

(g) $(A \backslash B) \cup B = A \cup B$.

(h) $A \supseteq A \cup B$.

(i) $A \cap B \subseteq A$.

(j) $A \cup B = A$ if and only if $B \supseteq A$.

(k) $A \cap B = A$ if and only if $A \subseteq B$.

(m) $A \backslash B = A \backslash (A \cap B)$.

(n) (DeMorgan's Theorem) $(A \backslash B) \cap (A \backslash C) = A \backslash (B \cup C)$ and
$$(A \backslash B) \cup (A \backslash C) = A \backslash (B \cap C).$$

(o) $(A \cup B)' = A' \cap B'$ and $(A \cap B)' = A' \cup B'$.

(p) $A \cup A' = I$ and $A \cap A' = \phi$.

9. A mathematical system S is a set $S = \{E, 0, A\}$ where E is a nonempty set of elements, 0 is a set of relations and operations on E, and A is a set of axioms, postulates, or assumptions concerning the elements of E and 0.

10. The Algebra of Sets provides an example of a mathematical system called a Boolean Algebra (or Boolean Ring) which is defined as:

Set E of elements $a, b, c, \ldots$;

Set 0 of 2 binary operations $\oplus$ and $\otimes$; (Here $a \oplus b$ denotes the image of (a, b) under the binary operation.)

Set A of axioms for all a, b, c of E:

A_1.   The binary operations are commutative; i.e.,

$$a \oplus b = b \oplus a \quad \text{and} \quad a \otimes b = b \otimes a.$$

A_2.   Each binary operation is distributive over the other; i.e.,

$$a \oplus (b \otimes c) = (a \oplus b) \otimes (a \oplus c) \quad \text{and} \quad a \otimes (b \oplus c) = (a \otimes b) + (a \otimes c).$$

A_3.   There exist elements e and z in E such that for each $a \in E$, $a \oplus z = a$ and $a \otimes e = a$.

A_4.   For each $a \in E$ there exists an element $a' \in E$ such that $a + a' = e$ and $a \times a' = z$.

    In the algebra of subsets of a (universal) set I, ϕ plays the role of z, I that of e, $\cup$ that of $\oplus$, and $\cap$ that of $\otimes$.

11. A Boolean Algebra has the Principle of Duality: If the interchanges of $\begin{Bmatrix} \oplus \text{ and } \otimes \\ e \text{ and } z \end{Bmatrix}$ are made in a correct statement, then the result is also a correct statement.

12. In addition to the Algrebra of Sets which is a Boolean Algebra, other representations of Boolean Algebra that are interesting of themselves and valuable for their applications are:

   (a) The Algebra of Symbolic Logic

   (b) The Algebra of Switching Currents

Algebra of Sets	Binary Operator	Symbolic Logic	Binary Operator	Switching Circuits	Binary Operator
Union of 2 sets	$\cup$	Disjunction of 2 propositions	$\vee$	2 switches in $\parallel$	$+$
Intersection of 2 sets	$\cap$	Conjunction of 2 propositions	$\wedge$	2 switches in series	$\times$
Complement of a set $A = \{a, b, c, \ldots\}$	$'$	Negation of a proposition T, F	$\sim$	on-off, or 1, 0	$'$

Both in symbolic logic and in switching circuits, we can consider "0" and "1" as the elements, in the former representing "False" and "True"; in the latter, "Off" and "On", satisfying the following "rules":

$$\left. \begin{array}{l} 0 + 0 = 0 \\ 1 + 1 = 1 \end{array} \right\} \text{ i.e. } a + a = a$$

$$\left. \begin{array}{l} 0 \times 0 = 0 \\ 1 \times 1 = 1 \end{array} \right\} \text{ i.e. } a \times a = a$$

$$0' = 1$$

$$1' = 0$$

$$\left. \begin{array}{l} 0 + 0' = 0 + 1 = 1 \\ 1 + 1' = 1 + 0 = 1 \end{array} \right\} \text{ i.e. } a + a' = 1$$

$$\left. \begin{array}{l} 0 \times 0' = 0 \times 1 = 0 \\ 1 \times 1' = 1 \times 0 = 0 \end{array} \right\} a \times a' = 0$$

Thus, 1 and 0 serve as U and Z.

In switching circuits:

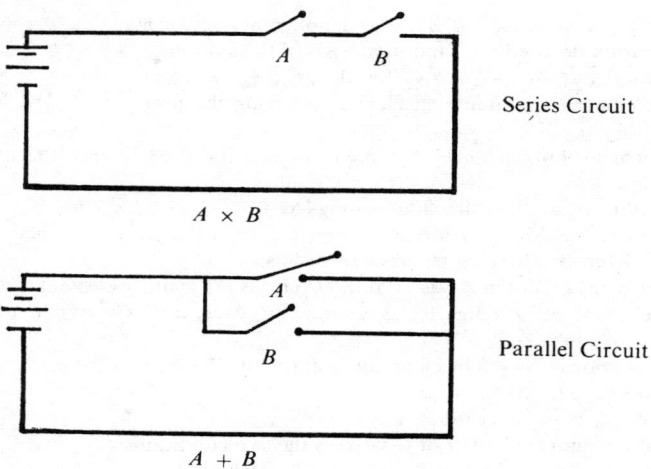

Series Circuit

$A \times B$

Parallel Circuit

$A + B$

here, "0" represents an open circuit: and "1"

$A = 0$

a closed circuit:

$A = 1$

In the Algebra of Symbolic Logic, we use *Truth Tables* to define the operations $\wedge$, $\vee$, $\sim$ as follows:

Other Operators Used

p	q	$p \wedge q$	$p \vee q$	$\sim p$	$*p \rightarrow q$	$p \leftrightarrow q*$
T	T	T	T	F	T	T
T	F	F	T	F	F	F
F	T	F	T	T	T	F
F	F	F	F	T	T	T

13. Two sets A and B are equivalent (have same cardinal) if and only if there exists a one-to-one correspondence between the elements of the two sets. This is an equivalence relation on the collection of subsets of set I.

A set is infinite if and only if it is equivalent with a proper subset of itself.

A set is called countably (denumerably) infinite if it is equivalent with the set of all positive integers. The set of all rational numbers is countably infinite but the set of all real numbers is noncountably infinite. The cardinal of the set of all rational numbers is denoted by (aleph null); the cardinal of the set of reals is denoted by (aleph).

II. ABSTRACT ALGEBRAIC SYSTEMS

1. *Semigroup.* A semigroup is a system $\{S, 0, A\}$; S is a nonempty set $\{a, b, c, \ldots\}$, θ consists of one binary operation on S, denoted by $*$, and A consists of the axiom

A_1. Associativity: $a * (b * c) = (a * b) * c$ for all $a, b \circ c \in S$.

Basic Theorem. (*Generalized Associativity*). If $a_1, a_2, \ldots, a_n$ are elements of S then all associations of the n elements yield the same "product". (For example,

$$a * ((b * c) * d) = a * (b * (c * d)) = (a * b) * (c * d), \text{etc.})$$

2. *Group.* A group is a system $\{G, 0, A\}$; G is a nonempty set $\{a, b, c, \ldots\}$, θ consists of one binary operation denoted by $\circ$, and A consists of the axioms:

A_1. Associativity: $a \circ (b \circ c) = (a \circ b) \circ c$ for all $a, b, c \in G$.

A_2. Identity Element: G contains an element e having the property, $a \circ e = e \circ a = a$ for every $a \in G$.

A_3. Inverse Element: For each $a \in G$ there is an element $a' \in G$ with the property, $a \circ a' = a' \circ a = e$.

If the following additional axiom belongs to A,

A_4. Commutativity: $a \circ b = b \circ a$ for all $a, b \in G$. Then the group is called Abelian (after Niels Henrik Abel). Some basic theorems:

(a) The element e (Axiom A_2) is unique. Then e is *the* identity element of G.

(b) The element a' (Axiom A_3) is unique for each $a \in G$. Then a' is *the* inverse of a in G.

(c) The equation $a \circ x = b$ has a unique solution in G, viz., $x = a' \circ b$.

(d) $(a')' = a$ and $(a \circ b)' = b' \circ a'$.

(e) $a \circ b = a \circ c$ if and only if $b = c$.

If a nonempty subset H of G satisfies the two conditions:

H_1. $a \circ b \in H$ whenever $a, b \in H$. (Closure)

H_2. $a \in H$ if and only if $a' \in H$.

then H is a *subgroup* of G.

(Lagrange). If G is a finite set then the number of elements in H divides the number of elements in G.

Example of group. Let G be the set of all one-to-one functions from a nonempty S onto itself. For any $f, g \in G$, define the function $f \circ g$ as the function which maps s onto $f(g(s))$, for each $s \in S$. Relative to this binary operation G is a group, the *symmetric group* of all permutations on S.

Each group is essentially a subgroup of the symmetric group of some set S.

3. *Ring.* A ring is a system $\{R, \theta, A\}$; R is a nonempty set $\{a, b, c, \ldots\}$, θ consists of two binary operations denoted by $+$ and $\times$, and A consists of the axioms:

A_0. Relative to addition (i.e., $+$) R is an Abelian group in which the identity element is denoted by z and the inverse of a is denoted by $-a$.

M_0. Relative to multiplication (i.e., $\times$) R is a semigroup.

D_1. Left distributive: $a \times (b + c) = (a \times b) + (a \times c)$, all $a, b, c \in R$.

D_2. Right distributive: $(b + c)a = (b \times a) + (c \times a)$, all $a, b, c \in R$.

EXAMPLE 1. The set of all integers (whole numbers) and ordinary addition and multiplication.

EXAMPLE 2. The set of all real functions continuous on the interval $0 \leq y \leq 1$, with addition and multiplication defined by $(f + g)(y) = f(y) + g(y)$, sum of real numbers, and $(f \times g)(y) = f(y) \times g(y)$, product of real numbers.

Special types of rings have been studied extensively.

3.1 *Integral Domain.* An integral domain is a ring R in which multiplication ($\times$) satisfies the additional assumptions:

M_1. Commutativity: $a \times b = b \times a$ for all a and b in R.

M_2. Multiplicative identity: R contains an element $e \neq z$ with the property $a \times e = e \times a = a$ for all a in R.

M_3. Cancellation: $a \times b = a \times c$ if and only if $b = c$.

An element u of integral domain R is a *unit* provided R contains v such that $u \times v = e$.

An element p of integral domain R is a *prime* (irreducible element) provided $p = a \times b$ implies that exactly one of the elements a or b is a unit.

The elements of integral domain R which differ from z and are neither units nor primes are *composites*.

In some integral domains (such as the ring of integers) each composite can be factored uniquely (up to unit factors) as the product of a finite set of primes. However in the integral domain of all entire functions this is not true.

3.2 *Field.* A field is an integral domain in which every element except z is a unit. In other words, the non-z elements form an Abelian group relative to multiplication ($\times$).

EXAMPLE 1. The rational field consisting of ordinary fractions, addition, and multiplication.

EXAMPLE 2. The set of all real numbers $a + b\sqrt{2}$, a and b rational. Then

$$(a + b\sqrt{2}) + (c + d\sqrt{2}) = (a + c) + (b + d)\sqrt{2} \text{ and}$$
$$(a + b\sqrt{2}) \times (c + d\sqrt{2}) = (ac + 2bd) + (ad + bc)\sqrt{2}.$$

Besides these well-known examples there exist finite fields (sometimes called Galois fields).

EXAMPLE 3. Let p be a prime integer. Denote by $GF(p)$ the p integers $0, 1, \ldots,$ $p - 1$. Define addition($\oplus$) of two of these elements a and b as the remainder of $a + b$ (ordinary addition) after division by p. (Thus $1 \oplus (p - 1) = 0$.)

Define $a \otimes b$, the product, to be the remainder of ab (ordinary multiplication) after division by p. (Thus, when $p = 3$, $2 \otimes 2 = 1$.) The resulting system $\{GF(p), \oplus, \otimes\}$ is the (modular) field of integers modulo p.

3.3 *Skew Field or Division Ring.* A skew field is a ring in which the non-z elements form a group relative to multiplication ($\times$).

The classical example of a skew field is the ring of real *quaternions*, first described by W. R. Hamilton. A quaternion is expressible in the form $ae + bi + cj + dk$ where $a, b, c,$ and d are real numbers and $e, i, j,$ and k are elements which commute with all real numbers and multiply as follows:

$$e \times e = e, \quad e \times i = i \times e = i, \quad e \times j = j \times e = j, \quad e \times k = k \times e = k;$$
$$i \times i = -e, \quad i \times j = k, \quad j \times i = -k, \quad i \times k = -j, \quad k \times i = j,$$
$$j \times j = -e, \quad j \times k = i, \quad k \times j = -i, \quad k \times k = -e.$$

These elements distribute over addition. e is generally identified with and written as the real number 1.

3.4 *Matric Ring.* The matric ring $M_n(R)$ over the ring R, where n is a positive integer, consists of all doubly-ordered sets of n^2 elements of R, written as an array

$$\begin{pmatrix} a_{1,1} & a_{1,2} \cdots a_{1,n} \\ a_{2,1} & a_{2,2} \cdots a_{2,n} \\ \vdots \\ a_{n,1} & \cdots \quad a_{n,n} \end{pmatrix} = (a_{i,j})$$

with addition and multiplication defined as follows:

$$(a_{i,j}) + (b_{i,j}) = (a_{i,j} + b_{i,j})$$
$$(a_{i,j}) \times (b_{i,j}) = (c_{i,j})$$

where

$$c_{i,j} = \sum_{k=1}^{n} a_{i,k}\, b_{k,j}, \quad i = 1, \ldots, n \quad \text{and} \quad j = 1, \ldots, n.$$

If $n > 1$, then multiplication is noncommutative in general; i.e., $(a_{i,j}) \times (b_{i,j})$ can differ from $(b_{i,j}) \times (a_{i,j})$. Moreover, the product of two nonzero matrices can be the zero matrix (which consists of only the element z in all n^2 positions).

A similar useful method for forming a new ring from a known ring utilizes sequences.

3.5 *Power Series and Polynomial Ring.* Let R be a ring in which multiplication ($\times$) is commutative. The set $PS(R)$ of all sequences $(a_0, a_1, \ldots)$ with $a_i \in R$ is the power series ring of R, with addition and multiplication defined as

$$(a_0, a_1, \ldots) \oplus (b_0, b_1, \ldots) = (a_0 + b_0, \quad a_1 + b_1, \ldots) \text{ and}$$
$$(a_0, a_1, \ldots) \oplus (b_0, b_1, \ldots) = (c_0, c_1, \ldots)$$

where

$$c_0 = a_0 \times b_0, \quad c_1 = a_0 \times b_1 + a_1 \times b_0, \ldots, \text{ and,}$$

generally,

$$c_n = a_0 \times b_n + a_1 \times b_{n-1} + \cdots + a_n \times b_0.$$

The subset $P(R)$ of $PS(R)$ consisting of those sequences $(a_0, a_1, \ldots)$ in which at most only finitely many of the a_i differ from z, form a ring relative to the addition and multiplication just defined. This ring $\{P(R), \oplus, \otimes\}$, is the polynomial ring of R.

Some theorems for rings, fields, etc.

(a) In a ring R, if $a = b$ and $c = d$, then $a + c = b + d$ and $a \times c = b \times d$.

(b) In a ring R, $-(-a) = a$; $(-a) \times b = a \times (-b) = -(a \times b)$; and $(-a) \times (-b) = a \times b$, for all $a,b \in R$.

(c) In a ring R, $a \times z = z \times a = z$, for all $a \in R$.

(d) In a ring R the equation $a + x = b$ has a unique solution, viz., $x = -a + b$.

(f) In a field, skew field, or integral domain, $a \times b = z$ if and only if a and/or b equals z.

(g) A finite integral domain is a field.

(h) The polynomial ring of an integral domain is also an integral domain.

(i) The power series ring of an integral domain is also an integral domain.

(j) A ring is a field provided it is both an integral domain and a skew field.

(k) If R is a (skew) field, then the equation $a \times y = b$, $a \neq z$, has a unique solution $y = a' \times b$.

(l) The polynomial ring and the power series ring of a field are unique factorization domains.

4. *Vector Space.* A vector space $V(F)$ over a field F consists of a nonempty set V (the vectors), a binary operation ($\oplus$) on V, a function (called *scalar multiplication*) from the product set $F \times V$ onto V with the image of (a,ν) denoted by $a \circ \nu$, and the following axioms:

A_0. Relative to addition ($\oplus$) V is an Abelian group in which the identity element (vector) is denoted by z and the inverse of ν is denoted by $-\nu$.

M_1. $a \circ (b \circ \nu) = (ab) \circ \nu$ for all $a,b \in F$ and $\nu \in F$. (Here ab denotes the product of a and b in F.)

M_2. $1 \circ \nu = \nu$ for all $\nu \in V$. (Here 1 denotes the multiplicative indentity element of F.)

D_1. $a \circ (\mu \oplus \nu) = (a \circ \mu) \oplus (a \circ \nu)$ for all $a \in F$, $\mu, \nu \in V$.

D_2. $(a + b) \circ \nu \doteq (a \circ \nu) \oplus (b \circ \nu)$ for all $a,b \in F$, $\nu \in V$. (Here $+$ denotes addition in the field F.)

The elements of F are referred to as *scalars*.

EXAMPLE 1. The polynomial ring $P(F)$ of a field F is a vector space over F. In this example scalar multiplication is a special case of the multiplication defined for $P(F)$.

EXAMPLE 2. Denote by $C_n(F)$ the set of all n-tuples, $(a_1, a_2, \ldots, a_n)$, n a positive integer, with all $a_i \in F$. Define

$$(a_1, \ldots, a_n) \oplus (b_1, \ldots, b_n) = (a_1 + b_1, \ldots, a_n + b_n) \quad \text{and}$$
$$c \circ (a_1, \ldots, a_n) = (c \times a_1, \ldots, c \times a_n),$$

where $+$ and $\times$ denote the addition and multiplication, respectively, of the field F. Relative to $\oplus$ and $\circ$, $C_n(F)$ is a vector space, called the *n-dimensional coordinate space* over F.

A vector space $V(F)$ is *n-dimensional* over F provided V contains n elements ν_1, ν_2, $\ldots, \nu_n$ such that each element $\nu \in V$ is uniquely expressible in the form

$$\nu = a_1 \circ \nu_1 \oplus a_2 \circ \nu_2 \oplus \cdots \oplus a_n \circ \nu_n$$

for some $a_1, a_2, \ldots, a_n \in F$.

Two vector spaces $V(F)$ and $W(F)$ over the field of scalars F are *isomorphic* provided there is a one-to-one correspondence between the elements of V and the elements of W which is preserved under the arithmetic of the two spaces.

Basic Theorem. An n-dimensional vector space $V(F)$ is isomorphic with the coordinate space $C_n(F)$ (of Example 2, above).

MATRICES AND DETERMINANTS

Dr. R. E. Bargmann

1. GENERAL DEFINITIONS

1.1. A matrix is an array of numbers, consisting of m rows and n columns. It is usually denoted by a bold-face capital letter, e.g.,

$$\mathbf{A} \qquad \mathbf{\Sigma} \qquad \mathbf{M}$$

1.2. The (i, j) element of a matrix is the element occurring in row i and column j. It is usually denoted by a lower-case letter with subscripts, e.g.,

$$a_{ij} \qquad \sigma_{ij} \qquad m_{ij}$$

Exceptions to this convention will be stated where required.

1.3. A matrix is called rectangular if m (number of rows) $\neq n$ (number of columns).

1.4. A matrix is called square if $m = n$.

1.5a. In the transpose of a matrix $\mathbf{A}$, denoted by $\mathbf{A}'$, the element in the j'th row and i'th column of $\mathbf{A}$ is equal to the element in the i'th row and j'th column of $\mathbf{A}'$. Formally $(\mathbf{A}')_{ij} = (\mathbf{A})_{ji}$ where the symbol $(\mathbf{A}')_{ij}$ denotes the (i, j) element of $\mathbf{A}'$.

1.5b. The Hermitian conjugate of a matrix $\mathbf{A}$, denoted by $\mathbf{A}^H$ or $\mathbf{A}^\dagger$ is obtained by transposing $\mathbf{A}$ and replacing each element by its conjugate complex. Hence if

$$a_{kl} = u_{kl} + iv_{kl}$$

then

$$(\mathbf{A}^H)_{kl} = u_{lk} - iv_{lk}$$

where typical elements have been denoted by (k, l) to avoid confusion with $i = \sqrt{-1}$.

1.6a. A square matrix is called symmetric if $\mathbf{A} = \mathbf{A}'$.

1.6b. A square matrix is called Hermitian if $\mathbf{A} = \mathbf{A}^H$.

1.7. A matrix with m rows and 1 column is called a column vector and is usually denoted by bold faced, lower-case letters, e.g.,

$$\boldsymbol{\beta} \qquad \mathbf{x} \qquad \mathbf{a}$$

1.8. A matrix with one row and n columns is called a row vector and is usually denoted by a primed, bold faced, lower-case letter, e.g.,

$$\mathbf{a}' \qquad \mathbf{c}' \qquad \boldsymbol{\mu}'$$

1.9. A matrix with one row and one column is called a scalar, and is usually denoted by a lower-case letter, occasionally italicized.

1.10. The diagonal extending from upper left (NW) to lower right (SE) is called the principal diagonal of a square matrix.

1.11a. A matrix with all elements above the principal diagonal equal to zero is called a lower triangular matrix.

Example

$$\mathbf{T} = \begin{bmatrix} t_{11} & 0 & 0 \\ t_{21} & t_{22} & 0 \\ t_{31} & t_{32} & t_{33} \end{bmatrix} \text{ is lower triangular}$$

1.11b. The transpose of a lower triangular matrix is called an upper triangular matrix.

1.12. A square matrix with all off-diagonal elements equal to zero is called a diagonal matrix, denoted by the letter **D** with subscript indicating the typical element in the principal diagonal.

Example

$$\mathbf{D}_a = \begin{bmatrix} a_1 & 0 & 0 \\ 0 & a_2 & 0 \\ 0 & 0 & a_3 \end{bmatrix} \text{ is diagonal}$$

2. ADDITION, SUBTRACTION, AND MULTIPLICATION

2.1. Two matrices **A** and **B** can be added (subtracted) if the number of rows (columns) in **A** equals the number of rows (columns) in **B**.

$$\mathbf{A} \pm \mathbf{B} = \mathbf{C}$$

implies

$$a_{ij} \pm b_{ij} = c_{ij} \quad \begin{aligned} i &= 1, 2, \ldots m \\ j &= 1, 2, \ldots n \end{aligned}$$

2.2. Multiplication of a matrix or vector by a scalar implies multiplication of each element by the scalar. If

$$\mathbf{B} = \gamma \mathbf{A}$$

then

$$b_{ij} = \gamma a_{ij}$$

for all elements.

2.3a. Two matrices, **A** and **B**, can be multiplied if the number of columns in **A** equals the number of rows in **B**.

2.3b. Let **A** be of order $(m \times n)$ (have m rows and n columns) and **B** of order $(n \times p)$. Then the product of two matrices $\mathbf{C} = \mathbf{AB}$, is a matrix of order $(m \times p)$ with elements

$$c_{ij} = \sum_{k=1}^{n} a_{ik} b_{kj}$$

This states that c_{ij} is the scalar product of the i'th row vector of **A** and the j'th column vector of **B**.

Example

$$\begin{bmatrix} 3 & 4 & 2 \\ 2 & 3 & -1 \end{bmatrix} \begin{bmatrix} 1 & -2 & -4 \\ 0 & -1 & 2 \\ 6 & -3 & 9 \end{bmatrix} = \begin{bmatrix} 15 & -16 & 14 \\ -4 & -4 & -11 \end{bmatrix}$$

e.g.,

$$c_{23} = \begin{bmatrix} 2 & 3 & -1 \end{bmatrix} \begin{bmatrix} -4 \\ 2 \\ 9 \end{bmatrix}$$

$$= 2 \times (-4) + 3 \times 2 + (-1) \times 9 = -11$$

2.3c. In general, matrix multiplication is not commutative

$$\mathbf{AB} \neq \mathbf{BA}$$

2.3d. Matrix multiplication is associative

$$\mathbf{A(BC)} = \mathbf{(AB)C}$$

2.3e. The distributive law for multiplication and addition holds as in the case of scalars,

$$\mathbf{(A + B)C} = \mathbf{AC} + \mathbf{BC}$$
$$\mathbf{C(A + B)} = \mathbf{CA} + \mathbf{CB}$$

2.4. In some applications, the term-by-term product of two matrices $\mathbf{A}$ and $\mathbf{B}$ of identical order is defined as

$$\mathbf{C} = \mathbf{A} * \mathbf{B}$$

where

$$c_{ij} = a_{ij}b_{ij}$$

2.5. $(\mathbf{ABC})' = \mathbf{C'B'A'}$
2.6. $(\mathbf{ABC})^H = \mathbf{C}^H\mathbf{B}^H\mathbf{A}^H$
2.7. If both $\mathbf{A}$ and $\mathbf{B}$ are symmetric, then $(\mathbf{AB})' = \mathbf{BA}$. Note that the product of two symmetric matrices is generally not symmetric.

3. RECOGNITION RULES AND SPECIAL FORMS

3.1. A column (row) vector with all elements equal to zero is called a null vector, and usually denoted by the symbol $\mathbf{0}$.

3.2. A null matrix has all elements equal to zero.

3.3a. A diagonal matrix with all elements equal to one in the principal diagonal is called the identity matrix $\mathbf{I}$.

3.3b. $\gamma\mathbf{I}$, i.e., a diagonal matrix with all diagonal elements equal to a constant γ, is called a scalar matrix.

3.4. A matrix which has only one element equal to one and all others equal to zero is called an elementary matrix $(\mathbf{EL})_{ij}$.

Example

$$(\mathbf{EL})_{23} = \begin{bmatrix} 0 & 0 & 0 & 0 & 0 \\ 0 & 0 & 1 & 0 & 0 \\ 0 & 0 & 0 & 0 & 0 \\ 0 & 0 & 0 & 0 & 0 \end{bmatrix}$$

The order of the matrix is usually implicit.

3.5a. The symbol $\mathbf{j}$ is reserved for a column vector with all elements equal to 1.

3.5b. The symbol $\mathbf{j}'$ is reserved for a row vector with all elements equal to 1.

3.6. An expression ending with a column vector is a column vector.

Example

$$\mathbf{ABx} = \mathbf{y}$$

(It is assumed that rule 2.3a is satisfied, else matrix multiplication would not be defined.)

3.7. An expression beginning with a row vector is a row vector.

Example

$$\mathbf{y'(A + BC)} = \mathbf{d'}$$

3.8. An expression beginning with a row vector and ending with a column vector, is a scalar.

Example

$$\mathbf{a}'\mathbf{Bc} = \gamma$$

3.9a. If $\mathbf{Q}$ is a square matrix, the scalar $\mathbf{x}'\mathbf{Qx}$ is called a quadratic form. If $\mathbf{Q}$ is non-symmetric, one can always find a symmetric matrix $\mathbf{Q}^*$ such that

$$\mathbf{x}'\mathbf{Qx} = \mathbf{x}'\mathbf{Q}^*\mathbf{x}$$

where

$$(\mathbf{Q}^*)_{ij} = \tfrac{1}{2}(q_{ij} + q_{ji})$$

3.9b. If $\mathbf{Q}$ is a square matrix the scalar $\mathbf{x}^H\mathbf{Qx}$ is called a Hermitian form.

3.10. A scalar $\mathbf{x}'\mathbf{Qy}$ is called a bilinear form.

3.11. The scalar $\mathbf{x}'\mathbf{x} = \Sigma x_i^2$, i.e., the sum of squares of all elements of $\mathbf{x}$.

3.12. The scalar $\mathbf{x}'\mathbf{y} = \Sigma x_i y_i$, i.e., the sum of products of elements in $\mathbf{x}$ by those in $\mathbf{y}$. $\mathbf{x}$ and $\mathbf{y}$ have the same number of elements.

3.13. The scalar $\mathbf{x}'\mathbf{D}_w\mathbf{x} = \Sigma w_i x_i^2$ is called a weighted sum of squares.

3.14. The scalar $\mathbf{x}'\mathbf{D}_w\mathbf{y} = \Sigma w_i x_i y_i$ is called a weighted sum of products.

3.15a. The vector $\mathbf{Aj}$ is a column vector whose elements are the row sums of $\mathbf{A}$.

3.15b. The vector $\mathbf{j}'\mathbf{A}$ is a row vector whose elements are the column sums of $\mathbf{A}$.

3.15c. The scalar $\mathbf{j}'\mathbf{Aj}$ is the sum of all elements in $\mathbf{A}$. Schematically

$\mathbf{A}$	$\mathbf{Aj}$
$\mathbf{j}'\mathbf{A}$	$\mathbf{j}'\mathbf{Aj}$

3.16a. If $\mathbf{B} = \mathbf{D}_w\mathbf{A}$; then $b_{ij} = w_i a_{ij}$.

3.16b. If $\mathbf{B} = \mathbf{AD}_w$; then $b_{ij} = a_{ij} w_j$.

3.17. Interchanging summation and matrix notation:

If

$$\mathbf{ABCD} = \mathbf{E}$$

then

$$e_{ij} = \sum_k \sum_l \sum_m a_{ik} b_{kl} c_{lm} d_{mj}$$

The second subscript of an element must coincide with the first of the next one. Reordering and transposing may be required.

Example

If

$$e_{ij} = \sum_k \sum_l \sum_m a_{kl} b_{ki} c_{jm} d_{ml}$$

$$= \sum_k \sum_l \sum_m b_{ki} a_{kl} d_{ml} c_{jm}$$

Then

$$\mathbf{E} = \mathbf{B}'\mathbf{AD}'\mathbf{C}'$$

3.18a. $\mathbf{A}'\mathbf{A}$ is a symmetric matrix whose (i,j) element is the scalar product of the i'th column vector and the j'th column vector of $\mathbf{A}$.

3.18b. $\mathbf{AA}'$ is a symmetric matrix whose (i,j) element is the scalar product of the i'th row vector and the j'th row vector of $\mathbf{A}$.

4. DETERMINANTS

4.1a. A determinant $|\mathbf{A}|$ or $\det(\mathbf{A})$ is a scalar function of a square matrix defined in such a way that

$$|\mathbf{A}|\,|\mathbf{B}| = |\mathbf{AB}|$$

and

$$\begin{vmatrix} a_{11} & a_{12} \\ a_{21} & a_{22} \end{vmatrix} = a_{11}a_{22} - a_{12}a_{21}$$

4.1b. $|\mathbf{A}| = |\mathbf{A}'|$

4.2.

$$\begin{vmatrix} a_{11} & a_{12} & a_{13} \\ a_{21} & a_{22} & a_{23} \\ a_{31} & a_{32} & a_{33} \end{vmatrix} = \begin{aligned} & a_{11}a_{22}a_{33} + a_{12}a_{23}a_{31} + a_{13}a_{21}a_{32} \\ & - a_{13}a_{22}a_{31} - a_{11}a_{23}a_{32} - a_{12}a_{21}a_{33} \end{aligned}$$

4.3.

$$\begin{vmatrix} a_{11} & a_{12} & \cdots & a_{1n} \\ a_{21} & a_{22} & \cdots & a_{2n} \\ a_{n1} & a_{n2} & \cdots & a_{nm} \end{vmatrix} = \sum (-1)^{\delta} a_{1i_1} a_{2i_2} \cdots a_{ni_n}$$

where the sum is over all permutations

$$i_1 \neq i_2 \neq \cdots i_n$$

and δ denotes the number of exchanges necessary to bring the sequence $(i_1, i_2, \ldots i_n)$ back into the natural order $(1, 2, \ldots n)$.

4.4. If two rows (columns) in a matrix are exchanged, the determinant will change its sign.

4.5. A determinant does not change its value if a linear combination of other rows (columns) is added to any given row (column).

Example

$$\begin{vmatrix} a_{11} & a_{12} & a_{13} & a_{14} \\ b_{21} & b_{22} & b_{23} & b_{24} \\ a_{31} & a_{32} & a_{33} & a_{34} \\ a_{41} & a_{42} & a_{43} & a_{44} \end{vmatrix} = \begin{vmatrix} a_{11} & a_{12} & a_{13} & a_{14} \\ a_{21} & a_{22} & a_{23} & a_{24} \\ a_{31} & a_{32} & a_{33} & a_{34} \\ a_{41} & a_{42} & a_{43} & a_{44} \end{vmatrix}$$

where

$$b_{2i} = a_{2i} + \gamma_1 a_{1i} + \gamma_3 a_{3i} + \gamma_4 a_{4i}$$
$$i = 1, 2, 3, 4$$

$\gamma_1, \gamma_3, \gamma_4$ arbitrary.

4.6. If the i'th row (column) equals (a constant times) the j'th row (column) of a matrix, its determinant is equal to zero, $(i \neq j)$.

4.7. If, in a matrix $\mathbf{A}$, each element of a row (column) is multiplied by a constant γ, the determinant is multiplied by γ.

4.8. $|\gamma \mathbf{A}| = \gamma^n |\mathbf{A}|$ assuming that $\mathbf{A}$ is of order $(n \times n)$.

4.9. The cofactor of a square matrix $\mathbf{A}$, $\mathrm{cof}_{ij}(\mathbf{A})$ is the determinant of a matrix obtained by striking the i'th row and j'th column of $\mathbf{A}$ and choosing positive (negative) sign if $i + j$ is even (odd).

Example

$$\text{cof}_{23}\begin{bmatrix} 2 & 4 & 3 \\ 6 & 1 & 5 \\ -2 & 1 & 3 \end{bmatrix} = -\begin{vmatrix} 2 & 4 \\ -2 & 1 \end{vmatrix}$$

$$= -(2 + 8) = -10$$

4.10. (Laplace Development)

$$| \mathbf{A} | = a_{i1}\text{cof}_{i1}(\mathbf{A}) + a_{i2}\text{cof}_{i2}(\mathbf{A}) + \cdots + a_{in}\text{cof}_{in}(\mathbf{A})$$

$$= a_{1j}\text{cof}_{1j}(\mathbf{A}) + a_{2j}\text{cof}_{2j}(\mathbf{A}) + \cdots + a_{nj}\text{cof}_{nj}(\mathbf{A})$$

for any row i or any column j.

4.11. Numerical Evaluation of the determinant of a symmetric matrix.

Note: If $\mathbf{A}$ is non-symmetric, form $\mathbf{A'A}$ or $\mathbf{AA'}$ by rule 3.18, obtain its determinant, and take the square root.

("Forward Doolittle Scheme", "left side")

Let

$$p_{11} = a_{11}, \quad p_{12} = a_{12} = a_{21}, \dots p_{1n} = a_{1n}$$

p_{11}	p_{12}	p_{13}	$\cdots$	p_{1n}
1	u_{12}	u_{13}	$\cdots$	u_{1n}
	a_{22}	a_{23}	$\cdots$	a_{2n}
	p_{22}	p_{23}	$\cdots$	p_{2n}
	1	u_{23}	$\cdots$	u_{2n}
		a_{33}	$\cdots$	a_{3n}
		p_{33}	$\cdots$	p_{3n}
		1	$\cdots$	u_{3n}
		$\cdot$	$\cdots$	$\cdot$
				a_{nn}
				p_{nn}
				1

$$u_{1i} = p_{1i}/p_{11} \qquad\qquad i = 1, 2, \dots n$$
$$p_{2i} = a_{2i} - u_{12}\,p_{1i} \qquad\qquad i = 2, 3, \dots n$$
$$u_{2i} = p_{2i}/p_{22}$$
$$p_{3i} = a_{3i} - u_{13}\,p_{1i} - u_{23}\,p_{2i} \qquad\qquad i = 3, 4, \dots n$$
$$u_{3i} = p_{3i}/p_{33}$$
$$p_{ki} = a_{ki} - u_{1k}\,p_{1i} - u_{2k}\,p_{2i} - \cdots - u_{k-1,k}\,p_{k-1,i} \qquad i = k, k+1, \dots n$$
$$\qquad\qquad\qquad\qquad\qquad\qquad\qquad\qquad\qquad\qquad\qquad k = 2, 3, \dots n$$
$$u_{ki} = p_{ki}/p_{kk}$$

If, at some stage, $p_{kk} = 0$, reordering of rows and columns may be required. If the matrix is positive-definite (see 8.16) (always true for $\mathbf{AA'}$ or $\mathbf{A'A}$, see rule 10.24), none of the

p_{kk} will be zero. The p_{ii} are called pivots. Then

$$|\mathbf{A}| = \prod_{i=1}^{n} p_{ii}$$

Further, if $\mathbf{A}$ is partitioned

$$\mathbf{A} = \begin{bmatrix} \mathbf{A}_{11} & \mathbf{A}_{12} \\ \mathbf{A}'_{12} & \mathbf{A}_{22} \end{bmatrix}$$

where $\mathbf{A}_{11}$ is of order $(k \times k)$, then

$$|\mathbf{A}_{11}| = \prod_{i=1}^{k} p_{ii}$$

(Numerical Examples: see 6.14.)

5. SINGULARITY AND RANK

5.1. A matrix $\mathbf{A}$ is called singular if there exists a vector $\mathbf{x} \neq \mathbf{0}$ such that $\mathbf{A}\mathbf{x} = \mathbf{0}$ or $\mathbf{A}'\mathbf{x} = \mathbf{0}$. Note $\mathbf{x} \neq \mathbf{0}$ if a single element of $\mathbf{x}$ is unequal 0. If a matrix is not singular, it is called non-singular.

5.2. If a matrix $\mathbf{A}_1$ can be formed by selection of r rows and columns of $\mathbf{A}$ such that $\mathbf{A}_1\mathbf{x} \neq \mathbf{0}$ or $\mathbf{A}'_1\mathbf{x} \neq \mathbf{0}$ for every $\mathbf{x} \neq \mathbf{0}$, and if addition of an $(r+1)st$ row and column would produce a singular matrix, r is called the rank of $\mathbf{A}$.

Example

$$\mathbf{A} = \begin{bmatrix} 2 & 4 & 6 \\ 1 & 3 & 7 \\ 3 & 7 & 13 \\ 1 & 1 & -1 \end{bmatrix}$$

Note that

$$[1, \quad 1, \quad -1] \begin{bmatrix} 2 & 4 & 6 \\ 1 & 3 & 7 \\ 3 & 7 & 13 \end{bmatrix} = [0 \quad 0 \quad 0]$$

and

$$[1, \quad -1, \quad -1] \begin{bmatrix} 2 & 4 & 6 \\ 1 & 3 & 7 \\ 1 & 1 & -1 \end{bmatrix} = [0 \quad 0 \quad 0]$$

but

$$\begin{bmatrix} 2 & 4 \\ 1 & 3 \end{bmatrix} \begin{bmatrix} x_1 \\ x_2 \end{bmatrix} \neq \begin{bmatrix} 0 \\ 0 \end{bmatrix}$$

or

$$[x_1 \quad x_2] \begin{bmatrix} 2 & 4 \\ 1 & 3 \end{bmatrix} \neq [0, \quad 0]$$

for any arbitrary

$$[x_1, \quad x_2] \neq [0, \quad 0].$$

Hence the matrix has rank 2.

5.3. If **A** has rank r and if $\mathbf{A}_1$ is a non-singular submatrix consisting of r rows and columns of **A**, then $\mathbf{A}_1$ is called a basis of **A**.

5.4a. The determinant of a square singular matrix is 0.

5.4b. The determinant of a non-singular matrix is $\neq 0$.

5.5. rank $(\mathbf{AB}) \leq$ min [rank $(\mathbf{A})$, rank $(\mathbf{B})$].

5.6. rank $(\mathbf{AA}') =$ rank $(\mathbf{A}'\mathbf{A}) =$ rank $(\mathbf{A})$.

5.7. $|\mathbf{A}'\mathbf{A}| = |\mathbf{AA}'| = |\mathbf{A}|^2$ if **A** is square.

5.8. $|\mathbf{A}'\mathbf{A}| = |\mathbf{AA}'| \geq 0$ for every **A** with real elements.

6. INVERSION

(Regular Case, non-singular matrices)

6.1. If **A** is square and non-singular ($|\mathbf{A}| \neq 0$) there exists a unique matrix $\mathbf{A}^{-1}$ such that $\mathbf{AA}^{-1} = \mathbf{A}^{-1}\mathbf{A} = \mathbf{I}$.

6.2. $(\mathbf{ABC})^{-1} = \mathbf{C}^{-1}\mathbf{B}^{-1}\mathbf{A}^{-1}$ (provided that all inverses exist).

6.3. $(\mathbf{A}^{-1})' = (\mathbf{A}')^{-1}$

6.4. $\mathbf{Ax} = \mathbf{b}$ is a system of linear equations. If **A** is square and non-singular, there exists a unique solution

$$\mathbf{x} = \mathbf{A}^{-1}\mathbf{b}$$

6.5. $(\gamma\mathbf{A})^{-1} = (1/\gamma)\mathbf{A}^{-1}$

6.6. $|\mathbf{A}^{-1}| = 1/|\mathbf{A}|$

6.7. $\mathbf{D}_w^{-1} = \mathbf{D}_{1/w}$ where **D** is a diagonal matrix.

6.8. If

$$\mathbf{A} = \mathbf{B} + \mathbf{uv}'$$

then

$$\mathbf{A}^{-1} = \mathbf{B}^{-1} - \lambda\mathbf{yz}'$$

where

$$\mathbf{y} = \mathbf{B}^{-1}\mathbf{u}, \quad \mathbf{z}' = \mathbf{v}'\mathbf{B}^{-1},$$

and

$$\lambda = 1/(1 + \mathbf{z}'\mathbf{u})$$

Example 6.8.1

$$\mathbf{A} = \begin{bmatrix} 4 & 2 & 4 & 5 \\ 3 & 9 & 12 & 15 \\ 2 & 4 & 11 & 10 \\ 1 & 2 & 4 & 10 \end{bmatrix}$$

This matrix can be written as

$$\begin{bmatrix} 3 & 0 & 0 & 0 \\ 0 & 3 & 0 & 0 \\ 0 & 0 & 3 & 0 \\ 0 & 0 & 0 & 5 \end{bmatrix} + \begin{bmatrix} 1 \\ 3 \\ 2 \\ 1 \end{bmatrix} \begin{bmatrix} 1 & 2 & 4 & 5 \end{bmatrix} = \mathbf{B} + \mathbf{uv}'$$

$$B^{-1} = \begin{bmatrix} 1/3 & 0 & 0 & 0 \\ 0 & 1/3 & 0 & 0 \\ 0 & 0 & 1/3 & 0 \\ 0 & 0 & 0 & 1/5 \end{bmatrix}$$

$$y = B^{-1}u = \begin{bmatrix} 1/3 \\ 1 \\ 2/3 \\ 1/5 \end{bmatrix}$$

$$z' = v'B^{-1} = [1/3 \quad 2/3 \quad 4/3 \quad 1]$$

$$z'u = 1/3 \times 1 + 2/3 \times 3 + 4/3 \times 2 + 1 \times 1 = 6$$

$$\lambda = 1/7$$

$$A^{-1} = \begin{bmatrix} 1/3 & 0 & 0 & 0 \\ 0 & 1/3 & 0 & 0 \\ 0 & 0 & 1/3 & 0 \\ 0 & 0 & 0 & 1/5 \end{bmatrix} - (1/7) \begin{bmatrix} 1/3 \\ 1 \\ 2/3 \\ 1/5 \end{bmatrix} [1/3 \quad 2/3 \quad 4/3 \quad 1]$$

$$= (1/315) \begin{bmatrix} 100 & -10 & -20 & -15 \\ -15 & 75 & -60 & -45 \\ -10 & -20 & 65 & -30 \\ -3 & -6 & -12 & 54 \end{bmatrix}$$

(This rule is especially useful if all off-diagonal elements are equal, then $u = kj$ and $v' = j'$ and B is diagonal.)

6.9. Let B (elements b_{ij}) have a known inverse, B^{-1} (elements b^{ij}). Let $A = B$ except for one element $a_{rs} = b_{rs} + k$. Then the elements of A^{-1} are

$$a^{ij} = b^{ij} - \frac{kb^{ir}b^{sj}}{1 + kb^{sr}}.$$

6.10. (Partitioning)

Let

$$\begin{array}{cc} & (p) \quad (q) \\ A = \begin{matrix}(p)\\(q)\end{matrix} & \begin{bmatrix} B & C \\ D & E \end{bmatrix} \end{array}$$

(letters in parentheses denote order of the submatrices)

Let B^{-1} and E^{-1} exist. Then

$$A^{-1} = \begin{bmatrix} X & Y \\ Z & U \end{bmatrix}$$

where

$$X = (B - CE^{-1}D)^{-1}$$
$$U = (E - DB^{-1}C)^{-1}$$
$$Y = -B^{-1}CU$$
$$Z = -E^{-1}DX$$

6.11. (Partitioning of Determinants)

Let

$$|\mathbf{A}| = \begin{vmatrix} \mathbf{B} & \mathbf{C} \\ \mathbf{D} & \mathbf{E} \end{vmatrix} \qquad \text{(same structure as in 6.10)}$$

Then

$$|\mathbf{A}| = |\mathbf{E}|\,|(\mathbf{B} - \mathbf{C}\mathbf{E}^{-1}\mathbf{D})| = |\mathbf{B}|\,|(\mathbf{E} - \mathbf{D}\mathbf{B}^{-1}\mathbf{C})|$$

6.12. Let

$$\mathbf{A} = \mathbf{B} + \mathbf{U}\mathbf{V}$$

where $\mathbf{B}(n \times n)$ has an inverse

$\mathbf{U}$ is of order $(n \times k)$, with k usually very small
$\mathbf{V}$ is of order $(k \times n)$

(the special case for $k = 1$ is treated in 6.8).

Then

$$\mathbf{A}^{-1} = \mathbf{B}^{-1} - \mathbf{Y}\Lambda\mathbf{Z}$$

where

$$\mathbf{Y} = \mathbf{B}^{-1}\mathbf{U}(n \times k)$$
$$\mathbf{Z} = \mathbf{V}\mathbf{B}^{-1}(k \times n)$$

and

$$\Lambda(k \times k) = [\mathbf{I} + \mathbf{Z}\mathbf{U}]^{-1}$$

6.13. Let a_{ij} denote the elements of $\mathbf{A}$ and a^{ij} those of $\mathbf{A}^{-1}$. Then

$$a^{ij} = \text{cof}_{ji}(\mathbf{A})/|\mathbf{A}|$$

where cof is the determinant defined in 4.9.

6.14. "Doolittle" Method of inverting symmetric matrices (see also 4.11). Let

$$p_{11} = a_{11}, \quad p_{12} = a_{12} = a_{21},\ldots p_{1n} = a_{1n} = a_{n1}$$

Forward Solution

p_{11}	p_{12}	p_{13}	$\cdots$	p_{1n}	1				
1	u_{12}	u_{13}	$\cdots$	u_{1n}	u_{11}				
	a_{22}	a_{23}	$\cdots$	a_{2n}	0	1			
	p_{22}	p_{23}	$\cdots$	p_{2n}	p_{21}	$p_{2\text{II}}$			
	1	u_{23}	$\cdots$	u_{2n}	u_{21}	$u_{2\text{II}}$			
		a_{33}	$\cdots$	a_{3n}	0	0	1		
		p_{33}	$\cdots$	p_{3n}	p_{31}	$p_{3\text{II}}$	$p_{3\text{III}}$		
		1	$\cdots$	u_{3n}	u_{31}	$u_{3\text{II}}$	$u_{3\text{III}}$		
			$\cdots$	$\cdot$	$\cdot$	$\cdots$	$\cdot$		
				a_{nn}	0	0	0	$\cdots$	1
				p_{nn}	p_{n1}	$p_{n\text{II}}$	$p_{n\text{III}}$	$\cdots$	p_{nN}
				1	u_{n1}	$u_{n\text{II}}$	$u_{n\text{III}}$	$\cdots$	u_{nN}

$$u_{1i} = p_{1i}/p_{11} \qquad\qquad i = 1, 2, \ldots n, \text{I}$$

$$p_{2i} = a_{2i} - u_{12}p_{1i} \qquad\qquad i = 2, 3, \ldots n, \text{I}, \text{II}$$

$$u_{2i} = p_{2i}/p_{22}$$

$$p_{3i} = a_{3i} - u_{13}p_{1i} - u_{23}p_{2i} \qquad\qquad i = 3, 4, \ldots n, \text{I}, \text{II}, \text{III}$$

$$u_{3i} = p_{3i}/p_{33}$$

$$p_{ki} = a_{ki} - u_{1k}p_{1i} - u_{2k}p_{2i} - \cdots - u_{k-1,k}p_{k-1,i} \quad \begin{array}{l} i = k, k+1, \ldots n, \text{I}, \text{II}, \ldots \text{K} \\ k = 2, 3, \ldots n \end{array}$$

$$u_{ki} = p_{ki}/p_{kk}$$

Backward Solution

(j refers to Arabic, J refers to Roman numerals)

The elements of $\mathbf{A}^{-1}$ are a^{ij}

$$a^{nj} = u_{nJ} \qquad\qquad\qquad\qquad \begin{array}{l} j = 1, 2, \ldots n; \\ J = \text{I}, \text{II}, \ldots N \end{array}$$

$$a^{n-1j} = u_{n-1,J} - u_{n-1,n}a^{nj} \qquad\qquad \begin{array}{l} j = 1, 2, \ldots (n-1); \\ J = \text{I}, \text{II}, \ldots (N-1) \end{array}$$

$$a^{n-2,j} = u_{n-2,J} - u_{n-2,n}a^{nj} - u_{n-2,n-1}a^{n-1,j} \qquad \begin{array}{l} j = 1, 2, \ldots (n-2); \\ J = \text{I}, \text{II}, \ldots (N-2) \end{array}$$

$$a^{n-k,j} = u_{n-k,J} - u_{n-k,n}a^{nj} - u_{n-k,n-1}a^{n-1,j} - \cdots - u_{n-k,n-k+1}a^{n-k+1,j} \quad \begin{array}{l} j = 1, 2, \ldots (n-k); \\ J = \text{I}, \text{II}, \ldots (N-k); \\ k = 1, 2, \ldots (n-1), \end{array}$$

and $a^{ji} = a^{ij}$.

Numerical Example 6.14.1.

Invert the Matrix

$$\begin{bmatrix} 25 & 30 & -10 \\ 30 & 40 & -6 \\ -10 & -6 & 17 \end{bmatrix}$$

a_1	25	30	-10	1		
u_1	1	1.2	-0.4	0.04		
a_2		40	-6	0	1	
p_2		4	6	-1.2	1	
u_2		1	1.5	-0.3	0.25	
a_3			17	0	0	1
p_3			4	2.2	-1.5	1
u_3			1	0.55	-0.375	0.25
	1.61	-1.125	0.55			
	-1.125	0.8125	-0.375			
	0.55	-0.375	0.25			

Enter row a_1.
Elements in u_1 = Elements in a_1 divided by $a_{11}(=25)$.
Enter row a_2.

$$p_{22} = 40 - 1.2 \times 30 = 4$$
$$p_{23} = -6 - 1.2 \times (-10) = 6$$
$$p_{21} = 0 - 1.2 \times 1 = -1.2$$
$$p_{211} = 1$$

Elements in u_2 = Elements in p_2 divided by $p_{22}(=4)$.
Enter row a_3.

$$p_{33} = 17 - (-0.4) \times (-10) - 1.5 \times 6 = 4$$
$$p_{31} = 0 - (-0.4) \times 1 - 1.5 \times (-1.2) = 2.2$$
$$p_{311} = 0 - 1.5 \times 1 = -1.5$$
$$p_{3111} = 1$$

Elements in u_3 = Elements in p_3 divided by $p_{33}(=4)$.
Copy the right-hand side of the last (third) u − row as the last column below the double line.

$$a^{21} = -0.3 - 1.5 \times 0.55 = -1.125$$
$$a^{22} = 0.25 - 1.5 \times (-0.375) = 0.8125$$
$$a^{23} = 0 - 1.5 \times 0.25 = -0.375 \quad \text{(check against } a^{32}\text{)}.$$

These are entered in the next to last (second) column below.

$$a^{11} = 0.04 - (-0.4) \times 0.55 - 1.2 \times (-1.125) = 1.61$$
$$a^{12} = 0 - (-0.4) \times (-0.375) - 1.2 \times 0.8125 = -1.125 \quad \text{(check against } a^{21}\text{)}$$
$$a^{13} = 0 - (-0.4) \times (0.25) - 1.2 \times (-0.375) = 0.55 \quad \text{(check against } a^{31}\text{)}.$$

6.15. A matrix is called orthogonal if $\mathbf{A}' = \mathbf{A}^{-1}$ (or $\mathbf{AA}' = \mathbf{I}$).

7. TRACES

7.1. If $\mathbf{A}$ is a square matrix then the trace of $\mathbf{A}$ is $tr\,\mathbf{A} = \sum_i a_{ii}$, i.e., the sum of the diagonal elements.

7.2. If $\mathbf{A}$ is of order $(m \times k)$ and $\mathbf{B}$ of order $(k \times m)$ then $tr(\mathbf{AB}) = tr(\mathbf{BA})$.

7.3. If $\mathbf{A}$ is of order $(m \times k)$, $\mathbf{B}$ of order $(k \times r)$ and $\mathbf{C}$ of order $(r \times m)$, then

$$tr(\mathbf{ABC}) = tr(\mathbf{BCA}) = tr(\mathbf{CAB}).$$

7.3a. If $\mathbf{b}$ is a column vector and $\mathbf{c}'$ a row vector, then

$$tr(\mathbf{Abc}') = tr(\mathbf{bc}'\mathbf{A}) = \mathbf{c}'\mathbf{Ab}$$

since the trace of a scalar is the scalar.

7.4. $tr(\mathbf{A} + \gamma\mathbf{B}) = tr\mathbf{A} + \gamma\,tr\mathbf{B}$; where γ is a scalar.

7.5. $tr(\mathbf{EL})_{ij}\mathbf{A} = tr\mathbf{A}(\mathbf{EL})_{ij} = a_{ji}$; where $(\mathbf{EL})_{ij}$ is an elementary matrix as defined in 3.4.

7.6. $tr(\mathbf{EL})_{ij}\mathbf{A}(\mathbf{EL})_{rs}\mathbf{B} = a_{jr}b_{si}$

(These rules are useful in matrix differentiation)

7.7. The trace of the second order of a square matrix $\mathbf{A}$ is the sum of the determinants of all $\binom{n}{2}$ matrices of order (2×2) which can be formed by intersecting rows i and j with columns i and j.

$$tr_2 \mathbf{A} = \begin{vmatrix} a_{11} & a_{12} \\ a_{21} & a_{22} \end{vmatrix} + \begin{vmatrix} a_{11} & a_{13} \\ a_{31} & a_{33} \end{vmatrix}$$

$$+ \cdots + \begin{vmatrix} a_{11} & a_{1n} \\ a_{n1} & a_{nn} \end{vmatrix} + \begin{vmatrix} a_{22} & a_{23} \\ a_{32} & a_{33} \end{vmatrix}$$

$$+ \cdots + \begin{vmatrix} a_{22} & a_{2n} \\ a_{n2} & a_{nn} \end{vmatrix} + \cdots + \begin{vmatrix} a_{n-1,n-1} & a_{n-1,n} \\ a_{n,n-1} & a_{nn} \end{vmatrix}.$$

7.8. The trace of the k'th order of a square matrix is the sum of the determinants of all $\binom{n}{k}$ matrices of order ($k \times k$) which can be formed by intersecting any k rows of $\mathbf{A}$ with the same k columns.

$$tr_k \mathbf{A} = \sum \begin{vmatrix} a_{i_1 i_1} & a_{i_1 i_2} & \cdots & a_{i_1 i_k} \\ a_{i_2 i_1} & a_{i_2 i_2} & \cdots & a_{i_2 i_k} \\ \cdot & \cdot & \cdots & \cdot \\ a_{i_k i_1} & a_{i_k i_2} & \cdots & a_{i_k i_k} \end{vmatrix}$$

where the sum extends over all combinations of n elements taken k at a time in order

$$i_1 < i_2 < \cdots < i_k.$$

7.9. Rules 7.2 and 7.3 (cyclic exchange) are valid for trace of k'th order.
7.10. $tr_n \mathbf{A} = |\mathbf{A}|$ if $\mathbf{A}$ is of order ($n \times n$).

8. CHARACTERISTIC ROOTS AND VECTORS

8.1. If $\mathbf{A}$ is a square matrix of order ($n \times n$), then $|\mathbf{A} - \lambda \mathbf{I}| = 0$ is called the characteristic equation of the matrix $\mathbf{A}$. It is a polynomial of the n'th degree in λ.

8.2. The n roots of the characteristic equation (not necessarily distinct) are called the characteristic roots of $\mathbf{A}$

$$ch(\mathbf{A}) = \lambda_1, \lambda_2, \ldots \lambda_n$$

8.3. The characteristic equation of $\mathbf{A}$ can be obtained by the relation

$$\lambda^n - (tr\mathbf{A})\lambda^{n-1} + (tr_2\mathbf{A})\lambda^{n-2} - (tr_3\mathbf{A})\lambda^{n-3} \cdots - (-1)^n(tr_{n-1}\mathbf{A})\lambda + (-1)^n |\mathbf{A}| = 0$$

where tr_k is defined in 7.8.

Example 8.3.1

$$\mathbf{A} = \begin{bmatrix} 25 & 30 & -10 \\ 30 & 40 & -6 \\ -10 & -6 & 17 \end{bmatrix}$$

$tr\mathbf{A} = 25 + 40 + 17 = 82$

$tr_2\mathbf{A} = (25 \times 40 - 30 \times 30) + (25 \times 17 - 10 \times 10) + (40 \times 17 - 6 \times 6) = 1069$

$tr_3\mathbf{A} = |\mathbf{A}| = 25 \times 4 \times 4 = 400$

    (cf. 6.14 and procedure stated in 4.11)

Hence

$$\lambda^3 - 82\lambda^2 + 1069\lambda - 400 = 0$$

The solutions (by Newton iteration) are

$$\lambda_1 = 65.86108$$
$$\lambda_2 = 15.75339$$
$$\lambda_3 = 0.38553$$

These are the characteristic roots of **A**.

8.4. $ch(\mathbf{A} + \gamma \mathbf{I}) = \gamma + ch(\mathbf{A})$

8.5. $ch(\mathbf{AB}) = ch(\mathbf{BA})$

      (except that **AB** or **BA** may have additional roots equal to zero).

8.6. $ch(\mathbf{A}^{-1}) = 1/ch(\mathbf{A})$

8.7. If $\lambda_1, \lambda_2, \ldots \lambda_n$ are the roots of **A** then

$$\sum_i \lambda_i = tr\,\mathbf{A}$$

$$\sum_{i<j} \lambda_i\lambda_j = tr_2\mathbf{A}$$

$$\sum_{i<j<k} \lambda_i\lambda_j\lambda_k = tr_3\mathbf{A}$$

$$\prod_i \lambda_i = |\mathbf{A}|$$

8.8. If $\mathbf{x}'$ denotes the radius vector (running coordinates $[x, y, z]$) and if a matrix **Q** is positive-definite, then

$$(\mathbf{x}' - \mathbf{x}_0')\mathbf{Q}^{-1}(\mathbf{x} - \mathbf{x}_0) = 1$$

is the equation of an ellipsoid with center at $[x_0, y_0, z_0] = \mathbf{x}_0'$ and semi-axes equal to the square roots of the characteristic roots of **Q**.

8.9. The characteristic roots of a triangular (or diagonal) matrix are the diagonal elements of the matrix.

8.10. If **A** is a real matrix with positive roots, then

$$ch_{min}(\mathbf{AA}') \leq [ch_{min}(\mathbf{A})]^2 \leq [ch_{max}(\mathbf{A})]^2 \leq ch_{max}(\mathbf{AA}')$$

where ch_{min} denotes the smallest and ch_{max} the largest root.

8.11. The ratio of two quadratic forms (**B** non-singular)

$$u = \frac{\mathbf{x}'\mathbf{Ax}}{\mathbf{x}'\mathbf{Bx}}$$

attains stationary values at the roots of $\mathbf{B}^{-1}\mathbf{A}$. In particular

$$u_{max} = ch_{max}(\mathbf{B}^{-1}\mathbf{A}) \quad \text{and} \quad u_{min} = ch_{min}(\mathbf{B}^{-1}\mathbf{A})$$

8.12. The equation system

$$\mathbf{Ax} = \lambda\mathbf{x}$$

permits non-zero solutions only if λ is one of the characteristic roots of **A**. Such a solution **x** is called a characteristic vector.

8.13. If **x** is a solution to 8.12, so is $\gamma\mathbf{x}$ for an arbitrary scalar γ.

8.14. A solution **x** which has unit length ($\mathbf{x}'\mathbf{x} = 1$) is called the eigenvector associated with the characteristic root λ of **A**. The vector is frequently denoted by **e**.

8.15. A real symmetric matrix has real roots.

8.16. A matrix **A** is called positive-definite (abbreviated p.d.) if the quadratic form $\mathbf{x}'\mathbf{Ax} > 0$ for every $\mathbf{x} \neq \mathbf{0}$.

8.17. A matrix **A** is called positive-semidefinite (abbreviated p.s.d.) if the quadratic form $\mathbf{x}'\mathbf{A}\mathbf{x} > 0$ and/or $\mathbf{x}'\mathbf{A}\mathbf{x} = 0$ for some $\mathbf{x} \neq \mathbf{0}$.

8.18. A positive-definite real symmetric matrix has only positive characteristic roots.

8.19. If a real symmetric matrix is positive-semidefinite, it has no negative roots. The number of non-zero roots equals the rank of the matrix.

8.20. If all roots of a real symmetric matrix are distinct, the associated eigenvectors are distinct.

8.21. The matrix of eigenvectors

$$\mathbf{E} = [\mathbf{e}_1, \mathbf{e}_2, \ldots \mathbf{e}_n]$$

of a real symmetric matrix is (or can be chosen to be) orthogonal.

8.22. $\mathbf{AE} = \mathbf{ED}_\lambda$.

8.23. For a real symmetric matrix, $\mathbf{A} = \mathbf{ED}_\lambda\mathbf{E}'$ (decomposition into matrices of unit rank)

$$\mathbf{E}'\mathbf{AE} = \mathbf{D}_\lambda$$

where $\mathbf{D}_\lambda$ denotes the diagonal matrix of characteristic roots ordered in the same way as the eigenvector columns in **E**.

8.24. If $f(\lambda)$ is a polynomial in λ, then

$$f(\mathbf{A}) = \mathbf{ED}_{f(\lambda)}\mathbf{E}^{-1}$$

where λ are the characteristic roots of **A** and **E** is the matrix of associated eigenvectors. If **A** is symmetric, $\mathbf{E}^{-1} = \mathbf{E}'$.

Example 8.24.1

Consider the matrix in 8.3 (and 6.14).

$$\mathbf{A} = \begin{bmatrix} 25 & 30 & -10 \\ 30 & 40 & -6 \\ -10 & -6 & 17 \end{bmatrix}$$

The characteristic roots were found in Example 8.3.1,

$$\lambda_1 = 65.86108 \qquad \lambda_2 = 15.75339 \qquad \lambda_3 = 0.38553.$$

To find some **x** such that $\mathbf{A}\mathbf{x} = \lambda_1\mathbf{x}$, we arbitrarily set the first element of **x** equal to 1. Using only the first two rows of **A** we solve the equation system

$$25 + 30x_2 - 10x_3 = 65.86108$$
$$30 + 40x_2 - 6x_3 = 65.86108x_2$$

which yields $x_2 = 1.24294$ and $x_3 = -0.35729$. Substitution of these values into the third equation

$$-10 - 6x_2 + 17x_3 = 65.86108x_3$$

yields zero to five decimal places, indicating the accuracy of the first characteristic root. To reduce to unit length the characteristic vector

$$[1 \qquad 1.24294 \qquad -0.35729]$$

we divide each element by

$$\sqrt{1 + 1.24294^2 + 0.35729^2}$$

and thus obtain the first eigenvector

$$[0.61170 \qquad 0.76030 \qquad -0.21855]$$

This, written as a column vector, is e_1. Repeating the same process for the second and third eigenvectors we obtain

$$e_2 = \begin{bmatrix} -0.08659 \\ 0.33896 \\ 0.93681 \end{bmatrix} \qquad e_3 = \begin{bmatrix} 0.78634 \\ -0.55412 \\ 0.27318 \end{bmatrix}$$

The three vectors can be placed into the eigenvector matrix E, which is easily seen to be orthogonal.

9. CONDITIONAL INVERSES

9.1. Any matrix **A** (singular or non-singular, rectangular or square) has some conditional or generalized inverse $A^{(-1)}$ defined by the relation

$$AA^{(-1)}A = A.$$

9.2. If (and only if) **A** is square and non-singular, $A^{(-1)}$ is unique and equals A^{-1}. Otherwise there will be infinitely many matrices $A^{(-1)}$ which satisfy the defining relation 9.1.

9.3a. If **A** is rectangular $(n \times m)$ of rank m, with $m < n$, then $A^{(-1)}$ is of order $(m \times n)$ and $A^{(-1)}A = I(m \times m)$. Then $A^{(-1)}$ is called an inverse from the left. $AA^{(-1)} \neq I$ in this case.

9.3b. If **A** is rectangular $(n \times m)$ of rank n, with $m > n$, then $A^{(-1)}$ is of order $(m \times n)$ and $AA^{(-1)} = I(n \times n)$. Then $A^{(-1)}$ is called an inverse to the right. In this case,

$$A^{(-1)}A \neq I.$$

9.3c. For a square, singular matrix, $AA^{(-1)} \neq I$ and $A^{(-1)}A \neq I$.

Example 9.3.1

$$A = \begin{bmatrix} 3 \\ 2 \\ 1 \end{bmatrix}$$

The row vector $[1/3 \quad 0 \quad 0]$ is an inverse from the left. The row vector

$$[x \quad y \quad (1 - 3x - 2y)]$$

is a conditional inverse of the above matrix **A** for any values of x and y. It is called the generalized inverse of **A**.

Example 9.3.2

$$A = \begin{bmatrix} 1 & 2 & 3 \\ 2 & 5 & 6 \\ 3 & 7 & 9 \end{bmatrix}$$

A conditional inverse is

$$A^{(-1)} = \begin{bmatrix} 5 & -2 & 0 \\ -2 & 1 & 0 \\ 0 & 0 & 0 \end{bmatrix}$$

Here it was obtained by inversion of the basis (the 2×2 matrix in the upper left-hand corner) and replacement of the other elements by zeros.

9.4. A square matrix A is called idempotent if $AA = A^2 = A$.

9.5. $AA^{(-1)}$ and $A^{(-1)}A$ are idempotent.

9.6. All characteristic roots of idempotent matrices are either zero or one.

9.7. A system of linear equations (m equations in n unknowns)

$$Ax = b$$

is called consistent if there exists some solution x which satisfies the equation system.

Example 9.7.1

The system

$$x + y = 2$$
$$2x + 2y = 4 \qquad \text{is consistent.}$$

Example 9.7.2

The system

$$x + y = 2$$
$$2x + 2y = 5 \qquad \text{is inconsistent,}$$

for no pair of values (x, y) will satisfy this system.

9.8. If, in a system of equations (rectangular or square)

$$Ax = b$$

$AA^{(-1)}b = b$ for some conditional inverse $A^{(-1)}$, then $AA^{(-1)}b = b$ for every conditional inverse of A, and $Ax = b$ is consistent. Conversely, if $AA^{(-1)}b \neq b$ for some conditional inverse $A^{(-1)}$ then $AA^{(-1)}b \neq b$ for every conditional inverse of A, and $Ax = b$ is inconsistent.

9.9. If $Ax = b$ is consistent, then $x = A^{(-1)}b$ is a solution (generally a different one for each $A^{(-1)}$).

9.10. Let y ($p \times 1$) be a set of linear functions of the solutions x ($n \times 1$) of a consistent system of equations $Ax = b$, given by the relation $y = Cx$. Then $y = Cx$ is called unique if the same values of y will result regardless which solution x is used.

Example 9.10.1

$$3x + 4y + 5z = 22$$
$$x + y + z = 6$$

is a consistent system. One solution would be

$$x = 3 \quad y = 2 \quad z = 1$$

Another solution is

$$x = 2 \quad y = 4 \quad z = 0$$

The linear function

$$[7 \quad 9 \quad 11] \begin{bmatrix} x \\ y \\ z \end{bmatrix} = u$$

($7x + 9y + 11z = u$) will have the same value (50) regardless which of the two (or any other) solutions is substituted. Thus u is unique.

9.11. Let $Ax = b$ be a consistent system of equations. For $Cx = y$ to be a unique linear combination of the solution x, it is necessary and sufficient that $CA^{(-1)}A = C$. If this relation holds for some $A^{(-1)}$ it will hold for every conditional inverse of A. If it is violated for some $A^{(-1)}$ it will be violated for every $A^{(-1)}$, and y will be non-unique.

9.12. Let A be of rank r and select r rows and r columns which form a basis of A. Then a conditional inverse of A can be obtained as follows: Invert the $(r \times r)$ matrix, place the inverse (without transposing) into the r rows corresponding to the column numbers and the r columns corresponding to the row numbers of the basis, and place zero into all remaining elements. Thus, if A is of order (5×4) and rank 3, and if rows 1, 2, 4 and columns 2, 3, 4 are selected as a basis, $A^{(-1)}$, of order (4×5) will contain the inverse elements of the basis in rows 2, 3, 4 and columns 1, 2, 4, and zeros elsewhere. (See example 9.3.2)

9.13. If A is a square, singular matrix of order $(n \times n)$ and rank r, let M be a matrix of order $[n \times (n - r)]$ and K another matrix of order $[(n - r) \times n]$ chosen in such a way that $A + MK$ is non-singular. Then $(A + MK)^{-1}$ is a conditional inverse of A.

Example 9.13.1

$$A = \begin{bmatrix} 3 & -1 & -1 & -1 \\ -1 & 3 & -1 & -1 \\ -1 & -1 & 3 & -1 \\ -1 & -1 & -1 & 3 \end{bmatrix}$$

is of order (4×4) and rank 3. Take $M = j$ (column vector of ones) and $K = j'$ (row vector of ones). Then $A + MK = A + jj' = 4I$. Hence $(1/4)I$ is a conditional inverse of A.

9.14. The "Doolittle" method (see 6.14) can be employed to obtain a conditional inverse of a symmetric matrix. If, at any stage, the leading element of the p-row is zero, that cycle is disregarded.

Example 9.14.1

Invert, conditionally, the matrix

$$A = \begin{bmatrix} 4 & 2 & -2 & 4 \\ 2 & 17 & 11 & 6 \\ -2 & 11 & 10 & 1 \\ 4 & 6 & 1 & 30 \end{bmatrix}$$

4	2	-2	4	1			
1	.5	-.5	1	.25			
	17	11	6	0	1		
	16	12	4	-.5	1		
	1	.75	.25	-.03125	.0625		
		10	1	0	0	1	
		0					
			30	0	0	0	1
			25	-.875	-.25	0	1
			1	-.035	-.01	0	.04

$$\begin{bmatrix} .29625 & -.0225 & 0 & -.035 \\ -.0225 & .065 & 0 & -.01 \\ 0 & 0 & 0 & 0 \\ -.035 & -.01 & 0 & .04 \end{bmatrix} = \mathbf{A}^{(-1)}$$

10. MATRIX DIFFERENTIATION

10.1a. If the elements of a matrix $\mathbf{Y}$ ($m \times n$) are functions of a scalar, x, the expression

$$\partial \mathbf{Y}/\partial x$$

denotes a matrix of order ($m \times n$) with elements $\partial y_{ij}/\partial x$.

10.1b. If the elements of a column (row) vector $\mathbf{y}$ ($\mathbf{y}'$) are functions of a scalar, x, the expression

$$\partial \mathbf{y}/\partial x \quad (\partial \mathbf{y}'/\partial x)$$

denotes a column (row) vector with elements $\partial y_i/\partial x$.

10.2a. If y is a scalar function of $m \times n$ variables, x_{ij}, arranged into a matrix $\mathbf{X}$, the expression

$$\partial y/\partial \mathbf{X}$$

denotes a matrix with elements $\partial y/\partial x_{ij}$.

(Note: Partial differentiation is performed with respect to the element in row i and column j of $\mathbf{X}$. If the same x-variable occurs in another place as, e.g., in a symmetric matrix, differentiation with respect to the distinct (repeated) variable is performed in two stages.)

Example 10.2.1

If $y = \mathbf{j}'\mathbf{Xj}$ (sum of all elements of a square matrix), $\partial y/\partial \mathbf{X}$ is a matrix of ones. If $\mathbf{X}$ is symmetric, one can introduce a new notation $x_{ij} = x_{ji} = z_{ij}$. Then

$$\begin{aligned} \partial y/\partial z_{ij} &= (\partial y/\partial x_{ij})(\partial x_{ij}/\partial z_{ij}) \\ &\quad + (\partial y/\partial x_{ji})(\partial x_{ji}/\partial z_{ij}) \\ &= 1 + 1 = 2 \quad (\text{if } i \neq j) \\ &= 1 \quad\quad\quad\; (\text{if } i = j). \end{aligned}$$

10.2b. If y is a scalar function of n variables, x_i, arranged into a column (row) vector $\mathbf{x}$ ($\mathbf{x}'$), the expression

$$\partial y/\partial \mathbf{x} \quad (\partial y/\partial \mathbf{x}')$$

denotes a column (row) vector with elements $\partial y/\partial x_i$.

10.3. If $\mathbf{y}$ is a column vector with m elements, each a function of n variables, x_i, arranged into a row vector $\mathbf{x}'$, the expression $\partial \mathbf{y}/\partial \mathbf{x}'$ denotes a matrix with m rows and n columns, with elements $\partial y_i/\partial x_j$.

10.4. $\partial \mathbf{Y}/\partial y_{ij} = (\mathbf{EL})_{ij}$ (see definition of $(\mathbf{EL})$ in 3.4).

10.5. $\partial \mathbf{UV}/\partial x = (\partial \mathbf{U}/\partial x)\mathbf{V} + \mathbf{U}(\partial \mathbf{V}/\partial x)$.

10.6. $\partial \mathbf{AY}/\partial x = \mathbf{A}(\partial \mathbf{Y}/\partial x)$ (if elements of $\mathbf{A}$ are not functions of x).

10.7. $\partial \mathbf{Y}'/\partial y_{ij} = (\mathbf{EL})_{ji}$

10.8. $\partial \mathbf{A}'\mathbf{YA}/\partial x = \mathbf{A}'(\partial \mathbf{Y}/\partial x)\mathbf{A}$

10.9: $\partial \mathbf{Y}'\mathbf{AY}/\partial x = (\partial \mathbf{Y}'/\partial x)\mathbf{AY} + \mathbf{Y}'\mathbf{A}(\partial \mathbf{Y}/\partial x)$

10.10. $\partial \mathbf{a}'\mathbf{x}/\partial \mathbf{x} = \mathbf{a}$

10.11. $\partial \mathbf{x}'\mathbf{x}/\partial \mathbf{x} = 2\mathbf{x}$

10.12. $\partial \mathbf{x}'\mathbf{A}\mathbf{x}/\partial \mathbf{x} = \mathbf{A}\mathbf{x} + \mathbf{A}'\mathbf{x}$

10.13. (Chain Rule No. 1) $\quad \partial y/\partial \mathbf{x}' = (\partial y/\partial \mathbf{z}')(\partial \mathbf{z}/\partial \mathbf{x}')$

10.14. $\partial \mathbf{A}\mathbf{x}/\partial \mathbf{x}' = \mathbf{A}$

10.15. $\partial tr\mathbf{X}/\partial \mathbf{X} = \mathbf{I}$

10.16. $\partial tr\mathbf{A}\mathbf{X}/\partial \mathbf{X} = \partial tr\mathbf{X}\mathbf{A}/\partial \mathbf{X} = \mathbf{A}'$

10.17. $\partial tr\mathbf{A}\mathbf{X}\mathbf{B}/\partial \mathbf{X} = \mathbf{A}'\mathbf{B}'$

10.18. $\partial tr\mathbf{X}'\mathbf{A}\mathbf{X}/\partial \mathbf{X} = \mathbf{A}\mathbf{X} + \mathbf{A}'\mathbf{X}$

10.19. $\partial \log |\mathbf{X}| /\partial \mathbf{X} = (\mathbf{X}')^{-1}$ $\quad$ (log to base e).

10.20. $\partial \mathbf{Y}^{-1}/\partial x = -\mathbf{Y}^{-1}(\partial \mathbf{Y}/\partial x)\,\mathbf{Y}^{-1}$.

10.21. (Chain Rule No. 2)

$$\partial y/\partial x = tr(\partial y/\partial \mathbf{Z})(\partial \mathbf{Z}'/\partial x)$$

where y and x are scalars. The scalar y is a function of $m \times n$ variables z_{ij}, and each of the z_{ij} is a function of x.

Example 10.21.1

Obtain $\log |\mathbf{R} - \mathbf{FF}'| /\partial \mathbf{F}$, where $\mathbf{R}$ is symmetric.

By Chain Rule No. 2:

$\partial \log |\mathbf{R} - \mathbf{FF}'| /\partial f_{ij}$

$\quad = tr[\partial \log |\mathbf{R} - \mathbf{FF}'| /\partial (\mathbf{R} - \mathbf{FF}')][\partial (\mathbf{R} - \mathbf{FF}')/\partial f_{ij}]$ $\quad$ (since $\mathbf{R}$ and $\mathbf{FF}'$ are symmetric)

$\quad = tr(\mathbf{R} - \mathbf{FF}')^{-1}[\partial (\mathbf{R} - \mathbf{FF}')/\partial f_{ij}]$ $\quad$ (by 10.19)

$\quad = tr(\mathbf{R} - \mathbf{FF}')^{-1}[-(\partial \mathbf{F}/\partial f_{ij})\,\mathbf{F}' - \mathbf{F}(\partial \mathbf{F}'/\partial f_{ij})]$ $\quad$ (by 10.5)

$\quad = tr(\mathbf{R} - \mathbf{FF}')^{-1}[-(\mathbf{EL})_{ij}\mathbf{F}' - \mathbf{F}(\mathbf{EL})_{ji}]$ $\quad$ (by 10.4 and 10.7)

$\quad = -tr(\mathbf{R} - \mathbf{FF}')^{-1}(\mathbf{EL})_{ij}\mathbf{F}' - tr(\mathbf{R} - \mathbf{FF}')^{-1}\mathbf{F}(\mathbf{EL})_{ji}$

$\quad = -tr(\mathbf{EL})_{ij}\mathbf{F}'(\mathbf{R} - \mathbf{FF}')^{-1} - tr(\mathbf{EL})_{ji}(\mathbf{R} - \mathbf{FF}')^{-1}\mathbf{F}$ $\quad$ (by 7.3)

$\quad = -[\mathbf{F}'(\mathbf{R} - \mathbf{FF}')^{-1}]_{ji} - [(\mathbf{R} - \mathbf{FF}')^{-1}\mathbf{F}]_{ij}$,

where $[\ ]_{ij}$ denotes the (i, j) element of the matrix in brackets (by 7.5),

$\quad = -[(\mathbf{R} - \mathbf{FF}')^{-1}\mathbf{F}]_{ij} - [(\mathbf{R} - \mathbf{FF}')^{-1}\mathbf{F}]_{ij}$ $\quad$ (since $\mathbf{R} - \mathbf{FF}'$ is symmetric)

$\quad = -2[(\mathbf{R} - \mathbf{FF}')^{-1}\mathbf{F}]_{ij}$.

Hence, by definition 10.2a

$$\partial \log |\mathbf{R} - \mathbf{FF}'| /\partial \mathbf{F} = -2(\mathbf{R} - \mathbf{FF}')^{-1}\mathbf{F}.$$

10.22. $|\partial \mathbf{y}/\partial \mathbf{x}'| = J(\mathbf{y}; \mathbf{x})$ is called the Jacobian or Functional Determinant used in variable transformation of multiple integrals. Formally, if $\mathbf{y}$ is a column vector with m elements, each a function of m variables x_i arranged into a row vector $\mathbf{x}'$,

$$dx_1 dx_2 \ldots dx_m = |\partial \mathbf{y}/\partial \mathbf{x}'|^{-1} dy_1 dy_2 \ldots dy_m.$$

10.23. For a scalar y (a function of m variables x_i) to attain a stationary value, it is necessary that

$$\partial y/\partial \mathbf{x} = \mathbf{0}.$$

10.24. For a stationary value to be a minimum (maximum) it is necessary that

$$\partial (\partial y/\partial \mathbf{x})/\partial \mathbf{x}' \quad (-\partial (\partial y/\partial \mathbf{x})/\partial \mathbf{x}')$$

be a positive-definite matrix for the value of $\mathbf{x}$ satisfying 10.23.

Example 10.24.1

Find the values of β which minimize $u = \mathbf{x}'\mathbf{x}$ (the sum of squares of x_i) where $\mathbf{x} = \mathbf{y} - \mathbf{A}\beta$ (with $\mathbf{y}$ and $\mathbf{A}$ known and fixed).

$$\partial u / \partial \beta' = (\partial u / \partial \mathbf{x}')(\partial \mathbf{x} / \partial \beta') \quad \text{(by Chain Rule No. 1)}$$
$$= -2\mathbf{x}'\mathbf{A} \quad \text{(by 10.11 and 10.14)}$$

Hence

$$\partial u / \partial \beta = -2\mathbf{A}'\mathbf{x}$$
$$= -2\mathbf{A}'(\mathbf{y} - \mathbf{A}\beta).$$

Hence, for a stationary value, by 10.23, it is necessary that

$$\mathbf{A}'\mathbf{A}\hat{\beta} = \mathbf{A}'\mathbf{y}$$

where $\hat{\beta}$ denotes the values which make u stationary. Now,

$$\partial (\partial u / \partial \beta) / \partial \beta' = 2\partial (\mathbf{A}'\mathbf{A}\beta) / \partial \beta' = 2\mathbf{A}'\mathbf{A}.$$

If **A** has real elements, and if **A'A** is non-singular, then it is positive-definite (since, given an arbitrary real $\mathbf{x} \neq \mathbf{0}$, $\mathbf{x}'\mathbf{A}'\mathbf{A}\mathbf{x} = \mathbf{z}'\mathbf{z}$, with $\mathbf{z} = \mathbf{A}\mathbf{x}$; thus this is a sum of squares). Hence $\hat{\beta}$ minimizes u.

10.25. (Generalized Newton Iteration)

Let $\mathbf{x}_0'$ be an initial estimate (m elements) of the roots of the m equations

$$\mathbf{f}(\mathbf{x}') = \mathbf{0}$$

where the m elements of the column vector **f** are each functions of $x_1, x_2, \ldots x_m$. Then an improved root is

$$\mathbf{x}_1 = \mathbf{x}_0 - \mathbf{Q}_0^{-1}\mathbf{f}(\mathbf{x}_0'),$$

where $\mathbf{Q}_0$ is the matrix of derivatives $\partial \mathbf{f} / \partial \mathbf{x}'$ evaluated at $\mathbf{x} = \mathbf{x}_0$. The usual procedure consists of evaluating $\mathbf{f}(\mathbf{x}_0')$, then solving $\mathbf{Q}_0\mathbf{u} = \mathbf{f}(\mathbf{x}_0')$ for **u**. Then $\mathbf{x}_1 = \mathbf{x}_0 - \mathbf{u}$.

Example 10.25.1

Solve

$$f_1(x, y) = x^3 - x^2 y + y^2 - 3.526 = 0$$
$$f_2(x, y) = x^3 + y^3 - 14.911 = 0$$

$$\mathbf{Q} = \begin{bmatrix} 3x^2 - 2xy & 2y - x^2 \\ 3x^2 & 3y^2 \end{bmatrix}$$

Take $x_0 = 1$, $y_0 = 2$

$$f_1(x_0, y_0) = -0.526$$
$$f_2(x_0, y_0) = -5.911$$

$$\mathbf{Q}_0 = \begin{bmatrix} -1 & 3 \\ 3 & 12 \end{bmatrix}$$

$$-u + 3v = -0.526$$
$$3u + 12v = -5.911$$

yields $u = -0.55$, $v = -0.36$.

Then,

$$x_1 = x_0 - u = 1.55$$
$$y_1 = y_0 - v = 2.36$$
$$f_1(x_1, y_1) = 0.0976$$
$$f_2(x_1, y_1) = 1.9572$$

$$Q_1 = \begin{bmatrix} -0.1085 & 2.3175 \\ 7.2075 & 16.7088 \end{bmatrix}$$

$$-0.1085u + 2.3175v = 0.0976$$
$$7.2075u + 16.7088v = 1.9572$$

yields $u = 0.157$, $v = 0.049$.

Then

$$x_2 = x_1 - u = 1.393$$
$$y_2 = y_1 - v = 2.311$$
$$f_1(x_2, y_2) = 0.03337$$
$$f_2(x_2, y_2) = 0.13443$$

$$Q_2 = \begin{bmatrix} -0.61710 & 2.68155 \\ 5.82135 & 16.02216 \end{bmatrix}$$

$$-0.61710u + 2.68155v = 0.03337$$
$$5.82135u + 16.02216v = 0.13443$$

yields $u = -0.0068$, $v = 0.0109$.

Then,

$$x_3 = x_2 - u = 1.3998$$
$$y_3 = y_2 - v = 2.3001$$

(The exact roots are $x = 1.4$ and $y = 2.3$).

11. STATISTICAL MATRIX FORMS

11.1. Let E denote the expectation operator, and let $\mathbf{y}$ be a set of p random variables. Then

$$E(\mathbf{y}) = \boldsymbol{\mu}$$

states that $E(y_i) = \mu_i$ $(i = 1, 2, \ldots p)$.

11.2. Let var denote variance. Then

$$\mathrm{var}(\mathbf{y}) = \boldsymbol{\Sigma}$$

denotes a $p \times p$ symmetric matrix whose elements are $\mathrm{cov}(y_i, y_j)$, and whose diagonal elements are $\mathrm{var}(y_i)$, where cov denotes covariance.

11.3. $E(\mathbf{AY} + \mathbf{b}) = AE(\mathbf{y}) + \mathbf{b} = A\boldsymbol{\mu} + \mathbf{b}$

11.4. $\mathrm{var}(A\mathbf{y} + \mathbf{b}) = A \, \mathrm{var}(\mathbf{y}) \, A' = A\boldsymbol{\Sigma}A'$

11.5. $\mathrm{cov}(\mathbf{y}, \mathbf{z}')$ denotes a matrix with elements $\mathrm{cov}(y_i, z_j)$.
$\mathrm{cov}(\mathbf{z}, \mathbf{y}') = [\mathrm{cov}(\mathbf{y}, \mathbf{z}')]'$.

11.6. $\mathrm{cov}(A\mathbf{y} + \mathbf{b}, \mathbf{z}'C + \mathbf{d}') = A \, \mathrm{cov}(\mathbf{y}, \mathbf{z}') \, C$

11.7. $\mathrm{var}(\mathbf{y}) = E(\mathbf{yy}') - E(\mathbf{y})E(\mathbf{y}')$

11.8. $\mathrm{cov}(\mathbf{y}, \mathbf{z}') = E(\mathbf{yz}') - E(\mathbf{y})E(\mathbf{z}')$

11.9. (Expected "sum of squares")

$$E(\mathbf{y}'Q\mathbf{y}) = tr[Q \, \mathrm{var}(\mathbf{y})] + E(\mathbf{y}')QE(\mathbf{y}).$$

11.10. If a matrix Q is symmetric and positive-definite, one can find a lower triangular matrix T (with positive diagonal terms, for uniqueness) such that $TT' = Q$. The matrices T and T^{-1} can be obtained from the Doolittle pattern (6.14) (Gauss elimination or square-root method) as follows: In each cycle, divide the p-row (left and right hand side) by $\sqrt{p_{ii}}$ (instead of p_{ii} for the u-row). Thus obtain rows designated as t-rows. The left-hand side (Arabic subscripts) is $\mathbf{T}'$, and the right-hand side (Roman subscripts) is $\mathbf{T}^{-1}$

11.11. If a coordinate system $\mathbf{x}$ is oblique, and if the cosines between reference vectors (scalar products of basis vectors of unit length) are stated in a symmetric matrix $\mathbf{Q}$, then $\mathbf{T}^{-1}\mathbf{x} = \mathbf{y}$ is an orthogonal system, where $\mathbf{T}$ is obtained from $\mathbf{Q}$ by 11.10.

11.12. The likelihood function of a sample of size n from a multivariate normal distribution (p responses), with common variance-covariance matrix $\Sigma(p \times p)$, and with means or main effects replaced by maximum-likelihood or least-squares estimates, can be written as

$$\log L = -\frac{np}{2} \log 2\pi - \frac{n}{2} \log |\Sigma| - \frac{n}{2} tr \Sigma^{-1}\mathbf{S}$$

where $\Sigma(p \times p)$ is the common variance-covariance matrix, and $\mathbf{S}$ is its maximum-likelihood estimate (matrix of sums of squares and products due to error, divided by sample size n).

11.13. If Σ has a structure under a model or null hypothesis, and if elements of Σ are to be estimated, by maximum-likelihood, two cases can be distinguished: (11.14) Σ^{-1} has the same structure (intraclass correlation, mixed model, compound symmetry, factor analysis). (11.15) Σ^{-1} has a different structure (autocorrelation, Simplex structure).

11.14. If the structure of Σ and Σ^{-1} is identical, and if u and v are elements (or functions of elements) of Σ^{-1} then estimates of Σ can be obtained from the relations (usually requiring Newton iteration, see 10.25):

$$\partial \log L/\partial u = \frac{n}{2} tr \mathbf{A}(\Sigma - \mathbf{S})$$

where $\mathbf{A} = \partial \Sigma^{-1}/\partial u$, is frequently an elementary matrix (see 3.4 and, especially, the rules 7.5 and 7.6).

$$\partial^2 \log L/\partial u \partial v = \frac{n}{2} tr(\partial \mathbf{A}/\partial v)(\Sigma - \mathbf{S}) + \frac{n}{2} tr \mathbf{A}\Sigma^{-1}\mathbf{B}\Sigma^{-1}$$

where $\mathbf{B} = \partial \Sigma^{-1}/\partial v$. These rules are useful to obtain Newton iterations and asymptotic variance-covariance matrices of the estimates.

11.15. If the structures of Σ and Σ^{-1} are different, then an estimate of Σ can be obtained from the relations

$$\partial \log L/\partial x = -\frac{n}{2} tr \mathbf{A}(\Sigma^{-1} - \mathbf{Q}),$$

where

$$\mathbf{Q} = \Sigma^{-1}\mathbf{S}\Sigma^{-1}$$

and

$$\mathbf{A} = \partial \Sigma/\partial x \qquad \text{(see comments in 11.14)}.$$

$$\partial^2 \log L/\partial x \partial y = -\frac{n}{2} tr(\partial \mathbf{A}/\partial y)(\Sigma^{-1} - \mathbf{Q}) + \frac{n}{2} tr \mathbf{A}\Sigma^{-1}\mathbf{B}(\Sigma^{-1} - \mathbf{Q}) - \frac{n}{2} tr \mathbf{A}\mathbf{Q}\mathbf{B}\Sigma^{-1},$$

where

$$\mathbf{B} = \partial \Sigma/\partial y$$

x and y are elements (or functions of elements) of Σ. The comments of 11.14 apply, but the iterative procedure is considerably more complex.

Suggestions for further reading:

A. S. Householder, *The Theory of Matrices in Numerical Analysis*, Blaisdell, 1964.
S. R. Searle, *Matrix Algebra for the Biological Sciences*, Wiley, 1966.
P. H. Schonemann, Matrix differentiation of traces and determinants, *Psychometrika*, 1966.

USE OF LOGARITHMS

LAWS OF EXPONENTS

For a any real number and m a positive integer, the exponential a^m is defined as

$$\underbrace{a \cdot a \cdot a \cdots a}_{m \text{ terms}}$$

Using this definition, it is easy to show that the following three *laws of exponents* hold:

I. $a^m \cdot a^n = a^{m+n}$

II. $\dfrac{a^m}{a^n} = \begin{cases} a^{m-n} & \text{if } m > n \\ 1 & \text{if } m = n \\ \dfrac{1}{a^{n-m}} & \text{if } m < n \end{cases}$

III. $(a^m)^n = a^{mn}$

The n-th root function is defined as the inverse of the n-th power function; that is, if

$$b^n = a, \quad \text{then} \quad b = \sqrt[n]{a}.$$

If n is odd, there will be a unique real number satisfying the above definition for $\sqrt[n]{a}$, for any real value of a. If n is even, for positive values of a there will be two real values for $\sqrt[n]{a}$, one positive and one negative. By convention, the symbol $\sqrt[n]{a}$ is understood to mean the positive value in this case. If n is even and a is negative, there are no real values for $\sqrt[n]{a}$.

If we now attempt to extend the definition of the exponential a^t to all rational values of the exponent t, in such a way that the three laws of exponents continue to hold, it is easily shown that the required definitions are:

$$a^0 = 1$$
$$a^{p/q} = \sqrt[q]{a^p}$$
$$a^{-t} = \frac{1}{a^t}$$

In order to avoid difficulties with imaginary numbers and division by zero, a must now be restricted to be positive.

With this extended definition, it is possible to restate the second law of exponents in a simpler form:

II′. $\dfrac{a^m}{a^n} = a^{m-n}$

It is shown in advanced calculus that this definition may be further extended so that the exponent may be any real number, and the laws of exponents continue to hold. When the quantity a^x thus defined is viewed as a function of the exponent x, with the base a held constant, it is a continuous function. Also, if $a > 1$, the exponential function is monotone increasing, and if $0 < a < 1$, it is monotone decreasing.

LOGARITHMS

Any monotone function has a single-valued inverse function, which is also monotone. Furthermore, if the original function is continuous, so is the inverse. Therefore, the inverse function to the exponential function a^x exists for all positive values of a, except $a = 1$. This function is given the name *logarithm to the base a*, abbreviated $\log_a$. That is, if

$$x = a^y, \quad \text{then} \quad y = \log_a x.$$

This function is defined and continuous for all positive values of x. It is monotone increasing if $a > 1$, and monotone decreasing if $a < 1$.

If the laws of exponents are rewritten in terms of logarithms, they become the *laws of logarithms*:

I. $\log_a(xy) = \log_a x + \log_a y$

II. $\log_a\left(\dfrac{x}{y}\right) = \log_a x - \log_a y$

III. $\log_a(x^n) = n \log_a x$

Logarithms derive their main usefulness in computation from the above laws, since they allow multiplication, division, and exponentiation to be replaced by the simpler operations of addition, subtraction, and multiplication, respectively. See the examples which follow.

Further recourse to the definition of logarithm leads to the following formula for change of base

$$\log_a x = \log_b x / \log_b a = (\log_b x) \cdot (\log_a b)$$

Two numbers are commonly used as bases for logarithms. Logarithms to the base 10 are most convenient for use in computation. These logarithm are called common or Briggsian logarithms.

The other usual base for logarithms is an irrational number denoted by e, whose value is approximately 2.71828 .... These logarithms are called natural, Naperian, or hyperbolic logarithms, and occur in many formulas of higher mathematics. The abbreviation ln is frequently used for the natural logarithm function.

Other bases for logarithms, such as 2 and 3, occur in certain applications. These applications are so infrequent that separate tables for these bases are usually not given. Instead, the formulas for change of base are applied to common or natural logarithms.

If the formulas for change of base are applied to the two usual bases, the following formulas result:

$$\log_{10} x = \log_e x / \log_e 10 = (\log_{10} e)(\log_e x) = M \log_e x$$
$$= 0.43429\ 44819 \log_e x$$
$$\log_e x = \log_{10} x / \log_{10} e = (\log_e 10)(\log_{10} x) = \frac{1}{M} \log_{10} x$$
$$= 2.30258\ 50930 \log_{10} x$$

The following remarks apply to common logarithms.

Since most numbers are irrational powers of ten, a common logarithm, in general, consists of an integer, which is called the characteristic, and an endless decimal, the mantissa.

It is to be observed that the common logarithms of all numbers expressed by the same figures in the same order with the decimal point in different positions have different characteristics but the same mantissa. To illustrate:—if the decimal point stand after the first figure of a number, counting from the left, the characteristic is 0; if after two figures, it is 1; if after three figures, it is 2; and so forth. If the decimal point stand before the first significant figure the characteristic is −1, usually written $\bar{1}$; if there is one zero between the decimal point and the first significant figure it is $\bar{2}$, and so on. For example: log 256 = 2.408240, log 2.56 = 0.408240, log 0.256 = $\bar{1}$.408240, log 0.00256 = $\bar{3}$.408240. The two latter are often written log 0.256 = 9.408240 − 10, log 0.00256 = 7.408240 − 10.

Notice that, although the common logarithm of a number less than one is a negative number, it is customarily written as a negative characteristic and a *positive* mantissa, since the mantissas are usually given in tables as positive numbers. This is the reason that the negative sign is written above the characteristic, since it does not apply to the mantissa. Thus log 0.00256 = $\bar{3}$.408240 = 7.408240 − 10 = −2.591760.

A method of determining characteristics of logarithms is to write the number with one figure to the left of the decimal point multiplied by the appropriate power of 10. The characteristic is then the exponent used. For example:

$$256\ 000\ 000 = 2.56 \times 10^8 \qquad \log = 8.408240$$
$$0.000\ 000\ 256 = 2.56 \times 10^{-7} \qquad \log = \bar{7}.408240 \quad \text{or} \quad 3.408240 - 10$$

Inasmuch as the characteristic may be determined by inspection, the mantissas only are given in tables of common logarithms.

USE OF LOGARITHM TABLES

To find the common logarithm of a number:

(*Note:* This description and examples refer specifically to the table entitled "Six-Place Mantissas for Common Logarithms." For the other tables, there will be minor differences from this description. Most of these differences are obvious. Notes with the individual tables explain any differences which are not immediately obvious.)

For a number of four figures, take out the tabular mantissa on a line with the first three figures of the number and under its fourth figure. The characteristic is determined as previously explained.

For a number of less than four figures, supply zeros to make a four figure number and take the value of the mantissa from the tables as before. For example: log 2 = log 2.000 = 0.301030.

(Notice that in some of the tables not all of the digits of the logarithm are given for every value. For example, in the table of six-place common logarithms, the first two digits of each mantissa are given only once for each line. The remaining four digits of each mantissa are given in the correct place in the table. When the leading two digits are not given on a line, they should be taken from the last line above it on which they do appear. When a mantissa is marked with an asterisk, it indicates that the value for the leading digits is to be taken from the *next* line instead of the present line. Similar remarks apply to the other tables in which this method of presenting the values are used.)

For a number of more than four figures, interpolation must be used. There are several precautions that must be observed when interpolating:

1. Linear interpolation, as described below, may only be used to add one extra digit to the argument (i.e., in the present case, for a five-digit argument).

2. Even though the mantissas given in the table are accurate to six decimal places, interpolated values are accurate only to the same number of places as in the argument, i.e. five places.

3. Because of the rapidly changing values in this region of the table, interpolation is not accurate if the first two digits of the argument are 11 or 12. For this reason, the table has been extended at the end so that such values may be read directly from

the table with five-digit arguments, without interpolation. (The four-place table is not so extended. If interpolation is required in this section of the four-place table, the value should be read instead from the six-place table without interpolation.)

If the above precautions cannot be observed, then higher order interpolation should be used.

Where applicable, linear interpolation is carried out as follows:

Take the tabular value of the mantissa for the first four figures; find the difference between the mantissa and the next greater tabular mantissa and multiply the difference so found by the remaining figures of the number as a decimal and add the product to the mantissa of the first four figures. For example, to find log 46.762:

$$\log 46.76 = 1.669875$$

Tabular difference between this mantissa and that for 4677 is .000092

$$\therefore \log 46.762 = 1.669875 + .2 \times .000092$$
$$= 1.669875 + .000018$$
$$= 1.669893$$

The last digit is not accurate, so must be rounded out. Thus

$$\log 46.762 = 1.66989$$

The accuracy will not ordinarily be affected by more than 1 in the last place if the mantissas are rounded to five decimal places before interpolation, and this makes the computation somewhat easier.

In the four-place logarithm table, a column of proportional parts is given at the end of each line. The number in the column under the fourth digit of the argument is the amount that must be added to any mantissa in that line to interpolate for the fourth digit. This number is to be added to the last place of the mantissa. These numbers are averages for the entire line, so may be off by 1 in the last place.

For example, to find log 33.74

$$\log 33.7 = 1.5276$$
$$\text{proportional part for } 4 = \underline{5}$$
$$\therefore \log 33.74 = 1.5281$$

To find the number corresponding to a given logarithm:

(*Note*: This number is called the antilogarithm, and is denoted by $\log^{-1}$. Since the logarithm function is the inverse of the exponential function, $\log_a^{-1} x = a^x$. Therefore, any procedure or table which calculates antilogarithms may also be used to calculate exponentials, and vice-versa. In particular, tables of e^x may be used to compute antilogarithms to the base e.)

The procedure given below refers to the six-place logarithm table. As before, any significant deviation for other tables will be noted.

If the mantissa is found exactly in the table, join the figure at the top which is directly above the given mantissa to the three figures on the line at the left and place the decimal point according to the characteristic of the logarithm. For example,

$$\log^{-1} 3.399674 = \text{antilog } 3.399674 = 2510.$$

If the mantissa is not found exactly in the table it is necessary to interpolate. For example, to find antilog 3.400280, we find in the table

$$\text{antilog } 3.400192 = 2513.$$
$$\text{antilog } \underline{3.400365} = 2514.$$
$$\text{tabular difference} \qquad 173$$

The required difference is 88, so we must add $\frac{88}{173}$ = .5.

$$\therefore \text{ antilog } 3.400280 = 2513.5$$

The same precautions must be observed for interpolation in finding antilogarithms as in finding logarithms.

A four-place antilogarithm table is also provided. When using this table, the mantissa of the logarithm is looked up on the margins of the table, and the significant digits of the antilogarithm are read from the body of the table. Lookup and interpolation are done in the same manner as when looking up logarithms in a table of logarithms.

Tables of natural logarithms are used in the same way as tables of common logarithms, except that they contain both the characteristics and the mantissas of the logarithms.

Examples of the use of logarithms in computation follow. Almost all computation with logarithms is done with common logarithms, since the computation of the characteristic is simpler, and since only the significant digits of the argument need be given in the table, without regard for the decimal point location. These examples all use the table of six-place common logarithms.

1. 52600 × 0.00381 × 2.74 = 549.11

```
log 52600        = 4.720986
log       0.00381 = 3.580925
log       2.74    = 0.437751
adding           = 2.739662
antilog          = 549.11
```

The sum is the logarithm of the product, the mantissa of which is 739662. On looking up this mantissa in the logarithm tables we see that it corresponds to the digits 54911. The characteristic is 2, hence there are three figures before the decimal point. The number corresponding to the logarithm, called the antilogarithm, is 549.11.

2. 0.00123 ÷ 52.7 = 0.000 023 34   An alternative method:

```
log  0.00123 = 3̄.089905          log  0.00123 = 7.089905 − 10
log 52.7     = 1.721811          log 52.7     = 1.721811
subtracting  = 5̄.368094                       5.368094 − 10
antilog      = 0.000 023 34
```

The characteristic 5̄(5. − 10) shows four zeros after the decimal point before the first significant figure.

3. $\dfrac{273 \times 780}{292 \times 760} \times 15 \times 0.09 = 1.2954$

```
log 273       = 2.436163          log 292              = 2.465383
log 780       = 2.892095          log 760              = 2.880814
log  15       = 1.176091          log denominator = 5.346197
log   0.09    = 2̄.954243
log numerator = 5.458592
```

```
log numerator   = 5.458592
log denominator = 5.346197
subtracting     = 0.112395
antilog         = 1.2954
```

As division may be accomplished by multiplying by the reciprocal of a number, the above may be considerably simplified. The logarithm of the reciprocal of a number, called the cologarithm, is readily obtained from the table by subtracting the logarithm of the number from zero. This may be readily read off from the table of mantissas. Change the sign of the characteristic algebraically adding to it -1, then mentally subtract each figure of the mantissa from 9 proceeding from left to right, the last figure being subtracted from 10. The example then is:

$$
\begin{array}{lll}
\log 273 & = & 2.436163 \\
\log 780 & = & 2.892095 \\
\log \ 15 & = & 1.176091 \\
\log \ \ 0.09 & = & \bar{2}.954243 \\
\text{colog } 292 & = & \bar{3}.534617 \\
\text{colog } 760 & = & \bar{3}.119186 \\
& & 0.112395
\end{array}
$$

4. $(0.00098)^4 = 9.2237 \times 10^{-13}$ An alternative method:

$$
\begin{array}{lll}
\log 0.00098 & = & \bar{4}.991226 \\
& & \underline{4} \\
& & 3.964904 \ \ (a) \\
\bar{4} \times 4 & = & \underline{\bar{16}.} \ \ \ (b) \\
\log (0.00098)^4 & = & \bar{13}.964904 \ \ (c) \\
\text{antilog} & = & 9.2237 \times 10^{-13}
\end{array}
$$

$$
\begin{array}{lll}
\log 0.00098 & = & 6.991226 - 10 \\
& & \underline{4} \\
& & 27.964904 - 40 \\
\text{or} & & 7.964904 - 20 \\
\text{or} & & \bar{13}.964904 \\
\text{antilog} & = & 9.2237 \times 10^{-13}
\end{array}
$$

In the above it will be noted that the mantissa is always positive, hence the multiplication of the mantissa shown at (a), while (b) shows the multiplication of the characteristic. (c) is the algebraic sum.

5. $\sqrt[5]{492} = 3.4546$
    $\log 492 = 2.691965$

Dividing the logarithm by 5 gives as the logarithm of the root 0.538393 the antilogarithm of which is 3.4546 both characteristic and mantissa being positive. When the characteristic is negative and not evenly divisible by the root to be taken, a modification of the logarithm is necessary, as the following example shows:

6. $\sqrt[3]{0.000372} = 0.07192$
    $\log 3.72 \times 10^{-4} = \bar{4}.570543$ (a)
              $= 26.570543 - 30$ (b)

Dividing (b) by 3 gives $8.856848 - 10$ which may be written $\bar{2}.856848$ and is the logarithm of the root sought, the antilogarithm of which is 0.07192.

7. $(0.000\ 372)^{1.2} = 0.000\ 076\ 675$
    $\log 0.000\ 372 = \bar{4}.570543$
            or $6.570543 - 10$
                    $\underline{1.2}$
                $7.884652 - 12$
    antilog $= 0.000\ 076\ 675$

8. $(0.000372)^{-1.32} = 33642$
    colog $0.000372 = 3.429457$
                  $\underline{1.32}$
                 4.526883
    antilog $= 33642$

*FOUR-PLACE MANTISSAS FOR COMMON LOGARITHMS OF DECIMAL FRACTIONS

N	0	1	2	3	4	5	6	7	8	9
.10	-1.000	$-.9957$	$-.9914$	$-.9872$	$-.9830$	$-.9788$	$-.9747$	$-.9706$	$-.9666$	$-.9626$
.11	$-.9586$	$-.9547$	$-.9508$	$-.9469$	$-.9431$	$-.9393$	$-.9355$	$-.9318$	$-.9281$	$-.9245$
.12	$-.9208$	$-.9172$	$-.9136$	$-.9101$	$-.9066$	$-.9031$	$-.8996$	$-.8962$	$-.8928$	$-.8894$
.13	$-.8861$	$-.8827$	$-.8794$	$-.8761$	$-.8729$	$-.8697$	$-.8665$	$-.8633$	$-.8601$	$-.8570$
.14	$-.8539$	$-.8508$	$-.8477$	$-.8447$	$-.8416$	$-.8386$	$-.8356$	$-.8327$	$-.8297$	$-.8268$
.15	$-.8239$	$-.8210$	$-.8182$	$-.8153$	$-.8125$	$-.8097$	$-.8069$	$-.8041$	$-.8013$	$-.7986$
.16	$-.7959$	$-.7932$	$-.7905$	$-.7878$	$-.7852$	$-.7825$	$-.7799$	$-.7773$	$-.7747$	$-.7721$
.17	$-.7696$	$-.7670$	$-.7645$	$-.7620$	$-.7595$	$-.7570$	$-.7545$	$-.7520$	$-.7496$	$-.7471$
.18	$-.7447$	$-.7423$	$-.7399$	$-.7375$	$-.7352$	$-.7328$	$-.7305$	$-.7282$	$-.7258$	$-.7235$
.19	$-.7212$	$-.7190$	$-.7167$	$-.7144$	$-.7122$	$-.7100$	$-.7077$	$-.7055$	$-.7033$	$-.7011$
.20	$-.6990$	$-.6968$	$-.6946$	$-.6925$	$-.6904$	$-.6882$	$-.6861$	$-.6840$	$-.6819$	$-.6799$
.21	$-.6778$	$-.6757$	$-.6737$	$-.6716$	$-.6696$	$-.6676$	$-.6655$	$-.6635$	$-.6615$	$-.6596$
.22	$-.6576$	$-.6556$	$-.6536$	$-.6517$	$-.6498$	$-.6478$	$-.6459$	$-.6440$	$-.6421$	$-.6402$
.23	$-.6383$	$-.6364$	$-.6345$	$-.6326$	$-.6308$	$-.6289$	$-.6271$	$-.6253$	$-.6234$	$-.6216$
.24	$-.6198$	$-.6180$	$-.6162$	$-.6144$	$-.6126$	$-.6108$	$-.6091$	$-.6073$	$-.6055$	$-.6038$
.25	$-.6021$	$-.6003$	$-.5986$	$-.5969$	$-.5952$	$-.5935$	$-.5918$	$-.5901$	$-.5884$	$-.5867$
.26	$-.5850$	$-.5834$	$-.5817$	$-.5800$	$-.5784$	$-.5768$	$-.5751$	$-.5735$	$-.5719$	$-.5702$
.27	$-.5686$	$-.5670$	$-.5654$	$-.5638$	$-.5622$	$-.5607$	$-.5591$	$-.5575$	$-.5560$	$-.5544$
.28	$-.5528$	$-.5513$	$-.5498$	$-.5482$	$-.5467$	$-.5452$	$-.5436$	$-.5421$	$-.5406$	$-.5391$
.29	$-.5376$	$-.5361$	$-.5346$	$-.5331$	$-.5317$	$-.5302$	$-.5287$	$-.5272$	$-.5258$	$-.5243$
.30	$-.5229$	$-.5214$	$-.5200$	$-.5186$	$-.5171$	$-.5157$	$-.5143$	$-.5129$	$-.5114$	$-.5100$
.31	$-.5086$	$-.5072$	$-.5058$	$-.5045$	$-.5031$	$-.5017$	$-.5003$	$-.4989$	$-.4976$	$-.4962$
.32	$-.4949$	$-.4935$	$-.4921$	$-.4908$	$-.4895$	$-.4881$	$-.4868$	$-.4855$	$-.4841$	$-.4828$
.33	$-.4815$	$-.4802$	$-.4789$	$-.4776$	$-.4763$	$-.4750$	$-.4737$	$-.4724$	$-.4711$	$-.4698$
.34	$-.4685$	$-.4672$	$-.4660$	$-.4647$	$-.4634$	$-.4622$	$-.4609$	$-.4597$	$-.4584$	$-.4572$
.35	$-.4559$	$-.4547$	$-.4535$	$-.4522$	$-.4510$	$-.4498$	$-.4486$	$-.4473$	$-.4461$	$-.4449$
.36	$-.4437$	$-.4425$	$-.4413$	$-.4401$	$-.4389$	$-.4377$	$-.4365$	$-.4353$	$-.4342$	$-.4330$
.37	$-.4318$	$-.4306$	$-.4295$	$-.4283$	$-.4271$	$-.4260$	$-.4248$	$-.4237$	$-.4225$	$-.4214$
.38	$-.4202$	$-.4191$	$-.4179$	$-.4168$	$-.4157$	$-.4145$	$-.4134$	$-.4123$	$-.4112$	$-.4101$
.39	$-.4089$	$-.4078$	$-.4067$	$-.4056$	$-.4045$	$-.4034$	$-.4023$	$-.4012$	$-.4001$	$-.3990$
.40	$-.3979$	$-.3969$	$-.3958$	$-.3947$	$-.3936$	$-.3925$	$-.3915$	$-.3904$	$-.3893$	$-.3883$
.41	$-.3872$	$-.3862$	$-.3851$	$-.3840$	$-.3830$	$-.3820$	$-.3809$	$-.3799$	$-.3788$	$-.3778$
.42	$-.3768$	$-.3757$	$-.3747$	$-.3737$	$-.3726$	$-.3716$	$-.3706$	$-.3696$	$-.3686$	$-.3675$
.43	$-.3665$	$-.3655$	$-.3645$	$-.3635$	$-.3625$	$-.3615$	$-.3605$	$-.3595$	$-.3585$	$-.3575$
.44	$-.3565$	$-.3556$	$-.3546$	$-.3536$	$-.3526$	$-.3516$	$-.3507$	$-.3497$	$-.3487$	$-.3478$
.45	$-.3468$	$-.3458$	$-.3449$	$-.3439$	$-.3429$	$-.3420$	$-.3410$	$-.3401$	$-.3391$	$-.3382$
.46	$-.3372$	$-.3363$	$-.3354$	$-.3344$	$-.3335$	$-.3325$	$-.3316$	$-.3307$	$-.3298$	$-.3288$
.47	$-.3279$	$-.3270$	$-.3261$	$-.3251$	$-.3242$	$-.3233$	$-.3224$	$-.3215$	$-.3206$	$-.3197$
.48	$-.3188$	$-.3179$	$-.3170$	$-.3161$	$-.3152$	$-.3143$	$-.3134$	$-.3125$	$-.3116$	$-.3107$
.49	$-.3098$	$-.3089$	$-.3080$	$-.3072$	$-.3063$	$-.3054$	$-.3045$	$-.3036$	$-.3028$	$-.3019$
.50	$-.3010$	$-.3002$	$-.2993$	$-.2984$	$-.2976$	$-.2967$	$-.2958$	$-.2950$	$-.2941$	$-.2933$
.51	$-.2924$	$-.2916$	$-.2907$	$-.2899$	$-.2890$	$-.2882$	$-.2874$	$-.2865$	$-.2857$	$-.2848$
.52	$-.2840$	$-.2832$	$-.2823$	$-.2815$	$-.2807$	$-.2798$	$-.2790$	$-.2782$	$-.2774$	$-.2765$
.53	$-.2757$	$-.2749$	$-.2741$	$-.2733$	$-.2725$	$-.2716$	$-.2708$	$-.2700$	$-.2692$	$-.2684$
.54	$-.2676$	$-.2668$	$-.2660$	$-.2652$	$-.2644$	$-.2636$	$-.2628$	$-.2620$	$-.2612$	$-.2604$

* This table gives the logarithms of the decimal fractions which are negative numbers.

For example log $0.61 = -0.2147 = 9.7853 - 10$. It should be noted that the entries as given can be used conveniently to find cologarithms of positive numbers. Every positive number $N = P \cdot (10)^k$, where $0 < P \leqq 1$. Since colog $N = -$ log N, it follows that colog $N = -$ log $P - k$.

For example colog $0.61 = -$ log $0.61 = 0.2147$; colog $61 = 0.2147 - 2$; and colog $0.00061 = 3.2147$.

*FOUR-PLACE MANTISSAS FOR COMMON LOGARITHMS OF DECIMAL FRACTIONS (Continued)

N	0	1	2	3	4	5	6	7	8	9
.55	− .2596	− .2588	− .2581	− .2573	− .2565	− .2557	− .2549	− .2541	− .2534	− .2526
.56	− .2518	− .2510	− .2503	− .2495	− .2487	− .2480	− .2472	− .2464	− .2457	− .2449
.57	− .2441	− .2434	− .2426	− .2418	− .2411	− .2403	− .2396	− .2388	− .2381	− .2373
.58	− .2366	− .2358	− .2351	− .2343	− .2336	− .2328	− .2321	− .2314	− .2306	− .2299
.59	− .2291	− .2284	− .2277	− .2269	− .2262	− .2255	− .2248	− .2240	− .2233	− .2226
.60	− .2218	− .2211	− .2204	− .2197	− .2190	− .2182	− .2175	− .2168	− .2161	− .2154
.61	− .2147	− .2140	− .2132	− .2125	− .2118	− .2111	− .2104	− .2097	− .2090	− .2083
.62	− .2076	− .2069	− .2062	− .2055	− .2048	− .2041	− .2034	− .2027	− .2020	− .2013
.63	− .2007	− .2000	− .1993	− .1986	− .1979	− .1972	− .1965	− .1959	− .1952	− .1945
.64	− .1938	− .1931	− .1925	− .1918	− .1911	− .1904	− .1898	− .1891	− .1884	− .1878
.65	− .1871	− .1864	− .1858	− .1851	− .1844	− .1838	− .1831	− .1824	− .1818	− .1811
.66	− .1805	− .1798	− .1791	− .1785	− .1778	− .1772	− .1765	− .1759	− .1752	− .1746
.67	− .1739	− .1733	− .1726	− .1720	− .1713	− .1707	− .1701	− .1694	− .1688	− .1681
.68	− .1675	− .1669	− .1662	− .1656	− .1649	− .1643	− .1637	− .1630	− .1624	− .1618
.69	− .1612	− .1605	− .1599	− .1593	− .1586	− .1580	− .1574	− .1568	− .1561	− .1555
.70	− .1549	− .1543	− .1537	− .1530	− .1524	− .1518	− .1512	− .1506	− .1500	− .1494
.71	− .1487	− .1481	− .1475	− .1469	− .1463	− .1457	− .1451	− .1445	− .1439	− .1433
.72	− .1427	− .1421	− .1415	− .1409	− .1403	− .1397	− .1391	− .1385	− .1379	− .1373
.73	− .1367	− .1361	− .1355	− .1349	− .1343	− .1337	− .1331	− .1325	− .1319	− .1314
.74	− .1308	− .1302	− .1296	− .1290	− .1284	− .1278	− .1273	− .1267	− .1261	− .1255
.75	− .1249	− .1244	− .1238	− .1232	− .1226	− .1221	− .1215	− .1209	− .1203	− .1198
.76	− .1192	− .1186	− .1180	− .1175	− .1169	− .1163	− .1158	− .1152	− .1146	− .1141
.77	− .1135	− .1129	− .1124	− .1118	− .1113	− .1107	− .1101	− .1096	− .1090	− .1085
.78	− .1079	− .1073	− .1068	− .1062	− .1057	− .1051	− .1046	− .1040	− .1035	− .1029
.79	− .1024	− .1018	− .1013	− .1007	− .1002	− .0996	− .0991	− .0985	− .0980	− .0975
.80	− .0969	− .0964	− .0958	− .0953	− .0947	− .0942	− .0937	− .0931	− .0926	− .0921
.81	− .0915	− .0910	− .0904	− .0899	− .0894	− .0888	− .0883	− .0878	− .0872	− .0867
.82	− .0862	− .0857	− .0851	− .0846	− .0841	− .0835	− .0830	− .0825	− .0820	− .0814
.83	− .0809	− .0804	− .0799	− .0794	− .0788	− .0783	− .0778	− .0773	− .0768	− .0762
.84	− .0757	− .0752	− .0747	− .0742	− .0737	− .0731	− .0726	− .0721	− .0716	− .0711
.85	− .0706	− .0701	− .0696	− .0691	− .0685	− .0680	− .0675	− .0670	− .0665	− .0660
.86	− .0655	− .0650	− .0645	− .0640	− .0635	− .0630	− .0625	− .0620	− .0615	− .0610
.87	− .0605	− .0600	− .0595	− .0590	− .0585	− .0580	− .0575	− .0570	− .0565	− .0560
.88	− .0555	− .0550	− .0545	− .0540	− .0535	− .0531	− .0526	− .0521	− .0516	− .0511
.89	− .0506	− .0501	− .0496	− .0491	− .0487	− .0482	− .0477	− .0472	− .0467	− .0462
.90	− .0458	− .0453	− .0448	− .0443	− .0438	− .0434	− .0429	− .0424	− .0419	− .0414
.91	− .0410	− .0405	− .0400	− .0395	− .0391	− .0386	− .0381	− .0376	− .0372	− .0367
.92	− .0362	− .0357	− .0353	− .0348	− .0343	− .0339	− .0334	− .0329	− .0325	− .0320
.93	− .0315	− .0311	− .0306	− .0301	− .0297	− .0292	− .0287	− .0283	− .0278	− .0273
.94	− .0269	− .0264	− .0259	− .0255	− .0250	− .0246	− .0241	− .0237	− .0232	− .0227
.95	− .0223	− .0218	− .0214	− .0209	− .0205	− .0200	− .0195	− .0191	− .0186	− .0182
.96	− .0177	− .0173	− .0168	− .0164	− .0159	− .0155	− .0150	− .0146	− .0141	− .0137
.97	− .0132	− .0128	− .0123	− .0119	− .0114	− .0110	− .0106	− .0101	− .0097	− .0092
.98	− .0088	− .0083	− .0079	− .0074	− .0070	− .0066	− .0061	− .0057	− .0052	− .0048
.99	− .0044	− .0039	− .0035	− .0031	− .0026	− .0022	− .0017	− .0013	− .0009	− .0004

* See footnote page 136.

FOUR-PLACE MANTISSAS FOR COMMON LOGARITHMS

N	0	1	2	3	4	5	6	7	8	9	Proportional Parts								
											1	2	3	4	5	6	7	8	9
10	0000	0043	0086	0128	0170	0212	0253	0294	0334	0374	*4	8	12	17	21	25	29	33	37
11	0414	0453	0492	0531	0569	0607	0645	0682	0719	0755	4	8	11	15	19	23	26	30	34
12	0792	0828	0864	0899	0934	0969	1004	1038	1072	1106	3	7	10	14	17	21	24	28	31
13	1139	1173	1206	1239	1271	1303	1335	1367	1399	1430	3	6	10	13	16	19	23	26	29
14	1461	1492	1523	1553	1584	1614	1644	1673	1703	1732	3	6	9	12	15	18	21	24	27
15	1761	1790	1818	1847	1875	1903	1931	1959	1987	2014	*3	6	8	11	14	17	20	22	25
16	2041	2068	2095	2122	2148	2175	2201	2227	2253	2279	3	5	8	11	13	16	18	21	24
17	2304	2330	2355	2380	2405	2430	2455	2480	2504	2529	2	5	7	10	12	15	17	20	22
18	2553	2577	2601	2625	2648	2672	2695	2718	2742	2765	2	5	7	9	12	14	16	19	21
19	2788	2810	2833	2856	2878	2900	2923	2945	2967	2989	2	4	7	9	11	13	16	18	20
20	3010	3032	3054	3075	3096	3118	3139	3160	3181	3201	2	4	6	8	11	13	15	17	19
21	3222	3243	3263	3284	3304	3324	3345	3365	3385	3404	2	4	6	8	10	12	14	16	18
22	3424	3444	3464	3483	3502	3522	3541	3560	3579	3598	2	4	6	8	10	12	14	15	17
23	3617	3636	3655	3674	3692	3711	3729	3747	3766	3784	2	4	6	7	9	11	13	15	17
24	3802	3820	3838	3856	3874	3892	3909	3927	3945	3962	2	4	5	7	9	11	12	14	16
25	3979	3997	4014	4031	4048	4065	4082	4099	4116	4133	2	3	5	7	9	10	12	14	15
26	4150	4166	4183	4200	4216	4232	4249	4265	4281	4298	2	3	5	7	8	10	11	13	15
27	4314	4330	4346	4362	4378	4393	4409	4425	4440	4456	2	3	5	6	8	9	11	13	14
28	4472	4487	4502	4518	4533	4548	4564	4579	4594	4609	2	3	5	6	8	9	11	12	14
29	4624	4639	4654	4669	4683	4698	4713	4728	4742	4757	1	3	4	6	7	9	10	12	13
30	4771	4786	4800	4814	4829	4843	4857	4871	4886	4900	1	3	4	6	7	9	10	11	13
31	4914	4928	4942	4955	4969	4983	4997	5011	5024	5038	1	3	4	6	7	8	10	11	12
32	5051	5065	5079	5092	5105	5119	5132	5145	5159	5172	1	3	4	5	7	8	9	11	12
33	5185	5198	5211	5224	5237	5250	5263	5276	5289	5302	1	3	4	5	6	8	9	10	12
34	5315	5328	5340	5353	5366	5378	5391	5403	5416	5428	1	3	4	5	6	8	9	10	11
35	5441	5453	5465	5478	5490	5502	5514	5527	5539	5551	1	2	4	5	6	7	9	10	11
36	5563	5575	5587	5599	5611	5623	5635	5647	5658	5670	1	2	4	5	6	7	8	10	11
37	5682	5694	5705	5717	5729	5740	5752	5763	5775	5786	1	2	3	5	6	7	8	9	10
38	5798	5809	5821	5832	5843	5855	5866	5877	5888	5899	1	2	3	5	6	7	8	9	10
39	5911	5922	5933	5944	5955	5966	5977	5988	5999	6010	1	2	3	4	5	7	8	9	10
40	6021	6031	6042	6053	6064	6075	6085	6096	6107	6117	1	2	3	4	5	6	8	9	10
41	6128	6138	6149	6160	6170	6180	6191	6201	6212	6222	1	2	3	4	5	6	7	8	9
42	6232	6243	6253	6263	6274	6284	6294	6304	6314	6325	1	2	3	4	5	6	7	8	9
43	6335	6345	6355	6365	6375	6385	6395	6405	6415	6425	1	2	3	4	5	6	7	8	9
44	6435	6444	6454	6464	6474	6484	6493	6503	6513	6522	1	2	3	4	5	6	7	8	9
45	6532	6542	6551	6561	6571	6580	6590	6599	6609	6618	1	2	3	4	5	6	7	8	9
46	6628	6637	6646	6656	6665	6675	6684	6693	6702	6712	1	2	3	4	5	6	7	7	8
47	6721	6730	6739	6749	6758	6767	6776	6785	6794	6803	1	2	3	4	5	5	6	7	8
48	6812	6821	6830	6839	6848	6857	6866	6875	6884	6893	1	2	3	4	4	5	6	7	8
49	6902	6911	6920	6928	6937	6946	6955	6964	6972	6981	1	2	3	4	4	5	6	7	8
50	6990	6998	7007	7016	7024	7033	7042	7050	7059	7067	1	2	3	3	4	5	6	7	8
51	7076	7084	7093	7101	7110	7118	7126	7135	7143	7152	1	2	3	3	4	5	6	7	8
52	7160	7168	7177	7185	7193	7202	7210	7218	7226	7235	1	2	2	3	4	5	6	7	7
53	7243	7251	7259	7267	7275	7284	7292	7300	7308	7316	1	2	2	3	4	5	6	6	7
54	7324	7332	7340	7348	7356	7364	7372	7380	7388	7396	1	2	2	3	4	5	6	6	7
N	0	1	2	3	4	5	6	7	8	9	1	2	3	4	5	6	7	8	9

* Interpolation in this section of the table is inaccurate.

Logarithm Tables

FOUR-PLACE MANTISSAS FOR COMMON LOGARITHMS (Continued)

N	0	1	2	3	4	5	6	7	8	9	1	2	3	4	5	6	7	8	9
											Proportional Parts								
55	7404	7412	7419	7427	7435	7443	7451	7459	7466	7474	1	2	2	3	4	5	5	6	7
56	7482	7490	7497	7505	7513	7520	7528	7536	7543	7551	1	2	2	3	4	5	5	6	7
57	7559	7566	7574	7582	7589	7597	7604	7612	7619	7627	1	2	2	3	4	5	5	6	7
58	7634	7642	7649	7657	7664	7672	7679	7686	7694	7701	1	1	2	3	4	4	5	6	7
59	7709	7716	7723	7731	7738	7745	7752	7760	7767	7774	1	1	2	3	4	4	5	6	7
60	7782	7789	7796	7803	7810	7818	7825	7832	7839	7846	1	1	2	3	4	4	5	6	6
61	7853	7860	7868	7875	7882	7889	7896	7903	7910	7917	1	1	2	3	4	4	5	6	6
62	7924	7931	7938	7945	7952	7959	7966	7973	7980	7987	1	1	2	3	3	4	5	6	6
63	7993	8000	8007	8014	8021	8028	8035	8041	8048	8055	1	1	2	3	3	4	5	5	6
64	8062	8069	8075	8082	8089	8096	8102	8109	8116	8122	1	1	2	3	3	4	5	5	6
65	8129	8136	8142	8149	8156	8162	8169	8176	8182	8189	1	1	2	3	3	4	5	5	6
66	8195	8202	8209	8215	8222	8228	8235	8241	8248	8254	1	1	2	3	3	4	5	5	6
67	8261	8267	8274	8280	8287	8293	8299	8306	8312	8319	1	1	2	3	3	4	5	5	6
68	8325	8331	8338	8344	8351	8357	8363	8370	8376	8382	1	1	2	3	3	4	4	5	6
69	8388	8395	8401	8407	8414	8420	8426	8432	8439	8445	1	1	2	2	3	4	4	5	6
70	8451	8457	8463	8470	8476	8482	8488	8494	8500	8506	1	1	2	2	3	4	4	5	6
71	8513	8519	8525	8531	8537	8543	8549	8555	8561	8567	1	1	2	2	3	4	4	5	5
72	8573	8579	8585	8591	8597	8603	8609	8615	8621	8627	1	1	2	2	3	4	4	5	5
73	8633	8639	8645	8651	8657	8663	8669	8675	8681	8686	1	1	2	2	3	4	4	5	5
74	8692	8698	8704	8710	8716	8722	8727	8733	8739	8745	1	1	2	2	3	4	4	5	5
75	8751	8756	8762	8768	8774	8779	8785	8791	8797	8802	1	1	2	2	3	3	4	5	5
76	8808	8814	8820	8825	8831	8837	8842	8848	8854	8859	1	1	2	2	3	3	4	5	5
77	8865	8871	8876	8882	8887	8893	8899	8904	8910	8915	1	1	2	2	3	3	4	4	5
78	8921	8927	8932	8938	8943	8949	8954	8960	8965	8971	1	1	2	2	3	3	4	4	5
79	8976	8982	8987	8993	8998	9004	9009	9015	9020	9025	1	1	2	2	3	3	4	4	5
80	9031	9036	9042	9047	9053	9058	9063	9069	9074	9079	1	1	2	2	3	3	4	4	5
81	9085	9090	9096	9101	9106	9112	9117	9122	9128	9133	1	1	2	2	3	3	4	4	5
82	9138	9143	9149	9154	9159	9165	9170	9175	9180	9186	1	1	2	2	3	3	4	4	5
83	9191	9196	9201	9206	9212	9217	9222	9227	9232	9238	1	1	2	2	3	3	4	4	5
84	9243	9248	9253	9258	9263	9269	9274	9279	9284	9289	1	1	2	2	3	3	4	4	5
85	9294	9299	9304	9309	9315	9320	9325	9330	9335	9340	1	1	2	2	3	3	4	4	5
86	9345	9350	9355	9360	9365	9370	9375	9380	9385	9390	1	1	2	2	3	3	4	4	5
87	9395	9400	9405	9410	9415	9420	9425	9430	9435	9440	0	1	1	2	2	3	3	4	4
88	9445	9450	9455	9460	9465	9469	9474	9479	9484	9489	0	1	1	2	2	3	3	4	4
89	9494	9499	9504	9509	9513	9518	9523	9528	9533	9538	0	1	1	2	2	3	3	4	4
90	9542	9547	9552	9557	9562	9566	9571	9576	9581	9586	0	1	1	2	2	3	3	4	4
91	9590	9595	9600	9605	9609	9614	9619	9624	9628	9633	0	1	1	2	2	3	3	4	4
92	9638	9643	9647	9652	9657	9661	9666	9671	9675	9680	0	1	1	2	2	3	3	4	4
93	9685	9689	9694	9699	9703	9708	9713	9717	9722	9727	0	1	1	2	2	3	3	4	4
94	9731	9736	9741	9745	9750	9754	9759	9763	9768	9773	0	1	1	2	2	3	3	4	4
95	9777	9782	9786	9791	9795	9800	9805	9809	9814	9818	0	1	1	2	2	3	3	4	4
96	9823	9827	9832	9836	9841	9845	9850	9854	9859	9863	0	1	1	2	2	3	3	4	4
97	9868	9872	9877	9881	9886	9890	9894	9899	9903	9908	0	1	1	2	2	3	3	4	4
98	9912	9917	9921	9926	9930	9934	9939	9943	9948	9952	0	1	1	2	2	3	3	4	4
99	9956	9961	9965	9969	9974	9978	9983	9987	9991	9996	0	1	1	2	2	3	3	3	4
N	0	1	2	3	4	5	6	7	8	9	1	2	3	4	5	6	7	8	9

ANTILOGARITHMS

	0	1	2	3	4	5	6	7	8	9	Proportional Parts 1	2	3	4	5	6	7	8	9
.00	1000	1002	1005	1007	1009	1012	1014	1016	1019	1021	0	0	1	1	1	1	2	2	2
.01	1023	1026	1028	1030	1033	1035	1038	1040	1042	1045	0	0	1	1	1	1	2	2	2
.02	1047	1050	1052	1054	1057	1059	1062	1064	1067	1069	0	0	1	1	1	1	2	2	2
.03	1072	1074	1076	1079	1081	1084	1086	1089	1091	1094	0	0	1	1	1	1	2	2	2
.04	1096	1099	1102	1104	1107	1109	1112	1114	1117	1119	0	1	1	1	1	2	2	2	2
.05	1122	1125	1127	1130	1132	1135	1138	1140	1143	1146	0	1	1	1	1	2	2	2	2
.06	1148	1151	1153	1156	1159	1161	1164	1167	1169	1172	0	1	1	1	1	2	2	2	2
.07	1175	1178	1180	1183	1186	1189	1191	1194	1197	1199	0	1	1	1	1	2	2	2	2
.08	1202	1205	1208	1211	1213	1216	1219	1222	1225	1227	0	1	1	1	1	2	2	2	3
.09	1230	1233	1236	1239	1242	1245	1247	1250	1253	1256	0	1	1	1	1	2	2	2	3
.10	1259	1262	1265	1268	1271	1274	1276	1279	1282	1285	0	1	1	1	1	2	2	2	3
.11	1288	1291	1294	1297	1300	1303	1306	1309	1312	1315	0	1	1	1	2	2	2	3	3
.12	1318	1321	1324	1327	1330	1334	1337	1340	1343	1346	0	1	1	1	2	2	2	3	3
.13	1349	1352	1355	1358	1361	1365	1368	1371	1374	1377	0	1	1	1	2	2	2	3	3
.14	1380	1384	1387	1390	1393	1396	1400	1403	1406	1409	0	1	1	1	2	2	2	3	3
.15	1413	1416	1419	1422	1426	1429	1432	1435	1439	1442	0	1	1	1	2	2	2	3	3
.16	1445	1449	1452	1455	1459	1462	1466	1469	1472	1476	0	1	1	1	2	2	2	3	3
.17	1479	1483	1486	1489	1493	1496	1500	1503	1507	1510	0	1	1	1	2	2	2	3	3
.18	1514	1517	1521	1524	1528	1531	1535	1538	1542	1545	0	1	1	1	2	2	2	3	3
.19	1549	1552	1556	1560	1563	1567	1570	1574	1578	1581	0	1	1	1	2	2	3	3	3
.20	1585	1589	1592	1596	1600	1603	1607	1611	1614	1618	0	1	1	1	2	2	3	3	3
.21	1622	1626	1629	1633	1637	1641	1644	1648	1652	1656	0	1	1	2	2	2	3	3	3
.22	1660	1663	1667	1671	1675	1679	1683	1687	1690	1694	0	1	1	2	2	2	3	3	3
.23	1698	1702	1706	1710	1714	1718	1722	1726	1730	1734	0	1	1	2	2	2	3	3	4
.24	1738	1742	1746	1750	1754	1758	1762	1766	1770	1774	0	1	1	2	2	2	3	3	4
.25	1778	1782	1786	1791	1795	1799	1803	1807	1811	1816	0	1	1	2	2	2	3	3	4
.26	1820	1824	1828	1832	1837	1841	1845	1849	1854	1858	0	1	1	2	2	3	3	3	4
.27	1862	1866	1871	1875	1879	1884	1888	1892	1897	1901	0	1	1	2	2	3	3	3	4
.28	1905	1910	1914	1919	1923	1928	1932	1936	1941	1945	0	1	1	2	2	3	3	4	4
.29	1950	1954	1959	1963	1968	1972	1977	1982	1986	1991	0	1	1	2	2	3	3	4	4
.30	1995	2000	2004	2009	2014	2018	2023	2028	2032	2037	0	1	1	2	2	3	3	4	4
.31	2042	2046	2051	2056	2061	2065	2070	2075	2080	2084	0	1	1	2	2	3	3	4	4
.32	2089	2094	2099	2104	2109	2113	2118	2123	2128	2133	0	1	1	2	2	3	3	4	4
.33	2138	2143	2148	2153	2158	2163	2168	2173	2178	2183	0	1	1	2	2	3	3	4	4
.34	2188	2193	2198	2203	2208	2213	2218	2223	2228	2234	1	1	2	2	3	3	4	4	5
.35	2239	2244	2249	2254	2259	2265	2270	2275	2280	2286	1	1	2	2	3	3	4	4	5
.36	2291	2296	2301	2307	2312	2317	2323	2328	2333	2339	1	1	2	2	3	3	4	4	5
.37	2344	2350	2355	2360	2366	2371	2377	2382	2388	2393	1	1	2	2	3	3	4	4	5
.38	2399	2404	2410	2415	2421	2427	2432	2438	2443	2449	1	1	2	2	3	3	4	5	5
.39	2455	2460	2466	2472	2477	2483	2489	2495	2500	2506	1	1	2	2	3	3	4	5	5
.40	2512	2518	2523	2529	2535	2541	2547	2553	2559	2564	1	1	2	2	3	4	4	5	5
.41	2570	2576	2582	2588	2594	2600	2606	2612	2618	2624	1	1	2	2	3	4	4	5	5
.42	2630	2636	2642	2649	2655	2661	2667	2673	2679	2685	1	1	2	2	3	4	4	5	6
.43	2692	2698	2704	2710	2716	2723	2729	2735	2742	2748	1	1	2	3	3	4	4	5	6
.44	2754	2761	2767	2773	2780	2786	2793	2799	2805	2812	1	1	2	3	3	4	4	5	6
.45	2818	2825	2831	2838	2844	2851	2858	2864	2871	2877	1	1	2	3	3	4	5	5	6
.46	2884	2891	2897	2904	2911	2917	2924	2931	2938	2944	1	1	2	3	3	4	5	5	6
.47	2951	2958	2965	2972	2979	2985	2992	2999	3006	3013	1	1	2	3	3	4	5	5	6
.48	3020	3027	3034	3041	3048	3055	3062	3069	3076	3083	1	1	2	3	4	4	5	6	6
.49	3090	3097	3105	3112	3119	3126	3133	3141	3148	3155	1	1	2	3	4	4	5	6	6
	0	1	2	3	4	5	6	7	8	9	1	2	3	4	5	6	7	8	9

Logarithm Tables

ANTILOGARITHMS (Continued)

	0	1	2	3	4	5	6	7	8	9	1	2	3	4	5	6	7	8	9
											Proportional Parts								
.50	3162	3170	3177	3184	3192	3199	3206	3214	3221	3228	1	1	2	3	4	4	5	6	7
.51	3236	3243	3251	3258	3266	3273	3281	3289	3296	3304	1	2	2	3	4	5	5	6	7
.52	3311	3319	3327	3334	3342	3350	3357	3365	3373	3381	1	2	2	3	4	5	5	6	7
.53	3388	3396	3404	3412	3420	3428	3436	3443	3451	3459	1	2	2	3	4	5	6	6	7
.54	3467	3475	3483	3491	3499	3508	3516	3524	3532	3540	1	2	2	3	4	5	6	6	7
.55	3548	3556	3565	3573	3581	3589	3597	3606	3614	3622	1	2	2	3	4	5	6	7	7
.56	3631	3639	3648	3656	3664	3673	3681	3690	3698	3707	1	2	3	3	4	5	6	7	8
.57	3715	3724	3733	3741	3750	3758	3767	3776	3784	3793	1	2	3	3	4	5	6	7	8
.58	3802	3811	3819	3828	3837	3846	3855	3864	3873	3882	1	2	3	4	4	5	6	7	8
.59	3890	3899	3908	3917	3926	3936	3945	3954	3963	3972	1	2	3	4	5	5	6	7	8
.60	3981	3990	3999	4009	4018	4027	4036	4046	4055	4064	1	2	3	4	5	6	6	7	8
.61	4074	4083	4093	4102	4111	4121	4130	4140	4150	4159	1	2	3	4	5	6	7	8	9
.62	4169	4178	4188	4198	4207	4217	4227	4236	4246	4256	1	2	3	4	5	6	7	8	9
.63	4266	4276	4285	4295	4305	4315	4325	4335	4345	4355	1	2	3	4	5	6	7	8	9
.64	4365	4375	4385	4395	4406	4416	4426	4436	4446	4457	1	2	3	4	5	6	7	8	9
.65	4467	4477	4487	4498	4508	4519	4529	4539	4550	4560	1	2	3	4	5	6	7	8	9
.66	4571	4581	4592	4603	4613	4624	4634	4645	4656	4667	1	2	3	4	5	6	7	9	10
.67	4677	4688	4699	4710	4721	4732	4742	4753	4764	4775	1	2	3	4	5	7	8	9	10
.68	4786	4797	4808	4819	4831	4842	4853	4864	4875	4887	1	2	3	4	6	7	8	9	10
.69	4898	4909	4920	4932	4943	4955	4966	4977	4989	5000	1	2	3	5	6	7	8	9	10
.70	5012	5023	5035	5047	5058	5070	5082	5093	5105	5117	1	2	4	5	6	7	8	9	11
.71	5129	5140	5152	5164	5176	5188	5200	5212	5224	5236	1	2	4	5	6	7	8	10	11
.72	5248	5260	5272	5284	5297	5309	5321	5333	5346	5358	1	2	4	5	6	7	9	10	11
.73	5370	5383	5395	5408	5420	5433	5445	5458	5470	5483	1	3	4	5	6	8	9	10	11
.74	5495	5508	5521	5534	5546	5559	5572	5585	5598	5610	1	3	4	5	6	8	9	10	12
.75	5623	5636	5649	5662	5675	5689	5702	5715	5728	5741	1	3	4	5	7	8	9	10	12
.76	5754	5768	5781	5794	5808	5821	5834	5848	5861	5875	1	3	4	5	7	8	9	11	12
.77	5888	5902	5916	5929	5943	5957	5970	5984	5998	6012	1	3	4	5	7	8	10	11	12
.78	6026	6039	6053	6067	6081	6095	6109	6124	6138	6152	1	3	4	6	7	8	10	11	13
.79	6166	6180	6194	6209	6223	6237	6252	6266	6281	6295	1	3	4	6	7	9	10	11	13
.80	6310	6324	6339	6353	6368	6383	6397	6412	6427	6442	1	3	4	6	7	9	10	12	13
.81	6457	6471	6486	6501	6516	6531	6546	6561	6577	6592	2	3	5	6	8	9	11	12	14
.82	6607	6622	6637	6653	6668	6683	6699	6714	6730	6745	2	3	5	6	8	9	11	12	14
.83	6761	6776	6792	6808	6823	6839	6855	6871	6887	6902	2	3	5	6	8	9	11	13	14
.84	6918	6934	6950	6966	6982	6998	7015	7031	7047	7063	2	3	5	6	8	10	11	13	15
.85	7079	7096	7112	7129	7145	7161	7178	7194	7211	7228	2	3	5	7	8	10	12	13	15
.86	7244	7261	7278	7295	7311	7328	7345	7362	7379	7396	2	3	5	7	8	10	12	13	15
.87	7413	7430	7447	7464	7482	7499	7516	7534	7551	7568	2	3	5	7	9	10	12	14	16
.88	7586	7603	7621	7638	7656	7674	7691	7709	7727	7745	2	4	5	7	9	11	12	14	16
.89	7762	7780	7798	7816	7834	7852	7870	7889	7907	7925	2	4	5	7	9	11	13	14	16
.90	7943	7962	7980	7998	8017	8035	8054	8072	8091	8110	2	4	6	7	9	11	13	15	17
.91	8128	8147	8166	8185	8204	8222	8241	8260	8279	8299	2	4	6	8	9	11	13	15	17
.92	8318	8337	8356	8375	8395	8414	8433	8453	8472	8492	2	4	6	8	10	12	14	15	17
.93	8511	8531	8551	8570	8590	8610	8630	8650	8670	8690	2	4	6	8	10	12	14	16	18
.94	8710	8730	8750	8770	8790	8810	8831	8851	8872	8892	2	4	6	8	10	12	14	16	18
.95	8913	8933	8954	8974	8995	9016	9036	9057	9078	9099	2	4	6	8	10	12	15	17	19
.96	9120	9141	9162	9183	9204	9226	9247	9268	9290	9311	2	4	6	8	11	13	15	17	19
.97	9333	9354	9376	9397	9419	9441	9462	9484	9506	9528	2	4	7	9	11	13	15	17	20
.98	9550	9572	9594	9616	9638	9661	9683	9705	9727	9750	2	4	7	9	11	13	16	18	20
.99	9772	9795	9817	9840	9863	9886	9908	9931	9954	9977	2	5	7	9	11	14	16	18	20
	0	1	2	3	4	5	6	7	8	9	1	2	3	4	5	6	7	8	9

FIVE-PLACE MANTISSAS FOR COMMON LOGARITHMS

N.	0	1	2	3	4	5	6	7	8	9
100	00 000	043	087	130	173	217	260	303	346	389
101	432	475	518	561	604	647	689	732	775	817
102	860	903	945	988	*030	*072	*115	*157	*199	*242
103	01 284	326	368	410	452	494	536	578	620	662
104	703	745	787	828	870	912	953	995	*036	*078
105	02 119	160	202	243	284	325	366	407	449	490
106	531	572	612	653	694	735	776	816	857	898
107	938	979	*019	*060	*100	*141	*181	*222	*262	*302
108	03 342	383	423	463	503	543	583	623	663	703
109	743	783	822	862	902	941	981	*021	*060	*100
110	04 139	179	218	258	297	336	376	415	454	493
111	532	571	610	650	689	727	766	805	844	883
112	922	961	999	*038	*077	*115	*154	*192	*231	*269
113	05 308	346	385	423	461	500	538	576	614	652
114	690	729	767	805	843	881	918	956	994	*032
115	06 070	108	145	183	221	258	296	333	371	408
116	446	483	521	558	595	633	670	707	744	781
117	819	856	893	930	967	*004	*041	*078	*115	*151
118	07 188	225	262	298	335	372	408	445	482	518
119	555	591	628	664	700	737	773	809	846	882
120	918	954	990	*027	*063	*099	*135	*171	*207	*243
121	08 279	314	350	386	422	458	493	529	565	600
122	636	672	707	743	778	814	849	884	920	955
123	991	*026	*061	*096	*132	*167	*202	*237	*272	*307
124	09 342	377	412	447	482	517	552	587	621	656
125	691	726	760	795	830	864	899	934	968	*003
126	10 037	072	106	140	175	209	243	278	312	346
127	380	415	449	483	517	551	585	619	653	687
128	721	755	789	823	857	890	924	958	992	*025
129	11 059	093	126	160	193	227	261	294	327	361
130	394	428	461	494	528	561	594	628	661	694
131	727	760	793	826	860	893	926	959	992	*024
132	12 057	090	123	156	189	222	254	287	320	352
133	385	418	450	483	516	548	581	613	646	678
134	710	743	775	808	840	872	905	937	969	*001
135	13 033	066	098	130	162	194	226	258	290	322
136	354	386	418	450	481	513	545	577	609	640
137	672	704	735	767	799	830	862	893	925	956
138	988	*019	*051	*082	*114	*145	*176	*208	*239	*270
139	14 301	333	364	395	426	457	489	520	551	582
140	613	644	675	706	737	768	799	829	860	891
141	922	953	983	*014	*045	*076	*106	*137	*168	*198
142	15 229	259	290	320	351	381	412	442	473	503
143	534	564	594	625	655	685	715	746	776	806
144	836	866	897	927	957	987	*017	*047	*077	*107
145	16 137	167	197	227	256	286	316	346	376	406
146	435	465	495	524	554	584	613	643	673	702
147	732	761	791	820	850	879	909	938	967	997
148	17 026	056	085	114	143	173	202	231	260	289
149	319	348	377	406	435	464	493	522	551	580
150	609	638	667	696	725	754	782	811	840	869

Proportional parts

	44	43	42
1	4.4	4.3	4.2
2	8.8	8.6	8.4
3	13.2	12.9	12.6
4	17.6	17.2	16.8
5	22.0	21.5	21.0
6	26.4	25.8	25.2
7	30.8	30.1	29.4
8	35.2	34.4	33.6
9	39.6	38.7	37.8

	41	40	39
1	4.1	4.0	3.9
2	8.2	8.0	7.8
3	12.3	12.0	11.7
4	16.4	16.0	15.6
5	20.5	20.0	19.5
6	24.6	24.0	23.4
7	28.7	28.0	27.3
8	32.8	32.0	31.2
9	36.9	36.0	35.1

	38	37	36
1	3.8	3.7	3.6
2	7.6	7.4	7.2
3	11.4	11.1	10.8
4	15.2	14.8	14.4
5	19.0	18.5	18.0
6	22.8	22.2	21.6
7	26.6	25.9	25.2
8	30.4	29.6	28.8
9	34.2	33.3	32.4

	35	34	33
1	3.5	3.4	3.3
2	7.0	6.8	6.6
3	10.5	10.2	9.9
4	14.0	13.6	13.2
5	17.5	17.0	16.5
6	21.0	20.4	19.8
7	24.5	23.8	23.1
8	28.0	27.2	26.4
9	31.5	30.6	29.7

	32	31	30
1	3.2	3.1	3.0
2	6.4	6.2	6.0
3	9.6	9.3	9.0
4	12.8	12.4	12.0
5	16.0	15.5	15.0
6	19.2	18.6	18.0
7	22.4	21.7	21.0
8	25.6	24.8	24.0
9	28.8	27.9	27.0

N.	0	1	2	3	4	5	6	7	8	9	Proportional parts

Logarithm Tables

FIVE-PLACE MANTISSAS FOR COMMON LOGARITHMS

N.	0	1	2	3	4	5	6	7	8	9	Proportional parts		
150	17 609	638	667	696	725	754	782	811	840	869		**29**	**28**
151	898	926	955	984	*013	*041	*070	*099	*127	*156	1	2.9	2.8
152	18 184	213	241	270	298	327	355	384	412	441	2	5.8	5.6
153	469	498	526	554	583	611	639	667	696	724	3	8.7	8.4
154	752	780	808	837	865	893	921	949	977	*005	4	11.6	11.2
155	19 033	061	089	117	145	173	201	229	257	285	5	14.5	14.0
156	312	340	368	396	424	451	479	507	535	562	6	17.4	16.8
157	590	618	645	673	700	728	756	783	811	838	7	20.3	19.6
158	866	893	921	948	976	*003	*030	*058	*085	*112	8	23.2	22.4
159	20 140	167	194	222	249	276	303	330	358	385	9	26.1	25.2
160	412	439	466	493	520	548	575	602	629	656		**27**	**26**
161	683	710	737	763	790	817	844	871	898	925	1	2.7	2.6
162	952	978	*005	*032	*059	*085	*112	*139	*165	*192	2	5.4	5.2
163	21 219	245	272	299	325	352	378	405	431	458	3	8.1	7.8
164	484	511	537	564	590	617	643	669	696	722	4	10.8	10.4
165	748	775	801	827	854	880	906	932	958	985	5	13.5	13.0
166	22 011	037	063	089	115	141	167	194	220	246	6	16.2	15.6
167	272	298	324	350	376	401	427	453	479	505	7	18.9	18.2
168	531	557	583	608	634	660	686	712	737	763	8	21.6	20.8
169	789	814	840	866	891	917	943	968	994	*019	9	24.3	23.4
170	23 045	070	096	121	147	172	198	223	249	274		**25**	
171	300	325	350	376	401	426	452	477	502	528	1	2.5	
172	553	578	603	629	654	679	704	729	754	779	2	5.0	
173	805	830	855	880	905	930	955	980	*005	*030	3	7.5	
174	24 055	080	105	130	155	180	204	229	254	279	4	10.0	
175	304	329	353	378	403	428	452	477	502	527	5	12.5	
176	551	576	601	625	650	674	699	724	748	773	6	15.0	
177	797	822	846	871	895	920	944	969	993	*018	7	17.5	
178	25 042	066	091	115	139	164	188	212	237	261	8	20.0	
179	285	310	334	358	382	406	431	455	479	503	9	22.5	
180	527	551	575	600	624	648	672	696	720	744		**24**	**23**
181	768	792	816	840	864	888	912	935	959	983	1	2.4	2.3
182	26 007	031	055	079	102	126	150	174	198	221	2	4.8	4.6
183	245	269	293	316	340	364	387	411	435	458	3	7.2	6.9
184	482	505	529	553	576	600	623	647	670	694	4	9.6	9.2
185	717	741	764	788	811	834	858	881	905	928	5	12.0	11.5
186	951	975	998	*021	*045	*068	*091	*114	*138	*161	6	14.4	13.8
187	27 184	207	231	254	277	300	323	346	370	393	7	16.8	16.1
188	416	439	462	485	508	531	554	577	600	623	8	19.2	18.4
189	646	669	692	715	738	761	784	807	830	852	9	21.6	20.7
190	875	898	921	944	967	989	*012	*035	*058	*081		**22**	**21**
191	28 103	126	149	171	194	217	240	262	285	307	1	2.2	2.1
192	330	353	375	398	421	443	466	488	511	533	2	4.4	4.2
193	556	578	601	623	646	668	691	713	735	758	3	6.6	6.3
194	780	803	825	847	870	892	914	937	959	981	4	8.8	8.4
195	29 003	026	048	070	092	115	137	159	181	203	5	11.0	10.5
196	226	248	270	292	314	336	358	380	403	425	6	13.2	12.6
197	447	469	491	513	535	557	579	601	623	645	7	15.4	14.7
198	667	688	710	732	754	776	798	820	842	863	8	17.6	16.8
199	885	907	929	951	973	994	*016	*038	*060	*081	9	19.8	18.9
200	30 103	125	146	168	190	211	233	255	276	298			

N.	0	1	2	3	4	5	6	7	8	9	Proportional parts		

FIVE-PLACE MANTISSAS FOR COMMON LOGARITHMS

N.	0	1	2	3	4	5	6	7	8	9	Proportional parts	
200	30 103	125	146	168	190	211	233	255	276	298	**22**	**21**
201	320	341	363	384	406	428	449	471	492	514	1 | 2.2	2.1
202	535	557	578	600	621	643	664	685	707	728	2 | 4.4	4.2
203	750	771	792	814	835	856	878	899	920	942	3 | 6.6	6.3
204	963	984	*006	*027	*048	*069	*091	*112	*133	*154	4 | 8.8	8.4
205	31 175	197	218	239	260	281	302	323	345	366	5 | 11.0	10.5
206	387	408	429	450	471	492	513	534	555	576	6 | 13.2	12.6
207	597	618	639	660	681	702	723	744	765	785	7 | 15.4	14.7
208	806	827	848	869	890	911	931	952	973	994	8 | 17.6	16.8
209	32 015	035	056	077	098	118	139	160	181	201	9 | 19.8	18.9
210	222	243	263	284	305	325	346	366	387	408	**20**	
211	428	449	469	490	510	531	552	572	593	613	1 | 2.0	
212	634	654	675	695	715	736	756	777	797	818	2 | 4.0	
213	838	858	879	899	919	940	960	980	*001	*021	3 | 6.0	
214	33 041	062	082	102	122	143	163	183	203	224	4 | 8.0	
215	244	264	284	304	325	345	365	385	405	425	5 | 10.0	
216	445	465	486	506	526	546	566	586	606	626	6 | 12.0	
217	646	666	686	706	726	746	766	786	806	826	7 | 14.0	
218	846	866	885	905	925	945	965	985	*005	*025	8 | 16.0	
219	34 044	064	084	104	124	143	163	183	203	223	9 | 18.0	
220	242	262	282	301	321	341	361	380	400	420	**19**	
221	439	459	479	498	518	537	557	577	596	616	1 | 1.9	
222	635	655	674	694	713	733	753	772	792	811	2 | 3.8	
223	830	850	869	889	908	928	947	967	986	*005	3 | 5.7	
224	35 025	044	064	083	102	122	141	160	180	199	4 | 7.6	
225	218	238	257	276	295	315	334	353	372	392	5 | 9.5	
226	411	430	449	468	488	507	526	545	564	583	6 | 11.4	
227	603	622	641	660	679	698	717	736	755	774	7 | 13.3	
228	793	813	832	851	870	889	908	927	946	965	8 | 15.2	
229	984	*003	*021	*040	*059	*078	*097	*116	*135	*154	9 | 17.1	
230	36 173	192	211	229	248	267	286	305	324	342	**18**	
231	361	380	399	418	436	455	474	493	511	530	1 | 1.8	
232	549	568	586	605	624	642	661	680	698	717	2 | 3.6	
233	736	754	773	791	810	829	847	866	884	903	3 | 5.4	
234	922	940	959	977	996	*014	*033	*051	*070	*088	4 | 7.2	
235	37 107	125	144	162	181	199	218	236	254	273	5 | 9.0	
236	291	310	328	346	365	383	401	420	438	457	6 | 10.8	
237	475	493	511	530	548	566	585	603	621	639	7 | 12.6	
238	658	676	694	712	731	749	767	785	803	822	8 | 14.4	
239	840	858	876	894	912	931	949	967	985	*003	9 | 16.2	
240	38 021	039	057	075	093	112	130	148	166	184	**17**	
241	202	220	238	256	274	292	310	328	346	364	1 | 1.7	
242	382	399	417	435	453	471	489	507	525	543	2 | 3.4	
243	561	578	596	614	632	650	668	686	703	721	3 | 5.1	
244	739	757	775	792	810	828	846	863	881	899	4 | 6.8	
245	917	934	952	970	987	*005	*023	*041	*058	*076	5 | 8.5	
246	39 094	111	129	146	164	182	199	217	235	252	6 | 10.2	
247	270	287	305	322	340	358	375	393	410	428	7 | 11.9	
248	445	463	480	498	515	533	550	568	585	602	8 | 13.6	
249	620	637	655	672	690	707	724	742	759	777	9 | 15.3	
250	794	811	829	846	863	881	898	915	933	950		
N.	0	1	2	3	4	5	6	7	8	9	Proportional parts	

FIVE-PLACE MANTISSAS FOR COMMON LOGARITHMS

N.	0	1	2	3	4	5	6	7	8	9	Proportional parts	
250	39 794	811	829	846	863	881	898	915	933	950		**18**
251	967	985	*002	*019	*037	*054	*071	*088	*106	*123	1	1.8
252	40 140	157	175	192	209	226	243	261	278	295	2	3.6
253	312	329	346	364	381	398	415	432	449	466	3	5.4
254	483	500	518	535	552	569	586	603	620	637	4	7.2
255	654	671	688	705	722	739	756	773	790	807	5	9.0
256	824	841	858	875	892	909	926	943	960	976	6	10.8
257	993	*010	*027	*044	*061	*078	*095	*111	*128	*145	7	12.6
258	41 162	179	196	212	229	246	263	280	296	313	8	14.4
259	330	347	363	380	397	414	430	447	464	481	9	16.2
260	497	514	531	547	564	581	597	614	631	647		**17**
261	664	681	697	714	731	747	764	780	797	814	1	1.7
262	830	847	863	880	896	913	929	946	963	979	2	3.4
263	996	*012	*029	*045	*062	*078	*095	*111	*127	*144	3	5.1
264	42 160	177	193	210	226	243	259	275	292	308	4	6.8
265	325	341	357	374	390	406	423	439	455	472	5	8.5
266	488	504	521	537	553	570	586	602	619	635	6	10.2
267	651	667	684	700	716	732	749	765	781	797	7	11.9
268	813	830	846	862	878	894	911	927	943	959	8	13.6
269	975	991	*008	*024	*040	*056	*072	*088	*104	*120	9	15.3
270	43 136	152	169	185	201	217	233	249	265	281		**16**
271	297	313	329	345	361	377	393	409	425	441	1	1.6
272	457	473	489	505	521	537	553	569	584	600	2	3.2
273	616	632	648	664	680	696	712	727	743	759	3	4.8
274	775	791	807	823	838	854	870	886	902	917	4	6.4
275	933	949	965	981	996	*012	*028	*044	*059	*075	5	8.0
276	44 091	107	122	138	154	170	185	201	217	232	6	9.6
277	248	264	279	295	311	326	342	358	373	389	7	11.2
278	404	420	436	451	467	483	498	514	529	545	8	12.8
279	560	576	592	607	623	638	654	669	685	700	9	14.4
280	716	731	747	762	778	793	809	824	840	855		**15**
281	871	886	902	917	932	948	963	979	994	*010	1	1.5
282	45 025	040	056	071	086	102	117	133	148	163	2	3.0
283	179	194	209	225	240	255	271	286	301	317	3	4.5
284	332	347	362	378	393	408	423	439	454	469	4	6.0
285	484	500	515	530	545	561	576	591	606	621	5	7.5
286	637	652	667	682	697	712	728	743	758	773	6	9.0
287	788	803	818	834	849	864	879	894	909	924	7	10.5
288	939	954	969	984	*000	*015	*030	*045	*060	*075	8	12.0
289	46 090	105	120	135	150	165	180	195	210	225	9	13.5
290	240	255	270	285	300	315	330	345	359	374		**14**
291	389	404	419	434	449	464	479	494	509	523	1	1.4
292	538	553	568	583	598	613	627	642	657	672	2	2.8
293	687	702	716	731	746	761	776	790	805	820	3	4.2
294	835	850	864	879	894	909	923	938	953	967	4	5.6
295	982	997	*012	*026	*041	*056	*070	*085	*100	*114	5	7.0
296	47 129	144	159	173	188	202	217	232	246	261	6	8.4
297	276	290	305	319	334	349	363	378	392	407	7	9.8
298	422	436	451	465	480	494	509	524	538	553	8	11.2
299	567	582	596	611	625	640	654	669	683	698	9	12.6
300	712	727	741	756	770	784	799	813	828	842		
N.	0	1	2	3	4	5	6	7	8	9	Proportional parts	

FIVE-PLACE MANTISSAS FOR COMMON LOGARITHMS

N.	0	1	2	3	4	5	6	7	8	9
300	47 712	727	741	756	770	784	799	813	828	842
301	857	871	885	900	914	929	943	958	972	986
302	48 001	015	029	044	058	073	087	101	116	130
303	144	159	173	187	202	216	230	244	259	273
304	287	302	316	330	344	359	373	387	401	416
305	430	444	458	473	487	501	515	530	544	558
306	572	586	601	615	629	643	657	671	686	700
307	714	728	742	756	770	785	799	813	827	841
308	855	869	883	897	911	926	940	954	968	982
309	996	*010	*024	*038	*052	*066	*080	*094	*108	*122
310	49 136	150	164	178	192	206	220	234	248	262
311	276	290	304	318	332	346	360	374	388	402
312	415	429	443	457	471	485	499	513	527	541
313	554	568	582	596	610	624	638	651	665	679
314	693	707	721	734	748	762	776	790	803	817
315	831	845	859	872	886	900	914	927	941	955
316	969	982	996	*010	*024	*037	*051	*065	*079	*092
317	50 106	120	133	147	161	174	188	202	215	229
318	243	256	270	284	297	311	325	338	352	365
319	379	393	406	420	433	447	461	474	488	501
320	515	529	542	556	569	583	596	610	623	637
321	651	664	678	691	705	718	732	745	759	772
322	786	799	813	826	840	853	866	880	893	907
323	920	934	947	961	974	987	*001	*014	*028	*041
324	51 055	068	081	095	108	121	135	148	162	175
325	188	202	215	228	242	255	268	282	295	308
326	322	335	348	362	375	388	402	415	428	441
327	455	468	481	495	508	521	534	548	561	574
328	587	601	614	627	640	654	667	680	693	706
329	720	733	746	759	772	786	799	812	825	838
330	851	865	878	891	904	917	930	943	957	970
331	983	996	*009	*022	*035	*048	*061	*075	*088	*101
332	52 114	127	140	153	166	179	192	205	218	231
333	244	257	270	284	297	310	323	336	349	362
334	375	388	401	414	427	440	453	466	479	492
335	504	517	530	543	556	569	582	595	608	621
336	634	647	660	673	686	699	711	724	737	750
337	763	776	789	802	815	827	840	853	866	879
338	892	905	917	930	943	956	969	982	994	*007
339	53 020	033	046	058	071	084	097	110	122	135
340	148	161	173	186	199	212	224	237	250	263
341	275	288	301	314	326	339	352	364	377	390
342	403	415	428	441	453	466	479	491	504	517
343	529	542	555	567	580	593	605	618	631	643
344	656	668	681	694	706	719	732	744	757	769
345	782	794	807	820	832	845	857	870	882	895
346	908	920	933	945	958	970	983	995	*008	*020
347	54 033	045	058	070	083	095	108	120	133	145
348	158	170	183	195	208	220	233	245	258	270
349	283	295	307	320	332	345	357	370	382	394
350	407	419	432	444	456	469	481	494	506	518

Proportional parts

	15		14		13		12
1	1.5	1	1.4	1	1.3	1	1.2
2	3.0	2	2.8	2	2.6	2	2.4
3	4.5	3	4.2	3	3.9	3	3.6
4	6.0	4	5.6	4	5.2	4	4.8
5	7.5	5	7.0	5	6.5	5	6.0
6	9.0	6	8.4	6	7.8	6	7.2
7	10.5	7	9.8	7	9.1	7	8.4
8	12.0	8	11.2	8	10.4	8	9.6
9	13.5	9	12.6	9	11.7	9	10.8

FIVE-PLACE MANTISSAS FOR COMMON LOGARITHMS

N.	0	1	2	3	4	5	6	7	8	9	Proportional parts	
350	54 407	419	432	444	456	469	481	494	506	518		
351	531	543	555	568	580	593	605	617	630	642		
352	654	667	679	691	704	716	728	741	753	765		
353	777	790	802	814	827	839	851	864	876	888		**13**
354	900	913	925	937	949	962	974	986	998	*011	1	1.3
355	55 023	035	047	060	072	084	096	108	121	133	2	2.6
356	145	157	169	182	194	206	218	230	242	255	3	3.9
357	267	279	291	303	315	328	340	352	364	376	4	5.2
358	388	400	413	425	437	449	461	473	485	497	5	6.5
359	509	522	534	546	558	570	582	594	606	618	6	7.8
											7	9.1
360	630	642	654	666	678	691	703	715	727	739	8	10.4
361	751	763	775	787	799	811	823	835	847	859	9	11.7
362	871	883	895	907	919	931	943	955	967	979		
363	991	*003	*015	*027	*038	*050	*062	*074	*086	*098		
364	56 110	122	134	146	158	170	182	194	205	217		
365	229	241	253	265	277	289	301	312	324	336		**12**
366	348	360	372	384	396	407	419	431	443	455	1	1.2
367	467	478	490	502	514	526	538	549	561	573	2	2.4
368	585	597	608	620	632	644	656	667	679	691	3	3.6
369	703	714	726	738	750	761	773	785	797	808	4	4.8
											5	6.0
370	820	832	844	855	867	879	891	902	914	926	6	7.2
371	937	949	961	972	984	996	*008	*019	*031	*043	7	8.4
372	57 054	066	078	089	101	113	124	136	148	159	8	9.6
373	171	183	194	206	217	229	241	252	264	276	9	10.8
374	287	299	310	322	334	345	357	368	380	392		
375	403	415	426	438	449	461	473	484	496	507		
376	519	530	542	553	565	576	588	600	611	623		
377	634	646	657	669	680	692	703	715	726	738		**11**
378	749	761	772	784	795	807	818	830	841	852	1	1.1
379	864	875	887	898	910	921	933	944	955	967	2	2.2
											3	3.3
380	978	990	*001	*013	*024	*035	*047	*058	*070	*081	4	4.4
381	58 092	104	115	127	138	149	161	172	184	195	5	5.5
382	206	218	229	240	252	263	274	286	297	309	6	6.6
383	320	331	343	354	365	377	388	399	410	422	7	7.7
384	433	444	456	467	478	490	501	512	524	535	8	8.8
385	546	557	569	580	591	602	614	625	636	647	9	9.9
386	659	670	681	692	704	715	726	737	749	760		
387	771	782	794	805	816	827	838	850	861	872		
388	883	894	906	917	928	939	950	961	973	984		
389	995	*006	*017	*028	*040	*051	*062	*073	*084	*095		**10**
											1	1.0
390	59 106	118	129	140	151	162	173	184	195	207	2	2.0
391	218	229	240	251	262	273	284	295	306	318	3	3.0
392	329	340	351	362	373	384	395	406	417	428	4	4.0
393	439	450	461	472	483	494	506	517	528	539	5	5.0
394	550	561	572	583	594	605	616	627	638	649	6	6.0
395	660	671	682	693	704	715	726	737	748	759	7	7.0
396	770	780	791	802	813	824	835	846	857	868	8	8.0
397	879	890	901	912	923	934	945	956	966	977	9	9.0
398	988	999	*010	*021	*032	*043	*054	*065	*076	*086		
399	60 097	108	119	130	141	152	163	173	184	195		
400	206	217	228	239	249	260	271	282	293	304		

N.	0	1	2	3	4	5	6	7	8	9	Proportional parts	

FIVE-PLACE MANTISSAS FOR COMMON LOGARITHMS

N.	0	1	2	3	4	5	6	7	8	9	Proportional parts	
400	60 206	217	228	239	249	260	271	282	293	304		
401	314	325	336	347	358	369	379	390	401	412		
402	423	433	444	455	466	477	487	498	509	520		
403	531	541	552	563	574	584	595	606	617	627		
404	638	649	660	670	681	692	703	713	724	735		
405	746	756	767	778	788	799	810	821	831	842		
406	853	863	874	885	895	906	917	927	938	949		
407	959	970	981	991	*002	*013	*023	*034	*045	*055		**11**
408	61 066	077	087	098	109	119	130	140	151	162	1	1.1
409	172	183	194	204	215	225	236	247	257	268	2	2.2
											3	3.3
410	278	289	300	310	321	331	342	352	363	374	4	4.4
411	384	395	405	416	426	437	448	458	469	479	5	5.5
412	490	500	511	521	532	542	553	563	574	584	6	6.6
413	595	606	616	627	637	648	658	669	679	690	7	7.7
414	700	711	721	731	742	752	763	773	784	794	8	8.8
415	805	815	826	836	847	857	868	878	888	899	9	9.9
416	909	920	930	941	951	962	972	982	993	*003		
417	62 014	024	034	045	055	066	076	086	097	107		
418	118	128	138	149	159	170	180	190	201	211		
419	221	232	242	252	263	273	284	294	304	315		
420	325	335	346	356	366	377	387	397	408	418		**10**
421	428	439	449	459	469	480	490	500	511	521	1	1.0
422	531	542	552	562	572	583	593	603	613	624	2	2.0
423	634	644	655	665	675	685	696	706	716	726	3	3.0
424	737	747	757	767	778	788	798	808	818	829	4	4.0
425	839	849	859	870	880	890	900	910	921	931	5	5.0
426	941	951	961	972	982	992	*002	*012	*022	*033	6	6.0
427	63 043	053	063	073	083	094	104	114	124	134	7	7.0
428	144	155	165	175	185	195	205	215	225	236	8	8.0
429	246	256	266	276	286	296	306	317	327	337	9	9.0
430	347	357	367	377	387	397	407	417	428	438		
431	448	458	468	478	488	498	508	518	528	538		
432	548	558	568	579	589	599	609	619	629	639		
433	649	659	669	679	689	699	709	719	729	739		
434	749	759	769	779	789	799	809	819	829	839		
435	849	859	869	879	889	899	909	919	929	939		
436	949	959	969	979	988	998	*008	*018	*028	*038		
437	64 048	058	068	078	088	098	108	118	128	137		
438	147	157	167	177	187	197	207	217	227	237		**9**
439	246	256	266	276	286	296	306	316	326	335	1	0.9
											2	1.8
440	345	355	365	375	385	395	404	414	424	434	3	2.7
441	444	454	464	473	483	493	503	513	523	532	4	3.6
442	542	552	562	572	582	591	601	611	621	631	5	4.5
443	640	650	660	670	680	689	699	709	719	729	6	5.4
444	738	748	758	768	777	787	797	807	816	826	7	6.3
445	836	846	856	865	875	885	895	904	914	924	8	7.2
446	933	943	953	963	972	982	992	*002	*011	*021	9	8.1
447	65 031	040	050	060	070	079	089	099	108	118		
448	128	137	147	157	167	176	186	196	205	215		
449	225	234	244	254	263	273	283	292	302	312		
450	321	331	341	350	360	369	379	389	398	408		

N.	0	1	2	3	4	5	6	7	8	9	Proportional parts

Logarithm Tables

FIVE-PLACE MANTISSAS FOR COMMON LOGARITHMS

N.	0	1	2	3	4	5	6	7	8	9
450	65 321	331	341	350	360	369	379	389	398	408
451	418	427	437	447	456	466	475	485	495	504
452	514	523	533	543	552	562	571	581	591	600
453	610	619	629	639	648	658	667	677	686	696
454	706	715	725	734	744	753	763	772	782	792
455	801	811	820	830	839	849	858	868	877	887
456	896	906	916	925	935	944	954	963	973	982
457	992	*001	*011	*020	*030	*039	*049	*058	*068	*077
458	66 087	096	106	115	124	134	143	153	162	172
459	181	191	200	210	219	229	238	247	257	266
460	276	285	295	304	314	323	332	342	351	361
461	370	380	389	398	408	417	427	436	445	455
462	464	474	483	492	502	511	521	530	539	549
463	558	567	577	586	596	605	614	624	633	642
464	652	661	671	680	689	699	708	717	727	736
465	745	755	764	773	783	792	801	811	820	829
466	839	848	857	867	876	885	894	904	913	922
467	932	941	950	960	969	978	987	997	*006	*015
468	67 025	034	043	052	062	071	080	089	099	108
469	117	127	136	145	154	164	173	182	191	201
470	210	219	228	237	247	256	265	274	284	293
471	302	311	321	330	339	348	357	367	376	385
472	394	403	413	422	431	440	449	459	468	477
473	486	495	504	514	523	532	541	550	560	569
474	578	587	596	605	614	624	633	642	651	660
475	669	679	688	697	706	715	724	733	742	752
476	761	770	779	788	797	806	815	825	834	843
477	852	861	870	879	888	897	906	916	925	934
478	943	952	961	970	979	988	997	*006	*015	*024
479	68 034	043	052	061	070	079	088	097	106	115
480	124	133	142	151	160	169	178	187	196	205
481	215	224	233	242	251	260	269	278	287	296
482	305	314	323	332	341	350	359	368	377	386
483	395	404	413	422	431	440	449	458	467	476
484	485	494	502	511	520	529	538	547	556	565
485	574	583	592	601	610	619	628	637	646	655
486	664	673	681	690	699	708	717	726	735	744
487	753	762	771	780	789	797	806	815	824	833
488	842	851	860	869	878	886	895	904	913	922
489	931	940	949	958	966	975	984	993	*002	*011
490	69 020	028	037	046	055	064	073	082	090	099
491	108	117	126	135	144	152	161	170	179	188
492	197	205	214	223	232	241	249	258	267	276
493	285	294	302	311	320	329	338	346	355	364
494	373	381	390	399	408	417	425	434	443	452
495	461	469	478	487	496	504	513	522	531	539
496	548	557	566	574	583	592	601	609	618	627
497	636	644	653	662	671	679	688	697	705	714
498	723	732	740	749	758	767	775	784	793	801
499	810	819	827	836	845	854	862	871	880	888
500	897	906	914	923	932	940	949	958	966	975

Proportional parts

	10		9		8
1	1.0	1	0.9	1	0.8
2	2.0	2	1.8	2	1.6
3	3.0	3	2.7	3	2.4
4	4.0	4	3.6	4	3.2
5	5.0	5	4.5	5	4.0
6	6.0	6	5.4	6	4.8
7	7.0	7	6.3	7	5.6
8	8.0	8	7.2	8	6.4
9	9.0	9	8.1	9	7.2

FIVE-PLACE MANTISSAS FOR COMMON LOGARITHMS

N.	0	1	2	3	4	5	6	7	8	9	Proportional parts	
500	69 897	906	914	923	932	940	949	958	966	975		
501	984	992	*001	*010	*018	*027	*036	*044	*053	*062		
502	70 070	079	088	096	105	114	122	131	140	148		
503	157	165	174	183	191	200	209	217	226	234		
504	243	252	260	269	278	286	295	303	312	321		
505	329	338	346	355	364	372	381	389	398	406		
506	415	424	432	441	449	458	467	475	484	492		
507	501	509	518	526	535	544	552	561	569	578		**9**
508	586	595	603	612	621	629	638	646	655	663	1	0.9
509	672	680	689	697	706	714	723	731	740	749	2	1.8
											3	2.7
510	757	766	774	783	791	800	808	817	825	834	4	3.6
511	842	851	859	868	876	885	893	902	910	919	5	4.5
512	927	935	944	952	961	969	978	986	995	*003	6	5.4
513	71 012	020	029	037	046	054	063	071	079	088	7	6.3
514	096	105	113	122	130	139	147	155	164	172	8	7.2
515	181	189	198	206	214	223	231	240	248	257	9	8.1
516	265	273	282	290	299	307	315	324	332	341		
517	349	357	366	374	383	391	399	408	416	425		
518	433	441	450	458	466	475	483	492	500	508		
519	517	525	533	542	550	559	567	575	584	592		
520	600	609	617	625	634	642	650	659	667	675		
521	684	692	700	709	717	725	734	742	750	759		**8**
522	767	775	784	792	800	809	817	825	834	842	1	0.8
523	850	858	867	875	883	892	900	908	917	925	2	1.6
524	933	941	950	958	966	975	983	991	999	*008	3	2.4
525	72 016	024	032	041	049	057	066	074	082	090	4	3.2
526	099	107	115	123	132	140	148	156	165	173	5	4.0
527	181	189	198	206	214	222	230	239	247	255	6	4.8
528	263	272	280	288	296	304	313	321	329	337	7	5.6
529	346	354	362	370	378	387	395	403	411	419	8	6.4
											9	7.2
530	428	436	444	452	460	469	477	485	493	501		
531	509	518	526	534	542	550	558	567	575	583		
532	591	599	607	616	624	632	640	648	656	665		
533	673	681	689	697	705	713	722	730	738	746		
534	754	762	770	779	787	795	803	811	819	827		
535	835	843	852	860	868	876	884	892	900	908		
536	916	925	933	941	949	957	965	973	981	989		
537	997	*006	*014	*022	*030	*038	*046	*054	*062	*070		
538	73 078	086	094	102	111	119	127	135	143	151		
539	159	167	175	183	191	199	207	215	223	231		**7**
											1	0.7
540	239	247	255	263	272	280	288	296	304	312	2	1.4
541	320	328	336	344	352	360	368	376	384	392	3	2.1
542	400	408	416	424	432	440	448	456	464	472	4	2.8
543	480	488	496	504	512	520	528	536	544	552	5	3.5
544	560	568	576	584	592	600	608	616	624	632	6	4.2
545	640	648	656	664	672	679	687	695	703	711	7	4.9
546	719	727	735	743	751	759	767	775	783	791	8	5.6
547	799	807	815	823	830	838	846	854	862	870	9	6.3
548	878	886	894	902	910	918	926	933	941	949		
549	957	965	973	981	989	997	*005	*013	*020	*028		
550	74 036	044	052	060	068	076	084	092	099	107		

N.	0	1	2	3	4	5	6	7	8	9	Proportional parts

Logarithm Tables

FIVE-PLACE MANTISSAS FOR COMMON LOGARITHMS

N.	0	1	2	3	4	5	6	7	8	9	Proportional parts		
550	74 036	044	052	060	068	076	084	092	099	107			
551	115	123	131	139	147	155	162	170	178	186			
552	194	202	210	218	225	233	241	249	257	265			
553	273	280	288	296	304	312	320	327	335	343			
554	351	359	367	374	382	390	398	406	414	421			
555	429	437	445	453	461	468	476	484	492	500			
556	507	515	523	531	539	547	554	562	570	578			
557	586	593	601	609	617	624	632	640	648	656			
558	663	671	679	687	695	702	710	718	726	733			
559	741	749	757	764	772	780	788	796	803	811			
560	819	827	834	842	850	858	865	873	881	889			**8**
561	896	904	912	920	927	935	943	950	958	966	1		0.8
562	974	981	989	997	*005	*012	*020	*028	*035	*043	2		1.6
563	75 051	059	066	074	082	089	097	105	113	120	3		2.4
564	128	136	143	151	159	166	174	182	189	197	4		3.2
565	205	213	220	228	236	243	251	259	266	274	5		4.0
566	282	289	297	305	312	320	328	335	343	351	6		4.8
567	358	366	374	381	389	397	404	412	420	427	7		5.6
568	435	442	450	458	465	473	481	488	496	504	8		6.4
569	511	519	526	534	542	549	557	565	572	580	9		7.2
570	587	595	603	610	618	626	633	641	648	656			
571	664	671	679	686	694	702	709	717	724	732			
572	740	747	755	762	770	778	785	793	800	808			
573	815	823	831	838	846	853	861	868	876	884			
574	891	899	906	914	921	929	937	944	952	959			
575	967	974	982	989	997	*005	*012	*020	*027	*035			
576	76 042	050	057	065	072	080	087	095	103	110			
577	118	125	133	140	148	155	163	170	178	185			
578	193	200	208	215	223	230	238	245	253	260			
579	268	275	283	290	298	305	313	320	328	335			
580	343	350	358	365	373	380	388	395	403	410			**7**
581	418	425	433	440	448	455	462	470	477	485	1		0.7
582	492	500	507	515	522	530	537	545	552	559	2		1.4
583	567	574	582	589	597	604	612	619	626	634	3		2.1
584	641	649	656	664	671	678	686	693	701	708	4		2.8
585	716	723	730	738	745	753	760	768	775	782	5		3.5
586	790	797	805	812	819	827	834	842	849	856	6		4.2
587	864	871	879	886	893	901	908	916	923	930	7		4.9
588	938	945	953	960	967	975	982	989	997	*004	8		5.6
589	77 012	019	026	034	041	048	056	063	070	078	9		6.3
590	085	093	100	107	115	122	129	137	144	151			
591	159	166	173	181	188	195	203	210	217	225			
592	232	240	247	254	262	269	276	283	291	298			
593	305	313	320	327	335	342	349	357	364	371			
594	379	386	393	401	408	415	422	430	437	444			
595	452	459	466	474	481	488	495	503	510	517			
596	525	532	539	546	554	561	568	576	583	590			
597	597	605	612	619	627	634	641	648	656	663			
598	670	677	685	692	699	706	714	721	728	735			
599	743	750	757	764	772	779	786	793	801	808			
600	815	822	830	837	844	851	859	866	873	880			
N.	0	1	2	3	4	5	6	7	8	9	Proportional parts		

FIVE-PLACE MANTISSAS FOR COMMON LOGARITHMS

N.	0	1	2	3	4	5	6	7	8	9	Proportional parts	
600	77 815	822	830	837	844	851	859	866	873	880		
601	887	895	902	909	916	924	931	938	945	952		
602	960	967	974	981	988	996	*003	*010	*017	*025		
603	78 032	039	046	053	061	068	075	082	089	097		
604	104	111	118	125	132	140	147	154	161	168		
605	176	183	190	197	204	211	219	226	233	240		
606	247	254	262	269	276	283	290	297	305	312		
607	319	326	333	340	347	355	362	369	376	383		
608	390	398	405	412	419	426	433	440	447	455		
609	462	469	476	483	490	497	504	512	519	526		**8**
											1	0.8
610	533	540	547	554	561	569	576	583	590	597	2	1.6
611	604	611	618	625	633	640	647	654	661	668	3	2.4
612	675	682	689	696	704	711	718	725	732	739	4	3.2
613	746	753	760	767	774	781	789	796	803	810	5	4.0
614	817	824	831	838	845	852	859	866	873	880	6	4.8
615	888	895	902	909	916	923	930	937	944	951	7	5.6
616	958	965	972	979	986	993	*000	*007	*014	*021	8	6.4
617	79 029	036	043	050	057	064	071	078	085	092	9	7.2
618	099	106	113	120	127	134	141	148	155	162		
619	169	176	183	190	197	204	211	218	225	232		
620	239	246	253	260	267	274	281	288	295	302		**7**
621	309	316	323	330	337	344	351	358	365	372	1	0.7
622	379	386	393	400	407	414	421	428	435	442	2	1.4
623	449	456	463	470	477	484	491	498	505	511	3	2.1
624	518	525	532	539	546	553	560	567	574	581	4	2.8
625	588	595	602	609	616	623	630	637	644	650	5	3.5
626	657	664	671	678	685	692	699	706	713	720	6	4.2
627	727	734	741	748	754	761	768	775	782	789	7	4.9
628	796	803	810	817	824	831	837	844	851	858	8	5.6
629	865	872	879	886	893	900	906	913	920	927	9	6.3
630	934	941	948	955	962	969	975	982	989	996		
631	80 003	010	017	024	030	037	044	051	058	065		
632	072	079	085	092	099	106	113	120	127	134		
633	140	147	154	161	168	175	182	188	195	202		**6**
634	209	216	223	229	236	243	250	257	264	271	1	0.6
635	277	284	291	298	305	312	318	325	332	339	2	1.2
636	346	353	359	366	373	380	387	393	400	407	3	1.8
637	414	421	428	434	441	448	455	462	468	475	4	2.4
638	482	489	496	502	509	516	523	530	536	543	5	3.0
639	550	557	564	570	577	584	591	598	604	611	6	3.6
											7	4.2
640	618	625	632	638	645	652	659	665	672	679	8	4.8
641	686	693	699	706	713	720	726	733	740	747	9	5.4
642	754	760	767	774	781	787	794	801	808	814		
643	821	828	835	841	848	855	862	868	875	882		
644	889	895	902	909	916	922	929	936	943	949		
645	956	963	969	976	983	990	996	*003	*010	*017		
646	81 023	030	037	043	050	057	064	070	077	084		
647	090	097	104	111	117	124	131	137	144	151		
648	158	164	171	178	184	191	198	204	211	218		
649	224	231	238	245	251	258	265	271	278	285		
650	291	298	305	311	318	325	331	338	345	351		
N.	0	1	2	3	4	5	6	7	8	9	Proportional parts	

FIVE-PLACE MANTISSAS FOR COMMON LOGARITHMS

N.	0	1	2	3	4	5	6	7	8	9	Proportional parts	
650	81 291	298	305	311	318	325	331	338	345	351		
651	358	365	371	378	385	391	398	405	411	418		
652	425	431	438	445	451	458	465	471	478	485		
653	491	498	505	511	518	525	531	538	544	551		
654	558	564	571	578	584	591	598	604	611	617		
655	624	631	637	644	651	657	664	671	677	684		
656	690	697	704	710	717	723	730	737	743	750		
657	757	763	770	776	783	790	796	803	809	816		
658	823	829	836	842	849	856	862	869	875	882		
659	889	895	902	908	915	921	928	935	941	948		
660	954	961	968	974	981	987	994	*000	*007	*014		**7**
661	82 020	027	033	040	046	053	060	066	073	079	1	0.7
662	086	092	099	105	112	119	125	132	138	145	2	1.4
663	151	158	164	171	178	184	191	197	204	210	3	2.1
664	217	223	230	236	243	249	256	263	269	276	4	2.8
665	282	289	295	302	308	315	321	328	334	341	5	3.5
666	347	354	360	367	373	380	387	393	400	406	6	4.2
667	413	419	426	432	439	445	452	458	465	471	7	4.9
668	478	484	491	497	504	510	517	523	530	536	8	5.6
669	543	549	556	562	569	575	582	588	595	601	9	6.3
670	607	614	620	627	633	640	646	653	659	666		
671	672	679	685	692	698	705	711	718	724	730		
672	737	743	750	756	763	769	776	782	789	795		
673	802	808	814	821	827	834	840	847	853	860		
674	866	872	879	885	892	898	905	911	918	924		
675	930	937	943	950	956	963	969	975	982	988		
676	995	*001	*008	*014	*020	*027	*033	*040	*046	*052		
677	83 059	065	072	078	085	091	097	104	110	117		
678	123	129	136	142	149	155	161	168	174	181		
679	187	193	200	206	213	219	225	232	238	245		
680	251	257	264	270	276	283	289	296	302	308		**6**
681	315	321	327	334	340	347	353	359	366	372	1	0.6
682	378	385	391	398	404	410	417	423	429	436	2	1.2
683	442	448	455	461	467	474	480	487	493	499	3	1.8
684	506	512	518	525	531	537	544	550	556	563	4	2.4
685	569	575	582	588	594	601	607	613	620	626	5	3.0
686	632	639	645	651	658	664	670	677	683	689	6	3.6
687	696	702	708	715	721	727	734	740	746	753	7	4.2
688	759	765	771	778	784	790	797	803	809	816	8	4.8
689	822	828	835	841	847	853	860	866	872	879	9	5.4
690	885	891	897	904	910	916	923	929	935	942		
691	948	954	960	967	973	979	985	992	998	*004		
692	84 011	017	023	029	036	042	048	055	061	067		
693	073	080	086	092	098	105	111	117	123	130		
694	136	142	148	155	161	167	173	180	186	192		
695	198	205	211	217	223	230	236	242	248	255		
696	261	267	273	280	286	292	298	305	311	317		
697	323	330	336	342	348	354	361	367	373	379		
698	386	392	398	404	410	417	423	429	435	442		
699	448	454	460	466	473	479	485	491	497	504		
700	510	516	522	528	535	541	547	553	559	566		
N.	0	1	2	3	4	5	6	7	8	9	Proportional parts	

FIVE-PLACE MANTISSAS FOR COMMON LOGARITHMS

N.	0	1	2	3	4	5	6	7	8	9	Proportional parts
700	84 510	516	522	528	535	541	547	553	559	566	
701	572	578	584	590	597	603	609	615	621	628	
702	634	640	646	652	658	665	671	677	683	689	
703	696	702	708	714	720	726	733	739	745	751	
704	757	763	770	776	782	788	794	800	807	813	
705	819	825	831	837	844	850	856	862	868	874	
706	880	887	893	899	905	911	917	924	930	936	
707	942	948	954	960	967	973	979	985	991	997	**7**
708	85 003	009	016	022	028	034	040	046	052	058	1 0.7
709	065	071	077	083	089	095	101	107	114	120	2 1.4
											3 2.1
710	126	132	138	144	150	156	163	169	175	181	4 2.8
711	187	193	199	205	211	217	224	230	236	242	5 3.5
712	248	254	260	266	272	278	285	291	297	303	6 4.2
713	309	315	321	327	333	339	345	352	358	364	7 4.9
714	370	376	382	388	394	400	406	412	418	425	8 5.6
715	431	437	443	449	455	461	467	473	479	485	9 6.3
716	491	497	503	509	516	522	528	534	540	546	
717	552	558	564	570	576	582	588	594	600	606	
718	612	618	625	631	637	643	649	655	661	667	
719	673	679	685	691	697	703	709	715	721	727	**6**
											1 0.6
720	733	739	745	751	757	763	769	775	781	788	2 1.2
721	794	800	806	812	818	824	830	836	842	848	3 1.8
722	854	860	866	872	878	884	890	896	902	908	4 2.4
723	914	920	926	932	938	944	950	956	962	968	5 3.0
724	974	980	986	992	998	*004	*010	*016	*022	*028	6 3.6
725	86 034	040	046	052	058	064	070	076	082	088	7 4.2
726	094	100	106	112	118	124	130	136	141	147	8 4.8
727	153	159	165	171	177	183	189	195	201	207	9 5.4
728	213	219	225	231	237	243	249	255	261	267	
729	273	279	285	291	297	303	308	314	320	326	
730	332	338	344	350	356	362	368	374	380	386	**5**
731	392	398	404	410	415	421	427	433	439	445	1 0.5
732	451	457	463	469	475	481	487	493	499	504	2 1.0
733	510	516	522	528	534	540	546	552	558	564	3 1.5
734	570	576	581	587	593	599	605	611	617	623	4 2.0
735	629	635	641	646	652	658	664	670	676	682	5 2.5
736	688	694	700	705	711	717	723	729	735	741	6 3.0
737	747	753	759	764	770	776	782	788	794	800	7 3.5
738	806	812	817	823	829	835	841	847	853	859	8 4.0
739	864	870	876	882	888	894	900	906	911	917	9 4.5
740	923	929	935	941	947	953	958	964	970	976	
741	982	988	994	999	*005	*011	*017	*023	*029	*035	
742	87 040	046	052	058	064	070	075	081	087	093	
743	099	105	111	116	122	128	134	140	146	151	
744	157	163	169	175	181	186	192	198	204	210	
745	216	221	227	233	239	245	251	256	262	268	
746	274	280	286	291	297	303	309	315	320	326	
747	332	338	344	349	355	361	367	373	379	384	
748	390	396	402	408	413	419	425	431	437	442	
749	448	454	460	466	471	477	483	489	495	500	
750	506	512	518	523	529	535	541	547	552	558	
N.	0	1	2	3	4	5	6	7	8	9	Proportional parts

Logarithm Tables

FIVE-PLACE MANTISSAS FOR COMMON LOGARITHMS

N.	0	1	2	3	4	5	6	7	8	9	Proportional parts		
750	87 506	512	518	523	529	535	541	547	552	558			
751	564	570	576	581	587	593	599	604	610	616			
752	622	628	633	639	645	651	656	662	668	674			
753	679	685	691	697	703	708	714	720	726	731			
754	737	743	749	754	760	766	772	777	783	789			
755	795	800	806	812	818	823	829	835	841	846			
756	852	858	864	869	875	881	887	892	898	904			
757	910	915	921	927	933	938	944	950	955	961			
758	967	973	978	984	990	996	*001	*007	*013	*018			
759	88 024	030	036	041	047	053	058	064	070	076			
760	081	087	093	098	104	110	116	121	127	133			**6**
761	138	144	150	156	161	167	173	178	184	190	1		0.6
762	195	201	207	213	218	224	230	235	241	247	2		1.2
763	252	258	264	270	275	281	287	292	298	304	3		1.8
764	309	315	321	326	332	338	343	349	355	360	4		2.4
765	366	372	377	383	389	395	400	406	412	417	5		3.0
766	423	429	434	440	446	451	457	463	468	474	6		3.6
767	480	485	491	497	502	508	513	519	525	530	7		4.2
768	536	542	547	553	559	564	570	576	581	587	8		4.8
769	593	598	604	610	615	621	627	632	638	643	9		5.4
770	649	655	660	666	672	677	683	689	694	700			
771	705	711	717	722	728	734	739	745	750	756			
772	762	767	773	779	784	790	795	801	807	812			
773	818	824	829	835	840	846	852	857	863	868			
774	874	880	885	891	897	902	908	913	919	925			
775	930	936	941	947	953	958	964	969	975	981			
776	986	992	997	*003	*009	*014	*020	*025	*031	*037			
777	89 042	048	053	059	064	070	076	081	087	092			
778	098	104	109	115	120	126	131	137	143	148			
779	154	159	165	170	176	182	187	193	198	204			
780	209	215	221	226	232	237	243	248	254	260			**5**
781	265	271	276	282	287	293	298	304	310	315	1		0.5
782	321	326	332	337	343	348	354	360	365	371	2		1.0
783	376	382	387	393	398	404	409	415	421	426	3		1.5
784	432	437	443	448	454	459	465	470	476	481	4		2.0
785	487	492	498	504	509	515	520	526	531	537	5		2.5
786	542	548	553	559	564	570	575	581	586	592	6		3.0
787	597	603	609	614	620	625	631	636	642	647	7		3.5
788	653	658	664	669	675	680	686	691	697	702	8		4.0
789	708	713	719	724	730	735	741	746	752	757	9		4.5
790	763	768	774	779	785	790	796	801	807	812			
791	818	823	829	834	840	845	851	856	862	867			
792	873	878	883	889	894	900	905	911	916	922			
793	927	933	938	944	949	955	960	966	971	977			
794	982	988	993	998	*004	*009	*015	*020	*026	*031			
795	90 037	042	048	053	059	064	069	075	080	086			
796	091	097	102	108	113	119	124	129	135	140			
797	146	151	157	162	168	173	179	184	189	195			
798	200	206	211	217	222	227	233	238	244	249			
799	255	260	266	271	276	282	287	293	298	304			
800	309	314	320	325	331	336	342	347	352	358			
N.	0	1	2	3	4	5	6	7	8	9	Proportional parts		

FIVE-PLACE MANTISSAS FOR COMMON LOGARITHMS

N.	0	1	2	3	4	5	6	7	8	9	Proportional parts	
800	90 309	314	320	325	331	336	342	347	352	358		
801	363	369	374	380	385	390	396	401	407	412		
802	417	423	428	434	439	445	450	455	461	466		
803	472	477	482	488	493	499	504	509	515	520		
804	526	531	536	542	547	553	558	563	569	574		
805	580	585	590	596	601	607	612	617	623	628		
806	634	639	644	650	655	660	666	671	677	682		
807	687	693	698	703	709	714	720	725	730	736		
808	741	747	752	757	763	768	773	779	784	789		
809	795	800	806	811	816	822	827	832	838	843		
810	849	854	859	865	870	875	881	886	891	897		**6**
811	902	907	913	918	924	929	934	940	945	950	1	0.6
812	956	961	966	972	977	982	988	993	998	*004	2	1.2
813	91 009	014	020	025	030	036	041	046	052	057	3	1.8
814	062	068	073	078	084	089	094	100	105	110	4	2.4
815	116	121	126	132	137	142	148	153	158	164	5	3.0
816	169	174	180	185	190	196	201	206	212	217	6	3.6
817	222	228	233	238	243	249	254	259	265	270	7	4.2
818	275	281	286	291	297	302	307	312	318	323	8	4.8
819	328	334	339	344	350	355	360	365	371	376	9	5.4
820	381	387	392	397	403	408	413	418	424	429		
821	434	440	445	450	455	461	466	471	477	482		
822	487	492	498	503	508	514	519	524	529	535		
823	540	545	551	556	561	566	572	577	582	587		
824	593	598	603	609	614	619	624	630	635	640		
825	645	651	656	661	666	672	677	682	687	693		
826	698	703	709	714	719	724	730	735	740	745		
827	751	756	761	766	772	777	782	787	793	798		
828	803	808	814	819	824	829	834	840	845	850		
829	855	861	866	871	876	882	887	892	897	903		
830	908	913	918	924	929	934	939	944	950	955		**5**
831	960	965	971	976	981	986	991	997	*002	*007	1	0.5
832	92 012	018	023	028	033	038	044	049	054	059	2	1.0
833	065	070	075	080	085	091	096	101	106	111	3	1.5
834	117	122	127	132	137	143	148	153	158	163	4	2.0
835	169	174	179	184	189	195	200	205	210	215	5	2.5
836	221	226	231	236	241	247	252	257	262	267	6	3.0
837	273	278	283	288	293	298	304	309	314	319	7	3.5
838	324	330	335	340	345	350	355	361	366	371	8	4.0
839	376	381	387	392	397	402	407	412	418	423	9	4.5
840	428	433	438	443	449	454	459	464	469	474		
841	480	485	490	495	500	505	511	516	521	526		
842	531	536	542	547	552	557	562	567	572	578		
843	583	588	593	598	603	609	614	619	624	629		
844	634	639	645	650	655	660	665	670	675	681		
845	686	691	696	701	706	711	716	722	727	732		
846	737	742	747	752	758	763	768	773	778	783		
847	788	793	799	804	809	814	819	824	829	834		
848	840	845	850	855	860	865	870	875	881	886		
849	891	896	901	906	911	916	921	927	932	937		
850	942	947	952	957	962	967	973	978	983	988		
N.	0	1	2	3	4	5	6	7	8	9	Proportional parts	

Logarithm Tables

FIVE-PLACE MANTISSAS FOR COMMON LOGARITHMS

N.	0	1	2	3	4	5	6	7	8	9
850	92 942	947	952	957	962	967	973	978	983	988
851	993	998	*003	*008	*013	*018	*024	*029	*034	*039
852	93 044	049	054	059	064	069	075	080	085	090
853	095	100	105	110	115	120	125	131	136	141
854	146	151	156	161	166	171	176	181	186	192
855	197	202	207	212	217	222	227	232	237	242
856	247	252	258	263	268	273	278	283	288	293
857	298	303	308	313	318	323	328	334	339	344
858	349	354	359	364	369	374	379	384	389	394
859	399	404	409	414	420	425	430	435	440	445
860	450	455	460	465	470	475	480	485	490	495
861	500	505	510	515	520	526	531	536	541	546
862	551	556	561	566	571	576	581	586	591	596
863	601	606	611	616	621	626	631	636	641	646
864	651	656	661	666	671	676	682	687	692	697
865	702	707	712	717	722	727	732	737	742	747
866	752	757	762	767	772	777	782	787	792	797
867	802	807	812	817	822	827	832	837	842	847
868	852	857	862	867	872	877	882	887	892	897
869	902	907	912	917	922	927	932	937	942	947
870	952	957	962	967	972	977	982	987	992	997
871	94 002	007	012	017	022	027	032	037	042	047
872	052	057	062	067	072	077	082	086	091	096
873	101	106	111	116	121	126	131	136	141	146
874	151	156	161	166	171	176	181	186	191	196
875	201	206	211	216	221	226	231	236	240	245
876	250	255	260	265	270	275	280	285	290	295
877	300	305	310	315	320	325	330	335	340	345
878	349	354	359	364	369	374	379	384	389	394
879	399	404	409	414	419	424	429	433	438	443
880	448	453	458	463	468	473	478	483	488	493
881	498	503	507	512	517	522	527	532	537	542
882	547	552	557	562	567	571	576	581	586	591
883	596	601	606	611	616	621	626	630	635	640
884	645	650	655	660	665	670	675	680	685	689
885	694	699	704	709	714	719	724	729	734	738
886	743	748	753	758	763	768	773	778	783	787
887	792	797	802	807	812	817	822	827	832	836
888	841	846	851	856	861	866	871	876	880	885
889	890	895	900	905	910	915	919	924	929	934
890	939	944	949	954	959	963	968	973	978	983
891	988	993	998	*002	*007	*012	*017	*022	*027	*032
892	95 036	041	046	051	056	061	066	071	075	080
893	085	090	095	100	105	109	114	119	124	129
894	134	139	143	148	153	158	163	168	173	177
895	182	187	192	197	202	207	211	216	221	226
896	231	236	240	245	250	255	260	265	270	274
897	279	284	289	294	299	303	308	313	318	323
898	328	332	337	342	347	352	357	361	366	371
899	376	381	386	390	395	400	405	410	415	419
900	424	429	434	439	444	448	453	458	463	468

Proportional parts

	6		5		4
1	0.6	1	0.5	1	0.4
2	1.2	2	1.0	2	0.8
3	1.8	3	1.5	3	1.2
4	2.4	4	2.0	4	1.6
5	3.0	5	2.5	5	2.0
6	3.6	6	3.0	6	2.4
7	4.2	7	3.5	7	2.8
8	4.8	8	4.0	8	3.2
9	5.4	9	4.5	9	3.6

N.	0	1	2	3	4	5	6	7	8	9	Proportional parts

FIVE-PLACE MANTISSAS FOR COMMON LOGARITHMS

N.	0	1	2	3	4	5	6	7	8	9
900	95 424	429	434	439	444	448	453	458	463	468
901	472	477	482	487	492	497	501	506	511	516
902	521	525	530	535	540	545	550	554	559	564
903	569	574	578	583	588	593	598	602	607	612
904	617	622	626	631	636	641	646	650	655	660
905	665	670	674	679	684	689	694	698	703	708
906	713	718	722	727	732	737	742	746	751	756
907	761	766	770	775	780	785	789	794	799	804
908	809	813	818	823	828	832	837	842	847	852
909	856	861	866	871	875	880	885	890	895	899
910	904	909	914	918	923	928	933	938	942	947
911	952	957	961	966	971	976	980	985	990	995
912	999	*004	*009	*014	*019	*023	*028	*033	*038	*042
913	96 047	052	057	061	066	071	076	080	085	090
914	095	099	104	109	114	118	123	128	133	137
915	142	147	152	156	161	166	171	175	180	185
916	190	194	199	204	209	213	218	223	227	232
917	237	242	246	251	256	261	265	270	275	280
918	284	289	294	298	303	308	313	317	322	327
919	332	336	341	346	350	355	360	365	369	374
920	379	384	388	393	398	402	407	412	417	421
921	426	431	435	440	445	450	454	459	464	468
922	473	478	483	487	492	497	501	506	511	515
923	520	525	530	534	539	544	548	553	558	562
924	567	572	577	581	586	591	595	600	605	609
925	614	619	624	628	633	638	642	647	652	656
926	661	666	670	675	680	685	689	694	699	703
927	708	713	717	722	727	731	736	741	745	750
928	755	759	764	769	774	778	783	788	792	797
929	802	806	811	816	820	825	830	834	839	844
930	848	853	858	862	867	872	876	881	886	890
931	895	900	904	909	914	918	923	928	932	937
932	942	946	951	956	960	965	970	974	979	984
933	988	993	997	*002	*007	*011	*016	*021	*025	*030
934	97 035	039	044	049	053	058	063	067	072	077
935	081	086	090	095	100	104	109	114	118	123
936	128	132	137	142	146	151	155	160	165	169
937	174	179	183	188	192	197	202	206	211	216
938	220	225	230	234	239	243	248	253	257	262
939	267	271	276	280	285	290	294	299	304	308
940	313	317	322	327	331	336	340	345	350	354
941	359	364	368	373	377	382	387	391	396	400
942	405	410	414	419	424	428	433	437	442	447
943	451	456	460	465	470	474	479	483	488	493
944	497	502	506	511	516	520	525	529	534	539
945	543	548	552	557	562	566	571	575	580	585
946	589	594	598	603	607	612	617	621	626	630
947	635	640	644	649	653	658	663	667	672	676
948	681	685	690	695	699	704	708	713	717	722
949	727	731	736	740	745	749	754	759	763	768
950	772	777	782	786	791	795	800	804	809	813

| N. | 0 | 1 | 2 | 3 | 4 | 5 | 6 | 7 | 8 | 9 |

Proportional parts

5
1	0.5
2	1.0
3	1.5
4	2.0
5	2.5
6	3.0
7	3.5
8	4.0
9	4.5

4
1	0.4
2	0.8
3	1.2
4	1.6
5	2.0
6	2.4
7	2.8
8	3.2
9	3.6

FIVE-PLACE MANTISSAS FOR COMMON LOGARITHMS

N.	0	1	2	3	4	5	6	7	8	9	Proportional parts
950	97 772	777	782	786	791	795	800	804	809	813	
951	818	823	827	832	836	841	845	850	855	859	
952	864	868	873	877	882	886	891	896	900	905	
953	909	914	918	923	928	932	937	941	946	950	
954	955	959	964	968	973	978	982	987	991	996	
955	98 000	005	009	014	019	023	028	032	037	041	
956	046	050	055	059	064	068	073	078	082	087	
957	091	096	100	105	109	114	118	123	127	132	
958	137	141	146	150	155	159	164	168	173	177	
959	182	186	191	195	200	204	209	214	218	223	
960	227	232	236	241	245	250	254	259	263	268	**5**
961	272	277	281	286	290	295	299	304	308	313	1 0.5
962	318	322	327	331	336	340	345	349	354	358	2 1.0
963	363	367	372	376	381	385	390	394	399	403	3 1.5
964	408	412	417	421	426	430	435	439	444	448	4 2.0
965	453	457	462	466	471	475	480	484	489	493	5 2.5
966	498	502	507	511	516	520	525	529	534	538	6 3.0
967	543	547	552	556	561	565	570	574	579	583	7 3.5
968	588	592	597	601	605	610	614	619	623	628	8 4.0
969	632	637	641	646	650	655	659	664	668	673	9 4.5
970	677	682	686	691	695	700	704	709	713	717	
971	722	726	731	735	740	744	749	753	758	762	
972	767	771	776	780	784	789	793	798	802	807	
973	811	816	820	825	829	834	838	843	847	851	
974	856	860	865	869	874	878	883	887	892	896	
975	900	905	909	914	918	923	927	932	936	941	
976	945	949	954	958	963	967	972	976	981	985	
977	989	994	998	*003	*007	*012	*016	*021	*025	*029	
978	99 034	038	043	047	052	056	061	065	069	074	
979	078	083	087	092	096	100	105	109	114	118	
980	123	127	131	136	140	145	149	154	158	162	**4**
981	167	171	176	180	185	189	193	198	202	207	1 0.4
982	211	216	220	224	229	233	238	242	247	251	2 0.8
983	255	260	264	269	273	277	282	286	291	295	3 1.2
984	300	304	308	313	317	322	326	330	335	339	4 1.6
985	344	348	352	357	361	366	370	374	379	383	5 2.0
986	388	392	396	401	405	410	414	419	423	427	6 2.4
987	432	436	441	445	449	454	458	463	467	471	7 2.8
988	476	480	484	489	493	498	502	506	511	515	8 3.2
989	520	524	528	533	537	542	546	550	555	559	9 3.6
990	564	568	572	577	581	585	590	594	599	603	
991	607	612	616	621	625	629	634	638	642	647	
992	651	656	660	664	669	673	677	682	686	691	
993	695	699	704	708	712	717	721	726	730	734	
994	739	743	747	752	756	760	765	769	774	778	
995	782	787	791	795	800	804	808	813	817	822	
996	826	830	835	839	843	848	852	856	861	865	
997	870	874	878	883	887	891	896	900	904	909	
998	913	917	922	926	930	935	939	944	948	952	
999	957	961	965	970	974	978	983	987	991	996	
1000	00 000	004	009	013	017	022	026	030	035	039	
N.	0	1	2	3	4	5	6	7	8	9	Proportional parts

SIX-PLACE MANTISSAS FOR COMMON LOGARITHMS

N	0	1	2	3	4	5	6	7	8	9
100	00 0000	0434	0868	1301	1734	2166	2598	3029	3461	3891
01	4321	4751	5181	5609	6038	6466	6894	7321	7748	8174
02	00 8600	9026	9451	9876	*0300	*0724	*1147	*1570	*1993	*2415
03	01 2837	3259	3680	4100	4521	4940	5360	5779	6197	6616
04	01 7033	7451	7868	8284	8700	9116	9532	9947	*0361	*0775
05	02 1189	1603	2016	2428	2841	3252	3664	4075	4486	4896
06	5306	5715	6125	6533	6942	7350	7757	8164	8571	8978
07	02 9384	9789	*0195	*0600	*1004	*1408	*1812	*2216	*2619	*3021
08	03 3424	3826	4227	4628	5029	5430	5830	6230	6629	7028
09	03 7426	7825	8223	8620	9017	9414	9811	*0207	*0602	*0998
110	04 1393	1787	2182	2576	2969	3362	3755	4148	4540	4932
11	5323	5714	6105	6495	6885	7275	7664	8053	8442	8830
12	04 9218	9606	9993	*0380	*0766	*1153	*1538	*1924	*2309	*2694
13	05 3078	3463	3846	4230	4613	4996	5378	5760	6142	6524
14	05 6905	7286	7666	8046	8426	8805	9185	9563	9942	*0320
15	06 0698	1075	1452	1829	2206	2582	2958	3333	3709	4083
16	4458	4832	5206	5580	5953	6326	6699	7071	7443	7815
17	06 8186	8557	8928	9298	9668	*0038	*0407	*0776	*1145	*1514
18	07 1882	2250	2617	2985	3352	3718	4085	4451	4816	5182
19	5547	5912	6276	6640	7004	7368	7731	8094	8457	8819
120	07 9181	9543	9904	*0266	*0626	*0987	*1347	*1707	*2067	*2426
21	08 2785	3144	3503	3861	4219	4576	4934	5291	5647	6004
22	6360	6716	7071	7426	7781	8136	8490	8845	9198	9552
23	08 9905	*0258	*0611	*0963	*1315	*1667	*2018	*2370	*2721	*3071
24	09 3422	3772	4122	4471	4820	5169	5518	5866	6215	6562
25	09 6910	7257	7604	7951	8298	8644	8990	9335	9681	*0026
26	10 0371	0715	1059	1403	1747	2091	2434	2777	3119	3462
27	3804	4146	4487	4828	5169	5510	5851	6191	6531	6871
28	10 7210	7549	7888	8227	8565	8903	9241	9579	9916	*0253
29	11 0590	0926	1263	1599	1934	2270	2605	2940	3275	3609
130	3943	4277	4611	4944	5278	5611	5943	6276	6608	6940
31	11 7271	7603	7934	8265	8595	8926	9256	9586	9915	*0245
32	12 0574	0903	1231	1560	1888	2216	2544	2871	3198	3525
33	3852	4178	4504	4830	5156	5481	5806	6131	6456	6781
34	12 7105	7429	7753	8076	8399	8722	9045	9368	9690	*0012
35	13 0334	0655	0977	1298	1619	1939	2260	2580	2900	3219
36	3539	3858	4177	4496	4814	5133	5451	5769	6086	6403
37	6721	7037	7354	7671	7989	8303	8618	8934	9249	9564
38	13 9879	*0194	*0508	*0822	*1136	*1450	*1763	*2076	*2389	*2702
39	14 3015	3327	3639	3851	4263	4574	4885	5196	5507	5818
140	6128	6438	6748	7058	7367	7676	7985	8294	8603	8911
41	14 9219	9527	9835	*0142	*0449	*0756	*1063	*1370	*1676	*1982
42	15 2288	2594	2900	3205	3510	3815	4120	4424	4728	5032
43	5336	5640	5943	6246	6549	6852	7154	7457	7759	8061
44	15 8362	8664	8965	9266	9567	9868	*0168	*0469	*0769	*1068
45	16 1368	1667	1967	2266	2564	2863	3161	3460	3758	4055
46	4353	4650	4947	5244	5541	5838	6134	6430	6726	7022
47	16 7317	7613	7908	8203	8497	8792	9086	9380	9674	9968
48	17 0262	0555	0848	1141	1434	1726	2019	2311	2603	2895
49	3186	3478	3769	4060	4351	4641	4932	5222	5512	5802
150	17 6091	6381	6670	6959	7248	7536	7825	8113	8401	8689
N	0	1	2	3	4	5	6	7	8	9

SIX-PLACE MANTISSAS FOR COMMON LOGARITHMS (Continued)

N	0	1	2	3	4	5	6	7	8	9
150	17 6091	6381	6670	6959	7248	7536	7825	8113	8401	8689
51	17 8977	9264	9552	9839	*0126	*0413	*0699	*0986	*1272	*1558
52	18 1844	2129	2415	2700	2985	3270	3555	3839	4123	4407
53	4691	4975	5259	5542	5825	6108	6391	6674	6956	7239
54	18 7521	7803	8084	8366	8647	8928	9209	9490	9771	*0051
55	19 0332	0612	0892	1171	1451	1730	2010	2289	2567	2846
56	3125	3403	3681	3959	4237	4514	4792	5069	5346	5623
57	5900	6176	6453	6829	7005	7281	7556	7832	8107	8382
58	19 8657	8932	9206	9481	9755	*0029	*0303	*0577	*0850	*1124
59	20 1397	1670	1943	2216	2488	2761	3033	3305	3577	3848
160	4120	4391	4663	4934	5204	5475	5746	6016	6286	6556
61	6826	7096	7365	7634	7904	8173	8441	8710	8979	9247
62	20 9515	9783	*0051	*0319	*0586	*0853	*1121	*1388	*1654	*1921
63	21 2188	2454	2720	2986	3252	3518	3783	4049	4314	4579
64	4844	5109	5373	5638	5902	6166	6430	6694	6957	7221
65	21 7484	7747	8010	8273	8536	8798	9060	9323	9585	9846
66	22 0108	0370	0631	0892	1153	1414	1675	1936	2196	2456
67	2716	2976	3236	3496	3755	4015	4274	4533	4792	5051
68	5309	5568	5826	6084	6342	6600	6858	7115	7372	7630
69	22 7887	8144	8400	8657	8913	9170	9426	9682	9938	*0193
170	23 0449	0704	0960	1215	1470	1724	1979	2234	2488	2742
71	2996	3250	3504	3757	4011	4264	4517	4770	5023	5276
72	5528	5781	6033	6285	6537	6789	7041	7292	7544	7795
73	23 8046	8297	8548	8799	9049	9299	9550	9800	*0050	*0300
74	24 0549	0799	1048	1297	1546	1795	2044	2293	2541	2790
75	3038	3286	3534	3782	4030	4277	4525	4772	5019	5266
76	5513	5759	6006	6252	6499	6745	6991	7237	7482	7728
77	24 7973	8219	8464	8709	8954	9198	9443	9687	9932	*0176
78	25 0420	0664	0908	1151	1395	1638	1881	2125	2368	2610
79	2853	3096	3338	3580	3822	4064	4306	4548	4790	5031
180	5273	5514	5755	5996	6237	6477	6718	6958	7198	7439
81	25 7679	7918	8158	8398	8637	8877	9116	9355	9594	9833
82	26 0071	0310	0548	0787	1025	1263	1501	1739	1976	2214
83	2451	2688	2925	3162	3399	3636	3873	4109	4346	4582
84	4818	5054	5290	5525	5761	5996	6232	6467	6702	6937
85	7172	7406	7641	7875	8110	8344	8578	8812	9046	9279
86	26 9513	9746	9980	*0213	*0446	*0679	*0912	*1144	*1377	*1609
87	27 1842	2074	2306	2538	2770	3001	3233	3464	3696	3927
88	4158	4389	4620	4850	5081	5311	5542	5772	6002	6232
89	6462	6692	6921	7151	7380	7609	7838	8067	8296	8525
190	27 8754	8982	9211	9439	9667	9895	*0123	*0351	*0578	*0806
91	28 1033	1261	1488	1715	1942	2169	2396	2622	2849	3075
92	3301	3527	3753	3979	4205	4431	4656	4882	5107	5332
93	5557	5782	6007	6232	6456	6681	6905	7130	7354	7578
94	28 7802	8026	8249	8473	8696	8920	9143	9366	9589	9812
95	29 0035	0257	0480	0702	0925	1147	1369	1591	1813	2034
96	2256	2478	2699	2920	3141	3363	3584	3804	4025	4246
97	4466	4687	4907	5127	5347	5567	5787	6007	6226	6446
98	6665	6884	7104	7323	7542	7761	7979	8198	8416	8635
99	29 8853	9071	9289	9507	9725	9943	*0161	*0378	*0595	*0813
200	30 1030	1247	1464	1681	1898	2114	2331	2547	2764	2980
N	0	1	2	3	4	5	6	7	8	9

SIX-PLACE MANTISSAS FOR COMMON LOGARITHMS (Continued)

N	0	1	2	3	4	5	6	7	8	9
200	30 1030	1247	1464	1681	1898	2114	2331	2547	2764	2980
01	3196	3412	3628	3844	4059	4275	4491	4706	4921	5136
02	5351	5566	5781	5996	6211	6425	6639	6854	7068	7282
03	7496	7710	7924	8137	8351	8564	8778	8991	9204	9417
04	30 9630	9843	*0056	*0268	*0481	*0693	*0906	*1118	*1330	*1542
05	31 1754	1966	2177	2389	2600	2812	3023	3234	3445	3656
06	3867	4078	4289	4499	4710	920	5130	5340	5551	5760
07	5970	6180	6390	6599	6809	7018	7227	7436	7646	7854
08	31 8063	8272	8481	8689	8898	9106	9314	9522	9730	9938
09	32 0146	0354	0562	0769	0977	1184	1391	1598	1805	2012
210	2219	2426	2633	2839	3046	3252	3458	3665	3871	4077
11	4282	4488	4694	4899	5105	5310	5516	5721	5926	6131
12	6336	6541	6745	6950	7155	7359	7563	7767	7972	8176
13	32 8380	8583	8787	8991	9194	9398	9601	9805	*0008	*0211
14	33 0414	0617	0819	1022	1225	1427	1630	1832	2034	2236
15	2438	2640	2842	3044	3246	3447	3649	3850	4051	4253
16	4454	4655	4856	5057	5257	5458	5658	5859	6059	6260
17	6460	6660	6860	7060	7260	7459	7659	7858	8058	8257
18	33 8456	8656	8855	9054	9253	9451	9650	9849	*0047	*0246
19	34 0444	0642	0841	1039	1237	1435	1632	1830	2028	2225
220	2423	2620	2817	3014	3212	3409	3606	3802	3999	4196
21	4392	4589	4785	4981	5178	5374	5570	5766	5962	6157
22	6353	6549	6744	6939	7135	7330	7525	7720	7915	8110
23	34 8305	8500	8694	8889	9083	9278	9472	9666	9860	*0054
24	35 0248	0442	0636	0829	1023	1216	1410	1603	1796	1989
25	2183	2375	2568	2761	2954	3147	3339	3532	3724	3916
26	4108	4301	4493	4685	4876	5068	5260	5452	5643	5834
27	6026	6217	6408	6599	6790	6981	7172	7363	7554	7744
28	7935	8125	8316	8506	8696	8886	9076	9266	9456	9646
29	35 9835	*0025	*0215	*0404	*0593	*0783	*0972	*1161	*1350	*1539
230	36 1728	1917	2105	2294	2482	2671	2859	3048	3236	3424
31	3612	3800	3988	4176	4363	4551	4739	4926	5113	5301
32	5488	5675	5862	6049	6236	6423	6610	6796	6983	7169
33	7356	7542	7729	7915	8101	8287	8473	8659	8845	9030
34	36 9216	9401	9587	9772	9958	*0143	*0328	*0513	*0698	*0883
35	37 1068	1253	1437	1622	1806	1991	2175	2360	2544	2728
36	2912	3096	3280	3464	3647	3831	4015	4198	4382	4565
37	4748	4932	5115	5298	5481	5664	5846	6029	6212	6394
38	6577	6759	6942	7124	7306	7488	7670	7852	8034	8216
39	37 8398	8580	8761	8943	9124	9306	9487	9668	9849	*0030
240	38 0211	0392	0573	0754	0934	1115	1296	1476	1656	1837
41	2017	2197	2377	2557	2737	2917	3097	3277	3456	3636
42	3815	3995	4174	4353	4533	4712	4891	5070	5249	5428
43	5606	5785	5964	6142	6321	6499	6677	6856	7034	7212
44	7390	7568	7746	7924	8101	8279	8456	8634	8811	8989
45	38 9166	9343	9520	9698	9875	*0051	*0228	*0405	*0582	*0759
46	39 0935	1112	1288	1464	1641	1817	1993	2169	2345	2521
47	2697	2873	3048	3224	3400	3575	3751	3926	4101	4277
48	4452	4627	4802	4977	5152	5326	5501	5676	5850	6025
49	6199	6374	6548	6722	6896	7071	7245	7419	7592	7766
250	39 7940	8114	8287	8461	8634	8808	8981	9154	9328	9501
N	0	1	2	3	4	5	6	7	8	9

SIX-PLACE MANTISSAS FOR COMMON LOGARITHMS (Continued)

N	0	1	2	3	4	5	6	7	8	9
250	39 7940	8114	8287	8461	8634	8808	8981	9154	9328	9501
51	39 9674	9847	*0020	*0192	*0365	*0538	*0711	*0883	*1056	*1228
52	40 1401	1573	1745	1917	2089	2261	2433	2605	2777	2949
53	3121	3292	3464	3635	3807	3978	4149	4320	4492	4663
54	4834	5005	5176	5346	5517	5688	5858	6029	6199	6370
55	6540	6710	6881	7051	7221	7391	7561	7731	7901	8070
56	8240	8410	8579	8749	8918	9087	9257	9426	9595	9764
57	40 9933	*0102	*0271	*0440	*0609	*0777	*0946	*1114	*1283	*1451
58	41 1620	1788	1956	2124	2293	2461	2629	2796	2964	3132
59	3300	3467	3635	3803	3970	4137	4305	4472	4639	4806
260	4973	5140	5307	5474	5641	5808	5974	6141	6308	6474
61	6641	6807	6973	7139	7306	7472	7638	7804	7970	8135
62	8301	8467	8633	8798	8964	9129	9295	9460	9625	9791
63	41 9956	*0121	*0286	*0451	*0616	*0781	*0945	*1110	*1275	*1439
64	42 1604	1768	1933	2097	2261	2426	2590	2754	2918	3082
65	3246	3410	3574	3737	3901	4065	4228	4392	4555	4718
66	4882	5045	5208	5371	5534	5697	5860	6023	6186	6349
67	6511	6674	6836	6999	7161	7324	7486	7648	7811	7973
68	8135	8297	8459	8621	8783	8944	9106	9268	9429	9591
69	42 9752	9914	*0075	*0236	*0398	*0559	*0720	*0881	*1042	*1203
270	43 1364	1525	1685	1846	2007	2167	2328	2488	2649	2809
71	2969	3130	3290	3450	3610	3770	3930	4090	4249	4409
72	4569	4729	4888	5048	5207	5367	5526	5685	5844	6004
73	6163	6322	6481	6640	6799	6957	7116	7275	7433	7592
74	7751	7909	8067	8226	8384	8542	8701	8859	9017	9175
75	43 9333	9491	9648	9806	9964	*0122	*0279	*0437	*0594	*0752
76	44 0909	1066	1224	1381	1538	1695	1852	2009	2166	2323
77	2480	2637	2793	2950	3106	3263	3419	3576	3732	3889
78	4045	4201	4357	4513	4669	4825	4981	5137	5293	5449
79	5604	5760	5915	6071	6226	6382	6537	6692	6848	7003
280	7158	7313	7468	7623	7778	7933	8088	8242	8397	8552
81	44 8706	8861	9015	9170	9324	9478	9633	9787	9941	*0095
82	45 0249	0403	0557	0711	0865	1018	1172	1326	1479	1633
83	1786	1940	2093	2247	2400	2553	2706	2859	3012	3165
84	3318	3471	3624	3777	3930	4082	4235	4387	4540	4692
85	4845	4997	5150	5302	5454	5606	5758	5910	6062	6214
86	6366	6518	6670	6821	6973	7125	7276	7428	7579	7731
87	7882	8033	8184	8336	8487	8638	8789	8940	9091	9242
88	45 9392	9543	9694	9845	9995	*0146	*0296	*0447	*0597	*0748
89	46 0898	1048	1198	1348	1499	1649	1799	1948	2098	2248
290	2398	2548	2697	2847	2997	3146	3296	3445	3594	3744
91	3893	4042	4191	4340	4490	4639	4788	4936	5085	5234
92	5383	5532	5680	5829	5977	6126	6274	6423	6571	6719
93	6868	7016	7164	7312	7460	7608	7756	7904	8052	8200
94	8347	8495	8643	8790	8938	9085	9233	9380	9527	9675
95	46 9822	9969	*0116	*0263	*0410	*0557	*0704	*0851	*0998	*1145
96	47 1292	1438	1585	1732	1878	2025	2171	2318	2464	2610
97	2756	2903	3049	3195	3341	3487	3633	3779	3925	4071
98	4216	4362	4508	4653	4799	4944	5090	5235	5381	5526
99	5671	5816	5962	6107	6252	6397	6542	6687	6832	6976
300	47 7121	7266	7411	7555	7700	7844	7989	8133	8278	8422
N	0	1	2	3	4	5	6	7	8	9

SIX-PLACE MANTISSAS FOR COMMON LOGARITHMS (Continued)

N	0	1	2	3	4	5	6	7	8	9
300	47 7121	7266	7411	7555	7700	7844	7989	8133	8278	8422
01	47 8566	8711	8855	8999	9143	9287	9431	9575	9719	9863
02	48 0007	0151	0294	0438	0582	0725	0869	1012	1156	1299
03	1443	1586	1729	1872	2016	2159	2302	2445	2588	2731
04	2874	3016	3159	3302	3445	3587	3730	3872	4015	4157
05	4300	4442	4585	4727	4869	5011	5153	5295	5437	5579
06	5721	5863	6005	6147	6289	6430	6572	6714	6855	6997
07	7138	7280	7421	7563	7704	7845	7986	8127	8269	8410
08	8551	8692	8833	8974	9114	9255	9396	9537	9677	9818
09	48 9958	*0099	*0239	*0380	*0520	*0661	*0801	*0941	*1081	*1222
310	49 1362	1502	1642	1782	1922	2062	2201	2341	2481	2621
11	2760	2900	3040	3179	3319	3458	3597	3737	3876	4015
12	4155	4294	4433	4572	4711	4850	4989	5128	5267	5406
13	5544	5683	5822	5960	6099	6238	6376	6515	6653	6791
14	6930	7068	7206	7344	7483	7621	7759	7897	8035	8173
15	8311	8448	8586	8724	8862	8999	9137	9275	9412	9550
16	49 9687	9824	9962	*0099	*0236	*0374	*0511	*0648	*0785	*0922
17	50 1059	1196	1333	1470	1607	1744	1880	2017	2154	2291
18	2427	2564	2700	2837	2973	3109	3246	3382	3518	3655
19	3791	3927	4063	4199	4335	4471	4607	4743	4878	5014
320	5150	5286	5421	5557	5693	5828	5964	6099	6234	6370
21	6505	6640	6776	6911	7046	7181	7316	7451	7586	7721
22	7856	7991	8126	8260	8395	8530	8664	8799	8934	9068
23	50 9203	9337	9471	9606	9740	9874	*0009	*0143	*0277	*0411
24	51 0545	0679	0813	0947	1081	1215	1349	1482	1616	1750
25	1883	2017	2151	2284	2418	2551	2684	2818	2951	3084
26	3218	3351	3484	3617	3750	3883	4016	4149	4282	4415
27	4548	4681	4813	4946	5079	5211	5344	5476	5609	5741
28	5874	6006	6139	6271	6403	6535	6668	6800	6932	7064
29	7196	7329	7460	7592	7724	7855	7987	8119	8251	8382
330	8514	8646	8777	8909	9040	9171	9303	9434	9566	9697
31	51 9828	9959	*0090	*0221	*0353	*0484	*0615	*0745	*0876	*1007
32	52 1138	1269	1400	1530	1661	1792	1922	2053	2183	2314
33	2444	2575	2705	2835	2966	3096	3226	3356	3486	3616
34	3746	3876	4006	4136	4266	4396	4526	4656	4785	4915
35	5045	5174	5304	5434	5563	5693	5822	5951	6081	6210
36	6339	6469	6598	6727	6856	6985	7114	7243	7372	7501
37	7630	7759	7888	8016	8145	8274*	8402	8531	8660	8788
38	52 8917	9045	9174	9312	9430	9559	9687	9815	9943	*0072
39	53 0200	0328	0456	0584	0712	0840	0968	1096	1223	1351
340	1479	1607	1734	1862	1990	2117	2245	2372	2500	2627
41	2754	2882	3009	3136	3264	3391	3518	3645	3772	3899
42	4026	4153	4280	4407	4534	4661	4787	4914	5041	5167
43	5294	5421	5547	5674	5800	5927	6053	6180	6306	6432
44	6558	6685	6811	6937	7063	7189	7315	7441	7567	7693
45	7819	7945	8071	8197	8322	8448	8574	8699	8825	8951
46	53 9076	9202	9327	9452	9578	9703	9829	9954	*0079	*0204
47	54 0329	0455	0580	0705	0830	0955	1080	1205	1330	1454
48	1579	1704	1829	1953	2078	2203	2327	2452	2576	2701
49	2825	2950	3074	3199	3323	3447	3571	3696	3820	3944
350	54 4068	4192	4316	4440	4564	4688	4812	4936	5060	5183

N	0	1	2	3	4	5	6	7	8	9

SIX-PLACE MANTISSAS FOR COMMON LOGARITHMS (Continued)

N	0	1	2	3	4	5	6	7	8	9
350	54 4068	4192	4316	4440	4564	4688	4812	4936	5060	5183
51	5307	5431	5555	5678	5802	5925	6049	6172	6296	6419
52	6543	6666	6789	6913	7036	7159	7282	7405	7529	7652
53	7775	7898	8021	8144	8267	8389	8512	8635	8758	8881
54	54 9003	9126	9249	9371	9494	9616	9739	9861	9984	*0106
55	55 0228	0351	0473	0595	0717	0840	0962	1084	1206	1328
56	1450	1572	1694	1816	1938	2060	2181	2303	2425	2547
57	2668	2790	2911	3033	3155	3276	3398	3519	3640	3762
58	3883	4004	4126	4247	4368	4489	4610	4731	4852	4973
59	5094	5215	5336	5457	5578	5699	5820	5940	6061	6182
360	6303	6423	6544	6664	6785	6905	7026	7146	7267	7387
61	7507	7627	7748	7868	7988	8108	8228	8349	8469	8589
62	8709	8829	8948	9068	9188	9308	9428	9548	9667	9787
63	55 9907	*0026	*0146	*0265	*0385	*0504	*0624	*0743	*0863	*0982
64	56 1101	1221	1340	1459	1578	1698	1817	1936	2055	2174
65	2293	2412	2531	2650	2769	2887	3006	3125	3244	3362
66	3481	3600	3718	3837	3955	4074	4192	4311	4429	4548
67	4666	4784	4903	5021	5139	5257	5376	5494	5612	5730
68	5848	5966	6084	6202	6320	6437	6555	6673	6791	6909
69	7026	7144	7262	7379	7497	7614	7732	7849	7967	8084
370	8202	8319	8436	8554	8671	8788	8905	9023	9140	9257
71	56 9374	9491	9608	9725	9842	9959	*0076	*0193	*0309	*0426
72	57 0543	0660	0776	0893	1010	1126	1243	1359	1476	1592
73	1709	1825	1942	2058	2174	2291	2407	2523	2639	2755
74	2872	2988	3104	3220	3336	3452	3568	3684	3800	3915
75	4031	4147	4263	4379	4494	4610	4726	4841	4957	5072
76	5188	5303	5419	5534	5650	5765	5880	5996	6111	6226
77	6341	6457	6572	6687	6802	6917	7032	7147	7262	7377
78	7492	7607	7722	7836	7951	8066	8181	8295	8410	8525
79	8639	8754	8868	8983	9097	9212	9326	9441	9555	9669
380	57 9784	9898	*0012	*0126	*0241	*0355	*0469	*0583	*0697	*0811
81	58 0925	1039	1153	1267	1381	1495	1608	1722	1836	1950
82	2063	2177	2291	2404	2518	2631	2745	2858	2972	3085
83	3199	3312	3426	3539	3652	3765	3879	3992	4105	4218
84	4331	4444	4557	4670	4783	4896	5009	5122	5235	5348
85	5461	5574	5686	5799	5912	6024	6137	6250	6362	6475
86	6587	6700	6812	6925	7037	7149	7262	7374	7486	7599
87	7711	7823	7935	8047	8160	8272	8384	8496	8608	8720
88	8832	8944	9056	9167	9279	9391	9503	9615	9726	9838
89	58 9950	*0061	*0173	*0284	*0396	*0507	*0619	*0730	*0842	*0953
390	59 1065	1176	1287	1399	1510	1621	1732	1843	1955	2066
91	2177	2288	2399	2510	2621	2732	2843	2954	3064	3175
92	3286	3397	3508	3618	3729	3840	3950	4061	4171	4282
93	4393	4503	4614	4724	4834	4945	5055	5165	5276	5386
94	5496	5606	5717	5827	5937	6047	6157	6267	6377	6487
95	6597	6707	6817	6927	7037	7146	7256	7366	7476	7586
96	7695	7805	7914	8024	8134	8243	8353	8462	8572	8681
97	8791	8900	9009	9119	9228	9337	9446	9556	9665	9774
98	9883	9992	*0101	*0210	*0319	*0428	*0537	*0646	*0755	*0864
99	60 0973	1082	1191	1299	1408	1517	1625	1734	1843	1951
400	60 2060	2169	2277	2386	2494	2603	2711	2819	2928	3036
N	0	1	2	3	4	5	6	7	8	9

SIX-PLACE MANTISSAS FOR COMMON LOGARITHMS (Continued)

N	0	1	2	3	4	5	6	7	8	9
400	60 2060	2169	2277	2386	2494	2603	2711	2819	2928	3036
01	3144	3253	3361	3469	3577	3686	3794	3902	4010	4118
02	4226	4334	4442	4550	5658	4766	4874	4982	5089	5197
03	5305	5413	5521	5628	5736	5844	5951	6059	6166	6274
04	6381	6489	6596	6704	6811	6919	7026	7133	7241	7348
05	7455	7562	7669	7777	7884	7991	8098	8205	8312	8419
06	8526	8633	8740	8847	8954	9061	9167	9274	9381	9488
07	60 9594	9701	9808	9914	*0021	*0128	*0234	*0341	*0447	*0554
08	61 0660	0767	0873	0979	1086	1192	1298	1405	1511	1617
09	1723	1829	1936	2042	2148	2254	2360	2466	2572	2678
410	2784	2890	2996	3102	3207	3313	3419	3525	3630	3736
11	3842	3947	4053	4159	4264	4370	4475	4581	4686	4792
12	4897	5003	5108	5213	5319	5425	5529	5634	5740	5845
13	5950	6055	6160	6265	6370	6476	6581	6686	6790	6895
14	7000	7105	7210	7315	7420	7525	7629	7734	7839	7943
15	8048	8153	8257	8362	8466	8571	8676	8780	8884	8989
16	61 9093	9198	9302	9406	9511	9615	9719	9824	9928	*0032
17	62 0136	0240	0344	0448	0552	0656	0760	0864	0968	1072
18	1176	1280	1384	1488	1592	1695	1799	1903	2007	2110
19	2214	2318	2421	2525	2628	2732	2835	2939	3042	3146
420	3249	3353	3456	3559	3663	3766	3869	3973	4076	4179
21	4282	4385	4488	4591	4695	4798	4901	5004	5107	5210
22	5312	5415	5518	5621	5724	5827	5929	6032	6135	6238
23	6340	6443	6546	6648	6751	6853	6956	7058	7161	7263
24	7366	7468	7571	7673	7775	7878	7980	8082	8185	8287
25	8389	8491	8593	8695	8797	8900	9002	9104	9206	9308
26	62 9410	9512	9613	9715	9817	9919	*0021	*0123	*0224	*0326
27	63 0428	0530	0631	0733	0835	0936	1038	1139	1241	1342
28	1444	1545	1647	1748	1849	1951	2052	2153	2255	2356
29	2457	2559	2660	2761	2862	2963	3064	3165	3266	3367
430	3468	3569	3670	3771	3872	3973	4074	4175	4276	4376
31	4477	4578	4679	4779	4880	4981	5081	5182	5283	5383
32	5484	5584	5685	5785	5886	5986	6087	6187	6287	6388
33	6488	6588	6688	6789	6889	6989	7089	7189	7290	7390
34	7490	7590	7690	7790	7890	7990	8090	8190	8290	8389
35	8489	8589	8689	8789	8888	8988	9088	9188	9287	9387
36	63 9486	9586	9686	9785	9885	9984	*0084	*0183	*0283	* 382
37	64 0481	0581	0680	0779	0879	0978	1077	1177	1276	1375
38	1474	1573	1672	1771	1871	1970	2069	2168	2267	2366
39	2465	2563	2662	2761	2860	2959	3058	3156	3255	3354
440	3453	3551	3650	3749	3847	3946	4044	4143	4242	4340
41	4439	4537	4636	4734	4832	4931	5029	5127	5226	5324
42	5422	5521	5619	5717	5815	5913	6011	6110	6208	6306
43	6404	6502	6600	6698	6796	6894	6992	7089	7187	7285
44	7383	7481	7579	7676	7774	7872	7969	8067	8165	8262
45	8360	8458	8555	8653	8750	8848	8945	9043	9140	9237
46	64 9335	9432	9530	9627	9724	9821	9919	*0016	*0113	*0210
47	65 0308	0405	0502	0599	0696	0793	0890	0987	1084	1181
48	1278	1375	1472	1569	1666	1762	1859	1956	2053	2150
49	2246	2343	2440	2536	2633	2730	2826	2923	3019	3116
450	65 3213	3309	3405	3502	3598	3695	3791	3888	3984	4080

N	0	1	2	3	4	5	6	7	8	9

Logarithm Tables

SIX-PLACE MANTISSAS FOR COMMON LOGARITHMS (Continued)

N	0	1	2	3	4	5	6	7	8	9
450	65 3213	3309	3405	3502	3598	3695	3791	3888	3984	4080
51	4177	4273	4369	4465	4562	4658	4754	4850	4946	5042
52	5138	5235	5331	5427	5523	5619	5715	5810	5906	6002
53	6098	6194	6290	6386	6482	6577	6673	6769	6864	6960
54	7056	7152	7247	7343	7438	7534	7629	7725	7820	7916
55	8011	8017	8202	8298	8393	8488	8584	8679	8774	8870
56	8965	9060	9155	9250	9346	9441	9536	9631	9726	8921
57	65 9916	*0011	*0106	*0201	*0296	*0391	*0486	*0581	*0676	*0771
58	66 0865	0960	1055	1150	1245	1339	1434	1529	1623	1718
59	1813	1907	2002	2096	2191	2286	2380	2475	2569	2663
460	2758	2852	2947	3041	3135	3230	3324	3418	3512	3607
61	3701	3795	3889	3983	4078	4172	4266	4360	4454	4548
62	4642	4736	4830	4924	5018	5112	5206	5200	5393	5487
63	5581	5675	5769	5862	5956	6050	6143	6237	6331	6424
64	6518	6612	6705	6799	6892	6986	7079	7173	7266	7360
65	7453	7546	7640	7733	7826	7920	8013	8106	8199	8293
66	8386	8479	8572	8665	8759	8852	8945	9038	9131	9224
67	66 9317	9410	9503	9506	9689	9782	9875	9967	*0060	*0153
68	67 0246	0339	0431	0524	0617	0710	0802	0895	0988	1080
69	1173	1265	1358	1451	1543	1636	1728	1821	1913	2005
470	2098	2190	2283	2375	2467	2560	2652	2744	2836	2929
71	3021	3113	3295	3207	3390	3482	3574	3666	3758	3850
72	3942	4034	4126	4218	4310	4402	4494	4586	4677	4769
73	4861	4953	5045	5137	5228	5320	5412	5503	5595	5687
74	5778	5870	5962	6053	6145	6236	6328	6419	6511	6602
75	6694	6785	6876	6968	7059	7151	7242	7333	7424	7516
76	7607	7698	7789	7881	7972	8063	8154	8245	8336	8427
77	8518	8609	8700	8791	8882	8973	9064	9155	9246	9337
78	67 9428	9519	9610	9700	9791	9882	9973	*0063	*0154	*0245
79	68 0336	0426	0517	0607	0698	0789	0879	0970	1060	1151
480	1241	1332	1422	1513	1603	1693	1784	1874	1964	2055
81	2145	2235	2326	2416	2506	2596	2686	2777	2867	2957
82	3047	3137	3227	3317	3407	3497	3587	3677	3767	3857
83	3947	4037	4127	4217	4307	4396	4486	4576	4666	4756
84	4845	4935	5025	5114	5204	5294	5383	5473	5563	5652
85	5742	5831	5921	6010	6100	6189	6279	6368	6458	6547
86	6636	6726	6815	6904	6994	7083	7172	7261	7351	7440
87	7529	7618	7707	7796	7886	7975	8064	8153	8242	8331
88	8420	8509	8598	8687	8776	8865	8953	9042	9131	9220
89	68 9309	9398	9486	9575	9664	9753	9841	9930	*0019	*0107
490	69 0196	0285	0373	0462	0550	0639	0728	0816	0905	0993
91	1081	1170	1258	1347	1435	1524	1612	1700	1789	1877
92	1965	2053	2142	2230	2318	2406	2494	2583	2671	2759
93	2847	2935	3023	3111	3199	3287	3375	3463	3551	3639
94	3727	3815	3903	3991	4078	4166	4254	4342	4430	4517
95	4605	4693	4781	4868	4956	5044	5131	5219	5307	5394
96	5482·	5569	5657	5744	5832	5919	6007	6094	6182	6269
97	6356	6444	6531	6618	6706	6793	6880	6968	7055	7142
98	7229	7317	7404	7491	7578	7665	7752	7839	7926	8014
99	8101	8188	8275	8362	8449	8535	8622	8709	8796	8883
500	69 8970	9051	9144	9231	9317	9404	9491	9578	9664	9751
N	0	1	2	3	4	5	6	7	8	9

SIX-PLACE MANTISSAS FOR COMMON LOGARITHMS (Continued)

N	0	1	2	3	4	5	6	7	8	9
500	69 8970	9057	9144	9231	9317	9404	9491	9578	9664	9751
01	69 9838	9924	*0011	*0098	*0184	*0271	*0358	*0444	*0531	*0617
02	70 0704	0790	0877	0963	1050	1136	1222	1309	1395	1482
03	1568	1654	1741	1827	1913	1999	2086	2172	2258	2344
04	2431	2517	2603	2689	2775	2861	2947	3033	3119	3205
05	3291	3377	3463	3549	3635	3721	3807	3893	3979	4065
06	4151	4236	4322	4408	4494	4579	4665	4751	4837	4922
07	5008	5094	5179	5265	5350	5463	5522	5607	5693	5778
08	5864	5949	6035	6120	6206	6291	6376	6462	6547	6632
09	6718	6803	6888	6974	7059	7144	7229	7315	7400	7485
510	7570	7655	7740	7826	7911	7996	8081	8166	8251	8336
11	8421	8506	8591	8676	8761	8846	8931	9015	9100	9185
12	70 9270	9355	9440	9524	9609	9694	9779	9863	9948	*0033
13	71 0117	0202	0287	0371	0456	0540	0625	0710	0794	0879
14	0963	1048	1132	1217	1301	1385	1470	1554	1639	1723
15	1807	1892	1976	2060	2144	2229	2313	2397	2481	2566
16	2650	2734	2818	2902	2986	3070	3154	3238	3323	3407
17	3491	3575	3659	3742	3826	3910	3994	4078	4162	4246
18	4330	4414	4497	4581	4665	4749	4833	4916	5000	5084
19	5167	5251	5335	5418	5502	5586	5669	5753	5836	5920
520	6003	6087	6170	6254	6337	6421	6504	6588	6671	6754
21	6838	6921	7004	7088	7171	7254	7338	7421	7504	7587
22	7671	7754	7837	7920	8003	8086	8169	8253	8336	8419
23	8502	8585	8668	8751	8834	8917	9000	9083	9165	9248
24	71 9331	9414	9497	9580	9663	9745	9828	9911	9994	*0077
25	72 0159	0242	0325	0407	0490	0573	0655	0738	0821	0903
26	0986	1068	1151	1233	1316	1398	1481	1563	1646	1728
27	1811	1893	1975	2058	2140	2222	2305	2387	2469	2552
28	2634	2716	2798	2881	2963	3045	3127	3209	3291	3374
29	3456	3538	3620	3702	3784	3866	3948	4030	4112	4194
530	4276	4358	4440	4522	4604	4685	4767	4849	4931	5013
31	5095	5176	5258	5340	5422	5503	5585	5667	5748	5830
32	5912	5993	6075	6156	6238	6320	6401	6483	6564	6646
33	6727	6809	6890	6972	7053	7134	7216	7297	7379	7460
34	7541	7623	7704	7785	7866	7948	8029	8110	8191	8273
35	8354	8435	8516	8597	8678	8759	8841	8922	9003	9084
36	9165	9246	9327	9408	9489	9570	9651	9732	9813	9893
37	72 9974	*0055	*0136	*0217	*0298	*0378	*0459	*0540	*0621	*0702
38	73 0782	0863	0944	1024	1105	1186	1266	1347	1428	1508
39	1589	1669	1750	1830	1911	1991	2072	2152	2233	2313
540	2394	2474	2555	2635	2715	2796	2876	2956	3037	3117
41	3197	3278	3358	3438	3518	3598	3679	3759	3839	3919
42	3999	4079	4160	4240	4320	4400	4480	4560	4640	4720
43	4800	4880	4960	5040	5120	5200	5279	5359	5439	5519
44	5599	5679	5759	5838	5918	5998	6078	6157	6237	6317
45	6397	6476	6556	6635	6715	6795	6874	6954	7034	7113
46	7193	7272	7352	7431	7511	7590	7670	7749	7829	7908
47	7987	8067	8146	8225	8305	8384	8463	8543	8622	8701
48	8781	8860	8939	9018	9097	9177	9256	9335	9414	9493
49	73 9572	9651	9731	9810	9889	9968	*0047	*0126	*0205	*0284
550	74 0363	0442	0521	0600	0678	0757	0836	0915	0994	1073

N	0	1	2	3	4	5	6	7	8	9

Logarithm Tables

SIX-PLACE MANTISSAS FOR COMMON LOGARITHMS (Continued)

N	0	1	2	3	4	5	6	7	8	9
550	74 0363	0442	0521	0600	0678	0757	0836	0915	0994	1073
51	1152	1230	1309	1388	1467	1546	1624	1703	1782	1800
52	1939	2018	2096	2175	2254	2332	2411	2489	2568	2647
53	2725	2804	2882	2961	3039	3118	3196	3275	3353	3431
54	3510	3588	3667	3745	3823	3902	3980	4058	4136	4215
55	4293	4371	4449	4528	4606	4684	4762	4840	4919	4997
56	5075	5153	5231	5309	5387	5465	5543	5621	5699	5777
57	5855	5933	6011	6089	6167	6245	6323	6401	6479	6556
58	6634	6712	6790	6868	6945	7023	7101	7179	7256	7334
59	7412	7489	7567	7645	7722	7800	7878	7955	8033	8110
560	8188	8266	8343	8421	8498	8576	8653	8731	8808	8885
61	8963	9040	9118	9195	9272	9350	9427	9504	9582	9659
62	74 9736	9814	9891	9968	*0045	*0123	*0200	*0277	*0354	*0431
63	75 0508	0586	0663	0740	0817	0894	0971	1048	1125	1202
64	1279	1356	1433	1510	1587	1664	1741	1818	1895	1972
65	2048	2125	2202	2279	2356	2433	2509	2586	2663	2740
66	2816	2893	2970	3047	3123	3200	3277	3353	3430	3506
67	3583	3660	3736	3813	3889	3966	4042	4119	4195	4272
68	4348	4425	4501	4578	4654	4730	4807	4883	4960	5036
69	5112	5189	5265	5341	5417	5494	5570	5646	5722	5799
570	5875	5951	6027	6103	6180	6256	6332	6408	6484	6560
71	6636	6712	6788	6864	6940	7016	7092	7168	7244	7320
72	7396	7472	7548	7624	7700	7775	7851	7927	8003	8079
73	8155	8230	8306	8382	8458	8533	8609	8685	8761	8836
74	8912	8988	9063	9139	9214	9290	9366	9441	9517	9592
75	75 9668	9743	9819	9894	9970	*0045	*0121	*0196	*0272	*0347
76	76 0422	0498	0573	0649	0724	0799	0875	0950	1025	1101
77	1176	1251	1326	1402	1477	1552	1627	1702	1778	1853
78	1928	2003	2078	2153	2228	2303	2378	2453	2529	2604
79	2679	2754	2829	2904	2978	3053	3128	3203	3278	3353
580	3428	3503	3578	3653	3727	3802	3877	3952	4027	4101
81	4176	4251	4326	4400	4475	4550	4624	4699	4774	4848
82	4923	4998	5072	5147	5221	5296	5370	5445	5520	5594
83	5669	5743	5818	5892	5966	6041	6115	6190	6264	6338
84	6413	6487	6562	6636	6710	6785	6859	6933	7007	7082
85	7156	7230	7304	7379	7453	7527	7601	7675	7749	7823
86	7898	7972	8046	8120	8194	8268	8342	8416	8490	8564
87	8638	8712	8786	8860	8934	9008	9082	9156	9230	9303
88	76 9377	9451	9525	9599	9673	9746	9820	9894	9968	*0042
89	77 0115	0189	0263	0336	0410	0484	0557	0631	0705	0778
590	0852	0926	0999	1073	1146	1220	1293	1367	1440	1514
91	1587	1661	1734	1808	1881	1955	2028	2102	2175	2248
92	2322	2395	2468	2542	2615	2688	2762	2835	2908	2981
93	3055	3128	3201	3274	3348	3421	3494	3567	3640	3713
94	3786	3860	3933	4006	4079	4152	4225	4298	4371	4444
95	4517	4590	4663	4736	4809	4882	4955	5028	5100	5173
96	5246	5319	5392	5465	5538	5610	5683	5756	5829	5902
97	5974	6047	6120	6193	6265	6338	6411	6483	6556	6629
98	6701	6774	6846	6919	6992	7064	7137	7209	7282	7354
99	7427	7499	7572	7644	7717	7789	7862	7934	8006	8079
600	77 8151	8224	8296	8368	8441	8513	8585	8658	8730	8802
N	0	1	2	3	4	5	6	7	8	9

SIX-PLACE MANTISSAS FOR COMMON LOGARITHMS (Continued)

N	0	1	2	3	4	5	6	7	8	9
600	77 8151	8224	8296	8368	8441	8513	8585	8658	8730	8802
01	8874	8947	9019	9091	9163	9236	9308	9380	9452	9524
02	77 9596	9669	9741	9813	9885	9957	*0029	*0101	*0173	*0245
03	78 0317	0389	0461	0533	0605	0677	0749	0821	0893	0965
04	1037	1109	1181	1253	1324	1396	1468	1540	1612	1684
05	1755	1827	1899	1971	2042	2114	2186	2258	2329	2401
06	2473	2544	2616	2688	2759	2831	2902	2974	3046	3117
07	3189	3260	3332	3403	3475	3546	3618	3689	3761	3832
08	3904	3975	4046	4118	4189	4261	4332	4403	4475	4546
09	4617	4689	4760	4831	4902	4974	5045	5116	5187	5259
610	5330	5401	5472	5543	5615	5686	5757	5828	5899	5970
11	6041	6112	6183	6254	6325	6396	6467	6538	6609	6680
12	6751	6822	6893	6964	7035	7106	7177	7248	7319	7390
13	7460	7531	7602	7673	7744	7815	7885	7956	8027	8098
14	8168	8239	8310	8381	8451	8522	8593	8663	8734	8804
15	8875	8946	9016	9087	9157	9228	9299	9369	9440	9510
16	78 9581	9651	9722	9762	9863	9933	*0004	*0074	*0144	*0215
17	79 0285	0356	0426	0496	0567	0637	0707	0778	0848	0918
18	0988	1059	1129	1199	1269	1340	1410	1480	1550	1620
19	1691	1761	1831	1901	1971	2041	2111	2181	2252	2322
620	2392	2462	2532	2602	2672	2742	2812	2882	2952	3022
21	3092	3162	3231	3301	3371	3441	3511	3581	3651	3721
22	3790	3860	3930	4000	4070	4139	4209	4279	4349	4418
23	4488	4558	4627	4697	4767	4836	4906	4976	5045	5115
24	5185	5254	5324	5393	5463	5532	5602	5672	5741	5811
25	5880	5949	6019	6088	6158	6227	6297	6366	6436	6505
26	6574	6644	6713	6782	6852	6921	6990	7060	7129	7198
27	7268	7337	7406	7475	7545	7614	7683	7752	7821	7890
28	7960	8029	8098	8167	8236	8305	8374	8443	8513	8582
29	8651	8720	8789	8858	8927	8996	9065	9134	9203	9272
630	79 9341	9409	9478	9547	9616	9685	9754	9823	9892	9961
31	80 0029	0098	0167	0236	0305	0373	0442	0511	0580	0648
32	0717	0786	0854	0923	0992	1061	1129	1198	1266	1335
33	1404	1472	1541	1609	1678	1747	1815	1884	1952	2021
34	2089	2158	2226	2295	2363	2432	2500	2568	2637	2705
35	2774	2842	2910	2979	3047	3116	3184	3252	3321	3389
36	3457	3525	3594	3662	3730	3798	3867	3935	4003	4071
37	4139	4208	4276	4344	4412	4480	4548	4616	4685	4753
38	4821	4889	4957	5025	5093	5161	5229	5297	5365	5433
39	5501	5569	5637	5705	5773	5841	5908	5976	6044	6112
640	6180	6248	6316	6384	6451	6519	6587	6655	6723	6790
41	6858	6926	6994	7061	7129	7197	7264	7332	7400	7467
42	7537	7603	7670	7738	7806	7873	7941	8008	8076	8143
43	8211	8279	8346	8414	8481	8549	8616	8684	8751	8818
44	8886	8953	9021	9088	9156	9223	9290	9358	9425	9492
45	80 9560	9627	9694	9762	9829	9896	9964	*0031	*0098	*0165
46	81 0233	0300	0367	0434	0501	0569	0636	0703	0770	0837
47	0904	0971	1039	1106	1173	1240	1307	1374	1441	1508
48	1575	1642	1709	1776	1843	1910	1977	2044	2111	2178
49	2245	2312	2379	2445	2512	2579	2646	2713	2780	2847
650	81 2913	2980	3047	3114	3181	3247	3314	3381	3448	3514
N	0	1	2	3	4	5	6	7	8	9

SIX-PLACE MANTISSAS FOR COMMON LOGARITHMS (Continued)

N	0	1	2	3	4	5	6	7	8	9
650	81 2913	2980	3047	3114	3181	3247	3314	3381	3448	3514
51	3581	3648	3714	3781	3848	3914	3981	4048	4114	4181
52	4248	4314	4381	4447	4514	4581	4647	4714	4780	4847
53	4913	4980	5046	5113	5179	5246	5312	5378	5445	5511
54	5578	5644	5711	5777	5843	5910	5976	6042	6109	6175
55	6241	6308	6374	6440	6506	6573	6639	6705	6771	6838
56	6904	6970	7036	7102	7169	7235	7301	7367	7433	7499
57	7565	7631	7698	7764	7830	7896	7962	8028	8094	8160
58	8226	8292	8358	8424	8490	8556	8622	8688	8754	8820
59	8885	8951	9017	9083	9149	9215	9281	9346	9412	9478
660	81 9544	9610	9676	9741	9807	9873	9939	*0004	*0070	*0136
61	82 0201	0267	0333	0399	0464	0530	0595	0661	0727	0792
62	0858	0924	0989	1055	1120	1186	1251	1317	1382	1448
63	1514	1579	1645	1710	1775	1841	1906	1972	2037	2103
64	2168	2233	2299	2364	2430	2495	2560	2626	2691	2756
65	2822	2887	2952	3018	3083	3148	3213	3279	3344	3409
66	3474	3539	3605	3670	3735	3800	3865	3930	3996	4061
67	4126	4191	4256	4321	4386	4451	4516	4581	4646	4711
68	4776	4841	4906	4971	5036	5101	5166	5231	5296	5361
69	5426	5491	5556	5621	5686	5751	5815	5880	5945	6010
670	6075	6140	6204	6269	6334	6399	6464	6528	6593	6658
71	6723	6787	6852	6917	6981	7046	7111	7175	7240	7305
72	7369	7434	7499	7563	7628	7692	7757	7821	7886	7951
73	8015	8080	8144	8209	8273	8338	8402	8467	8531	8595
74	8660	8724	8789	8853	8918	8982	9046	9111	9175	9239
75	9304	9368	9432	9497	9561	9625	9690	9754	9818	9882
76	82 9947	*0011	*0075	*0139	*0204	*0268	*0332	*0396	*0460	*0525
77	83 0589	0653	0717	0781	0845	0909	0973	1037	1102	1166
78	1230	1294	1358	1422	1486	1550	1614	1678	1742	1806
79	1870	1934	1998	2062	2126	2189	2253	2317	2381	2445
680	2509	2573	2637	2700	2764	2828	2892	2956	3020	3083
81	3147	3211	3275	3338	3402	3466	3530	3593	3657	3721
82	3784	3848	3912	3975	4039	4103	4166	4230	4294	4357
83	4421	4484	4548	4611	4675	4739	4802	4866	4929	4993
84	5056	5120	5183	5247	5310	5373	5437	5500	5564	5627
85	5691	5754	5817	5881	5944	6007	6071	6134	6197	6261
86	6324	6387	6451	6514	6577	6641	6704	6767	6830	6894
87	6957	7020	7083	7146	7210	7273	7336	7399	7462	7525
88	7588	7652	7715	7778	7841	7904	7967	8030	8093	8156
89	8219	8282	8345	8408	8471	8534	8597	8660	8723	8786
690	8849	8912	8975	9038	9101	9164	9227	9289	9352	9415
91	83 9478	9541	9604	9667	9729	9792	9855	9918	9981	*0043
92	84 0106	0169	0232	0294	0357	0420	0482	0545	0608	0671
93	0733	0796	0859	0921	0984	1046	1109	1172	1234	1297
94	1359	1422	1485	1547	1610	1672	1735	1797	1860	1922
95	1985	2047	2110	2172	2235	2297	2360	2422	2484	2547
96	2609	2672	2734	2796	2859	2921	2983	3046	3108	3170
97	3233	3295	3357	3420	3482	3544	3606	3669	3731	3793
98	3855	3918	3980	4042	4104	4166	4229	4291	4353	4415
99	4477	4539	4601	4664	4726	4788	4850	4912	4974	5036
700	84 5098	5160	5222	5284	5346	5408	5470	5532	5594	5656

| N | 0 | 1 | 2 | 3 | 4 | 5 | 6 | 7 | 8 | 9 |

SIX-PLACE MANTISSAS FOR COMMON LOGARITHMS: (Continued)

N	0	1	2	3	4	5	6	7	8	9
700	84 5098	5160	5222	5284	5346	5408	5470	5532	5594	5656
01	5718	5780	5842	5904	5966	6028	6090	6151	6213	6275
02	6337	6399	6461	6523	6585	6646	6708	6770	6832	6894
03	6955	7017	7079	7141	7202	7264	7326	7388	7449	7511
04	7573	7634	7696	7758	7819	7881	7943	8004	8066	8128
05	8189	8251	8312	8374	8435	8497	8559	8620	8682	8743
06	8805	8866	8928	8989	9051	9112	9174	9235	9297	9358
07	84 9419	9481	9542	9604	9665	9726	9788	9849	9911	9972
08	85 0033	0095	0156	0217	0279	0340	0401	0462	0524	0585
09	0646	0707	0769	0830	0891	0952	1014	1075	1136	1197
710	1258	1320	1381	1442	1503	1564	1625	1686	1747	1809
11	1870	1931	1992	2053	2114	2175	2236	2297	2358	2419
12	2480	2541	2602	2663	2724	2785	2846	2907	2968	3029
13	3090	3150	3211	3272	3333	3394	3455	3516	3577	3637
14	3698	3759	3820	3881	3941	4002	4063	4124	4185	4245
15	4306	4367	4428	4488	4549	4610	4670	4731	4792	4852
16	4913	4974	5034	5095	5156	5216	5277	5337	5398	5459
17	5519	5580	5640	5701	5761	5822	5882	5943	6003	6064
18	6124	6185	6245	6306	6366	6427	6487	6548	6608	6668
19	6729	6789	6850	6910	6970	7031	7091	7152	7212	7272
720	7332	7393	7453	7513	7574	7634	7694	7755	7815	7875
21	7935	7995	8056	8116	8176	8236	8297	8357	8417	8477
22	8537	8597	8657	8718	8778	8838	8898	8958	9018	9078
23	9138	9198	9258	9318	9379	9439	9499	9559	9619	9679
24	85 9739	9799	9859	9918	9978	*0038	*0098	*0158	*0218	*0278
25	86 0338	0398	0458	0518	0578	0637	0697	0757	0817	0877
26	0937	0996	1056	1116	1176	1236	1295	1355	1415	1475
27	1534	1594	1654	1714	1773	1833	1893	1952	2012	2072
28	2131	2191	2251	2310	2370	2430	2489	2549	2608	2668
29	2728	2787	2847	2906	2966	3025	3085	3144	3204	3263
730	3323	3382	3442	3501	3561	3620	3680	3739	3799	3858
31	3917	3977	4036	4096	4155	4214	4274	4333	4392	4452
32	4511	4570	4630	4689	4748	4808	4867	4926	4985	5045
33	5104	5163	5222	5282	5341	5400	5459	5519	5578	5637
34	5696	5755	5814	5874	5933	5992	6051	6110	6169	6228
35	6287	6346	6405	6465	6524	6583	6642	6701	6760	6819
36	6878	6937	6996	7055	7114	7173	7232	7291	7350	7409
37	7467	7526	7585	7644	7703	7762	7821	7880	7939	7998
38	8056	8115	8174	8233	8292	8350	8409	8468	8527	8586
39	8644	8703	8762	8821	8879	8938	8997	9056	9114	9173
740	9232	9290	9349	9408	9466	9525	9584	9642	9701	9760
41	86 9818	9877	9935	9994	*0053	*0111	*0170	*0228	*0287	*0345
42	87 0404	0462	0521	0579	0638	0696	0755	0813	0872	0930
43	0989	1047	1106	1164	1223	1281	1339	1398	1456	1515
44	1573	1631	1690	1748	1806	1865	1923	1981	2040	2098
45	2156	2215	2273	2331	2389	2448	2506	2564	2622	2681
46	2739	2797	2855	2913	2972	3030	3088	3146	3204	3262
47	3321	3379	3437	3495	3553	3611	3669	3727	3785	3844
48	3902	3960	4018	4076	4134	4192	4250	4308	4366	4424
49	4482	4540	4598	4656	4714	4772	4830	4888	4945	5003
750	87 5061	5119	5177	5235	5293	5351	5409	5466	5524	5582
N	0	1	2	3	4	5	6	7	8	9

SIX-PLACE MANTISSAS FOR COMMON LOGARITHMS: (Continued)

N	0	1	2	3	4	5	6	7	8	9
750	87 5061	5119	5177	5235	5293	5351	5409	5466	5524	5582
51	5640	5698	5756	5813	5871	5929	5987	6045	6102	6160
52	6218	6276	6333	6391	6449	6507	6564	6622	6680	6737
53	6795	6853	6910	6968	7026	7083	7141	7199	7256	7314
54	7371	7429	7487	7544	7602	7659	7717	7774	7832	7889
55	7947	8004	8062	8119	8177	8234	8292	8349	8407	8464
56	8522	8579	8637	8694	8752	8809	8866	8924	8981	9039
57	9096	9153	9211	9268	9325	9383	9440	9497	9555	9612
58	87 9669	9726	9784	9841	9898	9956	*0013	*0070	*0127	*0185
59	88 0242	0299	0356	0413	0417	0528	0585	0642	0699	0756
760	0814	0871	0928	0985	1042	1099	1156	1213	1271	1328
61	1385	1442	1499	1556	1613	1670	1727	1784	1841	1898
62	1955	2012	2069	2126	2183	2240	2297	2354	2411	2468
63	2525	2581	2638	2695	2752	2809	2866	2923	2980	3037
64	3093	3150	3207	3264	3321	3377	3434	3491	3548	3605
65	3661	3718	3775	3832	3888	3945	4002	4059	4115	4172
66	4229	4285	4342	4399	4455	4512	4569	4625	4682	4739
67	4795	4852	4909	4965	5022	5078	5135	5192	5248	5305
68	5361	5418	5474	5531	5587	5644	5700	5757	5813	5870
69	5926	5983	6039	6096	6152	6209	6265	6321	6378	6434
770	6491	6547	6604	6660	6716	6773	6829	6885	6942	6998
71	7054	7111	7167	7223	7280	7336	7392	7449	7505	7561
72	7617	7674	7730	7786	7842	7898	7955	8011	8067	8123
73	8179	8236	8292	8348	8404	8460	8516	8573	8629	8685
74	8741	8797	8853	8909	8965	9021	9077	9134	9190	9246
75	9302	9358	9414	9470	9526	9582	9638	9694	9750	9806
76	88 9862	9918	9974	*0030	*0086	*0141	*0197	*0253	*0309	*0365
77	89 0421	0477	0533	0589	0645	0700	0756	0812	0868	0924
78	0980	1035	1091	1147	1203	1259	1314	1370	1426	1482
79	1537	1593	1649	1705	1760	1816	1872	1928	1983	2039
780	2095	2150	2206	2262	2317	2373	2429	2484	2540	2595
81	2651	2707	2762	2818	2873	2929	2985	3040	3096	3151
82	3207	3262	3318	3373	3429	3484	3540	3595	3651	3706
83	3762	3817	3873	3928	3984	4039	4094	4150	4205	4261
84	4316	4371	4427	4482	4538	4593	4648	4704	4759	4814
85	4870	4925	4980	5036	5091	5146	5201	5257	5312	5367
86	5423	5478	5533	5588	5644	5699	5754	5809	5864	5920
87	5975	6030	6085	6140	6195	6251	6306	6361	6416	6471
88	6526	6581	6636	6692	6747	6802	6857	6912	6967	7022
89	7077	7132	7187	7242	7297	7352	7407	7462	7517	7572
790	7627	7682	7737	7792	7847	7902	7957	8012	8067	8122
91	8176	8231	8286	8341	8396	8451	8506	8561	8615	8670
92	8725	8780	8835	8890	8944	8999	9054	9109	9164	9218
93	9273	9328	9383	9437	9492	9547	9602	9656	9711	9766
94	89 9821	9875	9930	9985	*0039	*0094	*0149	*0203	*0258	*0312
95	90 0367	0422	0476	0531	0586	0640	0695	0749	0804	0859
96	0913	0968	1022	1077	1131	1186	1240	1295	1349	1404
97	1458	1513	1567	1622	1676	1731	1785	1840	1894	1948
98	2003	2057	2112	2166	2221	2275	2329	2384	2438	2492
99	2547	2601	2655	2710	2764	2818	2873	2927	2981	3036
800	90 3090	3144	3199	3253	3307	3361	3416	3470	3524	3578
N	0	1	2	3	4	5	6	7	8	9

SIX-PLACE MANTISSAS FOR COMMON LOGARITHMS: (Continued)

N	0	1	2	3	4	5	6	7	8	9
800	90 3090	3144	3199	3253	3307	3361	3416	3470	3524	3578
01	3633	3687	3741	3795	3849	3904	3958	4012	4066	4120
02	4174	4229	4283	4337	4391	4445	4499	4553	4607	4661
03	4716	4770	4824	4878	4932	4986	5040	5094	5148	5202
04	5256	5310	5364	5418	5472	5526	5580	5634	5688	5742
05	5796	5850	5904	5958	6012	6066	6119	6173	6227	6281
06	6335	6389	6443	6497	6551	6604	6658	6712	6766	6820
07	6874	6927	6981	7035	7089	7143	7196	7250	7304	7358
08	7411	7465	7519	7573	7626	7680	7734	7787	7841	7895
09	7949	8002	8056	8110	8163	8217	8270	8324	8378	8431
810	8485	8539	8592	8646	8699	8753	8807	8860	8914	8967
11	9021	9074	9128	9181	9235	9289	9342	9396	9449	9503
12	90 9556	9610	9663	9716	9770	9823	9877	9930	9984	*0037
13	91 0091	0144	0197	0251	0304	0358	0411	0464	0518	0571
14	0624	0678	0731	0784	0838	0891	0944	0998	1051	1104
15	1158	1211	1264	1317	1371	1424	1477	1530	1584	1637
16	1690	1743	1797	1850	1903	1956	2009	2063	2116	2169
17	2222	2275	2328	2381	2435	2488	2541	2594	2647	2700
18	2753	2806	2859	2913	2966	3019	3072	3125	3178	3231
19	3284	3337	3390	3443	3496	3549	3602	3655	3708	3761
820	3814	3867	3920	3973	4026	4079	4132	4184	4237	4290
21	4343	4396	4449	4502	4555	4608	4660	4713	4766	4819
22	4872	4925	4977	5030	5083	5136	5189	5241	5294	5347
23	5400	5453	5505	5558	5611	5664	5716	5769	5822	5875
24	5927	5980	6033	6085	6138	6191	6243	6296	6349	6401
25	6454	6507	6559	6612	6664	6717	6770	6822	6875	6927
26	6980	7033	7085	7138	7190	7243	7295	7348	7400	7453
27	7506	7558	7611	7663	7716	7768	7820	7873	7925	7978
28	8030	8083	8135	8188	8240	8293	8345	8397	8450	8502
29	8555	8607	8659	8712	8764	8816	8869	8921	8973	9026
830	9078	9130	9183	9235	9287	9340	9392	9444	9496	9549
31	91 9601	9653	9706	9758	9810	9862	9914	9967	*0019	*0071
32	92 0123	0176	0228	0280	0332	0384	0436	0489	0541	0593
33	0645	0697	0749	0801	0853	0906	0958	1010	1062	1114
34	1166	1218	1270	1322	1374	1426	1478	1530	1582	1634
35	1686	1738	1790	1842	1894	1946	1998	2050	2102	2154
36	2206	2258	2310	2362	2414	2466	2518	2570	2622	2674
37	2725	2777	2829	2881	2933	2985	3037	3089	3140	3192
38	3244	3296	3348	3399	3451	3503	3555	3607	3658	3710
39	3762	3814	3865	3917	3969	4021	4072	4124	4176	4228
840	4279	4331	4383	4434	4486	4538	4589	4641	4693	4744
41	4796	4848	4899	4951	5003	5054	5106	5157	5209	5261
42	5312	5364	5415	5467	5518	5570	5621	5673	5725	5776
43	5828	5879	5931	5982	6034	6085	6137	6188	6240	6291
44	6342	6394	6445	6497	6548	6600	6651	6702	6754	6805
45	6857	6908	6959	7011	7062	7114	7165	7216	7268	7319
46	7370	7422	7473	7524	7576	7627	7678	7730	7781	7832
47	7883	7935	7986	8037	8088	8140	8191	8242	8293	8345
48	8396	8447	8498	8549	8601	8652	8703	8754	8805	8857
49	8908	8959	9010	9061	9112	9163	9215	9266	9317	9368
850	92 9419	9470	9521	9572	9623	9674	9725	9776	9827	9879
N	0	1	2	3	4	5	6	7	8	9

SIX-PLACE MANTISSAS FOR COMMON LOGARITHMS: (Continued)

N	0	1	2	3	4	5	6	7	8	9
850	92 9419	9470	9521	9572	9623	9674	9725	9776	9827	9879
51	92 9930	9981	*0032	*0083	*0134	*0185	*0236	*0287	*0338	*0389
52	93 0440	0491	0542	0592	0643	0694	0745	0796	0847	0898
53	0949	1000	1051	1102	1153	1204	1254	1305	1356	1407
54	1458	1509	1560	1610	1661	1712	1763	1814	1865	1915
55	1966	2017	2068	2118	2169	2220	2271	2322	2372	2423
56	2474	2524	2575	2626	2677	2727	2778	2829	2879	2930
57	2981	3031	3082	3133	3183	3234	3285	3335	3386	3437
58	3487	3538	3589	3639	3690	3740	3791	3841	3892	3943
59	3993	4044	4094	4145	4195	4246	4296	4347	4397	4448
860	4498	4549	4599	4650	4700	4751	4801	4852	4902	4953
61	5003	5054	5104	5154	5205	5255	5306	5356	5406	5457
62	5507	5558	5608	5658	5709	5759	5809	5860	5910	5960
63	6011	6061	6111	6162	6212	6262	6313	6363	6413	6463
64	6514	6564	6614	6665	6715	6765	6815	6865	6916	6966
65	7016	7066	7117	7167	7217	7267	7317	7367	7418	7468
66	7518	7568	7618	7668	7718	7769	7819	7869	7919	7969
67	8019	8069	8119	8169	8219	8269	8320	8370	8420	8470
68	8520	8570	8620	8670	8720	8770	8820	8870	8920	8970
69	9020	9070	9120	9170	9220	9270	9320	9369	9419	9469
870	93 9519	9569	9619	9669	9719	9769	9819	9869	9918	9968
71	94 0018	0068	0118	0168	0218	0267	0317	0367	0417	0467
72	0516	9566	0616	0666	0716	0765	0815	0865	0915	0964
73	1014	1064	1114	1163	1213	1263	1313	1362	1412	1462
74	1511	1561	1611	1660	1710	1760	1809	1859	1909	1958
75	2008	2058	2107	2157	2207	2256	2306	2355	2405	2455
76	2504	2554	2603	2653	2702	2752	2801	2851	2901	2950
77	3000	3049	3099	3148	3198	3247	3297	3346	3396	3445
78	3495	3544	3593	3643	3692	3742	3791	3841	3890	3939
79	3989	4038	4088	4137	4186	4236	4285	4335	4384	4433
880	4483	4532	4581	4631	4680	4729	4779	4828	4877	4927
81	4976	5025	5074	5124	5173	5222	5272	5321	5370	5419
82	5469	5518	5567	5616	5665	5715	5764	5813	5862	5912
83	5961	6010	6059	6108	6157	6207	6256	6305	6354	6403
84	6452	6501	6551	6600	6649	6698	6747	6796	6845	6894
85	6943	6992	7041	7090	7140	7189	7238	7287	7336	7385
86	7434	7483	7532	7581	7630	7679	7728	7777	7826	7875
87	7924	7973	8022	8070	8119	8168	8217	8266	8315	8364
88	8413	8462	8511	8560	8609	8657	8706	8755	8804	8853
89	8902	8951	8999	9048	9097	9146	9195	9244	9292	9341
890	9390	9439	9488	9536	9585	9634	9683	9731	9780	9829
91	94 9878	9926	9975	*0024	*0073	*0121	*0170	*0219	*0267	*0316
92	95 0365	0414	0462	0511	0560	0608	0657	0706	0754	0803
93	0851	0900	0949	0997	1046	1095	1143	1192	1240	1289
94	1338	1386	1435	1483	1532	1580	1629	1677	1726	1775
95	1823	1872	1920	1969	2017	2066	2114	2163	2211	2260
96	2308	2356	2405	2453	2502	2550	2599	2647	2696	2744
97	2792	2841	2889	2938	2986	3034	3083	3131	3180	3228
98	3276	3325	3373	3421	3470	3518	3566	3615	3663	3711
99	3760	3808	3856	3905	3953	4001	4049	4098	4146	4194
900	95 4243	4291	4339	4387	4435	4484	4532	4580	4628	4677
N	0	1	2	3	4	5	6	7	8	9

SIX-PLACE MANTISSAS FOR COMMON LOGARITHMS: (Continued)

N	0	1	2	3	4	5	6	7	8	9
900	95 4243	4291	4339	4387	4435	4484	4532	4580	4628	4677
01	4725	4773	4821	4869	4918	4966	5014	5062	5110	5158
02	5207	5255	5303	5351	5399	5447	5495	5543	5592	5640
03	5688	5736	5784	5832	5880	5928	5976	6024	6072	6120
04	6168	6216	6265	6313	6361	6409	6457	6505	6553	6601
05	6649	6697	6745	6793	6840	6888	6936	6984	7032	7080
06	7128	7176	7224	7272	7320	7368	7416	7464	7512	7559
07	7607	7655	7703	7751	7799	7847	7894	7942	7990	8038
08	8086	8134	8181	8229	8277	8325	8373	8421	8468	8516
09	8564	8612	8659	8707	8755	8803	8850	8898	8946	8994
910	9041	9089	9137	9185	9232	9280	9328	9375	9423	9471
11	9518	9566	9614	9661	9709	9757	9804	9852	9900	9947
12	95 9995	*0042	*0090	*0138	*0185	*0233	*0280	*0328	*0376	*0423
13	96 0471	0518	0566	0613	0661	0709	0756	0804	0851	0899
14	0946	0994	1041	1089	1136	1184	1231	1279	1326	1374
15	1421	1469	1516	1563	1611	1658	1706	1753	1801	1848
16	1895	1943	1990	2038	2085	2132	2180	2227	2275	2322
17	2369	2417	2464	2511	2559	2606	2653	2701	2748	2795
18	2843	2890	2937	2985	3032	3079	3126	3174	3221	3268
19	3316	3363	3410	3457	3504	3552	3599	3646	3693	3741
920	3788	3835	3882	3929	3977	4024	4071	4118	4165	4212
21	4260	4307	4354	4401	4448	4495	4542	4590	4637	4684
22	4731	4778	4825	4872	4919	4966	5013	5061	5108	5155
23	5202	5249	5296	5343	5390	5437	5484	5531	5578	5625
24	5672	5719	5766	5813	5860	5907	5954	6001	6048	6095
25	6142	6189	6236	6283	6329	6376	6423	6470	6517	6564
26	6611	6658	6705	6752	6799	6845	6892	6939	6986	7033
27	7080	7127	7173	7220	7267	7314	7361	7408	7454	7501
28	7548	7595	7642	7688	7735	7782	7829	7875	7922	7969
29	8016	8062	8109	8156	8203	8249	8296	8343	8390	8436
930	8483	8530	8576	8623	8670	8716	8763	8810	8856	8903
31	8950	8996	9043	9090	9136	9183	9229	9276	9323	9369
32	9416	9463	9509	9556	9602	9649	9695	9742	9789	9835
33	96 9882	9928	9975	*0021	*0068	*0114	*0161	*0207	*0254	*0300
34	97 0347	0393	0440	0486	0533	0579	0626	0672	0719	0765
35	0812	0858	0904	0951	0997	1044	1090	1137	1183	1229
36	1276	1322	1369	1415	1461	1508	1554	1601	1647	1693
37	1740	1786	1832	1879	1925	1971	2018	2064	2110	2157
38	2203	2249	2295	2342	2388	2434	2481	2527	2573	2619
39	2666	2712	2758	2804	2851	2897	2943	2989	3035	3082
940	3128	3174	3220	3266	3313	3359	3405	3451	3497	3543
41	3590	3636	3682	3728	3774	3820	3866	3913	3959	4005
42	4051	4097	4143	4189	4235	4281	4327	4374	4420	4466
43	4512	4558	4604	4650	4696	4742	4788	4834	4880	4926
44	4972	5018	5064	5110	5156	5202	5248	5294	5340	5386
45	5432	5478	5524	5570	5616	5662	5707	5753	5799	5845
46	5891	5937	5983	6029	6075	6121	6167	6212	6258	6304
47	6350	6396	6442	6488	6533	6579	6625	6671	6717	6763
48	6808	6854	6900	6946	6992	7037	7083	7129	7175	7220
49	7266	7312	7358	7403	7449	7495	7541	7586	7632	7678
950	97 7724	7769	7815	7861	7906	7952	7998	8043	8089	8135
N	0	1	2	3	4	5	6	7	8	9

SIX-PLACE MANTISSAS FOR COMMON LOGARITHMS: (Continued)

N	0	1	2	3	4	5	6	7	8	9
950	97 7724	7769	7815	7861	7906	7952	7998	8043	8089	8135
51	8181	8226	8272	8317	8363	8409	8454	8500	8546	8591
52	8637	8683	8728	8774	8819	8865	8911	8956	9002	9047
53	9093	9138	9184	9230	9275	9321	9366	9412	9457	9503
54	97 9548	9594	9639	9685	9730	9776	9821	9867	9912	9958
55	98 0003	0049	0094	0140	0185	0231	0276	0322	0367	0412
56	0458	0503	0549	0594	0640	0685	0730	0776	0821	0867
57	0912	0957	1003	1048	1093	1139	1184	1229	1275	1320
58	1366	1411	1456	1501	1547	1592	1637	1683	1728	1773
59	1819	1864	1909	1954	2000	2045	2090	2135	2181	2226
960	2271	2316	2362	2407	2452	2497	2543	2588	2633	2678
61	2723	2769	2814	2859	2904	2949	2994	3040	3085	3130
62	3175	3220	3265	3310	3356	3401	3446	3491	3536	3581
63	3626	3671	3716	3762	3807	3852	3897	3942	3987	4032
64	4077	4122	4167	4212	4257	4302	4347	4392	4437	4482
65	4527	4572	4617	4662	4707	4752	4797	4842	4887	4932
66	4977	5022	5067	5112	5157	5202	5247	5292	5337	5382
67	5426	5471	5516	5561	5606	5651	5696	5741	5786	5830
68	5875	5920	5965	6010	6055	6100	6144	6189	6234	6279
69	6324	6369	6413	6458	6503	6548	6593	6637	6682	6727
970	6772	6817	6861	6906	6951	6996	7040	7085	7130	7175
71	7219	7264	7309	7353	7398	7443	7488	7532	7577	7622
72	7666	7711	7756	7800	7845	7890	7934	7979	8024	8068
73	8113	8157	8202	8247	8291	8336	8381	8425	8470	8514
74	8559	8604	8648	8693	8737	8782	8826	8871	8916	8960
75	9005	9049	9094	9138	9183	9227	9272	9316	9361	9405
76	9450	9494	9539	9583	9628	9672	9717	9761	9806	9850
77	98 9895	9939	9983	*0028	*0072	*0117	*0161	*0206	*0250	*0294
78	99 0339	0383	0428	0472	0516	0561	0605	0650	0694	0738
79	0783	0827	0871	0916	0960	1004	1049	1093	1137	1182
980	1226	1270	1315	1359	1403	1448	1492	1536	1580	1625
81	1669	1713	1758	1802	1846	1890	1935	1979	2023	2067
82	2111	2156	2200	2244	2288	2333	2377	2421	2465	2509
83	2554	2598	2642	2686	2730	2774	2819	2863	2907	2951
84	2995	3039	3083	3127	3172	3216	3260	3304	3348	3392
85	3436	3480	3524	3568	3613	3657	3701	3745	3789	3833
86	3877	3921	3965	4009	4053	4097	4141	4185	4229	4273
87	4317	4361	4405	4449	4493	4537	4581	4625	4669	4713
88	4757	4801	4845	4889	4933	4977	5021	5065	5108	5152
89	5196	5240	5284	5328	5372	5416	5460	5504	5547	5591
990	5635	5679	5723	5767	5811	5854	5898	5942	5986	6030
91	6074	6117	6161	6205	6249	6293	6337	6380	6424	6468
92	6512	6555	6599	6643	6687	6731	6774	6818	6862	6906
93	6949	6993	7037	7080	7124	7168	7212	7255	7299	7343
94	7386	7430	7474	7517	7561	7605	7648	7692	7736	7779
95	7823	7868	7910	7954	7998	8041	8085	8129	8172	8216
96	8259	8303	8347	8390	8434	8477	8521	8564	8608	8651
97	8695	9738	8782	8826	8869	8913	8956	9000	9043	9087
98	9131	9174	9218	9261	9305	9348	9392	9435	9479	9522
99	99 9565	9609	9652	9696	9739	9783	9826	9870	9913	9957
1000	00 0000	0043	0087	0130	0174	0217	0260	0304	0347	0391

N	0	1	2	3	4	5	6	7	8	9

SEVEN-PLACE MANTISSAS FOR COMMON LOGARITHMS:

N	0	1	2	3	4	5	6	7	8	9
1000 000 0000	0434	0869	1303	1737	2171	2605	3039	3473	3907	
1001 4341	4775	5208	5642	6076	6510	6943	7377	7810	8244	
1002 8677	9111	9544	9977	*0411	*0844	*1277	*1710	*2143	*2576	
1003 001 3009	3442	3875	4308	4741	5174	5607	6039	6472	6905	
1004 7337	7770	8202	8635	9067	9499	9932	*0364	*0796	*1228	
1005 002 1661	2093	2525	2957	3389	3821	4253	4685	5116	5548	
1006 5980	6411	6843	7275	7706	8138	8569	9001	9432	9863	
1007 003 0295	0726	1157	1588	2019	2451	2882	3313	3744	4174	
1008 4605	5036	5467	5898	6328	6759	7190	7620	8051	8481	
1009 8912	9342	9772	*0203	*0633	*1063	*1493	*1924	*2354	*2784	
1010 004 3214	3644	4074	4504	4933	5363	5793	6223	6652	7082	
1011 7512	7941	8371	8800	9229	9659	*0088	*0517	*0947	*1376	
1012 005 1805	2234	2663	3092	3521	3950	4379	4808	5237	5666	
1013 6094	6523	6952	7380	7809	8238	8666	9094	9523	9951	
1014 006 0380	0808	1236	1664	2092	2521	2949	3377	3805	4233	
1015 4660	5088	5516	5944	6372	6799	7227	7655	8082	8510	
1016 8937	9365	9792	*0219	*0647	*1074	*1501	*1928	*2355	*2782	
1017 007 3210	3637	4064	4490	4917	5344	5771	6198	6624	7051	
1018 7478	7904	8331	8757	9184	9610	*0037	*0463	*0889	*1316	
1019 008 1742	2168	2594	3020	3446	3872	4298	4724	5150	5576	
1020 6002	6427	6853	7279	7704	8130	8556	8981	9407	9832	
1021 009 0257	0683	1108	1533	1959	2384	2809	3234	3659	4084	
1022 4509	4934	5359	5784	6208	6633	7058	7483	7907	8332	
1023 8756	9181	9605	*0030	*0454	*0878	*1303	*1727	*2151	*2575	
1024 010 3000	3424	3848	4272	4696	5120	5544	5967	6391	6815	
1025 7239	7662	8086	8510	8933	9357	9780	*0204	*0627	*1050	
1026 011 1474	1897	2320	2743	3166	3590	4013	4436	4859	5282	
1027 5704	6127	6550	6973	7396	7818	8241	8664	9086	9509	
1028 9931	*0354	*0776	*1198	*1621	*2043	*2465	*2887	*3310	*3732	
1029 012 4154	4576	4998	5420	5842	6264	6685	7107	7529	7951	
1030 8372	8794	9215	9637	*0059	*0480	*0901	*1323	*1744	*2165	
1031 013 2587	3008	3429	3850	4271	4692	5113	5534	5955	6376	
1032 6797	7218	7639	8059	8480	8901	9321	9742	*0162	*0583	
1033 014 1003	1424	1844	2264	2685	3105	3525	3945	4365	4785	
1034 5205	5625	6045	6465	6885	7305	7725	8144	8564	8984	
1035 9403	9823	*0243	*0662	*1082	*1501	*1920	*2340	*2759	*3178	
1036 015 3598	4017	4436	4855	5274	5693	6112	6531	6950	7369	
1037 7788	8206	8625	9044	9462	9881	*0300	*0718	*1137	*1555	
1038 016 1974	2392	2810	3229	3647	4065	4483	4901	5319	5737	
1039 6155	6573	6991	7409	7827	8245	8663	9080	9498	9916	
1040 017 0333	0751	1168	1586	2003	2421	2838	3256	3673	4090	
1041 4507	4924	5342	5759	6176	6593	7010	7427	7844	8260	
1042 8677	9094	9511	9927	*0344	*0761	*1177	*1594	*2010	*2427	
1043 018 2843	3259	3676	4092	4508	4925	5341	5757	6173	6589	
1044 7005	7421	7837	8253	8669	9084	9500	9916	*0332	*0747	
1045 019 1163	1578	1994	2410	2825	3240	3656	4071	4486	4902	
1046 5317	5732	6147	6562	6977	7392	7807	8222	8637	9052	
1047 9467	9882	*0296	*0711	*1126	*1540	*1955	*2369	*2784	*3198	
1048 020 3613	4027	4442	4856	5270	5684	6099	6513	6927	7341	
1049 7755	8169	8583	8997	9411	9824	*0238	*0652	*1066	*1479	
1050 021 1893	2307	2720	3134	3547	3961	4374	4787	5201	5614	

N	0	1	2	3	4	5	6	7	8	9

SEVEN-PLACE MANTISSAS FOR COMMON LOGARITHMS: (Continued)

N	0	1	2	3	4	5	6	7	8	9
1050 021	1893	2307	2720	3134	3547	3961	4374	4787	5201	5614
1051	6027	6440	6854	7267	7680	8093	8506	8919	9332	9745
1052 022	0157	0570	0983	1396	1808	2221	2634	3046	3459	3871
1053	4284	4696	5109	5521	5933	6345	6758	7170	7582	7994
1054	8406	8818	9230	9642	*0054	*0466	*0878	*1289	*1701	*2113
1055 023	2525	2936	3348	3759	4171	4582	4994	5405	5817	6228
1056	6639	7050	7462	7873	8284	8695	9106	9517	9928	*0339
1057 024	0750	1161	1572	1982	2393	2804	3214	3625	4036	4446
1058	4857	5267	5678	6088	6498	6909	7319	7729	8139	8549
1059	8960	9370	9780	*0190	*0600	*1010	*1419	*1829	*2239	*2649
1060 025	3059	3468	3878	4288	4697	5107	5516	5926	6335	6744
1061	7154	7563	7972	8382	8791	9200	9609	*0018	*0427	*0836
1062 026	1245	1654	2063	2472	2881	3289	3698	4107	4515	4924
1063	5333	5741	6150	6558	6967	7375	7783	8192	8600	9008
1064	9416	9824	*0233	*0641	*1049	*1457	*1865	*2273	*2680	*3088
1065 027	3496	3904	4312	4719	5127	5535	5942	6350	6757	7165
1066	7572	7979	8387	8794	9201	9609	*0016	*0423	*0830	*1237
1067 028	1644	2051	2458	2865	3272	3679	4086	4492	4899	5306
1068	5713	6119	6526	6932	7339	7745	8152	8558	8964	9371
1069	9777	*0183	*0590	*0996	*1402	*1808	*2214	*2620	*3026	*3432
1070 029	3838	4244	4649	5055	5461	5867	6272	6678	7084	7489
1071	7895	8300	8706	9111	9516	9922	*0327	*0732	*1138	*1543
1072 030	1948	2353	2758	3163	3568	3973	4378	4783	5188	5592
1073	5997	6402	6807	7211	7616	8020	8425	8830	9234	9638
1074 031	0043	0447	0851	1256	1660	2064	2468	2872	3277	3681
1075	4085	4489	4893	5296	5700	6104	6508	6912	7315	7719
1076	8123	8526	8930	9333	9737	*0140	*0544	*0947	*1350	*1754
1077 032	2157	2560	2963	3367	3770	4173	4576	4979	5382	5785
1078	6188	6590	6993	7396	7799	8201	8604	9007	9409	9812
1079 033	0214	0617	1019	1422	1824	2226	2629	3031	3433	3835
1080	4238	4640	5042	5444	5846	6248	6650	7052	7453	7855
1081	8257	8659	9060	9462	9864	*0265	*0667	*1068	*1470	*1871
1082 034	2273	2674	3075	3477	3878	4279	4680	5081	5482	5884
1083	6285	6686	7087	7487	7888	8289	8690	9091	9491	9892
1084 035	0293	0693	1094	1495	1895	2296	2696	3096	3497	3897
1085	4297	4698	5098	5498	5898	6298	6698	7098	7498	7898
1086	8298	8698	9098	9498	9898	*0297	*0697	*1097	*1496	*1896
1087 036	2295	2695	3094	3494	3893	4293	4692	5091	5491	5890
1088	6289	6688	7087	7486	7885	8284	8683	9082	9481	9880
1089 037	0279	0678	1076	1475	1874	2272	2671	3070	3468	3867
1090	4265	4663	5062	5460	5858	6257	6655	7053	7451	7849
1091	8248	8646	9044	9442	9839	*0237	*0635	*1033	*1431	*1829
1092 038	2226	2624	3022	3419	3817	4214	4612	5009	5407	5804
1093	6202	6599	6996	7393	7791	8188	8585	8982	9379	9776
1094 039	0173	0570	0967	1364	1761	2158	2554	2951	3348	3745
1095	4141	4538	4934	5331	5727	6124	6520	6917	7313	7709
1096	8106	8502	8898	9294	9690	*0086	*0482	*0878	*1274	*1670
1097 040	2066	2462	2858	3254	3650	4045	4441	4837	5232	5628
1098	6023	6419	6814	7210	7605	8001	8396	8791	9187	9582
1099	9977	*0372	*0767	*1162	*1557	*1952	*2347	*2742	*3137	*3532
1100 041	3927	4322	4716	5111	5506	5900	6295	6690	7084	7479

N	0	1	2	3	4	5	6	7	8	9

SEVEN-PLACE MANTISSAS FOR COMMON LOGARITHMS: (Continued)

N	0	1	2	3	4	5	6	7	8	9
1100 041 3927	4322	4716	5111	5506	5900	6295	6690	7084	7479
1101 7873	8268	8662	9056	9451	9845	*0239	*0633	*1028	*1422
1102 042 1816	2210	2604	2998	3392	3786	4180	4574	4968	5361
1103 5755	6149	6543	6936	7330	7723	8117	8510	8904	9297
1104 9691	*0084	*0477	*0871	*1264	*1657	*2050	*2444	*2837	*3230
1105 043 3623	4016	4409	4802	5195	5587	5980	6373	6766	7159
1106 7551	7944	8337	8729	9122	9514	9907	*0299	*0692	*1084
1107 044 1476	1869	2261	2653	3045	3437	3829	4222	4614	5006
1108 5398	5790	6181	6573	6965	7357	7749	8140	8532	8924
1109 9315	9707	*0099	*0490	*0882	*1273	*1664	*2056	*2447	*2839
1110 045 3230	3621	4012	4403	4795	5186	5577	5968	6359	6750
1111 7141	7531	7922	8313	8704	9095	9485	9876	*0267	*0657
1112 046 1048	1438	1829	2219	2610	3000	3391	3781	4171	4561
1113 4952	5342	5732	6122	6512	6902	7292	7682	8072	8462
1114 8852	9242	9632	*0021	*0411	*0801	*1190	*1580	*1970	*2359
1115 047 2749	3138	3528	3917	4306	4696	5085	5474	5864	6253
1116 6642	7031	7420	7809	8198	8587	8976	9365	9754	*0143
1117 048 0532	0921	1309	1698	2087	2475	2864	3253	3641	4030
1118 4418	4806	5195	5583	5972	6360	6748	7136	7525	7913
1119 8301	8689	9077	9465	9853	*0241	*0629	*1017	*1405	*1792
1120 049 2180	2568	2956	3343	3731	4119	4506	4894	5281	5669
1121 6056	6444	6831	7218	7606	7993	8380	8767	9154	9541
1122 9929	*0316	*0703	*1090	*1477	*1863	*2250	*2637	*3024	*3411
1123 050 3798	4184	4571	4958	5344	5731	6117	6504	6890	7277
1124 7663	8049	8436	8822	9208	9595	9981	*0367	*0753	*1139
1125 051 1525	1911	2297	2683	3069	3455	3841	4227	4612	4998
1126 5384	5770	6155	6541	6926	7312	7697	8083	8468	8854
1127 9239	9624	*0010	*0395	*0780	*1166	*1551	*1936	*2321	*2706
1128 052 3091	3476	3861	4246	4631	5016	5400	5785	6170	6555
1129 6939	7324	7709	8093	8478	8862	9247	9631	*0016	*0400
1130 053 0784	1169	1553	1937	2321	2706	3090	3474	3858	4242
1131 4626	5010	5394	5778	6162	6546	6929	7313	7697	8081
1132 8464	8848	9232	9615	9999	*0382	*0766	*1149	*1532	*1916
1133 054 2299	2682	3066	3449	3832	4215	4598	4981	5365	5748
1134 6131	6514	6896	7279	7662	8045	8428	8811	9193	9576
1135 9959	*0341	*0724	*1106	*1489	*1871	*2254	*2636	*3019	*3401
1136 055 3783	4166	4548	4930	5312	5694	6077	6459	6841	7223
1137 7605	7987	8369	8750	9132	9514	9896	*0278	*0659	*1041
1138 056 1423	1804	2186	2567	2949	3330	3712	4093	4475	4856
1139 5237	5619	6000	6381	6762	7143	7524	7905	8287	8668
1140 9049	9429	9810	*0191	*0572	*0953	*1334	*1714	*2095	*2476
1141 057 2856	3237	3618	3998	4379	4759	5140	5520	5900	6281
1142 6661	7041	7422	7802	8182	8562	8942	9322	9702	*0082
1143 058 0462	0842	1222	1602	1982	2362	2741	3121	3501	3881
1144 4260	4640	5019	5399	5778	6158	6537	6917	7296	7676
1145 8055	8434	8813	9193	9572	9951	*0330	*0709	*1088	*1467
1146 059 1846	2225	2604	2983	3362	3741	4119	4498	4877	5256
1147 5634	6013	6391	6770	7148	7527	7905	8284	8662	9041
1148 9419	9797	*0175	*0554	*0932	*1310	*1688	*2066	*2444	*2822
1149 060 3200	3578	3956	· 4334	4712	5090	5468	5845	6223	6601
1150 6978	7356	7734	8111	8489	8866	9244	9621	9999	*0376

N	0	1	2	3	4	5	6	7	8	9

SEVEN-PLACE MANTISSAS FOR COMMON LOGARITHMS: (Continued)

N	0	1	2	3	4	5	6	7	8	9
1150	060 6978	7356	7734	8111	8489	8866	9244	9621	9999	*0376
1151	061 0753	1131	1508	1885	2262	2639	3017	3394	3771	4148
1152	4525	4902	5279	5656	6032	6409	6786	7163	7540	7916
1153	8293	8670	9046	9423	9799	*0176	*0552	*0929	*1305	*1682
1154	062 2058	2434	2811	3187	3563	3939	4316	4692	5068	5444
1155	5820	6196	6572	6948	7324	7699	8075	8451	8827	9203
1156	9578	9954	*0330	*0705	*1081	*1456	*1832	*2207	*2583	*2958
1157	063 3334	3709	4084	4460	4835	5210	5585	5960	6335	6711
1158	7086	7461	7836	8211	8585	8960	9335	9710	*0085	*0460
1159	064 0834	1209	1584	1958	2333	2708	3082	3457	3831	4205
1160	4580	4954	5329	5703	6077	6451	6826	7200	7574	7948
1161	8322	8696	9070	9444	9818	*0192	*0566	*0940	*1314	*1688
1162	065 2061	2435	2809	3182	3556	3930	4303	4677	5050	5424
1163	5797	6171	6544	6917	7291	7664	8037	8410	8784	9157
1164	9530	9903	*0276	*0649	*1022	*1395	*1768	*2141	*2514	*2886
1165	066 3259	3632	4005	4377	4750	5123	5495	5868	6241	6613
1166	6986	7358	7730	8103	8475	8847	9220	9592	9964	*0336
1167	067 0709	1081	1453	1825	2197	2569	2941	3313	3685	4057
1168	4428	4800	5172	5544	5915	6287	6659	7030	7402	7774
1169	8145	8517	8888	9259	9631	*0002	*0374	*0745	*1116	*1487
1170	068 1859	2230	2601	2972	3343	3714	4085	4456	4827	5198
1171	5569	5940	6311	6681	7052	7423	7794	8164	8535	8906
1172	9276	9647	*0017	*0388	*0758	*1129	*1499	*1869	*2240	*2610
1173	069 2980	3350	3721	4091	4461	4831	5201	5571	5941	6311
1174	6681	7051	7421	7791	8160	8530	8900	9270	9639	*0009
1175	070 0379	0748	1118	1487	1857	2226	2596	2965	3335	3704
1176	4073	4442	4812	5181	5550	5919	6288	6658	7027	7396
1177	7765	8134	8503	8871	9240	9609	9978	*0347	*0715	*1084
1178	071 1453	1822	2190	2559	2927	3296	3664	4033	4401	4770
1179	5138	5506	5875	6243	6611	6979	7348	7716	8084	8452
1180	8820	9188	9556	9924	*0292	*0660	*1028	*1396	*1763	*2131
1181	072 2499	2867	3234	3602	3970	4337	4705	5072	5440	5807
1182	6175	6542	6910	7277	7644	8011	8379	8746	9113	9480
1183	9847	*0215	*0582	*0949	*1316	*1683	*2050	*2416	*2783	*3150
1184	073 3517	3884	4251	4617	4984	5351	5717	6084	6450	6817
1185	7184	7550	7916	8283	8649	9016	9382	9748	*0114	*0481
1186	074 0847	1213	1579	1945	2311	2677	3043	3409	3775	4141
1187	4507	4873	5239	5605	5970	6336	6702	7068	7433	7799
1188	8164	8530	8895	9261	9626	9992	*0357	*0723	*1088	*1453
1189	075 1819	2184	2549	2914	3279	3644	4010	4375	4740	5105
1190	5470	5835	6199	6564	6929	7294	7659	8024	8388	8753
1191	9118	9482	9847	*0211	*0576	*0940	*1305	*1669	*2034	*2398
1192	076 2763	3127	3491	3855	4220	4584	4948	5312	5676	6040
1193	6404	6768	7132	7496	7860	8224	8588	8952	9316	9680
1194	077 0043	0407	0771	1134	1498	1862	2225	2589	2952	3316
1195	3679	4042	4406	4769	5133	5496	5859	6222	6585	6949
1196	7312	7675	8038	8401	8764	9127	9490	9853	*0216	*0579
1197	078 0942	1304	1667	2030	2393	2755	3118	3480	3843	4206
1198	4568	4931	5293	5656	6018	6380	6743	7105	7467	7830
1199	8192	8554	8916	9278	9640	*0003	*0365	*0727	*1089	*1451
1200	079 1812	2174	2536	2898	3260	3622	3983	4345	4707	5068

N	0	1	2	3	4	5	6	7	8	9

NATURAL OR NAPERIAN LOGARITHMS
0.000–0.499

N	0	1	2	3	4	5	6	7	8	9
0.00	− ∞	−6‡ .90776	−6 .21461	−5 .80914	−5 .52146	−5 .29832	−5 .11000	−4 .96185	−4 .82831	−4 .71053
.01	−4.60517	.50986	.42285	.34281	.26870	.19971	.13517	.07454	.01738	*.96332
.02	−3.91202	.86323	.81671	.77226	.72970	.68888	.64966	.61192	.57555	.54046
.03	.50656	.47377	.44202	.41125	.38139	.35241	.32424	.29684	.27017	.24419
.04	.21888	.19418	.17009	.14656	.12357	.10109	.07911	.05761	.03655	.01593
.05	−2.99573	.97593	.95651	.93746	.91877	.90042	.88240	.86470	.84731	.83022
.06	.81341	.79688	.78062	.76462	.74887	.73337	.71810	.70306	.68825	.67365
.07	.65926	.64508	.63109	.61730	.60369	.59027	.57702	.56395	.55105	.53831
.08	.52573	.51331	.50104	.48891	.47694	.46510	.45341	.44185	.43042	.41912
.09	.40795	.39690	.38597	.37516	.36446	.35388	.34341	.33304	.32279	.31264
0.10	−2.30259	.29263	.28278	.27303	.26336	.25379	.24432	.23493	.22562	.21641
.11	.20727	.19823	.18926	.18037	.17156	.16282	.15417	.14558	.13707	.12863
.12	.12026	.11196	.10373	.09557	.08747	.07944	.07147	.06357	.05573	.04794
.13	.04022	.03256	.02495	.01741	.00992	.00248	*.99510	*.98777	*.98050	*.97328
.14	−1.96611	.95900	.95193	.94491	.93794	.93102	.92415	.91732	.91054	.90381
.15	.89712	.89048	.88387	.87732	.87080	.86433	.85790	.85151	.84516	.83885
.16	.83258	.82635	.82016	.81401	.80789	.80181	.79577	.78976	.78379	.77786
.17	.77196	.76609	.76026	.75446	.74870	.74297	.73727	.73161	.72597	.72037
.18	.71480	.70926	.70375	.69827	.69282	.68740	.68201	.67665	.67131	.66601
.19	.66073	.65548	.65026	.64507	.63990	.63476	.62964	.62455	.61949	.61445
0.20	−1.60944	.60445	.59949	.59455	.58964	.58475	.57988	.57504	.57022	.56542
.21	.56065	.55590	.55117	.54646	.54178	.53712	.53248	.52786	.52326	.51868
.22	.51413	.50959	.50508	.50058	.49611	.49165	.48722	.48281	.47841	.47403
.23	.46968	.46534	.46102	.45672	.45243	.44817	.44392	.43970	.43548	.43129
.24	.42712	.42296	.41882	.41469	.41059	.40650	.40242	.39837	.39433	.39030
.25	.38629	.38230	.37833	.37437	.37042	.36649	.36258	.35868	.35480	.35093
.26	.34707	.34323	.33941	.33560	.33181	.32803	.32426	.32051	.31677	.31304
.27	.30933	.30564	.30195	.29828	.29463	.29098	.28735	.28374	.28013	.27654
.28	.27297	.26940	.26585	.26231	.25878	.25527	.25176	.24827	.24479	.24133
.29	.23787	.23443	.23100	.22758	.22418	.22078	.21740	.21402	.21066	.20731
0.30	−1.20397	.20065	.19733	.19402	.19073	.18744	.18417	.18091	.17766	.17441
.31	.17118	.16796	.16475	.16155	.15836	.15518	.15201	.14885	.14570	.14256
.32	.13943	.13631	.13320	.13010	.12701	.12393	.12086	.11780	.11474	.11170
.33	.10866	.10564	.10262	.09961	.09661	.09362	.09064	.08767	.08471	.08176
.34	.07881	.07587	.07294	.07002	.06711	.06421	.06132	.05843	.05555	.05268
.35	−1.04982	.04697	.04412	.04129	.03846	.03564	.03282	.03002	.02722	.02443
.36	.02165	.01888	.01611	.01335	.01060	.00786	.00512	.00239	*.99967	*.99696
.37	−0.99425	.99155	.98886	.98618	.98350	.98083	.97817	.97551	.97286	.97022
.38	.96758	.96496	.96233	.95972	.95711	.95451	.95192	.94933	.94675	.94418
.39	.94161	.93905	.93649	.93395	.93140	.92887	.92634	.92382	.92130	.91879
0.40	−0.91629	.91379	.91130	.90882	.90634	.90387	.90140	.89894	.89649	.89404
.41	.89160	.88916	.88673	.88431	.88189	.87948	.87707	.87467	.87227	.86988
.42	.86750	.86512	.86275	.86038	.85802	.85567	.85332	.85097	.84863	.84630
.43	.84397	.84165	.83933	.83702	.83471	.83241	.83011	.82782	.82554	.82326
.44	.82098	.81871	.81645	.81419	.81193	.80968	.80744	.80520	.80296	.80073
.45	.79851	.79629	.79407	.79186	.78966	.78746	.78526	.78307	.78089	.77871
.46	.77653	.77436	.77219	.77003	.76787	.76572	.76357	.76143	.75929	.75715
.47	.75502	.75290	.75078	.74866	.74655	.74444	.74234	.74024	.73814	.73605
.48	.73397	.73189	.72981	.72774	.72567	.72361	.72155	.71949	.71744	.71539
.49	.71335	.71131	.70928	.70725	.70522	.70320	.70118	.69917	.69716	.69515

‡ Note that the whole number values are given above the decimal values for the first line. In the second and following lines they are given at the left. All decimal values are negative on this page.

NATURAL OR NAPERIAN LOGARITHMS (Continued)
0.500–0.999

N	0	1	2	3	4	5	6	7	8	9
0.50	−0.69315	.69115	.68916	.68717	.68518	.68320	.68122	.67924	.67727	.67531
.51	.67334	.67139	.66934	.66748	.66553	.66359	.66165	.65971	.65778	.65585
.52	.65393	.65201	.65009	.64817	.64626	.64436	.64245	.64055	.63866	.63677
.53	.63488	.63299	.63111	.62923	.62736	.62549	.62362	.62176	.61990	.61804
.54	.61619	.61434	.61249	.61065	.60881	.60697	.60514	.60331	.60148	.59966
.55	.59784	.59602	.59421	.59240	.59059	.58879	.58699	.58519	.58340	.58161
.56	.57982	.57803	.57625	.57448	.57270	.57093	.56916	.56740	.56563	.56387
.57	.56212	.56037	.55862	.55687	.55513	.55339	.55165	.54991	.54818	.54645
.58	.54473	.54300	.54128	.53957	.53785	.53614	.53444	.53273	.53103	.52933
.59	.52763	.52594	.52425	.52256	.52088	.51919	.51751	.51584	.51416	.51249
0.60	−0.51083	.50916	.50750	.50584	.50418	.50253	.50088	.49923	.49758	.49594
.61	.49430	.49266	.49102	.48939	.48776	.48613	.48451	.48289	.48127	.47965
.62	.47804	.47642	.47482	.47321	.47160	.47000	.46840	.46681	.46522	.46362
.63	.46204	.46045	.45887	.45728	.45571	.45413	.45256	.45099	.44942	.44785
.64	.44629	.44473	.44317	.44161	.44006	.43850	.43696	.43541	.43386	.43232
.65	.43078	.42925	.42771	.42618	.42465	.42312	.42159	.42007	.41855	.41703
.66	.41552	.41400	.41249	.41098	.40947	.40797	.40647	.40497	.40347	.40197
.67	.40048	.39899	.39750	.39601	.39453	.39304	.39156	.39008	.38861	.38713
.68	.38566	.38419	.38273	.38126	.37980	.37834	.37688	.37542	.37397	.37251
.69	.37106	.36962	.36817	.36673	.36528	.36384	.36241	.36097	.35954	.35810
0.70	−0.35667	.35525	.35382	.35240	.35098	.34956	.34814	.34672	.34531	.34390
.71	.34249	.34108	.33968	.33827	.33687	.33547	.33408	.33268	.33129	.32989
.72	.32850	.32712	.32573	.32435	.32296	.32158	.32021	.31883	.31745	.31608
.73	.31471	.31334	.31197	.31061	.30925	.30788	.30653	.30517	.30381	.30246
.74	.30111	.29975	.29841	.29706	.29571	.29437	.29303	.29169	.29035	.28902
.75	.28768	.28635	.28502	.28369	.28236	.28104	.27971	.27839	.27707	.27575
.76	.27444	.27312	.27181	.27050	.26919	.26788	.26657	.26527	.26397	.26266
.77	.26136	.26007	.25877	.25748	.25618	.25489	.25360	.25231	.25103	.24974
.78	.24846	.24718	.24590	.24462	.24335	.24207	.24080	.23953	.23826	.23699
.79	.23572	.23446	.23319	.23193	.23067	.22941	.22816	.22690	.22565	.22439
0.80	−0.22314	.22189	.22065	.21940	.21816	.21691	.21567	.21433	.21319	.21196
.81	.21072	.20949	.20825	.20702	.20579	.20457	.20334	.20212	.20089	.19967
.82	.19845	.19723	.19601	.19480	.19358	.19237	.19116	.18995	.18874	.18754
.83	.18633	.18513	.18392	.18272	.18152	.18032	.17913	.17793	.17674	.17554
.84	.17435	.17316	.17198	.17079	.16960	.16842	.16724	.16605	.16487	.16370
.85	−0.16252	.16134	.16017	.15900	.15782	.15665	.15548	.15432	.15315	.15199
.86	.15082	.14966	.14850	.14734	.14618	.14503	.14387	.14272	.14156	.14041
.87	.13926	.13811	.13697	.13582	.13467	.13353	.13239	.13125	.13011	.12897
.88	.12783	.12670	.12556	.12443	.12330	.12217	.12104	.11991	.11878	.11766
.89	.11653	.11541	.11429	.11317	.11205	.11093	.10981	.10870	.10759	.10647
0.90	−0.10536	.10425	.10314	.10203	.10093	.09982	.09872	.09761	.09651	.09541
.91	.09431	.09321	.09212	.09102	.08992	.08883	.08744	.08665	.08556	.08447
.92	.08338	.08230	.08121	.08013	.07904	.07796	.07688	.07580	.07472	.07365
.93	.07257	.07150	.07042	.06935	.06828	.06721	.06614	.06507	.06401	.06294
.94	.06188	.06081	.05975	.05869	.05763	.05657	.05551	.05446	.05340	.05235
.95	.05129	.05024	.04919	.04814	.04709	.04604	.04500	.04395	.04291	.04186
.96	.04082	.03978	.03874	.03770	.03666	.03563	.03459	.03356	.03252	.03149
.97	.03046	.02943	.02840	.02737	.02634	.02532	.02429	.02327	.02225	.02122
.98	.02020	.01918	.01816	.01715	.01613	.01511	.01410	.01309	.01207	.01106
.99	.01005	.00904	.00803	.00702	.00602	.00501	.00401	.00300	.00200	.00100

NATURAL OR NAPERIAN LOGARITHMS (Continued)

To find the natural logarithm of a number which is $\frac{1}{10}$, $\frac{1}{100}$, $\frac{1}{1000}$, etc. of a number whose logarithm is given, subtract from the given logarithm $\log_e 10$, $2 \log_e 10$, $3 \log_e 10$, etc.

To find the natural logarithm of a number which is 10, 100, 1000, etc. times a number whose logarithm is given, add to the given logarithm $\log_e 10$, $2 \log_e 10$, $3 \log_e 10$, etc.

$\log_e 10 = 2.30258\ 50930$	$6 \log_e 10 = 13.81551\ 05580$
$2 \log_e 10 = 4.60517\ 01860$	$7 \log_e 10 = 16.11809\ 56510$
$3 \log_e 10 = 6.90775\ 52790$	$8 \log_e 10 = 18.42068\ 07440$
$4 \log_e 10 = 9.21034\ 03720$	$9 \log_e 10 = 20.72326\ 58369$
$5 \log_e 10 = 11.51292\ 54650$	$10 \log_e 10 = 23.02585\ 09299$

See preceding table for logarithms for numbers between 0.000 and 0.999.

1.00–4.99

N	0	1	2	3	4	5	6	7	8	9
1.0	0.00000	.00995	.01980	.02956	.03922	.04879	.05827	.06766	.07696	.08618
.1	.09531	.10436	.11333	.12222	.13103	.13976	.14842	.15700	.16551	.17395
.2	.18232	.19062	.19885	.20701	.21511	.22314	.23111	.23902	.24686	.25464
.3	.26236	.27003	.27763	.28518	.29267	.30010	.30748	.31481	.32208	.32930
.4	.33647	.34359	.35066	.35767	.36464	.37156	.37844	.38526	.39204	.39878
.5	.40547	.41211	.41871	.42527	.43178	.43825	.44469	.45108	.45742	.46373
.6	.47000	.47623	.48243	.48858	.49470	.50078	.50682	.51282	.51879	.52473
.7	.53063	.53649	.54232	.54812	.55389	.55962	.56531	.57098	.57661	.58222
.8	.58779	.59333	.59884	.60432	.60977	.61519	.62058	.62594	.63127	.63658
.9	.64185	.64710	.65233	.65752	.66269	.66783	.67294	.67803	.68310	.68813
2.0	0.69315	.69813	.70310	.70804	.71295	.71784	.72271	.72755	.73237	.73716
.1	.74194	.74669	.75142	.75612	.76081	.76547	.77011	.77473	.77932	.78390
.2	.78846	.79299	.79751	.80200	.80648	.81093	.81536	.81978	.82418	.82855
.3	.83291	.83725	.84157	.84587	.85015	.85442	.85866	.86289	.86710	.87129
.4	.87547	.87963	.88377	.88789	.89200	.89609	.90016	.90422	.90826	.91228
.5	.91629	.92028	.92426	.92822	.93216	.93609	.94001	.94391	.94779	.95166
.6	.95551	.95935	.96317	.96698	.97078	.97456	.97833	.98208	.98582	.98954
.7	.99325	.99695	*.00063	*.00430	*.00796	*.01160	*.01523	*.01885	*.02245	*.02604
.8	1.02962	.03318	.03674	.04028	.04380	.04732	.05082	.05431	.05779	.06126
.9	.06471	.06815	.07158	.07500	.07841	.08181	.08519	.08856	.09192	.09527
3.0	1.09861	.10194	.10526	.10856	.11186	.11514	.11841	.12168	.12493	.12817
.1	.13140	.13462	.13783	.14103	.14422	.14740	.15057	.15373	.15688	.16002
.2	.16315	.16627	.16938	.17248	.17557	.17865	.18173	.18479	.18784	.19089
.3	.19392	.19695	.19996	.20297	.20597	.20896	.21194	.21491	.21788	.22083
.4	.22378	.22671	.22964	.23256	.23547	.23837	.24127	.24415	.24703	.24990
.5	.25276	.25562	.25846	.26130	.26413	.26695	.26976	.27257	.27536	.27815
.6	.28093	.28371	.28647	.28923	.29198	.29473	.29746	.30019	.30291	.30563
.7	.30833	.31103	.31372	.31641	.31909	.32176	.32442	.32708	.32972	.33237
.8	.33500	.33763	.34025	.34286	.34547	.34807	.35067	.35325	.35584	.35841
.9	.36098	.36354	.36609	.36864	.37118	.37372	.37624	.37877	.38128	.38379
4.0	1.38629	.38879	.39128	.39377	.39624	.39872	.40118	.40364	.40610	.40854
.1	.41099	.41342	.41585	.41828	.42070	.42311	.42552	.42792	.43031	.43270
.2	.43508	.43746	.43984	.44220	.44456	.44692	.44927	.45161	.45395	.45629
.3	.45862	.46094	.46326	.46557	.46787	.47018	.47247	.47476	.47705	.47933
.4	.48160	.48387	.48614	.48840	.49065	.49290	.49515	.49739	.49962	.50185
.5	.50408	.50630	.50851	.51072	.51293	.51513	.51732	.51951	.52170	.52388
.6	.52606	.52823	.53039	.53256	.53471	.53687	.53902	.54116	.54330	.54543
.7	.54756	.54969	.55181	.55393	.55604	.55814	.56025	.56235	.56444	.56653
.8	.56862	.57070	.57277	.57485	.57691	.57898	.58104	.58309	.58515	.58719
.9	.58924	.59127	.59331	.59534	.59737	.59939	.60141	.60342	.60543	.60744

NATURAL OR NAPERIAN LOGARITHMS (Continued)
5.00–9.99

N	0	1	2	3	4	5	6	7	8	9
5.0	1.60944	.61144	.61343	.61542	.61741	.61939	.62137	.62334	.62531	.62728
.1	.62924	.63120	.63315	.63511	.63705	.63900	.64094	.64287	.64481	.64673
.2	.64866	.65058	.65250	.65441	.65632	.65823	.66013	.66203	.66393	.66582
.3	.66771	.66959	.67147	.67335	.67523	.67710	.67896	.68083	.68269	.68455
.4	.68640	.68825	.69010	.69194	.69378	.69562	.69745	.69928	.70111	.70293
.5	.70475	.70656	.70838	.71019	.71199	.71380	.71560	.71740	.71919	.72098
.6	.72277	.72455	.72633	.72811	.72988	.73166	.73342	.73519	.73695	.73871
.7	.74047	.74222	.74397	.74572	.74746	.74920	.75094	.75267	.75440	.75613
.8	.75786	.75958	.76130	.76302	.76473	.76644	.76815	.76985	.77156	.77326
.9	.77495	.77665	.77834	.78002	.78171	.78339	.78507	.78675	.78842	.79009
6.0	1.79176	.79342	.79509	.79675	.79840	.80006	.80171	.80336	.80500	.80665
.1	.80829	.80993	.81156	.81319	.81482	.81645	.81808	.81970	.82132	.82294
.2	.82455	.82616	.82777	.82938	.83098	.83258	.83418	.83578	.83737	.83896
.3	.84055	.84214	.84372	.84530	.84688	.84845	.85003	.85160	.85317	.85473
.4	.85630	.85786	.85942	.86097	.86253	.86408	.86563	.86718	.86872	.87026
.5	.87180	.87334	.87487	.87641	.87794	.87947	.88099	.88251	.88403	.88555
.6	.88707	.88858	.89010	.89160	.89311	.89462	.89612	.89762	.89912	.90061
.7	.90211	.90360	.90509	.90658	.90806	.90954	.91102	.91250	.91398	.91545
.8	.91692	.91839	.91986	.92132	.92279	.92425	.92571	.92716	.92862	.93007
.9	.93152	.93297	.93442	.93586	.93730	.93874	.94018	.94162	.94305	.94448
7.0	1.94591	.94734	.94876	.95019	.95161	.95303	.95445	.95586	.95727	.95869
.1	.96009	.96150	.96291	.96431	.96571	.96711	.96851	.96991	.97130	.97269
.2	.97408	.97547	.97685	.97824	.97962	.98100	.98238	.98376	.98513	.98650
.3	.98787	.98924	.99061	.99198	.99334	.99470	.99606	.99742	.99877	*.00013
.4	2.00148	.00283	.00418	.00553	.00687	.00821	.00956	.01089	.01223	.01357
.5	.01490	.01624	.01757	.01890	.02022	.02155	.02287	.02419	.02551	.02683
.6	.02815	.02946	.03078	.03209	.03340	.03471	.03601	.03732	.03862	.03992
.7	.04122	.04252	.04381	.04511	.04640	.04769	.04898	.05027	.05156	.05284
.8	.05412	.05540	.05668	.05796	.05924	.06051	.06179	.06306	.06433	.06560
.9	.06686	.06813	.06939	.07065	.07191	.07317	.07443	.07568	.07694	.07819
8.0	2.07944	.08069	.08194	.08318	.08443	.08567	.08691	.08815	.08939	.09063
.1	.09186	.09310	.09433	.09556	.09679	.09802	.09924	.10047	.10169	.10291
.2	.10413	.10535	.10657	.10779	.10900	.11021	.11142	.11263	.11384	.11505
.3	.11626	.11746	.11866	.11986	.12106	.12226	.12346	.12465	.12585	.12704
.4	.12823	.12942	.13061	.13180	.13298	.13417	.13535	.13653	.13771	.13889
.5	.14007	.14124	.14242	.14359	.14476	.14593	.14710	.14827	.14943	.15060
.6	.15176	.15292	.15409	.15524	.15640	.15756	.15871	.15987	.16102	.16217
.7	.16332	.16447	.16562	.16677	.16791	.16905	.17020	.17134	.17248	.17361
.8	.17475	.17589	.17702	.17816	.17929	.18042	.18155	.18267	.18380	.18493
.9	.18605	.18717	.18830	.18942	.19054	.19165	.19277	.19389	.19500	.19611
9.0	2.19722	.19834	.19944	.20055	.20166	.20276	.20387	.20497	.20607	.20717
.1	.20827	.20937	.21047	.21157	.21266	.21375	.21485	.21594	.21703	.21812
.2	.21920	.22029	.22138	.22246	.22354	.22462	.22570	.22678	.22786	.22894
.3	.23001	.23109	.23216	.23324	.23431	.23538	.23645	.23751	.23858	.23965
.4	.24071	.24177	.24284	.24390	.24496	.24601	.24707	.24813	.24918	.25024
.5	.25129	.25234	.25339	.25444	.25549	.25654	.25759	.25863	.25968	.26072
.6	.26176	.26280	.26384	.26488	.26592	.26696	.26799	.26903	.27006	.27109
.7	.27213	.27316	.27419	.27521	.27624	.27727	.27829	.27932	.28034	.28136
.8	.28238	.28340	.28442	.28544	.28646	.28747	.28849	.28950	.29051	.29152
.9	.29253	.29354	.29455	.29556	.29657	.29757	.29858	.29958	.30058	.30158

NATURAL OR NAPERIAN LOGARITHMS (Continued)

Constants

log$_e$ 10 = 2.30258 50930		6 log$_e$ 10 = 13.81551 05580
2 log$_e$ 10 = 4.60517 01860		7 log$_e$ 10 = 16.11809 56510
3 log$_e$ 10 = 6.90775 52790		8 log$_e$ 10 = 18.42068 07440
4 log$_e$ 10 = 9.21034 03720		9 log$_e$ 10 = 20.72326 58369
5 log$_e$ 10 = 11.51292 54650		10 log$_e$ 10 = 23.02585 09299

10.0–49.9

N	0	1	2	3	4	5	6	7	8	9
10.	2.30259	.31254	.32239	.33214	.34181	.35138	.36085	.37024	.37955	.38876
11.	.39790	.40695	.41591	.42480	.43361	.44235	.45101	.45959	.46810	.47654
12.	.48491	.49321	.50144	.50960	.51770	.52573	.53370	.54160	.54945	.55723
13.	.56495	.57261	.58022	.58776	.59525	.60269	.61007	.61740	.62467	.63189
14.	.63906	.64617	.65324	.66026	.66723	.67415	.68102	.68785	.69463	.70136
15.	.70805	.71469	.72130	.72785	.73437	.74084	.74727	.75366	.76001	.76632
16.	.77259	.77882	.78501	.79117	.79728	.80336	.80940	.81541	.82138	.82731
17.	.83321	.83908	.84491	.85071	.85647	.86220	.86790	.87356	.87920	.88480
18.	.89037	.89591	.90142	.90690	.91235	.91777	.92316	.92852	.93386	.93916
19.	.94444	.94969	.95491	.96011	.96527	.97041	.97553	.98062	.98568	.99072
20.	2.99573	*.00072	*.00568	*.01062	*.01553	*.02042	*.02529	*.03013	*.03495	*.03975
21.	3.04452	.04927	.05400	.05871	.06339	.06805	.07269	.07731	.08191	.08649
22.	.09104	.09558	.10009	.10459	.10906	.11352	.11795	.12236	.12676	.13114
23.	.13549	.13983	.14415	.14845	.15274	.15700	.16125	.16548	.16969	.17388
24.	.17805	.18221	.18635	.19048	.19458	.19867	.20275	.20680	.21084	.21487
25.	.21888	.22287	.22684	.23080	.23475	.23868	.24259	.24649	.25037	.25424
26.	.25810	.26194	.26576	.26957	.27336	.27714	.28091	.28466	.28840	.29213
27.	.29584	.29953	.30322	.30689	.31054	.31419	.31782	.32143	.32504	.32863
28.	.33220	.33577	.33932	.34286	.34639	.34990	.35341	.35690	.36038	.36384
29.	.36730	.37074	.37417	.37759	.38099	.38439	.38777	.39115	.39451	.39786
30.	3.40120	.40453	.40784	.41115	.41444	.41773	.42100	.42426	.42751	.43076
31.	.43399	.43721	.44042	.44362	.44681	.44999	.45316	.45632	.45947	.46261
32.	.46574	.46886	.47197	.47507	.47816	.48124	.48431	.48738	.49043	.49347
33.	.49651	.49953	.50255	.50556	.50856	.51155	.51453	.51750	.52046	.52342
34.	.52636	.52930	.53223	.53515	.53806	.54096	.54385	.54674	.54962	.55249
35.	.55535	.55820	.56105	.56388	.56671	.56953	.57235	.57515	.57795	.58074
36.	.58352	.58629	.58906	.59182	.59457	.59731	.60005	.60278	.60550	.60821
37.	.61092	.61362	.61631	.61899	.62167	.62434	.62700	.62966	.63231	.63495
38.	.63759	.64021	.64284	.64545	.64806	.65066	.65325	.65584	.65842	.66099
39.	.66356	.66612	.66868	.67122	.67377	.67630	.67883	.68135	.68387	.68638
40.	3.68888	.69138	.69387	.69635	.69883	.70130	.70377	.70623	.70868	.71113
41.	.71357	.71601	.71844	.72086	.72328	.72569	.72810	.73050	.73290	.73529
42.	.73767	.74005	.74242	.74479	.74715	.74950	.75185	.75420	.75654	.75887
43.	.76120	.76352	.76584	.76815	.77046	.77276	.77506	.77735	.77963	.78191
44.	.78419	.78646	.78872	.79098	.79324	.79549	.79773	.79997	.80221	.80444
45.	.80666	.80888	.81110	.81331	.81551	.81771	.81991	.82210	.82428	.82647
46.	.82864	.83081	.83298	.83514	.83730	.83945	.84160	.84374	.84588	.84802
47.	.85015	.85227	.85439	.85651	.85862	.86073	.86283	.86493	.86703	.86912
48.	.87120	.87328	.87536	.87743	.87950	.88156	.88362	.88568	.88773	.88978
49.	.89182	.89386	.89589	.89792	.89995	.90197	.90399	.90600	.90801	.91002

NATURAL OR NAPERIAN LOGARITHMS (Continued)
50.0–99.9

N	0	1	2	3	4	5	6	7	8	9
50.	3.91202	.91402	.91602	.91801	.91999	.92197	.92395	.92593	.92790	.92986
51.	.93183	.93378	.93574	.93769	.93964	.94158	.94352	.94546	.94739	.94932
52.	.95124	.95316	.95508	.95700	.95891	.96081	.96272	.96462	.96651	.96840
53.	.97029	.97218	.97406	.97594	.97781	.97968	.98155	.98341	.98527	.98713
54.	.98898	.99083	.99268	.99452	.99636	.99820	*.00003	*.00186	*.00369	*.00551
55.	4.00733	.00915	.01096	.01277	.01458	.01638	.01818	.01998	.02177	.02356
56.	.02535	.02714	.02892	.03069	.03247	.03424	.03601	.03777	.03954	.04130
57.	.04305	.04480	.04655	.04830	.05004	.05178	.05352	.05526	.05699	.05872
58.	.06044	.06217	.06389	.06560	.06732	.06903	.07073	.07244	.07414	.07584
59.	.07754	.07923	.08092	.08261	.08429	.08598	.08766	.08933	.09101	.09268
60.	4.09434	.09601	.09767	.09933	.10099	.10264	.10429	.10594	.10759	.10923
61.	.11087	.11251	.11415	.11578	.11741	.11904	.12066	.12228	.12390	.12552
62.	.12713	.12875	.13036	.13196	.13357	.13517	.13677	.13836	.13996	.14155
63.	.14313	.14472	.14630	.14789	.14946	.15104	.15261	.15418	.15575	.15732
64.	.15888	.16044	.16200	.16356	.16511	.16667	.16821	.16976	.17131	.17285
65.	.17439	.17592	.17746	.17899	.18052	.18205	.18358	.18510	.18662	.18814
66.	.18965	.19117	.19268	.19419	.19570	.19720	.19870	.20020	.20170	.20320
67.	.20469	.20618	.20767	.20916	.21065	.21213	.21361	.21509	.21656	.21804
68.	.21951	.22098	.22244	.22391	.22537	.22683	.22829	.22975	.23120	.23266
69.	.23411	.23555	.23700	.23844	.23989	.24133	.24276	.24420	.24563	.24707
70.	4.24850	.24992	.25135	.25277	.25419	.25561	.25703	.25845	.25986	.26127
71.	.26268	.26409	.26549	.26690	.26830	.26970	.27110	.27249	.27388	.27528
72.	.27667	.27805	.27944	.28082	.28221	.28359	.28496	.28634	.28772	.28909
73.	.29046	.29183	.29320	.29456	.29592	.29729	.29865	.30000	.30136	.30271
74.	.30407	.30542	.30676	.30811	.30946	.31080	.31214	.31348	.31482	.31615
75.	.31749	.31882	.32015	.32149	.32281	.32413	.32546	.32678	.32810	.32942
76.	.33073	.33205	.33336	.33467	.33598	.33729	.33860	.33990	.34120	.34251
77.	.34381	.34510	.34640	.34769	.34899	.35028	.35157	.35286	.35414	.35543
78.	.35671	.35800	.35927	.36055	.36182	.36310	.36437	.36564	.36691	.36818
79.	.36945	.37071	.37198	.37324	.37450	.37576	.37701	.37827	.37952	.38078
80.	4.38203	.38328	.38452	.38577	.38701	.38826	.38950	.39074	.39198	.39321
81.	.39445	.39568	.39692	.39815	.39938	.40060	.40183	.40305	.40428	.40550
82.	.40672	.40794	.40916	.41037	.41159	.41280	.41401	.41522	.41643	.41764
83.	.41884	.42004	.42125	.42245	.42365	.42485	.42604	.42724	.42843	.42963
84.	.43082	.43201	.43319	.43438	.43557	.43675	.43793	.43912	.44030	.44147
85.	.44265	.44383	.44500	.44617	.44735	.44852	.44969	.45085	.45202	.45318
86.	.45435	.45551	.45667	.45783	.45899	.46014	.46130	.46245	.46361	.46476
87.	.46591	.46706	.46820	.46935	.47050	.47164	.47278	.47392	.47506	.47620
88.	.47734	.47847	.47961	.48074	.48187	.48300	.48413	.48526	.48639	.48751
89.	.48864	.48976	.49088	.49200	.49312	.49424	.49536	.49647	.49758	.49870
90.	4.49981	.50092	.50203	.50314	.50424	.50535	.50645	.50756	.50866	.50976
91.	.51086	.51196	.51305	.51415	.51525	.51634	.51743	.51852	.51961	.52070
92.	.52179	.52287	.52396	.52504	.52613	.52721	.52829	.52937	.53045	.53152
93.	.53260	.53367	.53475	.53582	.53689	.53796	.53903	.54010	.54116	.54223
94.	.54329	.54436	.54542	.54648	.54754	.54860	.54966	.55071	.55177	.55282
95.	.55388	.55493	.55598	.55703	.55808	.55913	.56017	.56122	.56226	.56331
96.	.56435	.56539	.56643	.56747	.56851	.56954	.57058	.57161	.57265	.57368
97.	.57471	.57574	.57677	.57780	.57883	.57985	.58088	.58190	.58292	.58395
98.	.58497	.58599	.58701	.58802	.58904	.59006	.59107	.59208	.59310	.59411
99.	.59512	.59613	.59714	.59815	.59915	.60016	.60116	.60217	.60317	.60417

NATURAL OR NAPERIAN LOGARITHMS (Continued)
0–499

N	0	1	2	3	4	5	6	7	8	9
0	− ∞	0.00000	0.69315	1.09861	.38629	.60944	.79176	.94591	*.07944	*.19722
1	2.30259	.39790	.48491	.56495	.63906	.70805	.77259	.83321	.89037	.94444
2	.99573	*.04452	*.09104	*.13549	*.17805	*.21888	*.25810	*.29584	*.33220	*.36730
3	3.40120	.43399	.46574	.49651	.52636	.55535	.58352	.61092	.63759	.66356
4	.68888	.71357	.73767	.76120	.78419	.80666	.82864	.85015	.87120	.89182
5	.91202	.93183	.95124	.97029	.98898	*.00733	*02535	*.04305	* 4.6044	*.07754
6	4.09434	.11087	.12713	.14313	.15888	.17439	.18965	.20469	.21951	.23411
7	.24850	.26268	.27667	.29046	.30407	.31749	.33073	.34381	.35671	.36945
8	.38203	.39445	.40672	.41884	.43082	.44265	.45435	.46591	.47734	.48864
9	.49981	.51086	.52179	.53260	.54329	.55388	.56435	.57471	.58497	.59512
10	4.60517	.61512	.62497	.63473	.64439	.65396	.66344	.67283	.68213	.69135
11	.70048	.70953	.71850	.72739	.73620	.74493	.75359	.76217	.77068	.77912
12	.78749	.79579	.80402	.81218	.82028	.82831	.83628	.84419	.85203	.85981
13	.86753	.87520	.88280	.89035	.89784	.90527	.91265	.91998	.92725	.93447
14	.94164	.94876	.95583	.96284	.96981	.97673	.98361	.99043	.99721	*.00395
15	5.01064	.01728	.02388	.03044	.03695	.04343	.04986	.05625	.06260	.06890
16	.07517	.08140	.08760	.09375	.09987	.10595	.11199	.11799	.12396	.12990
17	.13580	.14166	.14749	.15329	.15906	.16479	.17048	.17615	.18178	.18739
18	.19296	.19850	.20401	.20949	.21494	.22036	.22575	.23111	.23644	.24175
19	.24702	.25227	.25750	.26269	.26786	.27300	.27811	.28320	.28827	.29330
20	5.29832	.30330	.30827	.31321	.31812	.32301	.32788	.33272	.33754	.34233
21	.34711	.35186	.35659	.36129	.36598	.37064	.37528	.37990	.38450	.38907
22	.39363	.39816	.40268	.40717	.41165	.41610	.42053	.42495	.42935	.43372
23	.43808	.44242	.44674	.45104	.45532	.45959	.46383	.46806	.47227	.47646
24	.48064	.48480	.48894	.49306	.49717	.50126	.50533	.50939	.51343	.51745
25	.52146	.52545	.52943	.53339	.53733	.54126	.54518	.54908	.55296	.55683
26	.56068	.56452	.56834	.57215	.57595	.57973	.58350	.58725	.59099	.59471
27	.59842	.60212	.60580	.60947	.61313	.61677	.62040	.62402	.62762	.63121
28	.63479	.63835	.64191	.64545	.64897	.65249	.65599	.65948	.66296	.66643
29	.66988	.67332	.67675	.68017	.68358	.68698	.69036	.69373	.69709	.70044
30	5.70378	.70711	.71043	.71373	.71703	.72031	.72359	.72685	.73010	.73334
31	.73657	.73979	.74300	.74620	.74939	.75257	.75574	.75890	.76205	.76519
32	.76832	.77144	.77455	.77765	.78074	.78383	.78690	.78996	.79301	.79606
33	.79909	.80212	.80513	.80814	.81114	.81413	.81711	.82008	.82305	.82600
34	.82895	.83188	.83481	.83773	.84064	.84354	.84644	.84932	.85220	.85507
35	.85793	.86079	.86363	.86647	.86930	.87212	.87493	.87774	.88053	.88332
36	.88610	.88888	.89164	.89440	.89715	.89990	.90263	.90536	.90808	.91080
37	.91350	.91620	.91889	.92158	.92426	.92693	.92959	.93225	.93489	.93754
38	.94017	.94280	.94542	.94803	.95064	.95324	.95584	.95842	.96101	.96358
39	.96615	.96871	.97126	.97381	.97635	.97889	.98141	.98394	.98645	.98896
40	5.99146	.99396	.99645	.99894	*.00141	*.00389	*.00635	*.00881	*.01127	*.01372
41	6.01616	.01859	.02102	.02345	.02587	.02828	.03069	.03309	.03548	.03787
42	.04025	.04263	.04501	.04737	.04973	.05209	.05444	.05678	.05912	.06146
43	.06379	.06611	.06843	.07074	.07304	.07535	.07764	.07993	.08222	.08450
44	.08677	.08904	.09131	.09357	.09582	.09807	.10032	.10256	.10479	.10702
45	.10925	.11147	.11368	.11589	.11810	.12030	.12249	.12468	.12687	.12905
46	.13123	.13340	.13556	.13773	.13988	.14204	.14419	.14633	.14847	.15060
47	.15273	.15486	.15698	.15910	.16121	.16331	.16542	.16752	.16961	.17170
48	.17379	.17587	.17794	.18002	.18208	.18415	.18621	.18826	.19032	.19236
49	.19441	.19644	.19848	.20051	.20254	.20456	.20658	.20859	.21060	.21261

NATURAL OR NAPERIAN LOGARITHMS (Continued)

500–999

N	0	1	2	3	4	5	6	7	8	9
50	6.21461	.21661	.21860	.22059	.22258	.22456	.22654	.22851	.23048	.23245
51	.23441	.23637	.23832	.24028	.24222	.24417	.24611	.24804	.24998	.25190
52	.25383	.25575	.25767	.25958	.26149	.26340	.26530	.26720	.26910	.27099
53	.27288	.27476	.27664	.27852	.28040	.28227	.28413	.28600	.28786	.28972
54	.29157	.29342	.29527	.29711	.29895	.30079	.30262	.30445	.30628	.30810
55	.30992	.31173	.31355	.31536	.31716	.31897	.32077	.32257	.32436	.32615
56	.32794	.32972	.33150	.33328	.33505	.33683	.33859	.34036	.34212	.34388
57	.34564	.34739	.34914	.35089	.35263	.35437	.35611	.35784	.35957	.36130
58	.36303	.36475	.36647	.36819	.36990	.37161	.37332	.37502	.37673	.37843
59	.38012	.38182	.38351	.38519	.38688	.38856	.39024	.39192	.39359	.39526
60	6.30693	.39859	.40026	.40192	.40357	.40523	.40688	.40853	.41017	.41182
61	.41346	.41510	.41673	.41836	.41999	.42162	.42325	.42487	.42649	.42811
62	.42972	.43133	.43294	.43455	.43615	.43775	.43935	.44095	.44254	.44413
63	.44572	.44731	.44889	.45047	.45205	.45362	.45520	.45677	.45834	.45990
64	.46147	.46303	.46459	.46614	.46770	.46925	.47080	.47235	.47389	.47543
65	.47697	.47851	.48004	.48158	.48311	.48464	.48616	.48768	.48920	.49072
66	.49224	.49375	.49527	.49677	.49828	.49979	.50129	.50279	.50429	.50578
67	.50728	.50877	.51026	.51175	.51323	.51471	.51619	.51767	.51915	.52062
68	.52209	.52356	.52503	.52649	.52796	.52942	.53088	.53233	.53379	.53524
69	.53669	.53814	.53959	.54103	.54247	.54391	.54535	.54679	.54822	.54965
70	6.55108	.55251	.55393	.55536	.55678	.55820	.55962	.56103	.56244	.56386
71	.56526	.56667	.56808	.56948	.57088	.57228	.57368	.57508	.57647	.57786
72	.57925	.58064	.58203	.58341	.58479	.58617	.58755	.58893	.59030	.59167
73	.59304	.59441	.59578	.59715	.59851	.59987	.60123	.60259	.60394	.60530
74	.60665	.60800	.60935	.61070	.61204	.61338	.61473	.61607	.61740	.61874
75	.62007	.62141	.62274	.62407	.62539	.62672	.62804	.62936	.63068	.63200
76	.63332	.63463	.63595	.63726	.63857	.63988	.64118	.64249	.64379	.64509
77	.64639	.64769	.64898	.65028	.65157	.65286	.65415	.65544	.65673	.65801
78	.65929	.66058	.66185	.66313	.66441	.66568	.66696	.66823	.66950	.67077
79	.67203	.67330	.67456	.67582	.67708	.67834	.67960	.68085	.68211	.68336
80	6.68461	.68586	.68711	.68835	.68960	.69084	.69208	.69332	.69456	.69580
81	.69703	.69827	.69950	.70073	.70196	.70319	.70441	.70564	.70686	.70808
82	.70930	.71052	.71174	.71296	.71417	.71538	.71659	.71780	.71901	.72022
83	.72143	.72263	.72383	.72503	.72623	.72743	.72863	.72982	.73102	.73221
84	.73340	.73459	.73578	.73697	.73815	.73934	.74052	.74170	.74288	.74406
85	.74524	.74641	.74759	.74876	.74993	.75110	.75227	.75344	.75460	.75577
86	.75693	.75809	.75926	.76041	.76157	.76273	.76388	.76504	.76619	.76734
87	.76849	.76964	.77079	.77194	.77308	.77422	.77537	.77651	.77765	.77878
88	.77992	.78106	.78219	.78333	.78446	.78559	.78672	.78784	.78897	.79010
89	.79122	.79234	.79347	.79459	.79571	.79682	.79794	.79906	.80017	.80128
90	6.80239	.80351	.80461	.80572	.80683	.80793	.80904	.81014	.81124	.81235
91	.81344	.81454	.81564	.81674	.81783	.81892	.82002	.82111	.82220	.82329
92	.82437	.82546	.82655	.82763	.82871	.82979	.83087	.83195	.83303	.83411
93	.83518	.83626	.83733	.83841	.83948	.84055	.84162	.84268	.84375	.84482
94	.84588	.84694	.84801	.84907	.85013	.85118	.85224	.85330	.85435	.85541
95	.85646	.85751	.85857	.85961	.86066	.86171	.86276	.86380	.86485	.86589
96	.86693	.86797	.86901	.87005	.87109	.87213	.87316	.87420	.87523	.87626
97	.87730	.87833	.87936	.88038	.88141	.88244	.88346	.88449	.88551	.88653
98	.88755	.88857	.88959	.89061	.89163	.89264	.89366	.89467	.89568	.89669
99	.89770	.89871	.89972	.90073	.90174	.90274	.90375	.90475	.90575	.90675

EXPONENTIAL FUNCTIONS

Values of e^x, log e^x and e^{-x} where e is the base of the natural system of logarithms 2.71828...
and x has values from 0 to 10. Facilitating the solution of exponential equations, these tables also
serve as a table of natural or Naperian antilogarithms. For instance, if the logarithm or exponent
$x = 3.26$, the corresponding number or value of e^x is 26.050. Its reciprocal e^{-x} is .038388.

x	e^x	$Log_{10}(e^x)$	e^{-x}	x	e^x	$Log_{10}(e^x)$	e^{-x}
0.00	1.0000	0.00000	1.000000	**0.50**	1.6487	0.21715	0.606531
0.01	1.0101	.00434	0.990050	0.51	1.6653	.22149	.600496
0.02	1.0202	.00869	.980199	0.52	1.6820	.22583	.594521
0.03	1.0305	.01303	.970446	0.53	1.6989	.23018	.588605
0.04	1.0408	.01737	.960789	0.54	1.7160	.23452	.582748
0.05	1.0513	0.02171	0.951229	**0.55**	1.7333	0.23886	0.576950
0.06	1.0618	.02606	.941765	0.56	1.7507	.24320	.571209
0.07	1.0725	.03040	.932394	0.57	1.7683	.24755	.565525
0.08	1.0833	.03474	.923116	0.58	1.7860	.25189	.559898
0.09	1.0942	.03909	.913931	0.59	1.8040	.25623	.554327
0.10	1.1052	0.04343	0.904837	**0.60**	1.8221	0.26058	0.548812
0.11	1.1163	.04777	.895834	0.61	1.8404	.26492	.543351
0.12	1.1275	.05212	.886920	0.62	1.8589	.26926	.537944
0.13	1.1388	.05646	.878095	0.63	1.8776	.27361	.532592
0.14	1.1503	.06080	.869358	0.64	1.8965	.27795	.527292
0.15	1.1618	0.06514	0.860708	**0.65**	1.9155	0.28229	0.522046
0.16	1.1735	.06949	.852144	0.66	1.9348	.28663	.516851
0.17	1.1853	.07383	.843665	0.67	1.9542	.29098	.511709
0.18	1.1972	.07817	.835270	0.68	1.9739	.29532	.506617
0.19	1.2092	.08252	.826959	0.69	1.9937	.29966	.501576
0.20	1.2214	0.08686	0.818731	**0.70**	2.0138	0.30401	0.496585
0.21	1.2337	.09120	.810584	0.71	2.0340	.30835	.491644
0.22	1.2461	.09554	.802519	0.72	2.0544	.31269	.486752
0.23	1.2586	.09989	.794534	0.73	2.0751	.31703	.481909
0.24	1.2712	.10423	.786628	0.74	2.0959	.32138	.477114
0.25	1.2840	0.10857	0.778801	**0.75**	2.1170	0.32572	0.472367
0.26	1.2969	.11292	.771052	0.76	2.1383	.33006	.467666
0.27	1.3100	.11726	.763379	0.77	2.1598	.33441	.463013
0.28	1.3231	.12160	.755784	0.78	2.1815	.33875	.458406
0.29	1.3364	.12595	.748264	0.79	2.2034	.34309	.453845
0.30	1.3499	0.13029	0.740818	**0.80**	2.2255	0.34744	0.449329
0.31	1.3634	.13463	.733447	0.81	2.2479	.35178	.444858
0.32	1.3771	.13897	.726149	0.82	2.2705	.35612	.440432
0.33	1.3910	.14332	.718924	0.83	2.2933	.36046	.436049
0.34	1.4049	.14766	.711770	0.84	2.3164	.36481	.431711
0.35	1.4191	0.15200	0.704688	**0.85**	2.3396	0.36915	0.427415
0.36	1.4333	.15635	.697676	0.86	2.3632	.37349	.423162
0.37	1.4477	.16069	.690734	0.87	2.3869	.37784	.418952
0.38	1.4623	.16503	.683861	0.88	2.4109	.38218	.414783
0.39	1.4770	.16937	.677057	0.89	2.4351	.38652	.410656
0.40	1.4918	0.17372	0.670320	**0.90**	2.4596	0.39087	0.406570
0.41	1.5068	.17806	.663650	0.91	2.4843	.39521	.402524
0.42	1.5220	.18240	.657047	0.92	2.5093	.39955	.398519
0.43	1.5373	.18675	.650509	0.93	2.5345	.40389	.394554
0.44	1.5527	.19109	.644036	0.94	2.5600	.40824	.390628
0.45	1.5683	0.19543	0.637628	**0.95**	2.5857	0.41258	0.386741
0.46	1.5841	.19978	.631284	0.96	2.6117	.41692	.382893
0.47	1.6000	.20412	.625002	0.97	2.6379	.42127	.379083
0.48	1.6161	.20846	.618783	0.98	2.6645	.42561	.375311
0.49	1.6323	.21280	.612626	0.99	2.6912	.42995	.371577
0.50	1.6487	0.21715	0.606531	**1.00**	2.7183	0.43429	0.367879

EXPONENTIAL FUNCTIONS (Continued)

x	e^x	$\text{Log}_{10}(e^x)$	e^{-x}	x	e^x	$\text{Log}_{10}(e^x)$	e^{-x}
1.00	2.7183	0.43429	0.367879	**1.50**	4.4817	0.65144	0.223130
1.01	2.7456	.43864	.364219	1.51	4.5267	.65578	.220910
1.02	2.7732	.44298	.360595	1.52	4.5722	.66013	.218712
1.03	2.8011	.44732	.357007	1.53	4.6182	.66447	.216536
1.04	2.8292	.45167	.353455	1.54	4.6646	.66881	.214381
1.05	2.8577	0.45601	0.349938	**1.55**	4.7115	0.67316	0.212248
1.06	2.8864	.46035	.346456	1.56	4.7588	.67750	.210136
1.07	2.9154	.46470	.343009	1.57	4.8066	.68184	.208045
1.08	2.9447	.46904	.339596	1.58	4.8550	.68619	.205975
1.09	2.9743	.47338	.336216	1.59	4.9037	.69053	.203926
1.10	3.0042	0.47772	0.332871	**1.60**	4.9530	0.69487	0.201897
1.11	3.0344	.48207	.329559	1.61	5.0028	.69921	.199888
1.12	3.0649	.48641	.326280	1.62	5.0531	.70356	.197899
1.13	3.0957	.49075	.323033	1.63	5.1039	.70790	.195930
1.14	3.1268	.49510	.319819	1.64	5.1552	.71224	.193980
1.15	3.1582	0.49944	0.316637	**1.65**	5.2070	0.71659	0.192050
1.16	3.1899	.50378	.313486	1.66	5.2593	.72093	.190139
1.17	3.2220	.50812	.310367	1.67	5.3122	.72527	.188247
1.18	3.2544	.51247	.307279	1.68	5.3656	.72961	.186374
1.19	3.2871	.51681	.304221	1.69	5.4195	.73396	.184520
1.20	3.3201	0.52115	0.301194	**1.70**	5.4739	0.73830	0.182684
1.21	3.3535	.52550	.298197	1.71	5.5290	.74264	.180866
1.22	3.3872	.52984	.295230	1.72	5.5845	.74699	.179066
1.23	3.4212	.53418	.292293	1.73	5.6407	.75133	.177284
1.24	3.4556	.53853	.289384	1.74	5.6973	.75567	.175520
1.25	3.4903	0.54287	0.286505	**1.75**	5.7546	0.76002	0.173774
1.26	3.5254	.54721	.283654	1.76	5.8124	.76436	.172045
1.27	3.5609	.55155	.280832	1.77	5.8709	.76870	.170333
1.28	3.5966	.55590	.278037	1.78	5.9299	.77304	.168638
1.29	3.6328	.56024	.275271	1.79	5.9895	.77739	.166960
1.30	3.6693	0.56458	0.272532	**1.80**	6.0496	0.78173	0.165299
1.31	3.7062	.56893	.269820	1.81	6.1104	.78607	.163654
1.32	3.7434	.57327	.267135	1.82	6.1719	.79042	.162026
1.33	3.7810	.57761	.264477	1.83	6.2339	.79476	.160414
1.34	3.8190	.58195	.261846	1.84	6.2965	.79910	.158817
1.35	3.8574	0.58630	0.259240	**1.85**	6.3598	0.80344	0.157237
1.36	3.8962	.59064	.256661	1.86	6.4237	.80779	.155673
1.37	3.9354	.59498	.254107	1.87	6.4883	.81213	.154124
1.38	3.9749	.59933	.251579	1.88	6.5535	.81647	.152590
1.39	4.0149	.60367	.249075	1.89	6.6194	.82082	.151072
1.40	4.0552	0.60801	0.246597	**1.90**	6.6859	0.82516	0.149569
1.41	4.0960	.61236	.244143	1.91	6.7531	.82950	.148080
1.42	4.1371	.61670	.241714	1.92	6.8210	.83385	.146607
1.43	4.1787	.62104	.239309	1.93	6.8895	.83819	.145148
1.44	4.2207	.62538	.236928	1.94	6.9588	.84253	.143704
1.45	4.2631	0.62973	0.234570	**1.95**	7.0287	0.84687	0.142274
1.46	4.3060	.63407	.232236	1.96	7.0993	.85122	.140858
1.47	4.3492	.63841	.229925	1.97	7.1707	.85556	.139457
1.48	4.3929	.64276	.227638	1.98	7.2427	.85990	.138069
1.49	4.4371	.64710	.225373	1.99	7.3155	.86425	.136695
1.50	4.4817	0.65144	0.223130	**2.00**	7.3891	0.86859	0.135335

EXPONENTIAL FUNCTIONS (Continued)

x	e^x	$Log_{10}(e^x)$	e^{-x}	x	e^x	$Log_{10}(e^x)$	e^{-x}
2.00	7.3891	0.86859	0.135335	**2.50**	12.182	1.08574	0.082085
2.01	7.4633	.87293	.133989	2.51	12.305	1.09008	.081268
2.02	7.5383	.87727	.132655	2.52	12.429	1.09442	.080460
2.03	7.6141	.88162	.131336	2.53	12.554	1.09877	.079659
2.04	7.6906	.88596	.130029	2.54	12.680	1.10311	.078866
2.05	7.7679	0.89030	0.128735	**2.55**	12.807	1.10745	0.078082
2.06	7.8460	.89465	.127454	2.56	12.936	1.11179	.077305
2.07	7.9248	.89899	.126186	2.57	13.066	1.11614	.076536
2.08	8.0045	.90333	.124930	2.58	13.197	1.12048	.075774
2.09	8.0849	.90768	.123687	2.59	13.330	1.12482	.075020
2.10	8.1662	0.91202	0.122456	**2.60**	13.464	1.12917	0.074274
2.11	8.2482	.91636	.121238	2.61	13.599	1.13351	.073535
2.12	8.3311	.92070	.120032	2.62	13.736	1.13785	.072803
2.13	8.4149	.92505	.118837	2.63	13.874	1.14219	.072078
2.14	8.4994	.92939	.117655	2.64	14.013	1.14654	.071361
2.15	8.5849	0.93373	0.116484	**2.65**	14.154	1.15088	0.070651
2.16	8.6711	.93808	.115325	2.66	14.296	1.15522	.069948
2.17	8.7583	.94242	.114178	2.67	14.440	1.15957	.069252
2.18	8.8463	.94676	.113042	2.68	14.585	1.16391	.068563
2.19	8.9352	.95110	.111917	2.69	14.732	1.16825	.067881
2.20	9.0250	0.95545	0.110803	**2.70**	14.880	1.17260	0.067206
2.21	9.1157	.95979	.109701	2.71	15.029	1.17694	.066537
2.22	9.2073	.96413	.108609	2.72	15.180	1.18128	.065875
2.23	9.2999	.96848	.107528	2.73	15.333	1.18562	.065219
2.24	9.3933	.97282	.106459	2.74	15.487	1.18997	.064570
2.25	9.4877	0.97716	0.105399	**2.75**	15.643	1.19431	0.063928
2.26	9.5831	.98151	.104350	2.76	15.800	1.19865	.063292
2.27	9.6794	.98585	.103312	2.77	15.959	1.20300	.062662
2.28	9.7767	.99019	.102284	2.78	16.119	1.20734	.062039
2.29	9.8749	.99453	.101266	2.79	16.281	1.21168	.061421
2.30	9.9742	0.99888	0.100259	**2.80**	16.445	1.21602	0.060810
2.31	10.074	1.00322	.099261	2.81	16.610	1.22037	.060205
2.32	10.176	1.00756	.098274	2.82	16.777	1.22471	.059606
2.33	10.278	1.01191	.097296	2.83	16.945	1.22905	.059013
2.34	10.381	1.01625	.096328	2.84	17.116	1.23340	.058426
2.35	10.486	1.02059	0.095369	**2.85**	17.288	1.23774	0.057844
2.36	10.591	1.02493	.094420	2.86	17.462	1.24208	.057269
2.37	10.697	1.02928	.093481	2.87	17.637	1.24643	.056699
2.38	10.805	1.03362	.092551	2.88	17.814	1.25077	.056135
2.39	10.913	1.03796	.091630	2.89	17.993	1.25511	.055576
2.40	11.023	1.04231	0.090718	**2.90**	18.174	1.25945	0.055023
2.41	11.134	1.04665	.089815	2.91	18.357	1.26380	.054476
2.42	11.246	1.05099	.088922	2.92	18.541	1.26814	.053934
2.43	11.359	1.05534	.088037	2.93	18.728	1.27248	.053397
2.44	11.473	1.05968	.087161	2.94	18.916	1.27683	.052866
2.45	11.588	1.06402	0.086294	**2.95**	19.106	1.28117	0.052340
2.46	11.705	1.06836	.085435	2.96	19.298	1.28551	.051819
2.47	11.822	1.07271	.084585	2.97	19.492	1.28985	.051303
2.48	11.941	1.07705	.083743	2.98	19.688	1.29420	.050793
2.49	12.061	1.08139	.082910	2.99	19.886	1.29854	.050287
2.50	12.182	1.08574	0.082085	**3.00**	20.086	1.30288	0.049787

EXPONENTIAL FUNCTIONS (Continued)

x	e^x	$\text{Log}_{10}(e^x)$	e^{-x}	x	e^x	$\text{Log}_{10}(e^x)$	e^{-x}
3.00	20.086	1.30288	0.049787	**3.50**	33.115	1.52003	0.030197
3.01	20.287	1.30723	.049292	3.51	33.448	1.52437	.029897
3.02	20.491	1.31157	.048801	3.52	33.784	1.52872	.029599
3.03	20.697	1.31591	.048316	3.53	34.124	1.53306	.029305
3.04	20.905	1.32026	.047835	3.54	34.467	1.53740	.029013
3.05	21.115	1.32460	0.047359	**3.55**	34.813	1.54175	0.028725
3.06	21.328	1.32894	.046888	3.56	35.163	1.54609	.028439
3.07	21.542	1.33328	.046421	3.57	35.517	1.55043	.028156
3.08	21.758	1.33763	.045959	3.58	35.874	1.55477	.027876
3.09	21.977	1.34197	.045502	3.59	36.234	1.55912	.027598
3.10	22.198	1.34631	0.045049	**3.60**	36.598	1.56346	0.027324
3.11	22.421	1.35066	.044601	3.61	36.966	1.56780	.027052
3.12	22.646	1.35500	.044157	3.62	37.338	1.57215	.026783
3.13	22.874	1.35934	.043718	3.63	37.713	1.57649	.026516
3.14	23.104	1.36368	.043283	3.64	38.092	1.58083	.026252
3.15	23.336	1.36803	0.042852	**3.65**	38.475	1.58517	0.025991
3.16	23.571	1.37237	.042426	3.66	38.861	1.58952	.025733
3.17	23.807	1.37671	.042004	3.67	39.252	1.59386	.025476
3.18	24.047	1.38106	.041586	3.68	39.646	1.59820	.025223
3.19	24.288	1.38540	.041172	3.69	40.045	1.60255	.024972
3.20	24.533	1.38974	0.040762	**3.70**	40.447	1.60689	0.024724
3.21	24.779	1.39409	.040357	3.71	40.854	1.61123	.024478
3.22	25.028	1.39843	.039955	3.72	41.264	1.61558	.024234
3.23	25.280	1.40277	.039557	3.73	41.679	1.61992	.023993
3.24	25.534	1.40711	.039164	3.74	42.098	1.62426	.023754
3.25	25.790	1.41146	0.038774	**3.75**	42.521	1.62860	0.023518
3.26	26.050	1.41580	.038388	3.76	42.948	1.63295	.023284
3.27	26.311	1.42014	.038006	3.77	43.380	1.63729	.023052
3.28	26.576	1.42449	.037628	3.78	43.816	1.64163	.022823
3.29	26.843	1.42883	.037254	3.79	44.256	1.64598	.022596
3.30	27.113	1.43317	0.036883	**3.80**	44.701	1.65032	0.022371
3.31	27.385	1.43751	.036516	3.81	45.150	1.65466	.022148
3.32	27.660	1.44186	.036153	3.82	45.604	1.65900	.021928
3.33	27.938	1.44620	.035793	3.83	46.063	1.66335	.021710
3.34	28.219	1.45054	.035437	3.84	46.525	1.66769	.021494
3.35	28.503	1.45489	0.035084	**3.85**	46.993	1.67203	0.021280
3.36	28.789	1.45923	.034735	3.86	47.465	1.67638	.021068
3.37	29.079	1.46357	.034390	3.87	47.942	1.68072	.020858
3.38	29.371	1.46792	.034047	3.88	48.424	1.68506	.020651
3.39	29.666	1.47226	.033709	3.89	48.911	1.68941	.020445
3.40	29.964	1.47660	0.033373	**3.90**	49.402	1.69375	0.020242
3.41	30.265	1.48094	.033041	3.91	49.899	1.69809	.020041
3.42	30.569	1.48529	.032712	3.92	50.400	1.70243	.019841
3.43	30.877	1.48963	.032387	3.93	50.907	1.70678	.019644
3.44	31.187	1.49397	.032065	3.94	51.419	1.71112	.019448
3.45	31.500	1.49832	0.031746	**3.95**	51.935	1.71546	0.019255
3.46	31.817	1.50266	.031430	3.96	52.457	1.71981	.019063
3.47	32.137	1.50700	.031117	3.97	52.985	1.72415	.018873
3.48	32.460	1.51134	.030807	3.98	53.517	1.72849	.018686
3.49	32.786	1.51569	.030501	3.99	54.055	1.73283	.018500
3.50	33.115	1.52003	0.030197	**4.00**	54.598	1.73718	0.018316

EXPONENTIAL FUNCTIONS (Continued)

x	e^x	$\text{Log}_{10}(e^x)$	e^{-x}	x	e^x	$\text{Log}_{10}(e^x)$	e^{-x}
4.00	54.598	1.73718	0.018316	**4.50**	90.017	1.95433	0.011109
4.01	55.147	1.74152	.018133	4.51	90.922	1.95867	.010998
4.02	55.701	1.74586	.017953	4.52	91.836	1.96301	.010889
4.03	56.261	1.75021	.017774	4.53	92.759	1.96735	.010781
4.04	56.826	1.75455	.017597	4.54	93.691	1.97170	.010673
4.05	57.397	1.75889	0.017422	**4.55**	94.632	1.97604	0.010567
4.06	57.974	1.76324	.017249	4.56	95.583	1.98038	.010462
4.07	58.557	1.76758	.017077	4.57	96.544	1.98473	.010358
4.08	59.145	1.77192	.016907	4.58	97.514	1.98907	.010255
4.09	59.740	1.77626	.016739	4.59	98.494	1.99341	.010153
4.10	60.340	1.78061	0.016573	**4.60**	99.484	1.99775	0.010052
4.11	60.947	1.78495	.016408	4.61	100.48	2.00210	.009952
4.12	61.559	1.78929	.016245	4.62	101.49	2.00644	.009853
4.13	62.178	1.79364	.016083	4.63	102.51	2.01078	.009755
4.14	62.803	1.79798	.015923	4.64	103.54	2.01513	.009658
4.15	63.434	1.80232	0.015764	**4.65**	104.58	2.01947	0.009562
4.16	64.072	1.80667	.015608	4.66	105.64	2.02381	.009466
4.17	64.715	1.81101	.015452	4.67	106.70	2.02816	.009372
4.18	65.366	1.81535	.015299	4.68	107.77	2.03250	.009279
4.19	66.023	1.81969	.015146	4.69	108.85	2.03684	.009187
4.20	66.686	1.82404	0.014996	**4.70**	109.95	2.04118	0.009095
4.21	67.357	1.82838	.014846	4.71	111.05	2.04553	.009005
4.22	68.033	1.83272	.014699	4.72	112.17	2.04987	.008915
4.23	68.717	1.83707	.014552	4.73	113.30	2.05421	.008826
4.24	69.408	1.84141	.014408	4.74	114.43	2.05856	.008739
4.25	70.105	1.84575	0.014264	**4.75**	115.58	2.06290	0.008652
4.26	70.810	1.85009	.014122	4.76	116.75	2.06724	.008566
4.27	71.522	1.85444	.013982	4.77	117.92	2.07158	.008480
4.28	72.240	1.85878	.013843	4.78	119.10	2.07593	.008396
4.29	72.966	1.86312	.013705	4.79	120.30	2.08027	.008312
4.30	73.700	1.86747	0.013569	**4.80**	121.51	2.08461	0.008230
4.31	74.440	1.87181	.013434	4.81	122.73	2.08896	.008148
4.32	75.189	1.87615	.013300	4.82	123.97	2.09330	.008067
4.33	75.944	1.88050	.013168	4.83	125.21	2.09764	.007987
4.34	76.708	1.88484	.013037	4.84	126.47	2.10199	.007907
4.35	77.478	1.88918	0.012907	**4.85**	127.74	2.10633	0.007828
4.36	78.257	1.89352	.012778	4.86	129.02	2.11067	.007750
4.37	79.044	1.89787	.012651	4.87	130.32	2.11501	.007673
4.38	79.838	1.90221	.012525	4.88	131.63	2.11936	.007597
4.39	80.640	1.90655	.012401	4.89	132.95	2.12370	.007521
4.40	81.451	1.91090	0.012277	**4.90**	134.29	2.12804	0.007447
4.41	82.269	1.91524	.012155	4.91	135.64	2.13239	.007372
4.42	83.096	1.91958	.012034	4.92	137.00	2.13673	.007299
4.43	83.931	1.92392	.011914	4.93	138.38	2.14107	.007227
4.44	84.775	1.92827	.011796	4.94	139.77	2.14541	.007155
4.45	85.627	1.93261	0.011679	**4.95**	141.17	2.14976	0.007083
4.46	86.488	1.93695	.011562	4.96	142.59	2.15410	.007013
4.47	87.357	1.94130	.011447	4.97	144.03	2.15844	.006943
4.48	88.235	1.94564	.011333	4.98	145.47	2.16279	.006874
4.49	89.121	1.94998	.011221	4.99	146.94	2.16713	.006806
4.50	90.017	1.95433	0.011109	**5.00**	148.41	2.17147	0.006738

EXPONENTIAL FUNCTIONS (Continued)

x	e^x	$Log_{10}(e^x)$	e^{-x}	x	e^x	$Log_{10}(e^x)$	e^{-x}
5.00	148.41	2.17147	0.006738	**5.50**	244.69	2.38862	0.0040868
5.01	149.90	2.17582	.006671	5.55	257.24	2.41033	.0038875
5.02	151.41	2.18016	.006605	5.60	270.43	2.43205	.0036979
5.03	152.93	2.18450	.006539	5.65	284.29	2.45376	.0035175
5.04	154.47	2.18884	.006474	5.70	298.87	2.47548	.0033460
5.05	156.02	2.19319	0.006409	**5.75**	314.19	2.49719	0.0031828
5.06	157.59	2.19753	.006346	5.80	330.30	2.51891	.0030276
5.07	159.17	2.20187	.006282	5.85	347.23	2.54062	.0028799
5.08	160.77	2.20622	.006220	5.90	365.04	2.56234	.0027394
5.09	162.39	2.21056	.006158	5.95	383.75	2.58405	.0026058
5.10	164.02	2.21490	0.006097	**6.00**	403.43	2.60577	0.0024788
5.11	165.67	2.21924	.006036	6.05	424.11	2.62748	.0023579
5.12	167.34	2.22359	.005976	6.10	445.86	2.64920	.0022429
5.13	169.02	2.22793	.005917	6.15	468.72	2.67091	.0021335
5.14	170.72	2.23227	.005858	6.20	492.75	2.69263	.0020294
5.15	172.43	2.23662	0.005799	**6.25**	518.01	2.71434	0.0019305
5.16	174.16	2.24096	.005742	6.30	544.57	2.73606	.0018363
5.17	175.91	2.24530	.005685	6.35	572.49	2.75777	.0017467
5.18	177.68	2.24965	.005628	6.40	601.85	2.77948	.0016616
5.19	179.47	2.25399	.005572	6.45	632.70	2.80120	.0015805
5.20	181.27	2.25833	0.005517	**6.50**	665.14	2.82291	0.0015034
5.21	183.09	2.26267	.005462	6.55	699.24	2.84463	.0014301
5.22	184.93	2.26702	.005407	6.60	735.10	2.86634	.0013604
5.23	186.79	2.27136	.005354	6.65	772.78	2.88806	.0012940
5.24	188.67	2.27570	.005300	6.70	812.41	2.90977	.0012309
5.25	190.57	2.28005	0.005248	**6.75**	854.06	2.93149	0.0011709
5.26	192.48	2.28439	.005195	6.80	897.85	2.95320	.0011138
5.27	194.42	2.28873	.005144	6.85	943.88	2.97492	.0010595
5.28	196.37	2.29307	.005092	6.90	992.27	2.99663	.0010078
5.29	198.34	2.29742	.005042	6.95	1043.1	3.01835	.0009586
5.30	200.34	2.30176	0.004992	**7.00**	1096.6	3.04006	0.0009119
5.31	202.35	2.30610	.004942	7.05	1152.9	3.06178	.0008674
5.32	204.38	2.31045	.004893	7.10	1212.0	3.08349	.0008251
5.33	206.44	2.31479	.004844	7.15	1274.1	3.10521	.0007849
5.34	208.51	2.31913	.004796	7.20	1339.4	3.12692	.0007466
5.35	210.61	2.32348	0.004748	**7.25**	1408.1	3.14863	0.0007102
5.36	212.72	2.32782	.004701	7.30	1480.3	3.17035	.0006755
5.37	214.86	2.33216	.004654	7.35	1556.2	3.19206	.0006426
5.38	217.02	2.33650	.004608	7.40	1636.0	3.21378	.0006113
5.39	219.20	2.34085	.004562	7.45	1719.9	3.23549	.0005814
5.40	221.41	2.34519	0.004517	**7.50**	1808.0	3.25721	0.0005531
5.41	223.63	2.34953	.004472	7.55	1900.7	3.27892	.0005261
5.42	225.88	2.35388	.004427	7.60	1998.2	3.30064	.0005005
5.43	228.15	2.35822	.004383	7.65	2100.6	3.32235	.0004760
5.44	230.44	2.36256	.004339	7.70	2208.3	3.34407	.0004528
5.45	232.76	2.36690	0.004296	**7.75**	2321.6	3.36578	0.0004307
5.46	235.10	2.37125	.004254	7.80	2440.6	3.38750	.0004097
5.47	237.46	2.37559	.004211	7.85	2565.7	3.40921	.0003898
5.48	239.85	2.37993	.004169	7.90	2697.3	3.43093	.0003707
5.49	242.26	2.38428	.004128	7.95	2835.6	3.45264	.0003527
5.50	244.69	2.38862	0.004087	**8.00**	2981.0	3.47436	0.0003355

EXPONENTIAL FUNCTIONS (Continued)

x	e^x	$Log_{10}(e^x)$	e^{-x}
8.00	2981.0	3.47436	0.0003355
8.05	3133.8	3.49607	.0003191
8.10	3294.5	3.51779	.0003035
8.15	3463.4	3.53950	.0002887
8.20	3641.0	3.56121	.0002747
8.25	3827.6	3.58293	0.0002613
8.30	4023.9	3.60464	.0002485
8.35	4230.2	3.62636	.0002364
8.40	4447.1	3.64807	.0002249
8.45	4675.1	3.66979	.0002139
8.50	4914.8	3.69150	0.0002035
8.55	5166.8	3.71322	.0001935
8.60	5431.7	3.73493	.0001841
8.65	5710.1	3.75665	.0001751
8.70	6002.9	3.77836	.0001666
8.75	6310.7	3.80008	0.0001585
8.80	6634.2	3.82179	.0001507
8.85	6974.4	3.84351	.0001434
8.90	7332.0	3.86522	.0001364
8.95	7707.9	3.88694	.0001297
9.00	8103.1	3.90865	0.0001234
9.05	8518.5	3.93037	.0001174
9.10	8955.3	3.95208	.0001117
9.15	9414.4	3.97379	.0001062
9.20	9897.1	3.99551	.0001010
9.25	10405	4.01722	0.0000961
9.30	10938	4.03894	.0000914
9.35	11499	4.06065	.0000870
9.40	12088	4.08237	.0000827
9.45	12708	4.10408	.0000787
9.50	13360	4.12580	0.0000749
9.55	14045	4.14751	.0000712
9.60	14765	4.16923	.0000677
9.65	15522	4.19094	.0000644
9.70	16318	4.21266	.0000613
9.75	17154	4.23437	0.0000583
9.80	18034	4.25609	.0000555
9.85	18958	4.27780	.0000527
9.90	19930	4.29952	.0000502
9.95	20952	4.32123	0.0000477
10.00	22026	4.34294	0.0000454

TRIGONOMETRY

DR. HOWARD EVES

PLANE TRIGONOMETRY

Angle

That part of a straight line lying entirely to one side of a point O on the line is called a *ray* (or a *half-line*); the point O is called the *origin* of the ray. A ray of origin O is identified by the notation OA, where A is any point of the ray.

If a ray OA is rotated, in a plane, about its origin O onto ray OB, an *angle AOB* is said to be generated. Ray OA is called the *initial side*, ray OB the *terminal side*, and point O the *vertex* of the angle. The angle is said to be *positive* or *negative* according as the generating rotation is counterclockwise or clockwise.

An angle is said to be in *standard position* if its vertex is at the origin O and its initial side is on the positive x-axis of a rectangular Cartesian coordinate system (see p. 496). If the terminal side of the angle falls on a coordinate axis, the angle is called a *quadrantal angle*; otherwise the angle is called a *first, second, third,* or *fourth quadrant angle* according as the terminal side falls in the first, second, third, or fourth quadrant of the coordinate system.

An angle of one *degree* is an angle in which the rotation is $1/360$ of one complete rotation.

A *straight angle* is an angle of 180° (180 degrees).

A *right angle* is an angle of 90°.

An *acute angle* is an angle between 0° and 90°.

An *obtuse angle* is an angle between 90° and 180°.

A *radian* is an angle subtended at the center of a circle by an arc whose length is equal to that of the radius.

$$180° = \pi \text{ radians}; \quad 1° = \frac{\pi}{180} \text{ radians}; \quad 1 \text{ radian} = \frac{180}{\pi} \text{ degrees}.$$

The Trigonometric Functions of an Acute Angle

In the right triangle ABC,

sine A = $\sin A$ = a/c

cosine A = $\cos a$ = b/c

tangent A = $\tan A$ = a/b

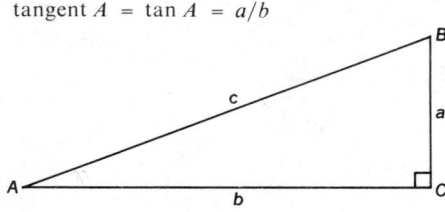

cosecant A = $\csc A$ = c/a

secant A = $\sec A$ = c/b

cotangent A = $\cot A$ = $\text{ctn } A$ = b/a

exsecant A = $\text{exsec } A$ = $\sec A - 1$

versine A = $\text{vers } A$ = $1 - \cos A$

coversine A = $\text{covers } A$ = $1 - \sin A$

haversine A = $\text{hav } A$ = $\frac{1}{2} \text{vers } A$

The Trigonometric Functions of an Arbitrary Angle

Let α be any angle in standard position and let $P(x,y)$ be any point on the terminal side of the angle. Denote the positive distance OP by r. Then

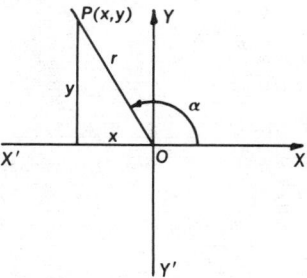

$$\sin \alpha = y/r \qquad\qquad \csc \alpha = r/y$$
$$\cos \alpha = x/r \qquad\qquad \sec \alpha = r/x$$
$$\tan \alpha = y/x \qquad\qquad \cot \alpha = \operatorname{ctn} \alpha = x/y$$
$$\operatorname{exsec} \alpha = \sec \alpha - 1 \qquad \operatorname{covers} \alpha = 1 - \sin \alpha$$
$$\operatorname{vers} \alpha = 1 - \cos \alpha \qquad \operatorname{hav} \alpha = \tfrac{1}{2} \operatorname{vers} \alpha$$
$$\operatorname{cis} \alpha = \cos \alpha + i \sin \alpha = e^{i\alpha}, \alpha \text{ in radians}, i = \sqrt{-1}$$

RELATIONS BETWEEN CIRCULAR (OR INVERSE CIRCULAR) FUNCTIONS

$$\left(0 \le x \le \frac{\pi}{2} \right)$$

	$\sin x = a$	$\cos x = a$	$\tan x = a$
$\sin x$	a	$(1 - a^2)^{1/2}$	$a(1 - a^2)^{-1/2}$
$\cos x$	$(1 - a^2)^{1/2}$	a	$(1 + a^2)^{-1/2}$
$\tan x$	$a(1 - a^2)^{-1/2}$	$a^{-1}(1 - a^2)^{1/2}$	a
$\csc x$	a^{-1}	$(1 - a^2)^{-1/2}$	$a^{-1}(1 + a^2)^{1/2}$
$\sec x$	$(1 - a^2)^{-1/2}$	a^{-1}	$(1 + a^2)^{1/2}$
$\cot x$	$a^{-1}(1 - a^2)^{1/2}$	$a(1 - a^2)^{-1/2}$	a^{-1}

	$\csc x = a$	$\sec x = a$	$\cot x = a$
$\sin x$	a^{-1}	$a^{-1}(a^2 - 1)^{1/2}$	$(1 + a^2)^{-1/2}$
$\cos x$	$a^{-1}(a^2 - 1)^{1/2}$	a^{-1}	$a(1 + a^2)^{-1/2}$
$\tan x$	$(a^2 - 1)^{-1/2}$	$(a^2 - 1)^{1/2}$	a^{-1}
$\csc x$	a	$a(a^2 - 1)^{-1/2}$	$(1 + a^2)^{1/2}$
$\sec x$	$a(a^2 - 1)^{-1/2}$	a	$a^{-1}(1 + a^2)^{1/2}$
$\cot x$	$(a^2 - 1)^{1/2}$	$(a^2 - 1)^{-1/2}$	a

Examples:

If $\sec x = a$, then $\tan x = (a^2 - 1)^{1/2}$
$\arctan a = \arccos (1 + a^2)^{-1/2}$

SIGNS OF THE TRIGONOMETRIC FUNCTIONS

Quadrant	sin	cos	tan	cot	sec	csc
I	+	+	+	+	+	+
II	+	−	−	−	−	+
III	−	−	+	+	−	−
IV	−	+	−	−	+	−

VARIATIONS OF THE TRIGONOMETRIC FUNCTIONS

Quadrant	sin	cos	tan	cot	sec	csc
I	$0 \to +1$	$+1 \to 0$	$0 \to +\infty$	$+\infty \to 0$	$+1 \to +\infty$	$+\infty \to +1$
II	$+1 \to 0$	$0 \to -1$	$-\infty \to 0$	$0 \to -\infty$	$-\infty \to -1$	$+1 \to +\infty$
III	$0 \to -1$	$-1 \to 0$	$0 \to +\infty$	$+\infty \to 0$	$-1 \to -\infty$	$-\infty \to -1$
IV	$-1 \to 0$	$0 \to +1$	$-\infty \to 0$	$0 \to -\infty$	$+\infty \to +1$	$-1 \to -\infty$

TRIGONOMETRIC FUNCTIONS OF SOME SPECIAL ANGLES

Angle	sin	cos	tan	cot	sec	csc
$0° = 0$	0	1	0	$\cdots$	1	$\cdots$
$15° = \dfrac{\pi}{12}$	$\dfrac{\sqrt{2}}{4}(\sqrt{3}-1)$	$\dfrac{\sqrt{2}}{4}(\sqrt{3}+1)$	$2-\sqrt{3}$	$2+\sqrt{3}$	$\sqrt{2}(\sqrt{3}-1)$	$\sqrt{2}(\sqrt{3}+1)$
$30° = \dfrac{\pi}{6}$	$1/2$	$\sqrt{3}/2$	$\sqrt{3}/3$	$\sqrt{3}$	$2\sqrt{3}/3$	2
$45° = \dfrac{\pi}{4}$	$\sqrt{2}/2$	$\sqrt{2}/2$	1	1	$\sqrt{2}$	$\sqrt{2}$
$60° = \dfrac{\pi}{3}$	$\sqrt{3}/2$	$1/2$	$\sqrt{3}$	$\sqrt{3}/3$	2	$2\sqrt{3}/3$
$75° = \dfrac{5\pi}{12}$	$\dfrac{\sqrt{2}}{4}(\sqrt{3}+1)$	$\dfrac{\sqrt{2}}{4}(\sqrt{3}-1)$	$2+\sqrt{3}$	$2-\sqrt{3}$	$\sqrt{2}(\sqrt{3}+1)$	$\sqrt{2}(\sqrt{3}-1)$
$90° = \dfrac{\pi}{2}$	1	0	$\cdots$	0	$\cdots$	1
$105° = \dfrac{7\pi}{12}$	$\dfrac{\sqrt{2}}{4}(\sqrt{3}+1)$	$-\dfrac{\sqrt{2}}{4}(\sqrt{3}-1)$	$-(2+\sqrt{3})$	$-(2-\sqrt{3})$	$-2(\sqrt{3}+1)$	$\sqrt{2}(\sqrt{3}-1)$
$120° = \dfrac{2\pi}{3}$	$\sqrt{3}/2$	$-1/2$	$-\sqrt{3}$	$-\sqrt{3}/3$	-2	$2\sqrt{3}/3$
$135° = \dfrac{3\pi}{4}$	$\sqrt{2}/2$	$-\sqrt{2}/2$	-1	-1	$-\sqrt{2}$	$\sqrt{2}$
$150° = \dfrac{5\pi}{6}$	$1/2$	$-\sqrt{3}/2$	$-\sqrt{3}/3$	$-\sqrt{3}$	$-2\sqrt{3}/3$	2
$165° = \dfrac{11\pi}{12}$	$\dfrac{\sqrt{2}}{4}(\sqrt{3}-1)$	$-\dfrac{\sqrt{2}}{4}(\sqrt{3}+1)$	$-(2-\sqrt{3})$	$-(2+\sqrt{3})$	$-\sqrt{2}(\sqrt{3}-1)$	$\sqrt{2}(\sqrt{3}+1)$
$180° = \pi$	0	-1	0	$\cdots$	-1	$\cdots$
$270° = \dfrac{3\pi}{2}$	-1	0	$\cdots$	0	$\cdots$	-1

Relations of the Functions

$$\sin x = \frac{1}{\csc x} \qquad\qquad\qquad \csc x = \frac{1}{\sin x}$$

$$\cos x = \frac{1}{\sec x} \qquad\qquad\qquad \sec x = \frac{1}{\cos x}$$

$$\tan x = \frac{1}{\cot x} = \frac{\sin x}{\cos x} \qquad\qquad \sin^2 x + \cos^2 x = 1$$

$$1 + \tan^2 x = \sec^2 x$$

$$\cot x = \frac{1}{\tan x} = \frac{\cos x}{\sin x} \qquad\qquad 1 + \cot^2 x = \csc^2 x$$

$$*\sin x = \pm\sqrt{1 - \cos^2 x} \qquad\qquad *\cos x = \pm\sqrt{1 - \sin^2 x}$$

$$*\tan x = \pm\sqrt{\sec^2 x - 1} \qquad\qquad *\sec x = \pm\sqrt{\tan^2 x + 1}$$

$$*\cot x = \pm\sqrt{\csc^2 x - 1} \qquad\qquad *\csc x = \pm\sqrt{\cot^2 x + 1}$$

$$\sin x = \cos(90° - x) = \sin(180° - x)$$

$$\cos x = \sin(90° - x) = -\cos(180° - x)$$

$$\tan x = \cot(90° - x) = -\tan(180° - x)$$

$$\cot x = \tan(90° - x) = -\cot(180° - x)$$

$$\csc x = \cot\frac{x}{2} - \cot x$$

*The sign in front of radical depends on quadrant in which x falls.

Reduction Formulae

$$\sin\alpha = +\cos(\alpha - 90°) = -\sin(\alpha - 180°) = -\cos(\alpha - 270°)$$

$$\cos\alpha = -\sin(\alpha - 90°) = -\cos(\alpha - 180°) = +\sin(\alpha - 270°)$$

$$\tan\alpha = -\cot(\alpha - 90°) = +\tan(\alpha - 180°) = -\cot(\alpha - 270°)$$

$$\cot\alpha = -\tan(\alpha - 90°) = +\cot(\alpha - 180°) = -\tan(\alpha - 270°)$$

$$\sec\alpha = -\csc(\alpha - 90°) = -\sec(\alpha - 180°) = +\csc(\alpha - 270°)$$

$$\csc\alpha = +\sec(\alpha - 90°) = -\csc(\alpha - 180°) = -\sec(\alpha - 270°)$$

FURTHER REDUCTION FORMULAE

	sin	cos	tan	cot	sec	csc
$-\alpha$	$-\sin\alpha$	$+\cos\alpha$	$-\tan\alpha$	$-\cot\alpha$	$+\sec\alpha$	$-\csc\alpha$
$90° + \alpha$	$+\cos\alpha$	$-\sin\alpha$	$-\cot\alpha$	$-\tan\alpha$	$-\csc\alpha$	$+\sec\alpha$
$90° - \alpha$	$+\cos\alpha$	$+\sin\alpha$	$+\cot\alpha$	$+\tan\alpha$	$+\csc\alpha$	$+\sec\alpha$
$180° + \alpha$	$-\sin\alpha$	$-\cos\alpha$	$+\tan\alpha$	$+\cot\alpha$	$-\sec\alpha$	$-\csc\alpha$
$180° - \alpha$	$+\sin\alpha$	$-\cos\alpha$	$-\tan\alpha$	$-\cot\alpha$	$-\sec\alpha$	$+\csc\alpha$
$270° + \alpha$	$-\cos\alpha$	$+\sin\alpha$	$-\cot\alpha$	$-\tan\alpha$	$+\csc\alpha$	$-\sec\alpha$
$270° - \alpha$	$-\cos\alpha$	$-\sin\alpha$	$+\cot\alpha$	$+\tan\alpha$	$-\csc\alpha$	$-\sec\alpha$
$360° + \alpha$	$+\sin\alpha$	$+\cos\alpha$	$+\tan\alpha$	$+\cot\alpha$	$+\sec\alpha$	$+\csc\alpha$
$360° - \alpha$	$-\sin\alpha$	$+\cos\alpha$	$-\tan\alpha$	$-\cot\alpha$	$+\sec\alpha$	$-\csc\alpha$

The above table may be summarized and extended by the following easily remembered rule:

$$f(\pm\alpha + n90°) = \pm g(\alpha)$$

where n may be any integer, positive, negative, or zero
        f is any one of the six trigonometric functions: sin, cos, tan, cot, sec, or csc
        α may be any real angle measure
If n is even, then g is the same function as f.   If n is odd, then g is the *cofunction* of f.

(Sine and cosine, tangent and cotangent, secant and cosecant, are cofunctions of each other.)

The second $\pm$ sign is not necessarily the same as the first one, but is determined as follows: For a given function f, a given value of n, and a given choice of the first $\pm$ sign, the second $\pm$ sign will be the same for all values of α.   Thus it is only necessary to check the sign for any one value of α, and the formula will be complete.

EXAMPLES:

   $\tan (\alpha + 270°) = \pm \cot \alpha$.   Since $n(=3)$ is odd, we use the cofunction.   To determine the sign, assume a value of α in the first quadrant.   Then $\alpha + 270°$ is in the fourth quadrant, where the tangent is negative, so a minus sign is required.   Thus the formula becomes

$$\tan (\alpha + 270°) = - \cot \alpha, \quad \text{valid for all values of } \alpha.$$

   $\cos (\alpha - 450°) = \pm \sin \alpha$.   Again assuming a value of α in the first quadrant, we find that $\alpha - 450°$ is in the fourth quadrant.   Thus $\cos (\alpha - 450°)$ would be positive, and no minus sign is needed.   Hence the formula becomes

$$\cos (\alpha - 450°) = \sin \alpha.$$

   $\sec (180° - \alpha) = \pm \sec \alpha$.   Here $n(=2)$ is even, so we use the same function.   To determine the sign, again assume a value of α in the first quadrant.   Then $180° - \alpha$ is in the second quadrant, where the secant is negative.   Thus the formula, valid for all values of α, is

$$\sec (180° - \alpha) = - \sec \alpha.$$

Fundamental Identities

Where a double sign appears in the following, the choice of sign depends upon the quadrant in which the angle terminates.

Reciprocal relations

$$\sin \alpha = \frac{1}{\csc \alpha}, \quad \cos \alpha = \frac{1}{\sec \alpha}, \quad \tan \alpha = \frac{1}{\cot \alpha}$$

$$\csc \alpha = \frac{1}{\sin \alpha}, \quad \sec \alpha = \frac{1}{\cos \alpha}, \quad \cot \alpha = \frac{1}{\tan \alpha}$$

Product relations

$$\sin \alpha = \tan \alpha \cos \alpha, \quad \cos \alpha = \cot \alpha \sin \alpha$$
$$\tan \alpha = \sin \alpha \sec \alpha, \quad \cot \alpha = \cos \alpha \csc \alpha$$
$$\sec \alpha = \csc \alpha \tan \alpha, \quad \csc \alpha = \sec \alpha \cot \alpha$$

Quotient relations

$$\sin \alpha = \frac{\tan \alpha}{\sec \alpha}, \quad \cos \alpha = \frac{\cot \alpha}{\csc \alpha}, \quad \tan \alpha = \frac{\sin \alpha}{\cos \alpha}$$

$$\csc \alpha = \frac{\sec \alpha}{\tan \alpha}, \quad \sec \alpha = \frac{\csc \alpha}{\cot \alpha}, \quad \cot \alpha = \frac{\cos \alpha}{\sin \alpha}$$

Pythagorean relations

$$\sin^2\alpha + \cos^2\alpha = 1, \qquad 1 + \tan^2\alpha = \sec^2\alpha, \qquad 1 + \cot^2\alpha = \csc^2\alpha$$

Angle-sum and angle-difference relations

$$\sin(\alpha + \beta) = \sin\alpha\cos\beta + \cos\alpha\sin\beta$$
$$\sin(\alpha - \beta) = \sin\alpha\cos\beta - \cos\alpha\sin\beta$$
$$\cos(\alpha + \beta) = \cos\alpha\cos\beta - \sin\alpha\sin\beta$$
$$\cos(\alpha - \beta) = \cos\alpha\cos\beta + \sin\alpha\sin\beta$$
$$\tan(\alpha + \beta) = \frac{\tan\alpha + \tan\beta}{1 - \tan\alpha\tan\beta}$$
$$\tan(\alpha - \beta) = \frac{\tan\alpha - \tan\beta}{1 + \tan\alpha\tan\beta}$$
$$\cot(\alpha + \beta) = \frac{\cot\beta\cot\alpha - 1}{\cot\beta + \cot\alpha}$$
$$\cot(\alpha - \beta) = \frac{\cot\beta\cot\alpha + 1}{\cot\beta - \cot\alpha}$$
$$\sin(\alpha + \beta)\sin(\alpha - \beta) = \sin^2\alpha - \sin^2\beta = \cos^2\beta - \cos^2\alpha$$
$$\cos(\alpha + \beta)\cos(\alpha - \beta) = \cos^2\alpha - \sin^2\beta = \cos^2\beta - \sin^2\alpha$$

Double-angle relations

$$\sin 2\alpha = 2\sin\alpha\cos\alpha = \frac{2\tan\alpha}{1 + \tan^2\alpha}$$
$$\cos 2\alpha = \cos^2\alpha - \sin^2\alpha = 2\cos^2\alpha - 1 = 1 - 2\sin^2\alpha = \frac{1 - \tan^2\alpha}{1 + \tan^2\alpha}$$
$$\tan 2\alpha = \frac{2\tan\alpha}{1 - \tan^2\alpha}, \qquad \cot 2\alpha = \frac{\cot^2\alpha - 1}{2\cot\alpha}$$

Multiple-angle relations

$$\sin 3\alpha = 3\sin\alpha - 4\sin^3\alpha$$
$$\cos 3\alpha = 4\cos^3\alpha - 3\cos\alpha$$
$$\sin 4\alpha = 4\sin\alpha\cos\alpha - 8\sin^3\alpha\cos\alpha$$
$$\cos 4\alpha = 8\cos^4\alpha - 8\cos^2\alpha + 1$$
$$\sin 5\alpha = 5\sin\alpha - 20\sin^3\alpha + 16\sin^5\alpha$$
$$\cos 5\alpha = 16\cos^5\alpha - 20\cos^3\alpha + 5\cos\alpha$$
$$\sin 6\alpha = 32\cos^5\alpha\sin\alpha - 32\cos^3\alpha\sin\alpha + 6\cos\alpha\sin\alpha$$
$$\cos 6\alpha = 32\cos^6\alpha - 48\cos^4\alpha + 18\cos^2\alpha - 1$$
$$\sin n\alpha = 2\sin(n - 1)\alpha\cos\alpha - \sin(n - 2)\alpha$$
$$\cos n\alpha = 2\cos(n - 1)\alpha\cos\alpha - \cos(n - 2)\alpha$$
$$\tan 3\alpha = \frac{3\tan\alpha - \tan^3\alpha}{1 - 3\tan^2\alpha}$$
$$\tan 4\alpha = \frac{4\tan\alpha - 4\tan^3\alpha}{1 - 6\tan^2\alpha + \tan^4\alpha}$$
$$\tan n\alpha = \frac{\tan(n - 1)\alpha + \tan\alpha}{1 - \tan(n - 1)\alpha\tan\alpha}$$

Function-product relations

$$\sin \alpha \sin \beta = \tfrac{1}{2}\cos(\alpha - \beta) - \tfrac{1}{2}\cos(\alpha + \beta)$$
$$\cos \alpha \cos \beta = \tfrac{1}{2}\cos(\alpha - \beta) + \tfrac{1}{2}\cos(\alpha + \beta)$$
$$\sin \alpha \cos \beta = \tfrac{1}{2}\sin(\alpha + \beta) + \tfrac{1}{2}\sin(\alpha - \beta)$$
$$\cos \alpha \sin \beta = \tfrac{1}{2}\sin(\alpha + \beta) - \tfrac{1}{2}\sin(\alpha - \beta)$$

Function-sum and function-difference relations

$$\sin \alpha + \sin \beta = 2 \sin \tfrac{1}{2}(\alpha + \beta) \cos \tfrac{1}{2}(\alpha - \beta)$$
$$\sin \alpha - \sin \beta = 2 \cos \tfrac{1}{2}(\alpha + \beta) \sin \tfrac{1}{2}(\alpha - \beta)$$
$$\cos \alpha + \cos \beta = 2 \cos \tfrac{1}{2}(\alpha + \beta) \cos \tfrac{1}{2}(\alpha - \beta)$$
$$\cos \alpha - \cos \beta = -2 \sin \tfrac{1}{2}(\alpha + \beta) \sin \tfrac{1}{2}(\alpha - \beta)$$

$$\tan \alpha + \tan \beta = \frac{\sin(\alpha + \beta)}{\cos \alpha \cos \beta}, \qquad \tan \alpha - \tan \beta = \frac{\sin(\alpha - \beta)}{\cos \alpha \cos \beta}$$

$$\cot \alpha + \cot \beta = \frac{\sin(\alpha + \beta)}{\sin \alpha \sin \beta}, \qquad \cot \alpha - \cot \beta = \frac{\sin(\beta - \alpha)}{\sin \alpha \sin \beta}$$

$$\frac{\sin \alpha + \sin \beta}{\sin \alpha - \sin \beta} = \frac{\tan \tfrac{1}{2}(\alpha + \beta)}{\tan \tfrac{1}{2}(\alpha - \beta)}, \qquad \frac{\sin \alpha + \sin \beta}{\cos \alpha - \cos \beta} = \cot \tfrac{1}{2}(\beta - \alpha)$$

$$\frac{\sin \alpha + \sin \beta}{\cos \alpha + \cos \beta} = \tan \tfrac{1}{2}(\alpha + \beta), \qquad \frac{\sin \alpha - \sin \beta}{\cos \alpha + \cos \beta} = \tan \tfrac{1}{2}(\alpha - \beta)$$

Half-angle relations

$$\sin \frac{\alpha}{2} = \pm \sqrt{\frac{1 - \cos \alpha}{2}}, \qquad \cos \frac{\alpha}{2} = \pm \sqrt{\frac{1 + \cos \alpha}{2}}$$

$$\tan \frac{\alpha}{2} = \pm \sqrt{\frac{1 - \cos \alpha}{1 + \cos \alpha}} = \frac{1 - \cos \alpha}{\sin \alpha} = \frac{\sin \alpha}{1 + \cos \alpha}$$

$$\cot \frac{\alpha}{2} = \pm \sqrt{\frac{1 + \cos \alpha}{1 - \cos \alpha}} = \frac{1 + \cos \alpha}{\sin \alpha} = \frac{\sin \alpha}{1 - \cos \alpha}$$

Power relations

$$\sin^2 \alpha = \tfrac{1}{2}(1 - \cos 2\alpha), \qquad \sin^3 \alpha = \tfrac{1}{4}(3 \sin \alpha - \sin 3\alpha)$$
$$\sin^4 \alpha = \tfrac{1}{8}(3 - 4 \cos 2\alpha + \cos 4\alpha)$$
$$\cos^2 \alpha = \tfrac{1}{2}(1 + \cos 2\alpha), \qquad \cos^3 \alpha = \tfrac{1}{4}(3 \cos \alpha + \cos 3\alpha)$$
$$\cos^4 \alpha = \tfrac{1}{8}(3 + 4 \cos 2\alpha + \cos 4\alpha)$$

$$\tan^2 \alpha = \frac{1 - \cos 2\alpha}{1 + \cos 2\alpha}, \qquad \cot^2 \alpha = \frac{1 + \cos 2\alpha}{1 - \cos 2\alpha}$$

Exponential relations (α in radians)

$$e^{i\alpha} = \cos \alpha + i \sin \alpha, \qquad i = \sqrt{-1}$$

$$\sin \alpha = \frac{e^{i\alpha} - e^{-i\alpha}}{2i}, \qquad \cos \alpha = \frac{e^{i\alpha} + e^{-i\alpha}}{2}$$

$$\tan \alpha = -i\left(\frac{e^{i\alpha} - e^{-i\alpha}}{e^{i\alpha} + e^{-i\alpha}}\right) = -i\left(\frac{e^{2i\alpha} - 1}{e^{2i\alpha} + 1}\right)$$

THE TRIGONOMETRIC FUNCTIONS IN TERMS OF ONE ANOTHER

Function	$\sin \alpha$	$\cos \alpha$	$\tan \alpha$	$\cot \alpha$	$\sec \alpha$	$\csc \alpha$
$\sin \alpha$	$\sin \alpha$	$\pm \sqrt{1 - \cos^2 \alpha}$	$\dfrac{\tan \alpha}{\pm \sqrt{1 + \tan^2 \alpha}}$	$\dfrac{1}{\pm \sqrt{1 + \cot^2 \alpha}}$	$\dfrac{\pm \sqrt{\sec^2 \alpha - 1}}{\sec \alpha}$	$\dfrac{1}{\csc \alpha}$
$\cos \alpha$	$\pm \sqrt{1 - \sin^2 \alpha}$	$\cos \alpha$	$\dfrac{1}{\pm \sqrt{1 + \tan^2 \alpha}}$	$\dfrac{\cot \alpha}{\pm \sqrt{1 + \cot^2 \alpha}}$	$\dfrac{1}{\sec \alpha}$	$\dfrac{\pm \sqrt{\csc^2 \alpha - 1}}{\csc \alpha}$
$\tan \alpha$	$\dfrac{\sin \alpha}{\pm \sqrt{1 - \sin^2 \alpha}}$	$\dfrac{\pm \sqrt{1 - \cos^2 \alpha}}{\cos \alpha}$	$\tan \alpha$	$\dfrac{1}{\cot \alpha}$	$\pm \sqrt{\sec^2 \alpha - 1}$	$\dfrac{1}{\pm \sqrt{\csc^2 \alpha - 1}}$
$\cot \alpha$	$\dfrac{\pm \sqrt{1 - \sin^2 \alpha}}{\sin \alpha}$	$\dfrac{\cos \alpha}{\pm \sqrt{1 - \cos^2 \alpha}}$	$\dfrac{1}{\tan \alpha}$	$\cot \alpha$	$\dfrac{1}{\pm \sqrt{\sec^2 \alpha - 1}}$	$\pm \sqrt{\csc^2 \alpha - 1}$
$\sec \alpha$	$\dfrac{1}{\pm \sqrt{1 - \sin^2 \alpha}}$	$\dfrac{1}{\cos \alpha}$	$\pm \sqrt{1 + \tan^2 \alpha}$	$\dfrac{\pm \sqrt{1 + \cot^2 \alpha}}{\cot \alpha}$	$\sec \alpha$	$\dfrac{\csc \alpha}{\pm \sqrt{\csc^2 \alpha - 1}}$
$\csc \alpha$	$\dfrac{1}{\sin \alpha}$	$\dfrac{1}{\pm \sqrt{1 - \cos^2 \alpha}}$	$\dfrac{\pm \sqrt{1 + \tan^2 \alpha}}{\tan \alpha}$	$\pm \sqrt{1 + \cot^2 \alpha}$	$\dfrac{\sec \alpha}{\pm \sqrt{\sec^2 \alpha - 1}}$	$\csc \alpha$

Note. The choice of sign depends upon the quadrant in which the angle terminates.

Principal Values of the Inverse Trigonometric Functions

The notation arcsin x (or $\sin^{-1}x$) is used to denote any angle whose sine is x; Arcsin x (or $\text{Sin}^{-1}x$) is usually used to denote the *principal value*. Similar notation is used for the other inverse trigonometric functions. The principal values of the inverse trigonometric functions are defined as follows:

$$-\pi/2 \leq \text{Arcsin } x \leq \pi/2, \qquad -1 \leq x \leq 1$$

$$0 \leq \text{Arccos } x \leq \pi, \qquad -1 \leq x \leq 1$$

$$-\pi/2 < \text{Arctan } x < \pi/2, \qquad -\infty < x < \infty$$

$$0 < \text{Arccsc } x \leq \pi/2, \qquad x \geq 1$$
$$-\pi < \text{Arccsc } x \leq -\pi/2, \qquad x \leq -1$$

$$0 \leq \text{Arcsec } x < \pi/2, \qquad x \geq 1$$
$$-\pi \leq \text{Arcsec } x < -\pi/2, \qquad x \leq -1$$

$$0 < \text{Arccot } x < \pi, \qquad -\infty < x < \infty$$

Note. There is no uniform agreement on the definitions of Arccsc x, Arcsec x, Arccot x for negative values of x.

Fundamental Identities Involving Principal Values

$$\text{Arcsin } x + \text{Arccos } x = \pi/2$$
$$\text{Arctan } x + \text{Arccot } x = \pi/2$$

If $\alpha = \text{Arcsin } x$, then

$$\sin \alpha = x, \qquad \cos \alpha = \sqrt{1 - x^2}, \qquad \tan \alpha = \frac{x}{\sqrt{1 - x^2}}$$

$$\csc \alpha = \frac{1}{x}, \qquad \sec \alpha = \frac{1}{\sqrt{1 - x^2}}, \qquad \cot \alpha = \frac{\sqrt{1 - x^2}}{x}$$

If $\alpha = \text{Arccos } x$, then

$$\sin \alpha = \sqrt{1 - x^2}, \qquad \cos \alpha = x, \qquad \tan \alpha = \frac{\sqrt{1 - x^2}}{x}$$

$$\csc \alpha = \frac{1}{\sqrt{1 - x^2}}, \qquad \sec \alpha = \frac{1}{x}, \qquad \cot \alpha = \frac{x}{\sqrt{1 - x^2}}$$

If $\alpha = \text{Arctan } x$, then

$$\sin \alpha = \frac{x}{\sqrt{1 + x^2}}, \qquad \cos \alpha = \frac{1}{\sqrt{1 + x^2}}, \qquad \tan \alpha = x$$

$$\csc \alpha = \frac{\sqrt{1 + x^2}}{x}, \qquad \sec \alpha = \sqrt{1 + x^2}, \qquad \cot \alpha = \frac{1}{x}$$

Relations Between Principal Values of Inverse Trigonometric Functions

The following additional relations between principal values of the inverse trigonometric functions are useful:

$$\text{Arcsin } x = \text{Arccos}(-x) - \frac{\pi}{2} = \frac{\pi}{2} - \text{Arccos } x$$

$$= -\text{Arcsin}(-x) = \text{Arctan } \frac{x}{\sqrt{1 - x^2}}$$

$$= \frac{\pi}{2} - \text{Arccot } \frac{x}{\sqrt{1 - x^2}}$$

$$\text{Arctan } x = \text{Arccot}(-x) - \frac{\pi}{2} = \frac{\pi}{2} - \text{Arccot } x$$

$$= -\text{Arctan}(-x) = \text{Arcsin } \frac{x}{\sqrt{x^2 + 1}}$$

$$= \frac{\pi}{2} - \text{Arccos } \frac{x}{\sqrt{x^2 + 1}}$$

$$\text{Arccos } x = \frac{\pi}{2} + \text{Arcsin}(-x) = \frac{\pi}{2} - \text{Arcsin } x$$

$$= \pi - \text{Arccos}(-x) = \text{Arccot } \frac{x}{\sqrt{1 - x^2}}$$

$$= \frac{\pi}{2} - \text{Arctan } \frac{x}{\sqrt{1 - x^2}}$$

$$\text{Arccot } x = \frac{\pi}{2} + \text{Arctan}(-x) = \frac{\pi}{2} - \text{Arctan } x$$

$$= \pi - \text{Arccot}(-x) = \text{Arccos } \frac{x}{\sqrt{x^2 + 1}}$$

$$= \frac{\pi}{2} - \text{Arcsin } \frac{x}{\sqrt{x^2 + 1}}$$

$$\text{Arccsc } x = \text{Arcsec } \frac{x}{\sqrt{x^2 - 1}}$$

$$\text{Arcsec } x = \text{Arccsc } \frac{x}{\sqrt{x^2 - 1}}$$

$$\cos(\text{Arcsin } x) = \sin(\text{Arccos } x) = \sqrt{1 - x^2}$$

$$\sec(\text{Arctan } x) = \csc(\text{Arccot } x) = \sqrt{x^2 + 1}$$

$$\tan(\text{Arcsec } x) = \cot(\text{Arccsc } x) = \sqrt{x^2 - 1}$$

The above are valid for x positive or negative. The following are valid only for $x \geq 0$.

$$\text{Arcsin } x = \text{Arccos } \sqrt{1 - x^2} = \text{Arccot } \frac{\sqrt{1 - x^2}}{x}$$

$$= \text{Arcsec } \frac{1}{\sqrt{1 - x^2}} = \text{Arccsc } \frac{1}{x}$$

$$= \frac{\pi}{2} - \text{Arcsin } \sqrt{1 - x^2}$$

$$\text{Arccos } x = \text{Arcsin } \sqrt{1 - x^2} = \text{Arctan } \frac{\sqrt{1 - x^2}}{x}$$

$$= \text{Arcsec } \frac{1}{x} = \text{Arccsc } \frac{1}{\sqrt{1 - x^2}}$$

$$= \frac{\pi}{2} - \text{Arccos } \sqrt{1 - x^2}$$

$$\text{Arctan } x = \text{Arccot } \frac{1}{x} = \text{Arccos } \frac{1}{\sqrt{x^2 + 1}}$$

$$= \text{Arcsec } \sqrt{x^2 + 1} = \text{Arccsc } \frac{\sqrt{x^2 + 1}}{x}$$

$$= \frac{\pi}{2} - \text{Arctan } \frac{1}{x}$$

$$\text{Arccot } x = \text{Arctan } \frac{1}{x} = \text{Arcsin } \frac{1}{\sqrt{x^2 + 1}}$$

$$= \text{Arcsec } \frac{\sqrt{x^2 + 1}}{x} = \text{Arccsc } \sqrt{x^2 + 1}$$

$$= \frac{\pi}{2} - \text{Arccot } \frac{1}{x}$$

$$\text{Arcsec } x = \text{Arctan } \sqrt{x^2 - 1} = \text{Arccot } \frac{1}{\sqrt{x^2 - 1}}$$

$$= \text{Arcsin } \frac{\sqrt{x^2 - 1}}{x} = \text{Arccos } \frac{1}{x} = \pi + \text{Arcsec}(-x)$$

$$= \frac{\pi}{2} - \text{Arccsc } x - \frac{\pi}{2} - \text{Arccsc}(-x)$$

$$\text{Arccsc } x = \text{Arctan } \frac{1}{\sqrt{x^2 - 1}} = \text{Arccot } \sqrt{x^2 - 1}$$

$$= \text{Arcsin } \frac{1}{x} = \text{Arccos } \frac{\sqrt{x^2 - 1}}{x} = \pi + \text{Arccsc}(-x)$$

$$= \frac{\pi}{2} - \text{Arcsec } x = -\frac{\pi}{2} - \text{Arcsec}(-x)$$

The following are valid if $x < 0$.

$$\text{Arcsin } x = -\text{Arccos } \sqrt{1 - x^2} = \text{Arccot } \frac{\sqrt{1 - x^2}}{x} - \pi$$

$$= -\pi - \text{Arccsc } \frac{1}{x} = -\text{Arcsec } \frac{1}{\sqrt{1 - x^2}}$$

$$= \text{Arcsin } \sqrt{1 - x^2} - \frac{\pi}{2}$$

$$\text{Arccos } x = \pi - \text{Arcsin } \sqrt{1 - x^2} = \pi + \text{Arctan } \frac{\sqrt{1 - x^2}}{x}$$

$$= \pi - \text{Arccsc } \frac{1}{\sqrt{1 - x^2}} = -\text{Arcsec } \frac{1}{x}$$

$$= \text{Arccos } \sqrt{1 - x^2} + \frac{\pi}{2}$$

$$\text{Arctan } x = \text{Arccot } \frac{1}{x} - \pi = -\text{Arccos } \frac{1}{\sqrt{x^2 + 1}}$$

$$= -\text{Arcsec } \sqrt{x^2 + 1} = -\pi - \text{Arccsc } \frac{\sqrt{x^2 + 1}}{x}$$

$$= -\frac{\pi}{2} - \text{Arctan } \frac{1}{x}$$

$$\text{Arccot } x = \pi + \text{Arctan } \frac{1}{x} = \pi - \text{Arcsin } \frac{1}{\sqrt{x^2 + 1}}$$

$$= -\text{Arcsec } \frac{\sqrt{x^2 + 1}}{x} = \pi - \text{Arccsc } \sqrt{x^2 + 1}$$

$$= \frac{3\pi}{2} - \text{Arccot } \frac{1}{x}$$

$$\text{Arcsec } x = \text{Arctan } \sqrt{x^2 - 1} - \pi = \text{Arccot } \frac{1}{\sqrt{x^2 - 1}} - \pi$$

$$= -\pi - \text{Arcsin } \frac{\sqrt{x^2 - 1}}{x} = -\text{Arccos } \frac{1}{x} = \text{Arcsec}(-x) - \pi$$

$$= -\frac{3\pi}{2} - \text{Arccsc } x = -\frac{\pi}{2} - \text{Arccsc}(-x)$$

$$\text{Arccsc } x = \text{Arctan } \frac{1}{\sqrt{x^2 - 1}} - \pi = \text{Arccot } \sqrt{x^2 - 1} - \pi$$

$$= -\pi - \text{Arcsin } \frac{1}{x} = -\text{Arccos } \frac{\sqrt{x^2 - 1}}{x} = \text{Arccsc}(-x) - \pi$$

$$= -\frac{3\pi}{2} - \text{Arcsec } x = -\frac{\pi}{2} - \text{Arcsec}(-x)$$

Plane Triangle Formulae

In the following, A, B, C denote the angles of any plane triangle, a, b, c the corresponding opposite sides, and $s = \frac{1}{2}(a + b + c)$.

Radius of inscribed circle:

$$r = \sqrt{\frac{(s - a)(s - b)(s - c)}{s}}$$

Radius of circumscribed circle:

$$R = \frac{a}{2 \sin A} = \frac{b}{2 \sin B} = \frac{c}{2 \sin C}$$

Law of sines:

$$\frac{a}{\sin A} = \frac{b}{\sin B} = \frac{c}{\sin C}$$

Law of cosines:

$$a^2 = b^2 + c^2 - 2bc \cos A, \qquad \cos A = \frac{b^2 + c^2 - a^2}{2bc},$$

$$b^2 = c^2 + a^2 - 2ca \cos B, \qquad \cos B = \frac{c^2 + a^2 - b^2}{2ca}$$

$$c^2 = a^2 + b^2 - 2ab \cos C, \qquad \cos C = \frac{a^2 + b^2 - c^2}{2ab}$$

Law of tangents:

$$\frac{b - c}{b + c} = \frac{\tan \frac{1}{2}(B - C)}{\tan \frac{1}{2}(B + C)}, \qquad \frac{c - a}{c + a} = \frac{\tan \frac{1}{2}(C - A)}{\tan \frac{1}{2}(C + A)}$$

$$\frac{a - b}{a + b} = \frac{\tan \frac{1}{2}(A - B)}{\tan \frac{1}{2}(A + B)}$$

Half-angle formulae:

$$\tan \frac{1}{2}A = \frac{r}{s - a}, \qquad \tan \frac{1}{2}B = \frac{r}{s - b}, \qquad \tan \frac{1}{2}C = \frac{r}{s - c}$$

$$\sin \frac{1}{2}A = \sqrt{\frac{(s - b)(s - c)}{bc}}, \qquad \cos \frac{1}{2}A = \sqrt{\frac{s(s - a)}{bc}}$$

$$\sin \frac{1}{2}B = \sqrt{\frac{(s - c)(s - a)}{ca}}, \qquad \cos \frac{1}{2}B = \sqrt{\frac{s(s - b)}{ca}}$$

$$\sin \frac{1}{2}C = \sqrt{\frac{(s - a)(s - b)}{ab}}, \qquad \cos \frac{1}{2}C = \sqrt{\frac{s(s - c)}{ab}}$$

Formulas for Use in Trigonometry

Area:

$$K = \tfrac{1}{2}bc \sin A = \tfrac{1}{2}ca \sin B = \tfrac{1}{2}ab \sin C$$

$$K = \frac{a^2 \sin B \sin C}{2 \sin A} = \frac{b^2 \sin C \sin A}{2 \sin B} = \frac{c^2 \sin A \sin B}{2 \sin C}$$

$$K = \sqrt{s(s-a)(s-b)(s-c)} = rs = \frac{abc}{4R}$$

Mollweide's formulae:

$$\frac{b-c}{a} = \frac{\sin \tfrac{1}{2}(B-C)}{\cos \tfrac{1}{2}A}, \qquad \frac{c-a}{b} = \frac{\sin \tfrac{1}{2}(C-A)}{\cos \tfrac{1}{2}B}$$

$$\frac{a-b}{c} = \frac{\sin \tfrac{1}{2}(A-B)}{\cos \tfrac{1}{2}C}$$

Newton's formulae:

$$\frac{b+c}{a} = \frac{\cos \tfrac{1}{2}(B-C)}{\sin \tfrac{1}{2}A}, \qquad \frac{c+a}{b} = \frac{\cos \tfrac{1}{2}(C-A)}{\sin \tfrac{1}{2}B}$$

$$\frac{a+b}{c} = \frac{\cos \tfrac{1}{2}(A-B)}{\sin \tfrac{1}{2}C}$$

Solution of Right Triangles

(a) Given acute angle A and opposite leg a.

$$B = 90° - A, \quad b = a/\tan A = a \cot A, \quad c = a/\sin A = a \csc A$$

(b) Given acute angle A and adjacent leg b.

$$B = 90° - A, \quad a = b \tan A, \quad c = b/\cos A = b \sec A$$

(c) Given acute angle A and hypotenuse c.

$$B = 90° - A, \quad a = c \sin A, \quad b = c \cos A$$

(d) Given legs a and b.

$$c = \sqrt{a^2 + b^2}, \quad \tan A = a/b, \quad B = 90° - A$$

(e) Given hypotenuse c and leg a.

$$b = \sqrt{(c+a)(c-a)}, \quad \sin A = a/c, \quad B = 90° - A$$

Solution of Oblique Triangles

(a) Given sides b and c and included angle A.

Nonlogarithmic solution

$$a^2 = b^2 + c^2 - 2bc \cos A, \quad \cos B = (c^2 + a^2 - b^2)/2ca,$$
$$\cos C = (a^2 + b^2 - c^2)/2ab$$

Logarithmic solution

$$\tfrac{1}{2}(B+C) = 90° - \tfrac{1}{2}A, \quad \tan \tfrac{1}{2}(B-C) = \frac{b-c}{b+c}\tan \tfrac{1}{2}(B+C),$$
$$B = \tfrac{1}{2}(B+C) + \tfrac{1}{2}(B-C), \quad C = \tfrac{1}{2}(B+C) - \tfrac{1}{2}(B-C),$$
$$a = (b \sin A)/\sin B, \quad K = \tfrac{1}{2}bc \sin A$$

Check. $A + B + C = 180°$, or use Newton's formula or law of sines.

(b) Given angles B and C and included side a.

$$A = 180° - (B + C), \quad b = (a \sin B)/\sin A,$$
$$c = (a \sin C)/\sin A, \quad K = \frac{a^2 \sin B \sin C}{2 \sin A}$$

Check. $a = b \cos C + c \cos B$, or use Newton's formula or law of tangents.

(c) Given sides a and c and opposite angle A.

$$\sin C = (c \sin A)/a, \quad B = 180° - (A + C),$$
$$b = (a \sin B)/\sin A, \quad K = \tfrac{1}{2}ac \sin B$$

Check. $a = b \cos C + c \cos B$, or use Newton's formula or law of tangents.

Note. In this case there may be two solutions, for C may have two values:

$C_1 < 90°$ and $C_2 = 180° - C_1 > 90°$. If $A + C_2 > 180°$, use only C_1.

(d) Given the three sides a, b, c.

Nonlogarithmic solution

$$\cos A = (b^2 + c^2 - a^2)/2bc, \quad \cos B = (c^2 + a^2 - b^2)/2ca,$$
$$\cos C = (a^2 + b^2 - c^2)/2ab$$

Logarithmic solution

$$s = \tfrac{1}{2}(a + b + c), \quad r = \sqrt{\frac{(s - a)(s - b)(s - c)}{s}},$$
$$\tan \tfrac{1}{2}A = \frac{r}{s - a}, \quad \tan \tfrac{1}{2}B = \frac{r}{s - b}, \quad \tan \tfrac{1}{2}C = \frac{r}{s - c},$$
$$K = \sqrt{s(s - a)(s - b)(s - c)}$$

Check. $A + B + C = 180°$.

Relations Between Accuracy of Computed Lengths and Angles

When solving a triangle for any of its parts, the following should be observed:

Significant figures for sides	Angles to the nearest
2	degree
3	ten minutes
4	minute
5	tenth of a minute

SPHERICAL TRIGONOMETRY

Right Spherical Triangles

Let a, b, c be the sides of a right spherical triangle with opposite angles A, B, $C = 90°$, respectively, where each side is measured by the angle subtended at the center of the sphere.

$$\sin a = \tan b \cot B, \qquad \sin a = \sin A \sin c$$
$$\sin b = \tan a \cot A, \qquad \sin b = \sin B \sin c$$
$$\cos A = \tan b \cot c, \qquad \cos A = \cos a \sin B$$
$$\cos B = \tan a \cot c, \qquad \cos B = \cos b \sin A$$
$$\cos c = \cot A \cot B, \qquad \cos c = \cos a \cos b$$

Napier's Rules of Circular Parts

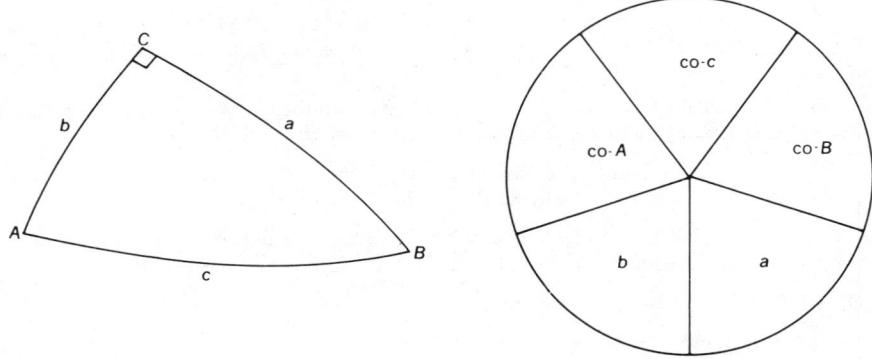

Arrange the five quantities a, b, co-A (complement of A), co-c, co-B of a right spherical triangle right-angled at C in cyclic order as pictured. If any one of these quantities is designated a *middle* part, then two of the other parts are *adjacent* to it, and the remaining two parts are *opposite* to it. The above formulae for a right spherical triangle may be recalled by the following two rules:

(a) The sine of any middle part is equal to the product of the *tangents* of the two *adjacent* parts.

(b) The sine of any middle part is equal to the product of the *cosines* of the two *opposite* parts.

Rules for Determining the Quadrant of a Calculated Part of a Right Spherical Triangle

(a) A leg and the angle opposite it are always of the same quadrant.

(b) If the hypotenuse if less than 90°, the legs are of the same quadrant.

(c) If the hypotenuse is greater than 90°, the legs are of unlike quadrants.

Oblique Spherical Triangles

In the following, a, b, c represent the sides of any spherical triangle, A, B, C the corresponding opposite angles, $s = \frac{1}{2}(a + b + c)$, $S = \frac{1}{2}(A + B + C)$, Δ = area of triangle, E = spherical excess of triangle, R = radius of the sphere upon which the triangle lies, and a', b', c', A', B', C' are the corresponding parts of the polar triangle.

$$0° < a + b + c < 360°, \qquad 180° < A + B + C < 540°$$
$$E = A + B + C - 180°, \qquad \Delta = \pi R^2 E/180$$
$$\tan \tfrac{1}{4} E = \sqrt{\tan \tfrac{s}{2} \tan \tfrac{1}{2}(s - a) \tan \tfrac{1}{2}(s - b) \tan \tfrac{1}{2}(s - c)}$$
$$A = 180° - a', \qquad B = 180° - b', \qquad C = 180° - c'$$
$$a = 180° - A', \qquad b = 180° - B', \qquad c = 180° - C'$$

Law of sines:

$$\frac{\sin a}{\sin A} = \frac{\sin b}{\sin B} = \frac{\sin c}{\sin C}$$

Law of cosines for sides:

$$\cos a = \cos b \cos c + \sin b \sin c \cos A$$
$$\cos b = \cos c \cos a + \sin c \sin a \cos B$$
$$\cos c = \cos a \cos b + \sin a \sin b \cos C$$

Law of cosines for angles:

$$\cos A = -\cos B \cos C + \sin B \sin C \cos a$$
$$\cos B = -\cos C \cos A + \sin C \sin A \cos b$$
$$\cos C = -\cos A \cos B + \sin A \sin B \cos c$$

Law of tangents:

$$\frac{\tan \tfrac{1}{2}(B - C)}{\tan \tfrac{1}{2}(B + C)} = \frac{\tan \tfrac{1}{2}(b - c)}{\tan \tfrac{1}{2}(b + c)}, \qquad \frac{\tan \tfrac{1}{2}(C - A)}{\tan \tfrac{1}{2}(C + A)} = \frac{\tan \tfrac{1}{2}(c - a)}{\tan \tfrac{1}{2}(c + a)}$$

$$\frac{\tan \tfrac{1}{2}(A - B)}{\tan \tfrac{1}{2}(A + B)} = \frac{\tan \tfrac{1}{2}(a - b)}{\tan \tfrac{1}{2}(a + b)}$$

Half-angle formulae:

$$\tan \tfrac{1}{2}A = \frac{k}{\sin(s - a)}, \qquad \tan \tfrac{1}{2}B = \frac{k}{\sin(s - b)}, \qquad \tan \tfrac{1}{2}C = \frac{k}{\sin(s - c)},$$

where

$$k^2 = \frac{\sin(s - a) \sin(s - b) \sin(s - c)}{\sin s}.$$

Half-side formulae:

$$\tan \tfrac{1}{2}\alpha = K \cos(S - A), \qquad \tan \tfrac{1}{2}b = K \cos(S - B),$$
$$\tan \tfrac{1}{2}c = K \cos(S - C),$$

where

$$K^2 = \frac{-\cos S}{\cos(S - A) \cos(S - B) \cos(S - C)}.$$

Gauss's formulae:

$$\frac{\sin \tfrac{1}{2}(a - b)}{\sin \tfrac{1}{2}c} = \frac{\sin \tfrac{1}{2}(A - B)}{\sin \tfrac{1}{2}C}, \qquad \frac{\cos \tfrac{1}{2}(a - b)}{\cos \tfrac{1}{2}c} = \frac{\sin \tfrac{1}{2}(A + B)}{\cos \tfrac{1}{2}C}$$

$$\frac{\sin \tfrac{1}{2}(a + b)}{\sin \tfrac{1}{2}c} = \frac{\cos \tfrac{1}{2}(A - B)}{\sin \tfrac{1}{2}C}, \qquad \frac{\cos \tfrac{1}{2}(a + b)}{\cos \tfrac{1}{2}c} = \frac{\cos \tfrac{1}{2}(A + B)}{\sin \tfrac{1}{2}C}$$

Napier's analogies:

$$\frac{\sin \tfrac{1}{2}(A - B)}{\sin \tfrac{1}{2}(A + B)} = \frac{\tan \tfrac{1}{2}(a - b)}{\tan \tfrac{1}{2}c}, \qquad \frac{\sin \tfrac{1}{2}(a - b)}{\sin \tfrac{1}{2}(a + b)} = \frac{\tan \tfrac{1}{2}(A - B)}{\cot \tfrac{1}{2}C}$$

$$\frac{\cos \tfrac{1}{2}(A - B)}{\cos \tfrac{1}{2}(A + B)} = \frac{\tan \tfrac{1}{2}(a + b)}{\tan \tfrac{1}{2}c}, \qquad \frac{\cos \tfrac{1}{2}(a - b)}{\cos \tfrac{1}{2}(a + b)} = \frac{\tan \tfrac{1}{2}(A + B)}{\cot \tfrac{1}{2}C}$$

Haversine formulae:

$$\text{hav } a = \text{hav}(b - c) + \sin b \sin c \, \text{hav } A$$

$$\text{hav } A = \frac{\sin(s - b) \sin(s - c)}{\sin b \sin c}$$

$$= \frac{\text{hav } a - \text{hav}(b - c)}{\sin b \sin c}$$

$$= \text{hav}[180° - (B + C)] + \sin B \sin C \, \text{hav } a$$

Rules for Determining the Quadrant of a Calculated Part of an Oblique Spherical Triangle

(a) If $A > B > C$, then $a > b > c$.

(b) A side (angle) which differs more from 90° than does another side (angle) is in the same quadrant as its opposite angle (side).

(c) Half the sum of any two sides and half the sum of the opposite angles are in the same quadrant.

SUMMARY OF SOLUTION OF OBLIQUE SPHERICAL TRIANGLES

Given	Solution	Check
Three sides	Half-angle formulae.	Law of sines
Three angles	Half-side formulae.	Law of sines
Two sides and included angle	Napier's analogies (to find sum and difference of unknown angles), then law of sines (to find remaining side).	Gauss's formula
Two angles and included side	Napier's analogies (to find sum and difference of unknown sides), then law of sines (to find remaining angle).	Gauss's formula
Two sides and an opposite angle	Law of sines (to find an angle), then Napier's analogies (to find remaining angle and side). Note number of solutions.	Gauss's formula
Two angles and an opposite side	Law of sines (to find a side), then Napier's analogies (to find remaining side and angle). Note number of solutions.	Gauss's formula

HYPERBOLIC TRIGONOMETRY

Geometrical Definitions

Let O be the center, A the vertex, and P any point of the branch $B'AB$ of a rectangular hyperbola. Set $OM = x$, $MP = y$, $OA = a$, and

$$u = \frac{\text{area } OPAP'}{a^2}.$$

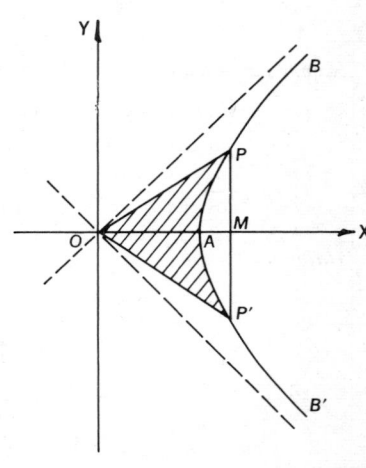

Then

hyperbolic sine of u = sinh u = y/a,

hyperbolic cosine of u = cosh u = x/a.

Exponential Definitions

$$\text{hyperbolic sine of } u = \sinh u = \tfrac{1}{2}(e^u - e^{-u})$$
$$\text{hyperbolic cosine of } u = \cosh u = \tfrac{1}{2}(e^u + e^{-u})$$
$$\text{hyperbolic tangent of } u = \tanh u = \frac{\sinh u}{\cosh u} = \frac{e^u - e^{-u}}{e^u + e^{-u}}$$

$$\operatorname{csch} u = \frac{1}{\sinh u}, \qquad \operatorname{sech} u = \frac{1}{\cosh u}, \qquad \coth u = \frac{1}{\tanh u}$$

Fundamental Identities

$$\sinh(-u) = -\sinh u, \qquad \operatorname{csch}(-u) = -\operatorname{csch} u$$
$$\cosh(-u) = \cosh u, \qquad \operatorname{sech}(-u) = \operatorname{sech} u$$
$$\tanh(-u) = -\tanh u, \qquad \coth(-u) = -\coth u$$

$$\cosh^2 u - \sinh^2 u = 1, \qquad \tanh^2 u + \operatorname{sech}^2 u = 1$$
$$\coth^2 u - \operatorname{csch}^2 u = 1, \qquad \operatorname{csch}^2 u - \operatorname{sech}^2 u = \operatorname{csch}^2 u \operatorname{sech}^2 u$$

$$\sinh(u + v) = \sinh u \cosh v + \cosh u \sinh v$$
$$\sinh(u - v) = \sinh u \cosh v - \cosh u \sinh v$$
$$\cosh(u + v) = \cosh u \cosh v + \sinh u \sinh v$$
$$\cosh(u - v) = \cosh u \cosh v - \sinh u \sinh v$$

$$\tanh(u + v) = \frac{\tanh u + \tanh v}{1 + \tanh u \tanh v}$$

$$\tanh(u - v) = \frac{\tanh u - \tanh v}{1 - \tanh u \tanh v}$$

$$\sinh(u + v) \sinh(u - v) = \sinh^2 u - \sinh^2 v = \cosh^2 u - \cosh^2 v$$
$$\cosh(u + v) \cosh(u - v) = \sinh^2 u + \cosh^2 v = \cosh^2 u + \sinh^2 v$$

$$\sinh u \cosh v = \tfrac{1}{2}\sinh(u + v) + \tfrac{1}{2}\sinh(u - v)$$
$$\cosh u \sinh v = \tfrac{1}{2}\sinh(u + v) - \tfrac{1}{2}\sinh(u - v)$$
$$\cosh u \cosh v = \tfrac{1}{2}\cosh(u + v) + \tfrac{1}{2}\cosh(u - v)$$
$$\sinh u \sinh v = \tfrac{1}{2}\cosh(u + v) - \tfrac{1}{2}\cosh(u - v)$$

$$\sinh u + \sinh v = 2 \sinh \tfrac{1}{2}(u + v) \cosh \tfrac{1}{2}(u - v)$$
$$\sinh u - \sinh v = 2 \cosh \tfrac{1}{2}(u + v) \sinh \tfrac{1}{2}(u - v)$$
$$\cosh u + \cosh v = 2 \cosh \tfrac{1}{2}(u + v) \cosh \tfrac{1}{2}(u - v)$$
$$\cosh u - \cosh v = 2 \sinh \tfrac{1}{2}(u + v) \sinh \tfrac{1}{2}(u - v)$$

$$\sinh u = \frac{2 \tanh \tfrac{1}{2}u}{1 - \tanh^2 \tfrac{1}{2}u} = \frac{\tanh u}{\sqrt{1 - \tanh^2 u}}$$

$$\cosh u = \frac{1 + \tanh^2 \tfrac{1}{2}u}{1 - \tanh^2 \tfrac{1}{2}u} = \frac{1}{\sqrt{1 - \tanh^2 u}}$$

$$\sinh u + \cosh u = \frac{1 + \tanh \tfrac{1}{2}u}{1 - \tanh \tfrac{1}{2}u}$$

$$\tanh u + \tanh v = \frac{\sinh(u + v)}{\cosh u \cosh v}$$

$$\tanh u - \tanh v = \frac{\sinh(u - v)}{\cosh u \cosh v}$$

$$\coth u + \coth v = \frac{\sinh(u + v)}{\sinh u \sinh v}$$

$$\coth u - \coth v = \frac{\sinh(v - u)}{\sinh u \sinh v}$$

$$\sinh 2u = 2 \sinh u \cosh u$$
$$\cosh 2u = \cosh^2 u + \sinh^2 u = 2 \cosh^2 u - 1 = 1 + 2 \sinh^2 u$$
$$\tanh 2u = \frac{2 \tanh u}{1 + \tanh^2 u}$$

$$\sinh 3u = 3 \sinh u + 4 \sinh^3 u$$
$$\cosh 3u = 4 \cosh^3 u - 3 \cosh u$$
$$\tanh 3u = \frac{3 \tanh u + \tanh^3 u}{1 + 3 \tanh^2 u}$$

$$\sinh \tfrac{1}{2} u = \pm \sqrt{\tfrac{1}{2}(\cosh u - 1)}$$
$$\cosh \tfrac{1}{2} u = \sqrt{\tfrac{1}{2}(\cosh u + 1)}$$
$$\tanh \tfrac{1}{2} u = \frac{\cosh u - 1}{\sinh u} = \frac{\sinh u}{\cosh u + 1}$$

Inverse Hyperbolic Functions*

$$\sinh^{-1} x = \log_e (x + \sqrt{x^2 + 1})$$
$$\cosh^{-1} x = \log_e (x \pm \sqrt{x^2 - 1}), \quad x \geqq 1. \text{ The plus sign is used for the}$$
$$\text{principal value.}$$

$$\tanh^{-1} x = \tfrac{1}{2} \log_e \left(\frac{1 + x}{1 - x} \right), \quad x^2 < 1$$

$$\operatorname{csch}^{-1} x = \log_e \left(\frac{1 \pm \sqrt{1 + x^2}}{x} \right). \text{ The plus sign is used if } x > 0, \text{ the minus}$$
$$\text{sign if } x < 0.$$

$$\operatorname{sech}^{-1} x = \log_e \left(\frac{1 \pm \sqrt{1 - x^2}}{x} \right), \quad 0 < x \leq 1. \text{ The plus sign is used for the}$$
$$\text{principal values.}$$

$$\coth^{-1} x = \tfrac{1}{2} \log_e \left(\frac{x + 1}{x - 1} \right), \quad x^2 > 1$$

*$\sinh^{-1}$, $\cosh^{-1}$, etc., are sometimes replaced by arg sinh, arg cosh etc., i.e. $\sinh^{-1} x = $ arg sinh x.

Relations with Circular Functions

$$\sinh iu = i \sin u, \qquad \sinh u = -i \sin iu$$
$$\cosh iu = \cos u, \qquad \cosh u = \cos iu$$
$$\tanh iu = i \tan u, \qquad \tanh u = -i \tan iu$$

$$\sinh(u + iv) = \sinh u \cos v + i \cosh u \sin v$$
$$\sinh(u - iv) = \sinh u \cos v - i \cosh u \sin v$$
$$\cosh(u + iv) = \cosh u \cos v + i \sinh u \sin v$$
$$\cosh(u - iv) = \cosh u \cos v - i \sinh u \sin v$$

$$\tanh(u + iv) = \frac{\sinh 2u + i \sin 2v}{\cosh 2u + \cos 2v}$$

$$\tanh(u - iv) = \frac{\sinh 2u - i \sin 2v}{\cosh 2u + \cos 2v}$$

$$\coth(u + iv) = \frac{\sinh 2u - i \sin 2v}{\cosh 2u - \cos 2v}$$

$$\coth(u - iv) = \frac{\sinh 2u + i \sin 2v}{\cosh 2u - \cos 2v}$$

$$\sinh(u + \tfrac{1}{2}\pi i) = i \cosh u, \qquad \cosh(u + \tfrac{1}{2}\pi i) = i \sinh u$$
$$\sinh(u + \pi i) = -\sinh u, \qquad \cosh(u + \pi i) = -\cosh u$$
$$\sinh(u + 2\pi i) = \sinh u, \qquad \cosh(u + 2\pi i) = \cosh u$$

$$e^u = \cosh u + \sinh u, \qquad e^{-u} = \cosh u - \sinh u$$
$$e^{iu} = \cos u + i \sin u, \qquad e^{-iu} = \cos u - i \sin u$$

The Gudermannian

If

$$x = \log_e \tan(\pi/4 + \theta/2) = \log_e(\sec\theta + \tan\theta),$$

then

$$\theta = \text{the gudermannian of } x = \text{gd } x = 2\tan^{-1}e^x - \tfrac{1}{2}\pi.$$
$$\sinh x = \tan\theta, \qquad \cosh x = \sec\theta$$
$$\tanh x = \sin\theta, \qquad \tanh\tfrac{1}{2}x = \tan\tfrac{1}{2}\theta$$
$$d\theta/dx = \text{sech } x$$

SPECIAL VALUES OF HYPERBOLIC FUNCTIONS

x	0	$\dfrac{\pi}{2}i$	πi	$\dfrac{3\pi}{2}i$	∞
$\sinh x$	0	i	0	$-i$	∞
$\cosh x$	1	0	-1	0	∞
$\tanh x$	0	∞i	0	$-\infty i$	1
$\text{csch } x$	∞	$-i$	∞	i	0
$\text{sech } x$	1	∞	-1	∞	0
$\coth x$	∞	0	∞	0	1

MILS—RADIANS—DEGREES

1 mil = 0.00098175 radians = 0.05625° = 3.375′ = 202.5″
1000 mils = 0.98175 radians = 56.25°
6400 mils = 360° = 2π radians
1 radian = 1018.6 mils
1° = 17.777778 mils
1′ = 0.296296 mils
1″ = 0.0049382 mils

DEGREES—RADIANS

1 radian = 57° 17′ 44″ .80625

		log
1 radian	= 57.29577 95131 degrees	1.75812 26324
1 radian	= 3437.74677 07849 minutes	3.53627 38828
1 radian	= 206264.80625 seconds	5.31442 51332
1 degree	= 0.01745 32925 19943 radians	8.24187 73676–10
1 minute	= 0.00029 08882 08666 radians	6.46372 61172–10
1 second	= 0.00000 48481 36811 radians	4.68557 48668–10

DEGREES, MINUTES, AND SECONDS TO RADIANS

Units in degrees, minutes *or* seconds	Degrees to Radians	Minutes to Radians	Seconds to Radians
10	0.174 5329	0.002 9089	0.000 0485
20	0.349 0659	0.005 8178	0.000 0970
30	0.523 5988	0.008 7266	0.000 1454
40	0.698 1317	0.011 6355	0.000 1939
50	0.872 6646	0.014 5444	0.000 2424
60	1.047 1976	0.017 4533	0.000 2909
70	1.221 7305	(0.020 3622)	(0.000 3394)
80	1.396 2634	(0.023 2711)	(0.000 3879)
90	1.570 7963	(0.026 1800)	(0.000 4364)
100	1.745 3293	....	....
200	3.490 6585	....	....
300	5.235 9878	....	....

where n = 1, 2, 3, 4, etc. n(100°) = n(1.745 3293)

*RADIANS TO DEGREES, MINUTES, AND SECONDS

Radians	1.0	0.1	0.01	0.001	0.0001
1	57° 17' 44.8"	5° 43' 46.5"	0° 34' 22.6"	0° 03' 26.3"	0° 00' 20.6"
2	114° 35' 29.6"	11° 27' 33.0"	1° 08' 45.3"	0° 06' 52.5"	0° 00' 41.3"
3	171° 53' 14.4"	17° 11' 19.4"	1° 43' 07.9 '	0° 10' 18.8"	0° 01' 01.9"
4	229° 10' 59.2"	22° 55' 05.9"	2° 17' 30.6"	0° 13' 45.1'	0° 01' 22.5"
5	286° 28' 44.0"	28° 38' 52.4"	2° 51' 53.2"	0° 17' 11.3"	0° 01' 43.1"
6	343° 46' 28.8"	34° 22' 38.9"	3° 26' 15.9"	0° 20' 37.6"	0° 02' 03.8"
7	401° 04' 13.6"	40° 06' 25.4"	4° 00' 38.5"	0° 24' 03.9"	0° 02' 24.4"
8	458° 21' 58.4"	45° 50' 11.8"	4° 35' 01.2"	0° 27' 30.1"	0° 02' 45.0"
9	515° 39' 43.3"	51° 33' 58.3"	5° 09' 23.8"	0° 30' 56.4"	0° 03' 05.6"

* If 3.214 is desired in degrees, minutes and seconds it is obtained as follows:

$$3 = 171° 53' 14.4''$$
$$.2 = 11° 27' 33.0''$$
$$.01 = 0° 34' 22.6''$$
$$.004 = 0° 13' 45.1''$$

$$3.214 = 184° \ 8' 55.1''$$

DEGREES—RADIANS

The table gives in radians the angle which is expressed in degrees and minutes at the side and top. Angles expressed to the nearest minute and second can readily be converted to radians by adding to the equivalent of the whole number of degrees the equivalents of the minutes and seconds found on the third page of this table.

°	00′	10	20	30	40	50
0	0.00000	0.00291	0.00582	0.00873	0.01164	0.01454
1	0.01745	0.02036	0.02327	0.02618	0.02909	0.03200
2	0.03491	0.03782	0.04072	0.04363	0.04654	0.04945
3	0.05236	0.05527	0.05818	0.06109	0.06400	0.06690
4	0.06981	0.07272	0.07563	0.07854	0.08145	0.08436
5	0.08727	0.09018	0.09308	0.09599	0.09890	0.10181
6	0.10472	0.10763	0.11054	0.11345	0.11636	0.11926
7	0.12217	0.12508	0.12799	0.13090	0.13381	0.13672
8	0.13963	0.14254	0.14544	0.14835	0.15126	0.15417
9	0.15708	0.15999	0.16290	0.16581	0.16872	0.17162
10	0.17453	0.17744	0.18035	0.18326	0.18617	0.18908
11	0.19199	0.19490	0.19780	0.20071	0.20362	0.20653
12	0.20944	0.21235	0.21526	0.21817	0.22108	0.22398
13	0.22689	0.22980	0.23271	0.23562	0.23853	0.24144
14	0.24435	0.24725	0.25016	0.25307	0.25598	0.25889
15	0.26180	0.26471	0.26762	0.27053	0.27343	0.27634
16	0.27925	0.28216	0.28507	0.28798	0.29089	0.29380
17	0.29671	0.29961	0.30252	0.30543	0.30834	0.31125
18	0.31416	0.31707	0.31998	0.32289	0.32579	0.32870
19	0.33161	0.33452	0.33743	0.34034	0.34325	0.34616
20	0.34907	0.35197	0.35488	0.35779	0.36070	0.36361
21	0.36652	0.36943	0.37234	0.37525	0.37815	0.38106
22	0.38397	0.38688	0.38979	0.39270	0.39561	0.39852
23	0.40143	0.40433	0.40724	0.41015	0.41306	0.41597
24	0.41888	0.42179	0.42470	0.42761	0.43051	0.43342
25	0.43633	0.43924	0.44215	0.44506	0.44797	0.45088
26	0.45379	0.45669	0.45960	0.46251	0.46542	0.46833
27	0.47124	0.47415	0.47706	0.47997	0.48287	0.48578
28	0.48869	0.49160	0.49451	0.49742	0.50033	0.50324
29	0.50615	0.50905	0.51196	0.51487	0.51778	0.52069
30	0.52360	0.52651	0.52942	0.53233	0.53523	0.53814
31	0.54105	0.54396	0.54687	0.54978	0.55269	0.55560
32	0.55851	0.56141	0.56432	0.56723	0.57014	0.57305
33	0.57596	0.57887	0.58178	0.58469	0.58759	0.59050
34	0.59341	0.59632	0.59923	0.60214	0.60505	0.60796
35	0.61087	0.61377	0.61668	0.61959	0.62250	0.62541
36	0.62832	0.63123	0.63414	0.63705	0.63995	0.64286
37	0.64577	0.64868	0.65159	0.65450	0.65741	0.66032
38	0.66323	0.66613	0.66904	0.67195	0.67486	0.67777
39	0.68068	0.68359	0.68650	0.68941	0.69231	0.69522
40	0.69813	0.70104	0.70395	0.70686	0.70977	0.71268
41	0.71558	0.71849	0.72140	0.72431	0.72722	0.73013
42	0.73304	0.73595	0.73886	0.74176	0.74467	0.74758
43	0.75049	0.75340	0.75631	0.75922	0.76213	0.76504
44	0.76794	0.77085	0.77376	0.77667	0.77958	0.78249
45	0.78540	0.78831	0.79122	0.79412	0.79703	0.79994
46	0.80285	0.80576	0.80867	0.81158	0.81449	0.81740
47	0.82030	0.82321	0.82612	0.82903	0.83194	0.83485
48	0.83776	0.84067	0.84358	0.84648	0.84939	0.85230
49	0.85521	0.85812	0.86103	0.86394	0.86685	0.86976

DEGREES—RADIANS (Continued)

°	00′	10	20	30	40	50
50	0.87266	0.87557	0.87848	0.88139	0.88430	0.88721
51	0.89012	0.89303	0.89594	0.89884	0.90175	0.90466
52	0.90757	0.91048	0.91339	0.91630	0.91921	0.92212
53	0.92502	0.92793	0.93084	0.93375	0.93666	0.93957
54	0.94248	0.94539	0.94830	0.95120	0.95411	0.95702
55	0.95993	0.96284	0.96575	0.96866	0.97157	0.97448
56	0.97738	0.98029	0.98320	0.98611	0.98902	0.99193
57	0.99484	0.99775	1.00066	1.00356	1.00647	1.00938
58	1.01229	1.01520	1.01811	1.02102	1.02393	1.02684
59	1.02974	1.03265	1.03556	1.03847	1.04138	1.04429
60	1.04720	1.05011	1.05302	1.05592	1.05883	1.06174
61	1.06465	1.06756	1.07047	1.07338	1.07629	1.07920
62	1.08210	1.08501	1.08792	1.09083	1.09374	1.09665
63	1.09956	1.10247	1.10538	1.10828	1.11119	1.11410
64	1.11701	1.11992	1.12283	1.12574	1.12865	1.13156
65	1.13446	1.13737	1.14028	1.14319	1.14610	1.14901
66	1.15192	1.15483	1.15774	1.16064	1.16355	1.16646
67	1.16937	1.17228	1.17519	1.17810	1.18101	1.18392
68	1.18682	1.18973	1.19264	1.19555	1.19846	1.20137
69	1.20428	1.20719	1.21009	1.21300	1.21591	1.21882
70	1.22173	1.22464	1.22755	1.23046	1.23337	1.23627
71	1.23918	1.24209	1.24500	1.24791	1.25082	1.25373
72	1.25664	1.25955	1.26245	1.26536	1.26827	1.27118
73	1.27409	1.27700	1.27991	1.28282	1.28573	1.28863
74	1.29154	1.29445	1.29736	1.30027	1.30318	1.30609
75	1.30900	1.31191	1.31481	1.31772	1.32063	1.32354
76	1.32645	1.32936	1.33227	1.33518	1.33809	1.34099
77	1.34390	1.34681	1.34972	1.35263	1.35554	1.35845
78	1.36136	1.36427	1.36717	1.37008	1.37299	1.37590
79	1.37881	1.38172	1.38463	1.38754	1.39045	1.39335
80	1.39626	1.39917	1.40208	1.40499	1.40790	1.41081
81	1.41372	1.41663	1.41953	1.42244	1.42535	1.42826
82	1.43117	1.43408	1.43699	1.43990	1.44281	1.44571
83	1.44862	1.45153	1.45444	1.45735	1.46026	1.46317
84	1.46608	1.46899	1.47189	1.47480	1.47771	1.48062
85	1.48353	1.48644	1.48935	1.49226	1.49517	1.49807
86	1.50098	1.50389	1.50680	1.50971	1.51262	1.51553
87	1.51844	1.52135	1.52425	1.52716	1.53007	1.53298
88	1.53589	1.53880	1.54171	1.54462	1.54753	1.55043
89	1.55334	1.55625	1.55916	1.56207	1.56498	1.56789
90	1.57080	1.57371	1.57661	1.57952	1.58243	1.58534
91	1.58825	1.59116	1.59407	1.59698	1.59989	1.60279
92	1.60570	1.60861	1.61152	1.61443	1.61734	1.62025
93	1.62316	1.62607	1.62897	1.63188	1.63479	1.63770
94	1.64061	1.64352	1.64643	1.64934	1.65225	1.65515
95	1.65806	1.66097	1.66388	1.66679	1.66970	1.67261
96	1.67552	1.67842	1.68133	1.68424	1.68715	1.69006
97	1.69297	1.69588	1.69879	1.70170	1.70460	1.70751
98	1.71042	1.71333	1.71624	1.71915	1.72206	1.72497
99	1.72788	1.73078	1.73369	1.73660	1.73951	1.74242
100	1.74533	1.74824	1.75115	1.75406	1.75696	1.75987
101	1.76278	1.76569	1.76860	1.77151	1.77442	1.77733
102	1.78024	1.78314	1.78605	1.78896	1.79187	1.79478
103	1.79769	1.80060	1.80351	1.80642	1.80932	1.81223
104	1.81514	1.81805	1.82096	1.82387	1.82678	1.82969
105	1.83260	1.83550	1.83841	1.84132	1.84423	1.84714
106	1.85004	1.85296	1.85587	1.85878	1.86168	1.86459
107	1.86750	1.87041	1.87332	1.87623	1.87914	1.88205
108	1.88496	1.88786	1.89077	1.89368	1.89659	1.89950
109	1.90241	1.90532	1.90823	1.91114	1.91404	1.91695
110	1.91986	1.92277	1.92568	1.92859	1.93150	1.93441

DEGREES—RADIANS (Continued)

Deg.	Radians	Deg.	Radians	Min.	Radians	Sec.	Radians
90	1.57080	150	2.61799	0	0.00000	0	0.00000
91	1.58825	151	2.63545	1	0.00029	1	0.00000
92	1.60570	152	2.65290	2	0.00058	2	0.00001
93	1.62316	153	2.67035	3	0.00087	3	0.00001
94	1.64061	154	2.68781	4	0.00116	4	0.00002
95	1.65806	155	2.70526	5	0.00145	5	0.00002
96	1.67552	156	2.72271	6	0.00175	6	0.00003
97	1.69297	157	2.74017	7	0.00204	7	0.00003
98	1.71042	158	2.75762	8	0.00233	8	0.00004
99	1.72788	159	2.77507	9	0.00262	9	0.00004
100	1.74533	160	2.79253	10	0.00291	10	0.00005
101	1.76278	161	2.80998	11	0.00320	11	0.00005
102	1.78024	162	2.82743	12	0.00349	12	0.00006
103	1.79769	163	2.84489	13	0.00378	13	0.00006
104	1.81514	164	2.86234	14	0.00407	14	0.00007
105	1.83260	165	2.87979	15	0.00436	15	0.00007
106	1.85005	166	2.89725	16	0.00465	16	0.00008
107	1.86750	167	2.91470	17	0.00495	17	0.00008
108	1.88496	168	2.93215	18	0.00524	18	0.00009
109	1.90241	169	2.94961	19	0.00553	19	0.00009
110	1.91986	170	2.96706	20	0.00582	20	0.00010
111	1.93732	171	2.98451	21	0.00611	21	0.00010
112	1.95477	172	3.00197	22	0.00640	22	0.00011
113	1.97222	173	3.01942	23	0.00669	23	0.00011
114	1.98968	174	3.03687	24	0.00698	24	0.00012
115	2.00713	175	3.05433	25	0.00727	25	0.00012
116	2.02458	176	3.07178	26	0.00756	26	0.00013
117	2.04204	177	3.08923	27	0.00785	27	0.00013
118	2.05949	178	3.10669	28	0.00814	28	0.00014
119	2.07694	179	3.12414	29	0.00844	29	0.00014
120	2.09440	180	3.14159	30	0.00873	30	0.00015
121	2.11185	190	3.31613	31	0.00902	31	0.00015
122	2.12930	200	3.49066	32	0.00931	32	0.00016
123	2.14676	210	3.66519	33	0.00960	33	0.00016
124	2.16421	220	3.83972	34	0.00989	34	0.00016
125	2.18166	230	4.01426	35	0.01018	35	0.00017
126	2.19911	240	4.18879	36	0.01047	36	0.00017
127	2.21657	250	4.36332	37	0.01076	37	0.00018
128	2.23402	260	4.53786	38	0.01105	38	0.00018
129	2.25147	270	4.71239	39	0.01134	39	0.00019
130	2.26893	280	4.88692	40	0.01164	40	0.00019
131	2.28638	290	5.06145	41	0.01193	41	0.00020
132	2.30383	300	5.23599	42	0.01222	42	0.00020
133	2.32129	310	5.41052	43	0.01251	43	0.00021
134	2.33874	320	5.58505	44	0.01280	44	0.00021
135	2.35619	330	5.75959	45	0.01309	45	0.00022
136	2.37365	340	5.93412	46	0.01338	46	0.00022
137	2.39110	350	6.10865	47	0.01367	47	0.00023
138	2.40855	360	6.28319	48	0.01396	48	0.00023
139	2.42601	370	6.45772	49	0.01425	49	0.00024
140	2.44346	380	6.63225	50	0.01454	50	0.00024
141	2.46091	390	6.80678	51	0.01484	51	0.00025
142	2.47837	400	6.98132	52	0.01513	52	0.00025
143	2.49582	410	7.15585	53	0.01542	53	0.00026
144	2.51327	420	7.33038	54	0.01571	54	0.00026
145	2.53073	430	7.50492	55	0.01600	55	0.00027
146	2.54818	440	7.67945	56	0.01629	56	0.00027
147	2.56563	450	7.85398	57	0.01658	57	0.00028
148	2.58309	460	8.02851	58	0.01687	58	0.00028
149	2.60054	470	8.20305	59	0.01716	59	0.00029
150	2.61799	480	8.37758	60	0.01745	60	0.00029

DEGREES AND DECIMAL FRACTIONS TO RADIANS

The table below facilitates conversion of an angle expressed in degrees and decimal fractions into radians. To convert 25.78 into radians, find the equivalents, successively, of 20°, 5°, 0°.7, 0°.08 and add.

Deg.	Radians	Deg.	Radians	Deg.	Radians	Deg.	Radians	Deg.	Radians
10	0.174533	1	0.017453	0.1	0.001745	0.01	0.000175	0.001	0.000017
20	0.349066	2	.034907	.2	.003491	.02	.000349	.002	.000035
30	0.523599	3	.052360	.3	.005236	.03	.000524	.003	.000052
40	0.698132	4	.069813	.4	.006981	.04	.000698	.004	.000070
50	0.872665	5	.087266	.5	.008727	.05	.000873	.005	.000087
60	1.047198	6	.104720	.6	.010472	.06	.001047	.006	.000105
70	1.221730	7	.122173	.7	.012217	.07	.001222	.007	.000122
80	1.396263	8	.139626	.8	.013963	.08	.001396	.008	.000140
90	1.570796	9	.157080	.9	.015708	.09	.001571	.009	.000157

RADIANS TO DEGREES AND DECIMALS

Radians	Degrees	Radians	Degrees	Radians	Degrees	Radians	Degrees
1	57.2958	0.1	5.7296	0.01	0.5730	0.001	0.0573
2	114.5916	.2	11.4592	.02	1.1459	.002	.1146
3	171.8873	.3	17.1887	.03	1.7189	.003	.1719
4	229.1831	.4	22.9183	.04	2.2918	.004	.2292
5	286.4789	.5	28.6479	.05	2.8648	.005	.2865
6	343.7747	.6	34.3775	.06	3.4377	.006	.3438
7	401.0705	.7	40.1070	.07	4.0107	.007	.4011
8	458.3662	.8	45.8366	.08	4.5837	.008	.4584
9	515.6620	.9	51.5662	.09	5.1566	.009	.5157
10	572.9578	1.0	57.2958	.10	5.7296	.010	.5730

RADIANS—DEGREES
Multiples and Fractions of π Radians in Degrees

Radians	Radians	Deg.	Radians	Radians	Deg.	Radians	Radians	Deg.
π	3.1416	180	$\pi/2$	1.5708	90	$2\pi/3$	2.0944	120
2π	6.2832	360	$\pi/3$	1.0472	60	$3\pi/4$	2.3562	135
3π	9.4248	540	$\pi/4$	0.7854	45	$5\pi/6$	2.6180	150
4π	12.5664	720	$\pi/5$	0.6283	36	$7\pi/6$	3.6652	210
5π	15.7080	900	$\pi/6$	0.5236	30	$5\pi/4$	3.9270	225
6π	18.8496	1080	$\pi/7$	0.4488	25.714	$4\pi/3$	4.1888	240
7π	21.9911	1260	$\pi/8$	0.3927	22.5	$3\pi/2$	4.7124	270
8π	25.1327	1440	$\pi/9$	0.3491	20	$5\pi/3$	5.2360	300
9π	28.2743	1620	$\pi/10$	0.3142	18	$7\pi/4$	5.4978	315
10π	31.4159	1800	$\pi/12$	0.2618	15	$11\pi/6$	5.7596	330

CONVERSION OF ANGLES FROM ARC TO TIME

Arc	Time	Arc	Time	Arc	Time	Arc	Time
°	h m	°	h m	″	s	″	s
′	m s	′	m s				
0	0 00	20	1 20	0	0.00	8	0.53
1	0 04	30	2 00	1	0.07	9	0.60
2	0 08	40	2 40	2	0.13	10	0.67
3	0 12	50	3 20	3	0.20	20	1.33
4	0 16	60	4 00	4	0.27	30	2.00
5	0 20	70	4 40	5	0.33	40	2.67
6	0 24	80	5 20	6	0.40	50	3.33
7	0 28	90	6 00	7	0.47	60	4.00
8	0 32	100	6 40				
9	0 36	200	13 20				
10	0 40	300	20 00				

MINUTES AND SECONDS TO DECIMAL PARTS OF A DEGREE

MINUTES AND SECONDS TO DECIMAL PARTS OF A DEG.				DECIMAL PARTS OF A DEGREE TO MINUTES AND SECONDS					
Min.	Degrees	Sec.	Degrees	Deg.	'	''	Deg.	'	''
0	0.00000	**0**	0.00000	**0.00**	0	00	**0.60**	36	
1	.01667	1	.00028	.01	0	36	.61	36	36
2	.03333	2	.00056	.02	1	12	.62	37	12
3	.05	3	.00083	.03	1	48	.63	37	48
4	.06667	4	.00111	.04	2	24	.64	38	24
5	.08333	5	.00139	.05	3		.65	39	
6	.10	6	.00167	.06	3	36	.66	39	36
7	.11667	7	.00194	.07	4	12	.67	40	12
8	.13333	8	.00222	.08	4	48	.68	40	48
9	.15	9	.0025	.09	5	24	.69	41	24
10	0.16667	**10**	0.00278	**0.10**	6		**0.70**	42	
11	.18333	11	.00306	.11	6	36	.71	42	36
12	.20	12	.00333	.12	7	12	.72	43	12
13	.21667	13	.00361	.13	7	48	.73	43	48
14	.23333	14	.00389	.14	8	24	.74	44	24
15	.25	15	.00417	.15	9		.75	45	
16	.26667	16	.00444	.16	9	36	.76	45	36
17	.28333	17	.00472	.17	10	12	.77	46	12
18	.30	18	.005	.18	10	48	.78	46	48
19	.31667	19	.00528	.19	11	24	.79	47	24
20	0.33333	**20**	0.00556	**0.20**	12		**0.80**	48	
21	.35	21	.00583	.21	12	36	.81	48	36
22	.36667	22	.00611	.22	13	12	.82	49	12
23	.38333	23	.00639	.23	13	48	.83	49	48
24	.40	24	.00667	.24	14	24	.84	50	24
25	.41667	25	.00694	.25	15		.85	51	
26	.43333	26	.00722	.26	15	36	.86	51	36
27	.45	27	.0075	.27	16	12	.87	52	12
28	.46667	28	.00778	.28	16	48	.88	52	48
29	.48333	29	.00806	.29	17	24	.89	53	24
30	0.50	**30**	0.00833	**0.30**	18		**0.90**	54	
31	.51667	31	.00861	.31	18	36	.91	54	36
32	.53333	32	.00889	.32	19	12	.92	55	12
33	.55	33	.00917	.33	19	48	.93	55	48
34	.56667	34	.00944	.34	20	24	94	56	24
35	.58333	35	.00972	.35	21		.95	57	
36	.60	36	.01	.36	21	36	.96	57	36
37	.61667	37	.01028	.37	22	12	.97	58	12
38	.63333	38	.01056	.38	22	48	.98	58	48
39	.65	39	.01083	.39	23	24	.99	59	24
40	0.66667	**40**	0.01111	**0.40**	24		**1.00**	60	
41	.68333	41	.01139	.41	24	36			
42	.70	42	.01167	.42	25	12			
43	.71667	43	.01194	.43	25	48			
44	.73333	44	.01222	.44	26	24			
45	.75	45	.0125	.45	27		Deg.		Sec.
46	.76667	46	.01278	.46	27	36	**0.000**		0.0
47	.78333	47	.01306	.47	28	12	.001		3.6
48	.80	48	.01333	.48	28	48	.002		7.2
49	.81667	49	.01361	.49	29	24	.003		10.8
50	0.83333	**50**	0.01389	**0.50**	30		.004		14.4
51	.85	51	.01417	.51	30	36	.005		18.
52	.86667	52	.01444	.52	31	12	.006		21.6
53	.88333	53	.01472	.53	31	48	.007		25.2
54	.90	54	.015	.54	32	24	.008		28.8
55	.91667	55	.01528	.55	33		.009		32.4
56	.93333	56	.01556	.56	33	36	**0.010**		36.
57	.95	57	.01583	.57	34	12			
58	.96667	58	.01611	.58	34	48			
59	.98333	59	.01639	.59	35	24			
60	1.00	**60**	0.01667	**0.60**	36				

NATURAL TRIGONOMETRIC FUNCTIONS
TO FIVE PLACES

Values of the trigonometric functions of angles for each minute from 0–360°.

For degrees indicated at the top of the page use the column headings at the top. For degrees indicated at the bottom use the column indications at the bottom.

With degrees at the left of each block (top or bottom), use the minute column at the left and with degrees at the right of each block use the minute column at the right.

If natural trigonometric function tables are used for angle measures greater than 90° and less than 360°, appropriate signs for the functions must be supplied in accordance with the quadrant in which the angle measure belongs.

Linear interpolation may be used to obtain values of the functions for tenths of degrees, except in regions where the functions are rapidly changing. See section on "Use of Logarithm Tables" for further discussion in interpolation practice.

NATURAL TRIGONOMETRIC FUNCTIONS
TO FIVE PLACES

180°)   (359)° 179°   1° (181°)   (358°) 178°

Sin	Tan	Cot	Cos	Sec	Csc	'
.00000	.00000	----	1.0000	1.0000	----	60
.00029	.00029	3437.7	1.0000	1.0000	3437.7	59
.00058	.00058	1718.9	1.0000	1.0000	1718.9	58
.00087	.00087	1145.9	1.0000	1.0000	1145.9	57
.00116	.00116	859.44	1.0000	1.0000	859.44	56
.00145	.00145	687.55	1.0000	1.0000	687.55	55
.00175	.00175	572.96	1.0000	1.0000	572.96	54
.00204	.00204	491.11	1.0000	1.0000	491.11	53
.00233	.00233	429.72	1.0000	1.0000	429.72	52
.00262	.00262	381.97	1.0000	1.0000	381.97	51
.00291	.00291	343.77	1.0000	1.0000	343.78	50
.00320	.00320	312.52	.99999	1.0000	312.52	49
.00349	.00349	286.48	.99999	1.0000	286.48	48
.00378	.00378	264.44	.99999	1.0000	264.44	47
.00407	.00407	245.55	.99999	1.0000	245.55	46
.00436	.00436	229.18	.99999	1.0000	229.18	45
.00465	.00465	214.86	.99999	1.0000	214.86	44
.00495	.00495	202.22	.99999	1.0000	202.22	43
.00524	.00524	190.98	.99999	1.0000	190.99	42
.00553	.00553	180.93	.99998	1.0000	180.93	41
.00582	.00582	171.89	.99998	1.0000	171.89	40
.00611	.00611	163.70	.99998	1.0000	163.70	39
.00640	.00640	156.26	.99998	1.0000	156.26	38
.00669	.00669	149.47	.99998	1.0000	149.47	37
.00698	.00698	143.24	.99998	1.0000	143.24	36
.00727	.00727	137.51	.99997	1.0000	137.51	35
.00756	.00756	132.22	.99997	1.0000	132.22	34
.00785	.00785	127.32	.99997	1.0000	127.33	33
.00814	.00815	122.77	.99997	1.0000	122.78	32
.00844	.00844	118.54	.99996	1.0000	118.54	31
.00873	.00873	114.59	.99996	1.0000	114.59	30
.00902	.00902	110.89	.99996	1.0000	110.90	29
.00931	.00931	107.43	.99996	1.0000	107.43	28
.00960	.00960	104.17	.99995	1.0000	104.18	27
.00989	.00989	101.11	.99995	1.0000	101.11	26
.01018	.01018	98.218	.99995	1.0001	98.223	25
.01047	.01047	95.489	.99995	1.0001	95.495	24
.01076	.01076	92.908	.99994	1.0001	92.914	23
.01105	.01105	90.463	.99994	1.0001	90.469	22
.01134	.01135	88.144	.99994	1.0001	88.149	21
.01164	.01164	85.940	.99993	1.0001	85.946	20
.01193	.01193	83.844	.99993	1.0001	83.849	19
.01222	.01222	81.847	.99993	1.0001	81.853	18
.01251	.01251	79.943	.99992	1.0001	79.950	17
.01280	.01280	78.126	.99992	1.0001	78.133	16
.01309	.01309	76.390	.99991	1.0001	76.397	15
.01338	.01338	74.729	.99991	1.0001	74.736	14
.01367	.01367	73.139	.99991	1.0001	73.146	13
.01396	.01396	71.615	.99990	1.0001	71.622	12
.01425	.01425	70.153	.99990	1.0001	70.160	11
.01454	.01455	68.750	.99989	1.0001	68.757	10
.01483	.01484	67.402	.99989	1.0001	67.409	9
.01513	.01513	66.105	.99989	1.0001	66.113	8
.01542	.01542	64.858	.99988	1.0001	64.866	7
.01571	.01571	63.657	.99988	1.0001	63.665	6
.01600	.01600	62.499	.99987	1.0001	62.507	5
.01629	.01629	61.383	.99987	1.0001	61.391	4
.01658	.01658	60.306	.99986	1.0001	60.314	3
.01687	.01687	59.266	.99986	1.0001	59.274	2
.01716	.01716	58.261	.99985	1.0001	58.270	1
.01745	.01746	57.290	.99985	1.0002	57.299	0
Cos	Cot	Tan	Sin	Csc	Sec	'

'	Sin	Tan	Cot	Cos	Sec	Csc	'
0	.01745	.01746	57.290	.99985	1.0002	57.299	60
1	.01774	.01775	56.351	.99984	1.0002	56.359	59
2	.01803	.01804	55.442	.99984	1.0002	55.451	58
3	.01832	.01833	54.561	.99983	1.0002	54.570	57
4	.01862	.01862	53.709	.99983	1.0002	53.718	56
5	.01891	.01891	52.882	.99982	1.0002	52.892	55
6	.01920	.01920	52.081	.99982	1.0002	52.090	54
7	.01949	.01949	51.303	.99981	1.0002	51.313	53
8	.01978	.01978	50.549	.99980	1.0002	50.558	52
9	.02007	.02007	49.816	.99980	1.0002	49.826	51
10	.02036	.02036	49.104	.99979	1.0002	49.114	50
11	.02065	.02066	48.412	.99979	1.0002	48.422	49
12	.02094	.02095	47.740	.99978	1.0002	47.750	48
13	.02123	.02124	47.085	.99977	1.0002	47.096	47
14	.02152	.02153	46.449	.99977	1.0002	46.460	46
15	.02181	.02182	45.829	.99976	1.0002	45.840	45
16	.02211	.02211	45.226	.99976	1.0002	45.237	44
17	.02240	.02240	44.639	.99975	1.0003	44.650	43
18	.02269	.02269	44.066	.99974	1.0003	44.077	42
19	.02298	.02298	43.508	.99974	1.0003	43.520	41
20	.02327	.02328	42.964	.99973	1.0003	42.976	40
21	.02356	.02357	42.433	.99972	1.0003	42.445	39
22	.02385	.02386	41.916	.99972	1.0003	41.928	38
23	.02414	.02415	41.411	.99971	1.0003	41.423	37
24	.02443	.02444	40.917	.99970	1.0003	40.930	36
25	.02472	.02473	40.436	.99969	1.0003	40.448	35
26	.02501	.02502	39.965	.99969	1.0003	39.978	34
27	.02530	.02531	39.506	.99968	1.0003	39.519	33
28	.02560	.02560	39.057	.99967	1.0003	39.070	32
29	.02589	.02589	38.618	.99966	1.0003	38.631	31
30	.02618	.02619	38.188	.99966	1.0003	38.202	30
31	.02647	.02648	37.769	.99965	1.0004	37.782	29
32	.02676	.02677	37.358	.99964	1.0004	37.371	28
33	.02705	.02706	36.956	.99963	1.0004	36.970	27
34	.02734	.02735	36.563	.99963	1.0004	36.576	26
35	.02763	.02764	36.178	.99962	1.0004	36.191	25
36	.02792	.02793	35.801	.99961	1.0004	35.815	24
37	.02821	.02822	35.431	.99960	1.0004	35.445	23
38	.02850	.02851	35.070	.99959	1.0004	35.084	22
39	.02879	.02881	34.715	.99959	1.0004	34.730	21
40	.02908	.02910	34.368	.99958	1.0004	34.382	20
41	.02938	.02939	34.027	.99957	1.0004	34.042	19
42	.02967	.02968	33.694	.99956	1.0004	33.708	18
43	.02996	.02997	33.366	.99955	1.0005	33.381	17
44	.03025	.03026	33.045	.99954	1.0005	33.060	16
45	.03054	.03055	32.730	.99953	1.0005	32.746	15
46	.03083	.03084	32.421	.99952	1.0005	32.437	14
47	.03112	.03114	32.118	.99952	1.0005	32.134	13
48	.03141	.03143	31.821	.99951	1.0005	31.836	12
49	.03170	.03172	31.528	.99950	1.0005	31.544	11
50	.03199	.03201	31.242	.99949	1.0005	31.258	10
51	.03228	.03230	30.960	.99948	1.0005	30.976	9
52	.03257	.03259	30.683	.99947	1.0005	30.700	8
53	.03286	.03288	30.412	.99946	1.0005	30.428	7
54	.03316	.03317	30.145	.99945	1.0006	30.161	6
55	.03345	.03346	29.882	.99944	1.0006	29.899	5
56	.03374	.03376	29.624	.99943	1.0006	29.641	4
57	.03403	.03405	29.371	.99942	1.0006	29.388	3
58	.03432	.03434	29.122	.99941	1.0006	29.139	2
59	.03461	.03463	28.877	.99940	1.0006	28.894	1
60	.03490	.03492	28.636	.99939	1.0006	28.654	0
'	Cos	Cot	Tan	Sin	Csc	Sec	'

NATURAL TRIGONOMETRIC FUNCTIONS
TO FIVE PLACES

2° (182°)   (357°) 177°

′	Sin	Tan	Cot	Cos	Sec	Csc	′
0	.03490	.03492	28.636	.99939	1.0006	28.654	60
1	.03519	.03521	28.399	.99938	1.0006	28.417	59
2	.03548	.03550	28.166	.99937	1.0006	28.184	58
3	.03577	.03579	27.937	.99936	1.0006	27.955	57
4	.03606	.03609	27.712	.99935	1.0007	27.730	56
5	.03635	.03638	27.490	.99934	1.0007	27.508	55
6	.03664	.03667	27.271	.99933	1.0007	27.290	54
7	.03693	.03696	27.057	.99932	1.0007	27.075	53
8	.03723	.03725	26.845	.99931	1.0007	26.864	52
9	.03752	.03754	26.637	.99930	1.0007	26.655	51
10	.03781	.03783	26.432	.99929	1.0007	26.451	50
11	.03810	.03812	26.230	.99927	1.0007	26.249	49
12	.03839	.03842	26.031	.99926	1.0007	26.050	48
13	.03868	.03871	25.835	.99925	1.0007	25.854	47
14	.03897	.03900	25.642	.99924	1.0008	25.661	46
15	.03926	.03929	25.452	.99923	1.0008	25.471	45
16	.03955	.03958	25.264	.99922	1.0008	25.284	44
17	.03984	.03987	25.080	.99921	1.0008	25.100	43
18	.04013	.04016	24.898	.99919	1.0008	24.918	42
19	.04042	.04046	24.719	.99918	1.0008	24.739	41
20	.04071	.04075	24.542	.99917	1.0008	24.562	40
21	.04100	.04104	24.368	.99916	1.0008	24.388	39
22	.04129	.04133	24.196	.99915	1.0009	24.216	38
23	.04159	.04162	24.026	.99913	1.0009	24.047	37
24	.04188	.04191	23.859	.99912	1.0009	23.880	36
25	.04217	.04220	23.695	.99911	1.0009	23.716	35
26	.04246	.04250	23.532	.99910	1.0009	23.553	34
27	.04275	.04279	23.372	.99909	1.0009	23.393	33
28	.04304	.04308	23.214	.99907	1.0009	23.235	32
29	.04333	.04337	23.058	.99906	1.0009	23.079	31
30	.04362	.04366	22.904	.99905	1.0010	22.926	30
31	.04391	.04395	22.752	.99904	1.0010	22.774	29
32	.04420	.04424	22.602	.99902	1.0010	22.624	28
33	.04449	.04454	22.454	.99901	1.0010	22.476	27
34	.04478	.04483	22.308	.99900	1.0010	22.330	26
35	.04507	.04512	22.164	.99898	1.0010	22.187	25
36	.04536	.04541	22.022	.99897	1.0010	22.044	24
37	.04565	.04570	21.881	.99896	1.0010	21.904	23
38	.04594	.04599	21.743	.99894	1.0011	21.766	22
39	.04623	.04628	21.606	.99893	1.0011	21.629	21
40	.04653	.04658	21.470	.99892	1.0011	21.494	20
41	.04682	.04687	21.337	.99890	1.0011	21.360	19
42	.04711	.04716	21.205	.99889	1.0011	21.229	18
43	.04740	.04745	21.075	.99888	1.0011	21.098	17
44	.04769	.04774	20.946	.99886	1.0011	20.970	16
45	.04798	.04803	20.819	.99885	1.0012	20.843	15
46	.04827	.04833	20.693	.99883	1.0012	20.717	14
47	.04856	.04862	20.569	.99882	1.0012	20.593	13
48	.04885	.04891	20.446	.99881	1.0012	20.471	12
49	.04914	.04920	20.325	.99879	1.0012	20.350	11
50	.04943	.04949	20.206	.99878	1.0012	20.230	10
51	.04972	.04978	20.087	.99876	1.0012	20.112	9
52	.05001	.05007	19.970	.99875	1.0013	19.995	8
53	.05030	.05037	19.855	.99873	1.0013	19.880	7
54	.05059	.05066	19.740	.99872	1.0013	19.766	6
55	.05088	.05095	19.627	.99870	1.0013	19.653	5
56	.05117	.05124	19.516	.99869	1.0013	19.541	4
57	.05146	.05153	19.405	.99867	1.0013	19.431	3
58	.05175	.05182	19.296	.99866	1.0013	19.322	2
59	.05205	.05212	19.188	.99864	1.0014	19.214	1
60	.05204	.05241	19.081	.99863	1.0014	19.107	0
′	Cos	Cot	Tan	Sin	Csc	Sec	′

3° (183°)   (356°)

′	Sin	Tan	Cot	Cos	Sec	Csc
0	.05234	.05241	19.081	.99863	1.0014	19.107
1	.05263	.05270	18.976	.99861	1.0014	19.002
2	.05292	.05299	18.871	.99860	1.0014	18.898
3	.05321	.05328	18.768	.99858	1.0014	18.794
4	.05350	.05357	18.666	.99857	1.0014	18.692
5	.05379	.05387	18.564	.99855	1.0014	18.591
6	.05408	.05416	18.464	.99854	1.0015	18.492
7	.05437	.05445	18.366	.99852	1.0015	18.393
8	.05466	.05474	18.268	.99851	1.0015	18.295
9	.05495	.05503	18.171	.99849	1.0015	18.198
10	.05524	.05533	18.075	.99847	1.0015	18.103
11	.05553	.05562	17.980	.99846	1.0015	18.008
12	.05582	.05591	17.886	.99844	1.0016	17.914
13	.05611	.05620	17.793	.99842	1.0016	17.822
14	.05640	.05649	17.702	.99841	1.0016	17.730
15	.05669	.05678	17.611	.99839	1.0016	17.639
16	.05698	.05708	17.521	.99838	1.0016	17.549
17	.05727	.05737	17.431	.99836	1.0016	17.460
18	.05756	.05766	17.343	.99834	1.0017	17.372
19	.05785	.05795	17.256	.99833	1.0017	17.285
20	.05814	.05824	17.169	.99831	1.0017	17.198
21	.05844	.05854	17.084	.99829	1.0017	17.113
22	.05873	.05883	16.999	.99827	1.0017	17.028
23	.05902	.05912	16.915	.99826	1.0017	16.945
24	.05931	.05941	16.832	.99824	1.0018	16.862
25	.05960	.05970	16.750	.99822	1.0018	16.779
26	.05989	.05999	16.668	.99821	1.0018	16.698
27	.06018	.06029	16.587	.99819	1.0018	16.618
28	.06047	.06058	16.507	.99817	1.0018	16.538
29	.06076	.06087	16.428	.99815	1.0019	16.459
30	.06105	.06116	16.350	.99813	1.0019	16.380
31	.06134	.06145	16.272	.99812	1.0019	16.303
32	.06163	.06175	16.195	.99810	1.0019	16.226
33	.06192	.06204	16.119	.99808	1.0019	16.150
34	.06221	.06233	16.043	.99806	1.0019	16.075
35	.06250	.06262	15.969	.99804	1.0020	16.000
36	.06279	.06291	15.895	.99803	1.0020	15.926
37	.06308	.06321	15.821	.99801	1.0020	15.853
38	.06337	.06350	15.748	.99799	1.0020	15.780
39	.06366	.06379	15.676	.99797	1.0020	15.708
40	.06395	.06408	15.605	.99795	1.0021	15.637
41	.06424	.06438	15.534	.99793	1.0021	15.566
42	.06453	.06467	15.464	.99792	1.0021	15.496
43	.06482	.06496	15.394	.99790	1.0021	15.427
44	.06511	.06525	15.325	.99788	1.0021	15.358
45	.06540	.06554	15.257	.99786	1.0021	15.290
46	.06569	.06584	15.189	.99784	1.0022	15.222
47	.06598	.06613	15.122	.99782	1.0022	15.155
48	.06627	.06642	15.056	.99780	1.0022	15.089
49	.06656	.06671	14.990	.99778	1.0022	15.023
50	.06685	.06700	14.924	.99776	1.0022	14.958
51	.06714	.06730	14.860	.99774	1.0023	14.893
52	.06743	.06759	14.795	.99772	1.0023	14.829
53	.06773	.06788	14.732	.99770	1.0023	14.766
54	.06802	.06817	14.669	.99768	1.0023	14.703
55	.06831	.06847	14.606	.99766	1.0023	14.640
56	.06860	.06876	14.544	.99764	1.0024	14.578
57	.06889	.06905	14.482	.99762	1.0024	14.517
58	.06918	.06934	14.421	.99760	1.0024	14.456
59	.06947	.06963	14.361	.99758	1.0024	14.395
60	.06976	.06993	14.301	.99756	1.0024	14.336
′	Cos	Cot	Tan	Sin	Csc	Sec

NATURAL TRIGONOMETRIC FUNCTIONS
TO FIVE PLACES

(184°)   (355°) 175°   5° (185°)   (354°) 174°

′	Sin	Tan	Cot	Cos	Sec	Csc	′
0	.06976	.06993	14.301	.99756	1.0024	14.336	60
1	.07005	.07022	14.241	.99754	1.0025	14.276	59
2	.07034	.07051	14.182	.99752	1.0025	14.217	58
3	.07063	.07080	14.124	.99750	1.0025	14.159	57
4	.07092	.07110	14.065	.99748	1.0025	14.101	56
5	.07121	.07139	14.008	.99746	1.0025	14.044	55
6	.07150	.07168	13.951	.99744	1.0026	13.987	54
7	.07179	.07197	13.894	.99742	1.0026	13.930	53
8	.07208	.07227	13.838	.99740	1.0026	13.874	52
9	.07237	.07256	13.782	.99738	1.0026	13.818	51
10	.07266	.07285	13.727	.99736	1.0027	13.763	50
11	.07295	.07314	13.672	.99734	1.0027	13.708	49
12	.07324	.07344	13.617	.99731	1.0027	13.654	48
13	.07353	.07373	13.563	.99729	1.0027	13.600	47
14	.07382	.07402	13.510	.99727	1.0027	13.547	46
15	.07411	.07431	13.457	.99725	1.0028	13.494	45
16	.07440	.07461	13.404	.99723	1.0028	13.441	44
17	.07469	.07490	13.352	.99721	1.0028	13.389	43
18	.07498	.07519	13.300	.99719	1.0028	13.337	42
19	.07527	.07548	13.248	.99716	1.0028	13.286	41
20	.07556	.07578	13.197	.99714	1.0029	13.235	40
21	.07585	.07607	13.146	.99712	1.0029	13.184	39
22	.07614	.07636	13.096	.99710	1.0029	13.134	38
23	.07643	.07665	13.046	.99708	1.0029	13.084	37
24	.07672	.07695	12.996	.99705	1.0030	13.035	36
25	.07701	.07724	12.947	.99703	1.0030	12.985	35
26	.07730	.07753	12.898	.99701	1.0030	12.937	34
27	.07759	.07782	12.850	.99699	1.0030	12.888	33
28	.07788	.07812	12.801	.99696	1.0030	12.840	32
29	.07817	.07841	12.754	.99694	1.0031	12.793	31
30	.07846	.07870	12.706	.99692	1.0031	12.745	30
31	.07875	.07899	12.659	.99689	1.0031	12.699	29
32	.07904	.07929	12.612	.99687	1.0031	12.652	28
33	.07933	.07958	12.566	.99685	1.0032	12.606	27
34	.07962	.07987	12.520	.99683	1.0032	12.560	26
35	.07991	.08017	12.474	.99680	1.0032	12.514	25
36	.08020	.08046	12.429	.99678	1.0032	12.469	24
37	.08049	.08075	12.384	.99676	1.0033	12.424	23
38	.08078	.08104	12.339	.99673	1.0033	12.379	22
39	.08107	.08134	12.295	.99671	1.0033	12.335	21
40	.08136	.08163	12.251	.99668	1.0033	12.291	20
41	.08165	.08192	12.207	.99666	1.0034	12.248	19
42	.08194	.08221	12.163	.99664	1.0034	12.204	18
43	.08223	.08251	12.120	.99661	1.0034	12.161	17
44	.08252	.08280	12.077	.99659	1.0034	12.119	16
45	.08281	.08309	12.035	.99657	1.0034	12.076	15
46	.08310	.08339	11.992	.99654	1.0035	12.034	14
47	.08339	.08368	11.950	.99652	1.0035	11.992	13
48	.08368	.08397	11.909	.99649	1.0035	11.951	12
49	.08397	.08427	11.867	.99647	1.0035	11.909	11
50	.08426	.08456	11.826	.99644	1.0036	11.868	10
51	.08455	.08485	11.785	.99642	1.0036	11.828	9
52	.08484	.08514	11.745	.99639	1.0036	11.787	8
53	.08513	.08544	11.705	.99637	1.0036	11.747	7
54	.08542	.08573	11.664	.99635	1.0037	11.707	6
55	.08571	.08602	11.625	.99632	1.0037	11.668	5
56	.08600	.08632	11.585	.99630	1.0037	11.628	4
57	.08629	.08661	11.546	.99627	1.0037	11.589	3
58	.08658	.08690	11.507	.99625	1.0038	11.551	2
59	.08687	.08720	11.468	.99622	1.0038	11.512	1
60	.08716	.08749	11.430	.99619	1.0038	11.474	0
	Cos	Cot	Tan	Sin	Csc	Sec	′

(274°)   (265°) 85°

′	Sin	Tan	Cot	Cos	Sec	Csc	′
0	.08716	.08749	11.430	.99619	1.0038	11.474	60
1	.08745	.08778	11.392	.99617	1.0038	11.436	59
2	.08774	.08807	11.354	.99614	1.0039	11.398	58
3	.08803	.08837	11.316	.99612	1.0039	11.360	57
4	.08831	.08866	11.279	.99609	1.0039	11.323	56
5	.08860	.08895	11.242	.99607	1.0039	11.286	55
6	.08889	.08925	11.205	.99604	1.0040	11.249	54
7	.08918	.08954	11.168	.99602	1.0040	11.213	53
8	.08947	.08983	11.132	.99599	1.0040	11.176	52
9	.08976	.09013	11.095	.99596	1.0041	11.140	51
10	.09005	.09042	11.059	.99594	1.0041	11.105	50
11	.09034	.09071	11.024	.99591	1.0041	11.069	49
12	.09063	.09101	10.988	.99588	1.0041	11.034	48
13	.09092	.09130	10.953	.99586	1.0042	10.998	47
14	.09121	.09159	10.918	.99583	1.0042	10.963	46
15	.09150	.09189	10.883	.99580	1.0042	10.929	45
16	.09179	.09218	10.848	.99578	1.0042	10.894	44
17	.09208	.09247	10.814	.99575	1.0043	10.860	43
18	.09237	.09277	10.780	.99572	1.0043	10.826	42
19	.09266	.09306	10.746	.99570	1.0043	10.792	41
20	.09295	.09335	10.712	.99567	1.0043	10.758	40
21	.09324	.09365	10.678	.99564	1.0044	10.725	39
22	.09353	.09394	10.645	.99562	1.0044	10.692	38
23	.09382	.09423	10.612	.99559	1.0044	10.659	37
24	.09411	.09453	10.579	.99556	1.0045	10.626	36
25	.09440	.09482	10.546	.99553	1.0045	10.593	35
26	.09469	.09511	10.514	.99551	1.0045	10.561	34
27	.09498	.09541	10.481	.99548	1.0045	10.529	33
28	.09527	.09570	10.449	.99545	1.0046	10.497	32
29	.09556	.09600	10.417	.99542	1.0046	10.465	31
30	.09585	.09629	10.385	.99540	1.0046	10.433	30
31	.09614	.09658	10.354	.99537	1.0047	10.402	29
32	.09642	.09688	10.322	.99534	1.0047	10.371	28
33	.09671	.09717	10.291	.99531	1.0047	10.340	27
34	.09700	.09746	10.260	.99528	1.0047	10.309	26
35	.09729	.09776	10.229	.99526	1.0048	10.278	25
36	.09758	.09805	10.199	.99523	1.0048	10.248	24
37	.09787	.09834	10.168	.99520	1.0048	10.217	23
38	.09816	.09864	10.138	.99517	1.0049	10.187	22
39	.09845	.09893	10.108	.99514	1.0049	10.157	21
40	.09874	.09923	10.078	.99511	1.0049	10.128	20
41	.09903	.09952	10.048	.99508	1.0049	10.098	19
42	.09932	.09981	10.019	.99506	1.0050	10.068	18
43	.09961	.10011	9.9893	.99503	1.0050	10.039	17
44	.09990	.10040	9.9601	.99500	1.0050	10.010	16
45	.10019	.10069	9.9310	.99497	1.0051	9.9812	15
46	.10048	.10099	9.9021	.99494	1.0051	9.9525	14
47	.10077	.10128	9.8734	.99491	1.0051	9.9239	13
48	.10106	.10158	9.8448	.99488	1.0051	9.8955	12
49	.10135	.10187	9.8164	.99485	1.0052	9.8672	11
50	.10164	.10216	9.7882	.99482	1.0052	9.8391	10
51	.10192	.10246	9.7601	.99479	1.0052	9.8112	9
52	.10221	.10275	9.7322	.99476	1.0053	9.7834	8
53	.10250	.10305	9.7044	.99473	1.0053	9.7558	7
54	.10279	.10334	9.6768	.99470	1.0053	9.7283	6
55	.10308	.10363	9.6493	.99467	1.0054	9.7010	5
56	.10337	.10393	9.6220	.99464	1.0054	9.6739	4
57	.10366	.10422	9.5949	.99461	1.0054	9.6469	3
58	.10395	.10452	9.5679	.99458	1.0054	9.6200	2
59	.10424	.10481	9.5411	.99455	1.0055	9.5933	1
60	.10453	.10510	9.5144	.99452	1.0055	9.5668	0
	Cos	Cot	Tan	Sin	Csc	Sec	′

95° (275°)   (264°) 84°

Tables for Use in Trigonometry

NATURAL TRIGONOMETRIC FUNCTIONS
TO FIVE PLACES

6° (186°) (353°) **173°**

′	Sin	Tan	Cot	Cos	Sec	Csc	′
0	.10453	.10510	9.5144	.99452	1.0055	9.5668	60
1	.10482	.10540	9.4878	.99449	1.0055	9.5404	59
2	.10511	.10569	9.4614	.99446	1.0056	9.5141	58
3	.10540	.10599	9.4352	.99443	1.0056	9.4880	57
4	.10569	.10628	9.4090	.99440	1.0056	9.4620	56
5	.10597	.10657	9.3831	.99437	1.0057	9.4362	55
6	.10626	.10687	9.3572	.99434	1.0057	9.4105	54
7	.10655	.10716	9.3315	.99431	1.0057	9.3850	53
8	.10684	.10746	9.3060	.99428	1.0058	9.3596	52
9	.10713	.10775	9.2806	.99424	1.0058	9.3343	51
10	.10742	.10805	9.2553	.99421	1.0058	9.3092	50
11	.10771	.10834	9.2302	.99418	1.0059	9.2842	49
12	.10800	.10863	9.2052	.99415	1.0059	9.2593	48
13	.10829	.10893	9.1803	.99412	1.0059	9.2346	47
14	.10858	.10922	9.1555	.99409	1.0059	9.2100	46
15	.10887	.10952	9.1309	.99406	1.0060	9.1855	45
16	.10916	.10981	9.1065	.99402	1.0060	9.1612	44
17	.10945	.11011	9.0821	.99399	1.0060	9.1370	43
18	.10973	.11040	9.0579	.99396	1.0061	9.1129	42
19	.11002	.11070	9.0338	.99393	1.0061	9.0890	41
20	.11031	.11099	9.0098	.99390	1.0061	9.0652	40
21	.11060	.11128	8.9860	.99386	1.0062	9.0415	39
22	.11089	.11158	8.9623	.99383	1.0062	9.0179	38
23	.11118	.11187	8.9387	.99380	1.0062	8.9944	37
24	.11147	.11217	8.9152	.99377	1.0063	8.9711	36
25	.11176	.11246	8.8919	.99374	1.0063	8.9479	35
26	.11205	.11276	8.8686	.99370	1.0063	8.9248	34
27	.11234	.11305	8.8455	.99367	1.0064	8.9019	33
28	.11263	.11335	8.8225	.99364	1.0064	8.8790	32
29	.11291	.11364	8.7996	.99360	1.0064	8.8563	31
30	.11320	.11394	8.7769	.99357	1.0065	8.8337	30
31	.11349	.11423	8.7542	.99354	1.0065	8.8112	29
32	.11378	.11452	8.7317	.99351	1.0065	8.7888	28
33	.11407	.11482	8.7093	.99347	1.0066	8.7665	27
34	.11436	.11511	8.6870	.99344	1.0066	8.7444	26
35	.11465	.11541	8.6648	.99341	1.0066	8.7223	25
36	.11494	.11570	8.6427	.99337	1.0067	8.7004	24
37	.11523	.11600	8.6208	.99334	1.0067	8.6786	23
38	.11552	.11629	8.5989	.99331	1.0067	8.6569	22
39	.11580	.11659	8.5772	.99327	1.0068	8.6353	21
40	.11609	.11688	8.5555	.99324	1.0068	8.6138	20
41	.11638	.11718	8.5340	.99320	1.0068	8.5924	19
42	.11667	.11747	8.5126	.99317	1.0069	8.5711	18
43	.11696	.11777	8.4913	.99314	1.0069	8.5500	17
44	.11725	.11806	8.4701	.99310	1.0069	8.5289	16
45	.11754	.11836	8.4490	.99307	1.0070	8.5079	15
46	.11783	.11865	8.4280	.99303	1.0070	8.4871	14
47	.11812	.11895	8.4071	.99300	1.0070	8.4663	13
48	.11840	.11924	8.3863	.99297	1.0071	8.4457	12
49	.11869	.11954	8.3656	.99293	1.0071	8.4251	11
50	.11898	.11983	8.3450	.99290	1.0072	8.4047	10
51	.11927	.12013	8.3245	.99286	1.0072	8.3843	9
52	.11956	.12042	8.3041	.99283	1.0072	8.3641	8
53	.11985	.12072	8.2838	.99279	1.0073	8.3439	7
54	.12014	.12101	8.2636	.99276	1.0073	8.3238	6
55	.12043	.12131	8.2434	.99272	1.0073	8.3039	5
56	.12071	.12160	8.2234	.99269	1.0074	8.2840	4
57	.12100	.12190	8.2035	.99265	1.0074	8.2642	3
58	.12129	.12219	8.1837	.99262	1.0074	8.2446	2
59	.12158	.12249	8.1640	.99258	1.0075	8.2250	1
60	.12187	.12278	8.1443	.99255	1.0075	8.2055	0
′	Cos	Cot	Tan	Sin	Csc	Sec	′

96° (276°) (263°) **83°**

7° (187°) (352°) 1

′	Sin	Tan	Cot	Cos	Sec	Csc	′
0	.12187	.12278	8.1443	.99255	1.0075	8.2055	6...
1	.12216	.12308	8.1248	.99251	1.0075	8.1861	5...
2	.12245	.12338	8.1054	.99248	1.0076	8.1668	5...
3	.12274	.12367	8.0860	.99244	1.0076	8.1476	5...
4	.12302	.12397	8.0667	.99240	1.0077	8.1285	5...
5	.12331	.12426	8.0476	.99237	1.0077	8.1095	5...
6	.12360	.12456	8.0285	.99233	1.0077	8.0905	5...
7	.12389	.12485	8.0095	.99230	1.0078	8.0717	5...
8	.12418	.12515	7.9906	.99226	1.0078	8.0529	5...
9	.12447	.12544	7.9718	.99222	1.0078	8.0342	5...
10	.12476	.12574	7.9530	.99219	1.0079	8.0156	5...
11	.12504	.12603	7.9344	.99215	1.0079	7.9971	4...
12	.12533	.12633	7.9158	.99211	1.0079	7.9787	4...
13	.12562	.12662	7.8973	.99208	1.0080	7.9604	4...
14	.12591	.12692	7.8789	.99204	1.0080	7.9422	4...
15	.12620	.12722	7.8606	.99200	1.0081	7.9240	4...
16	.12649	.12751	7.8424	.99197	1.0081	7.9059	4...
17	.12678	.12781	7.8243	.99193	1.0081	7.8879	4...
18	.12706	.12810	7.8062	.99189	1.0082	7.8700	4...
19	.12735	.12840	7.7882	.99186	1.0082	7.8522	4...
20	.12764	.12869	7.7704	.99182	1.0082	7.8344	4...
21	.12793	.12899	7.7525	.99178	1.0083	7.8168	3...
22	.12822	.12929	7.7348	.99175	1.0083	7.7992	3...
23	.12851	.12958	7.7171	.99171	1.0084	7.7817	3...
24	.12880	.12988	7.6996	.99167	1.0084	7.7642	3...
25	.12908	.13017	7.6821	.99163	1.0084	7.7469	3...
26	.12937	.13047	7.6647	.99160	1.0085	7.7296	3...
27	.12966	.13076	7.6473	.99156	1.0085	7.7124	3...
28	.12995	.13106	7.6301	.99152	1.0086	7.6953	3...
29	.13024	.13136	7.6129	.99148	1.0086	7.6783	3...
30	.13053	.13165	7.5958	.99144	1.0086	7.6613	3...
31	.13081	.13195	7.5787	.99141	1.0087	7.6444	2...
32	.13110	.13224	7.5618	.99137	1.0087	7.6276	2...
33	.13139	.13254	7.5449	.99133	1.0087	7.6109	2...
34	.13168	.13284	7.5281	.99129	1.0088	7.5942	2...
35	.13197	.13313	7.5113	.99125	1.0088	7.5776	2...
36	.13226	.13343	7.4947	.99122	1.0089	7.5611	2...
37	.13254	.13372	7.4781	.99118	1.0089	7.5446	2...
38	.13283	.13402	7.4615	.99114	1.0089	7.5282	2...
39	.13312	.13432	7.4451	.99110	1.0090	7.5119	2...
40	.13341	.13461	7.4287	.99106	1.0090	7.4957	2...
41	.13370	.13491	7.4124	.99102	1.0091	7.4795	1...
42	.13399	.13521	7.3962	.99098	1.0091	7.4635	1...
43	.13427	.13550	7.3800	.99094	1.0091	7.4474	1...
44	.13456	.13580	7.3639	.99091	1.0092	7.4315	1...
45	.13485	.13609	7.3479	.99087	1.0092	7.4156	1...
46	.13514	.13639	7.3319	.99083	1.0092	7.3998	1...
47	.13543	.13669	7.3160	.99079	1.0093	7.3840	1...
48	.13572	.13698	7.3002	.99075	1.0093	7.3684	1...
49	.13600	.13728	7.2844	.99071	1.0094	7.3527	1...
50	.13629	.13758	7.2687	.99067	1.0094	7.3372	1...
51	.13658	.13787	7.2531	.99063	1.0095	7.3217	9
52	.13687	.13817	7.2375	.99059	1.0095	7.3063	8
53	.13716	.13846	7.2220	.99055	1.0095	7.2909	7
54	.13744	.13876	7.2066	.99051	1.0096	7.2757	6
55	.13773	.13906	7.1912	.99047	1.0096	7.2604	5
56	.13802	.13935	7.1759	.99043	1.0097	7.2453	4
57	.13831	.13965	7.1607	.99039	1.0097	7.2302	3
58	.13860	.13995	7.1455	.99035	1.0097	7.2152	2
59	.13889	.14024	7.1304	.99031	1.0098	7.2002	1
60	.13917	.14054	7.1154	.99027	1.0098	7.1853	0
′	Cos	Cot	Tan	Sin	Csc	Sec	

97° (277°) (262°) 8...

NATURAL TRIGONOMETRIC FUNCTIONS
TO FIVE PLACES

8° (188°)   (351°) 171°   9° (189°)   (350°) 170°

'	Sin	Tan	Cot	Cos	Sec	Csc	'
0	.13917	.14054	7.1154	.99027	1.0098	7.1853	60
1	.13946	.14084	7.1004	.99023	1.0099	7.1705	59
2	.13975	.14113	7.0855	.99019	1.0099	7.1557	58
3	.14004	.14143	7.0706	.99015	1.0100	7.1410	57
4	.14033	.14173	7.0558	.99011	1.0100	7.1263	56
5	.14061	.14202	7.0410	.99006	1.0100	7.1117	55
6	.14090	.14232	7.0264	.99002	1.0101	7.0972	54
7	.14119	.14262	7.0117	.98998	1.0101	7.0827	53
8	.14148	.14291	6.9972	.98994	1.0102	7.0683	52
9	.14177	.14321	6.9827	.98990	1.0102	7.0539	51
10	.14205	.14351	6.9682	.98986	1.0102	7.0396	50
11	.14234	.14381	6.9538	.98982	1.0103	7.0254	49
12	.14263	.14410	6.9395	.98978	1.0103	7.0112	48
13	.14292	.14440	6.9252	.98973	1.0104	6.9971	47
14	.14320	.14470	6.9110	.98969	1.0104	6.9830	46
15	.14349	.14499	6.8969	.98965	1.0105	6.9690	45
16	.14378	.14529	6.8828	.98961	1.0105	6.9550	44
17	.14407	.14559	6.8687	.98957	1.0105	6.9411	43
18	.14436	.14588	6.8548	.98953	1.0106	6.9273	42
19	.14464	.14618	6.8408	.98948	1.0106	6.9135	41
20	.14493	.14648	6.8269	.98944	1.0107	6.8998	40
21	.14522	.14678	6.8131	.98940	1.0107	6.8861	39
22	.14551	.14707	6.7994	.98936	1.0108	6.8725	38
23	.14580	.14737	6.7856	.98931	1.0108	6.8589	37
24	.14608	.14767	6.7720	.98927	1.0108	6.8454	36
25	.14637	.14796	6.7584	.98923	1.0109	6.8320	35
26	.14666	.14826	6.7448	.98919	1.0109	6.8186	34
27	.14695	.14856	6.7313	.98914	1.0110	6.8052	33
28	.14723	.14886	6.7179	.98910	1.0110	6.7919	32
29	.14752	.14915	6.7045	.98906	1.0111	6.7787	31
30	.14781	.14945	6.6912	.98902	1.0111	6.7655	30
31	.14810	.14975	6.6779	.98897	1.0112	6.7523	29
32	.14838	.15005	6.6646	.98893	1.0112	6.7392	28
33	.14867	.15034	6.6514	.98889	1.0112	6.7262	27
34	.14896	.15064	6.6383	.98884	1.0113	6.7132	26
35	.14925	.15094	6.6252	.98880	1.0113	6.7003	25
36	.14954	.15124	6.6122	.98876	1.0114	6.6874	24
37	.14982	.15153	6.5992	.98871	1.0114	6.6745	23
38	.15011	.15183	6.5863	.98867	1.0115	6.6618	22
39	.15040	.15213	6.5734	.98863	1.0115	6.6490	21
40	.15069	.15243	6.5606	.98858	1.0116	6.6363	20
41	.15097	.15272	6.5478	.98854	1.0116	6.6237	19
42	.15126	.15302	6.5350	.98849	1.0116	6.6111	18
43	.15155	.15332	6.5223	.98845	1.0117	6.5986	17
44	.15184	.15362	6.5097	.98841	1.0117	6.5861	16
45	.15212	.15391	6.4971	.98836	1.0118	6.5736	15
46	.15241	.15421	6.4846	.98832	1.0118	6.5612	14
47	.15270	.15451	6.4721	.98827	1.0119	6.5489	13
48	.15299	.15481	6.4596	.98823	1.0119	6.5366	12
49	.15327	.15511	6.4472	.98818	1.0120	6.5243	11
50	.15356	.15540	6.4348	.98814	1.0120	6.5121	10
51	.15385	.15570	6.4225	.98809	1.0120	6.4999	9
52	.15414	.15600	6.4103	.98805	1.0121	6.4878	8
53	.15442	.15630	6.3980	.98800	1.0121	6.4757	7
54	.15471	.15660	6.3859	.98796	1.0122	6.4637	6
55	.15500	.15689	6.3737	.98791	1.0122	6.4517	5
56	.15529	.15719	6.3617	.98787	1.0123	6.4398	4
57	.15557	.15749	6.3496	.98782	1.0123	6.4279	3
58	.15586	.15779	6.3376	.98778	1.0124	6.4160	2
59	.15615	.15809	6.3257	.98773	1.0124	6.4042	1
60	.15643	.15838	6.3138	.98769	1.0125	6.3925	0
'	Cos	Cot	Tan	Sin	Csc	Sec	'

° (278°)   (261°) 81°

'	Sin	Tan	Cot	Cos	Sec	Csc	'
0	.15643	.15838	6.3138	.98769	1.0125	6.3925	60
1	.15672	.15868	6.3019	.98764	1.0125	6.3807	59
2	.15701	.15898	6.2901	.98760	1.0126	6.3691	58
3	.15730	.15928	6.2783	.98755	1.0126	6.3574	57
4	.15758	.15958	6.2666	.98751	1.0127	6.3458	56
5	.15787	.15988	6.2549	.98746	1.0127	6.3343	55
6	.15816	.16017	6.2432	.98741	1.0127	6.3228	54
7	.15845	.16047	6.2316	.98737	1.0128	6.3113	53
8	.15873	.16077	6.2200	.98732	1.0128	6.2999	52
9	.15902	.16107	6.2085	.98728	1.0129	6.2885	51
10	.15931	.16137	6.1970	.98723	1.0129	6.2772	50
11	.15959	.16167	6.1856	.98718	1.0130	6.2659	49
12	.15988	.16196	6.1742	.98714	1.0130	6.2546	48
13	.16017	.16226	6.1628	.98709	1.0131	6.2434	47
14	.16046	.16256	6.1515	.98704	1.0131	6.2323	46
15	.16074	.16286	6.1402	.98700	1.0132	6.2211	45
16	.16103	.16316	6.1290	.98695	1.0132	6.2100	44
17	.16132	.16346	6.1178	.98690	1.0133	6.1990	43
18	.16160	.16376	6.1066	.98686	1.0133	6.1880	42
19	.16189	.16405	6.0955	.98681	1.0134	6.1770	41
20	.16218	.16435	6.0844	.98676	1.0134	6.1661	40
21	.16246	.16465	6.0734	.98671	1.0135	6.1552	39
22	.16275	.16495	6.0624	.98667	1.0135	6.1443	38
23	.16304	.16525	6.0514	.98662	1.0136	6.1335	37
24	.16333	.16555	6.0405	.98657	1.0136	6.1227	36
25	.16361	.16585	6.0296	.98652	1.0137	6.1120	35
26	.16390	.16615	6.0188	.98648	1.0137	6.1013	34
27	.16419	.16645	6.0080	.98643	1.0138	6.0906	33
28	.16447	.16674	5.9972	.98638	1.0138	6.0800	32
29	.16476	.16704	5.9865	.98633	1.0139	6.0694	31
30	.16505	.16734	5.9758	.98629	1.0139	6.0589	30
31	.16533	.16764	5.9651	.98624	1.0140	6.0483	29
32	.16562	.16794	5.9545	.98619	1.0140	6.0379	28
33	.16591	.16824	5.9439	.98614	1.0141	6.0274	27
34	.16620	.16854	5.9333	.98609	1.0141	6.0170	26
35	.16648	.16884	5.9228	.98604	1.0142	6.0067	25
36	.16677	.16914	5.9124	.98600	1.0142	5.9963	24
37	.16706	.16944	5.9019	.98595	1.0143	5.9860	23
38	.16734	.16974	5.8915	.98590	1.0143	5.9758	22
39	.16763	.17004	5.8811	.98585	1.0144	5.9656	21
40	.16792	.17033	5.8708	.98580	1.0144	5.9554	20
41	.16820	.17063	5.8605	.98575	1.0145	5.9452	19
42	.16849	.17093	5.8502	.98570	1.0145	5.9351	18
43	.16878	.17123	5.8400	.98565	1.0146	5.9250	17
44	.16906	.17153	5.8298	.98561	1.0146	5.9150	16
45	.16935	.17183	5.8197	.98556	1.0147	5.9049	15
46	.16964	.17213	5.8095	.98551	1.0147	5.8950	14
47	.16992	.17243	5.7994	.98546	1.0148	5.8850	13
48	.17021	.17273	5.7894	.98541	1.0148	5.8751	12
49	.17050	.17303	5.7794	.98536	1.0149	5.8652	11
50	.17078	.17333	5.7694	.98531	1.0149	5.8554	10
51	.17107	.17363	5.7594	.98526	1.0150	5.8456	9
52	.17136	.17393	5.7495	.98521	1.0150	5.8358	8
53	.17164	.17423	5.7396	.98516	1.0151	5.8261	7
54	.17193	.17453	5.7297	.98511	1.0151	5.8164	6
55	.17222	.17483	5.7199	.98506	1.0152	5.8067	5
56	.17250	.17513	5.7101	.98501	1.0152	5.7970	4
57	.17279	.17543	5.7004	.98496	1.0153	5.7874	3
58	.17308	.17573	5.6906	.98491	1.0153	5.7778	2
59	.17336	.17603	5.6809	.98486	1.0154	5.7683	1
60	.17365	.17633	5.6713	.98481	1.0154	5.7588	0
'	Cos	Cot	Tan	Sin	Csc	Sec	'

99° (279°)   (260°) 80°

NATURAL TRIGONOMETRIC FUNCTIONS
TO FIVE PLACES

10° (190°)   (349°) 169°   11° (191°)   (348°)

′	Sin	Tan	Cot	Cos	Sec	Csc	′		′	Sin	Tan	Cot	Cos	Sec	Csc
0	.17365	.17633	5.6713	.98481	1.0154	5.7588	60		0	.19081	.19438	5.1446	.98163	1.0187	5.2408
1	.17393	.17663	5.6617	.98476	1.0155	5.7493	59		1	.19109	.19468	5.1366	.98157	1.0188	5.2330
2	.17422	.17693	5.6521	.98471	1.0155	5.7398	58		2	.19138	.19498	5.1286	.98152	1.0188	5.2252
3	.17451	.17723	5.6425	.98466	1.0156	5.7304	57		3	.19167	.19529	5.1207	.98146	1.0189	5.2174
4	.17479	.17753	5.6329	.98461	1.0156	5.7210	56		4	.19195	.19559	5.1128	.98140	1.0189	5.2097
5	.17508	.17783	5.6234	.98455	1.0157	5.7117	55		5	.19224	.19589	5.1049	.98135	1.0190	5.2019
6	.17537	.17813	5.6140	.98450	1.0157	5.7023	54		6	.19252	.19619	5.0970	.98129	1.0191	5.1942
7	.17565	.17843	5.6045	.98445	1.0158	5.6930	53		7	.19281	.19649	5.0892	.98124	1.0191	5.1865
8	.17594	.17873	5.5951	.98440	1.0158	5.6838	52		8	.19309	.19680	5.0814	.98118	1.0192	5.1789
9	.17623	.17903	5.5857	.98435	1.0159	5.6745	51		9	.19338	.19710	5.0736	.98112	1.0192	5.1712
10	.17651	.17933	5.5764	.98430	1.0160	5.6653	50		10	.19366	.19740	5.0658	.98107	1.0193	5.1636
11	.17680	.17963	5.5671	.98425	1.0160	5.6562	49		11	.19395	.19770	5.0581	.98101	1.0194	5.1560
12	.17708	.17993	5.5578	.98420	1.0161	5.6470	48		12	.19423	.19801	5.0504	.98096	1.0194	5.1484
13	.17737	.18023	5.5485	.98414	1.0161	5.6379	47		13	.19452	.19831	5.0427	.98090	1.0195	5.1409
14	.17766	.18053	5.5393	.98409	1.0162	5.6288	46		14	.19481	.19861	5.0350	.98084	1.0195	5.1333
15	.17794	.18083	5.5301	.98404	1.0162	5.6198	45		15	.19509	.19891	5.0273	.98079	1.0196	5.1258
16	.17823	.18113	5.5209	.98399	1.0163	5.6107	44		16	.19538	.19921	5.0197	.98073	1.0197	5.1183
17	.17852	.18143	5.5118	.98394	1.0163	5.6017	43		17	.19566	.19952	5.0121	.98067	1.0197	5.1109
18	.17880	.18173	5.5026	.98389	1.0164	5.5928	42		18	.19595	.19982	5.0045	.98061	1.0198	5.1034
19	.17909	.18203	5.4936	.98383	1.0164	5.5838	41		19	.19623	.20012	4.9969	.98056	1.0198	5.0960
20	.17937	.18233	5.4845	.98378	1.0165	5.5749	40		20	.19652	.20042	4.9894	.98050	1.0199	5.0886
21	.17966	.18263	5.4755	.98373	1.0165	5.5660	39		21	.19680	.20073	4.9819	.98044	1.0199	5.0813
22	.17995	.18293	5.4665	.98368	1.0166	5.5572	38		22	.19709	.20103	4.9744	.98039	1.0200	5.0739
23	.18023	.18323	5.4575	.98362	1.0166	5.5484	37		23	.19737	.20133	4.9669	.98033	1.0201	5.0666
24	.18052	.18353	5.4486	.98357	1.0167	5.5396	36		24	.19766	.20164	4.9594	.98027	1.0201	5.0593
25	.18081	.18384	5.4397	.98352	1.0168	5.5308	35		25	.19794	.20194	4.9520	.98021	1.0202	5.0520
26	.18109	.18414	5.4308	.98347	1.0168	5.5221	34		26	.19823	.20224	4.9446	.98016	1.0202	5.0447
27	.18138	.18444	5.4219	.98341	1.0169	5.5134	33		27	.19851	.20254	4.9372	.98010	1.0203	5.0375
28	.18166	.18474	5.4131	.98336	1.0169	5.5047	32		28	.19880	.20285	4.9298	.98004	1.0204	5.0302
29	.18195	.18504	5.4043	.98331	1.0170	5.4960	31		29	.19908	.20315	4.9225	.97998	1.0204	5.0230
30	.18224	.18534	5.3955	.98325	1.0170	5.4874	30		30	.19937	.20345	4.9152	.97992	1.0205	5.0159
31	.18252	.18564	5.3868	.98320	1.0171	5.4788	29		31	.19965	.20376	4.9078	.97987	1.0205	5.0087
32	.18281	.18594	5.3781	.98315	1.0171	5.4702	28		32	.19994	.20406	4.9006	.97981	1.0206	5.0016
33	.18309	.18624	5.3694	.98310	1.0172	5.4617	27		33	.20022	.20436	4.8933	.97975	1.0207	4.9944
34	.18338	.18654	5.3607	.98304	1.0173	5.4532	26		34	.20051	.20466	4.8860	.97969	1.0207	4.9873
35	.18367	.18684	5.3521	.98299	1.0173	5.4447	25		35	.20079	.20497	4.8788	.97963	1.0208	4.9803
36	.18395	.18714	5.3435	.98294	1.0174	5.4362	24		36	.20108	.20527	4.8716	.97958	1.0209	4.9732
37	.18424	.18745	5.3349	.98288	1.0174	5.4278	23		37	.20136	.20557	4.8644	.97952	1.0209	4.9662
38	.18452	.18775	5.3263	.98283	1.0175	5.4194	22		38	.20165	.20588	4.8573	.97946	1.0210	4.9591
39	.18481	.18805	5.3178	.98277	1.0175	5.4110	21		39	.20193	.20618	4.8501	.97940	1.0210	4.9521
40	.18509	.18835	5.3093	.98272	1.0176	5.4026	20		40	.20222	.20648	4.8430	.97934	1.0211	4.9452
41	.18538	.18865	5.3008	.98267	1.0176	5.3943	19		41	.20250	.20679	4.8359	.97928	1.0212	4.9382
42	.18567	.18895	5.2924	.98261	1.0177	5.3860	18		42	.20279	.20709	4.8288	.97922	1.0212	4.9313
43	.18595	.18925	5.2839	.98256	1.0178	5.3777	17		43	.20307	.20739	4.8218	.97916	1.0213	4.9244
44	.18624	.18955	5.2755	.98250	1.0178	5.3695	16		44	.20336	.20770	4.8147	.97910	1.0213	4.9175
45	.18652	.18986	5.2672	.98245	1.0179	5.3612	15		45	.20364	.20800	4.8077	.97905	1.0214	4.9106
46	.18681	.19016	5.2588	.98240	1.0179	5.3530	14		46	.20393	.20830	4.8007	.97899	1.0215	4.9037
47	.18710	.19046	5.2505	.98234	1.0180	5.3449	13		47	.20421	.20861	4.7937	.97893	1.0215	4.8969
48	.18738	.19076	5.2422	.98229	1.0180	5.3367	12		48	.20450	.20891	4.7867	.97887	1.0216	4.8901
49	.18767	.19106	5.2339	.98223	1.0181	5.3286	11		49	.20478	.20921	4.7798	.97881	1.0217	4.8833
50	.18795	.19136	5.2257	.98218	1.0181	5.3205	10		50	.20507	.20952	4.7729	.97875	1.0217	4.8765
51	.18824	.19166	5.2174	.98212	1.0182	5.3124	9		51	.20535	.20982	4.7659	.97869	1.0218	4.8697
52	.18852	.19197	5.2092	.98207	1.0183	5.3044	8		52	.20563	.21013	4.7591	.97863	1.0218	4.8630
53	.18881	.19227	5.2011	.98201	1.0183	5.2963	7		53	.20592	.21043	4.7522	.97857	1.0219	4.8563
54	.18910	.19257	5.1929	.98196	1.0184	5.2883	6		54	.20620	.21073	4.7453	.97851	1.0220	4.8496
55	.18938	.19287	5.1848	.98190	1.0184	5.2804	5		55	.20649	.21104	4.7385	.97845	1.0220	4.8429
56	.18967	.19317	5.1767	.98185	1.0185	5.2724	4		56	.20677	.21134	4.7317	.97839	1.0221	4.8362
57	.18995	.19347	5.1686	.98179	1.0185	5.2645	3		57	.20706	.21164	4.7249	.97833	1.0222	4.8296
58	.19024	.19378	5.1606	.98174	1.0186	5.2566	2		58	.20734	.21195	4.7181	.97827	1.0222	4.8229
59	.19052	.19408	5.1526	.98168	1.0187	5.2487	1		59	.20763	.21225	4.7114	.97821	1.0223	4.8163
60	.19081	.19438	5.1446	.98163	1.0187	5.2408	0		60	.20791	.21256	4.7046	.97815	1.0223	4.8097
′	Cos	Cot	Tan	Sin	Csc	Sec	′		′	Cos	Cot	Tan	Sin	Csc	Sec

NATURAL TRIGONOMETRIC FUNCTIONS
TO FIVE PLACES

192°)   (347°) 167°   13° (193°)   (346°) 166°

Sin	Tan	Cot	Cos	Sec	Csc	'		'	Sin	Tan	Cot	Cos	Sec	Csc	'
.20791	.21256	4.7046	.97815	1.0223	4.8097	60		0	.22495	.23087	4.3315	.97437	1.0263	4.4454	60
.20820	.21286	4.6979	.97809	1.0224	4.8032	59		1	.22523	.23117	4.3257	.97430	1.0264	4.4398	59
.20848	.21316	4.6912	.97803	1.0225	4.7966	58		2	.22552	.23148	4.3200	.97424	1.0264	4.4342	58
.20877	.21347	4.6845	.97797	1.0225	4.7901	57		3	.22580	.23179	4.3143	.97417	1.0265	4.4287	57
.20905	.21377	4.6779	.97791	1.0226	4.7836	56		4	.22608	.23209	4.3086	.97411	1.0266	4.4231	56
.20933	.21408	4.6712	.97784	1.0227	4.7771	55		5	.22637	.23240	4.3029	.97404	1.0266	4.4176	55
.20962	.21438	4.6646	.97778	1.0227	4.7706	54		6	.22665	.23271	4.2972	.97398	1.0267	4.4121	54
.20990	.21469	4.6580	.97772	1.0228	4.7641	53		7	.22693	.23301	4.2916	.97391	1.0268	4.4066	53
.21019	.21499	4.6514	.97766	1.0228	4.7577	52		8	.22722	.23332	4.2859	.97384	1.0269	4.4011	52
.21047	.21529	4.6448	.97760	1.0229	4.7512	51		9	.22750	.23363	4.2803	.97378	1.0269	4.3956	51
.21076	.21560	4.6382	.97754	1.0230	4.7448	50		10	.22778	.23393	4.2747	.97371	1.0270	4.3901	50
.21104	.21590	4.6317	.97748	1.0230	4.7384	49		11	.22807	.23424	4.2691	.97365	1.0271	4.3847	49
.21132	.21621	4.6252	.97742	1.0231	4.7321	48		12	.22835	.23455	4.2635	.97358	1.0271	4.3792	48
.21161	.21651	4.6187	.97735	1.0232	4.7257	47		13	.22863	.23485	4.2580	.97351	1.0272	4.3738	47
.21189	.21682	4.6122	.97729	1.0232	4.7194	46		14	.22892	.23516	4.2524	.97345	1.0273	4.3684	46
.21218	.21712	4.6057	.97723	1.0233	4.7130	45		15	.22920	.23547	4.2468	.97338	1.0273	4.3630	45
.21246	.21743	4.5993	.97717	1.0234	4.7067	44		16	.22948	.23578	4.2413	.97331	1.0274	4.3576	44
.21275	.21773	4.5928	.97711	1.0234	4.7004	43		17	.22977	.23608	4.2358	.97325	1.0275	4.3522	43
.21303	.21804	4.5864	.97705	1.0235	4.6942	42		18	.23005	.23639	4.2303	.97318	1.0276	4.3469	42
.21331	.21834	4.5800	.97698	1.0236	4.6879	41		19	.23033	.23670	4.2248	.97311	1.0276	4.3415	41
.21360	.21864	4.5736	.97692	1.0236	4.6817	40		20	.23062	.23700	4.2193	.97304	1.0277	4.3362	40
.21388	.21895	4.5673	.97686	1.0237	4.6755	39		21	.23090	.23731	4.2139	.97298	1.0278	4.3309	39
.21417	.21925	4.5609	.97680	1.0238	4.6693	38		22	.23118	.23762	4.2084	.97291	1.0278	4.3256	38
.21445	.21956	4.5546	.97673	1.0238	4.6631	37		23	.23146	.23793	4.2030	.97284	1.0279	4.3203	37
.21474	.21986	4.5483	.97667	1.0239	4.6569	36		24	.23175	.23823	4.1976	.97278	1.0280	4.3150	36
.21502	.22017	4.5420	.97661	1.0240	4.6507	35		25	.23203	.23854	4.1922	.97271	1.0281	4.3098	35
.21530	.22047	4.5357	.97655	1.0240	4.6446	34		26	.23231	.23885	4.1868	.97264	1.0281	4.3045	34
.21559	.22078	4.5294	.97648	1.0241	4.6385	33		27	.23260	.23916	4.1814	.97257	1.0282	4.2993	33
.21587	.22108	4.5232	.97642	1.0241	4.6324	32		28	.23288	.23946	4.1760	.97251	1.0283	4.2941	32
.21616	.22139	4.5169	.97636	1.0242	4.6263	31		29	.23316	.23977	4.1706	.97244	1.0283	4.2889	31
.21644	.22169	4.5107	.97630	1.0243	4.6202	30		30	.23345	.24008	4.1653	.97237	1.0284	4.2837	30
.21672	.22200	4.5045	.97623	1.0243	4.6142	29		31	.23373	.24039	4.1600	.97230	1.0285	4.2785	29
.21701	.22231	4.4983	.97617	1.0244	4.6081	28		32	.23401	.24069	4.1547	.97223	1.0286	4.2733	28
.21729	.22261	4.4922	.97611	1.0245	4.6021	27		33	.23429	.24100	4.1493	.97217	1.0286	4.2681	27
.21758	.22292	4.4860	.97604	1.0245	4.5961	26		34	.23458	.24131	4.1441	.97210	1.0287	4.2630	26
.21786	.22322	4.4799	.97598	1.0246	4.5901	25		35	.23486	.24162	4.1388	.97203	1.0288	4.2579	25
.21814	.22353	4.4737	.97592	1.0247	4.5841	24		36	.23514	.24193	4.1335	.97196	1.0288	4.2527	24
.21843	.22383	4.4676	.97585	1.0247	4.5782	23		37	.23542	.24223	4.1282	.97189	1.0289	4.2476	23
.21871	.22414	4.4615	.97579	1.0248	4.5722	22		38	.23571	.24254	4.1230	.97182	1.0290	4.2425	22
.21899	.22444	4.4555	.97573	1.0249	4.5663	21		39	.23599	.24285	4.1178	.97176	1.0291	4.2375	21
.21928	.22475	4.4494	.97566	1.0249	4.5604	20		40	.23627	.24316	4.1126	.97169	1.0291	4.2324	20
.21956	.22505	4.4434	.97560	1.0250	4.5545	19		41	.23656	.24347	4.1074	.97162	1.0292	4.2273	19
.21985	.22536	4.4373	.97553	1.0251	4.5486	18		42	.23684	.24377	4.1022	.97155	1.0293	4.2223	18
.22013	.22567	4.4313	.97547	1.0251	4.5428	17		43	.23712	.24408	4.0970	.97148	1.0294	4.2173	17
.22041	.22597	4.4253	.97541	1.0252	4.5369	16		44	.23740	.24439	4.0918	.97141	1.0294	4.2122	16
.22070	.22628	4.4194	.97534	1.0253	4.5311	15		45	.23769	.24470	4.0867	.97134	1.0295	4.2072	15
.22098	.22658	4.4134	.97528	1.0253	4.5253	14		46	.23797	.24501	4.0815	.97127	1.0296	4.2022	14
.22126	.22689	4.4075	.97521	1.0254	4.5195	13		47	.23825	.24532	4.0764	.97120	1.0297	4.1973	13
.22155	.22719	4.4015	.97515	1.0255	4.5137	12		48	.23853	.24562	4.0713	.97113	1.0297	4.1923	12
.22183	.22750	4.3956	.97508	1.0256	4.5079	11		49	.23882	.24593	4.0662	.97106	1.0298	4.1873	11
.22212	.22781	4.3897	.97502	1.0256	4.5022	10		50	.23910	.24624	4.0611	.97100	1.0299	4.1824	10
.22240	.22811	4.3838	.97496	1.0257	4.4964	9		51	.23938	.24655	4.0560	.97093	1.0299	4.1774	9
.22268	.22842	4.3779	.97489	1.0258	4.4907	8		52	.23966	.24686	4.0509	.97086	1.0300	4.1725	8
.22297	.22872	4.3721	.97483	1.0258	4.4850	7		53	.23995	.24717	4.0459	.97079	1.0301	4.1676	7
.22325	.22903	4.3662	.97476	1.0259	4.4793	6		54	.24023	.24747	4.0408	.97072	1.0302	4.1627	6
.22353	.22934	4.3604	.97470	1.0260	4.4736	5		55	.24051	.24778	4.0358	.97065	1.0302	4.1578	5
.22382	.22964	4.3546	.97463	1.0260	4.4679	4		56	.24079	.24809	4.0308	.97058	1.0303	4.1529	4
.22410	.22995	4.3488	.97457	1.0261	4.4623	3		57	.24108	.24840	4.0257	.97051	1.0304	4.1481	3
.22438	.23026	4.3430	.97450	1.0262	4.4566	2		58	.24136	.24871	4.0207	.97044	1.0305	4.1432	2
.22467	.23056	4.3372	.97444	1.0262	4.4510	1		59	.24164	.24902	4.0158	.97037	1.0305	4.1384	1
.22495	.23087	4.3315	.97437	1.0263	4.4454	0		60	.24192	.24933	4.0108	.97030	1.0306	4.1336	0
Cos	Cot	Tan	Sin	Csc	Sec	'		'	Cos	Cot	Tan	Sin	Csc	Sec	'

NATURAL TRIGONOMETRIC FUNCTIONS
TO FIVE PLACES

14° (194°)   (345°) 165°   15° (195°)   (344°

'	Sin	Tan	Cot	Cos	Sec	Csc	'		'	Sin	Tan	Cot	Cos	Sec	Csc
0	.24192	.24933	4.0108	.97030	1.0306	4.1336	60		0	.25882	.26795	3.7321	.96593	1.0353	3.8637
1	.24220	.24964	4.0058	.97023	1.0307	4.1287	59		1	.25910	.26826	3.7277	.96585	1.0354	3.8595
2	.24249	.24995	4.0009	.97015	1.0308	4.1239	58		2	.25938	.26857	3.7234	.96578	1.0354	3.8553
3	.24277	.25026	3.9959	.97008	1.0308	4.1191	57		3	.25966	.26888	3.7191	.96570	1.0355	3.8512
4	.24305	.25056	3.9910	.97001	1.0309	4.1144	56		4	.25994	.26920	3.7148	.96562	1.0356	3.8470
5	.24333	.25087	3.9861	.96994	1.0310	4.1096	55		5	.26022	.26951	3.7105	.96555	1.0357	3.8428
6	.24362	.25118	3.9812	.96987	1.0311	4.1048	54		6	.26050	.26982	3.7062	.96547	1.0358-	3.8387
7	.24390	.25149	3.9763	.96980	1.0311	4.1001	53		7	.26079	.27013	3.7019	.96540	1.0358	3.8346
8	.24418	.25180	3.9714	.96973	1.0312	4.0954	52		8	.26107	.27044	3.6976	.96532	1.0359	3.8304
9	.24446	.25211	3.9665	.96966	1.0313	4.0906	51		9	.26135	.27076	3.6933	.96524	1.0360	3.8263
10	.24474	.25242	3.9617	.96959	1.0314	4.0859	50		10	.26163	.27107	3.6891	.96517	1.0361	3.8222
11	.24503	.25273	3.9568	.96952	1.0314	4.0812	49		11	.26191	.27138	3.6848	.96509	1.0362	3.8181
12	.24531	.25304	3.9520	.96945	1.0315	4.0765	48		12	.26219	.27169	3.6806	.96502	1.0363	3.8140
13	.24559	.25335	3.9471	.96937	1.0316	4.0718	47		13	.26247	.27201	3.6764	.96494	1.0363	3.8100
14	.24587	.25366	3.9423	.96930	1.0317	4.0672	46		14	.26275	.27232	3.6722	.96486	1.0364	3.8059
15	.24615	.25397	3.9375	.96923	1.0317	4.0625	45		15	.26303	.27263	3.6680	.96479	1.0365	3.8018
16	.24644	.25428	3.9327	.96916	1.0318	4.0579	44		16	.26331	.27294	3.6638	.96471	1.0366	3.7978
17	.24672	.25459	3.9279	.96909	1.0319	4.0532	43		17	.26359	.27326	3.6596	.96463	1.0367	3.7937
18	.24700	.25490	3.9232	.96902	1.0320	4.0486	42		18	.26387	.27357	3.6554	.96456	1.0367	3.7897
19	.24728	.25521	3.9184	.96894	1.0321	4.0440	41		19	.26415	.27388	3.6512	.96448	1.0368	3.7857
20	.24756	.25552	3.9136	.96887	1.0321	4.0394	40		20	.26443	.27419	3.6470	.96440	1.0369	3.7817
21	.24784	.25583	3.9089	.96880	1.0322	4.0348	39		21	.26471	.27451	3.6429	.96433	1.0370	3.7777
22	.24813	.25614	3.9042	.96873	1.0323	4.0302	38		22	.26500	.27482	3.6387	.96425	1.0371	3.7737
23	.24841	.25645	3.8995	.96866	1.0324	4.0256	37		23	.26528	.27513	3.6346	.96417	1.0372	3.7697
24	.24869	.25676	3.8947	.96858	1.0324	4.0211	36		24	.26556	.27545	3.6305	.96410	1.0372	3.7657
25	.24897	.25707	3.8900	.96851	1.0325	4.0165	35		25	.26584	.27576	3.6264	.94602	1.0373	3.7617
26	.24925	.25738	3.8854	.96844	1.0326	4.0120	34		26	.26612	.27607	3.6222	.96394	1.0374	3.7577
27	.24954	.25769	3.8807	.96837	1.0327	4.0075	33		27	.26640	.27638	3.6181	.96386	1.0375	3.7538
28	.24982	.25800	3.8760	.96829	1.0327	4.0029	32		28	.26668	.27670	3.6140	.96379	1.0376	3.7498
29	.25010	.25831	3.8714	.96822	1.0328	3.9984	31		29	.26696	.27701	3.6100	.96371	1.0377	3.7459
30	.25038	.25862	3.8667	.96815	1.0329	3.9939	30		30	.26724	.27732	3.6059	.96363	1.0377	3.7420
31	.25066	.25893	3.8621	.96807	1.0330	3.9894	29		31	.26752	.27764	3.6018	.96355	1.0378	3.7381
32	.25094	.25924	3.8575	.96800	1.0331	3.9850	28		32	.26780	.27795	3.5978	.96347	1.0379	3.7341
33	.25122	.25955	3.8528	.96793	1.0331	3.9805	27		33	.26808	.27826	3.5937	.96340	1.0380	3.7302
34	.25151	.25986	3.8482	.96786	1.0332	3.9760	26		34	.26836	.27858	3.5897	.96332	1.0381	3.7263
35	.25179	.26017	3.8436	.96778	1.0333	3.9716	25		35	.26864	.27889	3.5856	.96324	1.0382	3.7225
36	.25207	.26048	3.8391	.96771	1.0334	3.9672	24		36	.26892	.27921	3.5816	.96316	1.0382	3.7186
37	.25235	.26079	3.8345	.96764	1.0334	3.9627	23		37	.26920	.27952	3.5776	.96308	1.0383	3.7147
38	.25263	.26110	3.8299	.96756	1.0335	3.9583	22		38	.26948	.27983	3.5736	.96301	1.0384	3.7108
39	.25291	.26141	3.8254	.96749	1.0336	3.9539	21		39	.26976	.28015	3.5696	.96293	1.0385	3.7070
40	.25320	.26172	3.8208	.96742	1.0337	3.9495	20		40	.27004	.28046	3.5656	.96285	1.0386	3.7032
41	.25348	.26203	3.8163	.96734	1.0338	3.9451	19		41	.27032	.28077	3.5616	.96277	1.0387	3.6993
42	.25376	.26235	3.8118	.96727	1.0338	3.9408	18		42	.27060	.28109	3.5576	.96269	1.0388	3.6955
43	.25404	.26266	3.8073	.96719	1.0339	3.9364	17		43	.27088	.28140	3.5536	.96261	1.0388	3.6917
44	.25432	.26297	3.8028	.96712	1.0340	3.9320	16		44	.27116	.28172	3.5497	.96253	1.0389	3.6879
45	.25460	.26328	3.7983	.96705	1.0341	3.9277	15		45	.27144	.28203	3.5457	.96246	1.0390	3.6840
46	.25488	.26359	3.7938	.96697	1.0342	3.9234	14		46	.27172	.28234	3.5418	.96238	1.0391	3.6803
47	.25516	.26390	3.7893	.96690	1.0342	3.9190	13		47	.27200	.28266	3.5379	.96230	1.0392	3.6765
48	.25545	.26421	3.7848	.96682	1.0343	3.9147	12		48	.27228	.28297	3.5339	.96222	1.0393	3.6727
49	.25573	.26452	3.7804	.96675	1.0344	3.9104	11		49	.27256	.28329	3.5300	.96214	1.0394	3.6689
50	.25601	.26483	3.7760	.96667	1.0345	3.9061	10		50	.27284	.28360	3.5261	.96206	1.0394	3.6652
51	.25629	.26515	3.7715	.96660	1.0346	3.9018	9		51	.27312	.28391	3.5222	.96198	1.0395	3.6614
52	.25657	.26546	3.7671	.96653	1.0346	3.8976	8		52	.27340	.28423	3.5183	.96190	1.0396	3.6575
53	.25685	.26577	3.7627	.96645	1.0347	3.8933	7		53	.27368	.28454	3.5144	.96182	1.0397	3.6539
54	.25713	.26608	3.7583	.96638	1.0348	3.8890	6		54	.27396	.28486	3.5105	.96174	1.0398	3.6502
55	.25741	.26639	3.7539	.96630	1.0349	3.8848	5		55	.27424	.28517	3.5067	.96166	1.0399	3.6465
56	.25769	.26670	3.7495	.96623	1.0350	3.8806	4		56	.27452	.28549	3.5028	.96158	1.0400	3.6427
57	.25798	.26701	3.7451	.96615	1.0350	3.8763	3		57	.27480	.28580	3.4989	.96150	1.0400	3.6390
58	.25826	.26733	3.7408	.96608	1.0351	3.8721	2		58	.27508	.28612	3.4951	.96142	1.0401	3.6353
59	.25854	.26764	3.7364	.96600	1.0352	3.8679	1		59	.27536	.28643	3.4912	.96134	1.0402	3.6316
60	.25882	.26795	3.7321	.96593	1.0353	3.8637	0		60	.27564	.28675	3.4874	.96126	1.0403	3.6280
'	Cos	Cot	Tan	Sin	Csc	Sec	'		'	Cos	Cot	Tan	Sin	Csc	Sec

NATURAL TRIGONOMETRIC FUNCTIONS
TO FIVE PLACES

196°)   (343°) 163°   17° (197°)   (342°) 162°

Sin	Tan	Cot	Cos	Sec	Csc	′		′	Sin	Tan	Cot	Cos	Sec	Csc	′
.27564	.28675	3.4874	.96126	1.0403	3.6280	60		0	.29237	.30573	3.2709	.95630	1.0457	3.4203	60
.27592	.28706	3.4836	.96118	1.0404	3.6243	59		1	.29265	.30605	3.2675	.95622	1.0458	3.4171	59
.27620	.28738	3.4798	.96110	1.0405	3.6206	58		2	.29293	.30637	3.2641	.95613	1.0459	3.4138	58
.27648	.28769	3.4760	.96102	1.0406	3.6169	57		3	.29321	.30669	3.2607	.95605	1.0460	3.4106	57
.27676	.28801	3.4722	.96094	1.0406	3.6133	56		4	.29348	.30700	3.2573	.95596	1.0461	3.4073	56
.27704	.28832	3.4684	.96086	1.0407	3.6097	55		5	.29376	.30732	3.2539	.95588	1.0462	3.4041	55
.27731	.28864	3.4646	.96078	1.0408	3.6060	54		6	.29404	.30764	3.2506	.95579	1.0463	3.4009	54
.27759	.28895	3.4608	.96070	1.0409	3.6024	53		7	.29432	.30796	3.2472	.95571	1.0463	3.3977	53
.27787	.28927	3.4570	.96062	1.0410	3.5988	52		8	.29460	.30828	3.2438	.95562	1.0464	3.3945	52
.27815	.28958	3.4533	.96054	1.0411	3.5951	51		9	.29487	.30860	3.2405	.95554	1.0465	3.3913	51
.27843	.28990	3.4495	.96046	1.0412	3.5915	50		10	.29515	.30891	3.2371	.95545	1.0466	3.3881	50
.27871	.29021	3.4458	.96037	1.0413	3.5879	49		11	.29543	.30923	3.2338	.95536	1.0467	3.3849	49
.27899	.29053	3.4420	.96029	1.0413	3.5843	48		12	.29571	.30955	3.2305	.95528	1.0468	3.3817	48
.27927	.29084	3.4383	.96021	1.0414	3.5808	47		13	.29599	.30987	3.2272	.95519	1.0469	3.3785	47
.27955	.29116	3.4346	.96013	1.0415	3.5772	46		14	.29626	.31019	3.2238	.95511	1.0470	3.3754	46
.27983	.29147	3.4308	.96005	1.0416	3.5736	45		15	.29654	.31051	3.2205	.95502	1.0471	3.3722	45
.28011	.29179	3.4271	.95997	1.0417	3.5700	44		16	.29682	.31083	3.2172	.95493	1.0472	3.3691	44
.28039	.29210	3.4234	.95989	1.0418	3.5665	43		17	.29710	.31115	3.2139	.95485	1.0473	3.3659	43
.28067	.29242	3.4197	.95981	1.0419	3.5629	42		18	.29737	.31147	3.2106	.95476	1.0474	3.3628	42
.28095	.29274	3.4160	.95972	1.0420	3.5594	41		19	.29765	.31178	3.2073	.95467	1.0475	3.3596	41
.28123	.29305	3.4124	.95964	1.0421	3.5559	40		20	.29793	.31210	3.2041	.95459	1.0476	3.3565	40
.28150	.29337	3.4087	.95956	1.0421	3.5523	39		21	.29821	.31242	3.2008	.95450	1.0477	3.3534	39
.28178	.29368	3.4050	.95948	1.0422	3.5488	38		22	.29849	.31274	3.1975	.95441	1.0478	3.3502	38
.28206	.29400	3.4014	.95940	1.0423	3.5453	37		23	.29876	.31306	3.1943	.95433	1.0479	3.3471	37
.28234	.29432	3.3977	.95931	1.0424	3.5418	36		24	.29904	.31338	3.1910	.95424	1.0480	3.3440	36
.28262	.29463	3.3941	.95923	1.0425	3.5383	35		25	.29932	.31370	3.1878	.95415	1.0480	3.3409	35
.28290	.29495	3.3904	.95915	1.0426	3.5348	34		26	.29960	.31402	3.1845	.95407	1.0481	3.3378	34
.28318	.29526	3.3868	.95907	1.0427	3.5313	33		27	.29987	.31434	3.1813	.95398	1.0482	3.3347	33
.28346	.29558	3.3832	.95898	1.0428	3.5279	32		28	.30015	.31466	3.1780	.95389	1.0483	3.3317	32
.28374	.29590	3.3796	.95890	1.0429	3.5244	31		29	.30043	.31498	3.1748	.95380	1.0484	3.3286	31
.28402	.29621	3.3759	.95882	1.0429	3.5209	30		30	.30071	.31530	3.1716	.95372	1.0485	3.3255	30
.28429	.29653	3.3723	.95874	1.0430	3.5175	29		31	.30098	.31562	3.1684	.95363	1.0486	3.3224	29
.28457	.29685	3.3687	.95865	1.0431	3.5140	28		32	.30126	.31594	3.1652	.95354	1.0487	3.3194	28
.28485	.29716	3.3652	.95857	1.0432	3.5106	27		33	.30154	.31626	3.1620	.95345	1.0488	3.3163	27
.28513	.29748	3.3616	.95849	1.0433	3.5072	26		34	.30182	.31658	3.1588	.95337	1.0489	3.3133	26
.28541	.29780	3.3580	.95841	1.0434	3.5037	25		35	.30209	.31690	3.1556	.95328	1.0490	3.3102	25
.28569	.29811	3.3544	.95832	1.0435	3.5003	24		36	.30237	.31722	3.1524	.95319	1.0491	3.3072	24
.28597	.29843	3.3509	.95824	1.0436	3.4969	23		37	.30265	.31754	3.1492	.95310	1.0492	3.3042	23
.28625	.29875	3.3473	.95816	1.0437	3.4935	22		38	.30292	.31786	3.1460	.95301	1.0493	3.3012	22
.28652	.29906	3.3438	.95807	1.0438	3.4901	21		39	.30320	.31818	3.1429	.95293	1.0494	3.2981	21
.28680	.29938	3.3402	.95799	1.0439	3.4867	20		40	.30348	.31850	3.1397	.95284	1.0495	3.2951	20
.28708	.29970	3.3367	.95791	1.0439	3.4833	19		41	.30376	.31882	3.1366	.95275	1.0496	3.2921	19
.28736	.30001	3.3332	.95782	1.0440	3.4799	18		42	.30403	.31914	3.1334	.95266	1.0497	3.2891	18
.28764	.30033	3.3297	.95774	1.0441	3.4766	17		43	.30431	.31946	3.1303	.95257	1.0498	3.2861	17
.28792	.30065	3.3261	.95766	1.0442	3.4732	16		44	.30459	.31978	3.1271	.95248	1.0499	3.2831	16
.28820	.30097	3.3226	.95757	1.0443	3.4699	15		45	.30486	.32010	3.1240	.95240	1.0500	3.2801	15
.28847	.30128	3.3191	.95749	1.0444	3.4665	14		46	.30514	.32042	3.1209	.95231	1.0501	3.2772	14
.28875	.30160	3.3156	.95740	1.0445	3.4632	13		47	.30542	.32074	3.1178	.95222	1.0502	3.2742	13
.28903	.30192	3.3122	.95732	1.0446	3.4598	12		48	.30570	.32106	3.1146	.95213	1.0503	3.2712	12
.28931	.30224	3.3087	.95724	1.0447	3.4565	11		49	.30597	.32139	3.1115	.95204	1.0504	3.2683	11
.28959	.30255	3.3052	.95715	1.0448	3.4532	10		50	.30625	.32171	3.1084	.95195	1.0505	3.2653	10
.28987	.30287	3.3017	.95707	1.0449	3.4499	9		51	.30653	.32203	3.1053	.95186	1.0506	3.2624	9
.29015	.30319	3.2983	.95698	1.0450	3.4465	8		52	.30680	.32235	3.1022	.95177	1.0507	3.2594	8
.29042	.30351	3.2948	.95690	1.0450	3.4432	7		53	.30708	.32267	3.0991	.95168	1.0508	3.2565	7
.29070	.30382	3.2914	.95681	1.0451	3.4399	6		54	.30736	.32299	3.0961	.95159	1.0509	3.2535	6
.29098	.30414	3.2879	.95673	1.0452	3.4367	5		55	.30763	.32331	3.0930	.95150	1.0510	3.2506	5
.29126	.30446	3.2845	.95664	1.0453	3.4334	4		56	.30791	.32363	3.0899	.95142	1.0511	3.2477	4
.29154	.30478	3.2811	.95656	1.0454	3.4301	3		57	.30819	.32396	3.0868	.95133	1.0512	3.2448	3
.29182	.30509	3.2777	.95647	1.0455	3.4268	2		58	.30846	.32428	3.0838	.95124	1.0513	3.2419	2
.29209	.30541	3.2743	.95639	1.0456	3.4236	1		59	.30874	.32460	3.0807	.95115	1.0514	3.2390	1
.29237	.30573	3.2709	.95630	1.0457	3.4203	0		60	.30902	.32492	3.0777	.95106	1.0515	3.2361	0
Cos	Cot	Tan	Sin	Csc	Sec	′		′	Cos	Cot	Tan	Sin	Csc	Sec	′

(286°)   (253°) 73°   107° (287°)   (252°) 72°

NATURAL TRIGONOMETRIC FUNCTIONS
TO FIVE PLACES

18° (198°)   (341°) 161°   19° (199°)   (340°

'	Sin	Tan	Cot	Cos	Sec	Csc	'		'	Sin	Tan	Cot	Cos	Sec	Csc
0	.30902	.32492	3.0777	.95106	1.0515	3.2361	60		0	.32557	.34433	2.9042	.94552	1.0576	3.0716
1	.30929	.32524	3.0746	.95097	1.0516	3.2332	59		1	.32584	.34465	2.9015	.94542	1.0577	3.0690
2	.30957	.32556	3.0716	.95088	1.0517	3.2303	58		2	.32612	.34498	2.8987	.94533	1.0578	3.0664
3	.30985	.32588	3.0686	.95079	1.0518	3.2274	57		3	.32639	.34530	2.8960	.94523	1.0579	3.0638
4	.31012	.32621	3.0655	.95070	1.0519	3.2245	56		4	.32667	.34563	2.8933	.94514	1.0580	3.0612
5	.31040	.32653	3.0625	.95061	1.0520	3.2217	55		5	.32694	.34596	2.8905	.94504	1.0582	3.0586
6	.31068	.32685	3.0595	.95052	1.0521	3.2188	54		6	.32722	.34628	2.8878	.94495	1.0583	3.0561
7	.31095	.32717	3.0565	.95043	1.0522	3.2159	53		7	.32749	.34661	2.8851	.94485	1.0584	3.0535
8	.31123	.32749	3.0535	.95033	1.0523	3.2131	52		8	.32777	.34693	2.8824	.94476	1.0585	3.0509
9	.31151	.32782	3.0505	.95024	1.0524	3.2102	51		9	.32804	.34726	2.8797	.94466	1.0586	3.0484
10	.31178	.32814	3.0475	.95015	1.0525	3.2074	50		10	.32832	.34758	2.8770	.94457	1.0587	3.0458
11	.31206	.32846	3.0445	.95006	1.0526	3.2045	49		11	.32859	.34791	2.8743	.94447	1.0588	3.0433
12	.31233	.32878	3.0415	.94997	1.0527	3.2017	48		12	.32887	.34824	2.8716	.94438	1.0589	3.0407
13	.31261	.32911	3.0385	.94988	1.0528	3.1989	47		13	.32914	.34856	2.8689	.94428	1.0590	3.0382
14	.31289	.32943	3.0356	.94979	1.0529	3.1960	46		14	.32942	.34889	2.8662	.94418	1.0591	3.0357
15	.31316	.32975	3.0326	.94970	1.0530	3.1932	45		15	.32969	.34922	2.8636	.94409	1.0592	3.0331
16	.31344	.33007	3.0296	.94961	1.0531	3.1904	44		16	.32997	.34954	2.8609	.94399	1.0593	3.0306
17	.31372	.33040	3.0267	.94952	1.0532	3.1876	43		17	.33024	.34987	2.8582	.94390	1.0594	3.0281
18	.31399	.33072	3.0237	.94943	1.0533	3.1848	42		18	.33051	.35020	2.8556	.94380	1.0595	3.0256
19	.31427	.33104	3.0208	.94933	1.0534	3.1820	41		19	.33079	.35052	2.8529	.94370	1.0597	3.0231
20	.31454	.33136	3.0178	.94924	1.0535	3.1792	40		20	.33106	.35085	2.8502	.94361	1.0598	3.0206
21	.31482	.33169	3.0149	.94915	1.0536	3.1764	39		21	.33134	.35118	2.8476	.94351	1.0599	3.0181
22	.31510	.33201	3.0120	.94906	1.0537	3.1736	38		22	.33161	.35150	2.8449	.94342	1.0600	3.0156
23	.31537	.33233	3.0090	.94897	1.0538	3.1708	37		23	.33189	.35183	2.8423	.94332	1.0601	3.0131
24	.31565	.33266	3.0061	.94888	1.0539	3.1681	36		24	.33216	.35216	2.8397	.94322	1.0602	3.0106
25	.31593	.33298	3.0032	.94878	1.0540	3.1653	35		25	.33244	.35248	2.8370	.94313	1.0603	3.0081
26	.31620	.33330	3.0003	.94869	1.0541	3.1625	34		26	.33271	.35281	2.8344	.94303	1.0604	3.0056
27	.31648	.33363	2.9974	.94860	1.0542	3.1598	33		27	.33298	.35314	2.8318	.94293	1.0605	3.0031
28	.31675	.33395	2.9945	.94851	1.0543	3.1570	32		28	.33326	.35346	2.8291	.94284	1.0606	3.0007
29	.31703	.33427	2.9916	.94842	1.0544	3.1543	31		29	.33353	.35379	2.8265	.94274	1.0607	2.9982
30	.31730	.33460	2.9887	.94832	1.0545	3.1515	30		30	.33381	.35412	2.8239	.94264	1.0608	2.9957
31	.31758	.33492	2.9858	.94823	1.0546	3.1488	29		31	.33408	.35445	2.8213	.94254	1.0610	2.9933
32	.31786	.33524	2.9829	.94814	1.0547	3.1461	28		32	.33436	.35477	2.8187	.94245	1.0611	2.9908
33	.31813	.33557	2.9800	.94805	1.0548	3.1433	27		33	.33463	.35510	2.8161	.94235	1.0612	2.9884
34	.31841	.33589	2.9772	.94795	1.0549	3.1406	26		34	.33490	.35543	2.8135	.94225	1.0613	2.9859
35	.31868	.33621	2.9743	.94786	1.0550	3.1379	25		35	.33518	.35576	2.8109	.94215	1.0614	2.9835
36	.31896	.33654	2.9714	.94777	1.0551	3.1352	24		36	.33545	.35608	2.8083	.94206	1.0615	2.9811
37	.31923	.33686	2.9686	.94768	1.0552	3.1325	23		37	.33573	.35641	2.8057	.94196	1.0616	2.9786
38	.31951	.33718	2.9657	.94758	1.0553	3.1298	22		38	.33600	.35674	2.8032	.94186	1.0617	2.9762
39	.31979	.33751	2.9629	.94749	1.0554	3.1271	21		39	.33627	.35707	2.8006	.94176	1.0618	2.9738
40	.32006	.33783	2.9600	.94740	1.0555	3.1244	20		40	.33655	.35740	2.7980	.94167	1.0619	2.9713
41	.32034	.33816	2.9572	.94730	1.0556	3.1217	19		41	.33682	.35772	2.7955	.94157	1.0621	2.9689
42	.32061	.33848	2.9544	.94721	1.0557	3.1190	18		42	.33710	.35805	2.7929	.94147	1.0622	2.9665
43	.32089	.33881	2.9515	.94712	1.0558	3.1163	17		43	.33737	.35838	2.7903	.94137	1.0623	2.9641
44	.32116	.33913	2.9487	.94702	1.0559	3.1137	16		44	.33764	.35871	2.7878	.94127	1.0624	2.9617
45	.32144	.33945	2.9459	.94693	1.0560	3.1110	15		45	.33792	.35904	2.7852	.94118	1.0625	2.9593
46	.32171	.33978	2.9431	.94684	1.0561	3.1083	14		46	.33819	.35937	2.7827	.94108	1.0626	2.9569
47	.32199	.34010	2.9403	.94674	1.0563	3.1057	13		47	.33846	.35969	2.7801	.94098	1.0627	2.9545
48	.32227	.34043	2.9375	.94665	1.0564	3.1030	12		48	.33874	.36002	2.7776	.94088	1.0628	2.9521
49	.32254	.34075	2.9347	.94656	1.0565	3.1004	11		49	.33901	.36035	2.7751	.94078	1.0629	2.9498
50	.32282	.34108	2.9319	.94646	1.0566	3.0977	10		50	.33929	.36068	2.7725	.94068	1.0631	2.9474
51	.32309	.34140	2.9291	.94637	1.0567	3.0951	9		51	.33956	.36101	2.7700	.94058	1.0632	2.9450
52	.32337	.34173	2.9263	.94627	1.0568	3.0925	8		52	.33983	.36134	2.7675	.94049	1.0633	2.9426
53	.32364	.34205	2.9235	.94618	1.0569	3.0898	7		53	.34011	.36167	2.7650	.94039	1.0634	2.9403
54	.32392	.34238	2.9208	.94609	1.0570	3.0872	6		54	.34038	.36199	2.7625	.94029	1.0635	2.9379
55	.32419	.34270	2.9180	.94599	1.0571	3.0846	5		55	.34065	.36232	2.7600	.94019	1.0636	2.9355
56	.32447	.34303	2.9152	.94590	1.0572	3.0820	4		56	.34093	.36265	2.7575	.94009	1.0637	2.9332
57	.32474	.34335	2.9125	.94580	1.0573	3.0794	3		57	.34120	.36298	2.7550	.93999	1.0638	2.9308
58	.32502	.34368	2.9097	.94571	1.0574	3.0768	2		58	.34147	.36331	2.7525	.93989	1.0640	2.9285
59	.32529	.34400	2.9070	.94561	1.0575	3.0742	1		59	.34175	.36364	2.7500	.93979	1.0641	2.9261
60	.32557	.34433	2.9042	.94552	1.0576	3.0716	0		60	.34202	.36397	2.7475	.93969	1.0642	2.9238
'	Cos	Cot	Tan	Sin	Csc	Sec	'		'	Cos	Cot	Tan	Sin	Csc	Sec

108° (288°)   (251°) 71°   109° (289°)   (250°

NATURAL TRIGONOMETRIC FUNCTIONS
TO FIVE PLACES

20° (200°)   (339°) **159°**

′	Sin	Tan	Cot	Cos	Sec	Csc	′
0	.34202	.36397	2.7475	.93969	1.0642	2.9238	60
1	.34229	.36430	2.7450	.93959	1.0643	2.9215	59
2	.34257	.36463	2.7425	.93949	1.0644	2.9191	58
3	.34284	.36496	2.7400	.93939	1.0645	2.9168	57
4	.34311	.36529	2.7376	.93929	1.0646	2.9145	56
5	.34339	.36562	2.7351	.93919	1.0647	2.9122	55
6	.34366	.36595	2.7326	.93909	1.0649	2.9099	54
7	.34393	.36628	2.7302	.93899	1.0650	2.9075	53
8	.34421	.36661	2.7277	.93889	1.0651	2.9052	52
9	.34448	.36694	2.7253	.93879	1.0652	2.9029	51
10	.34475	.36727	2.7228	.93869	1.0653	2.9006	50
11	.34503	.36760	2.7204	.93859	1.0654	2.8983	49
12	.34530	.36793	2.7179	.93849	1.0655	2.8960	48
13	.34557	.36826	2.7155	.93839	1.0657	2.8938	47
14	.34584	.36859	2.7130	.93829	1.0658	2.8915	46
15	.34612	.36892	2.7106	.93819	1.0659	2.8892	45
16	.34639	.36925	2.7082	.93809	1.0660	2.8869	44
17	.34666	.36958	2.7058	.93799	1.0661	2.8846	43
18	.34694	.36991	2.7034	.93789	1.0662	2.8824	42
19	.34721	.37024	2.7009	.93779	1.0663	2.8801	41
20	.34748	.37057	2.6985	.93769	1.0665	2.8779	40
21	.34775	.37090	2.6961	.93759	1.0666	2.8756	39
22	.34803	.37123	2.6937	.93748	1.0667	2.8733	38
23	.34830	.37157	2.6913	.93738	1.0668	2.8711	37
24	.34857	.37190	2.6889	.93728	1.0669	2.8688	36
25	.34884	.37223	2.6865	.93718	1.0670	2.8666	35
26	.34912	.37256	2.6841	.93708	1.0671	2.8644	34
27	.34939	.37289	2.6818	.93698	1.0673	2.8621	33
28	.34966	.37322	2.6794	.93688	1.0674	2.8599	32
29	.34993	.37355	2.6770	.93677	1.0675	2.8577	31
30	.35021	.37388	2.6746	.93667	1.0676	2.8555	30
31	.35048	.37422	2.6723	.93657	1.0677	2.8532	29
32	.35075	.37455	2.6699	.93647	1.0678	2.8510	28
33	.35102	.37488	2.6675	.93637	1.0680	2.8488	27
34	.35130	.37521	2.6652	.93626	1.0681	2.8466	26
35	.35157	.37554	2.6628	.93616	1.0682	2.8444	25
36	.35184	.37588	2.6605	.93606	1.0683	2.8422	24
37	.35211	.37621	2.6581	.93596	1.0684	2.8400	23
38	.35239	.37654	2.6558	.93585	1.0685	2.8378	22
39	.35266	.37687	2.6534	.93575	1.0687	2.8356	21
40	.35293	.37720	2.6511	.93565	1.0688	2.8334	20
41	.35320	.37754	2.6488	.93555	1.0689	2.8312	19
42	.35347	.37787	2.6464	.93544	1.0690	2.8291	18
43	.35375	.37820	2.6441	.93534	1.0691	2.8269	17
44	.35402	.37853	2.6418	.93524	1.0692	2.8247	16
45	.35429	.37887	2.6395	.93514	1.0694	2.8225	15
46	.35456	.37920	2.6371	.93503	1.0695	2.8204	14
47	.35484	.37953	2.6348	.93493	1.0696	2.8182	13
48	.35511	.37986	2.6325	.93483	1.0697	2.8161	12
49	.35538	.38020	2.6302	.93472	1.0698	2.8139	11
50	.35565	.38053	2.6279	.93462	1.0700	2.8117	10
51	.35592	.38086	2.6256	.93452	1.0701	2.8096	9
52	.35619	.38120	2.6233	.93441	1.0702	2.8075	8
53	.35647	.38153	2.6210	.93431	1.0703	2.8053	7
54	.35674	.38186	2.6187	.93420	1.0704	2.8032	6
55	.35701	.38220	2.6165	.93410	1.0705	2.8010	5
56	.35728	.38253	2.6142	.93400	1.0707	2.7989	4
57	.35755	.38286	2.6119	.93389	1.0708	2.7968	3
58	.35782	.38320	2.6096	.93379	1.0709	2.7947	2
59	.35810	.38353	2.6074	.93368	1.0710	2.7925	1
60	.35837	.38386	2.6051	.93358	1.0711	2.7904	0
′	Cos	Cot	Tan	Sin	Csc	Sec	′

110° (290°)   (249°) **69°**

21° (201°)   (338°) **158°**

′	Sin	Tan	Cot	Cos	Sec	Csc	′
0	.35837	.38386	2.6051	.93358	1.0711	2.7904	60
1	.35864	.38420	2.6028	.93348	1.0713	2.7883	59
2	.35891	.38453	2.6006	.93337	1.0714	2.7862	58
3	.35918	.38487	2.5983	.93327	1.0715	2.7841	57
4	.35945	.38520	2.5961	.93316	1.0716	2.7820	56
5	.35973	.38553	2.5938	.93306	1.0717	2.7799	55
6	.36000	.38587	2.5916	.93295	1.0719	2.7778	54
7	.36027	.38620	2.5893	.93285	1.0720	2.7757	53
8	.36054	.38654	2.5871	.93274	1.0721	2.7736	52
9	.36081	.38687	2.5848	.93264	1.0722	2.7715	51
10	.36108	.38721	2.5826	.93253	1.0723	2.7695	50
11	.36135	.38754	2.5804	.93243	1.0725	2.7674	49
12	.36162	.38787	2.5782	.93232	1.0726	2.7653	48
13	.36190	.38821	2.5759	.93222	1.0727	2.7632	47
14	.36217	.38854	2.5737	.93211	1.0728	2.7612	46
15	.36244	.38888	2.5715	.93201	1.0730	2.7591	45
16	.36271	.38921	2.5693	.93190	1.0731	2.7570	44
17	.36298	.38955	2.5671	.93180	1.0732	2.7550	43
18	.36325	.38988	2.5649	.93169	1.0733	2.7529	42
19	.36352	.39022	2.5627	.93159	1.0734	2.7509	41
20	.36379	.39055	2.5605	.93148	1.0736	2.7488	40
21	.36406	.39089	2.5583	.93137	1.0737	2.7468	39
22	.36434	.39122	2.5561	.93127	1.0738	2.7447	38
23	.36461	.39156	2.5539	.93116	1.0739	2.7427	37
24	.36488	.39190	2.5517	.93106	1.0740	2.7407	36
25	.36515	.39223	2.5495	.93095	1.0742	2.7386	35
26	.36542	.39257	2.5473	.93084	1.0743	2.7366	34
27	.36569	.39290	2.5452	.93074	1.0744	2.7346	33
28	.36596	.39324	2.5430	.93063	1.0745	2.7325	32
29	.36623	.39357	2.5408	.93052	1.0747	2.7305	31
30	.36650	.39391	2.5386	.93042	1.0748	2.7285	30
31	.36677	.39425	2.5365	.93031	1.0749	2.7265	29
32	.36704	.39458	2.5343	.93020	1.0750	2.7245	28
33	.36731	.39492	2.5322	.93010	1.0752	2.7225	27
34	.36758	.39526	2.5300	.92999	1.0753	2.7205	26
35	.36785	.39559	2.5279	.92988	1.0754	2.7185	25
36	.36812	.39593	2.5257	.92978	1.0755	2.7165	24
37	.36839	.39626	2.5236	.92967	1.0757	2.7145	23
38	.36867	.39660	2.5214	.92956	1.0758	2.7125	22
39	.36894	.39694	2.5193	.92945	1.0759	2.7105	21
40	.36921	.39727	2.5172	.92935	1.0760	2.7085	20
41	.36948	.39761	2.5150	.92924	1.0761	2.7065	19
42	.36975	.39795	2.5129	.92913	1.0763	2.7046	18
43	.37002	.39829	2.5108	.92902	1.0764	2.7026	17
44	.37029	.39862	2.5086	.92892	1.0765	2.7006	16
45	.37056	.39896	2.5065	.92881	1.0766	2.6986	15
46	.37083	.39930	2.5044	.92870	1.0768	2.6967	14
47	.37110	.39963	2.5023	.92859	1.0769	2.6947	13
48	.37137	.39997	2.5002	.92849	1.0770	2.6927	12
49	.37164	.40031	2.4981	.92838	1.0771	2.6908	11
50	.37191	.40065	2.4960	.92827	1.0773	2.6888	10
51	.37218	.40098	2.4939	.92816	1.0774	2.6869	9
52	.37245	.40132	2.4918	.92805	1.0775	2.6849	8
53	.37272	.40166	2.4897	.92794	1.0777	2.6830	7
54	.37299	.40200	2.4876	.92784	1.0778	2.6811	6
55	.37326	.40234	2.4855	.92773	1.0779	2.6791	5
56	.37353	.40267	2.4834	.92762	1.0780	2.6772	4
57	.37380	.40301	2.4813	.92751	1.0782	2.6752	3
58	.37407	.40335	2.4792	.92740	1.0783	2.6733	2
59	.37434	.40369	2.4772	.92729	1.0784	2.6714	1
60	.37461	.40403	2.4751	.92718	1.0785	2.6695	0
′	Cos	Cot	Tan	Sin	Csc	Sec	′

111° (291°)   (248°) **68°**

NATURAL TRIGONOMETRIC FUNCTIONS
TO FIVE PLACES

22° (202°)   (337°) 157°

'	Sin	Tan	Cot	Cos	Sec	Csc	'
0	.37461	.40403	2.4751	.92718	1.0785	2.6695	60
1	.37488	.40436	2.4730	.92707	1.0787	2.6675	59
2	.37515	.40470	2.4709	.92697	1.0788	2.6656	58
3	.37542	.40504	2.4689	.92686	1.0789	2.6637	57
4	.37569	.40538	2.4668	.92675	1.0790	2.6618	56
5	.37595	.40572	2.4648	.92664	1.0792	2.6599	55
6	.37622	.40606	2.4627	.92653	1.0793	2.6580	54
7	.37649	.40640	2.4606	.92642	1.0794	2.6561	53
8	.37676	.40674	2.4586	.92631	1.0796	2.6542	52
9	.37703	.40707	2.4566	.92620	1.0797	2.6523	51
10	.37730	.40741	2.4545	.92609	1.0798	2.6504	50
11	.37757	.40775	2.4525	.92598	1.0799	2.6485	49
12	.37784	.40809	2.4504	.92587	1.0801	2.6466	48
13	.37811	.40843	2.4484	.92576	1.0802	2.6447	47
14	.37838	.40877	2.4464	.92565	1.0803	2.6429	46
15	.37865	.40911	2.4443	.92554	1.0804	2.6410	45
16	.37892	.40945	2.4423	.92543	1.0806	2.6391	44
17	.37919	.40979	2.4403	.92532	1.0807	2.6372	43
18	.37946	.41013	2.4383	.92521	1.0808	2.6354	42
19	.37973	.41047	2.4362	.92510	1.0810	2.6335	41
20	.37999	.41081	2.4342	.92499	1.0811	2.6316	40
21	.38026	.41115	2.4322	.92488	1.0812	2.6298	39
22	.38053	.41149	2.4302	.92477	1.0814	2.6279	38
23	.38080	.41183	2.4282	.92466	1.0815	2.6260	37
24	.38107	.41217	2.4262	.92455	1.0816	2.6242	36
25	.38134	.41251	2.4242	.92444	1.0817	2.6223	35
26	.38161	.41285	2.4222	.92432	1.0819	2.6205	34
27	.38188	.41319	2.4202	.92421	1.0820	2.6186	33
28	.38215	.41353	2.4182	.92410	1.0821	2.6168	32
29	.38241	.41387	2.4162	.92399	1.0823	2.6150	31
30	.38268	.41421	2.4142	.92388	1.0824	2.6131	30
31	.38295	.41455	2.4122	.92377	1.0825	2.6113	29
32	.38322	.41490	2.4102	.92366	1.0827	2.6095	28
33	.38349	.41524	2.4083	.92355	1.0828	2.6076	27
34	.38376	.41558	2.4063	.92343	1.0829	2.6058	26
35	.38403	.41592	2.4043	.92332	1.0830	2.6040	25
36	.38430	.41626	2.4023	.92321	1.0832	2.6022	24
37	.38456	.41660	2.4004	.92310	1.0833	2.6003	23
38	.38483	.41694	2.3984	.92299	1.0834	2.5985	22
39	.38510	.41728	2.3964	.92287	1.0836	2.5967	21
40	.38537	.41763	2.3945	.92276	1.0837	2.5949	20
41	.38564	.41797	2.3925	.92265	1.0838	2.5931	19
42	.38591	.41831	2.3906	.92254	1.0840	2.5913	18
43	.38617	.41865	2.3886	.92243	1.0841	2.5895	17
44	.38644	.41899	2.3867	.92231	1.0842	2.5877	16
45	.38671	.41933	2.3847	.92220	1.0844	2.5859	15
46	.38698	.41968	2.3828	.92209	1.0845	2.5841	14
47	.38725	.42002	2.3808	.92198	1.0846	2.5823	13
48	.38752	.42036	2.3789	.92186	1.0848	2.5805	12
49	.38778	.42070	2.3770	.92175	1.0849	2.5788	11
50	.38805	.42105	2.3750	.92164	1.0850	2.5770	10
51	.38832	.42139	2.3731	.92152	1.0852	2.5752	9
52	.38859	.42173	2.3712	.92141	1.0853	2.5734	8
53	.38886	.42207	2.3693	.92130	1.0854	2.5716	7
54	.38912	.42242	2.3673	.92119	1.0856	2.5699	6
55	.38939	.42276	2.3654	92107	1.0857	2.5681	5
56	.38966	.42310	2.3635	.92096	1.0858	2.5663	4
57	.38993	.42345	2.3616	.92085	1.0860	2.5646	3
58	.39020	.42379	2.3597	.92073	1.0861	2.5628	2
59	.39046	.42413	2.3578	.92062	1.0862	2.5611	1
60	.39073	.42447	2.3559	.92050	1.0864	2.5593	0
'	Cos	Cot	Tan	Sin	Csc	Sec	'

112° (292°)   (247°) 67°

23° (203°)   (336°) 15

'	Sin	Tan	Cot	Cos	Sec	Csc	'
0	.39073	.42447	2.3559	.92050	1.0864	2.5593	60
1	.39100	.42482	2.3539	.92039	1.0865	2.5576	59
2	.39127	.42516	2.3520	.92028	1.0866	2.5558	58
3	.39153	.42551	2.3501	.92016	1.0868	2.5541	57
4	.39180	.42585	2 3483	92005	1.0869	2.5523	56
5	.39207	.42619	2.3464	.91994	1.0870	2.5506	55
6	.39234	.42654	2.3445	.91982	1.0872	2.5488	54
7	.39260	.42688	2.3426	.91971	1.0873	2.5471	53
8	.39287	.42722	2.3407	.91959	1.0874	2.5454	52
9	.39314	.42757	2.3388	.91948	1.0876	2.5436	51
10	.39341	.42791	2.3369	.91936	1.0877	2.5419	50
11	.39367	.42826	2.3351	.91925	1.0878	2.5402	49
12	.39394	.42860	2.3332	.91914	1.0880	2.5384	48
13	.39421	.42894	2.3313	.91902	1.0881	2.5367	47
14	.39448	.42929	2.3294	.91891	1.0883	2.5350	46
15	.39474	.42963	2.3276	.91879	1.0884	2.5333	45
16	.39501	.42998	2.3257	.91868	1.0885	2.5316	44
17	.39528	.43032	2.3238	.91856	1.0887	2.5299	43
18	.39555	.43067	2.3220	.91845	1.0888	2.5282	42
19	.39581	.43101	2.3201	.91833	1.0889	2.5264	41
20	.39608	.43136	2.3183	.91822	1.0891	2.5247	40
21	.39635	.43170	2.3164	.91810	1.0892	2.5230	39
22	.39661	.43205	2.3146	.91799	1.0893	2.5213	38
23	.39688	.43239	2.3127	.91787	1.0895	2.5196	37
24	.39715	.43274	2.3109	.91775	1.0896	2.5180	36
25	.39741	.43308	2.3090	.91764	1.0898	2.5163	35
26	.39768	.43343	2.3072	.91752	1.0899	2.5146	34
27	.39795	.43378	2.3053	.91741	1.0900	2.5129	33
28	.39822	.43412	2.3035	.91729	1.0902	2.5112	32
29	.39848	.43447	2.3017	.91718	1.0903	2.5095	31
30	.39875	.43481	2.2998	.91706	1.0904	2.5078	30
31	.39902	.43516	2.2980	.91694	1.0906	2.5062	29
32	.39928	.43550	2.2962	.91683	1.0907	2.5045	28
33	.39955	.43585	2.2944	.91671	1.0909	2.5028	27
34	.39982	.43620	2.2925	.91660	1.0910	2.5012	26
35	.40008	.43654	2.2907	.91648	1.0911	2.4995	25
36	.40035	.43689	2.2889	.91636	1.0913	2.4978	24
37	.40062	.43724	2.2871	.91625	1.0914	2.4962	23
38	.40088	.43758	2.2853	.91613	1.0915	2.4945	22
39	.40115	.43793	2.2835	.91601	1.0917	2.4928	21
40	.40141	.43828	2.2817	.91590	1.0918	2.4912	20
41	.40168	.43862	2.2799	.91578	1.0920	2.4895	19
42	.40195	.43897	2.2781	.91566	1.0921	2.4879	18
43	.40221	.43932	2.2763	.91555	1.0922	2.4862	17
44	.40248	.43966	2.2745	.91543	1.0924	2.4846	16
45	.40275	.44001	2.2727	.91531	1.0925	2.4830	15
46	.40301	.44036	2.2709	.91519	1.0927	2.4813	14
47	.40328	.44071	2.2691	.91508	1.0928	2.4797	13
48	.40355	.44105	2.2673	.91496	1.0929	2.4780	12
49	.40381	.44140	2.2655	.91484	1.0931	2.4764	11
50	.40408	.44175	2.2637	.91472	1.0932	2.4748	10
51	.40434	.44210	2.2620	.91461	1.0934	2.4731	9
52	.40461	.44244	2.2602	.91449	1.0935	2.4715	8
53	.40488	.44279	2.2584	.91437	1.0936	2.4699	7
54	.40514	.44314	2.2566	.91425	1.0938	2.4683	6
55	.40541	.44349	2.2549	.91414	1.0939	2.4667	5
56	.40567	.44384	2.2531	.91402	1.0941	2.4650	4
57	.40594	.44418	2.2513	.91390	1.0942	2.4634	3
58	.40621	.44453	2.2496	.91378	1.0944	2.4618	2
59	.40647	.44488	2.2478	.91366	1.0945	2.4602	1
60	.40674	.44523	2.2460	.91355	1.0946	2.4586	0
'	Cos	Cot	Tan	Sin	Csc	Sec	'

113° (293°)   (246°) 6

NATURAL TRIGONOMETRIC FUNCTIONS
TO FIVE PLACES

24° (204°)   (335°) 155°

′	Sin	Tan	Cot	Cos	Sec	Csc	′
0	.40674	.44523	2.2460	.91355	1.0946	2.4586	60
1	.40700	.44558	2.2443	.91343	1.0948	2.4570	59
2	.40727	.44593	2.2425	.91331	1.0949	2.4554	58
3	.40753	.44627	2.2408	.91319	1.0951	2.4538	57
4	.40780	.44662	2.2390	.91307	1.0952	2.4522	56
5	.40806	.44697	2.2373	.91295	1.0953	2.4506	55
6	.40833	.44732	2.2355	.91283	1.0955	2.4490	54
7	.40860	.44767	2.2338	.91272	1.0956	2.4474	53
8	.40886	.44802	2.2320	.91260	1.0958	2.4458	52
9	.40913	.44837	2.2303	.91248	1.0959	2.4442	51
10	.40939	.44872	2.2286	.91236	1.0961	2.4426	50
11	.40966	.44907	2.2268	.91224	1.0962	2.4411	49
12	.40992	.44942	2.2251	.91212	1.0963	2.4395	48
13	.41019	.44977	2.2234	.91200	1.0965	2.4379	47
14	.41045	.45012	2.2216	.91188	1.0966	2.4363	46
15	.41072	.45047	2.2199	.91176	1.0968	2.4348	45
16	.41098	.45082	2.2182	.91164	1.0969	2.4332	44
17	.41125	.45117	2.2165	.91152	1.0971	2.4316	43
18	.41151	.45152	2.2148	.91140	1.0972	2.4300	42
19	.41178	.45187	2.2130	.91128	1.0974	2.4285	41
20	.41204	.45222	2.2113	.91116	1.0975	2.4269	40
21	.41231	.45257	2.2096	.91104	1.0976	2.4254	39
22	.41257	.45292	2.2079	.91092	1.0978	2.4238	38
23	.41284	.45327	2.2062	.91080	1.0979	2.4222	37
24	.41310	.45362	2.2045	.91068	1.0981	2.4207	36
25	.41337	.45397	2.2028	.91056	1.0982	2.4191	35
26	.41363	.45432	2.2011	.91044	1.0984	2.4176	34
27	.41390	.45467	2.1994	.91032	1.0985	2.4160	33
28	.41416	.45502	2.1977	.91020	1.0987	2.4145	32
29	.41443	.45538	2.1960	.91008	1.0988	2.4130	31
30	.41469	.45573	2.1943	.90996	1.0989	2.4114	30
31	.41496	.45608	2.1926	.90984	1.0991	2.4099	29
32	.41522	.45643	2.1909	.90972	1.0992	2.4083	28
33	.41549	.45678	2.1892	.90960	1.0994	2.4068	27
34	.41575	.45713	2.1876	.90948	1.0995	2.4053	26
35	.41602	.45748	2.1859	.90936	1.0997	2.4038	25
36	.41628	.45784	2.1842	.90924	1.0998	2.4022	24
37	.41655	.45819	2.1825	.90911	1.1000	2.4007	23
38	.41681	.45854	2.1808	.90899	1.1001	2.3992	22
39	.41707	.45889	2.1792	.90887	1.1003	2.3977	21
40	.41734	.45924	2.1775	.90875	1.1004	2.3961	20
41	.41760	.45960	2.1758	.90863	1.1006	2.3946	19
42	.41787	.45995	2.1742	.90851	1.1007	2.3931	18
43	.41813	.46030	2.1725	.90839	1.1009	2.3916	17
44	.41840	.46065	2.1708	.90826	1.1010	2.3901	16
45	.41866	.46101	2.1692	.90814	1.1011	2.3886	15
46	.41892	.46136	2.1675	.90802	1.1013	2.3871	14
47	.41919	.46171	2.1659	.90790	1.1014	2.3856	13
48	.41945	.46206	2.1642	.90778	1.1016	2.3841	12
49	.41972	.46242	2.1625	.90766	1.1017	2.3826	11
50	.41998	.46277	2.1609	.90753	1.1019	2.3811	10
51	.42024	.46312	2.1592	.90741	1.1020	2.3796	9
52	.42051	.46348	2.1576	.90729	1.1022	2.3781	8
53	.42077	.46383	2.1560	.90717	1.1023	2.3766	7
54	.42104	.46418	2.1543	.90704	1.1025	2.3751	6
55	.42130	.46454	2.1527	.90692	1.1026	2.3736	5
56	.42156	.46489	2.1510	.90680	1.1028	2.3721	4
57	.42183	.46525	2.1494	.90668	1.1029	2.3706	3
58	.42209	.46560	2.1478	.90655	1.1031	2.3692	2
59	.42235	.46595	2.1461	.90643	1.1032	2.3677	1
60	.42262	.46631	2.1445	.90631	1.1034	2.3662	0
′	Cos	Cot	Tan	Sin	Csc	Sec	′

25° (205°)   (334°) 154°

′	Sin	Tan	Cot	Cos	Sec	Csc	′
0	.42262	.46631	2.1445	.90631	1.1034	2.3662	60
1	.42288	.46666	2.1429	.90618	1.1035	2.3647	59
2	.42315	.46702	2.1413	.90606	1.1037	2.3633	58
3	.42341	.46737	2.1396	.90594	1.1038	2.3618	57
4	.42367	.46772	2.1380	.90582	1.1040	2.3603	56
5	.42394	.46808	2.1364	.90569	1.1041	2.3588	55
6	.42420	.46843	2.1348	.90557	1.1043	2.3574	54
7	.42446	.46879	2.1332	.90545	1.1044	2.3559	53
8	.42473	.46914	2.1315	.90532	1.1046	2.3545	52
9	.42499	.46950	2.1299	.90520	1.1047	2.3530	51
10	.42525	.46985	2.1283	.90507	1.1049	2.3515	50
11	.42552	.47021	2.1267	.90495	1.1050	2.3501	49
12	.42578	.47056	2.1251	.90483	1.1052	2.3486	48
13	.42604	.47092	2.1235	.90470	1.1053	2.3472	47
14	.42631	.47128	2.1219	.90458	1.1055	2.3457	46
15	.42657	.47163	2.1203	.90446	1.1056	2.3443	45
16	.42683	.47199	2.1187	.90433	1.1058	2.3428	44
17	.42709	.47234	2.1171	.90421	1.1059	2.3414	43
18	.42736	.47270	2.1155	.90408	1.1061	2.3400	42
19	.42762	.47305	2.1139	.90396	1.1062	2.3385	41
20	.42788	.47341	2.1123	.90383	1.1064	2.3371	40
21	.42815	.47377	2.1107	.90371	1.1066	2.3356	39
22	.42841	.47412	2.1092	.90358	1.1067	2.3342	38
23	.42867	.47448	2.1076	.90346	1.1069	2.3328	37
24	.42894	.47483	2.1060	.90334	1.1070	2.3314	36
25	.42920	.47519	2.1044	.90321	1.1072	2.3299	35
26	.42946	.47555	2.1028	.90309	1.1073	2.3285	34
27	.42972	.47590	2.1013	.90296	1.1075	2.3271	33
28	.42999	.47626	2.0997	.90284	1.1076	2.3257	32
29	.43025	.47662	2.0981	.90271	1.1078	2.3242	31
30	.43051	.47698	2.0965	.90259	1.1079	2.3228	30
31	.43077	.47733	2.0950	.90246	1.1081	2.3214	29
32	.43104	.47769	2.0934	.90233	1.1082	2.3200	28
33	.43130	.47805	2.0918	.90221	1.1084	2.3186	27
34	.43156	.47840	2.0903	.90208	1.1085	2.3172	26
35	.43182	.47876	2.0887	.90196	1.1087	2.3158	25
36	.43209	.47912	2.0872	.90183	1.1089	2.3144	24
37	.43235	.47948	2.0856	.90171	1.1090	2.3130	23
38	.43261	.47984	2.0840	.90158	1.1092	2.3115	22
39	.43287	.48019	2.0825	.90146	1.1093	2.3101	21
40	.43313	.48055	2.0809	.90133	1.1095	2.3088	20
41	.43340	.48091	2.0794	.90120	1.1096	2.3074	19
42	.43366	.48127	2.0778	.90108	1.1098	2.3060	18
43	.43392	.48163	2.0763	.90095	1.1099	2.3046	17
44	.43418	.48198	2.0748	.90082	1.1101	2.3032	16
45	.43445	.48234	2.0732	.90070	1.1102	2.3018	15
46	.43471	.48270	2.0717	.90057	1.1104	2.3004	14
47	.43497	.48306	2.0701	.90045	1.1106	2.2990	13
48	.43523	.48342	2.0686	.90032	1.1107	2.2976	12
49	.43549	.48378	2.0671	.90019	1.1109	2.2962	11
50	.43575	.48414	2.0655	.90007	1.1110	2.2949	10
51	.43602	.48450	2.0640	.89994	1.1112	2.2935	9
52	.43628	.48486	2.0625	.89981	1.1113	2.2921	8
53	.43654	.48521	2.0609	.89968	1.1115	2.2907	7
54	.43680	.48557	2.0594	.89956	1.1117	2.2894	6
55	.43706	.48593	2.0579	.89943	1.1118	2.2880	5
56	.43733	.48629	2.0564	.89930	1.1120	2.2866	4
57	.43759	.48665	2.0549	.89918	1.1121	2.2853	3
58	.43785	.48701	2.0533	.89905	1.1123	2.2839	2
59	.43811	.48737	2.0518	.89892	1.1124	2.2825	1
60	.43837	.48773	2.0503	.89879	1.1126	2.2812	0
′	Cos	Cot	Tan	Sin	Csc	Sce	′

NATURAL TRIGONOMETRIC FUNCTIONS
TO FIVE PLACES

26° (206°)   (333°) **153°**   27° (207°)   (332°) **15**

'	Sin	Tan	Cot	Cos	Sec	Csc	'		'	Sin	Tan	Cot	Cos	Sec	Csc	'
0	.43837	.48773	2.0503	.89879	1.1126	2.2812	60		0	.45399	.50953	1.9626	.89101	1.1223	2.2027	60
1	.43863	.48809	2.0488	.89867	1.1128	2.2798	59		1	.45425	.50989	1.9612	.89087	1.1225	2.2014	59
2	.43889	.48845	2.0473	.89854	1.1129	2.2785	58		2	.45451	.51026	1.9598	.89074	1.1227	2.2002	58
3	.43916	.48881	2.0458	.89841	1.1131	2.2771	57		3	.45477	.51063	1.9584	.89061	1.1228	2.1989	57
4	.43942	.48917	2.0443	.89828	1.1132	2.2757	56		4	.45503	.51099	1.9570	.89048	1.1230	2.1977	56
5	.43968	.48953	2.0428	.89816	1.1134	2.2744	55		5	.45529	.51136	1.9556	.89035	1.1232	2.1964	55
6	.43994	.48989	2.0413	.89803	1.1136	2.2730	54		6	.45554	.51173	1.9542	.89021	1.1233	2.1952	54
7	.44020	.49026	2.0398	.89790	1.1137	2.2717	53		7	.45580	.51209	1.9528	.89008	1.1235	2.1939	53
8	.44046	.49062	2.0383	.89777	1.1139	2.2703	52		8	.45606	.51246	1.9514	.88995	1.1237	2.1927	52
9	.44072	.49098	2.0368	.89764	1.1140	2.2690	51		9	.45632	.51283	1.9500	.88981	1.1238	2.1914	51
10	.44098	.49134	2.0353	.89752	1.1142	2.2677	50		10	.45658	.51319	1.9486	.88968	1.1240	2.1902	50
11	.44124	.49170	2.0338	.89739	1.1143	2.2663	49		11	.45684	.51356	1.9472	.88955	1.1242	2.1890	49
12	.44151	.49206	2.0323	.89726	1.1145	2.2650	48		12	.45710	.51393	1.9458	.88942	1.1243	2.1877	48
13	.44177	.49242	2.0308	.89713	1.1147	2.2636	47		13	.45736	.51430	1.9444	.88928	1.1245	2.1865	47
14	.44203	.49278	2.0293	.89700	1.1148	2.2623	46		14	.45762	.51467	1.9430	.88915	1.1247	2.1852	46
15	.44229	.49315	2.0278	.89687	1.1150	2.2610	45		15	.45787	.51503	1.9416	.88902	1.1248	2.1840	45
16	.44255	.49351	2.0263	.89674	1.1151	2.2596	44		16	.45813	.51540	1.9402	.88888	1.1250	2.1828	44
17	.44281	.49387	2.0248	.89662	1.1153	2.2583	43		17	.45839	.51577	1.9388	.88875	1.1252	2.1815	43
18	.44307	.49423	2.0233	.89649	1.1155	2.2570	42		18	.45865	.51614	1.9375	.88862	1.1253	2.1803	42
19	.44333	.49459	2.0219	.89636	1.1156	2.2556	41		19	.45891	.51651	1.9361	.88848	1.1255	2.1791	41
20	.44359	.49495	2.0204	.89623	1.1158	2.2543	40		20	.45917	.51688	1.9347	.88835	1.1257	2.1779	40
21	.44385	.49532	2.0189	.89610	1.1159	2.2530	39		21	.45942	.51724	1.9333	.88822	1.1259	2.1766	39
22	.44411	.49568	2.0174	.89597	1.1161	2.2517	38		22	.45968	.51761	1.9319	.88808	1.1260	2.1754	38
23	.44437	.49604	2.0160	.89584	1.1163	2.2504	37		23	.45994	.51798	1.9306	.88795	1.1262	2.1742	37
24	.44464	.49640	2.0145	.89571	1.1164	2.2490	36		24	.46020	.51835	1.9292	.88782	1.1264	2.1730	36
25	.44490	.49677	2.0130	.89558	1.1166	2.2477	35		25	.46046	.51872	1.9278	.88768	1.1265	2.1718	35
26	.44516	.49713	2.0115	.89545	1.1168	2.2464	34		26	.46072	.51909	1.9265	.88755	1.1267	2.1705	34
27	.44542	.49749	2.0101	.89532	1.1169	2.2451	33		27	.46097	.51946	1.9251	.88741	1.1269	2.1693	33
28	.44568	.49786	2.0086	.89519	1.1171	2.2438	32		28	.46123	.51983	1.9237	.88728	1.1270	2.1681	32
29	.44594	.49822	2.0072	.89506	1.1172	2.2425	31		29	.46149	.52020	1.9223	.88715	1.1272	2.1669	31
30	.44620	.49858	2.0057	.89493	1.1174	2.2412	30		30	.46175	.52057	1.9210	.88701	1.1274	2.1657	30
31	.44646	.49894	2.0042	.89480	1.1176	2.2399	29		31	.46201	.52094	1.9196	.88688	1.1276	2.1645	29
32	.44672	.49931	2.0028	.89467	1.1177	2.2385	28		32	.46226	.52131	1.9183	.88674	1.1277	2.1633	28
33	.44698	.49967	2.0013	.89454	1.1179	2.2372	27		33	.46252	.52168	1.9169	.88661	1.1279	2.1621	27
34	.44724	.50004	1.9999	.89441	1.1180	2.2359	26		34	.46278	.52205	1.9155	.88647	1.1281	2.1609	26
35	.44750	.50040	1.9984	.89428	1.1182	2.2346	25		35	.46304	.52242	1.9142	.88634	1.1282	2.1596	25
36	.44776	.50076	1.9970	.89415	1.1184	2.2333	24		36	.46330	.52279	1.9128	.88620	1.1284	2.1584	24
37	.44802	.50113	1.9955	.89402	1.1185	2.2320	23		37	.46355	.52316	1.9115	.88607	1.1286	2.1572	23
38	.44828	.50149	1.9941	.89389	1.1187	2.2308	22		38	.46381	.52353	1.9101	.88593	1.1288	2.1560	22
39	.44854	.50185	1.9926	.89376	1.1189	2.2295	21		39	.46407	.52390	1.9088	.88580	1.1289	2.1549	21
40	.44880	.50222	1.9912	.89363	1.1190	2.2282	20		40	.46433	.52427	1.9074	.88566	1.1291	2.1537	20
41	.44906	.50258	1.9897	.89350	1.1192	2.2269	19		41	.46458	.52464	1.9061	.88553	1.1293	2.1525	19
42	.44932	.50295	1.9883	.89337	1.1194	2.2256	18		42	.46484	.52501	1.9047	.88539	1.1294	2.1513	18
43	.44958	.50331	1.9868	.89324	1.1195	2.2243	17		43	.46510	.52538	1.9034	.88526	1.1296	2.1501	17
44	.44984	.50368	1.9854	.89311	1.1197	2.2230	16		44	.46536	.52575	1.9020	.88512	1.1298	2.1489	16
45	.45010	.50404	1.9840	.89298	1.1198	2.2217	15		45	.46561	.52613	1.9007	.88499	1.1300	2.1477	15
46	.45036	.50441	1.9825	.89285	1.1200	2.2205	14		46	.46587	.52650	1.8993	.88485	1.1301	2.1465	14
47	.45062	.50477	1.9811	.89272	1.1202	2.2192	13		47	.46613	.52687	1.8980	.88472	1.1303	2.1453	13
48	.45088	.50514	1.9797	.89259	1.1203	2.2179	12		48	.46639	.52724	1.8967	.88458	1.1305	2.1441	12
49	.45114	.50550	1.9782	.89245	1.1205	2.2166	11		49	.46664	.52761	1.8953	.88445	1.1307	2.1430	11
50	.45140	.50587	1.9768	.89232	1.1207	2.2153	10		50	.46690	.52798	1.8940	.88431	1.1308	2.1418	10
51	.45166	.50623	1.9754	.89219	1.1208	2.2141	9		51	.46716	.52836	1.8927	.88417	1.1310	2.1406	9
52	.45192	.50660	1.9740	.89206	1.1210	2.2128	8		52	.46742	.52873	1.8913	.88404	1.1312	2.1394	8
53	.45218	.50696	1.9725	.89193	1.1212	2.2115	7		53	.46767	.52910	1.8900	.88390	1.1313	2.1382	7
54	.45243	.50733	1.9711	.89180	1.1213	2.2103	6		54	.46793	.52947	1.8887	.88377	1.1315	2.1371	6
55	.45269	.50769	1.9697	.89167	1.1215	2.2090	5		55	.46819	.52985	1.8873	.88363	1.1317	2.1359	5
56	.45295	.50806	1.9683	.89153	1.1217	2.2077	4		56	.46844	.53022	1.8860	.88349	1.1319	2.1347	4
57	.45321	.50843	1.9669	.89140	1.1218	2.2065	3		57	.46870	.53059	1.8847	.88336	1.1320	2.1336	3
58	.45347	.50879	1.9654	.89127	1.1220	2.2052	2		58	.46896	.53096	1.8834	.88322	1.1322	2.1324	2
59	.45373	.50916	1.9640	.89114	1.1222	2.2039	1		59	.46921	.53134	1.8820	.88308	1.1324	2.1312	1
60	.45399	.50953	1.9626	.89101	1.1223	2.2027	0		60	.46947	.53171	1.8807	.88295	1.1326	2.1301	0
'	Cos	Cot	Tan	Sin	Csc	Sec	'		'	Cos	Cot	Tan	Sin	Csc	Sec	'

NATURAL TRIGONOMETRIC FUNCTIONS
TO FIVE PLACES

28° (208°) (331°) **151°**

′	Sin	Tan	Cot	Cos	Sec	Csc	′
0	.46947	.53171	1.8807	.88295	1.1326	2.1301	60
1	.46973	.53208	1.8794	.88281	1.1327	2.1289	59
2	.46999	.53246	1.8781	.88267	1.1329	2.1277	58
3	.47024	.53283	1.8768	.88254	1.1331	2.1266	57
4	.47050	.53320	1.8755	.88240	1.1333	2.1254	56
5	.47076	.53358	1.8741	.88226	1.1334	2.1242	55
6	.47101	.53395	1.8728	.88213	1.1336	2.1231	54
7	.47127	.53432	1.8715	.88199	1.1338	2.1219	53
8	.47153	.53470	1.8702	.88185	1.1340	2.1208	52
9	.47178	.53507	1.8689	.88172	1.1342	2.1196	51
10	.47204	.53545	1.8676	.88158	1.1343	2.1185	50
11	.47229	.53582	1.8663	.88144	1.1345	2.1173	49
12	.47255	.53620	1.8650	.88130	1.1347	2.1162	48
13	.47281	.53657	1.8637	.88117	1.1349	2.1150	47
14	.47306	.53694	1.8624	.88103	1.1350	2.1139	46
15	.47332	.53732	1.8611	.88089	1.1352	2.1127	45
16	.47358	.53769	1.8598	.88075	1.1354	2.1116	44
17	.47383	.53807	1.8585	.88062	1.1356	2.1105	43
18	.47409	.53844	1.8572	.88048	1.1357	2.1093	42
19	.47434	.53882	1.8559	.88034	1.1359	2.1082	41
20	.47460	.53920	1.8546	.88020	1.1361	2.1070	40
21	.47486	.53957	1.8533	.88006	1.1363	2.1059	39
22	.47511	.53995	1.8520	.87993	1.1365	2.1048	38
23	.47537	.54032	1.8507	.87979	1.1366	2.1036	37
24	.47562	.54070	1.8495	.87965	1.1368	2.1025	36
25	.47588	.54107	1.8482	.87951	1.1370	2.1014	35
26	.47614	.54145	1.8469	.87937	1.1372	2.1002	34
27	.47639	.54183	1.8456	.87923	1.1374	2.0991	33
28	.47665	.54220	1.8443	.87909	1.1375	2.0980	32
29	.47690	.54258	1.8430	.87896	1.1377	2.0969	31
30	.47716	.54296	1.8418	.87882	1.1379	2.0957	30
31	.47741	.54333	1.8405	.87868	1.1381	2.0946	29
32	.47767	.54371	1.8392	.87854	1.1383	2.0935	28
33	.47793	.54409	1.8379	.87840	1.1384	2.0924	27
34	.47818	.54446	1.8367	.87826	1.1386	2.0913	26
35	.47844	.54484	1.8354	.87812	1.1388	2.0901	25
36	.47869	.54522	1.8341	.87798	1.1390	2.0890	24
37	.47895	.54560	1.8329	.87784	1.1392	2.0879	23
38	.47920	.54597	1.8316	.87770	1.1393	2.0868	22
39	.47946	.54635	1.8303	.87756	1.1395	2.0857	21
40	.47971	.54673	1.8291	.87743	1.1397	2.0846	20
41	.47997	.54711	1.8278	.87729	1.1399	2.0835	19
42	.48022	.54748	1.8265	.87715	1.1401	2.0824	18
43	.48048	.54786	1.8253	.87701	1.1402	2.0813	17
44	.48073	.54824	1.8240	.87687	1.1404	2.0802	16
45	.48099	.54862	1.8228	.87673	1.1406	2.0791	15
46	.48124	.54900	1.8215	.87659	1.1408	2.0779	14
47	.48150	.54938	1.8202	.87645	1.1410	2.0768	13
48	.48175	.54975	1.8190	.87631	1.1412	2.0757	12
49	.48201	.55013	1.8177	.87617	1.1413	2.0747	11
50	.48226	.55051	1.8165	.87603	1.1415	2.0736	10
51	.48252	.55089	1.8152	.87589	1.1417	2.0725	9
52	.48277	.55127	1.8140	.87575	1.1419	2.0714	8
53	.48303	.55165	1.8127	.87561	1.1421	2.0703	7
54	.48328	.55203	1.8115	.87546	1.1423	2.0692	6
55	.48354	.55241	1.8103	.87532	1.1424	2.0681	5
56	.48379	.55279	1.8090	.87518	1.1426	2.0670	4
57	.48405	.55317	1.8078	.87504	1.1428	2.0659	3
58	.48430	.55355	1.8065	.87490	1.1430	2.0648	2
59	.48456	.55393	1.8053	.87476	1.1432	2.0637	1
60	.48481	.55431	1.8040	.87462	1.1434	2.0627	0
′	Cos	Cot	Tan	Sin	Csc	Sec	′

29° (209°) (330)° **150°**

′	Sin	Tan	Cot	Cos	Sec	Csc	′
0	.48481	.55431	1.8040	.87462	1.1434	2.0627	60
1	.48506	.55469	1.8028	.87448	1.1435	2.0616	59
2	.48532	.55507	1.8016	.87434	1.1437	2.0605	58
3	.48557	.55545	1.8003	.87420	1.1439	2.0594	57
4	.48583	.55583	1.7991	.87406	1.1441	2.0583	56
5	.48608	.55621	1.7979	.87391	1.1443	2.0573	55
6	.48634	.55659	1.7966	.87377	1.1445	2.0562	54
7	.48659	.55697	1.7954	.87363	1.1446	2.0551	53
8	.48684	.55736	1.7942	.87349	1.1448	2.0540	52
9	.48710	.55774	1.7930	.87335	1.1450	2.0530	51
10	.48735	.55812	1.7917	.87321	1.1452	2.0519	50
11	.48761	.55850	1.7905	.87306	1.1454	2.0508	49
12	.48786	.55888	1.7893	.87292	1.1456	2.0498	48
13	.48811	.55926	1.7881	.87278	1.1458	2.0487	47
14	.48837	.55964	1.7868	.87264	1.1460	2.0476	46
15	.48862	.56003	1.7856	.87250	1.1461	2.0466	45
16	.48888	.56041	1.7844	.87235	1.1463	2.0455	44
17	.48913	.56079	1.7832	.87221	1.1465	2.0445	43
18	.48938	.56117	1.7820	.87207	1.1467	2.0434	42
19	.48964	.56156	1.7808	.87193	1.1469	2.0423	41
20	.48989	.56194	1.7796	.87178	1.1471	2.0413	40
21	.49014	.56232	1.7783	.87164	1.1473	2.0402	39
22	.49040	.56270	1.7771	.87150	1.1474	2.0392	38
23	.49065	.56309	1.7759	.87136	1.1476	2.0381	37
24	.49090	.56347	1.7747	.87121	1.1478	2.0371	36
25	.49116	.56385	1.7735	.87107	1.1480	2.0360	35
26	.49141	.56424	1.7723	.87093	1.1482	2.0350	34
27	.49166	.56462	1.7711	.87079	1.1484	2.0339	33
28	.49192	.56501	1.7699	.87064	1.1486	2.0329	32
29	.49217	.56539	1.7687	.87050	1.1488	2.0318	31
30	.49242	.56577	1.7675	.87036	1.1490	2.0308	30
31	.49268	.56616	1.7663	.87021	1.1491	2.0297	29
32	.49293	.56654	1.7651	.87007	1.1493	2.0287	28
33	.49318	.56693	1.7639	.86993	1.1495	2.0276	27
34	.49344	.56731	1.7627	.86978	1.1497	2.0266	26
35	.49369	.56769	1.7615	.86964	1.1499	2.0256	25
36	.49394	.56808	1.7603	.86949	1.1501	2.0245	24
37	.49419	.56846	1.7591	.86935	1.1503	2.0235	23
38	.49445	.56885	1.7579	.86921	1.1505	2.0225	22
39	.49470	.56923	1.7567	.86906	1.1507	2.0214	21
40	.49495	.56962	1.7556	.86892	1.1509	2.0204	20
41	.49521	.57000	1.7544	.86878	1.1510	2.0194	19
42	.49546	.57039	1.7532	.86863	1.1512	2.0183	18
43	.49571	.57078	1.7520	.86849	1.1514	2.0173	17
44	.49596	.57116	1.7508	.86834	1.1516	2.0163	16
45	.49622	.57155	1.7496	.86820	1.1518	2.0152	15
46	.49647	.57193	1.7485	.86805	1.1520	2.0142	14
47	.49672	.57232	1.7473	.86791	1.1522	2.0132	13
48	.49697	.57271	1.7461	.86777	1.1524	2.0122	12
49	.49723	.57309	1.7449	.86762	1.1526	2.0112	11
50	.49748	.57348	1.7437	.86748	1.1528	2.0101	10
51	.49773	.57386	1.7426	.86733	1.1530	2.0091	9
52	.49798	.57425	1.7414	.86719	1.1532	2.0081	8
53	.49824	.57464	1.7402	.86704	1.1533	2.0071	7
54	.49849	.57503	1.7391	.86690	1.1535	2.0061	6
55	.49874	.57541	1.7379	.86675	1.1537	2.0051	5
56	.49899	.57580	1.7367	.86661	1.1539	2.0040	4
57	.49924	.57619	1.7355	.86646	1.1541	2.0030	3
58	.49950	.57657	1.7344	.86632	1.1543	2.0020	2
59	.49975	.57696	1.7332	.86617	1.1545	2.0010	1
60	.50000	.57735	1.7321	.86603	1.1547	2.0000	0
′	Cos	Cot	Tan	Sin	Csc	Sec	′

NATURAL TRIGONOMETRIC FUNCTIONS
TO FIVE PLACES

30° (210°)   (329°) **149°**   **31° (211°)**   (328°) 14

′	Sin	Tan	Cot	Cos	Sec	Csc	′
0	.50000	.57735	1.7321	.86603	1.1547	2.0000	60
1	.50025	.57774	1.7309	.86588	1.1549	1.9990	59
2	.50050	.57813	1.7297	.86573	1.1551	1.9980	58
3	.50076	.57851	1.7286	.86559	1.1553	1.9970	57
4	.50101	.57890	1.7274	.86544	1.1555	1.9960	56
5	.50126	.57929	1.7262	.86530	1.1557	1.9950	55
6	.50151	.57968	1.7251	.86515	1.1559	1.9940	54
7	.50176	.58007	1.7239	.86501	1.1561	1.9930	53
8	.50201	.58046	1.7228	.86486	1.1563	1.9920	52
9	.50227	.58085	1.7216	.86471	1.1565	1.9910	51
10	.50252	.58124	1.7205	.86457	1.1566	1.9900	50
11	.50277	.58162	1.7193	.86442	1.1568	1.9890	49
12	.50302	.58201	1.7182	.86427	1.1570	1.9880	48
13	.50327	.58240	1.7170	.86413	1.1572	1.9870	47
14	.50352	.58279	1.7159	.86398	1.1574	1.9860	46
15	.50377	.58318	1.7147	.86384	1.1576	1.9850	45
16	.50403	.58357	1.7136	.86369	1.1578	1.9840	44
17	.50428	.58396	1.7124	.86354	1.1580	1.9830	43
18	.50453	.58435	1.7113	.86340	1.1582	1.9821	42
19	.50478	.58474	1.7102	.86325	1.1584	1.9811	41
20	.50503	.58513	1.7090	.86310	1.1586	1.9801	40
21	.50528	.58552	1.7079	.86295	1.1588	1.9791	39
22	.50553	.58591	1.7067	.86281	1.1590	1.9781	38
23	.50578	.58631	1.7056	.86266	1.1592	1.9771	37
24	.50603	.58670	1.7045	.86251	1.1594	1.9762	36
25	.50628	.58709	1.7033	.86237	1.1596	1.9752	35
26	.50654	.58748	1.7022	.86222	1.1598	1.9742	34
27	.50679	.58787	1.7011	.86207	1.1600	1.9732	33
28	.50704	.58826	1.6999	.86192	1.1602	1.9722	32
29	.50729	.58865	1.6988	.86178	1.1604	1.9713	31
30	.50754	.58905	1.6977	.86163	1.1606	1.9703	30
31	.50779	.58944	1.6965	.86148	1.1608	1.9693	29
32	.50804	.58983	1.6954	.86133	1.1610	1.9684	28
33	.50829	.59022	1.6943	.86119	1.1612	1.9674	27
34	.50854	.59061	1.6932	.86104	1.1614	1.9664	26
35	.50879	.59101	1.6920	.86089	1.1616	1.9654	25
36	.50904	.59140	1.6909	.86074	1.1618	1.9645	24
37	.50929	.59179	1.6898	.86059	1.1620	1.9635	23
38	.50954	.59218	1.6887	.86045	1.1622	1.9625	22
39	.50979	.59258	1.6875	.86030	1.1624	1.9616	21
40	.51004	.59297	1.6864	.86015	1.1626	1.9606	20
41	.51029	.59336	1.6853	.86000	1.1628	1.9597	19
42	.51054	.59376	1.6842	.85985	1.1630	1.9587	18
43	.51079	.59415	1.6831	.85970	1.1632	1.9577	17
44	.51104	.59454	1.6820	.85956	1.1634	1.9568	16
45	.51129	.59494	1.6808	.85941	1.1636	1.9558	15
46	.51154	.59533	1.6797	.85926	1.1638	1.9549	14
47	.51179	.59573	1.6786	.85911	1.1640	1.9539	13
48	.51204	.59612	1.6775	.85896	1.1642	1.9530	12
49	.51229	.59651	1.6764	.85881	1.1644	1.9520	11
50	.51254	.59691	1.6753	.85866	1.1646	1.9511	10
51	.51279	.59730	1.6742	.85851	1.1648	1.9501	9
52	.51304	.59770	1.6731	.85836	1.1650	1.9492	8
53	.51329	.59809	1.6720	.85821	1.1652	1.9482	7
54	.51354	.59849	1.6709	.85806	1.1654	1.9473	6
55	.51379	.59888	1.6698	.85792	1.1656	1.9463	5
56	.51404	.59928	1.6687	.85777	1.1658	1.9454	4
57	.51429	.59967	1.6676	.85762	1.1660	1.9444	3
58	.51454	.60007	1.6665	.85747	1.1662	1.9435	2
59	.51479	.60046	1.6654	.85732	1.1664	1.9425	1
60	.51504	.60086	1.6643	.85717	1.1666	1.9416	0
′	Cos	Cot	Tan	Sin	Csc	Sec	′

120° (300°)   (239°) **59°**

31° (211°)   (328°) 14

′	Sin	Tan	Cot	Cos	Sec	Csc	′
0	.51504	.60086	1.6643	.85717	1.1666	1.9416	60
1	.51529	.60126	1.6632	.85702	1.1668	1.9407	59
2	.51554	.60165	1.6621	.85687	1.1670	1.9397	58
3	.51579	.60205	1.6610	.85672	1.1672	1.9388	57
4	.51604	.60245	1.6599	.85657	1.1675	1.9379	56
5	.51628	.60284	1.6588	.85642	1.1677	1.9369	55
6	.51653	.60324	1.6577	.85627	1.1679	1.9360	54
7	.51678	.60364	1.6566	.85612	1.1681	1.9351	53
8	.51703	.60403	1.6555	.85597	1.1683	1.9341	52
9	.51728	.60443	1.6545	.85582	1.1685	1.9332	51
10	.51753	.60483	1.6534	.85567	1.1687	1.9323	50
11	.51778	.60522	1.6523	.85551	1.1689	1.9313	49
12	.51803	.60562	1.6512	.85536	1.1691	1.9304	48
13	.51828	.60602	1.6501	.85521	1.1693	1.9295	47
14	.51852	.60642	1.6490	.85506	1.1695	1.9285	46
15	.51877	.60681	1.6479	.85491	1.1697	1.9276	45
16	.51902	.60721	1.6469	.85476	1.1699	1.9267	44
17	.51927	.60761	1.6458	.85461	1.1701	1.9258	43
18	.51952	.60801	1.6447	.85446	1.1703	1.9249	42
19	.51977	.60841	1.6436	.85431	1.1705	1.9239	41
20	.52002	.60881	1.6426	.85416	1.1707	1.9230	40
21	.52026	.60921	1.6415	.85401	1.1710	1.9221	39
22	.52051	.60960	1.6404	.85385	1.1712	1.9212	38
23	.52076	.61000	1.6393	.85370	1.1714	1.9203	37
24	.52101	.61040	1.6383	.85355	1.1716	1.9194	36
25	.52126	.61080	1.6372	.85340	1.1718	1.9184	35
26	.52151	.61120	1.6361	.85325	1.1720	1.9175	34
27	.52175	.61160	1.6351	.85310	1.1722	1.9166	33
28	.52200	.61200	1.6340	.85294	1.1724	1.9157	32
29	.52225	.61240	1.6329	.85279	1.1726	1.9148	31
30	.52250	.61280	1.6319	.85264	1.1728	1.9139	30
31	.52275	.61320	1.6308	.85249	1.1730	1.9130	29
32	.52299	.61360	1.6297	.85234	1.1732	1.9121	28
33	.52324	.61400	1.6287	.85218	1.1735	1.9112	27
34	.52349	.61440	1.6276	.85203	1.1737	1.9103	26
35	.52374	.61480	1.6265	.85188	1.1739	1.9094	25
36	.52399	.61520	1.6255	.85173	1.1741	1.9084	24
37	.52423	.61561	1.6244	.85157	1.1743	1.9075	23
38	.52448	.61601	1.6234	.85142	1.1745	1.9066	22
39	.52473	.61641	1.6223	.85127	1.1747	1.9057	21
40	.52498	.61681	1.6212	.85112	1.1749	1.9048	20
41	.52522	.61721	1.6202	.85096	1.1751	1.9039	19
42	.52547	.61761	1.6191	.85081	1.1753	1.9031	18
43	.52572	.61801	1.6181	.85066	1.1756	1.9022	17
44	.52597	.61842	1.6170	.85051	1.1758	1.9013	16
45	.52621	.61882	1.6160	.85035	1.1760	1.9004	15
46	.52646	.61922	1.6149	.85020	1.1762	1.8995	14
47	.52671	.61962	1.6139	.85005	1.1764	1.8986	13
48	.52696	.62003	1.6128	.84989	1.1766	1.8977	12
49	.52720	.62043	1.6118	.84974	1.1768	1.8968	11
50	.52745	.62083	1.6107	.84959	1.1770	1.8959	10
51	.52770	.62124	1.6097	.84943	1.1773	1.8950	9
52	.52794	.62164	1.6087	.84928	1.1775	1.8941	8
53	.52819	.62204	1.6076	.84913	1.1777	1.8933	7
54	.52844	.62245	1.6066	.84897	1.1779	1.8924	6
55	.52869	.62285	1.6055	.84882	1.1781	1.8915	5
56	.52893	.62325	1.6045	.84866	1.1783	1.8906	4
57	.52918	.62366	1.6034	.84851	1.1785	1.8897	3
58	.52943	.62406	1.6024	.84836	1.1788	1.8888	2
59	.52967	.62446	1.6014	.84820	1.1790	1.8880	1
60	.52992	.62487	1.6003	.84805	1.1792	1.8871	0
′	Cos	Cot	Tan	Sin	Csc	Sec	′

121° (301°)   (238°) 5

NATURAL TRIGONOMETRIC FUNCTIONS
TO FIVE PLACES

2° (212°)   (327°) 147°

′	Sin	Tan	Cot	Cos	Sec	Csc	′
0	.52992	.62487	1.6003	.84805	1.1792	1.8871	60
1	.53017	.62527	? 5993	.84789	1.1794	1.8862	59
2	.53041	.62568	1.5983	.84774	1.1796	1.8853	58
3	.53066	.62608	1.5972	.84759	1.1798	1.8844	57
4	.53091	.62649	1.5962	.84743	1.1800	1.8836	56
5	.53115	.62689	1.5952	.84728	1.1803	1.8827	55
6	.53140	.62730	1.5941	.84712	1.1805	1.8818	54
7	.53164	.62770	1.5931	.84697	1.1807	1.8810	53
8	.53189	.62811	1.5921	.84681	1.1809	1.8801	52
9	.53214	.62852	1.5911	.84666	1.1811	1.8792	51
10	.53238	.62892	1.5900	.84650	1.1813	1.8783	50
11	.53263	.62933	1.5890	.84635	1.1815	1.8775	49
12	.53288	.62973	1.5880	.84619	1.1818	1.8766	48
13	.53312	.63014	1.5869	.84604	1.1820	1.8757	47
14	.53337	.63055	1.5859	.84588	1.1822	1.8749	46
15	.53361	.63095	1.5849	.84573	1.1824	1.8740	45
16	.53386	.63136	1.5839	.84557	1.1826	1.8731	44
17	.53411	.63177	1.5829	.84542	1.1828	1.8723	43
18	.53435	.63217	1.5818	.84526	1.1831	1.8714	42
19	.53460	.63258	1.5808	.84511	1.1833	1.8706	41
20	.53484	.63299	1.5798	.84495	1.1835	1.8697	40
21	.53509	.63340	1.5788	.84480	1.1837	1.8688	39
22	.53534	.63380	1.5778	.84464	1.1840	1.8680	38
23	.53558	.63421	1.5768	.84448	1.1842	1.8671	37
24	.53583	.63462	1.5757	.84433	1.1844	1.8663	36
25	.53607	.63503	1.5747	.84417	1.1846	1.8654	35
26	.53632	.63544	1.5737	.84402	1.1848	1.8646	34
27	.53656	.63584	1.5727	.84386	1.1850	1.8637	33
28	.53681	.63625	1.5717	.84370	1.1852	1.8629	32
29	.53705	.63666	1.5707	.84355	1.1855	1.8620	31
30	.53730	.63707	1.5697	.84339	1.1857	1.8612	30
31	.53754	.63748	1.5687	.84324	1.1859	1.8603	29
32	.53779	.63789	1.5677	.84308	1.1861	1.8595	28
33	.53804	.63830	1.5667	.84292	1.1863	1.8586	27
34	.53828	.63871	1.5657	.84277	1.1866	1.8578	26
35	.53853	.63912	1.5647	.84261	1.1868	1.8569	25
36	.53877	.63953	1.5637	.84245	1.1870	1.8561	24
37	.53902	.63994	1.5627	.84230	1.1872	1.8552	23
38	.53926	.64035	1.5617	.84214	1.1875	1.8544	22
39	.53951	.64076	1.5607	.84198	1.1877	1.8535	21
40	.53975	.64117	1.5597	.84182	1.1879	1.8527	20
41	.54000	.64158	1.5587	.84167	1.1881	1.8519	19
42	.54024	.64199	1.5577	.84151	1.1883	1.8510	18
43	.54049	.64240	1.5567	.84135	1.1886	1.8502	17
44	.54073	.64281	1.5557	.84120	1.1888	1.8494	16
45	.54097	.64322	1.5547	.84104	1.1890	1.8485	15
46	.54122	.64363	1.5537	.84088	1.1892	1.8477	14
47	.54146	.64404	1.5527	.84072	1.1895	1.8468	13
48	.54171	.64446	1.5517	.84057	1.1897	1.8460	12
49	.54195	.64487	1.5507	.84041	1.1899	1.8452	11
50	.54220	.64528	1.5497	.84025	1.1901	1.8443	10
51	.54244	.64569	1.5487	.84009	1.1903	1.8435	9
52	.54269	.64610	1.5477	.83994	1.1906	1.8427	8
53	.54293	.64652	1.5468	.83978	1.1908	1.8419	7
54	.54317	.64693	1.5458	.83962	1.1910	1.8410	6
55	.54342	.64734	1.5448	.83946	1.1912	1.8402	5
56	.54366	.64775	1.5438	.83930	1.1915	1.8394	4
57	.54391	.64817	1.5428	.83915	1.1917	1.8385	3
58	.54415	.64858	1.5418	.83899	1.1919	1.8377	2
59	.54440	.64899	1.5408	.83883	1.1921	1.8369	1
60	.54464	.64941	1.5399	.83867	1.1924	1.8361	0
′	Cos	Cot	Tan	Sin	Csc	Sec	′

22° (302°)   (237°) 57°

33° (213°)   (326°) 146°

′	Sin	Tan	Cot	Cos	Sec	Csc	′
0	.54464	.64941	1.5399	.83867	1.1924	1.8361	60
1	.54488	.64982	1.5389	.83851	1.1926	1.8353	59
2	.54513	.65024	1.5379	.83835	1.1928	1.8344	58
3	.54537	.65065	1.5369	.83819	1.1930	1.8336	57
4	.54561	.65106	1.5359	.83804	1.1933	1.8328	56
5	.54586	.65148	1.5350	.83788	1.1935	1.8320	55
6	.54610	.65189	1.5340	.83772	1.9137	1.8312	54
7	.54635	.65231	1.5330	.83756	1.1939	1.8303	53
8	.54659	.65272	1.5320	.83740	1.1942	1.8295	52
9	.54683	.65314	1.5311	.83724	1.1944	1.8287	51
10	.54708	.65355	1.5301	.83708	1.1946	1.8279	50
11	.54732	.65397	1.5291	.83692	1.1949	1.8271	49
12	.54756	.65438	1.5282	.83676	1.1951	1.8263	48
13	.54781	.65480	1.5272	.83660	1.1953	1.8255	47
14	.54805	.65521	1.5262	.83645	1.1955	1.8247	46
15	.54829	.65563	1.5253	.83629	1.1958	1.8238	45
16	.54854	.65604	1.5243	.83613	1.1960	1.8230	44
17	.54878	.65646	1.5233	.83597	1.1962	1.8222	43
18	.54902	.65688	1.5224	.83581	1.1964	1.8214	42
19	.54927	.65729	1.5214	.83565	1.1967	1.8206	41
20	.54951	.65771	1.5204	.83549	1.1969	1.8198	40
21	.54975	.65813	1.5195	.83533	1.1971	1.8190	39
22	.54999	.65854	1.5185	.83517	1.1974	1.8182	38
23	.55024	.65896	1.5175	.83501	1.1976	1.8174	37
24	.55048	.65938	1.5166	.83485	1.1978	1.8166	36
25	.55072	.65980	1.5156	.83469	1.1981	1.8158	35
26	.55097	.66021	1.5147	.83453	1.1983	1.8150	34
27	.55121	.66063	1.5137	.83437	1.1985	1.8142	33
28	.55145	.66105	1.5127	.83421	1.1987	1.8134	32
29	.55169	.66147	1.5118	.83405	1.1990	1.8126	31
30	.55194	.66189	1.5108	.83389	1.1992	1.8118	30
31	.55218	.66230	1.5099	.83373	1.1994	1.8110	29
32	.55242	.66272	1.5089	.83356	1.1997	1.8102	28
33	.55266	.66314	1.5080	.83340	1.1999	1.8094	27
34	.55291	.66356	1.5070	.83324	1.2001	1.8086	26
35	.55315	.66398	1.5061	.83308	1.2004	1.8078	25
36	.55339	.66440	1.5051	.83292	1.2006	1.8070	24
37	.55363	.66482	1.5042	.83276	1.2008	1.8062	23
38	.55388	.66524	1.5032	.83260	1.2011	1.8055	22
39	.55412	.66566	1.5023	.83244	1.2013	1.8047	21
40	.55436	.66608	1.5013	.83228	1.2015	1.8039	20
41	.55460	.66650	1.5004	.83212	1.2018	1.8031	19
42	.55484	.66692	1.4994	.83195	1.2020	1.8023	18
43	.55509	.66734	1.4985	.83179	1.2022	1.8015	17
44	.55533	.66776	1.4975	.83163	1.2025	1.8007	16
45	.55557	.66818	1.4966	.83147	1.2027	1.8000	15
46	.55581	.66860	1.4957	.83131	1.2029	1.7992	14
47	.55605	.66902	1.4947	.83115	1.2032	1.7984	13
48	.55630	.66944	1.4938	.83098	1.2034	1.7976	12
49	.55654	.66986	1.4928	.83082	1.2036	1.7968	11
50	.55678	.67028	1.4919	.83066	1.2039	1.7960	10
51	.55702	.67071	1.4910	.83050	1.2041	1.7953	9
52	.55726	.67113	1.4900	.83034	1.2043	1.7945	8
53	.55750	.67155	1.4891	.83017	1.2046	1.7937	7
54	.55775	.67197	1.4882	.83001	1.2048	1.7929	6
55	.55799	.67239	1.4872	.82985	1.2050	1.7922	5
56	.55823	.67282	1.4863	.82969	1.2053	1.7914	4
57	.55847	.67324	1.4854	.82953	1.2055	1.7906	3
58	.55871	.67366	1.4844	.82936	1.2057	1.7898	2
59	.55895	.67409	1.4835	.82920	1.2060	1.7891	1
60	.55919	.67451	1.4826	.82904	1.2062	1.7883	0
′	Cos	Cot	Tan	Sin	Csc	Sec	′

123° (303°)   (236°) 56°

Tables for Use in Trigonometry

NATURAL TRIGONOMETRIC FUNCTIONS
TO FIVE PLACES

34° (214°)   (325°) **145°**

'	Sin	Tan	Cot	Cos	Sec	Csc	'
0	.55919	.67451	1.4826	.82904	1.2062	1.7883	60
1	.55943	.67493	1.4816	.82887	1.2065	1.7875	59
2	.55968	.67536	1.4807	.82871	1.2067	1.7868	58
3	.55992	.67578	1.4798	.82855	1.2069	1.7860	57
4	.56016	.67620	1.4788	.82839	1.2072	1.7852	56
5	.56040	.67663	1.4779	.82822	1.2074	1.7844	55
6	.56064	.67705	1.4770	.82806	1.2076	1.7837	54
7	.56088	.67748	1.4761	.82790	1.2079	1.7829	53
8	.56112	.67790	1.4751	.82773	1.2081	1.7821	52
9	.56136	.67832	1.4742	.82757	1.2084	1.7814	51
10	.56160	.67875	1.4733	.82741	1.2086	1.7806	50
11	.56184	.67917	1.4724	.82724	1.2088	1.7799	49
12	.56208	.67960	1.4715	.82708	1.2091	1.7791	48
13	.56232	.68002	1.4705	.82692	1.2093	1.7783	47
14	.56256	.68045	1.4696	.82675	1.2096	1.7776	46
15	.56280	.68088	1.4687	.82659	1.2098	1.7768	45
16	.56305	.68130	1.4678	.82643	1.2100	1.7761	44
17	.56329	.68173	1.4669	.82626	1.2103	1.7753	43
18	.56353	.68215	1.4659	.82610	1.2105	1.7745	42
19	.56377	.68258	1.4650	.82593	1.2108	1.7738	41
20	.56401	.68301	1.4641	.82577	1.2110	1.7730	40
21	.56425	.68343	1.4632	.82561	1.2112	1.7723	39
22	.56449	.68386	1.4623	.82544	1.2115	1.7715	38
23	.56473	.68429	1.4614	.82528	1.2117	1.7708	37
24	.56497	.68471	1.4605	.82511	1.2120	1.7700	36
25	.56521	.68514	1.4596	.82495	1.2122	1.7693	35
26	.56545	.68557	1.4586	.82478	1.2124	1.7685	34
27	.56569	.68600	1.4577	.82462	1.2127	1.7678	33
28	.56593	.68642	1.4568	.82446	1.2129	1.7670	32
29	.56617	.68685	1.4559	.82429	1.2132	1.7663	31
30	.56641	.68728	1.4550	.82413	1.2134	1.7655	30
31	.56665	.68771	1.4541	.82396	1.2136	1.7648	29
32	.56689	.68814	1.4532	.82380	1.2139	1.7640	28
33	.56713	.68857	1.4523	.82363	1.2141	1.7633	27
34	.56736	.68900	1.4514	.82347	1.2144	1.7625	26
35	.56760	.68942	1.4505	.82330	1.2146	1.7618	25
36	.56784	.68985	1.4496	.82314	1.2149	1.7610	24
37	.56808	.69028	1.4487	.82297	1.2151	1.7603	23
38	.56832	.69071	1.4478	.82281	1.2154	1.7596	22
39	.56856	.69114	1.4469	.82264	1.2156	1.7588	21
40	.56880	.69157	1.4460	.82248	1.2158	1.7581	20
41	.56904	.69200	1.4451	.82231	1.2161	1.7573	19
42	.56928	.69243	1.4442	.82214	1.2163	1.7566	18
43	.56952	.69286	1.4433	.82198	1.2166	1.7559	17
44	.56976	.69329	1.4424	.82181	1.2168	1.7551	16
45	.57000	.69372	1.4415	.82165	1.2171	1.7544	15
46	.57024	.69416	1.4406	.82148	1.2173	1.7537	14
47	.57047	.69459	1.4397	.82132	1.2176	1.7529	13
48	.57071	.69502	1.4388	.82115	1.2178	1.7522	12
49	.57095	.69545	1.4379	.82098	1.2181	1.7515	11
50	.57119	.69588	1.4370	.82082	1.2183	1.7507	10
51	.57143	.69631	1.4361	.82065	1.2185	1.7500	9
52	.57167	.69675	1.4352	.82048	1.2188	1.7493	8
53	.57191	.69718	1.4344	.82032	1.2190	1.7485	7
54	.57215	.69761	1.4335	.82015	1.2193	1.7478	6
55	.57238	.69804	1.4326	.81999	1.2195	1.7471	5
56	.57262	.69847	1.4317	.81982	1.2198	1.7463	4
57	.57286	.69891	1.4308	.81965	1.2200	1.7456	3
58	.57310	.69934	1.4299	.81949	1.2203	1.7449	2
59	.57334	.69977	1.4290	.81932	1.2205	1.7442	1
60	.57358	.70021	1.4281	.81915	1.2208	1.7434	0
'	Cos	Cot	Tan	Sin	Csc	Sec	'

124° (304°)   (235°) **55°**

35° (215°)   (324°) **14**

'	Sin	Tan	Cot	Cos	Sec	Csc	'
0	.57358	.70021	1.4281	.81915	1.2208	1.7434	60
1	.57381	.70064	1.4273	.81899	1.2210	1.7427	59
2	.57405	.70107	1.4264	.81882	1.2213	1.7420	58
3	.57429	.70151	1.4255	.81865	1.2215	1.7413	57
4	.57453	.70194	1.4246	.81848	1.2218	1.7406	56
5	.57477	.70238	1.4237	.81832	1.2220	1.7398	55
6	.57501	.70281	1.4229	.81815	1.2223	1.7391	54
7	.57524	.70325	1.4220	.81798	1.2225	1.7384	53
8	.57548	.70368	1.4211	.81782	1.2228	1.7377	52
9	.57572	.70412	1.4202	.81765	1.2230	1.7370	51
10	.57596	.70455	1.4193	.81748	1.2233	1.7362	50
11	.57619	.70499	1.4185	.81731	1.2235	1.7355	49
12	.57643	.70542	1.4176	.81714	1.2238	1.7348	48
13	.57667	.70586	1.4167	.81698	1.2240	1.7341	47
14	.57691	.70629	1.4158	.81681	1.2243	1.7334	46
15	.57715	.70673	1.4150	.81664	1.2245	1.7327	45
16	.57738	.70717	1.4141	.81647	1.2248	1.7320	44
17	.57762	.70760	1.4132	.81631	1.2250	1.7312	43
18	.57786	.70804	1.4124	.81614	1.2253	1.7305	42
19	.57810	.70848	1.4115	.81597	1.2255	1.7298	41
20	.57833	.70891	1.4106	.81580	1.2258	1.7291	40
21	.57857	.70935	1.4097	.81563	1.2260	1.7284	39
22	.57881	.70979	1.4089	.81546	1.2263	1.7277	38
23	.57904	.71023	1.4080	.81530	1.2265	1.7270	37
24	.57928	.71066	1.4071	.81513	1.2268	1.7263	36
25	.57952	.71110	1.4063	.81496	1.2271	1.7256	35
26	.57976	.71154	1.4054	.81479	1.2273	1.7249	34
27	.57999	.71198	1.4045	.81462	1.2276	1.7242	33
28	.58023	.71242	1.4037	.81445	1.2278	1.7235	32
29	.58047	.71285	1.4028	.81428	1.2281	1.7228	31
30	.58070	.71329	1.4019	.81412	1.2283	1.7221	30
31	.58094	.71373	1.4011	.81395	1.2286	1.7213	29
32	.58118	.71417	1.4002	.81378	1.2288	1.7206	28
33	.58141	.71461	1.3994	.81361	1.2291	1.7199	27
34	.58165	.71505	1.3985	.81344	1.2293	1.7192	26
35	.58189	.71549	1.3976	.81327	1.2296	1.7185	25
36	.58212	.71593	1.3968	.81310	1.2299	1.7179	24
37	.58236	.71637	1.3959	.81293	1.2301	1.7172	23
38	.58260	.71681	1.3951	.81276	1.2304	1.7165	22
39	.58283	.71725	1.3942	.81259	1.2306	1.7158	21
40	.58307	.71769	1.3934	.81242	1.2309	1.7151	20
41	.58330	.71813	1.3925	.81225	1.2311	1.7144	19
42	.58354	.71857	1.3916	.81208	1.2314	1.7137	18
43	.58378	.71901	1.3908	.81191	1.2317	1.7130	17
44	.58401	.71946	1.3899	.81174	1.2319	1.7123	16
45	.58425	.71990	1.3891	.81157	1.2322	1.7116	15
46	.58449	.72034	1.3882	.81140	1.2324	1.7109	14
47	.58472	.72078	1.3874	.81123	1.2327	1.7102	13
48	.58496	.72122	1.3865	.81106	1.2329	1.7095	12
49	.58519	.72167	1.3857	.81089	1.2332	1.7088	11
50	.58543	.72211	1.3848	.81072	1.2335	1.7081	10
51	.58567	.72255	1.3840	.81055	1.2337	1.7075	9
52	.58590	.72299	1.3831	.81038	1.2340	1.7068	8
53	.58614	.72344	1.3823	.81021	1.2342	1.7061	7
54	.58637	.72388	1.3814	.81004	1.2345	1.7054	6
55	.58661	.72432	1.3806	.80987	1.2348	1.7047	5
56	.58684	.72477	1.3798	.80970	1.2350	1.7040	4
57	.58708	.72521	1.3789	.80953	1.2353	1.7033	3
58	.58731	.72565	1.3781	.80936	1.2355	1.7027	2
59	.58755	.72610	1.3772	.80919	1.2358	1.7020	1
60	.58779	.72654	1.3764	.80902	1.2361	1.7013	0
'	Cos	Cot	Tan	Sin	Csc	Sec	'

125° (305°)   (234°) **54**

NATURAL TRIGONOMETRIC FUNCTIONS
TO FIVE PLACES

36° (216°)   (323°) **143°**   **37° (217°)**   (322°) **142°**

′	Sin	Tan	Cot	Cos	Sec	Csc	′	′	Sin	Tan	Cot	Cos	Sec	Csc	′
0	.58779	.72654	1.3764	.80902	1.2361	1.7013	60	0	.60182	.75355	1.3270	.79864	1.2521	1.6616	60
1	.58802	.72699	1.3755	.80885	1.2363	1.7006	59	1	.60205	.75401	1.3262	.79846	1.2524	1.6610	59
2	.58826	.72743	1.3747	.80867	1.2366	1.6999	58	2	.60228	.75447	1.3254	.79829	1.2527	1.6604	58
3	.58849	.72788	1.3739	.80850	1.2369	1.6993	57	3	.60251	.75492	1.3246	.79811	1.2530	1.6597	57
4	.58873	.72832	1.3730	.80833	1.2371	1.6986	56	4	.60274	.75538	1.3238	.79793	1.2532	1.6591	56
5	.58896	.72877	1.3722	.80816	1.2374	1.6979	55	5	.60298	.75584	1.3230	.79776	1.2535	1.6584	55
6	.58920	.72921	1.3713	.80799	1.2376	1.6972	54	6	.60321	.75629	1.3222	.79758	1.2538	1.6578	54
7	.58943	.72966	1.3705	.80782	1.2379	1.6966	53	7	.60344	.75675	1.3214	.79741	1.2541	1.6572	53
8	.58967	.73010	1.3697	.80765	1.2382	1.6959	52	8	.60367	.75721	1.3206	.79723	1.2543	1.6565	52
9	.58990	.73055	1.3688	.80748	1.2384	1.6952	51	9	.60390	.75767	1.3198	.79706	1.2546	1.6559	51
10	.59014	.73100	1.3680	.80730	1.2387	1.6945	50	10	.60414	.75812	1.3190	.79688	1.2549	1.6553	50
11	.59037	.73144	1.3672	.80713	1.2390	1.6939	49	11	.60437	.75858	1.3182	.79671	1.2552	1.6546	49
12	.59061	.73189	1.3663	.80696	1.2392	1.6932	48	12	.60460	.75904	1.3175	.79653	1.2554	1.6540	48
13	.59084	.73234	1.3655	.80679	1.2395	1.6925	47	13	.60483	.75950	1.3167	.79635	1.2557	1.6534	47
14	.59108	.73278	1.3647	.80662	1.2397	1.6918	46	14	.60506	.75996	1.3159	.79618	1.2560	1.6527	46
15	.59131	.73323	1.3638	.80644	1.2400	1.6912	45	15	.60529	.76042	1.3151	.79600	1.2563	1.6521	45
16	.59154	.73368	1.3630	.80627	1.2403	1.6905	44	16	.60553	.76088	1.3143	.79583	1.2566	1.6515	44
17	.59178	.73413	1.3622	.80610	1.2405	1.6898	43	17	.60576	.76134	1.3135	.79565	1.2568	1.6508	43
18	.59201	.73457	1.3613	.80593	1.2408	1.6892	42	18	.60599	.76180	1.3127	.79547	1.2571	1.6502	42
19	.59225	.73502	1.3605	.80576	1.2411	1.6885	41	19	.60622	.76226	1.3119	.79530	1.2574	1.6496	41
20	.59248	.73547	1.3597	.80558	1.2413	1.6878	40	20	.60645	.76272	1.3111	.79512	1.2577	1.6489	40
21	.59272	.73592	1.3588	.80541	1.2416	1.6871	39	21	.60668	.76318	1.3103	.79494	1.2579	1.6483	39
22	.59295	.73637	1.3580	.80524	1.2419	1.6865	38	22	.60691	.76364	1.3095	.79477	1.2582	1.6477	38
23	.59318	.73681	1.3572	.80507	1.2421	1.6858	37	23	.60714	.76410	1.3087	.79459	1.2585	1.6471	37
24	.59342	.73726	1.3564	.80489	1.2424	1.6852	36	24	.60738	.76456	1.3079	.79441	1.2588	1.6464	36
25	.59365	.73771	1.3555	.80472	1.2427	1.6845	35	25	.60761	.76502	1.3072	.79424	1.2591	1.6458	35
26	.59389	.73816	1.3547	.80455	1.2429	1.6838	34	26	.60784	.76548	1.3064	.79406	1.2593	1.6452	34
27	.59412	.73861	1.3539	.80438	1.2432	1.6832	33	27	.60807	.76594	1.3056	.79388	1.2596	1.6446	33
28	.59436	.73906	1.3531	.80420	1.2435	1.6825	32	28	.60830	.76640	1.3048	.79371	1.2599	1.6439	32
29	.59459	.73951	1.3522	.80403	1.2437	1.6818	31	29	.60853	.76686	1.3040	.79353	1.2602	1.6433	31
30	.59482	.73996	1.3514	.80386	1.2440	1.6812	30	30	.60876	.76733	1.3032	.79335	1.2605	1.6427	30
31	.59506	.74041	1.3506	.80368	1.2443	1.6805	29	31	.60899	.76779	1.3024	.79318	1.2608	1.6421	29
32	.59529	.74086	1.3498	.80351	1.2445	1.6799	28	32	.60922	.76825	1.3017	.79300	1.2610	1.6414	28
33	.59552	.74131	1.3490	.80334	1.2448	1.6792	27	33	.60945	.76871	1.3009	.79282	1.2613	1.6408	27
34	.59576	.74176	1.3481	.80316	1.2451	1.6785	26	34	.60968	.76918	1.3001	.79264	1.2616	1.6402	26
35	.59599	.74221	1.3473	.80299	1.2453	1.6779	25	35	.60991	.76964	1.2993	.79247	1.2619	1.6396	25
36	.59622	.74267	1.3465	.80282	1.2456	1.6772	24	36	.61015	.77010	1.2985	.79229	1.2622	1.6390	24
37	.59646	.74312	1.3457	.80264	1.2459	1.6766	23	37	.61038	.77057	1.2977	.79211	1.2624	1.6383	23
38	.59669	.74357	1.3449	.80247	1.2462	1.6759	22	38	.61061	.77103	1.2970	.79193	1.2627	1.6377	22
39	.59693	.74402	1.3440	.80230	1.2464	1.6753	21	39	.61084	.77149	1.2962	.79176	1.2630	1.6371	21
40	.59716	.74447	1.3432	.80212	1.2467	1.6746	20	40	.61107	.77196	1.2954	.79158	1.2633	1.6365	20
41	.59739	.74492	1.3424	.80195	1.2470	1.6739	19	41	.61130	.77242	1.2946	.79140	1.2636	1.6359	19
42	.59763	.74538	1.3416	.80178	1.2472	1.6733	18	42	.61153	.77289	1.2938	.79122	1.2639	1.6353	18
43	.59786	.74583	1.3408	.80160	1.2475	1.6726	17	43	.61176	.77335	1.2931	.79105	1.2641	1.6346	17
44	.59809	.74628	1.3400	.80143	1.2478	1.6720	16	44	.61199	.77382	1.2923	.79087	1.2644	1.6340	16
45	.59832	.74674	1.3392	.80125	1.2480	1.6713	15	45	.61222	.77428	1.2915	.79069	1.2647	1.6334	15
46	.59856	.74719	1.3384	.80108	1.2483	1.6707	14	46	.61245	.77475	1.2907	.79051	1.2650	1.6328	14
47	.59879	.74764	1.3375	.80091	1.2486	1.6700	13	47	.61268	.77521	1.2900	.79033	1.2653	1.6322	13
48	.59902	.74810	1.3367	.80073	1.2489	1.6694	12	48	.61291	.77568	1.2892	.79016	1.2656	1.6316	12
49	.59926	.74855	1.3359	.80056	1.2491	1.6687	11	49	.61314	.77615	1.2884	.78998	1.2659	1.6310	11
50	.59949	.74900	1.3351	.80038	1.2494	1.6681	10	50	.61337	.77661	1.2876	.78980	1.2661	1.6303	10
51	.59972	.74946	1.3343	.80021	1.2497	1.6674	9	51	.61360	.77708	1.2869	.78962	1.2664	1.6297	9
52	.59995	.74991	1.3335	.80003	1.2499	1.6668	8	52	.61383	.77754	1.2861	.78944	1.2667	1.6291	8
53	.60019	.75037	1.3327	.79986	1.2502	1.6661	7	53	.61406	.77801	1.2853	.78926	1.2670	1.6285	7
54	.60042	.75082	1.3319	.79968	1.2505	1.6655	6	54	.61429	.77848	1.2846	.78908	1.2673	1.6279	6
55	.60065	.75128	1.3311	.79951	1.2508	1.6649	5	55	.61451	.77895	1.2838	.78891	1.2676	1.6273	5
56	.60089	.75173	1.3303	.79934	1.2510	1.6642	4	56	.61474	.77941	1.2830	.78873	1.2679	1.6267	4
57	.60112	.75219	1.3295	.79916	1.2513	1.6636	3	57	.61497	.77988	1.2822	.78855	1.2682	1.6261	3
58	.60135	.75264	1.3287	.79899	1.2516	1.6629	2	58	.61520	.78035	1.2815	.78837	1.2684	1.6255	2
59	.60158	.75310	1.3278	.79881	1.2519	1.6623	1	59	.61543	.78082	1.2807	.78819	1.2687	1.6249	1
60	.60182	.75355	1.3270	.79864	1.2521	1.6616	0	60	.61566	.78129	1.2799	.78801	1.2690	1.6243	0
′	Cos	Cot	Tan	Sin	Csc	Sec	′	′	Cos	Cot	Tan	Sin	Csc	Sec	′

126° (306°)   (233°) **53°**   **127° (307°)**   (232°) **52°**

NATURAL TRIGONOMETRIC FUNCTIONS
TO FIVE PLACES

38° (218°)   (321°) **141°**

′	Sin	Tan	Cot	Cos	Sec	Csc	′
0	.61566	.78129	1.2799	.78801	1.2690	1.6243	60
1	.61589	.78175	1.2792	.78783	1.2693	1.6237	59
2	.61612	.78222	1.2784	.78765	1.2696	1.6231	58
3	.61635	.78269	1.2776	.78747	1.2699	1.6225	57
4	.61658	.78316	1.2769	.78729	1.2702	1.6219	56
5	.61681	.78363	1.2761	.78711	1.2705	1.6213	55
6	.61704	.78410	1.2753	.78694	1.2708	1.6207	54
7	.61726	.78457	1.2746	.78676	1.2710	1.6201	53
8	.61749	.78504	1.2738	.78658	1.2713	1.6195	52
9	.61772	.78551	1.2731	.78640	1.2716	1.6189	51
10	.61795	.78598	1.2723	.78622	1.1719	1.6183	50
11	.61818	.78645	1.2715	.78604	1.2722	1.6177	49
12	.61841	.78692	1.2708	.78586	1.2725	1.6171	48
13	.61864	.78739	1.2700	.78568	1.2728	1.6165	47
14	.61887	.78786	1.2693	.78550	1.2731	1.6159	46
15	.61909	.78834	1.2685	.78532	1.2734	1.6153	45
16	.61932	.78881	1.2677	.78514	1.2737	1.6147	44
17	.61955	.78928	1.2670	.78496	1.2740	1.6141	43
18	.61978	.78975	1.2662	.78478	1.2742	1.6135	42
19	.62001	.79022	1.2655	.78460	1.2745	1.6129	41
20	.62024	.79070	1.2647	.78442	1.2748	1.6123	40
21	.62046	.79117	1.2640	.78424	1.2751	1.6117	39
22	.62069	.79164	1.2632	.78405	1.2754	1.6111	38
23	.62092	.79212	1.2624	.78387	1.2757	1.6105	37
24	.62115	.79259	1.2617	.78369	1.2760	1.6099	36
25	.62138	.79306	1.2609	.78351	1.2763	1.6093	35
26	.62160	.79354	1.2602	.78333	1.2766	1.6087	34
27	.62183	.79401	1.2594	.78315	1.2769	1.6082	33
28	.62206	.79449	1.2587	.78297	1.2772	1.6076	32
29	.62229	.79496	1.2579	.78279	1.2775	1.6070	31
30	.62251	.79544	1.2572	.78261	1.2778	1.6064	30
31	.62274	.79591	1.2564	.78243	1.2781	1.6058	29
32	.62297	.79639	1.2557	.78225	1.2784	1.6052	28
33	.62320	.79686	1.2549	.78206	1.2787	1.6046	27
34	.62342	.79734	1.2542	.78188	1.2790	1.6040	26
35	.62365	.79781	1.2534	.78170	1.2793	1.6035	25
36	.62388	.79829	1.2527	.78152	1.2796	1.6029	24
37	.62411	.79877	1.2519	.78134	1.2799	1.6023	23
38	.62433	.79924	1.2512	.78116	1.2802	1.6017	22
39	.62456	.79972	1.2504	.78098	1.2804	1.6011	21
40	.62479	.80020	1.2497	.78079	1.2807	1.6005	20
41	.62502	.80067	1.2489	.78061	1.2810	1.6000	19
42	.62524	.80115	1.2482	.78043	1.2813	1.5994	18
43	.62547	.80163	1.2475	.78025	1.2816	1.5988	17
44	.62570	.80211	1.2467	.78007	1.2819	1.5982	16
45	.62592	.80258	1.2460	.77988	1.2822	1.5976	15
46	.62615	.80306	1.2452	.77970	1.2825	1.5971	14
47	.62638	.80354	1.2445	.77952	1.2828	1.5965	13
48	.62660	.80402	1.2437	.77934	1.2831	1.5959	12
49	.62683	.80450	1.2430	.77916	1.2834	1.5953	11
50	.62706	.80498	1.2423	.77897	1.2837	1.5948	10
51	.62728	.80546	1.2415	.77879	1.2840	1.5942	9
52	.62751	.80594	1.2408	.77861	1.2843	1.5936	8
53	.62774	.80642	1.2401	.77843	1.2846	1.5930	7
54	.62796	.80690	1.2393	.77824	1.2849	1.5925	6
55	.62819	.80738	1.2386	.77806	1.2852	1.5919	5
56	.62842	.80786	1.2378	.77788	1.2855	1.5913	4
57	.62864	.80834	1.2371	.77769	1.2859	1.5907	3
58	.62887	.80882	1.2364	.77751	1.2862	1.5902	2
59	.62909	.80930	1.2356	.77733	1.2865	1.5896	1
60	.62932	.80978	1.2349	.77715	1.2868	1.5890	0
′	Cos	Cot	Tan	Sin	Csc	Sec	′

39° (219°)   (320°)

′	Sin	Tan	Cot	Cos	Sec	Csc	′
0	.62932	.80978	1.2349	.77715	1.2868	1.5890	60
1	.62955	.81027	1.2342	.77696	1.2871	1.5884	59
2	.62977	.81075	1.2334	.77678	1.2874	1.5879	58
3	.63000	.81123	1.2327	.77660	1.2877	1.5873	57
4	.63022	.81171	1.2320	.77641	1.2880	1.5867	56
5	.63045	.81220	1.2312	.77623	1.2883	1.5862	55
6	.63068	.81268	1.2305	.77605	1.2886	1.5856	54
7	.63090	.81316	1.2298	.77586	1.2889	1.5850	53
8	.63113	.81364	1.2290	.77568	1.2892	1.5845	52
9	.63135	.81413	1.2283	.77550	1.2895	1.5839	51
10	.63158	.81461	1.2276	.77531	1.2898	1.5833	50
11	.63180	.81510	1.2268	.77513	1.2901	1.5828	49
12	.63203	.81558	1.2261	.77494	1.2904	1.5822	48
13	.63225	.81606	1.2254	.77476	1.2907	1.5816	47
14	.63248	.81655	1.2247	.77458	1.2910	1.5811	46
15	.63271	.81703	1.2239	.77439	1.2913	1.5805	45
16	.63293	.81752	1.2232	.77421	1.2916	1.5800	44
17	.63316	.81800	1.2225	.77402	1.2919	1.5794	43
18	.63338	.81849	1.2218	.77384	1.2923	1.5788	42
19	.63361	.81898	1.2210	.77366	1.2926	1.5783	41
20	.63383	.81946	1.2203	.77347	1.2929	1.5777	40
21	.63406	.81995	1.2196	.77329	1.2932	1.5771	39
22	.63428	.82044	1.2189	.77310	1.2935	1.5766	38
23	.63451	.82092	1.2181	.77292	1.2938	1.5760	37
24	.63473	.82141	1.2174	.77273	1.2941	1.5755	36
25	.63496	.82190	1.2167	.77255	1.2944	1.5749	35
26	.63518	.82238	1.2160	.77236	1.2947	1.5744	34
27	.63540	.82287	1.2153	.77218	1.2950	1.5738	33
28	.63563	.82336	1.2145	.77199	1.2953	1.5732	32
29	.63585	.82385	1.2138	.77181	1.2957	1.5727	31
30	.63608	.82434	1.2131	.77162	1.2960	1.5721	30
31	.63630	.82483	1.2124	.77144	1.2963	1.5716	29
32	.63653	.82531	1.2117	.77125	1.2966	1.5710	28
33	.63675	.82580	1.2109	.77107	1.2969	1.5705	27
34	.63698	.82629	1.2102	.77088	1.2972	1.5699	26
35	.63720	.82678	1.2095	.77070	1.2975	1.5694	25
36	.63742	.82727	1.2088	.77051	1.2978	1.5688	24
37	.63765	.82776	1.2081	.77033	1.2981	1.5683	23
38	.63787	.82825	1.2074	.77014	1.2985	1.5677	22
39	.63810	.82874	1.2066	.76996	1.2988	1.5672	21
40	.63832	.82923	1.2059	.76977	1.2991	1.5666	20
41	.63854	.82972	1.2052	.76959	1.2994	1.5661	19
42	.63877	.83022	1.2045	.76940	1.2997	1.5655	18
43	.63899	.83071	1.2038	.76921	1.3000	1.5650	17
44	.63922	.83120	1.2031	.76903	1.3003	1.5644	16
45	.63944	.83169	1.2024	.76884	1.3007	1.5639	15
46	.63966	.83218	1.2017	.76866	1.3010	1.5633	14
47	.63989	.83268	1.2009	.76847	1.3013	1.5628	13
48	.64011	.83317	1.2002	.76828	1.3016	1.5622	12
49	.64033	.83366	1.1995	.76810	1.3019	1.5617	11
50	.64056	.83415	1.1988	.76791	1.3022	1.5611	10
51	.64078	.83465	1.1981	.76772	1.3026	1.5606	9
52	.64100	.83514	1.1974	.76754	1.3029	1.5601	8
53	.64123	.83564	1.1967	.76735	1.3032	1.5595	7
54	.64145	.83613	1.1960	.76717	1.3035	1.5590	6
55	.64167	.83662	1.1953	.76698	1.3038	1.5584	5
56	.64190	.83712	1.1946	.76679	1.3041	1.5579	4
57	.64212	.83761	1.1939	.76661	1.3045	1.5573	3
58	.64234	.83811	1.1932	.76642	1.3048	1.5568	2
59	.64256	.83860	1.1925	.76623	1.3051	1.5563	1
60	.64279	.83910	1 1918	.76604	1.3054	1.5557	0
′	Cos	Cot	Tan	Sin	Csc	Sec	′

NATURAL TRIGONOMETRIC FUNCTIONS
TO FIVE PLACES

40° (220°)   **(319°) 139°**   **41° (221°)**   **(318°) 138°**

′	Sin	Tan	Cot	Cos	Sec	Csc	′		′	Sin	Tan	Cot	Cos	Sec	Csc	′
0	.64279	.83910	1.1918	.76604	1.3054	1.5557	60		0	.65606	.86929	1.1504	.75471	1.3250	1.5243	60
1	.64301	.83960	1.1910	.76586	1.3057	1.5552	59		1	.65628	.86980	1.1497	.75452	1.3253	1.5237	59
2	.64323	.84009	1.1903	.76567	1.3060	1.5546	58		2	.65650	.87031	1.1490	.75433	1.3257	1.5232	58
3	.64346	.84059	1.1896	.76548	1.3064	1.5541	57		3	.65672	.87082	1.1483	.75414	1.3260	1.5227	57
4	.64368	.84108	1.1889	.76530	1.3067	1.5536	56		4	.65694	.87133	1.1477	.75395	1.3264	1.5222	56
5	.64390	.84158	1.1882	.76511	1.3070	1.5530	55		5	.65716	.87184	1.1470	.75375	1.3267	1.5217	55
6	.64412	.84208	1.1875	.76492	1.3073	1.5525	54		6	.65738	.87236	1.1463	.75356	1.3270	1.5212	54
7	.64435	.84258	1.1868	.76473	1.3076	1.5520	53		7	.65759	.87287	1.1456	.75337	1.3274	1.5207	53
8	.64457	.84307	1.1861	.76455	1.3080	1.5514	52		8	.65781	.87338	1.1450	.75318	1.3277	1.5202	52
9	.64479	.84357	1.1854	.76436	1.3083	1.5509	51		9	.65803	.87389	1.1443	.75299	1.3280	1.5197	51
10	.64501	.84407	1.1847	.76417	1.3086	1.5504	50		10	.65825	.87441	1.1436	.75280	1.3284	1.5192	50
11	.64524	.84457	1.1840	.76398	1.3089	1.5498	49		11	.65847	.87492	1.1430	.75261	1.3287	1.5187	49
12	.64546	.84507	1.1833	.76380	1.3093	1.5493	48		12	.65869	.87543	1.1423	.75241	1.3291	1.5182	48
13	.64568	.84556	1.1826	.76361	1.3096	1.5488	47		13	.65891	.87595	1.1416	.75222	1.3294	1.5177	47
14	.64590	.84606	1.1819	.76342	1.3099	1.5482	46		14	.65913	.87646	1.1410	.75203	1.3297	1.5172	46
15	.64612	.84656	1.1812	.76323	1.3102	1.5477	45		15	.65935	.87698	1.1403	.75184	1.3301	1.5167	45
16	.64635	.84706	1.1806	.76304	1.3105	1.5472	44		16	.65956	.87749	1.1396	.75165	1.3304	1.5162	44
17	.64657	.84756	1.1799	.76286	1.3109	1.5466	43		17	.65978	.87801	1.1389	.75146	1.3307	1.5156	43
18	.64679	.84806	1.1792	.76267	1.3112	1.5461	42		18	.66000	.87852	1.1383	.75126	1.3311	1.5151	42
19	.64701	.84856	1.1785	.76248	1.3115	1.5456	41		19	.66022	.87904	1.1376	.75107	1.3314	1.5146	41
20	.64723	.84906	1.1778	.76229	1.3118	1.5450	40		20	.66044	.87955	1.1369	.75088	1.3318	1.5141	40
21	.64746	.84956	1.1771	.76210	1.3122	1.5445	39		21	.66066	.88007	1.1363	.75069	1.3321	1.5136	39
22	.64768	.85006	1.1764	.76192	1.3125	1.5440	38		22	.66088	.88059	1.1356	.75050	1.3325	1.5131	38
23	.64790	.85057	1.1757	.76173	1.3128	1.5435	37		23	.66109	.88110	1.1349	.75030	1.3328	1.5126	37
24	.64812	.85107	1.1750	.76154	1.3131	1.5429	36		24	.66131	.88162	1.1343	.75011	1.3331	1.5121	36
25	.64834	.85157	1.1743	.76135	1.3135	1.5424	35		25	.66153	.88214	1.1336	.74992	1.3335	1.5116	35
26	.64856	.85207	1.1736	.76116	1.3138	1.5419	34		26	.66175	.88265	1.1329	.74973	1.3338	1.5111	34
27	.64878	.85257	1.1729	.76097	1.3141	1.5413	33		27	.66197	.88317	1.1323	.74953	1.3342	1.5107	33
28	.64901	.85308	1.1722	.76078	1.3144	1.5408	32		28	.66218	.88369	1.1316	.74934	1.3345	1.5102	32
29	.64923	.85358	1.1715	.76059	1.3148	1.5403	31		29	.66240	.88421	1.1310	.74915	1.3348	1.5097	31
30	.64945	.85408	1.1708	.76041	1.3151	1.5398	30		30	.66262	.88473	1.1303	.74896	1.3352	1.5092	30
31	.64967	.85458	1.1702	.76022	1.3154	1.5392	29		31	.66284	.88524	1.1296	.74876	1.3355	1.5087	29
32	.64989	.85509	1.1695	.76003	1.3157	1.5387	28		32	.66306	.88576	1.1290	.74857	1.3359	1.5082	28
33	.65011	.85559	1.1688	.75984	1.3161	1.5382	27		33	.66327	.88628	1.1283	.74838	1.3362	1.5077	27
34	.65033	.85609	1.1681	.75965	1.3164	1.5377	26		34	.66349	.88680	1.1276	.74818	1.3366	1.5072	26
35	.65055	.85660	1.1674	.75946	1.3167	1.5372	25		35	.66371	.88732	1.1270	.74799	1.3369	1.5067	25
36	.65077	.85710	1.1667	.75927	1.3171	1.5366	24		36	.66393	.88784	1.1263	.74780	1.3373	1.5062	24
37	.65100	.85761	1.1660	.75908	1.3174	1.5361	23		37	.66414	.88836	1.1257	.74760	1.3376	1.5057	23
38	.65122	.85811	1.1653	.75889	1.3177	1.5356	22		38	.66436	.88888	1.1250	.74741	1.3380	1.5052	22
39	.65144	.85862	1.1647	.75870	1.3180	1.5351	21		39	.66458	.88940	1.1243	.74722	1.3383	1.5047	21
40	.65166	.85912	1.1640	.75851	1.3184	1.5345	20		40	.66480	.88992	1.1237	.74703	1.3386	1.5042	20
41	.65188	.85963	1.1633	.75832	1.3187	1.5340	19		41	.66501	.89045	1.1230	.74683	1.3390	1.5037	19
42	.65210	.86014	1.1626	.75813	1.3190	1.5335	18		42	.66523	.89097	1.1224	.74664	1.3393	1.5032	18
43	.65232	.86064	1.1619	.75794	1.3194	1.5330	17		43	.66545	.89149	1.1217	.74644	1.3397	1.5027	17
44	.65254	.86115	1.1612	.75775	1.3197	1.5325	16		44	.66566	.89201	1.1211	.74625	1.3400	1.5023	16
45	.65276	.86166	1.1606	.75756	1.3200	1.5320	15		45	.66588	.89253	1.1204	.74606	1.3404	1.5018	15
46	.65298	.86216	1.1599	.75738	1.3203	1.5314	14		46	.66610	.89306	1.1197	.74586	1.3407	1.5013	14
47	.65320	.86267	1.1592	.75719	1.3207	1.5309	13		47	.66632	.89358	1.1191	.74567	1.3411	1.5008	13
48	.65342	.86318	1.1585	.75700	1.3210	1.5304	12		48	.66653	.89410	1.1184	.74548	1.3414	1.5003	12
49	.65364	.86368	1.1578	.75680	1.3213	1.5299	11		49	.66675	.89463	1.1178	.74528	1.3418	1.4998	11
50	.65386	.86419	1.1571	.75661	1.3217	1.5294	10		50	.66697	.89515	1.1171	.74509	1.3421	1.4993	10
51	.65408	.86470	1.1565	.75642	1.3220	1.5289	9		51	.66718	.89567	1.1165	.74489	1.3425	1.4988	9
52	.65430	.86521	1.1558	.75623	1.3223	1.5283	8		52	.66740	.89620	1.1158	.74470	1.3428	1.4984	8
53	.65452	.86572	1.1551	.75604	1.3227	1.5278	7		53	.66762	.89672	1.1152	.74451	1.3432	1.4979	7
54	.65474	.86623	1.1544	.75585	1.3230	1.5273	6		54	.66783	.89725	1.1145	.74431	1.3435	1.4974	6
55	.65496	.86674	1.1538	.75566	1.3233	1.5268	5		55	.66805	.89777	1.1139	.74412	1.3439	1.4969	5
56	.65518	.86725	1.1531	.75547	1.3237	1.5263	4		56	.66827	.89830	1.1132	.74392	1.3442	1.4964	4
57	.65540	.86776	1.1524	.75528	1.3240	1.5258	3		57	.66848	.89883	1.1126	.74373	1.3446	1.4959	3
58	.65562	.86827	1.1517	.75509	1.3243	1.5253	2		58	.66870	.89935	1.1119	.74353	1.3449	1.4954	2
59	.65584	.86878	1.1510	.75490	1.3247	1.5248	1		59	.66891	.89988	1.1113	.74334	1.3453	1.4950	1
60	.65606	.86929	1.1504	.75471	1.3250	1.5243	0		60	.66913	.90040	1.1106	.74314	1.3456	1.4945	0
′	Cos	Cot	Tan	Sin	Csc	Sec	′		′	Cos	Cot	Tan	Sin	Csc	Sec	′

Tables for Use in Trigonometry

NATURAL TRIGONOMETRIC FUNCTIONS
TO FIVE PLACES

42° (222°)   (317°) 137°

′	Sin	Tan	Cot	Cos	Sec	Csc	′
0	.66913	.90040	1.1106	.74314	1.3456	1.4945	60
1	.66935	.90093	1.1100	.74295	1.3460	1.4940	59
2	.66956	.90146	1.1093	.74276	1.3463	1.4935	58
3	.66978	.90199	1.1087	.74256	1.3467	1.4930	57
4	.66999	.90251	1.1080	.74237	1.3470	1.4925	56
5	.67021	.90304	1.1074	.74217	1.3474	1.4921	55
6	.67043	.90357	1.1067	.74198	1.3478	1.4916	54
7	.67064	.90410	1.1061	.74178	1.3481	1.4911	53
8	.67086	.90463	1.1054	.74159	1.3485	1.4906	52
9	.67107	.90516	1.1048	.74139	1.3488	1.4901	51
10	.67129	.90569	1.1041	.74120	1.3492	1.4897	50
11	.67151	.90621	1.1035	.74100	1.3495	1.4892	49
12	.67172	.90674	1.1028	.74080	1.3499	1.4887	48
13	.67194	.90727	1.1022	.74061	1.3502	1.4882	47
14	.67215	.90781	1.1016	.74041	1.3506	1.4878	46
15	.67237	.90834	1.1009	.74022	1.3510	1.4873	45
16	.67258	.90887	1.1003	.74002	1.3513	1.4868	44
17	.67280	.90940	1.0996	.73983	1.3517	1.4863	43
18	.67301	.90993	1.0990	.73963	1.3520	1.4859	42
19	.67323	.91046	1.0983	.73944	1.3524	1.4854	41
20	.67344	.91099	1.0977	.73924	1.3527	1.4849	40
21	.67366	.91153	1.0971	.73904	1.3531	1.4844	39
22	.67387	.91206	1.0964	.73885	1.3535	1.4840	38
23	.67409	.91259	1.0958	.73865	1.3538	1.4835	37
24	.67430	.91313	1.0951	.73846	1.3542	1.4830	36
25	.67452	.91366	1.0945	.73826	1.3545	1.4825	35
26	.67473	.91419	1.0939	.73806	1.3549	1.4821	34
27	.67495	.91473	1.0932	.73787	1.3553	1.4816	33
28	.67516	.91526	1.0926	.73767	1.3556	1.4811	32
29	.67538	.91580	1.0919	.73747	1.3560	1.4807	31
30	.67559	.91633	1.0913	.73728	1.3563	1.4802	30
31	.67580	.91687	1.0907	.73708	1.3567	1.4797	29
32	.67602	.91740	1.0900	.73688	1.3571	1.4792	28
33	.67623	.91794	1.0894	.73669	1.3574	1.4788	27
34	.67645	.91847	1.0888	.73649	1.3578	1.4783	26
35	.67666	.91901	1.0881	.73629	1.3582	1.4778	25
36	.67688	.91955	1.0875	.73610	1.3585	1.4774	24
37	.67709	.92008	1.0869	.73590	1.3589	1.4769	23
38	.67730	.92062	1.0862	.73570	1.3592	1.4764	22
39	.67752	.92116	1.0856	.73551	1.3596	1.4760	21
40	.67773	.92170	1.0850	.73531	1.3600	1.4755	20
41	.67795	.92224	1.0843	.73511	1.3603	1.4750	19
42	.67816	.92277	1.0837	.73491	1.3607	1.4746	18
43	.67837	.92331	1.0831	.73472	1.3611	1.4741	17
44	.67859	.92385	1.0824	.73452	1.3614	1.4737	16
45	.67880	.92439	1.0818	.73432	1.3618	1.4732	15
46	.67901	.92493	1.0812	.73413	1.3622	1.4727	14
47	.67923	.92547	1.0805	.73393	1.3625	1.4723	13
48	.67944	.92601	1.0799	.73373	1.3629	1.4718	12
49	.67965	.92655	1.0793	.73353	1.3633	1.4713	11
50	.67987	.92709	1.0786	.73333	1.3636	1.4709	10
51	.68008	.92763	1.0780	.73314	1.3640	1.4704	9
52	.68029	.92817	1.0774	.73294	1.3644	1.4700	8
53	.68051	.92872	1.0768	.73274	1.3647	1.4695	7
54	.68072	.92926	1.0761	.73254	1.3651	1.4690	6
55	.68093	.92980	1.0755	.73234	1.3655	1.4686	5
56	.68115	.93034	1.0749	.73215	1.3658	1.4681	4
57	.68136	.93088	1.0742	.73195	1.3662	1.4677	3
58	.68157	.93143	1.0736	.73175	1.3666	1.4672	2
59	.68179	.93197	1.0730	.73155	1.3670	1.4667	1
60	.68200	.93252	1.0724	.73135	1.3673	1.4663	0
′	Cos	Cot	Tan	Sin	Csc	Sec	′

43° (223°)   (316°) 1

′	Sin	Tan	Cot	Cos	Sec	Csc	′
0	.68200	.93252	1.0724	.73135	1.3673	1.4663	60
1	.68221	.93306	1.0717	.73116	1.3677	1.4658	59
2	.68242	.93360	1.0711	.73096	1.3681	1.4654	58
3	.68264	.93415	1.0705	.73076	1.3684	1.4649	57
4	.68285	.93469	1.0699	.73056	1.3688	1.4645	56
5	.68306	.93524	1.0692	.73036	1.3692	1.4640	55
6	.68327	.93578	1.0686	.73016	1.3696	1.4635	54
7	.68349	.93633	1.0680	.72996	1.3699	1.4631	53
8	.68370	.93688	1.0674	.72976	1.3703	1.4626	52
9	.68391	.93742	1.0668	.72957	1.3707	1.4622	51
10	.68412	.93797	1.0661	.72937	1.3711	1.4617	50
11	.68434	.93852	1.0655	.72917	1.3714	1.4613	49
12	.68455	.93906	1.0649	.72897	1.3718	1.4608	48
13	.68476	.93961	1.0643	.72877	1.3722	1.4604	47
14	.68497	.94016	1.0637	.72857	1.3726	1.4599	46
15	.68518	.94071	1.0630	.72837	1.3729	1.4595	45
16	.68539	.94125	1.0624	.72817	1.3733	1.4590	44
17	.68561	.94180	1.0618	.72797	1.3737	1.4586	43
18	.68582	.94235	1.0612	.72777	1.3741	1.4581	42
19	.68603	.94290	1.0606	.72757	1.3744	1.4577	41
20	.68624	.94345	1.0599	.72737	1.3748	1.4572	40
21	.68645	.94400	1.0593	.72717	1.3752	1.4568	39
22	.68666	.94455	1.0587	.72697	1.3756	1.4563	38
23	.68688	.94510	1.0581	.72677	1.3759	1.4559	37
24	.68709	.94565	1.0575	.72657	1.3763	1.4554	36
25	.68730	.94620	1.0569	.72637	1.3767	1.4550	35
26	.68751	.94676	1.0562	.72617	1.3771	1.4545	34
27	.68772	.94731	1.0556	.72597	1.3775	1.4541	33
28	.68793	.94786	1.0550	.72577	1.3778	1.4536	32
29	.68814	.94841	1.0544	.72557	1.3782	1.4532	31
30	.68835	.94896	1.0538	.72537	1.3786	1.4527	30
31	.68857	.94952	1.0532	.72517	1.3790	1.4523	29
32	.68878	.95007	1.0526	.72497	1.3794	1.4518	28
33	.68899	.95062	1.0519	.72477	1.3797	1.4514	27
34	.68920	.95118	1.0513	.72457	1.3801	1.4510	26
35	.68941	.95173	1.0507	.72437	1.3805	1.4505	25
36	.68962	.95229	1.0501	.72417	1.3809	1.4501	24
37	.68983	.95284	1.0495	.72397	1.3813	1.4496	23
38	.69004	.95340	1.0489	.72377	1.3817	1.4492	22
39	.69025	.95395	1.0483	.72357	1.3820	1.4487	21
40	.69046	.95451	1.0477	.72337	1.3824	1.4483	20
41	.69067	.95506	1.0470	.72317	1.3828	1.4479	19
42	.69088	.95562	1.0464	.72297	1.3832	1.4474	18
43	.69109	.95618	1.0458	.72277	1.3836	1.4470	17
44	.69130	.95673	1.0452	.72257	1.3840	1.4465	16
45	.69151	.95729	1.0446	.72236	1.3843	1.4461	15
46	.69172	.95785	1.0440	.72216	1.3847	1.4457	14
47	.69193	.95841	1.0434	.72196	1.3851	1.4452	13
48	.69214	.95897	1.0428	.72176	1.3855	1.4448	12
49	.69235	.95952	1.0422	.72156	1.3859	1.4443	11
50	.69256	.96008	1.0416	.72136	1.3863	1.4439	10
51	.69277	.96064	1.0410	.72116	1.3867	1.4435	9
52	.69298	.96120	1.0404	.72095	1.3871	1.4430	8
53	.69319	.96176	1.0398	.72075	1.3874	1.4426	7
54	.69340	.96232	1.0392	.72055	1.3878	1.4422	6
55	.69361	.96288	1.0385	.72035	1.3882	1.4417	5
56	.69382	.96344	1.0379	.72015	1.3886	1.4413	4
57	.69403	.96400	1.0373	.71995	1.3890	1.4409	3
58	.69424	.96457	1.0367	.71974	1.3894	1.4404	2
59	.69445	.96513	1.0361	.71954	1.3898	1.4400	1
60	.69466	.96569	1.0355	.71934	1.3902	1.4396	0
′	Cos	Cot	Tan	Sin	Csc	Sec	′

NATURAL TRIGONOMETRIC FUNCTIONS
TO FIVE PLACES

44° (224°)   (315°) 135°

′	Sin	Tan	Cot	Cos	Sec	Csc	′
0	.69466	.96569	1.0355	.71934	1.3902	1.4396	**60**
1	.69487	.96625	1.0349	.71914	1.3906	1.4391	59
2	.69508	.96681	1.0343	.71894	1.3909	1.4387	58
3	.69529	.96738	1.0337	.71873	1.3913	1.4383	57
4	.69549	.96794	1.0331	.71853	1.3917	1.4378	56
5	.69570	.96850	1.0325	.71833	1.3921	1.4374	**55**
6	.69591	.96907	1.0319	.71813	1.3925	1.4370	54
7	.69612	.96963	1.0313	.71792	1.3929	1.4365	53
8	.69633	.97020	1.0307	.71772	1.3933	1.4361	52
9	.69654	.97076	1.0301	.71752	1.3937	1.4357	51
10	.69675	.97133	1.0295	.71732	1.3941	1.4352	**50**
11	.69696	.97189	1.0289	.71711	1.3945	1.4348	49
12	.69717	.97246	1.0283	.71691	1.3949	1.4344	48
13	.69737	.97302	1.0277	.71671	1.3953	1.4340	47
14	.69758	.97359	1.0271	.71650	1.3957	1.4335	46
15	.69779	.97416	1.0265	.71630	1.3961	1.4331	**45**
16	.69800	.97472	1.0259	.71610	1.3965	1.4327	44
17	.69821	.97529	1.0253	.71590	1.3969	1.4322	43
18	.69842	.97586	1.0247	.71569	1.3972	1.4318	42
19	.69862	.97643	1.0241	.71549	1.3976	1.4314	41
20	.69883	.97700	1.0235	.71529	1.3980	1.4310	**40**
21	.69904	.97756	1.0230	.71508	1.3984	1.4305	39
22	.69925	.97813	1.0224	.71488	1.3988	1.4301	38
23	.69946	.97870	1.0218	.71468	1.3992	1.4297	37
24	.69966	.97927	1.0212	.71447	1.3996	1.4293	36
25	.69987	.97984	1.0206	.71427	1.4000	1.4288	**35**
26	.70008	.98041	1.0200	.71407	1.4004	1.4284	34
27	.70029	.98098	1.0194	.71386	1.4008	1.4280	33
28	.70049	.98155	1.0188	.71366	1.4012	1.4276	32
29	.70070	.98213	1.0182	.71345	1.4016	1.4271	31
30	.70091	.98270	1.0176	.71325	1.4020	1.4267	**30**
31	.70112	.98327	1.0170	.71305	1.4024	1.4263	29
32	.70132	.98384	1.0164	.71284	1.4028	1.4259	28
33	.70153	.98441	1.0158	.71264	1.4032	1.4255	27
34	.70174	.98499	1.0152	.71243	1.4036	1.4250	26
35	.70195	.98556	1.0147	.71223	1.4040	1.4246	**25**
36	.70215	.98613	1.0141	.71203	1.4044	1.4242	24
37	.70236	.98671	1.0135	.71182	1.4048	1.4238	23
38	.70257	.98728	1.0129	.71162	1.4052	1.4234	22
39	.70277	.98786	1.0123	.71141	1.4057	1.4229	21
40	.70298	.98843	1.0117	.71121	1.4061	1.4225	**20**
41	.70319	.98901	1.0111	.71100	1.4065	1.4221	19
42	.70339	.98958	1.0105	.71080	1.4069	1.4217	18
43	.70360	.99016	1.0099	.71059	1.4073	1.4213	17
44	.70381	.99073	1.0094	.71039	1.4077	1.4208	16
45	.70401	.99131	1.0088	.71019	1.4081	1.4204	**15**
46	.70422	.99189	1.0082	.70998	1.4085	1.4200	14
47	.70443	.99247	1.0076	.70978	1.4089	1.4196	13
48	.70463	.99304	1.0070	.70957	1.4093	1.4192	12
49	.70484	.99362	1.0064	.70937	1.4097	1.4188	11
50	.70505	.99420	1.0058	.70916	1.4101	1.4183	**10**
51	.70525	.99478	1.0052	.70896	1.4105	1.4179	9
52	.70546	.99536	1.0047	.70875	1.4109	1.4175	8
53	.70567	.99594	1.0041	.70855	1.4113	1.4171	7
54	.70587	.99652	1.0035	.70834	1.4118	1.4167	6
55	.70608	.99710	1.0029	.70813	1.4122	1.4163	**5**
56	.70628	.99768	1.0023	.70793	1.4126	1.4159	4
57	.70649	.99826	1.0017	.70772	1.4130	1.4154	3
58	.70670	.99884	1.0012	.70752	1.4134	1.4150	2
59	.70690	.99942	1.0006	.70731	1.4138	1.4146	1
60	.70711	1.0000	1.0000	.70711	1.4142	1.4142	**0**
′	Cos	Cot	Tan	Sin	Csc	Sec	′

134° (314°)   (225°) 45°

NATURAL TRIGONOMETRIC FUNCTIONS
SINE, COSINE, TANGENT, COTANGENT,
FOR ANGLES IN DEGREES AND DECIMALS

The table that follows, NATURAL TRIGONOMETRIC FUNCTIONS, SINE, COSINE, TANGENT, COTANGENT, FOR ANGLES IN DEGREES AND DECIMALS, gives the values of the sine, cosine, tangent, and cotangent for each tenth of a degree from 0° to 90° where the entries are correct to five significant digits.

For angle values in the left column, use the column headings at the top of each column. For angle values in the right column, use the column headings at the bottom of each column.

Linear interpolation may be used to obtain functional values for angles expressed to hundredths of a degree, except where the functions are rapidly varying.

This is followed by the table NATURAL TRIGONOMETRIC FUNCTIONS TO FIVE TENTHS OF A DEGREE (SECANTS AND COSECANTS), which gives the values of the secant and cosecant for equally spaced intervals of one-half degree from 0° to 90°, and the entries are correct to six significant digits.

NATURAL TRIGONOMETRIC FUNCTIONS
SINE, COSINE, TANGENT, COTANGENT,
FOR ANGLES IN DEGREES AND DECIMALS

Deg.	Sin	* Tan	* Cot	Cos	
0.0	0 00000	0.00000	∞	1.0000	**90.0**
.1	.00175	00175	573.0	1.0000	89.9
.2	.00349	00349	286.5	1.0000	.8
.3	.00524	00524	191.0	1.0000	.7
.4	.00698	.00698	143.24	1 0000	.6
.5	00873	.00873	114.59	1.0000	.5
.6	.01047	.01047	95.49	0.9999	.4
.7	.01222	.01222	81 85	.9999	.3
.8	.01396	.01396	71.62	.9999	.2
.9	.01571	.01571	63.66	.9999	89.1
1.0	0.01745	0.01746	57.29	0.9998	**89.0**
.1	.01920	01920	52.08	9998	88.9
.2	02094	02095	47.74	.9998	.8
.3	.02269	02269	44.07	.9997	.7
.4	.02443	.02444	40.92	.9997	.6
.5	.02618	.02619	38.19	.9997	.5
.6	.02792	.02793	35.80	.9996	.4
.7	.02967	.02968	33.69	.9996	.3
.8	03141	.03143	31.82	.9995	.2
.9	.03316	.03317	30.14	.9995	88.1
2.0	0.03490	0.03492	28.64	0.9994	**88.0**
.1	.03664	.03667	27.27	9993	87.9
.2	.03839	03842	26.03	.9993	.8
.3	.04013	.04016	24.90	.9992	.7
.4	.04188	04191	23.86	.9991	.6
.5	.04362	.04366	22.90	.9990	.5
.6	.04536	.04541	22 02	.9990	.4
.7	.04711	.04716	21.20	.9989	.3
.8	.04885	.04891	20.45	.9988	.2
.9	.05059	.05066	19.74	.9987	87.1
3.0	0.05234	0.05241	19.081	0.9986	**87.0**
.1	.05408	.05416	18.464	.9985	86.9
.2	.05582	.05591	17.886	.9984	.8
.3	.05756	.05766	17.343	.9983	.7
.4	.05931	.05941	16.832	9982	.6
.5	.06105	.06116	16.350	.9981	.5
.6	06279	06291	15.895	.9980	.4
.7	.06453	.06467	15.464	.9979	.3
.8	06627	.06642	15.056	.9978	.2
.9	.06802	.06817	14.669	.9977	86.1
4.0	0.06976	0.06993	14.301	0.9976	**86.0**
.1	.07150	.07168	13.951	.9974	85.9
.2	.07324	.07344	13.617	.9973	.8
.3	07498	.07519	13.300	.9972	.7
.4	.07672	.07695	12.996	.9971	.6
.5	.07846	.07870	12.706	.9969	.5
.6	.08020	.08046	12.429	.9968	.4
.7	.08194	.08221	12.163	.9966	.3
.8	.08368	.08397	11.909	.9965	.2
.9	.08542	.08573	11.664	.9963	85.1
5.0	0.08716	0.08749	11.430	0.9962	**85.0**
.1	.08889	.08925	11.205	.9960	84.9
.2	.09063	.09101	10.988	.9959	.8
.3	.09237	.09277	10.780	.9957	.7
.4	.09411	.09453	10.579	.9956	.6
.5	.09585	.09629	10.385	.9954	.5
.6	.09758	.09805	10.199	.9952	4
.7	.09932	.09981	10.019	.9951	.3
.8	.10106	.10158	9.845	.9949	.2
.9	.10279	.10334	9.677	.9947	84.1
6.0	0.10453	0.10510	9.514	0.9945	**84.0**
	Cos	* Cot	* Tan	Sin	Deg.

Deg.	Sin	Tan	Cot	Cos	
6.0	0.10453	0.10510	9 514	0.9945	**84.0**
.1	.10626	.10687	9.357	.9943	83.9
.2	.10800	10863	9.205	.9942	.8
.3	.10973	.11040	9.058	9940	.7
.4	.11147	.11217	8.915	9938	.6
.5	.11320	.11394	8.777	.9936	.5
.6	.11494	.11570	8.643	.9934	.4
.7	.11667	.11747	8.513	.9932	.3
.8	.11840	.11924	8.386	.9930	.2
.9	.12014	.12101	8.264	.9928	83.1
7.0	0.12187	0.12278	8.144	0.9925	**83.0**
.1	.12360	.12456	8.028	.9923	82.9
.2	.12533	.12633	7.916	.9921	.8
.3	.12706	.12810	7.806	.9919	.7
.4	.12880	.12988	7.700	.9917	.6
.5	.13053	.13165	7 596	.9914	.5
.6	.13226	13343	7.495	.9912	.4
.7	.13399	.13521	7.396	.9910	.3
.8	.13572	.13698	7.300	.9907	.2
.9	.13744	.13876	7.207	.9905	82.1
8.0	0.13917	0.14054	7.115	0.9903	**82.0**
.1	.14090	.14232	7.026	.9900	81.9
.2	.14263	.14410	6.940	.9898	.8
.3	.14436	.14588	6.855	.9895	.7
.4	.14608	.14767	6.772	.9893	.6
.5	.14781	.14945	6.691	.9890	.5
.6	.14954	.15124	6.612	.9888	.4
.7	.15126	.15302	6.535	.9885	.3
.8	.15299	.15481	6.460	.9882	.2
.9	.15471	.15660	6.386	.9880	81.1
9.0	0.15643	0.15838	6.314	0.9877	**81.0**
.1	.15816	.16017	6.243	.9874	80.9
.2	.15988	.16196	6.174	.9871	.8
.3	.16160	.16376	6.107	.9869	.7
.4	.16333	.16555	6.041	.9866	.6
.5	.16505	.16734	5.976	.9863	.5
.6	.16677	.16914	5.912	.9860	.4
.7	.16849	.17093	5.850	.9857	.3
.8	.17021	.17273	5.789	.9854	.2
.9	.17193	.17453	5.730	.9851	80.1
10.0	0.1736	0.1763	5.671	0.9848	**80.0**
.1	.1754	.1781	5.614	.9845	79.9
.2	.1771	.1799	5.558	.9842	.8
.3	.1788	.1817	5.503	.9839	.7
.4	.1805	.1835	5.449	.9836	.6
.5	.1822	.1853	5.396	.9833	.5
.6	.1840	.1871	5.343	.9829	.4
.7	.1857	.1890	5.292	.9826	.3
.8	.1874	.1908	5.242	.9823	.2
.9	.1891	.1926	5.193	.9820	79.1
11.0	0.1908	0.1944	5.145	0.9816	**79.0**
.1	.1925	.1962	5.097	.9813	78.9
.2	.1942	.1980	5.050	.9810	.8
.3	.1959	.1998	5.005	.9806	.7
.4	.1977	.2016	4.959	.9803	.6
.5	.1994	.2035	4.915	.9799	.5
.6	.2011	.2053	4.872	.9796	.4
.7	.2028	.2071	4.829	.9792	.3
.8	.2045	.2089	4.787	.9789	.2
.9	.2062	.2107	4.745	.9785	78.1
12.0	0.2079	0.2126	4.705	0.9781	**78.0**
	Cos	Cot	Tan	Sin	Deg.

* Interpolation in this section of the table is inaccurate.

NATURAL TRIGONOMETRIC FUNCTIONS
SINE, COSINE, TANGENT, COTANGENT,
FOR ANGLES IN DEGREES AND DECIMALS (Continued)

Deg.	Sin	Tan	Cot	Cos		Deg.	Sin	Tan	Cot	Cos	
12.0	0.2079	0.2126	4.705	0.9781	**78.0**	**18.0**	0.3090	0.3249	3.078	0.9511	**72.0**
.1	.2096	.2144	4.665	.9778	77.9	.1	.3107	.3269	3.060	.9505	71.9
.2	.2113	.2162	4.625	.9774	.8	.2	.3123	.3288	3.042	.9500	.8
.3	.2130	.2180	4.586	.9770	.7	.3	.3140	.3307	3.024	.9494	.7
.4	.2147	.2199	4.548	.9767	.6	.4	.3156	.3327	3.006	.9489	.6
.5	.2164	.2217	4.511	.9763	.5	.5	.3173	.3346	2.989	.9483	.5
.6	.2181	.2235	4.474	.9759	.4	.6	.3190	.3365	2.971	.9478	.4
.7	.2198	.2254	4.437	.9755	.3	.7	.3206	.3385	2.954	.9472	.3
.8	.2215	.2272	4.402	.9751	.2	.8	.3223	.3404	2.937	.9466	.2
.9	.2233	.2290	4.366	.9748	77.1	.9	.3239	.3424	2.921	.9461	71.1
13.0	0.2250	0.2309	4.331	0.9744	**77.0**	**19.0**	0.3256	0.3443	2.904	0.9455	**71.0**
.1	.2267	.2327	4.297	.9740	76.9	.1	.3272	.3463	2.888	.9449	70.9
.2	.2284	.2345	4.264	.9736	.8	.2	.3289	.3482	2.872	.9444	.8
.3	.2300	.2364	4.230	.9732	.7	.3	.3305	.3502	2.856	.9438	.7
.4	.2317	.2382	4.198	.9728	.6	.4	.3322	.3522	2.840	.9432	.6
.5	.2334	.2401	4.165	.9724	.5	.5	.3338	.3541	2.824	.9426	.5
.6	.2351	.2419	4.134	.9720	.4	.6	.3355	.3561	2.808	.9421	.4
.7	.2368	.2438	4.102	.9715	.3	.7	.3371	.3581	2.793	.9415	.3
.8	.2385	.2456	4.071	.9711	.2	.8	.3387	.3600	2.778	.9409	.2
.9	.2402	.2475	4.041	.9707	76.1	.9	.3404	.3620	2.762	.9403	70.1
14.0	0.2419	0.2493	4.011	0.9703	**76.0**	**20.0**	0.3420	0.3640	2.747	0.9397	**70.0**
.1	.2436	.2512	3.981	.9699	75.9	.1	.3437	.3659	2.733	.9391	69.9
.2	.2453	.2530	3.952	.9694	.8	.2	.3453	.3679	2.718	.9385	.8
.3	.2470	.2549	3.923	.9690	.7	.3	.3469	.3699	2.703	.9379	.7
.4	.2487	.2568	3.895	.9686	.6	.4	.3486	.3719	2.689	.9373	.6
.5	.2504	.2586	3.867	.9681	.5	.5	.3502	.3739	2.675	.9367	.5
.6	.2521	.2605	3.839	.9677	.4	.6	.3518	.3759	2.660	.9361	.4
.7	.2538	.2623	3.812	.9673	.3	.7	.3535	.3779	2.646	.9354	.3
.8	.2554	.2642	3.785	.9668	.2	.8	.3551	.3799	2.633	.9348	.2
.9	.2571	.2661	3.758	.9664	75.1	.9	.3567	.3819	2.619	.9342	69.1
15.0	0.2588	0.2679	3.732	0.9659	**75.0**	**21.0**	0.3584	0.3839	2.605	0.9336	**69.0**
.1	.2605	.2698	3.706	.9655	74.9	.1	.3600	.3859	2.592	.9330	68.9
.2	.2622	.2717	3.681	.9650	.8	.2	.3616	.3879	2.578	.9323	.8
.3	.2639	.2736	3.655	.9646	.7	.3	.3633	.3899	2.565	.9317	.7
.4	.2656	.2754	3.630	.9641	.6	.4	.3649	.3919	2.552	.9311	.6
.5	.2672	.2773	3.606	.9636	.5	.5	.3665	.3939	2.539	.9304	.5
.6	.2689	.2792	3.582	.9632	.4	.6	.3681	.3959	2.526	.9298	.4
.7	.2706	.2811	3.558	.9627	.3	.7	.3697	.3979	2.513	.9291	.3
.8	.2723	.2830	3.534	.9622	.2	.8	.3714	.4000	2.500	.9285	.2
.9	.2740	.2849	3.511	.9617	74.1	.9	.3730	.4020	2.488	.9278	68.1
16.0	0.2756	0.2867	3.487	0.9613	**74.0**	**22.0**	0.3746	0.4040	2.475	0.9272	**68.0**
.1	.2773	.2886	3.465	.9608	73.9	.1	.3762	.4061	2.463	.9265	67.9
.2	.2790	.2905	3.442	.9603	.8	.2	.3778	.4081	2.450	.9259	.8
.3	.2807	.2924	3.420	.9598	.7	.3	.3795	.4101	2.438	.9252	.7
.4	.2823	.2943	3.398	.9593	.6	.4	.3811	.4122	2.426	.9245	.6
.5	.2840	.2962	3.376	.9588	.5	.5	.3827	.4142	2.414	.9239	.5
.6	.2857	.2981	3.354	.9583	.4	.6	.3843	.4163	2.402	.9232	.4
.7	.2874	.3000	3.333	.9578	.3	.7	.3859	.4183	2.391	.9225	.3
.8	.2890	.3019	3.312	.9573	.2	.8	.3875	.4204	2.379	.9219	.2
.9	.2907	.3038	3.291	.9568	73.1	.9	.3891	.4224	2.367	.9212	67.1
17.0	0.2924	0.3057	3.271	0.9563	**73.0**	**23.0**	0.3907	0.4245	2.356	0.9205	**67.0**
.1	.2940	.3076	3.251	.9558	72.9	.1	.3923	.4265	2.344	.9198	66.9
.2	.2957	.3096	3.230	.9553	.8	.2	.3939	.4286	2.333	.9191	.8
.3	.2974	.3115	3.211	.9548	.7	.3	.3955	.4307	2.322	.9184	.7
.4	.2990	.3134	3.191	.9542	.6	.4	.3971	.4327	2.311	.9178	.6
.5	.3007	.3153	3.172	.9537	.5	.5	.3987	.4348	2.300	.9171	.5
.6	.3024	.3172	3.152	.9532	.4	.6	.4003	.4369	2.289	.9164	.4
.7	.3040	.3191	3.133	.9527	.3	.7	.4019	.4390	2.278	.9157	.3
.8	.3057	.3211	3.115	.9521	.2	.8	.4035	.4411	2.267	.9150	.2
.9	.3074	.3230	3.096	.9516	72.1	.9	.4051	.4431	2.257	.9143	66.1
18.0	0.3090	0.3249	3.078	0.9511	**72.0**	**24.0**	0.4067	0.4452	2.246	0.9135	**66.0**
	Cos	Cot	Tan	Sin	Deg.		Cos	Cot	Tan	Sin	Deg.

NATURAL TRIGONOMETRIC FUNCTIONS
SINE, COSINE, TANGENT, COTANGENT,
FOR ANGLES IN DEGREES AND DECIMALS (Continued)

Deg.	Sin	Tan	Cot	Cos	
24.0	0.4067	0.4452	2.246	0.9135	**66.0**
.1	.4083	.4473	2.236	.9128	65.9
.2	.4099	.4494	2.225	.9121	.8
.3	.4115	.4515	2.215	.9114	.7
.4	.4131	.4536	2.204	.9107	.6
.5	.4147	.4557	2.194	.9100	.5
.6	.4163	.4578	2.184	.9092	.4
.7	.4179	.4599	2.174	.9085	.3
.8	.4195	.4621	2.164	.9078	.2
.9	.4210	.4642	2.154	.9070	65.1
25.0	0.4226	0.4663	2.145	0.9063	**65.0**
.1	.4242	.4684	2.135	.9056	64.9
.2	.4258	.4706	2.125	.9048	.8
.3	.4274	.4727	2.116	.9041	.7
.4	.4289	.4748	2.106	.9033	.6
.5	.4305	.4770	2.097	.9026	.5
.6	.4321	.4791	2.087	.9018	.4
.7	.4337	.4813	2.078	.9011	.3
.8	.4352	.4834	2.069	.9003	.2
.9	.4368	.4856	2.059	.8996	64.1
26.0	0.4384	0.4877	2.050	0.8988	**64.0**
.1	.4399	.4899	2.041	.8980	63.9
.2	.4415	.4921	2.032	.8973	.8
.3	.4431	.4942	2.023	.8965	.7
.4	.4446	.4964	2.014	.8957	.6
.5	.4462	.4986	2.006	.8949	.5
.6	.4478	.5008	1.997	.8942	.4
.7	.4493	.5029	1.988	.8934	.3
.8	.4509	.5051	1.980	.8926	.2
.9	.4524	.5073	1.971	.8918	63.1
27.0	0.4540	0.5095	1.963	0.8910	**63.0**
.1	.4555	.5117	1.954	.8902	62.9
.2	.4571	.5139	1.946	.8894	.8
.3	.4586	.5161	1.937	.8886	.7
.4	.4602	.5184	1.929	.8878	.6
.5	.4617	.5206	1.921	.8870	.5
.6	.4633	.5228	1.913	.8862	.4
.7	.4648	.5250	1.905	.8854	.3
.8	.4664	.5272	1.897	.8846	.2
.9	.4679	.5295	1.889	.8838	62.1
28.0	0.4695	0.5317	1.881	0.8829	**62.0**
.1	.4710	.5340	1.873	.8821	61.9
.2	.4726	.5362	1.865	.8813	.8
.3	.4741	.5384	1.857	.8805	.7
.4	.4756	.5407	1.849	.8796	.6
.5	.4772	.5430	1.842	.8788	.5
.6	.4787	.5452	1.834	.8780	.4
.7	.4802	.5475	1.827	.8771	.3
.8	.4818	.5498	1.819	.8763	.2
.9	.4833	.5520	1.811	.8755	61.1
29.0	0.4848	0.5543	1.804	0.8746	**61.0**
.1	.4863	.5566	1.797	.8738	60.9
.2	.4879	.5589	1.789	.8729	.8
.3	.4894	.5612	1.782	.8721	.7
.4	.4909	.5635	1.775	.8712	.6
.5	.4924	.5658	1.767	.8704	.5
.6	.4939	.5681	1.760	.8695	.4
.7	.4955	.5704	1.753	.8686	.3
.8	.4970	.5727	1.746	.8678	.2
.9	.4985	.5750	1.739	.8669	60.1
30.0	0.5000	0.5774	1.732	0.8660	**60.0**
	Cos	Cot	Tan	Sin	Deg.

Deg.	Sin	Tan	Cot	Cos	
30.0	0.5000	0.5774	1.7321	0.8660	**60.0**
.1	.5015	.5797	1.7251	.8652	59.9
.2	.5030	.5820	1.7182	.8643	.8
.3	.5045	.5844	1.7113	.8634	.7
.4	.5060	.5867	1.7045	.8625	.6
.5	.5075	.5890	1.6977	.8616	.5
.6	.5090	.5914	1.6909	.8607	.4
.7	.5105	.5938	1.6842	.8599	.3
.8	.5120	.5961	1.6775	.8590	.2
.9	.5135	.5985	1.6709	.8581	59.1
31.0	0.5150	0.6009	1.6643	0.8572	**59.0**
.1	.5165	.6032	1.6577	.8563	58.9
.2	.5180	.6056	1.6512	.8554	.8
.3	.5195	.6080	1.6447	.8545	.7
.4	.5210	.6104	1.6383	.8536	.6
.5	.5225	.6128	1.6319	.8526	.5
.6	.5240	.6152	1.6255	.8517	.4
.7	.5255	.6176	1.6191	.8508	.3
.8	.5270	.6200	1.6128	.8499	.2
.9	.5284	.6224	1.6066	.8490	58.1
32.0	0.5299	0.6249	1.6003	0.8480	**58.0**
.1	.5314	.6273	1.5941	.8471	57.9
.2	.5329	.6297	1.5880	.8462	.8
.3	.5344	.6322	1.5818	.8453	.7
.4	.5358	.6346	1.5757	.8443	.6
.5	.5373	.6371	1.5697	.8434	.5
.6	.5388	.6395	1.5637	.8425	.4
.7	.5402	.6420	1.5577	.8415	.3
.8	.5417	.6445	1.5517	.8406	.2
.9	.5432	.6469	1.5458	.8396	57.1
33.0	0.5446	0.6494	1.5399	0.8387	**57.0**
.1	.5461	.6519	1.5340	.8377	56.9
.2	.5476	.6544	1.5282	.8368	.8
.3	.5490	.6569	1.5224	.8358	.7
.4	.5505	.6594	1.5166	.8348	.6
.5	.5519	.6619	1.5108	.8339	.5
.6	.5534	.6644	1.5051	.8329	.4
.7	.5548	.6669	1.4994	.8320	.3
.8	.5563	.6694	1.4938	.8310	.2
.9	.5577	.6720	1.4882	.8300	56.1
34.0	0.5592	0.6745	1.4826	0.8290	**56.0**
.1	.5606	.6771	1.4770	.8281	55.9
.2	.5621	.6796	1.4715	.8271	.8
.3	.5635	.6822	1.4659	.8261	.7
.4	.5650	.6847	1.4605	.8251	.6
.5	.5664	.6873	1.4550	.8241	.5
.6	.5678	.6899	1.4496	.8231	.4
.7	.5693	.6924	1.4442	.8221	.3
.8	.5707	.6950	1.4388	.8211	.2
.9	.5721	.6976	1.4335	.8202	55.1
35.0	0.5736	0.7002	1.4281	0.8192	**55.0**
.1	.5750	.7028	1.4229	.8181	54.9
.2	.5764	.7054	1.4176	.8171	.8
.3	.5779	.7080	1.4124	.8161	.7
.4	.5793	.7107	1.4071	.8151	.6
.5	.5807	.7133	1.4019	.8141	.5
.6	.5821	.7159	1.3968	.8131	.4
.7	.5835	.7186	1.3916	.8121	.3
.8	.5850	.7212	1.3865	.8111	.2
.9	.5864	.7239	1.3814	.8100	54.1
36.0	0.5878	0.7265	1.3764	0.8090	**54.0**
	Cos	Cot	Tan	Sin	Deg.

NATURAL TRIGONOMETRIC FUNCTIONS
SINE, COSINE, TANGENT, COTANGENT,
FOR ANGLES IN DEGREES AND DECIMALS (Continued)

Deg.	Sin	Tan	Cot	Cos		Deg.	Sin	Tan	Cot	Cos	
36.0	0.5878	0.7265	1.3764	0.8090	54.0	40.5	0.6494	0.8541	1.1708	0.7604	49.5
.1	.5892	.7292	1.3713	.8080	53.9	.6	.6508	.8571	1.1667	.7593	.4
.2	.5906	.7319	1.3663	.8070	.8	.7	.6521	.8601	1.1626	.7581	.3
.3	.5920	.7346	1.3613	.8059	.7	.8	.6534	.8632	1.1585	.7570	.2
.4	.5934	.7373	1.3564	.8049	.6	.9	.6547	.8662	1.1544	.7559	49.1
.5	.5948	.7400	1.3514	.8039	.5	41.0	0.6561	0.8693	1.1504	0.7547	49.0
.6	.5962	.7427	1.3465	.8028	.4	.1	.6574	.8724	1.1463	.7536	48.9
.7	.5976	.7454	1.3416	.8018	.3	.2	.6587	.8754	1.1423	.7524	.8
.8	.5990	.7481	1.3367	.8007	.2	.3	.6600	.8785	1.1383	.7513	.7
.9	.6004	.7508	1.3319	.7997	53.1	.4	.6613	.8816	1.1343	.7501	.6
37.0	0.6018	0.7536	1.3270	0.7986	53.0	.5	.6626	.8847	1.1303	.7490	.5
.1	.6032	.7563	1.3222	7976	52.9	.6	.6639	.8878	1.1263	.7478	.4
.2	.6046	.7590	1.3175	.7965	.8	.7	.6652	.8910	1.1224	.7466	.3
.3	.6060	.7618	1.3127	.7955	.7	.8	.6665	.8941	1.1184	.7455	.2
.4	.6074	.7646	1.3079	.7944	.6	.9	.6678	.8972	1.1145	.7443	48.1
.5	.6088	.7673	1.3032	.7934	.5	42.0	0.6691	0.9004	1.1106	0.7431	48.0
.6	.6101	.7701	1.2985	.7923	.4	.1	.6704	.9036	1.1067	.7420	47.9
.7	.6115	.7729	1.2938	.7912	.3	.2	.6717	.9067	1.1028	.7408	.8
.8	.6129	.7757	1.2892	.7902	.2	.3	.6730	.9099	1.0990	.7396	.7
.9	.6143	.7785	1.2846	.7891	52.1	.4	.6743	.9131	1.0951	.7385	.6
38.0	0.6157	0.7813	1.2799	0.7880	52.0	.5	.6756	.9163	1.0913	.7373	.5
.1	.6170	.7841	1.2753	.7869	51.9	.6	.6769	.9195	1.0875	.7361	.4
.2	.6184	.7869	1.2708	.7859	.8	.7	.6782	.9228	1.0837	.7349	.3
.3	.6198	.7898	1.2662	.7848	.7	.8	.6794	.9260	1.0799	.7337	.2
.4	.6211	.7926	1.2617	.7837	.6	.9	.6807	.9293	1.0761	.7325	47.1
.5	.6225	.7954	1.2572	.7826	.5	43.0	0.6820	0.9325	1.0724	0.7314	47.0
.6	.6239	.7983	1.2527	.7815	.4	.1	.6833	.9358	1.0686	.7302	46.9
.7	.6252	.8012	1.2482	.7804	.3	.2	.6845	.9391	1.0649	.7290	.8
.8	.6266	.8040	1.2437	.7793	.2	.3	.6858	.9424	1.0612	.7278	.7
.9	.6280	.8069	1.2393	.7782	51.1	.4	.6871	9457	1.0575	.7266	.6
39.0	0.6293	0.8098	1.2349	0.7771	51.0	.5	.6884	.9490	1.0538	.7254	.5
.1	.6307	.8127	1.2305	.7760	50.9	.6	.6896	.9523	1.0501	.7242	.4
.2	.6320	.8156	1.2261	.7749	.8	.7	.6909	.9556	1.0464	.7230	.3
.3	.6334	.8185	1.2218	.7738	.7	.8	.6921	.9590	1.0428	.7218	.2
.4	.6347	.8214	1.2174	.7727	.6	.9	.6934	.9623	1.0392	.7206	46.1
.5	.6361	.8243	1.2131	.7716	.5	44.0	0.6947	0.9657	1.0355	0.7193	46.0
.6	.6374	.8273	1.2088	.7705	.4	.1	.6959	.9691	1.0319	.7181	45.9
.7	.6388	.8302	1.2045	.7694	.3	.2	.6972	.9725	1.0283	.7169	.8
.8	.6401	.8332	1.2002	.7683	.2	.3	.6984	.9759	1.0247	.7157	.7
.9	.6414	.8361	1.1960	.7672	50.1	.4	.6997	.9793	1.0212	.7145	.6
40.0	0.6428	0.8391	1.1918	0.7660	50.0	.5	.7009	.9827	1.0176	.7133	.5
.1	.6441	.8421	1.1875	.7649	49.9	.6	.7022	.9861	1.0141	.7120	.4
.2	.6455	.8451	1.1833	.7638	.8	.7	.7034	.9896	1.0105	.7108	.3
.3	.6468	.8481	1.1792	.7627	.7	.8	.7046	.9930	1.0070	.7096	.2
.4	.6481	.8511	1.1750	.7615	.6	.9	.7059	.9965	1.0035	.7083	45.1
40.5	0.6494	0.8541	1.1708	0.7604	49.5	45.0	0.7071	1.0000	1.0000	0.7071	45.0
	Cos	Cot	Tan	Sin	Deg.		Cos	Cot	Tan	Sin	Deg.

NATURAL TRIGONOMETRIC FUNCTIONS TO FIVE TENTHS OF A DEGREE
(SECANTS AND COSECANTS)

Deg.	Sec	Csc	Deg.		Deg.	Sec	Csc	Deg.
0.0	1.00000	∞	90.0		22.5	1.08239	2.61313	67.5
0.5	1.00004	114.59301	89.5		23.0	1.08636	2.55930	67.0
1.0	1.00015	57.29869	89.0		23.5	1.09044	2.50784	66.5
1.5	1.00034	38.20155	88.5		24.0	1.09464	2.45859	66.0
2.0	1.00061	28.65371	88.0		24.5	1.09895	2.41142	65.5
2.5	1.00095	22.92559	87.5		25.0	1.10338	2.36620	65.0
3.0	1.00137	19.10732	87.0		25.5	1.10793	2.32282	64.5
3.5	1.00187	16.38041	86.5		26.0	1.11260	2.28117	64.0
4.0	1.00244	14.33559	86.0		26.5	1.11740	2.24116	63.5
4.5	1.00309	12.74549	85.5		27.0	1.12233	2.20269	63.0
5.0	1.00382	11.47371	85.0		27.5	1.12738	2.16568	62.5
5.5	1.00463	10.43343	84.5		28.0	1.13257	2.13005	62.0
6.0	1.00551	9.56677	84.0		28.5	1.13789	2.09574	61.5
6.5	1.00647	8.83367	83.5		29.0	1.14335	2.06267	61.0
7.0	1.00751	8.20551	83.0		29.5	1.14896	2.03077	60.5
7.5	1.00863	7.66130	82.5		30.0	1.15470	2.00000	60.0
8.0	1.00983	7.18530	82.0		30.5	1.16059	1.97029	59.5
8.5	1.01111	6.76547	81.5		31.0	1.16663	1.94160	59.0
9.0	1.01247	6.39245	81.0		31.5	1.17283	1.91388	58.5
9.5	1.01391	6.05886	80.5		32.0	1.17918	1.88708	58.0
10.0	1.01543	5.75877	80.0		32.5	1.18569	1.86116	57.5
10.5	1.01703	5.48740	79.5		33.0	1.19236	1.83608	57.0
11.0	1.01872	5.24084	79.0		33.5	1.19920	1.81180	56.5
11.5	1.02049	5.01585	78.5		34.0	1.20622	1.78829	56.0
12.0	1.02234	4.80973	78.0		34.5	1.21341	1.76552	55.5
12.5	1.02428	4.62023	77.5		35.0	1.22077	1.74345	55.0
13.0	1.02630	4.44541	77.0		35.5	1.22833	1.72205	54.5
13.5	1.02842	4.28366	76.5		36.0	1.23607	1.70130	54.0
14.0	1.03061	4.13357	76.0		36.5	1.24400	1.68117	53.5
14.5	1.03290	3.99393	75.5		37.0	1.25214	1.66164	53.0
15.0	1.03528	3.86370	75.0		37.5	1.26047	1.64268	52.5
15.5	1.03774	3.74198	74.5		38.0	1.26902	1.62427	52.0
16.0	1.04030	3.62796	74.0		38.5	1.27778	1.60639	51.5
16.5	1.04295	3.52094	73.5		39.0	1.28676	1.58902	51.0
17.0	1.04569	3.42030	73.0		39.5	1.29597	1.57213	50.5
17.5	1.04853	3.32551	72.5		40.0	1.30541	1.55572	50.0
18.0	1.05146	3.23607	72.0		40.5	1.31509	1.53977	49.5
18.5	1.05449	3.15155	71.5		41.0	1.32501	1.52425	49.0
19.0	1.05762	3.07155	71.0		41.5	1.33519	1.50916	48.5
19.5	1.06085	2.99574	70.5		42.0	1.34563	1.49448	48.0
20.0	1.06418	2.92380	70.0		42.5	1.35634	1.48019	47.5
20.5	1.06761	2.85545	69.5		43.0	1.36733	1.46628	47.0
21.0	1.07114	2.79043	69.0		43.5	1.37860	1.45274	46.5
21.5	1.07479	2.72850	68.5		44.0	1.39016	1.43956	46.0
22.0	1.07853	2.66947	68.0		44.5	1.40203	1.42672	45.5
22.5	1.08239	2.61313	67.5		45.0	1.41421	1.41421	45.0
	Csc	Sec				Csc	Sec	

Tables for Use in Trigonometry
NATURAL TRIGONOMETRIC FUNCTIONS
FOR ANGLES IN *x* RADIANS

x	Sin	Tan	Cot	Cos	x	Sin	Tan	Cot	Cos
.00	.00000	.00000	∞	1.00000	**.50**	.47943	.54630	1.8305	.87758
01	.01000	.01000	99.997	0.99995	.51	.48818	.55936	1.7878	.87274
02	.02000	.02000	49.993	.99980	.52	.49688	.57256	1.7465	.86782
03	.03000	.03001	33.323	.99955	.53	.50553	.58592	1.7067	.86281
04	.03999	.04002	24.987	.99920	.54	.51414	.59943	1.6683	.85771
.05	.04998	.05004	19.983	.99875	.55	.52269	.61311	1.6310	.85252
.06	.05996	.06007	16.647	.99820	.56	.53119	.62695	1.5950	.84726
.07	.06994	.07011	14.262	.99755	.57	.53963	.64097	1.5601	.84190
.08	.07991	.08017	12.473	.99680	.58	.54802	.65517	1.5263	.83646
.09	.08988	.09024	11.081	.99595	.59	.55636	.66956	1.4935	.83094
.10	.09983	.10033	9.9666	.99500	**.60**	.56464	.68414	1.4617	.82534
.11	.10978	.11045	9.0542	.99396	.61	.57287	.69892	1.4308	.81965
.12	.11971	.12058	8.2933	.99281	.62	.58104	.71391	1.4007	.81388
.13	.12963	.13074	7.6489	.99156	.63	.58914	.72911	1.3715	.80803
.14	.13954	.14092	7.0961	.99022	.64	.59720	.74454	1.3431	.80210
.15	.14944	.15114	6.6166	.98877	.65	.60519	.76020	1.3154	.79608
.16	.15932	.16138	6.1966	.98723	.66	.61312	.77610	1.2885	.78999
.17	.16918	.17166	5.8256	.98558	.67	.62099	.79225	1.2622	.78382
.18	.17903	.18197	5.4954	.98384	.68	.62879	.80866	1.2366	.77757
.19	.18886	.19232	5.1997	.98200	.69	.63654	.82534	1.2116	.77125
.20	.19867	.20271	4.9332	.98007	**.70**	.64422	.84229	1.1872	.76484
.21	.20846	.21314	4.6917	.97803	.71	.65183	.85953	1.1634	.75836
.22	.21823	.22362	4.4719	.97590	.72	.65938	.87707	1.1402	.75181
.23	.22798	.23414	4.2709	.97367	.73	.66687	.89492	1.1174	.74517
.24	.23770	.24472	4.0864	.97134	.74	.67429	.91309	1.0952	.73847
.25	.24740	.25534	3.9163	.96891	.75	.68164	.93160	1.0734	.73169
.26	.25708	.26602	3.7591	.96639	.76	.68892	.95045	1.0521	.72484
.27	.26673	.27676	3.6133	.96377	.77	.69614	.96967	1.0313	.71791
.28	.27636	.28755	3.4776	.96106	.78	.70328	.98926	1.0109	.71091
.29	.28595	.29841	3.3511	.95824	.79	.71035	1.0092	.99084	.70385
.30	.29552	.30934	3.2327	.95534	**.80**	.71736	1.0296	.97121	.69671
.31	.30506	.32033	3.1218	.95233	.81	.72429	1.0505	.95197	.68950
.32	.31457	.33139	3.0176	.94924	.82	.73115	1.0717	.93309	.68222
.33	.32404	.34252	2.9195	.94604	.83	.73793	1.0934	.91455	.67488
.34	.33349	.35374	2.8270	.94275	.84	.74464	1.1156	.89635	.66746
.35	.34290	.36503	2.7395	.93937	.85	.75128	1.1383	.87848	.65998
.36	.35227	.37640	2.6567	.93590	.86	.75784	1.1616	.86091	.65244
.37	.36162	.38786	2.5782	.93233	.87	.76433	1.1853	.84365	.64483
.38	.37092	.39941	2.5037	.92866	.88	.77074	1.2097	.82668	.63715
.39	.38019	.41105	2.4328	.92491	.89	.77707	1.2346	.80998	.62941
.40	.38942	.42279	2.3652	.92106	**.90**	.78333	1.2602	.79355	.62161
.41	.39861	.43463	2.3008	.91712	.91	.78950	1.2864	.77738	.61375
.42	.40776	.44657	2.2393	.91309	.92	.79560	1.3133	.76146	.60582
.43	.41687	.45862	2.1804	.90897	.93	.80162	1.3409	.74578	.59783
.44	.42594	.47078	2.1241	.90475	.94	.80756	1.3692	.73034	.58979
.45	.43497	.48306	2.0702	.90045	.95	.81342	1.3984	.71511	.58168
.46	.44395	.49545	2.0184	.89605	.96	.81919	1.4284	.70010	.57352
.47	.45289	.50797	1.9686	.89157	.97	.82489	1.4592	.68531	.56530
.48	.46178	.52061	1.9208	.88699	.98	.83050	1.4910	.67071	.55702
.49	.47063	.53339	1.8748	.88233	.99	.83603	1.5237	.65631	.54869
.50	.47943	.54630	1.8305	.87758	**1.00**	.84147	1.5574	.64209	.54030
x	Sin	Tan	Cot	Cos	x	Sin	Tan	Cot	Cos

NATURAL TRIGONOMETRIC FUNCTIONS

FOR ANGLES IN *x* RADIANS (Continued)

x	Sin	Tan	Cot	Cos	x	Sin	Tan	Cot	Cos
1.00	.84147	1.5574	.64209	.54030	**1.50**	.99749	14.101	.07091	.07074
1.01	.84683	1.5922	.62806	.53186	1.51	.99815	16.428	.06087	.06076
1.02	.85211	1.6281	.61420	.52337	1.52	.99871	19.670	.05084	.05077
1.03	.85730	1.6652	.60051	.51482	1.53	.99917	24.498	.04082	.04079
1.04	.86240	1.7036	.58699	.50622	1.54	.99953	32.461	.03081	.03079
1.05	.86742	1.7433	.57362	.49757	1.55	.99978	48.078	.02080	.02079
1.06	.87236	1.7844	.56040	.48887	1.56	.99994	92.621	.01080	.01080
1.07	.87720	1.8270	.54734	.48012	1.57	1.00000	1255.8	.00080	.00080
1.08	.88196	1.8712	.53441	.47133	1.58	.99996	−108.65	−.00920	−.00920
1.09	.88663	1.9171	.52162	.46249	1.59	.99982	−52.067	−.01921	−.01920
1.10	.89121	1.9648	.50897	.45360	**1.60**	.99957	−34.233	−.02921	−.02920
1.11	.89570	2.0143	.49644	.44466	1.61	.99923	−25.495	−.03922	−.03919
1.12	.90010	2.0660	.48404	.43568	1.62	.99879	−20.307	−.04924	−.04918
1.13	.90441	2.1198	.47175	.42666	1.63	.99825	−16.871	−.05927	−.05917
1.14	.90863	2.1759	.45959	.41759	1.64	.99761	−14.427	−.06931	−.06915
1.15	.91276	2.2345	.44753	.40849	1.65	.99687	−12.599	−.07937	−.07912
1.16	.91680	2.2958	.43558	.39934	1.66	.99602	−11.181	−.08944	−.08909
1.17	.92075	2.3600	.42373	.39015	1.67	.99508	−10.047	−.09953	−.09904
1.18	.92461	2.4273	.41199	.38092	1.68	.99404	− 9.1208	−.10964	−.10899
1.19	.92837	2.4979	.40034	.37166	1.69	.99290	− 8.3492	−.11977	−.11892
1.20	.93204	2.5722	.38878	.36236	**1.70**	.99166	− 7.6966	−.12993	−.12884
1.21	.93562	2.6503	.37731	.35302	1.71	.99033	− 7.1373	−.14011	−.13875
1.22	.93910	2.7328	.36593	.34365	1.72	.98889	− 6.6524	−.15032	−.14865
1.23	.94249	2.8198	.35463	.33424	1.73	.98735	− 6.2281	−.16056	−.15853
1.24	.94578	2.9119	.34341	.32480	1.74	.98572	− 5.8535	−.17084	−.16840
1.25	.94898	3.0096	.33227	.31532	1.75	.98399	− 5.5204	−.18115	−.17825
1.26	.95209	3.1133	.32121	.30582	1.76	.98215	− 5.2221	−.19149	−.18808
1.27	.95510	3.2236	.31021	.29628	1.77	.98022	− 4.9534	−.20188	−.19789
1.28	.95802	3.3413	.29928	.28672	1.78	.97820	− 4.7101	−.21231	−.20768
1.29	.96084	3.4672	.28842	.27712	1.79	.97607	− 4.4887	−.22278	−.21745
1.30	.96356	3.6021	.27762	.26750	**1.80**	.97385	− 4.2863	−.23330	−.22720
1.31	.96618	3.7471	.26687	.25785	1.81	.97153	− 4.1005	−.24387	−.23693
1.32	.96872	3.9033	.25619	.24818	1.82	.96911	− 3.9294	−.25449	−.24663
1.33	.97115	4.0723	.24556	.23848	1.83	.96659	− 3.7712	−.26517	−.25631
1.34	.97348	4.2556	.23498	.22875	1.84	.96398	− 3.6245	−.27590	−.26596
1.35	.97572	4.4552	.22446	.21901	1.85	.96128	− 3.4881	−.28669	−.27559
1.36	.97786	4.6734	.21398	.20924	1.86	.95847	− 3.3608	−.29755	−.28519
1.37	.97991	4.9131	.20354	.19945	1.87	.95557	− 2.2419	−.30846	−.29476
1.38	.98185	5.1774	.19315	.18964	1.88	.95258	− 3.1304	−.31945	−.30430
1.39	.98370	5.4707	.18279	.17981	1.89	.94949	− 3.0257	−.33051	−.31381
1.40	.98545	5.7979	.17248	.16997	**1.90**	.94630	− 2.9271	−.34164	−.32329
1.41	.98710	6.1654	.16220	.16010	1.91	.94302	− 2.8341	−.35284	−.33274
1.42	.98865	6.5811	.15195	.15023	1.92	.93965	− 2.7463	−.36413	−.34215
1.43	.99010	7.0555	.14173	.14033	1.93	.93618	− 2.6632	−.37549	−.35153
1.44	.99146	7.6018	.13155	.13042	1.94	.93262	− 2.5843	−.38695	−.36087
1.45	.99271	8.2381	.12139	.12050	1.95	.92896	− 2.5095	−.39849	−.37018
1.46	.99387	8.9886	.11125	.11057	1.96	.92521	− 2.4383	−.41012	−.37945
1.47	.99492	9.8874	.10114	.10063	1.97	.92137	− 2.3705	−.42185	−.38868
1.48	.99588	10.983	.09105	.09067	1.98	.91744	− 2.3058	−.43368	−.39788
1.49	.99674	12.350	.08097	.08071	1.99	.91341	− 2.2441	−.44562	−.40703
1.50	.99749	14.101	.07091	.07074	**2.00**	.90930	− 2.1850	−.45766	−.41615
x	Sin	Tan	Cot	Cos	x	Sin	Tan	Cot	Cos

NATURAL TRIGONOMETRIC FUNCTIONS
SECANTS AND COSECANTS
FOR ANGLES IN RADIANS

x	sec x	csc x	x	sec x	csc x	x	sec x	csc x
0.00	1.00000	∞	0.55	1.17299	1.91319	1.10	2.20460	1.12207
0.01	1.00005	100.00167	0.56	1.18028	1.88258	1.11	2.24890	1.11644
0.02	1.00020	50.00333	0.57	1.18779	1.85311	1.12	2.29525	1.11099
0.03	1.00045	33.33833	0.58	1.19551	1.82474	1.13	2.34379	1.10569
0.04	1.00080	25.00667	0.59	1.20345	1.79739	1.14	2.39467	1.10055
0.05	1.00125	20.00834	0.60	1.21163	1.77103	1.15	2.44806	1.09557
0.06	1.00180	16.67667	0.61	1.22003	1.74560	1.16	2.50413	1.09075
0.07	1.00246	14.29739	0.62	1.22868	1.72107	1.17	2.56311	1.08607
0.08	1.00321	12.51334	0.63	1.23758	1.69738	1.18	2.62519	1.08154
0.09	1.00406	11.12613	0.64	1.24673	1.67449	1.19	2.69063	1.07716
0.10	1.00502	10.01669	0.65	1.25615	1.65238	1.20	2.75970	1.07292
0.11	1.00608	9.10927	0.66	1.26583	1.63101	1.21	2.83271	1.06881
0.12	1.00724	8.35337	0.67	1.27580	1.61034	1.22	2.90997	1.06485
0.13	1.00851	7.71402	0.68	1.28605	1.59035	1.23	2.99188	1.06102
0.14	1.00988	7.16624	0.69	1.29660	1.57100	1.24	3.07885	1.05732
0.15	1.01136	6.69173	0.70	1.30746	1.55227	1.24	3.17136	1.05376
0.16	1.01294	6.27675	0.71	1.31863	1.53413	1.26	3.26993	1.05032
0.17	1.01463	5.91078	0.72	1.33013	1.51657	1.27	3.37518	1.04701
0.18	1.01642	5.58567	0.73	1.34197	1.49954	1.28	3.48778	1.04382
0.19	1.01833	5.29496	0.74	1.35415	1.48305	1.29	3.60853	1.04076
0.20	1.02034	5.03349	0.75	1.36670	1.46705	1.30	3.73833	1.03782
0.21	1.02246	4.79709	0.76	1.37962	1.45154	1.31	3.87822	1.03500
0.22	1.02470	4.58233	0.77	1.39293	1.43650	1.32	4.02941	1.03230
0.23	1.02705	4.38640	0.78	1.40664	1.42191	1.33	4.19329	1.02971
0.24	1.02951	4.20692	0.79	1.42077	1.40775	1.34	4.37153	1.02724
0.25	1.03208	4.04197	0.80	1.43532	1.39401	1.35	4.56607	1.02428
0.26	1.03478	3.88983	0.81	1.45033	1.38067	1.36	4.77923	1.02264
0.27	1.03759	3.74909	0.82	1.46580	1.36772	1.37	5.01379	1.02050
0.28	1.04052	3.61853	0.83	1.48175	1.35514	1.38	5.27313	1.01848
0.29	1.04358	3.49709	0.84	1.49821	1.34292	1.39	5.56133	1.01657
0.30	1.04675	3.38386	0.85	1.51519	1.33106	1.40	5.88349	1.01477
0.31	1.05005	3.27806	0.86	1.53271	1.31954	1.41	6.24593	1.01307
0.32	1.05348	3.17898	0.87	1.55080	1.30834	1.42	6.65666	1.01148
0.33	1.05704	3.08601	0.88	1.56949	1.29746	1.43	7.12598	1.00999
0.34	1.06072	2.99862	0.89	1.58878	1.28688	1.44	7.66732	1.00862
0.35	1.06454	2.91632	0.90	1.60873	1.27661	1.45	8.29856	1.00734
0.36	1.06849	2.83870	0.91	1.62934	1.26662	1.46	9.04406	1.00617
0.37	1.07258	2.76537	0.92	1.65065	1.25691	1.47	9.93781	1.00510
0.38	1.07682	2.69600	0.93	1.67270	1.24747	1.48	11.02881	1.00414
0.39	1.08119	2.63027	0.94	1.69552	1.23830	1.49	12.39028	1.00327
0.40	1.08570	2.56793	0.95	1.71915	1.22938	1.50	14.13683	1.00251
0.41	1.09037	2.50872	0.96	1.74362	1.22072	1.51	16.45850	1.00185
0.42	1.09518	2.45242	0.97	1.76897	1.21229	1.52	19.69493	1.00129
0.43	1.10015	2.39882	0.98	1.79526	1.20410	1.53	24.51881	1.00083
0.44	1.10528	2.34775	0.99	1.82252	1.19614	1.54	32.47654	1.00047
0.45	1.11056	2.29903	1.00	1.85082	1.18840	1.55	48.08888	1.00022
0.46	1.11601	2.25252	1.01	1.88019	1.18087	1.56	92.62589	1.00006
0.47	1.12162	2.20806	1.02	1.91071	1.17356	1.57	+1255.76599	1.00000
0.48	1.12740	2.16553	1.03	1.94243	1.16645	1.58	− 108.65381	1.00004
0.49	1.13336	2.12483	1.04	1.97542	1.15955	1.59	− 52.07657	1.00018
0.50	1.13949	2.08583	1.05	2.00976	1.15284	1.60	− 34.24714	1.00043
0.51	1.14581	2.04844	1.06	2.04552	1.14632			
0.52	1.15231	2.01256	1.07	2.08279	1.13999			
0.53	1.15901	1.97811	1.08	2.12166	1.13384			
0.54	1.16580	1.94501	1.09	2.16223	1.12787			
0.55	1.17299	1.91319	1.10	2.20460	1.12207			

NATURAL TRIGONOMETRIC FUNCTIONS
SINE, TANGENT, COTANGENT, COSINE
FOR ANGLES IN π RADIANS

x		Sin (πx)	Tan (πx)	Cot (πx)	Cos (πx)
.00 or	1.00	.00000	.00000	inf	1.00000
.01	.99	.03141	.03143	31.821	.99951
.02	.98	.06279	.06291	15.895	.99803
.03	.97	.09411	.09453	10.579	.99556
.04	.96	.12533	.12633	7.9158	.99211
.05	.95	.15643	.15838	6.3138	.98769
.06	.94	.18738	.19076	5.2422	.98229
.07	.93	.21814	.22353	4.4737	.97592
.08	.92	.24869	.25676	3.8947	.96858
.09	.91	.27399	.29053	3.4420	.96029
.10	.90	.30902	.32492	3.0777	.95106
.11	.89	.33874	.36002	2.7776	.94088
.12	.88	.36812	.39593	2.5257	.92978
.13	.87	.39715	.43274	2.3109	.91775
.14	.86	.42578	.47056	2.1251	.90483
.15	.85	.45399	.50953	1.9626	.89101
.16	.84	.48175	.54975	1.8190	.87631
.17	.83	.50904	.59140	1.6909	.86074
.18	.82	.53583	.63462	1.5757	.84433
.19	.81	.56208	.67960	1.4715	.82708
.20	.80	.58779	.72654	1.3764	.80902
.21	.79	.61291	.77568	1.2892	.79016
.22	.78	.63742	.82727	1.2088	.77051
.23	.77	.66131	.88162	1.1343	.75011
.24	.76	.68455	.93906	1.0649	.72897
.25	.75	.70711	1.0000	1.0000	.70711
.26	.74	.72897	1.0649	.93906	.68455
.27	.73	.75011	1.1343	.88162	.66131
.28	.72	.77051	1.2088	.82727	.63742
.29	.71	.79016	1.2892	.77568	.61291
.30	.70	.80902	1.3764	.72654	.58779
.31	.69	.82708	1.4715	.67960	.56208
.32	.68	.84433	1.5757	.63462	.53583
.33	.67	.86074	1.6909	.59140	.50904
.34	.66	.87631	1.8190	.54975	.48175
.35	.65	.89101	1.9626	.50953	.45399
.36	.64	.90483	2.1251	.47056	.42578
.37	.63	.91775	2.3109	.43274	.39715
.38	.62	.92978	2.5257	.39593	.36812
.39	.61	.94088	2.7776	.36002	.33874
.40	.60	.95106	3.0777	.32492	.30902
.41	.59	.96029	3.4420	.29053	.27899
.42	.58	.96858	3.8947	.25676	.24869
.43	.57	.97592	4.4737	.22353	.21814
.44	.56	.98229	5.2422	.19076	.18738
.45	.55	.98769	6.3138	.15838	.15643
.46	.54	.99211	7.9158	.12633	.12533
.47	.53	.99556	10.579	.09453	.09411
.48	.52	.99803	15.895	.06291	.06279
.49	.51	.99951	31.821	.03143	.03141
.50	.50	1.0000	inf	.00000	.00000

These functions are useful in the solution of wave equations such as the displacement equation of a sound wave in the form:

$$y = A \sin 2\pi n x$$

without the necessity of reducing the angular rotation either to radians or to degrees in order to find the value of the function.

The algebraic sign of the function follows the familiar Quadrant Law for the particular function desired. Thus a numerical value of 9.13π radians becomes (by the subtraction of the greatest multiple of 2π radians) 1.13π radians. This is the same as $.13\pi$ radians in the 3rd Quadrant, which would give, from the tables above, a value of the sine function of $-.39715$.

Submitted by J. A. Blythe Jr.

COMMON LOGARITHMS OF THE
TRIGONOMETRIC FUNCTIONS

Logarithms of the functions are given for each minute from 0–360°.

The quantity −10 is to be appended to all logarithms of the sine and cosine, to logarithms of the tangent from 0–45° and of the cotangent from 45–90°.

With degrees indicated at either side of top of the page use the column headings at the top. With degrees stated at bottom of the page use the column designations at the bottom.

With degrees at the left (top or bottom) use the minute column at the left, and with degrees on the right side of the page use the minute column at the right.

To illustrate the proper employment of headings for angles in the four quadrants—

log sin 6° 23′ = 9.04603 − 10	log sin 186° 23′ = 9.04603 − 10
log sin 83° 15′ = 9.99698 − 10	log sin 263° 15′ = 9.99698 − 10
log cos 96° 41′ = 9.06589 − 10	log cos 276° 41′ = 9.06589 − 10
log cos 173° 49′ = 9.99747 − 10	log cos 353° 49′ = 9.99747 − 10

For the accurate determination of values where the tabular differences are large, the values of CS and CT are given. The following equations indicate their use.

To find the logarithm of the functions of an angle:

For angles 0–3°	For angles 87–90°
$\log \sin \theta = \log \theta'' - CS$	$\log \cos \theta = \log (90° - \theta)'' - CS$
$\log \tan \theta = \log \theta'' - CT$	$\log \cot \theta = \log (90° - \theta)'' - CT$
$\log \cot \theta = \text{colog} \tan \theta$	$\log \tan \theta = \text{colog} \cot \theta$

To find the angle:

For angles 0–3°	For angles 87–90°
$\log \theta'' = \log \sin \theta + CS$	$\log (90° - \theta)'' = \log \cos \theta + CS$
$\log \theta'' = \log \tan \theta + CT$	$\log (90° - \theta)'' = \log \cot \theta + CT$

In the above expressions, θ'' and $(90° - \theta)''$ are used to indicate the value of the angles expressed in seconds. The values in the body of the table are the cologarithms and should be used as indicated above.

The values of the logarithms S and T are also given in a separate table. For these the following relations hold:

To find the function of an angle:

$\log \sin \theta = \log \theta'' + S$	$\log \cos \theta = \log (90° - \theta)'' + S$
$\log \tan \theta = \log \theta'' + T$	$\log \cot \theta = \log (90° - \theta)'' + T$

To find the angle:

$\log \theta'' = \log \sin \theta - S$	$\log (90° - \theta)'' = \log \cos \theta - S$
$\log \theta'' = \log \tan \theta - T$	$\log (90° - \theta)'' = \log \cot \theta - T$

Where the values of CS and CT are given, the angles expressed in seconds are given in the supplementary column at the left.

The tabular differences are given under the headings "d." and "c.d.", the latter referring to the common difference for the tangent and cotangent. Tables of proportional parts ("p.p.") facilitate interpolation. At the bottom of each column will be found special proportional parts between the tabular differences for the tangent or cotangent and those for the sine or cosine. These are useful when one function is to be obtained directly from the other without determining the angle.

For example, suppose log tan θ is given as 9.67644 and log cos θ is required. The difference between the given logarithm and that given in the table, 9.67622 (opposite 25° 23′), is 22. The tabular differences of the two logarithmic functions at this place are 32 and 6. In the proportional table for $\frac{6}{32}$, 22 corresponds to 4; this, subtracted from the tabular logarithmic cosine 9.95591, gives the required log cos θ = 9.95587.

The symbols $\bar{5}$ and $\underset{\cdot}{5}$ are used to indicate how the terminal 5 has been derived. For example, the logarithm 8.8307$\bar{5}$ is more fully given as 8.8307495 while the value 9.40825 is derived from 9.4082539. Thus, in rounding off to four places, a number ending in $\bar{5}$ should be decreased but a number ending in 5 should be increased.

COMMON LOGARITHMS OF THE TRIGONOMETRIC FUNCTIONS
Values of S and T

Min.	Values of S, −10 to be appended					Values of T, −10 to be appended					Sec.
	0°	1°	2°	3°	4°	0°	1°	2°	3°	4°	
0′	4.68 557	555	549	538	522	4.68 557	562	575	597	628	0″
1	557	555	549	537	522	557	562	575	598	629	60
2	557	555	548	537	522	557	562	576	598	629	120
3	557	555	548	537	521	557	562	576	599	630	180
4	557	555	548	537	521	558	563	576	599	631	240
5	557	555	548	537	521	558	563	577	599	631	300
6	557	555	548	536	520	558	563	577	600	632	360
7	557	555	548	536	520	558	563	577	600	632	420
8	557	555	548	536	520	558	563	578	601	633	480
9	557	555	547	536	520	558	563	578	601	634	540
10	4.68 557	555	547	535	519	4.68 558	564	578	602	634	600
11	557	554	547	535	519	558	564	579	602	635	660
12	557	554	547	535	519	558	564	579	603	635	720
13	557	554	547	535	518	558	564	579	603	636	780
14	557	554	547	534	518	558	564	580	604	637	840
15	557	554	546	534	518	558	564	580	604	637	900
16	557	554	546	534	517	558	565	580	605	638	960
17	557	554	546	534	517	558	565	581	605	639	1020
18	557	554	546	534	517	558	565	581	606	639	1080
19	557	554	546	533	516	558	565	581	606	640	1140
20	4.68 557	554	546	533	516	4.68 558	565	582	607	640	1200
21	557	554	545	533	516	558	566	582	607	641	1260
22	557	553	545	533	515	558	566	582	608	642	1320
23	557	553	545	532	515	558	566	583	608	642	1380
24	557	553	545	532	515	558	566	583	609	643	1440
25	557	553	545	532	515	558	566	583	609	644	1500
26	557	553	544	532	514	558	567	584	610	644	1560
27	557	553	544	531	514	558	567	584	610	645	1620
28	557	553	544	531	514	558	567	584	611	646	1680
29	557	553	544	531	513	559	567	585	611	646	1740
30	4.68 557	553	544	531	513	4.68 559	567	585	612	647	1800
31	557	552	544	530	513	559	568	585	612	648	1860
32	557	552	543	530	512	559	568	586	613	648	1920
33	557	552	543	530	512	559	568	586	613	649	1980
34	557	552	543	529	512	559	568	587	614	650	2040
35	557	552	543	529	511	559	569	587	614	650	2100
36	557	552	543	529	511	559	569	587	615	651	2160
37	557	552	542	529	511	559	569	588	615	652	2220
38	557	552	542	528	510	559	569	588	616	652	2280
39	557	552	542	528	510	559	570	589	616	653	2340
40	4.68 557	551	542	528	510	4.68 559	570	589	617	654	2400
41	556	551	542	528	509	560	570	589	617	654	2460
42	556	551	541	527	509	560	570	590	618	655	2520
43	556	551	541	527	508	560	571	590	619	656	2580
44	556	551	541	527	508	560	571	591	619	656	2640
45	556	551	541	527	508	560	571	591	620	657	2700
46	556	551	541	526	507	560	571	591	620	658	2760
47	556	551	540	526	507	560	572	592	621	659	2820
48	556	550	540	526	507	560	572	592	621	659	2880
49	556	550	540	525	506	560	572	593	622	660	2940
50	4.68 556	550	540	525	506	4.68 561	572	593	622	661	3000
51	556	550	540	525	506	561	573	593	623	661	3060
52	556	550	539	525	505	561	573	594	624	662	3120
53	556	550	539	524	505	561	573	594	624	663	3180
54	556	550	539	524	505	561	573	595	625	664	3240
55	556	549	539	524	504	561	574	595	625	664	3300
56	556	549	539	523	504	561	574	596	626	665	3360
57	556	549	538	523	503	562	574	596	626	666	3420
58	555	549	538	523	503	562	575	596	627	667	3480
59	555	549	538	523	503	562	575	597	628	667	3540
60	4.68 555	549	538	522	502	4.68 562	575	597	628	668	3600

COMMON LOGARITHMS OF THE TRIGONOMETRIC
FUNCTIONS (Continued)

0° (180°)   (359°) **179°**

"	'	L. Sin.	*d.	C. S.	C. T.	L. Tan	*c.d.	L. Cot.	L. Cos.	'
0	0	―		―	―	―		∞	0.00 000	60
60	1	6.46 373	30103	5.31 443	5.31 443	6.46 373	30103	3.53 627	0.00 000	59
120	2	6.76 476	17609	5.31 443	5.31 443	6.76 476	17609	3.23 524	0.00 000	58
180	3	6.94 085	12494	5.31 443	5.31 443	6.94 085	12494	3.05 915	0.00 000	57
240	4	7.06 579	9691	5.31 443	5.31 442	7.06 579	9691	2.93 421	0.00 000	56
300	5	7.16 270	7918	5.31 443	5.31 442	7.16 270	7918	2.83 730	0.00 000	55
360	6	7.24 188	6694	5.31 443	5.31 442	7.24 188	6694	2.75 812	0.00 000	54
420	7	7.30 882	5800	5.31 443	5.31 442	7.30 882	5800	2.69 118	0.00 000	53
480	8	7.36 682	5115	5.31 443	5.31 442	7.36 682	5115	2.63 318	0.00 000	52
540	9	7.41 797	4576	5.31 443	5.31 442	7.41 797	4576	2.58 203	0.00 000	51
600	10	7.46 373	4139	5.31 443	5.31 442	7.46 373	4139	2.53 627	0.00 000	50
660	11	7.50 512	3779	5.31 443	5.31 442	7.50 512	3779	2.49 488	0.00 000	49
720	12	7.54 291	3476	5.31 443	5.31 442	7.54 291	3476	2.45 709	0.00 000	48
780	13	7.57 767	3218	5.31 443	5.31 442	7.57 767	3219	2.42 233	0.00 000	47
840	14	7.60 985	2997	5.31 443	5.31 442	7.60 986	2996	2.39 014	0.00 000	46
900	15	7.63 982	2802	5.31 443	5.31 442	7.63 982	2803	2.36 018	0.00 000	45
960	16	7.66 784	2633	5.31 443	5.31 442	7.66 785	2633	2.33 215	0.00 000	44
1020	17	7.69 417	2483	5.31 443	5.31 442	7.69 418	2482	2.30 582	9.99 999	43
1080	18	7.71 900	2348	5.31 443	5.31 442	7.71 900	2348	2.28 100	9.99 999	42
1140	19	7.74 248	2227	5.31 443	5.31 442	7.74 248	2228	2.25 752	9.99 999	41
1200	20	7.76 475	2119	5.31 443	5.31 442	7.76 476	2119	2.23 524	9.99 999	40
1260	21	7.78 594	2021	5.31 443	5.31 442	7.78 595	2020	2.21 405	9.99 999	39
1320	22	7.80 615	1930	5.31 443	5.31 442	7.80 615	1931	2.19 385	9.99 999	38
1380	23	7.82 545	1848	5.31 443	5.31 442	7.82 546	1848	2.17 454	9.99 999	37
1440	24	7.84 393	1773	5.31 443	5.31 442	7.84 394	1773	2.15 606	9.99 999	36
1500	25	7.86 166	1704	5.31 443	5.31 442	7.86 167	1704	2.13 833	9.99 999	35
1560	26	7.87 870	1639	5.31 443	5.31 442	7.87 871	1639	2.12 129	9.99 999	34
1620	27	7.89 509	1579	5.31 443	5.31 442	7.89 510	1579	2.10 490	9.99 999	33
1680	28	7.91 088	1524	5.31 443	5.31 442	7.91 089	1524	2.08 911	9.99 999	32
1740	29	7.92 612	1472	5.31 443	5.31 441	7.92 613	1473	2.07 387	9.99 998	31
1800	30	7.94 084	1424	5.31 443	5.31 441	7.94 086	1424	2.05 914	9.99 998	30
1860	31	7.95 508	1379	5.31 443	5.31 441	7.95 510	1379	2.04 490	9.99 998	29
1920	32	7.96 887	1336	5.31 443	5.31 441	7.96 889	1336	2.03 111	9.99 998	28
1980	33	7.98 223	1297	5.31 443	5.31 441	7.98 225	1297	2.01 775	9.99 998	27
2040	34	7.99 520	1259	5.31 443	5.31 441	7.99 522	1259	2.00 478	9.99 998	26
2100	35	8.00 779	1223	5.31 443	5.31 441	8.00 781	1223	1.99 219	9.99 998	25
2160	36	8.02 002	1190	5.31 443	5.31 441	8.02 004	1190	1.97 996	9.99 998	24
2220	37	8.03 192	1158	5.31 443	5.31 441	8.03 194	1159	1.96 806	9.99 997	23
2280	38	8.04 350	1128	5.31 443	5.31 441	8.04 353	1128	1.95 647	9.99 997	22
2340	39	8.05 478	1100	5.31 443	5.31 441	8.05 481	1100	1.94 519	9.99 997	21
2400	40	8.06 578	1072	5.31 443	5.31 441	8.06 581	1072	1.93 419	9.99 997	20
2460	41	8.07 650	1046	5.31 444	5.31 440	8.07 653	1047	1.92 347	9.99 997	19
2520	42	8.08 696	1022	5.31 444	5.31 440	8.08 700	1022	1.91 300	9.99 997	18
2580	43	8.09 718	999	5.31 444	5.31 440	8.09 722	998	1.90 278	9.99 997	17
2640	44	8.10 717	976	5.31 444	5.31 440	8.10 720	976	1.89 280	9.99 996	16
2700	45	8.11 693	954	5.31 444	5.31 440	8.11 696	955	1.88 304	9.99 996	15
2760	46	8.12 647	934	5.31 444	5.31 440	8.12 651	934	1.87 349	9.99 996	14
2820	47	8.13 581	914	5.31 444	5.31 440	8.13 585	915	1.86 415	9.99 996	13
2880	48	8.14 495	896	5.31 444	5.31 440	8.14 500	895	1.85 500	9.99 996	12
2940	49	8.15 391	877	5.31 444	5.31 440	8.15 395	878	1.84 605	9.99 996	11
3000	50	8.16 268	860	5.31 444	5.31 439	8.16 273	860	1.83 727	9.99 995	10
3060	51	8.17 128	843	5.31 444	5.31 439	8.17 133	843	1.82 867	9.99 995	9
3120	52	8.17 971	827	5.31 444	5.31 439	8.17 976	828	1.82 024	9.99 995	8
3180	53	8.18 798	812	5.31 444	5.31 439	8.18 804	812	1.81 196	9.99 995	7
3240	54	8.19 610	797	5.31 444	5.31 439	8.19 616	797	1.80 384	9.99 995	6
3300	55	8.20 407	782	5.31 444	5.31 439	8.20 413	782	1.79 587	9.99 994	5
3360	56	8.21 189	769	5.31 444	5.31 439	8.21 195	769	1.78 805	9.99 994	4
3420	57	8.21 958	755	5.31 445	5.31 439	8.21 964	756	1.78 036	9.99 994	3
3480	58	8.22 713	743	5.31 445	5.31 438	8.22 720	742	1.77 280	9.99 994	2
3540	59	8.23 456	730	5.31 445	5.31 438	8.23 462	730	1.76 538	9.99 994	1
3600	60	8.24 186		5.31 445	5.31 438	8.24 192		1.75 808	9.99 993	0
"	'	L. Cos.	d.	C. S.	C. T.	L. Cot.	c. d.	L. Tan.	L. Sin.	'

90° (270°)   (269°) **89°**

* Interpolation in this section of the table is not accurate.

COMMON LOGARITHMS OF THE TRIGONOMETRIC
FUNCTIONS (Continued)

1° (181°)   (358°) **178°**

"	'	L. Sin.	*d.	C. S.	C. T.	L. Tan.	*c.d.	L. Cot.	L. Cos.	'
3600	0	8.24 186	717	5.31 445	5.31 438	8.24 192	718	1.75 808	9.99 993	60
3660	1	8.24 903	706	5.31 445	5.31 438	8.24 910	706	1.75 090	9.99 993	59
3720	2	8.25 609	695	5.31 445	5.31 438	8.25 616	696	1.74 384	9.99 993	58
3780	3	8.26 304	684	5.31 445	5.31 438	8.26 312	684	1.73 688	9.99 993	57
3840	4	8.26 988	673	5.31 445	5.31 437	8.26 996	673	1.73 004	9.99 992	56
3900	5	8.27 661	663	5.31 445	5.31 437	8.27 669	663	1.72 331	9.99 992	55
3960	6	8.28 324	653	5.31 445	5.31 437	8.28 332	654	1.71 668	9.99 992	54
4020	7	8.28 977	644	5.31 445	5.31 437	8.28 986	643	1.71 014	9.99 992	53
4080	8	8.29 621	634	5.31 445	5.31 437	8.29 629	634	1.70 371	9.99 991	52
4140	9	8.30 255	624	5.31 445	5.31 437	8.30 263	625	1.69 737	9.99 991	51
4200	10	8.30 879	616	5.31 446	5.31 437	8.30 888	617	1.69 112	9.99 991	50
4260	11	8.31 495	608	5.31 446	5.31 436	8.31 505	607	1.68 495	9.99 991	49
4320	12	8.32 103	599	5.31 446	5.31 436	8.32 112	599	1.67 888	9.99 990	48
4380	13	8.32 702	590	5.31 446	5.31 436	8.32 711	591	1.67 289	9.99 990	47
4440	14	8.33 292	583	5.31 446	5.31 436	8.33 302	584	1.66 698	9.99 990	46
4500	15	8.33 875	575	5.31 446	5.31 436	8.33 886	575	1.66 114	9.99 990	45
4560	16	8.34 450	568	5.31 446	5.31 435	8.34 461	568	1.65 539	9.99 989	44
4620	17	8.35 018	560	5.31 446	5.31 435	8.35 029	561	1.64 971	9.99 989	43
4680	18	8.35 578	553	5.31 446	5.31 435	8.35 590	553	1.64 410	9.99 989	42
4740	19	8.36 131	547	5.31 446	5.31 435	8.36 143	546	1.63 857	9.99 989	41
4800	20	8.36 678	539	5.31 446	5.31 435	8.36 689	540	1.63 311	9.99 988	40
4860	21	8.37 217	533	5.31 447	5.31 434	8.37 229	533	1.62 771	9.99 988	39
4920	22	8.37 750	526	5.31 447	5.31 434	8.37 762	527	1.62 238	9.99 988	38
4980	23	8.38 276	520	5.31 447	5.31 434	8.38 289	520	1.61 711	9.99 987	37
5040	24	8.38 796	514	5.31 447	5.31 434	8.38 809	514	1.61 191	9.99 987	36
5100	25	8.39 310	508	5.31 447	5.31 434	8.39 323	509	1.60 677	9.99 987	35
5160	26	8.39 818	502	5.31 447	5.31 433	8.39 832	502	1.60 168	9.99 986	34
5220	27	8.40 320	496	5.31 447	5.31 433	8.40 334	496	1.59 666	9.99 986	33
5280	28	8.40 816	491	5.31 447	5.31 433	8.40 830	491	1.59 170	9.99 986	32
5340	29	8.41 307	485	5.31 447	5.31 433	8.41 321	486	1.58 679	9.99 985	31
5400	30	8.41 792	480	5.31 447	5.31 433	8.41 807	480	1.58 193	9.99 985	30
5460	31	8.42 272	474	5.31 448	5.31 432	8.42 287	475	1.57 713	9.99 985	29
5520	32	8.42 746	470	5.31 448	5.31 432	8.42 762	470	1.57 238	9.99 984	28
5580	33	8.43 216	464	5.31 448	5.31 432	8.43 232	464	1.56 768	9.99 984	27
5640	34	8.43 680	459	5.31 448	5.31 432	8.43 696	459	1.56 304	9.99 984	26
5700	35	8.44 139	455	5.31 448	5.31 431	8.44 156	455	1.55 844	9.99 983	25
5760	36	8.44 594	450	5.31 448	5.31 431	8.44 611	450	1.55 389	9.99 983	24
5820	37	8.45 044	445	5.31 448	5.31 431	8.45 061	446	1.54 939	9.99 983	23
5880	38	8.45 489	441	5.31 448	5.31 431	8.45 507	441	1.54 493	9.99 982	22
5940	39	8.45 930	436	5.31 449	5.31 431	8.45 948	437	1.54 052	9.99 982	21
6000	40	8.46 366	433	5.31 449	5.31 430	8.46 385	432	1.53 615	9.99 982	20
6060	41	8.46 799	427	5.31 449	5.31 430	8.46 817	428	1.53 183	9.99 981	19
6120	42	8.47 226	424	5.31 449	5.31 430	8.47 245	424	1.52 755	9.99 981	18
6180	43	8.47 650	419	5.31 449	5.31 430	8.47 669	420	1.52 331	9.99 981	17
6240	44	8.48 069	416	5.31 449	5.31 429	8.48 089	416	1.51 911	9.99 980	16
6300	45	8.48 485	411	5.31 449	5.31 429	8.48 505	412	1.51 495	9.99 980	15
6360	46	8.48 896	408	5.31 449	5.31 429	8.48 917	408	1.51 083	9.99 979	14
6420	47	8.49 304	404	5.31 450	5.31 428	8.49 325	404	1.50 675	9.99 979	13
6480	48	8.49 708	400	5.31 450	5.31 428	8.49 729	401	1.50 271	9.99 979	12
6540	49	8.50 108	396	5.31 450	5.31 428	8.50 130	397	1.49 870	9.99 978	11
6600	50	8.50 504	393	5.31 450	5.31 428	8.50 527	393	1.49 473	9.99 978	10
6660	51	8.50 897	390	5.31 450	5.31 427	8.50 920	390	1.49 080	9.99 977	9
6720	52	8.51 287	386	5.31 450	5.31 427	8.51 310	386	1.48 690	9.99 977	8
6780	53	8.51 673	382	5.31 450	5.31 427	8.51 696	383	1.48 304	9.99 977	7
6840	54	8.52 055	379	5.31 450	5.31 427	8.52 079	380	1.47 921	9.99 976	6
6900	55	8.52 434	376	5.31 451	5.31 426	8.52 459	376	1.47 541	9.99 976	5
6960	56	8.52 810	373	5.31 451	5.31 426	8.52 835	373	1.47 165	9.99 975	4
7020	57	8.53 183	369	5.31 451	5.31 426	8.53 208	370	1.46 792	9.99 975	3
7080	58	8.53 552	367	5.31 451	5.31 425	8.53 578	367	1.46 422	9.99 974	2
7140	59	8.53 919	363	5.31 451	5.31 425	8.53 945	363	1.46 055	9.99 974	1
7200	60	8.54 282		5.31 451	5.31 425	8.54 308		1.45 692	9.99 974	0
"	'	L. Cos.	d.	C. S.	C. T.	L. Cot.	c.d.	L. Tan.	L. Sin.	'

91° (271°)   (268°) **88°**

* Interpolation in this section of the table is not accurate.

COMMON LOGARITHMS OF THE TRIGONOMETRIC FUNCTIONS (Continued)

2° (182°)   **(357°) 177°**

"	'	L. Sin.	*d.	C. S.	C. T.	L. Tan.	*c.d.	L. Cot.	L. Cos.	'
7200	0	8.54 282	360	5.31 451	5.31 423	8.54 308	361	1.45 692	9.99 974	60
7260	1	8.54 642	357	5.31 451	5.31 423	8.54 669	358	1.45 331	9.99 973	59
7320	2	8.54 999	355	5.31 452	5.31 424	8.55 027	355	1.44 973	9.99 973	58
7380	3	8.55 354	351	5.31 452	5.31 424	8.55 382	352	1.44 618	9.99 972	57
7440	4	8.55 705	349	5.31 452	5.31 424	8.55 734	349	1.44 266	9.99 972	56
7500	5	8.56 054	346	5.31 452	5.31 423	8.56 083	346	1.43 917	9.99 971	55
7560	6	8.56 400	343	5.31 452	5.31 423	8.56 429	344	1.43 571	9.99 971	54
7620	7	8.56 743	341	5.31 452	5.31 423	8.56 773	341	1.43 227	9.99 970	53
7680	8	8.57 084	337	5.31 453	5.31 422	8.57 114	338	1.42 886	9.99 970	52
7740	9	8.57 421	336	5.31 453	5.31 422	8.57 452	336	1.42 548	9.99 969	51
7800	10	8.57 757	332	5.31 453	5.31 422	8.57 788	333	1.42 212	9.99 969	50
7860	11	8.58 089	330	5.31 453	5.31 421	8.58 121	330	1.41 879	9.99 968	49
7920	12	8.58 419	328	5.31 453	5.31 421	8.58 451	328	1.41 549	9.99 968	48
7980	13	8.58 747	325	5.31 453	5.31 421	8.58 779	326	1.41 221	9.99 967	47
8040	14	8.59 072	323	5.31 454	5.31 421	8.59 105	323	1.40 895	9.99 967	46
8100	15	8.59 395	320	5.31 454	5.31 420	8.59 428	321	1.40 572	9.99 967	45
8160	16	8.59 715	318	5.31 454	5.31 420	8.59 749	319	1.40 251	9.99 966	44
8220	17	8.60 033	316	5.31 454	5.31 420	8.60 068	316	1.39 932	9.99 966	43
8280	18	8.60 349	313	5.31 454	5.31 419	8.60 384	314	1.39 616	9.99 965	42
8340	19	8.60 662	311	5.31 454	5.31 419	8.60 698	311	1.39 302	9.99 964	41
8400	20	8.60 973	309	5.31 455	5.31 418	8.61 009	310	1.38 991	9.99 964	40
8460	21	8.61 282	307	5.31 455	5.31 418	8.61 319	307	1.38 681	9.99 963	39
8520	22	8.61 589	305	5.31 455	5.31 418	8.61 626	305	1.38 374	9.99 963	38
8580	23	8.61 894	302	5.31 455	5.31 417	8.61 931	303	1.38 069	9.99 962	37
8640	24	8.62 196	301	5.31 455	5.31 417	8.62 234	301	1.37 766	9.99 962	36
8700	25	8.62 497	298	5.31 455	5.31 417	8.62 535	299	1.37 465	9.99 961	35
8760	26	8.62 795	296	5.31 456	5.31 416	8.62 834	297	1.37 166	9.99 961	34
8820	27	8.63 091	294	5.31 456	5.31 416	8.63 131	295	1.36 869	9.99 960	33
8880	28	8.63 385	293	5.31 456	5.31 416	8.63 426	293	1.36 574	9.99 960	32
8940	29	8.63 678	290	5.31 456	5.31 415	8.63 718	291	1.36 282	9.99 959	31
9000	30	8.63 968	288	5.31 456	5.31 415	8.64 009	289	1.35 991	9.99 959	30
9060	31	8.64 256	287	5.31 456	5.31 415	8.64 298	287	1.35 702	9.99 958	29
9120	32	8.64 543	284	5.31 457	5.31 414	8.64 585	285	1.35 415	9.99 958	28
9180	33	8.64 827	283	5.31 457	5.31 414	8.64 870	284	1.35 130	9.99 957	27
9240	34	8.65 110	281	5.31 457	5.31 413	8.65 154	281	1.34 846	9.99 956	26
9300	35	8.65 391	279	5.31 457	5.31 413	8.65 435	280	1.34 565	9.99 956	25
9360	36	8.65 670	277	5.31 457	5.31 413	8.65 715	278	1.34 285	9.99 955	24
9420	37	8.65 947	276	5.31 458	5.31 412	8.65 993	276	1.34 007	9.99 955	23
9480	38	8.66 223	274	5.31 458	5.31 412	8.66 269	274	1.33 731	9.99 954	22
9540	39	8.66 497	272	5.31 458	5.31 412	8.66 543	273	1.33 457	9.99 954	21
9600	40	8.66 769	270	5.31 458	5.31 411	8.66 816	271	1.33 184	9.99 953	20
9660	41	8.67 039	269	5.31 458	5.31 411	8.67 087	269	1.32 913	9.99 952	19
9720	42	8.67 308	267	5.31 459	5.31 410	8.67 356	268	1.32 644	9.99 952	18
9780	43	8.67 575	266	5.31 459	5.31 410	8.67 624	266	1.32 376	9.99 951	17
9840	44	8.67 841	263	5.31 459	5.31 410	8.67 890	264	1.32 110	9.99 951	16
9900	45	8.68 104	263	5.31 459	5.31 409	8.68 154	263	1.31 846	9.99 950	15
9960	46	8.68 367	260	5.31 459	5.31 409	8.68 417	261	1.31 583	9.99 949	14
10020	47	8.68 627	259	5.31 460	5.31 408	8.68 678	260	1.31 322	9.99 949	13
10080	48	8.68 886	258	5.31 460	5.31 408	8.68 938	258	1.31 062	9.99 948	12
10140	49	8.69 144	256	5.31 460	5.31 408	8.69 196	257	1.30 804	9.99 948	11
10200	50	8.69 400	254	5.31 460	5.31 407	8.69 453	255	1.30 547	9.99 947	10
10260	51	8.69 654	253	5.31 460	5.31 407	8.69 708	254	1.30 292	9.99 946	9
10320	52	8.69 907	252	5.31 461	5.31 406	8.69 962	252	1.30 038	9.99 946	8
10380	53	8.70 159	250	5.31 461	5.31 406	8.70 214	251	1.29 786	9.99 945	7
10440	54	8.70 409	249	5.31 461	5.31 405	8.70 465	249	1.29 535	9.99 944	6
10500	55	8.70 658	247	5.31 461	5.31 405	8.70 714	248	1.29 286	9.99 944	5
10560	56	8.70 905	246	5.31 461	5.31 405	8.70 962	246	1.29 038	9.99 943	4
10620	57	8.71 151	244	5.31 462	5.31 404	8.71 208	245	1.28 792	9.99 942	3
10680	58	8.71 395	243	5.31 462	5.31 404	8.71 453	244	1.28 547	9.99 942	2
10740	59	8.71 638	242	5.31 462	5.31 403	8.71 697	243	1.28 303	9.99 941	1
10800	60	8.71 880		5.31 462	5.31 403	8.71 940		1.28 060	9.99 940	0
"	'	L. Cos.	d.	C. S.	C. T.	L. Cot.	c.d.	L. Tan.	L. Sin.	

* Interpolation in this section of the table is not accurate.

COMMON LOGARITHMS OF THE TRIGONOMETRIC
FUNCTIONS (Continued)

3° (183°)   (356°) **176°**

′	L. Sin.	*d.	L. Tan.	*c.d.	L. Cot.	L. Cos.	′	P. P.				
0	8.71 880		8.71 940		1.28 060	9.99 940	60	″	**241**	**239**	**237**	**235**	**234**
1	8.72 120	240	8.72 181	241	1.27 819	9.99 940	59	1	4.0	4.0	4.0	3.9	3.9
2	8.72 359	239	8.72 420	239	1.27 580	9.99 939	58	2	8.0	8.0	7.9	7.8	7.8
3	8.72 597	238	8.72 659	239	1.27 341	9.99 938	57	3	12.0	12.0	11.8	11.8	11.7
4	8.72 834	237	8.72 896	237	1.27 104	9.99 938	56	4	16.1	15.9	15.8	15.7	15.6
		235		236									
5	8.73 069		8.73 132		1.26 868	9.99 937	55	5	20.1	19.9	19.8	19.6	19.5
6	8.73 303	234	8.73 366	234	1.26 634	9.99 936	54	6	24.1	23.9	23.7	23.5	23.4
7	8.73 535	232	8.73 600	234	1.26 400	9.99 936	53	7	28.1	27.9	27.6	27.4	27.3
8	8.73 767	232	8.73 832	232	1.26 168	9.99 935	52	8	32.1	31.9	31.6	31.3	31.2
9	8.73 997	230	8.74 063	231	1.25 937	9.99 934	51	9	36.2	35.8	35.6	35.2	35.1
		229		229									
10	8.74 226		8.74 292		1.25 708	9.99 934	50	″	**232**	**229**	**227**	**225**	**223**
11	8.74 454	228	8.74 521	229	1.25 479	9.99 933	49	1	3.9	3.8	3.8	3.8	3.7
12	8.74 680	226	8.74 748	227	1.25 252	9.99 932	48	2	7.7	7.6	7.6	7.5	7.4
13	8.74 906	226	8.74 974	226	1.25 026	9.99 932	47	3	11.6	11.4	11.4	11.2	11.2
14	8.75 130	224	8.75 199	225	1.24 801	9.99 931	46	4	15.5	15.3	15.1	15.0	14.9
		223		224									
15	8.75 353		8.75 423		1.24 577	9.99 930	45	5	19.3	19.1	18.9	18.8	18.6
16	8.75 575	222	8.75 645	222	1.24 355	9.99 929	44	6	23.2	22.9	22.7	22.5	22.3
17	8.75 795	220	8.75 867	222	1.24 133	9.99 929	43	7	27.1	26.7	26.5	26.2	26.0
18	8.76 015	220	8.76 087	220	1.23 913	9.99 928	42	8	30.9	30.5	30.3	30.0	29.7
19	8.76 234	219	8.76 306	219	1.23 694	9.99 927	41	9	34.8	34.4	34.0	33.8	33.4
		217		219									
20	8.76 451		8.76 525		1.23 475	9.99 926	40	″	**222**	**220**	**217**	**215**	**213**
21	8.76 667	216	8.76 742	217	1.23 258	9.99 926	39	1	3.7	3.7	3.6	3.6	3.6
22	8.76 883	216	8.76 958	216	1.23 042	9.99 925	38	2	7.4	7.3	7.2	7.2	7.1
23	8.77 097	214	8.77 173	215	1.22 827	9.99 924	37	3	11.1	11.0	10.8	10.8	10.6
24	8.77 310	213	8.77 387	214	1.22 613	9.99 923	36	4	14.8	14.7	14.5	14.3	14.2
		212		213									
25	8.77 522		8.77 600		1.22 400	9.99 923	35	5	18.5	18.3	18.1	17.9	17.8
26	8.77 733	211	8.77 811	211	1.22 189	9.99 922	34	6	22.2	22.0	21.7	21.5	21.3
27	8.77 943	210	8.78 022	211	1.21 978	9.99 921	33	7	25.9	25.7	25.3	25.1	24.8
28	8.78 152	209	8.78 232	210	1.21 768	9.99 920	32	8	29.6	29.3	28.9	28.7	28.4
29	8.78 360	208	8.78 441	209	1.21 559	9.99 920	31	9	33.3	33.0	32.6	32.2	32.0
		208		208									
30	8.78 568		8.78 649		1.21 351	9.99 919	30	″	**211**	**208**	**206**	**203**	**201**
31	8.78 774	206	8.78 855	206	1.21 145	9.99 918	29	1	3.5	3.5	3.4	3.4	3.4
32	8.78 979	205	8.79 061	206	1.20 939	9.99 917	28	2	7.0	6.9	6.9	6.8	6.7
33	8.79 183	204	8.79 266	205	1.20 734	9.99 917	27	3	10.6	10.4	10.3	10.2	10.0
34	8.79 386	203	8.79 470	204	1.20 530	9.99 916	26	4	14.1	13.9	13.7	13.5	13.4
		202		203									
35	8.79 588		8.79 673		1.20 327	9.99 915	25	5	17.6	17.3	17.2	16.9	16.8
36	8.79 789	201	8.79 875	202	1.20 125	9.99 914	24	6	21.1	20.8	20.6	20.3	20.1
37	8.79 990	201	8.80 076	201	1.19 924	9.99 913	23	7	24.6	24.3	24.0	23.7	23.4
38	8.80 189	199	8.80 277	201	1.19 723	9.99 913	22	8	28.1	27.7	27.5	27.1	26.8
39	8.80 388	199	8.80 476	199	1.19 524	9.99 912	21	9	31.6	31.2	30.9	30.4	30.2
		197		198									
40	8.80 585		8.80 674		1.19 326	9.99 911	20	″	**199**	**197**	**195**	**193**	**192**
41	8.80 782	197	8.80 872	198	1.19 128	9.99 910	19	1	3.3	3.3	3.2	3.2	3.2
42	8.80 978	196	8.81 068	196	1.18 932	9.99 909	18	2	6.6	6.6	6.5	6.4	6.4
43	8.81 173	195	8.81 264	196	1.18 736	9.99 909	17	3	10.0	9.8	9.8	9.6	9.6
44	8.81 367	194	8.81 459	195	1.18 541	9.99 908	16	4	13.3	13.1	13.0	12.9	12.8
		193		194									
45	8.81 560		8.81 653		1.18 347	9.99 907	15	5	16.6	16.4	16.2	16.1	16.0
46	8.81 752	192	8.81 846	193	1.18 154	9.99 906	14	6	19.9	19.7	19.5	19.3	19.2
47	8.81 944	192	8.82 038	192	1.17 962	9.99 905	13	7	23.2	23.0	22.8	22.5	22.4
48	8.82 134	190	8.82 230	192	1.17 770	9.99 904	12	8	26.5	26.3	26.0	25.7	25.6
49	8.82 324	190	8.82 420	190	1.17 580	9.99 904	11	9	29.8	29.6	29.2	29.0	28.8
		189		190									
50	8.82 513		8.82 610		1.17 390	9.99 903	10	″	**189**	**187**	**185**	**183**	**181**
51	8.82 701	188	8.82 799	189	1.17 201	9.99 902	9	1	3.2	3.1	3.1	3.0	3.0
52	8.82 888	187	8.82 987	188	1.17 013	9.99 901	8	2	6.3	6.2	6.2	6.1	6.0
53	8.83 075	187	8.83 175	188	1.16 825	9.99 900	7	3	9.4	9.4	9.2	9.2	9.0
54	8.83 261	186	8.83 361	186	1.16 639	9.99 899	6	4	12.6	12.5	12.3	12.2	12.1
		185		186									
55	8.83 446		8.83 547		1.16 453	9.99 898	5	5	15.8	15.6	15.4	15.2	15.1
56	8.83 630	184	8.83 732	185	1.16 263	9.99 898	4	6	18.9	18.7	18.5	18.3	18.1
57	8.83 813	183	8.83 916	184	1.16 084	9.99 897	3	7	22.0	21.8	21.6	21.4	21.1
58	8.83 996	183	8.84 100	184	1.15 900	9.99 896	2	8	25.2	24.9	24.7	24.4	24.1
59	8.84 177	181	8.84 282	182	1.15 718	9.99 895	1	9	28.4	28.0	27.8	27.4	27.2
		181		182									
60	8.84 358		8.84 464		1.15 536	9.99 894	0	10	31.5	31.2	30.8	30.5	30.2
′	L. Cos.	d.	L. Cot.	c.d	L. Tan.	L. Sin.	′		P. P.				

* Interpolation in this section of the table is not accurate.

COMMON LOGARITHMS OF THE TRIGONOMETRIC FUNCTIONS (Continued)

4° (184°)   (355°) 175°

'	L. Sin.	*d.	L. Tan.	*c.d.	L. Cot.	L. Cos.	'
0	8.84 358	181	8.84 464	182	1.15 536	9.99 894	60
1	8.84 539	179	8.84 646	180	1.15 354	9.99 893	59
2	8.84 718	179	8.84 826	180	1.15 174	9.99 892	58
3	8.84 897	178	8.85 006	179	1.14 994	9.99 891	57
4	8.85 075	177	8.85 185	178	1.14 815	9.99 891	56
5	8.85 252	177	8.85 363	177	1.14 637	9.99 890	55
6	8.85 429	176	8.85 540	177	1.14 460	9.99 889	54
7	8.85 605	175	8.85 717	177	1.14 283	9.99 888	53
8	8.85 780	175	8.85 893	176	1.14 107	9.99 887	52
9	8.85 955	173	8.86 069	174	1.13 931	9.99 886	51
10	8.86 128	173	8.86 243	174	1.13 757	9.99 885	50
11	8.86 301	173	8.86 417	174	1.13 583	9.99 884	49
12	8.86 474	171	8.86 591	172	1.13 409	9.99 883	48
13	8.86 645	171	8.86 763	172	1.13 237	9.99 882	47
14	8.86 816	171	8.86 935	171	1.13 065	9.99 881	46
15	8.86 987	169	8.87 106	171	1.12 894	9.99 880	45
16	8.87 156	169	8.87 277	170	1.12 723	9.99 879	44
17	8.87 325	169	8.87 447	169	1.12 553	9.99 879	43
18	8.87 494	167	8.87 616	169	1.12 384	9.99 878	42
19	8.87 661	168	8.87 785	168	1.12 215	9.99 877	41
20	8.87 829	166	8.87 953	167	1.12 047	9.99 876	40
21	8.87 995	166	8.88 120	167	1.11 880	9.99 875	39
22	8.88 161	165	8.88 287	166	1.11 713	9.99 874	38
23	8.88 326	164	8.88 453	165	1.11 547	9.99 873	37
24	8.88 490	164	8.88 618	165	1.11 382	9.99 872	36
25	8.88 654	163	8.88 783	165	1.11 217	9.99 870	35
26	8.88 817	163	8.88 948	163	1.11 052	9.99 870	34
27	8.88 980	162	8.89 111	163	1.10 889	9.99 869	33
28	8.89 142	162	8.89 274	163	1.10 726	9.99 868	32
29	8.89 304	160	8.89 437	161	1.10 563	9.99 867	31
30	8.89 464	161	8.89 598	162	1.10 402	9.99 866	30
31	8.89 625	159	8.89 760	160	1.10 240	9.99 865	29
32	8.89 784	159	8.89 920	160	1.10 080	9.99 864	28
33	8.89 943	159	8.90 080	160	1.09 920	9.99 863	27
34	8.90 102	158	8.90 240	159	1.09 760	9.99 862	26
35	8.90 260	157	8.90 399	158	1.09 601	9.99 861	25
36	8.90 417	157	8.90 557	158	1.09 443	9.99 860	24
37	8.90 574	156	8.90 715	157	1.09 285	9.99 859	23
38	8.90 730	157	8.90 872	157	1.09 128	9.99 858	22
39	8.90 885	155	8.91 029	156	1.08 971	9.99 857	21
40	8.91 040	155	8.91 185	155	1.08 815	9.99 856	20
41	8.91 195	154	8.91 340	155	1.08 660	9.99 855	19
42	8.91 349	153	8.91 495	155	1.08 505	9.99 854	18
43	8.91 502	153	8.91 650	153	1.08 350	9.99 853	17
44	8.91 655	152	8.91 803	154	1.08 197	9.99 852	16
45	8.91 807	152	8.91 957	153	1.08 043	9.99 851	15
46	8.91 959	151	8.92 110	152	1.07 890	9.99 850	14
47	8.92 110	151	8.92 262	152	1.07 738	9.99 848	13
48	8.92 261	150	8.92 414	151	1.07 586	9.99 847	12
49	8.92 411	150	8.92 565	151	1.07 435	9.99 846	11
50	8.92 561	149	8.92 716	150	1.07 284	9.99 845	10
51	8.92 710	149	8.92 866	150	1.07 134	9.99 844	9
52	8.92 859	148	8.93 016	149	1.06 984	9.99 843	8
53	8.93 007	147	8.93 165	148	1.06 835	9.99 842	7
54	8.93 154	147	8.93 313	149	1.06 687	9.99 841	6
55	8.93 301	147	8.93 462	147	1.06 538	9.99 840	5
56	8.93 448	146	8.93 609	147	1.06 391	9.99 839	4
57	8.93 594	146	8.93 756	147	1.06 244	9.99 838	3
58	8.93 740	145	8.93 903	146	1.06 097	9.99 837	2
59	8.93 885	145	8.94 049	146	1.05 951	9.99 836	1
60	8.94 030		8.94 195		1.05 805	9.99 834	0

L. Cos.	d.	L. Cot.	c.d.	L. Tan.	L. Sin.	'

P. P.

''	182	181	179	178	177
1	3.0	3.0	3.0	3.0	3.0
2	6.1	6.0	6.0	5.9	5.9
3	9.1	9.0	9.0	8.9	8.8
4	12.1	12.1	11.9	11.9	11.8
5	15.2	15.1	14.9	14.8	14.8
6	18.2	18.1	17.9	17.8	17.7
7	21.2	21.1	20.9	20.8	20.6
8	24.3	24.1	23.9	23.7	23.6
9	27.3	27.2	26.8	26.7	26.6

''	176	175	174	173	172
1	2.9	2.9	2.9	2.9	2.9
2	5.9	5.8	5.8	5.8	5.7
3	8.8	8.8	8.7	8.6	8.6
4	11.7	11.7	11.6	11.5	11.5
5	14.7	14.6	14.5	14.4	14.3
6	17.6	17.5	17.4	17.3	17.2
7	20.5	20.4	20.3	20.2	20.1
8	23.5	23.3	23.2	23.1	22.9
9	26.4	26.2	26.1	26.0	25.8

''	171	170	169	168	167
1	2.8	2.8	2.8	2.8	2.8
2	5.7	5.7	5.6	5.6	5.6
3	8.6	8.5	8.4	8.4	8.3
4	11.4	11.3	11.3	11.2	11.1
5	14.2	14.2	14.1	14.0	13.9
6	17.1	17.0	16.9	16.8	16.7
7	20.0	19.8	19.7	19.6	19.5
8	22.8	22.7	22.5	22.4	22.3
9	25.6	25.5	25.4	25.2	25.0

''	166	165	164	163	162
1	2.8	2.8	2.7	2.7	2.7
2	5.5	5.5	5.5	5.4	5.4
3	8.3	8.2	8.2	8.2	8.1
4	11.1	11.0	10.9	10.9	10.8
5	13.8	13.8	13.7	13.6	13.5
6	16.6	16.5	16.4	16.3	16.2
7	19.4	19.2	19.1	19.0	18.9
8	22.1	22.0	21.9	21.7	21.6
9	24.9	24.8	24.6	24.4	24.3

''	161	160	159	158	157
1	2.7	2.7	2.6	2.6	2.6
2	5.4	5.3	5.3	5.3	5.2
3	8.0	8.0	8.0	7.9	7.8
4	10.7	10.7	10.6	10.5	10.5
5	13.4	13.3	13.2	13.2	13.1
6	16.1	16.0	15.9	15.8	15.7
7	18.8	18.7	18.6	18.4	18.3
8	21.5	21.3	21.2	21.1	20.9
9	24.2	24.0	23.8	23.7	23.6

''	156	155	154	153	152
1	2.6	2.6	2.6	2.6	2.5
2	5.2	5.2	5.1	5.1	5.1
3	7.8	7.8	7.7	7.6	7.6
4	10.4	10.3	10.3	10.2	10.1
5	13.0	12.9	12.8	12.8	12.7
6	15.6	15.5	15.4	15.3	15.2
7	18.2	18.1	18.0	17.8	17.7
8	20.8	20.7	20.5	20.4	20.3
9	23.4	23.2	23.1	23.0	22.8
10	26.0	25.8	25.7	25.5	25.3

* Interpolation in this section of the table is not accurate.

COMMON LOGARITHMS OF THE TRIGONOMETRIC
FUNCTIONS (Continued)

5° (185°) (354°) **174°**

'	L. Sin.	d.	L. Tan.	c.d.	L. Cot.	L. Cos.	'				P. P.		
0	8.94 030	144	8.94 195	145	1.05 805	9.99 834	60	"	151	149	148	147	146
1	8.94 174	143	8.94 340	145	1.05 660	9.99 833	59	1	2.5	2.5	2.5	2.4	2.4
2	8.94 317	144	8.94 485	145	1.05 515	9.99 832	58	2	5.0	5.0	4.9	4.9	4.9
3	8.94 461	142	8.94 630	143	1.05 370	9.99 831	57	3	7.6	7.4	7.4	7.4	7.3
4	8.94 603	143	8.94 773	144	1.05 227	9.99 830	56	4	10.1	9.9	9.9	9.8	9.7
5	8.94 746	141	8.94 917	143	1.05 083	9.99 829	55	5	12.6	12.4	12.3	12.2	12.2
6	8.94 887	142	8.95 060	142	1.04 940	9.99 828	54	6	15.1	14.9	14.8	14.7	14.6
7	8.95 029	141	8.95 202	142	1.04 798	9.99 827	53	7	17.6	17.4	17.3	17.2	17.0
8	8.95 170	140	8.95 344	142	1.04 656	9.99 825	52	8	20.1	19.9	19.7	19.6	19.5
9	8.95 310	140	8.95 486	141	1.04 514	9.99 824	51	9	22.6	22.4	22.2	22.0	21.9
10	8.95 450	139	8.95 627	140	1.04 373	9.99 823	50	"	145	144	143	142	141
11	8.95 589	139	8.95 767	141	1.04 233	9.99 822	49	1	2.4	2.4	2.4	2.4	2.4
12	8.95 728	139	8.95 908	139	1.04 092	9.99 821	48	2	4.8	4.8	4.8	4.7	4.7
13	8.95 867	138	8.96 047	140	1.03 953	9.99 820	47	3	7.2	7.2	7.2	7.1	7.0
14	8.96 005	138	8.96 187	138	1.03 813	9.99 819	46	4	9.7	9.6	9.5	9.5	9.4
15	8.96 143	137	8.96 325	139	1.03 675	9.99 817	45	5	12.1	12.0	11.9	11.8	11.8
16	8.96 280	137	8.96 464	138	1.03 536	9.99 816	44	6	14.5	14.4	14.3	14.2	14.1
17	8.96 417	136	8.96 602	137	1.03 398	9.99 815	43	7	16.9	16.8	16.7	16.6	16.4
18	8.96 553	136	8.96 739	138	1.03 261	9.99 814	42	8	19.3	19.2	19.1	18.9	18.8
19	8.96 689	136	8.96 877	136	1.03 123	9.99 813	41	9	21.8	21.6	21.4	21.3	21.2
20	8.96 825	135	8.97 013	137	1.02 987	9.99 812	40	"	140	139	138	137	136
21	8.96 960	135	8.97 150	135	1.02 850	9.99 810	39	1	2.3	2.3	2.3	2.3	2.3
22	8.97 095	134	8.97 285	136	1.02 715	9.99 809	38	2	4.7	4.6	4.6	4.6	4.5
23	8.97 229	134	8.97 421	135	1.02 579	9.99 808	37	3	7.0	7.0	6.9	6.8	6.8
24	8.97 363	133	8.97 556	135	1.02 444	9.99 807	36	4	9.3	9.3	9.2	9.1	9.1
25	8.97 496	133	8.97 691	134	1.02 309	9.99 806	35	5	11.7	11.6	11.5	11.4	11.3
26	8.97 629	133	8.97 825	134	1.02 175	9.99 804	34	6	14.0	13.9	13.8	13.7	13.6
27	8.97 762	132	8.97 959	133	1.02 041	9.99 803	33	7	16.3	16.2	16.1	16.0	15.9
28	8.97 894	132	8.98 092	133	1.01 908	9.99 802	32	8	18.7	18.5	18.4	18.3	18.1
29	8.98 026	131	8.98 225	133	1.01 775	9.99 801	31	9	21.0	20.8	20.7	20.6	20.4
30	8.98 157	131	8.98 358	132	1.01 642	9.99 800	30	"	135	134	133	132	131
31	8.98 288	131	8.98 490	132	1.01 510	9.99 798	29	1	2.2	2.2	2.2	2.2	2.2
32	8.98 419	130	8.98 622	131	1.01 378	9.99 797	28	2	4.5	4.5	4.4	4.4	4.4
33	8.98 549	130	8.98 753	131	1.01 247	9.99 796	27	3	6.8	6.7	6.6	6.6	6.6
34	8.98 679	129	8.98 884	131	1.01 116	9.99 795	26	4	9.0	8.9	8.9	8.8	8.7
35	8.98 808	129	8.99 015	130	1.00 985	9.99 793	25	5	11.2	11.2	11.1	11.0	10.9
36	8.98 937	129	8.99 145	130	1.00 855	9.99 792	24	6	13.5	13.4	13.3	13.2	13.1
37	8.99 066	128	8.99 275	130	1.00 725	9.99 791	23	7	15.8	15.6	15.5	15.4	15.3
38	8.99 194	128	8.99 405	129	1.00 595	9.99 790	22	8	18.0	17.9	17.7	17.6	17.5
39	8.99 322	128	8.99 534	128	1.00 466	9.99 788	21	9	20.2	20.1	20.0	19.8	19.6
40	8.99 450	127	8.99 662	129	1.00 338	9.99 787	20	"	130	129	128	127	126
41	8.99 577	127	8.99 791	128	1.00 209	9.99 786	19	1	2.2	2.2	2.1	2.1	2.1
42	8.99 704	126	8.99 919	127	1.00 081	9.99 785	18	2	4.3	4.3	4.3	4.2	4.2
43	8.99 830	126	9.00 046	128	0.99 954	9.99 783	17	3	6.5	6.4	6.4	6.4	6.3
44	8.99 956	126	9.00 174	127	0.99 826	9.99 782	16	4	8.7	8.6	8.5	8.5	8.4
45	9.00 082	125	9.00 301	126	0.99 699	9.99 781	15	5	10.8	10.8	10.7	10.6	10.5
46	9.00 207	125	9.00 427	126	0.99 573	9.99 780	14	6	13.0	12.9	12.8	12.7	12.6
47	9.00 332	124	9.00 553	126	0.99 447	9.99 778	13	7	15.2	15.0	14.9	14.8	14.7
48	9.00 456	125	9.00 679	126	0.99 321	9.99 777	12	8	17.3	17.2	17.1	16.9	16.8
49	9.00 581	123	9.00 805	125	0.99 195	9.99 776	11	9	19.5	19.4	19.2	19.0	18.9
50	9.00 704	124	9.00 930	125	0.99 070	9.99 775	10	"	125	124	123	122	121
51	9.00 828	123	9.01 055	124	0.98 945	9.99 773	9	1	2.1	2.1	2.0	2.0	2.0
52	9.00 951	123	9.01 179	124	0.98 821	9.99 772	8	2	4.2	4.1	4.1	4.1	4.0
53	9.01 074	122	9.01 303	124	0.98 697	9.99 771	7	3	6.2	6.2	6.2	6.1	6.0
54	9.01 196	122	9.01 427	123	0.98 573	9.99 769	6	4	8.3	8.3	8.2	8.1	8.1
55	9.01 318	122	9.01 550	123	0.98 450	9.99 768	5	5	10.4	10.3	10.2	10.2	10.1
56	9.01 440	121	9.01 673	123	0.98 327	9.99 767	4	6	12.5	12.4	12.3	12.2	12.1
57	9.01 561	121	9.01 796	122	0.98 204	9.99 765	3	7	14.6	14.5	14.4	14.2	14.1
58	9.01 682	121	9.01 918	122	0.98 082	9.99 764	2	8	16.7	16.5	16.4	16.3	16.1
59	9.01 803	120	9.02 040	122	0.97 960	9.99 763	1	9	18.8	18.6	18.4	18.3	18.2
60	9.01 923		9.02 162		0.97 838	9.99 761	0	10	20.8	20.7	20.5	20.3	20.2
'	L. Cos.	d.	L. Cot.	c.d.	L. Tan.	L. Sin.	'				P. P.		

95° (275°) (264°) **84°**

COMMON LOGARITHMS OF THE TRIGONOMETRIC FUNCTIONS (Continued)

6° (186°)   **(353°) 173°**

′	L. Sin.	d.	L. Tan.	c.d.	L. Cot.	L. Cos.	′	P. P.				
0	9.01 923	120	9.02 162	121	0.97 838	9.99 761	60	″	121	120	119	118
1	9.02 043	120	9.02 283	121	0.97 717	9.99 760	59	1	2.0	2.0	2.0	2.0
2	9.02 163	120	9.02 404	121	0.97 596	9.99 759	58	2	4.0	4.0	4.0	3.9
3	9.02 283	119	9.02 525	120	0.97 475	9.99 757	57	3	6.0	6.0	6.0	5.9
4	9.02 402	118	9.02 645	121	0.97 355	9.99 756	56	4	8.1	8.0	7.9	7.9
5	9.02 520	119	9.02 766	119	0.97 234	9.99 755	55	5	10.1	10.0	9.9	9.8
6	9.02 639	118	9.02 885	120	0.97 115	9.99 753	54	6	12.1	12.0	11.9	11.8
7	9.02 757	117	9.03 005	119	0.96 995	9.99 752	53	7	14.1	14.0	13.9	13.8
8	9.02 874	118	9.03 124	118	0.96 876	9.99 751	52	8	16.1	16.0	15.9	15.7
9	9.02 992	117	9.03 242	119	0.96 758	9.99 749	51	9	18.2	18.0	17.8	17.7
10	9.03 109	117	9.03 361	118	0.96 639	9.99 748	50	10	20.2	20.0	19.8	19.7
11	9.03 226	116	9.03 479	118	0.96 521	9.99 747	49	20	40.3	40.0	39.7	39.3
12	9.03 342	116	9.03 597	117	0.96 403	9.99 745	48	30	60.5	60.0	59.5	59.0
13	9.03 458	116	9.03 714	118	0.96 286	9.99 744	47	40	80.7	80.0	79.3	78.7
14	9.03 574	116	9.03 832	116	0.96 168	9.99 742	46	50	100.8	100.0	99.2	98.3
15	9.03 690	115	9.03 948	117	0.96 052	9.99 741	45	″	117	116	115	114
16	9.03 805	115	9.04 065	116	0.95 935	9.99 740	44	1	2.0	1.9	1.9	1.9
17	9.03 920	114	9.04 181	116	0.95 819	9.99 738	43	2	3.9	3.9	3.8	3.8
18	9.04 034	115	9.04 297	116	0.95 703	9.99 737	42	3	5.8	5.8	5.8	5.7
19	9.04 149	113	9.04 413	115	0.95 587	9.99 736	41	4	7.8	7.7	7.7	7.6
20	9.04 262	114	9.04 528	115	0.95 472	9.99 734	40	5	9.8	9.7	9.6	9.5
21	9.04 376	114	9.04 643	115	0.95 357	9.99 733	39	6	11.7	11.6	11.5	11.4
22	9.04 490	113	9.04 758	115	0.95 242	9.99 731	38	7	13.6	13.5	13.4	13.3
23	9.04 603	112	9.04 873	114	0.95 127	9.99 730	37	8	15.6	15.5	15.3	15.2
24	9.04 715	113	9.04 987	114	0.95 013	9.99 728	36	9	17.6	17.4	17.2	17.1
25	9.04 828	112	9.05 101	113	0.94 899	9.99 727	35	10	19.5	19.3	19.2	19.0
26	9.04 940	112	9.05 214	114	0.94 786	9.99 726	34	20	39.0	38.7	38.3	38.0
27	9.05 052	112	9.05 328	113	0.94 672	9.99 724	33	30	58.5	58.0	57.5	57.0
28	9.05 164	111	9.05 441	112	0.94 559	9.99 723	32	40	78.0	77.3	76.7	76.0
29	9.05 275	111	9.05 553	113	0.94 447	9.99 721	31	50	97.5	96.7	95.8	95.0
30	9.05 386	111	9.05 666	112	0.94 334	9.99 720	30	″	113	112	111	110
31	9.05 497	110	9.05 778	112	0.94 222	9.99 718	29	1	1.9	1.9	1.8	1.8
32	9.05 607	110	9.05 890	112	0.94 110	9.99 717	28	2	3.8	3.7	3.7	3.7
33	9.05 717	110	9.06 002	111	0.93 998	9.99 716	27	3	5.6	5.6	5.6	5.5
34	9.05 827	110	9.06 113	111	0.93 887	9.99 714	26	4	7.5	7.5	7.4	7.3
35	9.05 937	109	9.06 224	111	0.93 776	9.99 713	25	5	9.4	9.3	9.2	9.2
36	9.06 046	109	9.06 335	110	0.93 665	9.99 711	24	6	11.3	11.2	11.1	11.0
37	9.06 155	109	9.06 445	111	0.93 555	9.99 710	23	7	13.2	13.1	13.0	12.8
38	9.06 264	108	9.06 556	110	0.93 444	9.99 708	22	8	15.1	14.9	14.8	14.7
39	9.06 372	109	9.06 666	109	0.93 334	9.99 707	21	9	17.0	16.8	16.6	16.5
40	9.06 481	108	9.06 775	110	0.93 225	9.99 705	20	10	18.8	18.7	18.5	18.3
41	9.06 589	107	9.06 885	109	0.93 115	9.99 704	19	20	37.7	37.3	37.0	36.7
42	9.06 696	108	9.06 994	109	0.93 006	9.99 702	18	30	56.5	56.0	55.5	55.0
43	9.06 804	107	9.07 103	108	0.92 897	9.99 701	17	40	75.3	74.7	74.0	73.3
44	9.06 911	107	9.07 211	109	0.92 789	9.99 699	16	50	94.2	93.3	92.5	91.7
45	9.07 018	106	9.07 320	108	0.92 680	9.99 698	15	″	109	108	107	106
46	9.07 124	107	9.07 428	108	0.92 572	9.99 696	14	1	1.8	1.8	1.8	1.8
47	9.07 231	106	9.07 536	107	0.92 464	9.99 695	13	2	3.6	3.6	3.6	3.5
48	9.07 337	105	9.07 643	108	0.92 357	9.99 693	12	3	5.4	5.4	5.4	5.3
49	9.07 442	106	9.07 751	107	0.92 249	9.99 692	11	4	7.3	7.2	7.1	7.1
50	9.07 548	105	9.07 858	106	0.92 142	9.99 690	10	5	9.1	9.0	8.9	8.8
51	9.07 653	105	9.07 964	107	0.92 036	9.99 689	9	6	10.9	10.8	10.7	10.6
52	9.07 758	105	9.08 071	106	0.91 929	9.99 687	8	7	12.7	12.6	12.5	12.4
53	9.07 863	105	9.08 177	106	0.91 823	9.99 686	7	8	14.5	14.4	14.3	14.1
54	9.07 968	104	9.08 283	106	0.91 717	9.99 684	6	9	16.4	16.2	16.0	15.9
55	9.08 072	104	9.08 389	106	0.91 611	9.99 683	5	10	18.2	18.0	17.8	17.7
56	9.08 176	104	9.08 495	105	0.91 505	9.99 681	4	20	36.3	36.0	35.7	35.3
57	9.08 280	103	9.08 600	105	0.91 400	9.99 680	3	30	54.5	54.0	53.5	53.0
58	9.08 383	103	9.08 705	105	0.91 295	9.99 678	2	40	72.7	72.0	71.3	70.7
59	9.08 486	103	9.08 810	104	0.91 190	9.99 677	1	50	90.8	90.0	89.2	88.3
60	9.08 589		9.08 914		0.91 086	9.99 675	0					
′	L. Cos.	d.	L. Cot.	c.d.	L. Tan.	L. Sin.	′	P. P.				

96° (276°)   **(263°) 83°**

COMMON LOGARITHMS OF THE TRIGONOMETRIC FUNCTIONS (Continued)

7° (187°)   **(352°) 172°**

'	L. Sin.	d.	L. Tan.	c.d.	L. Cot.	L. Cos.	'
0	9.08 589	103	9.08 914	105	0.91 086	9.99 675	60
1	9.08 692	103	9.09 019	104	0.90 981	9.99 674	59
2	9.08 795	102	9.09 123	104	0.90 877	9.99 672	58
3	9.08 897	102	9.09 227	103	0.90 773	9.99 670	57
4	9.08 999	102	9.09 330	104	0.90 670	9.99 669	56
5	9.09 101	101	9.09 434	103	0.90 566	9.99 667	55
6	9.09 202	102	9.09 537	103	0.90 463	9.99 666	54
7	9.09 304	101	9.09 640	102	0.90 360	9.99 664	53
8	9.09 405	101	9.09 742	103	0.90 258	9.99 663	52
9	9.09 506	100	9.09 845	102	0.90 155	9.99 661	51
10	9.09 606	101	9.09 947	102	0.90 053	9.99 659	50
11	9.09 707	100	9.10 049	101	0.89 951	9.99 658	49
12	9.09 807	100	9.10 150	102	0.89 850	9.99 656	48
13	9.09 907	99	9.10 252	101	0.89 748	9.99 655	47
14	9.10 006	100	9.10 353	101	0.89 647	9.99 653	46
15	9.10 106	99	9.10 454	101	0.89 546	9.99 651	45
16	9.10 205	99	9.10 555	101	0.89 445	9.99 650	44
17	9.10 304	98	9.10 656	100	0.89 344	9.99 648	43
18	9.10 402	99	9.10 756	100	0.89 244	9.99 647	42
19	9.10 501	98	9.10 856	100	0.89 144	9.99 645	41
20	9.10 599	98	9.10 956	100	0.89 044	9.99 643	40
21	9.10 697	98	9.11 056	99	0.88 944	9.99 642	39
22	9.10 795	98	9.11 155	99	0.88 845	9.99 640	38
23	9.10 893	97	9.11 254	99	0.88 746	9.99 638	37
24	9.10 990	97	9.11 353	99	0.88 647	9.99 637	36
25	9.11 087	97	9.11 452	99	0.88 548	9.99 635	35
26	9.11 184	97	9.11 551	98	0.88 449	9.99 633	34
27	9.11 281	96	9.11 649	98	0.88 351	9.99 632	33
28	9.11 377	97	9.11 747	98	0.88 253	9.99 630	32
29	9.11 474	96	9.11 845	98	0.88 155	9.99 629	31
30	9.11 570	96	9.11 943	97	0.88 057	9.99 627	30
31	9.11 666	95	9.12 040	98	0.87 960	9.99 625	29
32	9.11 761	96	9.12 138	97	0.87 862	9.99 624	28
33	9.11 857	95	9.12 235	97	0.87 765	9.99 622	27
34	9.11 952	95	9.12 332	96	0.87 668	9.99 620	26
35	9.12 047	95	9.12 428	97	0.87 572	9.99 618	25
36	9.12 142	94	9.12 525	96	0.87 475	9.99 617	24
37	9.12 236	95	9.12 621	96	0.87 379	9.99 615	23
38	9.12 331	94	9.12 717	96	0.87 283	9.99 613	22
39	9.12 425	94	9.12 813	96	0.87 187	9.99 612	21
40	9.12 519	93	9.12 909	95	0.87 091	9.99 610	20
41	9.12 612	94	9.13 004	95	0.86 996	9.99 608	19
42	9.12 706	93	9.13 099	95	0.86 901	9.99 607	18
43	9.12 799	93	9.13 194	95	0.86 806	9.99 605	17
44	9.12 892	93	9.13 289	95	0.86 711	9.99 603	16
45	9.12 985	93	9.13 384	94	0.86 616	9.99 601	15
46	9.13 078	93	9.13 478	95	0.86 522	9.99 600	14
47	9.13 171	92	9.13 573	94	0.86 427	9.99 598	13
48	9.13 263	92	9.13 667	94	0.86 333	9.99 596	12
49	9.13 355	92	9.13 761	93	0.86 239	9.99 595	11
50	9.13 447	92	9.13 854	94	0.86 146	9.99 593	10
51	9.13 539	91	9.13 948	93	0.86 052	9.99 591	9
52	9.13 630	92	9.14 041	93	0.85 959	9.99 589	8
53	9.13 722	91	9.14 134	93	0.85 866	9.99 588	7
54	9.13 813	91	9.14 227	93	0.85 773	9.99 586	6
55	9.13 904	90	9.14 320	92	0.85 680	9.99 584	5
56	9.13 994	91	9.14 412	92	0.85 588	9.99 582	4
57	9.14 085	90	9.14 504	93	0.85 496	9.99 581	3
58	9.14 175	91	9.14 597	91	0.85 403	9.99 579	2
59	9.14 266	90	9.14 688	92	0.85 312	9.99 577	1
60	9.14 356		9.14 780		0.85 220	9.99 575	0

| ' | L. Cos. | d. | L. Cot. | c.d. | L. Tan. | L. Sin. | ' |

97° (277°)   **(262°) 82°**

P. P.

''	105	104	103	102
1	1.8	1.7	1.7	1.7
2	3.5	3.5	3.4	3.4
3	5.2	5.2	5.2	5.1
4	7.0	6.9	6.9	6.8
5	8.8	8.7	8.6	8.5
6	10.5	10.4	10.3	10.2
7	12.2	12.1	12.0	11.9
8	14.0	13.9	13.7	13.6
9	15.8	15.6	15.4	15.3
10	17.5	17.3	17.2	17.0
20	35.0	34.7	34.3	34.0
30	52.5	52.0	51.5	51.0
40	70.0	69.3	68.7	68.0
50	87.5	86.7	85.8	85.0

''	101	100	99	98
1	1.7	1.7	1.6	1.6
2	3.4	3.3	3.3	3.3
3	5.0	5.0	5.0	4.9
4	6.7	6.7	6.6	6.5
5	8.4	8.3	8.2	8.2
6	10.1	10.0	9.9	9.8
7	11.8	11.7	11.6	11.4
8	13.5	13.3	13.2	13.1
9	15.2	15.0	14.8	14.7
10	16.8	16.7	16.5	16.3
20	33.7	33.3	33.0	32.7
30	50.5	50.0	49.5	49.0
40	67.3	66.7	66.0	65.3
50	84.2	83.3	82.5	81.7

''	97	96	95	94
1	1.6	1.6	1.6	1.6
2	3.2	3.2	3.2	3.1
3	4.8	4.8	4.8	4.7
4	6.5	6.4	6.3	6.3
5	8.1	8.0	7.9	7.8
6	9.7	9.6	9.5	9.4
7	11.3	11.2	11.1	11.0
8	12.9	12.8	12.7	12.5
9	14.6	14.4	14.2	14.1
10	16.2	16.0	15.8	15.7
20	32.3	32.0	31.7	31.3
30	48.5	48.0	47.5	47.0
40	64.7	64.0	63.3	62.7
50	80.8	80.0	79.2	78.3

''	93	92	91	90
1	1.6	1.5	1.5	1.5
2	3.1	3.1	3.0	3.0
3	4.6	4.6	4.6	4.5
4	6.2	6.1	6.1	6.0
5	7.8	7.7	7.6	7.5
6	9.3	9.2	9.1	9.0
7	10.8	10.7	10.6	10.5
8	12.4	12.3	12.1	12.0
9	14.0	13.8	13.6	13.5
10	15.5	15.3	15.2	15.0
20	31.0	30.7	30.3	30.0
30	46.5	46.0	45.5	45.0
40	62.0	61.3	60.7	60.0
50	77.5	76.7	75.8	75.0

COMMON LOGARITHMS OF THE TRIGONOMETRIC
FUNCTIONS (Continued)

8° (188°)   (351°) **171°**

′	L. Sin.	d.	L. Tan.	c.d.	L. Cot.	L. Cos.	′		P. P.		
0	9.14 356	89	9.14 780	92	0.85 220	9.99 575	60	″	**92**	**91**	**90**
1	9.14 445	90	9.14 872	91	0.85 128	9.99 574	59	1	1.5	1.5	1.5
2	9.14 535	89	9.14 963	91	0.85 037	9.99 572	58	2	3.1	3.0	3.0
3	9.14 624	90	9.15 054	91	0.84 946	9.99 570	57	3	4.6	4.6	4.5
4	9.14 714	89	9.15 145	91	0.84 855	9.99 568	56	4	6.1	6.1	6.0
5	9.14 803	88	9.15 236	91	0.84 764	9.99 566	55	5	7.7	7.6	7.5
6	9.14 891	89	9.15 327	90	0.84 673	9.99 565	54	6	9.2	9.1	9.0
7	9.14 980	89	9.15 417	91	0.84 583	9.99 563	53	7	10.7	10.6	10.5
8	9.15 069	88	9.15 508	90	0.84 492	9.99 561	52	8	12.3	12.1	12.0
9	9.15 157	88	9.15 598	90	0.84 402	9.99 559	51	9	13.8	13.6	13.5
10	9.15 245	88	9.15 688	89	0.84 312	9.99 557	50	10	15.3	15.2	15.0
11	9.15 333	88	9.15 777	90	0.84 223	9.99 556	49	20	30.7	30.3	30.0
12	9.15 421	87	9.15 867	89	0.84 133	9.99 554	48	30	46.0	45.5	45.0
13	9.15 508	88	9.15 956	90	0.84 044	9.99 552	47	40	61.3	60.7	60.0
14	9.15 596	87	9.16 046	89	0.83 954	9.99 550	46	50	76.7	75.8	75.0
15	9.15 683	87	9.16 135	89	0.83 865	9.99 548	45	″	**89**	**88**	**87**
16	9.15 770	87	9.16 224	88	0.83 776	9.99 546	44	1	1.5	1.5	1.4
17	9.15 857	87	9.16 312	89	0.83 688	9.99 545	43	2	3.0	2.9	2.9
18	9.15 944	86	9.16 401	88	0.83 599	9.99 543	42	3	4.4	4.4	4.4
19	9.16 030	86	9.16 489	88	0.83 511	9.99 541	41	4	5.9	5.9	5.8
20	9.16 116	87	9.16 577	88	0.83 423	9.99 539	40	5	7.4	7.3	7.2
21	9.16 203	86	9.16 665	88	0.83 335	9.99 537	39	6	8.9	8.8	8.7
22	9.16 289	85	9.16 753	88	0.83 247	9.99 535	38	7	10.4	10.3	10.2
23	9.16 374	86	9.16 841	87	0.83 159	9.99 533	37	8	11.9	11.7	11.6
24	9.16 460	85	9.16 928	88	0.83 072	9.99 532	36	9	13.4	13.2	13.0
25	9.16 545	86	9.17 016	87	0.82 984	9.99 530	35	10	14.8	14.7	14.5
26	9.16 631	85	9.17 103	87	0.82 897	9.99 528	34	20	29.7	29.3	29.0
27	9.16 716	85	9.17 190	87	0.82 810	9.99 526	33	30	44.5	44.0	43.5
28	9.16 801	85	9.17 277	86	0.82 723	9.99 524	32	40	59.3	58.7	58.0
29	9.16 886	84	9.17 363	87	0.82 637	9.99 522	31	50	74.2	73.3	72.5
30	9.16 970	85	9.17 450	86	0.82 550	9.99 520	30	″	**86**	**85**	**84**
31	9.17 055	84	9.17 536	86	0.82 464	9.99 518	29	1	1.4	1.4	1.4
32	9.17 139	84	9.17 622	86	0.82 378	9.99 517	28	2	2.9	2.8	2.8
33	9.17 223	84	9.17 708	86	0.82 292	9.99 515	27	3	4.3	4.2	4.2
34	9.17 307	84	9.17 794	86	0.82 206	9.99 513	26	4	5.7	5.7	5.6
35	9.17 391	83	9.17 880	85	0.82 120	9.99 511	25	5	7.2	7.1	7.0
36	9.17 474	84	9.17 965	86	0.82 035	9.99 509	24	6	8.6	8.5	8.4
37	9.17 558	83	9.18 051	85	0.81 949	9.99 507	23	7	10.0	9.9	9.8
38	9.17 641	83	9.18 136	85	0.81 864	9.99 506	22	8	11.5	11.3	11.2
39	9.17 724	83	9.18 221	85	0.81 779	9.99 503	21	9	12.9	12.8	12.6
40	9.17 807	83	9.18 306	85	0.81 694	9.99 501	20	10	14.3	14.2	14.0
41	9.17 890	83	9.18 391	84	0.81 609	9.99 499	19	20	28.7	28.3	28.0
42	9.17 973	82	9.18 475	85	0.81 525	9.99 497	18	30	43.0	42.5	42.0
43	9.18 055	82	9.18 560	84	0.81 440	9.99 495	17	40	57.3	56.7	56.0
44	9.18 137	83	9.18 644	84	0.81 356	9.99 494	16	50	71.7	70.8	70.0
45	9.18 220	82	9.18 728	84	0.81 272	9.99 492	15	″	**83**	**82**	**81**
46	9.18 302	81	9.18 812	84	0.81 188	9.99 490	14	1	1.4	1.4	1.4
47	9.18 383	82	9.18 896	83	0.81 104	9.99 488	13	2	2.8	2.7	2.7
48	9.18 465	82	9.18 979	84	0.81 021	9.99 486	12	3	4.2	4.1	4.0
49	9.18 547	81	9.19 063	83	0.80 937	9.99 484	11	4	5.5	5.5	5.4
50	9.18 628	81	9.19 146	83	0.80 854	9.99 482	10	5	6.9	6.8	6.8
51	9.18 709	81	9.19 229	83	0.80 771	9.99 480	9	6	8.3	8.2	8.1
52	9.18 790	81	9.19 312	83	0.80 688	9.99 478	8	7	9.7	9.6	9.4
53	9.18 871	81	9.19 395	83	0.80 605	9.99 476	7	8	11.1	10.9	10.8
54	9.18 952	81	9.19 478	83	0.80 522	9.99 474	6	9	12.4	12.3	12.2
55	9.19 033	80	9.19 561	82	0.80 439	9.99 472	5	10	13.8	13.7	13.5
56	9.19 113	80	9.19 643	82	0.80 357	9.99 470	4	20	27.7	27.3	27.0
57	9.19 193	80	9.19 725	82	0.80 275	9.99 468	3	30	41.5	41.0	40.5
58	9.19 273	80	9.19 807	82	0.80 193	9.99 466	2	40	55.3	54.7	54.0
59	9.19 353	80	9.19 889	82	0.80 111	9.99 464	1	50	69.2	68.3	67.5
60	9.19 433		9.19 971		0.80 029	9.99 462	0				
′	L. Cos.	d.	L. Cot.	c.d.	L. Tan.	L. Sin.	′		P. P.		

COMMON LOGARITHMS OF THE TRIGONOMETRIC FUNCTIONS (Continued)

9° (189°)　　　　　　　　　　　　　　　　(350°) **170°**

'	L. Sin.	d.	L. Tan.	c.d.	L. Cot.	L. Cos.	'
0	9.19 433	80	9.19 971	82	0.80 029	9.99 462	60
1	9.19 513	79	9.20 053	81	0.79 947	9.99 460	59
2	9.19 592	80	9.20 134	82	0.79 866	9.99 458	58
3	9.19 672	79	9.20 216	81	0.79 784	9.99 456	57
4	9.19 751	79	9.20 297	81	0.79 703	9.99 454	56
5	9.19 830	79	9.20 378	81	0.79 622	9.99 452	55
6	9.19 909	79	9.20 459	81	0.79 541	9.99 450	54
7	9.19 988	79	9.20 540	81	0.79 460	9.99 448	53
8	9.20 067	78	9.20 621	80	0.79 379	9.99 446	52
9	9.20 145	78	9.20 701	81	0.79 299	9.99 444	51
10	9.20 223	79	9.20 782	80	0.79 218	9.99 442	50
11	9.20 302	78	9.20 862	80	0.79 138	9.99 440	49
12	9.20 380	78	9.20 942	80	0.79 058	9.99 438	48
13	9.20 458	77	9.21 022	80	0.78 978	9.99 436	47
14	9.20 535	78	9.21 102	80	0.78 898	9.99 434	46
15	9.20 613	78	9.21 182	79	0.78 818	9.99 432	45
16	9.20 691	77	9.21 261	80	0.78 739	9.99 429	44
17	9.20 768	77	9.21 341	79	0.78 659	9.99 427	43
18	9.20 845	77	9.21 420	79	0.78 580	9.99 425	42
19	9.20 922	77	9.21 499	79	0.78 501	9.99 423	41
20	9.20 999	77	9.21 578	79	0.78 422	9.99 421	40
21	9.21 076	77	9.21 657	79	0.78 343	9.99 419	39
22	9.21 153	76	9.21 736	78	0.78 264	9.99 417	38
23	9.21 229	77	9.21 814	79	0.78 186	9.99 415	37
24	9.21 306	76	9.21 893	78	0.78 107	9.99 413	36
25	9.21 382	76	9.21 971	78	0.78 029	9.99 411	35
26	9.21 458	76	9.22 049	78	0.77 951	9.99 409	34
27	9.21 534	76	9.22 127	78	0.77 873	9.99 407	33
28	9.21 610	75	9.22 205	78	0.77 795	9.99 404	32
29	9.21 685	76	9.22 283	78	0.77 717	9.99 402	31
30	9.21 761	75	9.22 361	77	0.77 639	9.99 400	30
31	9.21 836	76	9.22 438	78	0.77 562	9.99 398	29
32	9.21 912	75	9.22 516	77	0.77 484	9.99 396	28
33	9.21 987	75	9.22 593	77	0.77 407	9.99 394	27
34	9.22 062	75	9.22 670	77	0.77 330	9.99 392	26
35	9.22 137	74	9.22 747	77	0.77 253	9.99 390	25
36	9.22 211	75	9.22 824	77	0.77 176	9.99 388	24
37	9.22 286	75	9.22 901	76	0.77 099	9.99 385	23
38	9.22 361	74	9.22 977	77	0.77 023	9.99 383	22
39	9.22 435	74	9.23 054	76	0.76 946	9.99 381	21
40	9.22 509	74	9.23 130	76	0.76 870	9.99 379	20
41	9.22 583	74	9.23 206	77	0.76 794	9.99 377	19
42	9.22 657	74	9.23 283	76	0.76 717	9.99 375	18
43	9.22 731	74	9.23 359	76	0.76 641	9.99 372	17
44	9.22 805	73	9.23 435	75	0.76 565	9.99 370	16
45	9.22 878	74	9.23 510	76	0.76 490	9.99 368	15
46	9.22 952	73	9.23 586	75	0.76 414	9.99 366	14
47	9.23 025	73	9.23 661	76	0.76 339	9.99 364	13
48	9.23 098	73	9.23 737	75	0.76 263	9.99 362	12
49	9.23 171	73	9.23 812	75	0.76 188	9.99 359	11
50	9.23 244	73	9.23 887	75	0.76 113	9.99 357	10
51	9.23 317	73	9.23 962	75	0.76 038	9.99 355	9
52	9.23 390	72	9.24 037	75	0.75 963	9.99 353	8
53	9.23 462	73	9.24 112	74	0.75 888	9.99 351	7
54	9.23 535	72	9.24 186	75	0.75 814	9.99 348	6
55	9.23 607	72	9.24 261	74	0.75 739	9.99 346	5
56	9.23 679	73	9.24 335	75	0.75 665	9.99 344	4
57	9.23 752	71	9.24 410	74	0.75 590	9.99 342	3
58	9.23 823	72	9.24 484	74	0.75 516	9.99 340	2
59	9.23 895	72	9.24 558	74	0.75 442	9.99 337	1
60	9.23 967		9.24 632		0.75 368	9.99 335	0

'	L. Cos.	d.	L. Cot.	c.d.	L. Tan.	L. Sin.	'

99° (279°)　　　　　　　　　　　　　　　　(260°) **80°**

P. P.

"	80	79	78	77
1	1.3	1.3	1.3	1.3
2	2.7	2.6	2.6	2.6
3	4.0	4.0	3.9	3.8
4	5.3	5.3	5.2	5.1
5	6.7	6.6	6.5	6.4
6	8.0	7.9	7.8	7.7
7	9.3	9.2	9.1	9.0
8	10.7	10.5	10.4	10.3
9	12.0	11.8	11.7	11.6
10	13.3	13.2	13.0	12.8
20	26.7	26.3	26.0	25.7
30	40.0	39.5	39.0	38.5
40	53.3	52.7	52.0	51.3
50	66.7	65.8	65.0	64.2

"	76	75	74	73
1	1.3	1.2	1.2	1.2
2	2.5	2.5	2.5	2.4
3	3.8	3.8	3.7	3.6
4	5.1	5.0	4.9	4.9
5	6.3	6.2	6.2	6.1
6	7.6	7.5	7.4	7.3
7	8.9	8.8	8.6	8.5
8	10.1	10.0	9.9	9.7
9	11.4	11.2	11.1	11.0
10	12.7	12.5	12.3	12.2
20	25.3	25.0	24.7	24.3
30	38.0	37.5	37.0	36.5
40	50.7	50.0	49.3	48.7
50	63.3	62.5	61.7	60.8

"	72	71	3	2
1	1.2	1.2	0.0	0.0
2	2.4	2.4	0.1	0.1
3	3.6	3.6	0.2	0.1
4	4.8	4.7	0.2	0.1
5	6.0	5.9	0.2	0.2
6	7.2	7.1	0.3	0.2
7	8.4	8.3	0.4	0.2
8	9.6	9.5	0.4	0.3
9	10.8	10.6	0.4	0.3
10	12.0	11.8	0.5	0.3
20	24.0	23.7	1.0	0.7
30	36.0	35.5	1.5	1.0
40	48.0	47.3	2.0	1.3
50	60.0	59.2	2.5	1.7

	3	3	3
	79	78	77
0			
1	13.2	13.0	12.8
2	39.5	39.0	38.5
3	65.8	65.0	64.2

	3	3	3
	76	75	74
0			
1	12.7	12.5	12.3
2	38.0	37.5	37.0
3	63.3	62.5	61.7

COMMON LOGARITHMS OF THE TRIGONOMETRIC
FUNCTIONS (Continued)

10° (190°) (349°) **169°**

′	L. Sin.	d.	L. Tan.	c.d.	L. Cot.	L. Cos.	d.	′
0	9.23 967	72	9.24 632	74	0.75 368	9.99 335	2	60
1	9.24 039	71	9.24 706	73	0.75 294	9.99 333	2	59
2	9.24 110	71	9.24 779	74	0.75 221	9.99 331	3	58
3	9.24 181	72	9.24 853	73	0.75 147	9.99 328	2	57
4	9.24 253	71	9.24 926	74	0.75 074	9.99 326	2	56
5	9.24 324	71	9.25 000	73	0.75 000	9.99 324	2	55
6	9.24 395	71	9.25 073	73	0.74 927	9.99 322	3	54
7	9.24 466	70	9.25 146	73	0.74 854	9.99 319	2	53
8	9.24 536	71	9.25 219	73	0.74 781	9.99 317	2	52
9	9.24 607	70	9.25 292	73	0.74 708	9.99 315	2	51
10	9.24 677	71	9.25 365	72	0.74 635	9.99 313	3	50
11	9.24 748	70	9.25 437	73	0.74 563	9.99 310	2	49
12	9.24 818	70	9.25 510	72	0.74 490	9.99 308	2	48
13	9.24 888	70	9.25 582	73	0.74 418	9.99 306	2	47
14	9.24 958	70	9.25 655	72	0.74 345	9.99 304	3	46
15	9.25 028	70	9.25 727	72	0.74 273	9.99 301	2	45
16	9.25 098	70	9.25 799	72	0.74 201	9.99 299	2	44
17	9.25 168	69	9.25 871	72	0.74 129	9.99 297	3	43
18	9.25 237	70	9.25 943	72	0.74 057	9.99 294	2	42
19	9.25 307	69	9.26 015	71	0.73 985	9.99 292	2	41
20	9.25 376	69	9.26 086	72	0.73 914	9.99 290	2	40
21	9.25 445	69	9.26 158	71	0.73 842	9.99 288	3	39
22	9.25 514	69	9.26 229	72	0.73 771	9.99 285	2	38
23	9.25 583	69	9.26 301	71	0.73 699	9.99 283	2	37
24	9.25 652	69	9.26 372	71	0.73 628	9.99 281	3	36
25	9.25 721	69	9.26 443	71	0.73 557	9.99 278	2	35
26	9.25 790	68	9.26 514	71	0.73 486	9.99 276	2	34
27	9.25 858	69	9.26 585	70	0.73 415	9.99 274	3	33
28	9.25 927	68	9.26 655	71	0.73 345	9.99 271	2	32
29	9.25 995	68	9.26 726	71	0.73 274	9.99 269	2	31
30	9.26 063	68	9.26 797	70	0.73 203	9.99 267	3	30
31	9.26 131	68	9.26 867	70	0.73 133	9.99 264	2	29
32	9.26 199	68	9.26 937	71	0.73 063	9.99 262	2	28
33	9.26 267	68	9.27 008	70	0.72 992	9.99 260	3	27
34	9.26 335	68	9.27 078	70	0.72 922	9.99 257	2	26
35	9.26 403	67	9.27 148	70	0.72 852	9.99 255	2	25
36	9.26 470	68	9.27 218	70	0.72 782	9.99 252	2	24
37	9.26 538	67	9.27 288	69	0.72 712	9.99 250	2	23
38	9.26 605	67	9.27 357	70	0.72 643	9.99 248	3	22
39	9.26 672	67	9.27 427	69	0.72 573	9.99 245	2	21
40	9.26 739	67	9.27 496	70	0.72 504	9.99 243	2	20
41	9.26 806	67	9.27 566	69	0.72 434	9.99 241	3	19
42	9.26 873	67	9.27 635	69	0.72 365	9.99 238	2	18
43	9.26 940	67	9.27 704	69	0.72 296	9.99 236	3	17
44	9.27 007	66	9.27 773	69	0.72 227	9.99 233	2	16
45	9.27 073	67	9.27 842	69	0.72 158	9.99 231	2	15
46	9.27 140	66	9.27 911	69	0.72 089	9.99 229	3	14
47	9.27 206	67	9.27 980	69	0.72 020	9.99 226	2	13
48	9.27 273	66	9.28 049	68	0.71 951	9.99 224	3	12
49	9.27 339	66	9.28 117	69	0.71 883	9.99 221	2	11
50	9.27 405	66	9.28 186	68	0.71 814	9.99 219	2	10
51	9.27 471	66	9.28 254	69	0.71 746	9.99 217	3	9
52	9.27 537	65	9.28 323	68	0.71 677	9.99 214	2	8
53	9.27 602	66	9.28 391	68	0.71 609	9.99 212	3	7
54	9.27 668	66	9.28 459	68	0.71 541	9.99 209	2	6
55	9.27 734	65	9.28 527	68	0.71 473	9.99 207	3	5
56	9.27 799	65	9.28 595	67	0.71 405	9.99 204	2	4
57	9.27 864	66	9.28 662	68	0.71 338	9.99 202	2	3
58	9.27 930	65	9.28 730	68	0.71 270	9.99 200	3	2
59	9.27 995	65	9.28 798	67	0.71 202	9.99 197	2	1
60	9.28 060		9.28 865		0.71 135	9.99 195		0
′	L. Cos.	d.	L. Cot.	c.d.	L. Tan.	L. Sin.	d.	′

P. P.

″	74	73	72
1	1.2	1.2	1.2
2	2.5	2.4	2.4
3	3.7	3.6	3.6
4	4.9	4.9	4.8
5	6.2	6.1	6.0
6	7.4	7.3	7.2
7	8.6	8.5	8.4
8	9.9	9.7	9.6
9	11.1	11.0	10.8
10	12.3	12.2	12.0
20	24.7	24.3	24.0
30	37.0	36.5	36.0
40	49.3	48.7	48.0
50	61.7	60.8	60.0

″	71	70	69
1	1.2	1.2	1.2
2	2.4	2.3	2.3
3	3.6	3.5	3.4
4	4.7	4.7	4.6
5	5.9	5.8	5.8
6	7.1	7.0	6.9
7	8.3	8.2	8.0
8	9.5	9.3	9.2
9	10.6	10.5	10.4
10	11.8	11.7	11.5
20	23.7	23.3	23.0
30	35.5	35.0	34.5
40	47.3	46.7	46.0
50	59.2	58.3	57.5

″	68	67	66
1	1.1	1.1	1.1
2	2.3	2.2	2.2
3	3.4	3.4	3.3
4	4.5	4.5	4.4
5	5.7	5.6	5.5
6	6.8	6.7	6.6
7	7.9	7.8	7.7
8	9.1	8.9	8.8
9	10.2	10.0	9.9
10	11.3	11.2	11.0
20	22.7	22.3	22.0
30	34.0	33.5	33.0
40	45.3	44.7	44.0
50	56.7	55.8	55.0

	3	3	3
	74	73	72
0	12.3	12.2	12.0
1	37.0	36.5	36.0
2	61.7	60.8	60.0
3			

	3	3	3	3
	71	70	69	68
0	11.8	11.7	11.5	11.3
1	35.5	35.0	34.5	34.0
2	59.2	58.3	57.5	56.7
3				

P. P.

COMMON LOGARITHMS OF THE TRIGONOMETRIC
FUNCTIONS (Continued)

11° (191°)   (348°) **168°**

′	L. Sin.	d.	L. Tan.	c.d.	L. Cot.	L. Cos.	d.	′	P. P.		
0	9.28 060	65	9.28 865	68	0.71 135	9.99 195	3	60			
1	9.28 125	65	9.28 933	67	0.71 067	9.99 192	2	59	″	**65** **64** **63**	
2	9.28 190	64	9.29 000	67	0.71 000	9.99 190	3	58	1	1.1 1.1 1.0	
3	9.28 254	65	9.29 067	67	0.70 933	9.99 187	2	57	2	2.2 2.1 2.1	
4	9.28 319	65	9.29 134	67	0.70 866	9.99 185	3	56	3	3.2 3.2 3.2	
									4	4.3 4.3 4.2	
5	9.28 384	64	9.29 201	67	0.70 799	9.99 182	2	55			
6	9.28 448	64	9.29 268	67	0.70 732	9.99 180	3	54	5	5.4 5.3 5.2	
7	9.28 512	65	9.29 335	67	0.70 665	9.99 177	2	53	6	6.5 6.4 6.3	
8	9.28 577	64	9.29 402	66	0.70 598	9.99 175	3	52	7	7.6 7.5 7.4	
9	9.28 641	64	9.29 468	67	0.70 532	9.99 172	2	51	8	8.7 8.5 8.4	
									9	9.8 9.6 9.4	
10	9.28 705	64	9.29 535	66	0.70 465	9.99 170	3	50			
11	9.28 769	64	9.29 601	67	0.70 399	9.99 167	2	49	10	10.8 10.7 10.5	
12	9.28 833	63	9.29 668	66	0.70 332	9.99 165	3	48	20	21.7 21.3 21.0	
13	9.28 896	64	9.29 734	66	0.70 266	9.99 162	2	47	30	32.5 32.0 31.5	
14	9.28 960	64	9.29 800	66	0.70 200	9.99 160	3	46	40	43.3 42.7 42.0	
									50	54.2 53.3 52.5	
15	9.29 024	63	9.29 866	66	0.70 134	9.99 157	2	45			
16	9.29 087	63	9.29 932	66	0.70 068	9.99 155	3	44	″	**62** **61** **60**	
17	9.29 150	64	9.29 998	66	0.70 002	9.99 152	2	43	1	1.0 1.0 1.0	
18	9.29 214	63	9.30 064	66	0.69 936	9.99 150	3	42	2	2.1 2.0 2.0	
19	9.29 277	63	9.30 130	65	0.69 870	9.99 147	2	41	3	3.1 3.0 3.0	
									4	4.1 4.1 4.0	
20	9.29 340	63	9.30 195	66	0.69 805	9.99 145	3	40			
21	9.29 403	63	9.30 261	65	0.69 739	9.99 142	2	39	5	5.2 5.1 5.0	
22	9.29 466	63	9.30 326	65	0.69 674	9.99 140	3	38	6	6.2 6.1 6.0	
23	9.29 529	62	9.30 391	66	0.69 609	9.99 137	3	37	7	7.2 7.1 7.0	
24	9.29 591	63	9.30 457	65	0.69 543	9.99 135	3	36	8	8.3 8.1 8.0	
									9	9.3 9.2 9.0	
25	9.29 654	62	9.30 522	65	0.69 478	9.99 132	2	35			
26	9.29 716	63	9.30 587	65	0.69 413	9.99 130	3	34	10	10.3 10.2 10.0	
27	9.29 779	62	9.30 652	65	0.69 348	9.99 127	3	33	20	20.7 20.3 20.0	
28	9.29 841	62	9.30 717	65	0.69 283	9.99 124	2	32	30	31.0 30.5 30.0	
29	9.29 903	63	9.30 782	64	0.69 218	9.99 122	3	31	40	41.3 40.7 40.0	
									50	51.7 50.8 50.0	
30	9.29 966	62	9.30 846	65	0.69 154	9.99 119	2	30			
31	9.30 028	62	9.30 911	64	0.69 089	9.99 117	3	29	″	**59** **3** **2**	
32	9.30 090	61	9.30 975	65	0.69 025	9.99 114	2	28	1	1.0 0.0 0.0	
33	9.30 151	62	9.31 040	64	0.68 960	9.99 112	3	27	2	2.0 0.1 0.1	
34	9.30 213	62	9.31 104	64	0.68 896	9.99 109	3	26	3	3.0 0.2 0.1	
									4	3.9 0.2 0.1	
35	9.30 275	61	9.31 168	65	0.68 832	9.99 106	2	25			
36	9.30 336	62	9.31 233	64	0.68 767	9.99 104	3	24	5	4.9 0.2 0.2	
37	9.30 398	61	9.31 297	64	0.68 703	9.99 101	2	23	6	5.9 0.3 0.2	
38	9.30 459	62	9.31 361	64	0.68 639	9.99 099	3	22	7	6.9 0.4 0.2	
39	9.30 521	61	9.31 425	64	0.68 575	9.99 096	3	21	8	7.9 0.4 0.3	
									9	8.8 0.4 0.3	
40	9.30 582	61	9.31 489	63	0.68 511	9.99 093	2	20			
41	9.30 643	61	9.31 552	64	0.68 448	9.99 091	3	19	10	9.8 0.5 0.3	
42	9.30 704	61	9.31 616	63	0.68 384	9.99 088	2	18	20	19.7 1.0 0.7	
43	9.30 765	61	9.31 679	64	0.68 321	9.99 086	3	17	30	29.5 1.5 1.0	
44	9.30 826	61	9.31 743	63	0.68 257	9.99 083	2	16	40	39.3 2.0 1.3	
									50	49.2 2.5 1.7	
45	9.30 887	60	9.31 806	64	0.68 194	9.99 080	3	15			
46	9.30 947	61	9.31 870	63	0.68 130	9.99 078	3	14			
47	9.31 008	60	9.31 933	63	0.68 067	9.99 075	2	13		**3** **3** **3**	
48	9.31 068	61	9.31 996	63	0.68 004	9.99 072	2	12		— — —	
49	9.31 129	60	9.32 059	63	0.67 941	9.99 070	2	11		**67** **66** **65**	
50	9.31 189	61	9.32 122	63	0.67 878	9.99 067	3	10	0	11.2 11.0 10.8	
51	9.31 250	60	9.32 185	63	0.67 815	9.99 064	2	9	1	33.5 33.0 32.5	
52	9.31 310	60	9.32 248	63	0.67 752	9.99 062	3	8	2	55.8 55.0 54.2	
53	9.31 370	60	9.32 311	62	0.67 689	9.99 059	3	7	3		
54	9.31 430	60	9.32 373	63	0.67 627	9.99 056	2	6		**3** **3** **3**	
55	9.31 490	59	9.32 436	62	0.67 564	9.99 054	3	5		— — —	
56	9.31 549	60	9.32 498	63	0.67 502	9.99 051	3	4		**64** **63** **62**	
57	9.31 609	60	9.32 561	62	0.67 439	9.99 048	3	3			
58	9.31 669	59	9.32 623	62	0.67 377	9.99 046	2	2	0	10.7 10.5 10.3	
59	9.31 728	60	9.32 685	62	0.67 315	9.99 043	3	1	1	32.0 31.5 31.0	
									2	53.3 52.5 51.7	
60	9.31 788		9.32 747		0.67 253	9.99 040		0	3		

′	L. Cos.	d.	L. Cot.	c.d.	L. Tan.	L. Sin.	d.	′	P. P.		

COMMON LOGARITHMS OF THE TRIGONOMETRIC
FUNCTIONS (Continued)

12° (192°)   (347°) **167°**

′	L. Sin.	d.	L. Tan.	c.d.	L. Cot.	L. Cos.	d.	′
0	9.31 788	59	9.32 747	63	0.67 253	9.99 040	2	**60**
1	9.31 847	60	9.32 810	62	0.67 190	9.99 038	3	59
2	9.31 907	59	9.32 872	61	0.67 128	9.99 035	3	58
3	9.31 966	59	9.32 933	62	0.67 067	9.99 032	2	57
4	9.32 025	59	9.32 995	62	0.67 005	9.99 030	3	56
5	9.32 084	59	9.33 057	62	0.66 943	9.99 027	3	55
6	9.32 143	59	9.33 119	61	0.66 881	9.99 024	2	54
7	9.32 202	59	9.33 180	62	0.66 820	9.99 022	3	53
8	9.32 261	58	9.33 242	61	0.66 758	9.99 019	3	52
9	9.32 319	59	9.33 303	62	0.66 697	9.99 016	3	51
10	9.32 378	59	9.33 365	61	0.66 635	9.99 013	2	**50**
11	9.32 437	58	9.33 426	61	0.66 574	9.99 011	3	49
12	9.32 495	58	9.33 487	61	0.66 513	9.99 008	3	48
13	9.32 553	59	9.33 548	61	0.66 452	9.99 005	3	47
14	9.32 612	58	9.33 609	61	0.66 391	9.99 002	2	46
15	9.32 670	58	9.33 670	61	0.66 330	9.99 000	3	45
16	9.32 728	58	9.33 731	61	0.66 269	9.98 997	3	44
17	9.32 786	58	9.33 792	61	0.66 208	9.98 994	3	43
18	9.32 844	58	9.33 853	60	0.66 147	9.98 991	2	42
19	9.32 902	58	9.33 913	61	0.66 087	9.98 989	3	41
20	9.32 960	58	9.33 974	60	0.66 026	9.98 986	3	**40**
21	9.33 018	57	9.34 034	61	0.65 966	9.98 983	3	39
22	9.33 075	58	9.34 095	60	0.65 905	9.98 980	2	38
23	9.33 133	57	9.34 155	60	0.65 845	9.98 978	3	37
24	9.33 190	58	9.34 215	61	0.65 785	9.98 975	3	36
25	9.33 248	57	9.34 276	60	0.65 724	9.98 972	3	35
26	9.33 305	57	9.34 336	60	0.65 664	9.98 969	2	34
27	9.33 362	58	9.34 396	60	0.65 604	9.98 967	3	33
28	9.33 420	57	9.34 456	60	0.65 544	9.98 964	3	32
29	9.33 477	57	9.34 516	60	0.65 484	9.98 961	3	31
30	9.33 534	57	9.34 576	59	0.65 424	9.98 958	3	**30**
31	9.33 591	56	9.34 635	60	0.65 365	9.98 955	2	29
32	9.33 647	57	9.34 695	60	0.65 305	9.98 953	3	28
33	9.33 704	57	9.34 755	59	0.65 245	9.98 950	3	27
34	9.33 761	57	9.34 814	60	0.65 186	9.98 947	3	26
35	9.33 818	56	9.34 874	59	0.65 126	9.98 944	3	25
36	9.33 874	57	9.34 933	59	0.65 067	9.98 941	3	24
37	9.33 931	56	9.34 992	59	0.65 008	9.98 938	3	23
38	9.33 987	56	9 35 051	60	0.64 949	9.98 936	3	22
39	9.34 043	57	9.35 111	59	0.64 889	9.98 933	3	21
40	9.34 100	56	9.35 170	59	0.64 830	9.98 930	3	**20**
41	9.34 156	56	9.35 229	59	0.64 771	9.98 927	3	19
42	9.34 212	56	9.35 288	59	0.64 712	9.98 924	3	18
43	9.34 268	56	9.35 347	59	0.64 653	9.98 921	2	17
44	9.34 324	56	9.35 405	59	0.64 595	9.98 919	3	16
45	9.34 380	56	9 35 464	59	0.64 536	9.98 916	3	15
46	9.34 436	55	9 35 523	58	0.64 477	9.98 913	3	14
47	9.34 491	56	9 35 581	59	0.64 419	9.98 910	3	13
48	9.34 547	55	9 35 640	58	0.64 360	9.98 907	3	12
49	9.34 602	56	9 35 698	59	0.64 302	9.98 904	3	11
50	9.34 658	55	9 35 757	58	0.64 243	9.98 901	3	**10**
51	9.34 713	56	9 35 815	58	0 64 185	9.98 898	2	9
52	9.34 769	55	9 35 873	58	0 64 127	9.98 896	3	8
53	9.34 824	55	9 35 931	58	0.64 069	9.98 893	3	7
54	9.34 879	55	9.35 989	58	0.64 011	9.98 890	3	6
55	9.34 934	55	9 36 047	58	0.63 953	9.98 887	3	5
56	9.34 989	55	9 36 105	58	0.63 895	9.98 884	3	4
57	9.35 044	55	9 36 163	58	0.63 837	9.98 881	3	3
58	9.35 099	55	9 36 221	58	0.63 779	9.98 878	3	2
59	9.35 154	55	9.36 279	57	0.63 721	9.98 875	3	1
60	9.35 209		9.36 336		0.63 664	9.98 872		**0**
′	L. Cos.	d.	L. Cot.	c.d.	L. Tan.	L. Sin.	d.	′

P. P.

″	63	62	61
1	1.0	1.0	1.0
2	2.1	2.1	2.0
3	3.2	3.1	3.0
4	4.2	4.1	4.1
5	5.2	5.2	5.1
6	6.3	6.2	6.1
7	7.4	7.2	7.1
8	8.4	8.3	8.1
9	9.4	9.3	9.2
10	10.5	10.3	10.2
20	21.0	20.7	20.3
30	31.5	31.0	30.5
40	42.0	41.3	40.7
50	52.5	51.7	50.8

″	60	59	58
1	1.0	1.0	1.0
2	2.0	2.0	1.9
3	3.0	3.0	2.9
4	4.0	3.9	3.8
5	5.0	4.9	4.8
6	6.0	5.9	5.8
7	7.0	6.9	6.8
8	8.0	7.9	7.7
9	9.0	8.8	8.7
10	10.0	9.8	9.7
20	20.0	19.7	19.3
30	30.0	29.5	29.0
40	40.0	39.3	38.7
50	50.0	49.2	48.3

″	57	56	55
1	1.0	0.9	0.9
2	1.9	1.9	1.8
3	2.8	2.8	2.8
4	3.8	3.7	3.7
5	4.8	4.7	4.6
6	5.7	5.6	5.5
7	6.6	6.5	6.4
8	7.6	7.5	7.3
9	8.6	8.4	8.2
10	9.5	9.3	9.2
20	19.0	18.7	18.3
30	28.5	28.0	27.5
40	38.0	37.3	36.7
50	47.5	46.7	45.8

	3	3	3
	62	61	60
0	10.3	10.2	10.0
1	31.0	30.5	30.0
2	51.7	50.8	50.0
3			

	3	3	3
	59	58	57
0	9.8	9.7	9.5
1	29.5	29.0	28.5
2	49.2	48.3	47.5
3			

102° (282°)   (257°) **77°**

COMMON LOGARITHMS OF THE TRIGONOMETRIC FUNCTIONS (Continued)

13° (193°)   **(346°) 166°**

'	L. Sin.	d.	L. Tan.	c.d.	L. Cot.	L. Cos.	d.	'
0	9.35 209	34	9.36 336	58	0.63 664	9.98 872	3	60
1	9.35 263	55	9.36 394	58	0.63 606	9.98 869	2	59
2	9.35 318	55	9.36 452	57	0.63 548	9.98 867	3	58
3	9.35 373	54	9.36 509	57	0.63 491	9.98 864	3	57
4	9.35 427	54	9.36 566	58	0.63 434	9.98 861	3	56
5	9.35 481	55	9.36 624	57	0.63 376	9.98 858	3	55
6	9.35 536	54	9.36 681	57	0.63 319	9.98 855	3	54
7	9.35 590	54	9.36 738	57	0.63 262	9.98 852	3	53
8	9.35 644	54	9.36 795	57	0.63 205	9.98 849	3	52
9	9.35 698	54	9.36 852	57	0.63 148	9.98 846	3	51
10	9.35 752	54	9.36 909	57	0.63 091	9.98 843	3	50
11	9.35 806	54	9.36 966	57	0.63 034	9.98 840	3	49
12	9.35 860	54	9.37 023	57	0.62 977	9.98 837	3	48
13	9.35 914	54	9.37 080	57	0.62 920	9.98 834	3	47
14	9.35 968	54	9.37 137	56	0.62 863	9.98 831	3	46
15	9.36 022	53	9.37 193	57	0.62 807	9.98 828	3	45
16	9.36 075	54	9.37 250	57	0.62 750	9.98 825	3	44
17	9.36 129	53	9.37 306	57	0.62 694	9.98 822	3	43
18	9.36 182	54	9.37 363	56	0.62 637	9.98 819	3	42
19	9.36 236	53	9.37 419	57	0.62 581	9.98 816	3	41
20	9.36 289	53	9.37 476	56	0.62 524	9.98 813	3	40
21	9.36 342	53	9.37 532	56	0.62 468	9.98 810	3	39
22	9.36 395	53	9.37 588	56	0.62 412	9.98 807	3	38
23	9.36 449	53	9.37 644	56	0.62 356	9.98 804	3	37
24	9.36 502	53	9.37 700	56	0.62 300	9.98 801	3	36
25	9.36 555	53	9.37 756	56	0.62 244	9.98 798	3	35
26	9.36 608	52	9.37 812	56	0.62 188	9.98 795	3	34
27	9.36 660	53	9.37 868	56	0.62 132	9.98 792	3	33
28	9.36 713	53	9.37 924	56	0.62 076	9.98 789	3	32
29	9.36 766	53	9.37 980	55	0.62 020	9.98 786	3	31
30	9.36 819	52	9.38 035	56	0.61 965	9.98 783	3	30
31	9.36 871	53	9.38 091	56	0.61 909	9.98 780	3	29
32	9.36 924	52	9.38 147	55	0.61 853	9.98 777	3	28
33	9.36 976	52	9.38 202	55	0.61 798	9.98 774	3	27
34	9.37 028	53	9.38 257	56	0.61 743	9.98 771	3	26
35	9.37 081	52	9.38 313	55	0.61 687	9.98 768	3	25
36	9.37 133	52	9.38 368	55	0.61 632	9.98 765	3	24
37	9.37 185	52	9.38 423	56	0.61 577	9.98 762	3	23
38	9.37 237	52	9.38 479	55	0.61 521	9.98 759	3	22
39	9.37 289	52	9.38 534	55	0.61 466	9.98 756	3	21
40	9.37 341	52	9.38 589	55	0.61 411	9.98 753	4	20
41	9.37 393	52	9.38 644	55	0.61 356	9.98 750	3	19
42	9.37 445	52	9.38 699	55	0.61 301	9.98 746	3	18
43	9.37 497	52	9.38 754	54	0.61 246	9.98 743	3	17
44	9.37 549	51	9.38 808	55	0.61 192	9.98 740	3	16
45	9.37 600	52	9.38 863	55	0.61 137	9.98 737	3	15
46	9.37 652	51	9.38 918	54	0.61 082	9.98 734	3	14
47	9.37 703	52	9.38 972	55	0.61 028	9.98 731	3	13
48	9.37 755	51	9.39 027	54	0.60 973	9.98 728	3	12
49	9.37 806	52	9.39 082	54	0.60 918	9.98 725	3	11
50	9.37 858	51	9.39 136	54	0.60 864	9.98 722	3	10
51	9.37 909	51	9.39 190	55	0.60 810	9.98 719	4	9
52	9.37 960	51	9.39 245	54	0.60 755	9.98 715	3	8
53	9.38 011	51	9.39 299	54	0.60 701	9.98 712	3	7
54	9.38 062	51	9.39 353	54	0.60 647	9.98 709	3	6
55	9.38 113	51	9.39 407	54	0.60 593	9.98 706	3	5
56	9.38 164	51	9.39 461	54	0.60 539	9.98 703	3	4
57	9.38 215	51	9.39 515	54	0.60 485	9.98 700	3	3
58	9.38 266	51	9.39 569	54	0.60 431	9.98 697	3	2
59	9.38 317	51	9.39 623	54	0.60 377	9.98 694	4	1
60	9.38 368		9.39 677		0.60 323	9.98 690		0

| ' | L. Cos. | d. | L. Cot. | c.d. | L. Tan. | L. Sin. | d. | ' |

P. P.

	57	56	55
1	1.0	0.9	0.9
2	1.9	1.9	1.8
3	2.8	2.8	2.8
4	3.8	3.7	3.7
5	4.8	4.7	4.6
6	5.7	5.6	5.5
7	6.6	6.5	6.4
8	7.6	7.5	7.3
9	8.6	8.4	8.2
10	9.5	9.3	9.2
20	19.0	18.7	18.3
30	28.5	28.0	27.5
40	38.0	37.3	36.7
50	47.5	46.7	45.8

	54	53	52
1	0.0	0.9	0.9
2	1.8	1.8	1.7
3	2.7	2.6	2.6
4	3.6	3.5	3.5
5	4.5	4.4	4.3
6	5.4	5.3	5.2
7	6.3	6.2	6.1
8	7.2	7.1	6.9
9	8.1	8.0	7.8
10	9.0	8.8	8.7
20	18.0	17.7	17.3
30	27.0	26.5	26.0
40	36.0	35.3	34.7
50	45.0	44.2	43.3

	51	4	3	2
1	0.8	0.1	0.0	0.0
2	1.7	0.1	0.1	0.1
3	2.6	0.2	0.2	0.1
4	3.4	0.3	0.2	0.1
5	4.2	0.3	0.2	0.2
6	5.1	0.4	0.3	0.2
7	6.0	0.5	0.4	0.2
8	6.8	0.5	0.4	0.3
9	7.6	0.6	0.4	0.3
10	8.5	0.7	0.5	0.3
20	17.0	1.3	1.0	0.7
30	25.5	2.0	1.5	1.0
40	34.0	2.7	2.0	1.3
50	42.5	3.3	2.5	1.7

	4 / 55	4 / 54	3 / 58	3 / 57
0	6.9	6.8	9.7	9.5
1	20.6	20.2	29.0	28.5
2	34.4	33.8	48.3	47.5
3	48.1	47.2		

	3 / 56	3 / 55	3 / 54
0	9.3	9.2	9.3
1	28.0	27.5	27.0
2	46.7	45.8	45.0

page 284

Tables for Use in Trigonometry

COMMON LOGARITHMS OF THE TRIGONOMETRIC FUNCTIONS (Continued)

14° (194°)   **(345°) 165°**

'	L. Sin.	d.	L. Tan.	c.d.	L. Cot.	L. Cos.	d.	'
0	9.38 368	50	9.39 677	54	0.60 323	9.98 690	3	60
1	9.38 418	51	9.39 731	54	0.60 269	9.98 687	3	59
2	9.38 469	50	9.39 785	53	0.60 215	9.98 684	3	58
3	9.38 519	51	9.39 838	54	0.60 162	9.98 681	3	57
4	9.38 570	50	9.39 892	53	0.60 108	9.98 678	3	56
5	9.38 620	50	9.39 945	54	0.60 055	9.98 675	4	55
6	9.38 670	51	9.39 999	53	0.60 001	9.98 671	3	54
7	9.38 721	50	9.40 052	54	0.59 948	9.98 668	3	53
8	9.38 771	50	9.40 106	53	0.59 894	9.98 665	3	52
9	9.38 821	50	9.40 159	53	0.59 841	9.98 662	3	51
10	9.38 871	50	9.40 212	54	0.59 788	9.98 659	3	50
11	9.38 921	50	9.40 266	53	0.59 734	9.98 656	4	49
12	9.38 971	50	9.40 319	53	0.59 681	9.98 652	3	48
13	9.39 021	50	9.40 372	53	0.59 628	9.98 649	3	47
14	9.39 071	50	9.40 425	53	0.59 575	9.98 646	3	46
15	9.39 121	49	9.40 478	53	0.59 522	9.98 643	3	45
16	9.39 170	50	9.40 531	53	0.59 469	9.98 640	4	44
17	9.39 220	50	9.40 584	52	0.59 416	9.98 636	3	43
18	9.39 270	49	9.40 636	53	0.59 364	9.98 633	3	42
19	9.39 319	50	9.40 689	53	0.59 311	9.98 630	3	41
20	9.39 369	49	9.40 742	53	0.59 258	9.98 627	4	40
21	9.39 418	49	9.40 795	52	0.59 205	9.98 623	3	39
22	9.39 467	50	9.40 847	53	0.59 153	9.98 620	3	38
23	9.39 517	49	9.40 900	52	0.59 100	9.98 617	3	37
24	9.39 566	49	9.40 952	53	0.59 048	9.98 614	4	36
25	9.39 615	49	9.41 005	52	0.58 995	9.98 610	3	35
26	9.39 664	49	9.41 057	52	0.58 943	9.98 607	3	34
27	9.39 713	49	9.41 109	52	0.58 891	9.98 604	3	33
28	9.39 762	49	9.41 161	53	0.58 839	9.98 601	3	32
29	9.39 811	49	9.41 214	52	0.58 786	9.98 597	3	31
30	9.39 860	49	9.41 266	52	0.58 734	9.98 594	3	30
31	9.39 909	49	9.41 318	52	0.58 682	9.98 591	3	29
32	9.39 958	48	9.41 370	52	0.58 630	9.98 588	4	28
33	9.40 006	49	9.41 422	52	0.58 578	9.98 584	3	27
34	9.40 055	48	9.41 474	52	0.58 526	9.98 581	3	26
35	9.40 103	49	9.41 526	52	0.58 474	9.98 578	4	25
36	9.40 152	48	9.41 578	51	0.58 422	9.98 574	3	24
37	9.40 200	49	9.41 629	52	0.58 371	9.98 571	3	23
38	9.40 249	48	9.41 681	52	0.58 319	9.98 568	3	22
39	9.40 297	49	9.41 733	51	0.58 267	9.98 565	4	21
40	9.40 346	48	9.41 784	52	0.58 216	9.98 561	3	20
41	9.40 394	48	9.41 836	51	0.58 164	9.98 558	3	19
42	9.40 442	48	9.41 887	52	0.58 113	9.98 555	4	18
43	9.40 490	48	9.41 939	51	0.58 061	9.98 551	3	17
44	9.40 538	48	9.41 990	51	0.58 010	9.98 548	3	16
45	9.40 586	48	9.42 041	52	0.57 959	9.98 545	4	15
46	9.40 634	48	9.42 093	51	0.57 907	9.98 541	3	14
47	9.40 682	48	9.42 144	51	0.57 856	9.98 538	3	13
48	9.40 730	48	9.42 195	51	0.57 805	9.98 535	4	12
49	9.40 778	47	9.42 246	51	0.57 754	9.98 531	3	11
50	9.40 825	48	9.42 297	51	0.57 703	9.98 528	3	10
51	9.40 873	48	9.42 348	51	0.57 652	9.98 525	4	9
52	9.40 921	47	9.42 399	51	0.57 601	9.98 521	3	8
53	9.40 968	48	9.42 450	51	0.57 550	9.98 518	3	7
54	9.41 016	47	9.42 501	51	0.57 499	9.98 515	4	6
55	9.41 063	48	9.42 552	51	0.57 448	9.98 511	3	5
56	9.41 111	47	9.42 603	50	0.57 397	9.98 508	3	4
57	9.41 158	47	9.42 653	51	0.57 347	9.98 505	4	3
58	9.41 205	47	9.42 704	51	0.57 296	9.98 501	3	2
59	9.41 252	48	9.42 755	50	0.57 245	9.98 498	4	1
60	9.41 300		9.42 805		0.57 195	9.98 494		0

| | L. Cos. | d. | L. Cot. | c.d. | L. Tan. | L. Sin. | d. | ' |

104° (284°)   **(255°) 75°**

P. P.

"	54	53	52
1	0.9	0.9	0.9
2	1.8	1.8	1.7
3	2.7	2.6	2.6
4	3.6	3.5	3.5
5	4.5	4.4	4.3
6	5.4	5.3	5.2
7	6.3	6.2	6.1
8	7.2	7.1	6.9
9	8.1	8.0	7.8
10	9.0	8.8	8.7
20	18.0	17.7	17.3
30	27.0	26.5	26.0
40	36.0	35.3	34.7
50	45.0	44.2	43.3

"	51	50	49
1	0.8	0.8	0.8
2	1.7	1.7	1.6
3	2.6	2.5	2.4
4	3.4	3.3	3.3
5	4.2	4.2	4.1
6	5.1	5.0	4.9
7	6.0	5.8	5.7
8	6.8	6.7	6.5
9	7.6	7.5	7.4
10	8.5	8.3	8.2
20	17.0	16.7	16.3
30	25.5	25.0	24.5
40	34.0	33.3	32.7
50	42.5	41.7	40.8

"	48	47	4	3
1	0.8	0.8	0.1	0.0
2	1.6	1.6	0.1	0.1
3	2.4	2.4	0.2	0.2
4	3.2	3.1	0.3	0.2
5	4.0	3.9	0.3	0.2
6	4.8	4.7	0.4	0.3
7	5.6	5.5	0.5	0.4
8	6.4	6.3	0.5	0.4
9	7.2	7.6	0.6	0.4
10	8.0	7.8	0.7	0.5
20	16.0	15.7	1.3	1.0
30	24.0	23.5	2.0	1.5
40	32.0	31.3	2.7	2.0
50	40.0	39.2	3.3	2.5

	4	4	4	4
	54	53	52	51
0	6.8	6.6	6.5	6.4
1	20.2	19.9	19.5	19.1
2	33.8	33.1	32.5	31.9
3	47.2	46.4	45.5	44.6
4				

	3	3	3	3
	54	53	52	51
0	9.0	8.8	8.7	8.5
1	27.0	26.5	26.0	25.5
2	45.0	44.2	43.3	42.5
3				

P. P.

COMMON LOGARITHMS OF THE TRIGONOMETRIC
FUNCTIONS (Continued)

15° (195°) (344°) **164°**

′	L. Sin.	d.	L. Tan.	c.d.	L.Cot.	L. Cos.	d.	′
0	9.41 300	47	9.42 805	51	0.57 195	9.98 494	3	60
1	9.41 347	47	9.42 856	50	0.57 144	9.98 491	3	59
2	9.41 394	47	9.42 906	51	0.57 094	9.98 488	3	58
3	9.41 441	47	9.42 957	50	0.57 043	9.98 484	3	57
4	9.41 488	47	9.43 007	50	0.56 993	9.98 481	4	56
5	9.41 535	47	9.43 057	51	0.56 943	9.98 477	3	55
6	9.41 582	46	9.43 108	50	0.56 892	9.98 474	3	54
7	9.41 628	47	9.43 158	50	0.56 842	9.98 471	4	53
8	9.41 675	47	9.43 208	50	0.56 792	9.98 467	3	52
9	9.41 722	46	9.43 258	50	0.56 742	9.98 464	4	51
10	9.41 768	47	9.43 308	50	0.56 692	9.98 460	3	50
11	9.41 815	46	9.43 358	50	0.56 642	9.98 457	4	49
12	9.41 861	47	9.43 408	50	0.56 592	9.98 453	3	48
13	9.41 908	46	9.43 458	50	0.56 542	9.98 450	3	47
14	9.41 954	47	9.43 508	50	0.56 492	9.98 447	4	46
15	9.42 001	46	9.43 558	49	0.56 442	9.98 443	3	45
16	9.42 047	46	9.43 607	50	0.56 393	9.98 440	4	44
17	9.42 093	47	9.43 657	50	0.56 343	9.98 436	4	43
18	9.42 140	46	9.43 707	49	0.56 293	9.98 433	4	42
19	9.42 186	46	9.43 756	50	0.56 244	9.98 429	3	41
20	9.42 232	46	9.43 806	49	0.56 194	9.98 426	4	40
21	9.42 278	46	9.43 855	50	0.56 145	9.98 422	4	39
22	9.42 324	46	9.43 905	49	0.56 095	9.98 419	4	38
23	9.42 370	46	9.43 954	50	0.56 046	9.98 415	3	37
24	9.42 416	45	9.44 004	49	0.55 996	9.98 412	3	36
25	9.42 461	46	9.44 053	49	0.55 947	9.98 409	4	35
26	9.42 507	46	9.44 102	49	0.55 898	9.98 405	3	34
27	9.42 553	46	9.44 151	50	0.55 849	9.98 402	4	33
28	9.42 599	45	9.44 201	49	0.55 799	9.98 398	3	32
29	9.42 644	46	9.44 250	49	0.55 750	9.98 395	4	31
30	9.42 690	45	9.44 299	49	0.55 701	9.98 391	3	30
31	9.42 735	46	9.44 348	49	0.55 652	9.98 388	4	29
32	9.42 781	45	9.44 397	49	0.55 603	9.98 384	3	28
33	9.42 826	46	9.44 446	49	0.55 554	9.98 381	4	27
34	9.42 872	45	9.44 495	49	0.55 505	9.98 377	4	26
35	9.42 917	45	9.44 544	48	0.55 456	9.98 373	3	25
36	9.42 962	46	9.44 592	49	0.55 408	9.98 370	4	24
37	9.43 008	45	9.44 641	49	0.55 359	9.98 366	3	23
38	9.43 053	45	9.44 690	48	0.55 310	9.98 363	4	22
39	9.43 098	45	9.44 738	49	0.55 262	9.98 359	3	21
40	9.43 143	45	9.44 787	49	0.55 213	9.98 356	4	20
41	9.43 188	45	9.44 836	48	0.55 164	9.98 352	4	19
42	9.43 233	45	9.44 884	49	0.55 116	9.98 349	4	18
43	9.43 278	45	9.44 933	48	0.55 067	9.98 345	4	17
44	9.43 323	44	9.44 981	48	0.55 019	9.98 342	4	16
45	9.43 367	45	9.45 029	49	0.54 971	9.98 338	4	15
46	9.43 412	45	9.45 078	48	0.54 922	9.98 334	3	14
47	9.43 457	45	9.45 126	48	0.54 874	9.98 331	4	13
48	9.43 502	45	9.45 174	48	0.54 826	9.98 327	3	12
49	9.43 546	45	9.45 222	49	0.54 778	9.98 324	4	11
50	9.43 591	44	9.45 271	48	0.54 729	9.98 320	3	10
51	9.43 635	45	9.45 319	48	0.54 681	9.98 317	4	9
52	9.43 680	44	9.45 367	48	0.54 633	9.98 313	4	8
53	9.43 724	45	9.45 415	48	0.54 585	9.98 309	3	7
54	9.43 769	44	9.45 463	48	0.54 537	9.98 306	4	6
55	9.43 813	44	9.45 511	48	0.54 489	9.98 302	3	5
56	9.43 857	44	9.45 559	47	0.54 441	9.98 299	4	4
57	9.43 901	45	9.45 606	48	0.54 394	9.98 295	4	3
58	9.43 946	44	9.45 654	48	0.54 346	9.98 291	3	2
59	9.43 990	44	9.45 702	48	0.54 298	9.98 288	4	1
60	9.44 034		9.45 750		0.54 250	9.98 284		0

′	L. Cos.	d.	L. Cot.	c.d.	L. Tan.	L. Sin.	d.	′

105° (285°) (254°) **74°**

P. P.

	51	50	49
1	0.8	0.8	0.8
2	1.7	1.7	1.6
3	2.6	2.5	2.4
4	3.4	3.3	3.3
5	4.2	4.2	4.1
6	5.1	5.0	4.9
7	6.0	5.8	5.7
8	6.8	6.7	6.5
9	7.6	7.5	7.4
10	8.5	8.3	8.2
20	17.0	16.7	16.3
30	25.5	25.0	24.5
40	34.0	33.3	32.7
50	42.5	41.7	40.8

	48	47	46
1	0.8	0.8	0.8
2	1.6	1.6	1.5
3	2.4	2.4	2.3
4	3.2	3.1	3.1
5	4.0	3.9	3.8
6	4.3	4.7	4.6
7	5.6	5.5	5.4
8	6.4	6.3	6.1
9	7.2	7.0	6.9
10	8.0	7.8	7.7
20	16.0	15.7	15.3
30	24.0	23.5	23.0
40	32.0	31.3	30.7
50	40.0	39.2	38.3

	45	44	4	3
1	0.8	0.7	0.1	0.0
2	1.5	1.5	0.1	0.1
3	2.2	2.2	0.2	0.2
4	3.0	2.9	0.3	0.2
5	3.8	3.7	0.3	0.2
6	4.5	4.4	0.4	0.3
7	5.2	5.1	0.5	0.4
8	6.0	5.9	0.5	0.4
9	6.8	6.6	0.6	0.4
10	7.5	7.3	0.7	0.5
20	15.0	14.7	1.3	1.0
30	22.5	22.0	2.0	1.5
40	30.0	29.3	2.7	2.0
50	37.5	36.7	3.3	2.5

	4	4	4	4
	50	49	48	47
0	6.2	6.1	6.0	5.9
1	18.8	18.4	18.0	17.6
2	31.2	30.6	30.0	29.4
3	43.8	42.9	42.0	41.1
4				

	3	3	3	3
	51	50	49	48
0	8.5	8.3	8.2	8.0
1	25.5	25.0	24.5	24.0
2	42.5	41.7	40.8	40.0
3				

COMMON LOGARITHMS OF THE TRIGONOMETRIC
FUNCTIONS (Continued)

16° (196°)   **(343°) 163°**

'	L. Sin.	d.	L. Tan.	c.d.	L. Cot.	L. Cos.	d.	'	P. P.
0	9.44 034	44	9.45 750	47	0.54 250	9.98 284	3	60	
1	9.44 078	44	9.45 797	48	0.54 203	9.98 281	4	59	**" 48 47 46**
2	9.44 122	44	9.45 845	47	0.54 155	9.98 277	4	58	1 0.8 0.8 0.8
3	9.44 166	44	9.45 892	48	0.54 108	9.98 273	3	57	2 1.6 1.6 1.5
4	9.44 210	43	9.45 940	47	0.54 060	9.98 270	4	56	3 2.4 2.4 2.3
									4 3.2 3.1 3.1
5	9.44 253	44	9.45 987	48	0.54 013	9.98 266	4	55	
6	9.44 297	44	9.46 035	47	0.53 965	9.98 262	3	54	5 4.0 3.9 3.8
7	9.44 341	44	9.46 082	48	0.53 918	9.98 259	4	53	6 4.8 4.7 4.6
8	9.44 385	43	9.46 130	47	0.53 870	9.98 255	4	52	7 5.6 5.5 5.4
9	9.44 428	44	9.46 177	47	0.53 823	9.98 251	3	51	8 6.4 6.3 6.1
									9 7.2 7.0 6.9
10	9.44 472	44	9.46 224	47	0.53 776	9.98 248	4	50	
11	9.44 516	43	9.46 271	48	0.53 729	9.98 244	4	49	10 8.0 7.8 7.7
12	9.44 559	43	9.46 319	47	0.53 681	9.98 240	3	48	20 16.0 15.7 15.3
13	9.44 602	44	9.46 366	47	0.53 634	9.98 237	4	47	30 24.0 23.5 23.0
14	9.44 646	43	9.46 413	47	0.53 587	9.98 233	4	46	40 32.0 31.3 30.7
									50 40.0 39.2 38.3
15	9.44 689	44	9.46 460	47	0.53 540	9.98 229	3	45	
16	9.44 733	43	9.46 507	47	0.53 493	9.98 226	4	44	**" 45 44 43**
17	9.44 776	43	9.46 554	47	0.53 446	9.98 222	4	43	1 0.8 0.7 0.7
18	9.44 819	43	9.46 601	47	0.53 399	9.98 218	3	42	2 1.5 1.5 1.4
19	9.44 862	43	9.46 648	46	0.53 352	9.98 215	4	41	3 2.2 2.2 2.2
									4 3.0 2.9 2.9
20	9.44 905	43	9.46 694	47	0.53 306	9.98 211	4	40	
21	9.44 948	44	9.46 741	47	0.53 259	9.98 207	3	39	5 3.8 3.7 3.6
22	9.44 992	43	9.46 788	47	0.53 212	9.98 204	4	38	6 4.5 4.4 4.3
23	9.45 035	42	9.46 835	46	0.53 165	9.98 200	4	37	7 5.2 5.1 5.0
24	9.45 077	43	9.46 881	47	0.53 119	9.98 196	4	36	8 6.0 5.9 5.7
									9 6.8 6.6 6.4
25	9.45 120	43	9.46 928	47	0.53 072	9.98 192	3	35	
26	9.45 163	43	9.46 975	46	0.53 025	9.98 189	4	34	10 7.5 7.3 7.2
27	9.45 206	43	9.47 021	47	0.52 979	9.98 185	4	33	20 15.0 14.7 14.3
28	9.45 249	43	9.47 068	46	0.52 932	9.98 181	4	32	30 22.5 22.0 21.5
29	9.45 292	42	9.47 114	46	0.52 886	9.98 177	3	31	40 30.0 29.3 28.7
									50 37.5 36.7 35.8
30	9.45 334	43	9.47 160	47	0.52 840	9.98 174	4	30	
31	9.45 377	42	9.47 207	46	0.52 793	9.98 170	4	29	**" 42 41 4 3**
32	9.45 419	43	9.47 253	46	0.52 747	9.98 166	4	28	1 0.7 0.7 0.1 0.0
33	9.45 462	42	9.47 299	47	0.52 701	9.98 162	3	27	2 1.4 1.4 0.1 0.1
34	9.45 504	43	9.47 346	46	0.52 654	9.98 159	4	26	3 2.1 2.0 0.2 0.2
									4 2.8 2.7 0.3 0.2
35	9.45 547	42	9.47 392	46	0.52 608	9.98 155	4	25	
36	9.45 589	43	9.47 438	46	0.52 562	9.98 151	4	24	5 3.5 3.4 0.3 0.2
37	9.45 632	42	9.47 484	46	0.52 516	9.98 147	3	23	6 4.2 4.1 0.4 0.3
38	9.45 674	42	9.47 530	46	0.52 470	9.98 144	4	22	7 4.9 4.8 0.5 0.4
39	9.45 716	42	9.47 576	46	0.52 424	9.98 140	4	21	8 5.6 5.5 0.5 0.4
									9 6.3 6.2 0.6 0.4
40	9.45 758	43	9.47 622	46	0.52 378	9.98 136	4	20	
41	9.45 801	42	9.47 668	46	0.52 332	9.98 132	3	19	10 7.0 6.8 0.7 0.5
42	9.45 843	42	9.47 714	46	0.52 286	9.98 129	4	18	20 14.0 13.7 1.3 1.0
43	9.45 885	42	9.47 760	46	0.52 240	9.98 125	4	17	30 21.0 20.5 2.0 1.5
44	9.45 927	42	9.47 806	46	0.52 194	9.98 121	4	16	40 28.0 27.3 2.7 2.0
									50 35.0 34.2 3.3 2.5
45	9.45 969	42	9.47 852	45	0.52 148	9.98 117	4	15	
46	9.46 011	42	9.47 897	46	0.52 103	9.98 113	3	14	
47	9.46 053	42	9 47 943	46	0.52 057	9.98 110	4	13	**4 4 4 4**
48	9.46 095	41	9.47 989	46	0.52 011	9.98 106	4	12	**48 47 46 45**
49	9.46 136	42	9.48 035	45	0.51 965	9.98 102	4	11	
50	9.46 178	42	9.48 080	46	0.51 920	9.98 098	4	10	0 6.0 5.9 5.8 5.6
51	9.46 220	42	9.48 126	45	0.51 874	9.98 094	4	9	1 18.0 17.6 17.2 16.9
52	9.46 262	41	9.48 171	46	0.51 829	9.98 090	3	8	2 30.0 29.4 28.8 28.1
53	9.46 303	42	9.48 217	45	0.51 783	9.98 087	4	7	3 42.0 41.1 40.2 39.4
54	9.46 345	41	9.48 262	45	0.51 738	9.98 083	4	6	4
									3 3 3 3
55	9.46 386	42	9.48 307	46	0.51 693	9.98 079	4	5	**48 47 46 45**
56	9.46 428	41	9.48 353	45	0.51 647	9.98 075	4	4	
57	9.46 469	42	9.48 398	45	0.51 602	9.98 071	4	3	0 8.0 7.8 7.7 7.5
58	9.46 511	41	9.48 443	46	0.51 557	9.98 067	4	2	1 24.0 23.5 23.0 22.5
59	9.46 552	42	9.48 489	45	0.51 511	9.98 063	3	1	2 40.0 39.2 38.3 37.5
									3
60	9.46 594		9.48 534		0.51 466	9.98 060		0	

| ' | L. Cos. | d. | L. Cot. | c.d. | L. Tan. | L. Sin. | d. | ' | P. P. |

106° (286°)   **(253°) 73°**

COMMON LOGARITHMS OF THE TRIGONOMETRIC
FUNCTIONS (Continued)

17° (197°)   (342°) **162°**

'	L. Sin.	d.	L. Tan.	c.d.	L. Cot.	L. Cos.	d.	'		P. P.		
0	9.46 594	41	9.48 534	45	0.51 466	9.98 060	4	60	''	**45**	**44**	**43**
1	9.46 635	41	9.48 579	45	0.51 421	9.98 056	4	59	1	0.8	0.7	0.7
2	9.46 676	41	9.48 624	45	0.51 376	9.98 052	4	58	2	1.5	1.5	1.4
3	9.46 717	41	9.48 669	45	0.51 331	9.98 048	4	57	3	2.2	2.2	2.2
4	9.46 758	42	9.48 714	45	0.51 286	9.98 044	4	56	4	3.0	2.9	2.9
5	9.46 800	41	9.48 759	45	0.51 241	9.98 040	4	55	5	3.8	3.7	3.6
6	9.46 841	41	9.48 804	45	0.51 196	9.98 036	4	54	6	4.5	4.4	4.3
7	9.46 882	41	9.48 849	45	0.51 151	9.98 032	3	53	7	5.2	5.1	5.0
8	9.46 923	41	9.48 894	45	0.51 106	9.98 029	4	52	8	6.0	5.9	5.7
9	9.46 964	41	9.48 939	45	0.51 061	9.98 025	4	51	9	6.8	6.6	6.4
10	9.47 005	40	9.48 984	45	0.51 016	9.98 021	4	50	10	7.5	7.3	7.2
11	9.47 045	41	9.49 029	44	0.50 971	9.98 017	4	49	20	15.0	14.7	14.3
12	9.47 086	41	9.49 073	45	0.50 927	9.98 013	4	48	30	22.5	22.0	21.5
13	9.47 127	41	9.49 118	45	0.50 882	9.98 009	4	47	40	30.0	29.3	28.7
14	9.47 168	41	9.49 163	44	0.50 837	9.98 005	4	46	50	37.5	36.7	35.8
15	9.47 209	40	9.49 207	45	0.50 793	9.98 001	4	45	''	**42**	**41**	**40**
16	9.47 249	41	9.49 252	44	0.50 748	9.97 997	4	44	1	0.7	0.7	0.7
17	9.47 290	40	9.49 296	45	0.50 704	9.97 993	4	43	2	1.4	1.4	1.3
18	9.47 330	41	9.49 341	44	0.50 659	9.97 989	3	42	3	2.1	2.0	2.0
19	9.47 371	40	9.49 385	45	0.50 615	9.97 986	4	41	4	2.8	2.7	2.7
20	9.47 411	41	9.49 430	44	0.50 570	9.97 982	4	40	5	3.5	3.4	3.3
21	9.47 452	40	9.49 474	45	0.50 526	9.97 978	4	39	6	4.2	4.1	4.0
22	9.47 492	41	9.49 519	44	0.50 481	9.97 974	4	38	7	4.9	4.8	4.7
23	9.47 533	40	9.49 563	44	0.50 437	9.97 970	4	37	8	5.6	5.5	5.3
24	9.47 573	40	9.49 607	45	0.50 393	9.97 966	4	36	9	6.3	6.2	6.0
25	9.47 613	41	9.49 652	44	0.50 348	9.97 962	4	35	10	7.0	6.8	6.7
26	9.47 654	40	9.49 696	44	0.50 304	9.97 958	4	34	20	14.0	13.7	13.3
27	9.47 694	40	9.49 740	44	0.50 260	9.97 954	4	33	30	21.0	20.5	20.0
28	9.47 734	40	9.49 784	44	0.50 216	9.97 950	4	32	40	28.0	27.3	26.7
29	9.47 774	40	9.49 828	44	0.50 172	9.97 946	4	31	50	35.0	34.2	33.3
30	9.47 814	40	9.49 872	44	0.50 128	9.97 942	4	30	''	**39**	**5**	**4**	**3**
31	9.47 854	40	9.49 916	44	0.50 084	9.97 938	4	29	1	0.6	0.1	0.1	0.0
32	9.47 894	40	9.49 960	44	0.50 040	9.97 934	4	28	2	1.3	0.2	0.1	0.1
33	9.47 934	40	9.50 004	44	0.49 996	9.97 930	4	27	3	2.0	0.2	0.2	0.2
34	9.47 974	40	9.50 048	44	0.49 952	9.97 926	4	26	4	2.6	0.3	0.3	0.2
35	9.48 014	40	9.50 092	44	0.49 908	9.97 922	4	25	5	3.2	0.4	0.3	0.2
36	9.48 054	40	9.50 136	44	0.49 864	9.97 918	4	24	6	3.9	0.5	0.4	0.3
37	9.48 094	39	9.50 180	43	0.49 820	9.97 914	4	23	7	4.6	0.6	0.5	0.4
38	9.48 133	40	9.50 223	44	0.49 777	9.97 910	4	22	8	5.2	0.7	0.5	0.4
39	9.48 173	40	9.50 267	44	0.49 733	9.97 906	4	21	9	5.8	0.8	0.6	0.4
40	9.48 213	39	9.50 311	44	0.49 689	9.97 902	4	20	10	6.5	0.8	0.7	0.5
41	9.48 252	40	9.50 355	43	0.49 645	9.97 898	4	19	20	13.0	1.7	1.3	1.0
42	9.48 292	40	9.50 398	44	0.49 602	9.97 894	4	18	30	19.5	2.5	2.0	1.5
43	9.48 332	39	9.50 442	43	0.49 558	9.97 890	4	17	40	26.0	3.3	2.7	2.0
44	9.48 371	40	9.50 485	44	0.49 515	9.97 886	4	16	50	32.5	4.2	3.3	2.5
45	9.48 411	39	9.50 529	43	0.49 471	9.97 882	4	15		**5**	**4**	**4**
46	9.48 450	40	9.50 572	44	0.49 428	9.97 878	4	14				
47	9.48 490	39	9.50 616	43	0.49 384	9.97 874	4	13		**43**	**45**	**44**
48	9.48 529	39	9.50 659	44	0.49 341	9.97 870	4	12				
49	9.48 568	39	9.50 703	43	0.49 297	9.97 866	5	11	0	4.3	5.6	5.5
50	9.48 607	40	9.50 746	43	0.49 254	9.97 861	4	10	1	12.9	16.9	16.5
51	9.48 647	39	9.50 789	44	0.49 211	9.97 857	4	9	2	21.5	28.1	27.5
52	9.48 686	39	9.50 833	43	0.49 167	9.97 853	4	8	3	30.1	39.4	38.5
53	9.48 725	39	9.50 876	43	0.49 124	9.97 849	4	7	4	38.7	—	—
54	9.48 764	39	9.50 919	43	0.49 081	9.97 845	4	6	5	**4**	**3**	**3**
55	9.48 803	39	9.50 962	43	0.49 038	9.97 841	4	5		**43**	**45**	**44**
56	9.48 842	39	9.51 005	43	0.48 995	9.97 837	4	4				
57	9.48 881	39	9.51 048	44	0.48 952	9.97 833	4	3	0			
58	9.48 920	39	9.51 092	43	0.48 908	9.97 829	4	2	1	5.4	7.5	7.3
59	9.48 959	39	9.51 135	43	0.48 865	9.97 825	4	1	2	16.1	22.5	22.0
									3	26.9	37.5	36.7
60	9.48 998		9.51 178		0.48 822	9.97 821		0	4	37.6	—	—
'	L. Cos.	d.	L. Cot.	c.d.	L. Tan.	L. Sin.	d.	'		P. P.		

107° (287°)   (252°) **72°**

COMMON LOGARITHMS OF THE TRIGONOMETRIC
FUNCTIONS (Continued)

18° (198°)   **(341°) 161°**

′	L. Sin.	d.	L. Tan.	c.d.	L. Cot.	L. Cos.	d.	′	P. P.		
0	9.48 998	39	9.51 178	43	0.48 822	9.97 821	4	60	″	**43**	**42**	**41**
1	9.49 037	39	9.51 221	43	0.48 779	9.97 817	5	59	1	0.7	0.7	0.7
2	9.49 076	39	9.51 264	42	0.48 736	9.97 812	4	58	2	1.4	1.4	1.4
3	9.49 115	38	9.51 306	43	0.48 694	9.97 808	4	57	3	2.2	2.1	2.0
4	9.49 153	39	9.51 349	43	0.48 651	9.97 804	4	56	4	2.9	2.8	2.7
5	9.49 192	39	9.51 392	43	0.48 608	9.97 800	4	55	5	3.6	3.5	3.4
6	9.49 231	38	9.51 435	43	0.48 565	9.97 796	4	54	6	4.3	4.2	4.1
7	9.49 269	39	9.51 478	42	0.48 522	9.97 792	4	53	7	5.0	4.9	4.8
8	9.49 308	39	9.51 520	43	0.48 480	9.97 788	4	52	8	5.7	5.6	5.5
9	9.49 347	38	9.51 563	43	0.48 437	9.97 784	5	51	9	6.4	6.3	6.2
10	9.49 385	39	9.51 606	42	0.48 394	9.97 779	4	50	10	7.2	7.0	6.8
11	9.49 424	38	9.51 648	43	0.48 352	9.97 775	4	49	20	14.3	14.0	13.7
12	9.49 462	38	9.51 691	43	0.48 309	9.97 771	4	48	30	21.5	21.0	20.5
13	9.49 500	39	9.51 734	42	0.48 266	9.97 767	4	47	40	28.7	28.0	27.3
14	9.49 539	38	9.51 776	43	0.48 224	9.97 763	4	46	50	35.8	35.0	34.2
15	9.49 577	38	9.51 819	42	0.48 181	9.97 759	5	45	″	**39**	**38**	**37**
16	9.49 615	39	9.51 861	42	0.48 139	9.97 754	4	44	1	0.6	0.6	0.6
17	9.49 654	38	9.51 903	43	0.48 097	9.97 750	4	43	2	1.3	1.3	1.2
18	9.49 692	38	9.51 946	42	0.48 054	9.97 746	4	42	3	2.0	1.9	1.8
19	9.49 730	38	9.51 988	43	0.48 012	9.97 742	4	41	4	2.6	2.5	2.5
20	9.49 768	38	9.52 031	42	0.47 969	9.97 738	4	40	5	3.2	3.2	3.1
21	9.49 806	38	9.52 073	42	0.47 927	9.97 734	5	39	6	3.9	3.8	3.7
22	9.49 844	38	9.52 115	42	0.47 885	9.97 729	4	38	7	4.6	4.4	4.3
23	9.49 882	38	9.52 157	43	0.47 843	9.97 725	4	37	8	5.2	5.1	4.9
24	9.49 920	38	9.52 200	42	0.47 800	9.97 721	4	36	9	5.8	5.7	5.6
25	9.49 958	38	9.52 242	42	0.47 758	9.97 717	4	35	10	6.5	6.3	6.2
26	9.49 996	38	9.52 284	42	0.47 716	9.97 713	5	34	20	13.0	12.7	12.3
27	9.50 034	38	9.52 326	42	0.47 674	9.97 708	4	33	30	19.5	19.0	18.5
28	9.50 072	38	9.52 368	42	0.47 632	9.97 704	4	32	40	26.0	25.3	24.7
29	9.50 110	38	9.52 410	42	0.47 590	9.97 700	4	31	50	32.5	31.7	30.8
30	9.50 148	37	9.52 452	42	0.47 548	9.97 696	5	30	″	**36**	**5**	**4**
31	9.50 185	38	9.52 494	42	0.47 506	9.97 691	4	29	1	0.6	0.1	0.1
32	9.50 223	38	9.52 536	42	0.47 464	9.97 687	4	28	2	1.2	0.2	0.1
33	9.50 261	37	9.52 578	42	0.47 422	9.97 683	4	27	3	1.8	0.2	0.2
34	9.50 298	38	9.52 620	41	0.47 380	9.97 679	5	26	4	2.4	0.3	0.3
35	9.50 336	38	9.52 661	42	0.47 339	9.97 674	4	25	5	3.0	0.4	0.3
36	9.50 374	37	9.52 703	42	0.47 297	9.97 670	4	24	6	3.6	0.5	0.4
37	9.50 411	38	9.52 745	42	0.47 255	9.97 666	4	23	7	4.2	0.6	0.5
38	9.50 449	37	9.52 787	42	0.47 213	9.97 662	5	22	8	4.8	0.7	0.5
39	9.50 486	37	9.52 829	41	0.47 171	9.97 657	4	21	9	5.4	0.8	0.6
40	9.50 523	38	9.52 870	42	0.47 130	9.97 653	4	20	10	6.0	0.8	0.7
41	9.50 561	37	9.52 912	41	0.47 088	9.97 649	4	19	20	12.0	1.7	1.3
42	9.50 598	37	9.52 953	42	0.47 047	9.97 645	5	18	30	18.0	2.5	2.0
43	9.50 635	38	9.52 995	42	0.47 005	9.97 640	4	17	40	24.0	3.3	2.7
44	9.50 673	37	9.53 037	41	0.46 963	9.97 636	4	16	50	30.0	4.2	3.3
45	9.50 710	37	9.53 078	42	0.46 922	9.97 632	4	15		**5**	**5**	**5**
46	9.50 747	37	9.53 120	41	0.46 880	9.97 628	5	14				
47	9.50 784	37	9.53 161	41	0.46 839	9.97 623	4	13		**43**	**42**	**41**
48	9.50 821	37	9.53 202	42	0.46 798	9.97 619	4	12	0	4.3	4.2	4.1
49	9.50 858	38	9.53 244	41	0.46 756	9.97 615	5	11	1	12.9	12.6	12.3
50	9.50 896	37	9.53 285	42	0.46 715	9.97 610	4	10	2 / 3	21.5	21.0	20.5
51	9.50 933	37	9.53 327	41	0.46 673	9.97 606	4	9	4	30.1	29.4	28.7
52	9.50 970	37	9.53 368	41	0.46 632	9.97 602	5	8	5	38.7	37.8	36.9
53	9.51 007	36	9.53 409	41	0.46 591	9.97 597	4	7				
54	9.51 043	37	9.53 450	42	0.46 550	9.97 593	4	6		**4**	**4**	**4**
55	9.51 080	37	9.53 492	41	0.46 508	9.97 589	5	5		**43**	**42**	**41**
56	9.51 117	37	9.53 533	41	0.46 467	9.97 584	4	4				
57	9.51 154	37	9.53 574	41	0.46 426	9.97 580	4	3	0	5.4	5.2	5.1
58	9.51 191	36	9.53 615	41	0.46 385	9.97 576	5	2	1	16.1	15.8	15.4
59	9.51 227	37	9.53 656	41	0.46 344	9.97 571	4	1	2 / 3	26.9	26.2	25.6
60	9.51 264		9.53 697		0.46 303	9.97 567		0	4	37.6	36.8	35.9

′	L. Cos.	d.	L. Cot.	c.d.	L. Tan.	L. Sin.	d.	′	P. P.		

COMMON LOGARITHMS OF THE TRIGONOMETRIC
FUNCTIONS (Continued)

19° (199°)   (340°) **160°**

'	L. Sin.	d.	L. Tan.	c.d.	L. Cot.	L. Cos.	d.	'
0	9.51 264	37	9.53 697	41	0.46 303	9.97 567	4	60
1	9.51 301	37	9.53 738	41	0.46 262	9.97 563	5	59
2	9.51 338	36	9.53 779	41	0.46 221	9.97 558	4	58
3	9.51 374	37	9.53 820	41	0.46 180	9.97 554	4	57
4	9.51 411	36	9.53 861	41	0.46 139	9.97 550	5	56
5	9.51 447	37	9.53 902	41	0.46 098	9.97 545	4	55
6	9.51 484	36	9.53 943	41	0.46 057	9.97 541	5	54
7	9.51 520	37	9.53 984	41	0.46 016	9.97 536	4	53
8	9.51 557	36	9.54 025	40	0.45 975	9.97 532	4	52
9	9.51 593	36	9.54 065	41	0.45 935	9.97 528	5	51
10	9.51 629	37	9.54 106	41	0.45 894	9.97 523	4	50
11	9.51 666	36	9.54 147	40	0.45 853	9.97 519	4	49
12	9.51 702	36	9.54 187	41	0.45 813	9.97 515	5	48
13	9.51 738	36	9.54 228	41	0.45 772	9.97 510	4	47
14	9.51 774	37	9.54 269	40	0.45 731	9.97 506	5	46
15	9.51 811	36	9.54 309	41	0.45 691	9.97 501	4	45
16	9.51 847	36	9.54 350	40	0.45 650	9.97 497	5	44
17	9.51 883	36	9.54 390	41	0.45 610	9.97 492	4	43
18	9.51 919	36	9.54 431	40	0.45 569	9.97 488	4	42
19	9.51 955	36	9.54 471	41	0.45 529	9.97 484	5	41
20	9.51 991	36	9.54 512	40	0.45 488	9.97 479	4	40
21	9.52 027	36	9.54 552	41	0.45 448	9.97 475	4	39
22	9.52 063	36	9.54 593	40	0.45 407	9.97 470	5	38
23	9.52 099	36	9.54 633	40	0.45 367	9.97 466	4	37
24	9.52 135	36	9.54 673	41	0.45 327	9.97 461	5	36
25	9.52 171	36	9.54 714	40	0.45 286	9.97 457	4	35
26	9.52 207	35	9.54 754	40	0.45 246	9.97 453	5	34
27	9.52 242	36	9.54 794	41	0.45 206	9.97 448	4	33
28	9.52 278	36	9.54 835	40	0.45 165	9.97 444	5	32
29	9.52 314	36	9.54 875	40	0.45 125	9.97 439	4	31
30	9.52 350	35	9.54 915	40	0.45 085	9.97 435	5	30
31	9.52 385	36	9.54 955	40	0.45 045	9.97 430	4	29
32	9.52 421	35	9.54 995	40	0.45 005	9.97 426	5	28
33	9.52 456	36	9.55 035	40	0.44 965	9.97 421	4	27
34	9.52 492	35	9.55 075	40	0.44 925	9.97 417	5	26
35	9.52 527	36	9.55 115	40	0.44 885	9.97 412	4	25
36	9.52 563	35	9.55 155	40	0.44 845	9.97 408	5	24
37	9.52 598	36	9.55 195	40	0.44 805	9.97 403	4	23
38	9.52 634	35	9.55 235	40	0.44 765	9.97 399	5	22
39	9.52 669	36	9.55 275	40	0.44 725	9.97 394	4	21
40	9.52 705	35	9.55 315	40	0.44 685	9.97 390	5	20
41	9.52 740	35	9.55 355	40	0.44 645	9.97 385	4	19
42	9.52 775	36	9.55 395	39	0.44 605	9.97 381	5	18
43	9.52 811	35	9.55 434	40	0.44 566	9.97 376	5	17
44	9.52 846	35	9.55 474	40	0.44 526	9.97 372	4	16
45	9.52 881	35	9.55 514	40	0.44 486	9.97 367	5	15
46	9.52 916	35	9.55 554	39	0.44 446	9.97 363	5	14
47	9.52 951	35	9.55 593	40	0.44 407	9.97 358	5	13
48	9.52 986	35	9.55 633	40	0.44 367	9.97 353	4	12
49	9.53 021	35	9.55 673	39	0.44 327	9.97 349	5	11
50	9.53 056	36	9.55 712	40	0.44 288	9.97 344	4	10
51	9.53 092	34	9.55 752	39	0.44 248	9.97 340	5	9
52	9.53 126	35	9.55 791	40	0.44 209	9.97 335	5	8
53	9.53 161	35	9.55 831	39	0.44 169	9.97 331	5	7
54	9.53 196	35	9.55 870	40	0.44 130	9.97 326	4	6
55	9.53 231	35	9.55 910	39	0.44 090	9.97 322	5	5
56	9.53 266	35	9.55 949	40	0.44 051	9.97 317	5	4
57	9.53 301	35	9.55 989	39	0.44 011	9.97 312	4	3
58	9.53 336	34	9.56 028	39	0.43 972	9.97 308	5	2
59	9.53 370	35	9.56 067	40	0.43 933	9.97 303	4	1
60	9.53 405		9.56 107		0.43 893	9.97 299		0

P. P.

"	41	40	39
1	0.7	0.7	0.6
2	1.4	1.3	1.3
3	2.0	2.0	2.0
4	2.7	2.7	2.6
5	3.4	3.3	3.2
6	4.1	4.0	3.9
7	4.8	4.7	4.6
8	5.5	5.3	5.2
9	6.2	6.0	5.8
10	6.8	6.7	6.5
20	13.7	13.3	13.0
30	20.5	20.0	19.5
40	27.3	26.7	26.0
50	34.2	33.3	32.5

"	37	36	35
1	0.6	0.6	0.6
2	1.2	1.2	1.2
3	1.8	1.8	1.8
4	2.5	2.4	2.3
5	3.1	3.0	2.9
6	3.7	3.6	3.5
7	4.3	4.2	4.1
8	4.9	4.8	4.7
9	5.6	5.4	5.2
10	6.2	6.0	5.8
20	12.3	12.0	11.7
30	18.5	18.0	17.5
40	24.7	24.0	23.3
50	30.8	30.0	29.2

"	34	5	4
1	0.6	0.1	0.1
2	1.1	0.2	0.1
3	1.7	0.2	0.2
4	2.3	0.3	0.3
5	2.8	0.4	0.3
6	3.4	0.5	0.4
7	4.0	0.6	0.5
8	4.5	0.7	0.5
9	5.1	0.8	0.6
10	5.7	0.8	0.7
20	11.3	1.7	1.3
30	17.0	2.5	2.0
40	22.7	3.3	2.7
50	28.3	4.2	3.3

5	5	5
41	40	39
4.1	4.0	3.9
12.3	12.0	11.7
20.5	20.0	19.5
28.7	28.0	27.3
36.9	36.0	35.1

4	4	4
41	40	39
5.1	5.0	4.9
15.4	15.0	14.6
25.6	25.0	24.4
35.9	35.0	34.1

'	L. Cos.	d.	L. Cot.	c.d.	L. Tan.	L. Sin.	d.	'	P. P.

109° (289°)   (250°) **70°**

COMMON LOGARITHMS OF THE TRIGONOMETRIC
FUNCTIONS (Continued)

20° (200°)   (339°) **159°**

′	L. Sin.	d.	L. Tan.	c.d.	L. Cot.	L. Cos.	d.	′	P. P.		
0	9.53 405	35	9.56 107	39	0.43 893	9.97 299	5	60			
1	9.53 440	35	9.56 146	39	0.43 854	9.97 294	5	59	″	40	39	38
2	9.53 475	34	9.56 185	39	0.43 815	9.97 289	4	58	1	0.7	0.6	0.6
3	9.53 509	35	9.56 224	40	0.43 776	9.97 285	5	57	2	1.3	1.3	1.3
4	9.53 544	34	9.56 264	39	0.43 736	9.97 280	4	56	3	2.0	2.0	1.9
									4	2.7	2.6	2.5
5	9.53 578	35	9.56 303	39	0.43 697	9.97 276	5	55				
6	9.53 613	34	9.56 342	39	0.43 658	9.97 271	5	54	5	3.3	3.2	3.2
7	9.53 647	35	9.56 381	39	0.43 619	9.97 266	4	53	6	4.0	3.9	3.8
8	9.53 682	34	9.56 420	39	0.43 580	9.97 262	5	52	7	4.7	4.6	4.4
9	9.53 716	35	9.56 459	39	0.43 541	9.97 257	5	51	8	5.3	5.2	5.1
									9	6.0	5.8	5.7
10	9.53 751	34	9.56 498	39	0.43 502	9.97 252	4	50				
11	9.53 785	34	9.56 537	39	0.43 463	9.97 248	5	49	10	6.7	6.5	6.3
12	9.53 819	35	9.56 576	39	0.43 424	9.97 243	5	48	20	13.3	13.0	12.7
13	9.53 854	34	9.56 615	39	0.43 385	9.97 238	4	47	30	20.0	19.5	19.0
14	9.53 888	34	9.56 654	39	0.43 346	9.97 234	5	46	40	26.7	26.0	25.3
										50	33.3	32.5	31.7
15	9.53 922	35	9.56 693	39	0.43 307	9.97 229	5	45				
16	9.53 957	34	9.56 732	39	0.43 268	9.97 224	4	44	″	37	35	34
17	9.53 991	34	9.56 771	39	0.43 229	9.97 220	5	43	1	0.6	0.6	0.6
18	9.54 025	34	9.56 810	39	0.43 190	9.97 215	5	42	2	1.2	1.2	1.1
19	9.54 059	34	9.56 849	38	0.43 151	9.97 210	4	41	3	1.8	1.8	1.7
									4	2.5	2.3	2.3
20	9.54 093	34	9.56 887	39	0.43 113	9.97 206	5	40				
21	9.54 127	34	9.56 926	39	0.43 074	9.97 201	5	39	5	3.1	2.9	2.8
22	9.54 161	34	9.56 965	39	0.43 035	9.97 196	4	38	6	3.7	3.5	3.4
23	9.54 195	34	9.57 004	38	0.42 996	9.97 192	5	37	7	4.3	4.1	4.0
24	9.54 229	34	9.57 042	39	0.42 958	9.97 187	5	36	8	4.9	4.7	4.5
									9	5.6	5.2	5.1
25	9.54 263	34	9.57 081	39	0.42 919	9.97 182	4	35				
26	9.54 297	34	9.57 120	38	0.42 880	9.97 178	5	34	10	6.2	5.8	5.7
27	9.54 331	34	9.57 158	39	0.42 842	9.97 173	5	33	20	12.3	11.7	11.3
28	9.54 365	34	9.57 197	38	0.42 803	9.97 168	5	32	30	18.5	17.5	17.0
29	9.54 399	34	9.57 235	39	0.42 765	9.97 163	4	31	40	24.7	23.3	22.7
										50	30.8	29.2	28.3
30	9.54 433	33	9.57 274	38	0.42 726	9.97 159	5	30				
31	9.54 466	34	9.57 312	39	0.42 688	9.97 154	5	29	″	33	5	4
32	9.54 500	34	9.57 351	38	0.42 649	9.97 149	5	28	1	0.6	0.1	0.1
33	9.54 534	33	9.57 389	39	0.42 611	9.97 145	5	27	2	1.1	0.2	0.1
34	9.54 567	34	9.57 428	38	0.42 572	9.97 140	5	26	3	1.6	0.2	0.2
									4	2.2	0.3	0.3
35	9.54 601	34	9.57 466	38	0.42 534	9.97 135	5	25				
36	9.54 635	33	9.57 504	39	0.42 496	9.97 130	4	24	5	2.8	0.4	0.3
37	9.54 668	34	9.57 543	38	0.42 457	9.97 126	5	23	6	3.3	0.5	0.4
38	9.54 702	33	9.57 581	38	0.42 419	9.97 121	5	22	7	3.8	0.6	0.5
39	9.54 735	34	9.57 619	39	0.42 381	9.97 116	5	21	8	4.4	0.7	0.5
									9	5.0	0.8	0.6
40	9.54 769	33	9.57 658	38	0.42 342	9.97 111	4	20				
41	9.54 802	34	9.57 696	38	0.42 304	9.97 107	5	19	10	5.5	0.8	0.7
42	9.54 836	33	9.57 734	38	0.42 266	9.97 102	5	18	20	11.0	1.7	1.3
43	9.54 869	34	9.57 772	38	0.42 228	9.97 097	5	17	30	16.5	2.5	2.0
44	9.54 903	33	9.57 810	39	0.42 190	9.97 092	5	16	40	22.0	3.3	2.7
										50	27.5	4.2	3.3
45	9.54 936	33	9.57 849	38	0.42 151	9.97 087	4	15				
46	9.54 969	34	9.57 887	38	0.42 113	9.97 083	5	14		5	5	5
47	9.55 003	33	9.57 925	38	0.42 075	9.97 078	5	13		—	—	—
48	9.55 036	33	9.57 963	38	0.42 037	9.97 073	5	12		40	39	38
49	9.55 069	33	9.58 001	38	0.41 999	9.97 068	5	11	0			
									1	4.0	3.9	3.8
50	9.55 102	34	9.58 039	38	0.41 961	9.97 063	4	10	2	12.0	11.7	11.4
51	9.55 136	33	9.58 077	38	0.41 923	9.97 059	5	9	3	20.0	19.5	19.0
52	9.55 169	33	9.58 115	38	0.41 885	9.97 054	5	8	4	28.0	27.3	26.6
53	9.55 202	33	9.58 153	38	0.41 847	9.97 049	5	7	5	36.0	35.1	34.2
54	9.55 235	33	9.58 191	38	0.41 809	9.97 044	5	6		5	4	4
55	9.55 268	33	9.58 229	38	0.41 771	9.97 039	4	5		37	39	38
56	9.55 301	33	9.58 267	37	0.41 733	9.97 035	5	4	0			
57	9.55 334	33	9.58 304	38	0.41 696	9.97 030	5	3	1	3.7	4.9	4.8
58	9.55 367	33	9.58 342	38	0.41 658	9.97 025	5	2	2	11.1	14.6	14.2
59	9.55 400	33	9.58 380	38	0.41 620	9.97 020	5	1	3	18.5	24.4	23.8
									4	25.9	34.1	33.2
60	9.55 433		9.58 418		0.41 582	9.97 015		0	5	33.3	—	—
′	L. Cos.	d.	L. Cot.	c.d.	L. Tan.	L. Sin.	d.	′	P. P.		

110° (290°)   (249°) **69°**

COMMON LOGARITHMS OF THE TRIGONOMETRIC
FUNCTIONS (Continued)

21° (201°)   (338°)**158°**

′	L. Sin.	d.	L. Tan.	c.d.	L. Cot.	L. Cos.	d.	′	P. P.		
0	9.55 433	33	9.58 418	37	0.41 582	9.97 015	5	**60**	″	**38**	**37**	**36**
1	9.55 466	33	9.58 455	38	0.41 545	9.97 010	5	59	1	0.6	0.6	0.6
2	9.55 499	33	9.58 493	38	0.41 507	9.97 005	4	58	2	1.3	1.2	1.2
3	9.55 532	32	9.58 531	38	0.41 469	9.97 001	5	57	3	1.9	1.8	1.8
4	9.55 564	33	9.58 569	37	0.41 431	9.96 996	5	56	4	2.5	2.5	2.4
5	9.55 597	33	9.58 606	38	0.41 394	9.96 991	5	55	5	3.2	3.1	3.0
6	9.55 630	33	9.58 644	37	0.41 356	9.96 986	5	54	6	3.8	3.7	3.6
7	9.55 663	32	9.58 681	38	0.41 319	9.96 981	5	53	7	4.4	4.3	4.2
8	9.55 695	33	9.58 719	38	0.41 281	9.96 976	5	52	8	5.1	4.9	4.8
9	9.55 728	33	9.58 757	37	0.41 243	9.96 971	5	51	9	5.7	5.6	5.4
10	9.55 761	32	9.58 794	38	0.41 206	9.96 966	4	**50**	10	6.3	6.2	6.0
11	9.55 793	33	9.58 832	37	0.41 168	9.96 962	5	49	20	12.7	12.3	12.0
12	9.55 826	32	9.58 869	38	0.41 131	9.96 957	5	48	30	19.0	18.5	18.0
13	9.55 858	33	9.58 907	37	0.41 093	9.96 952	5	47	40	25.3	24.7	24.0
14	9.55 891	32	9.58 944	37	0.41 056	9.96 947	5	46	50	31.7	30.8	30.0
15	9.55 923	33	9.58 981	38	0.41 019	9.96 942	5	45	″	**33**	**32**	**31**
16	9.55 956	32	9.59 019	37	0.40 981	9.96 937	5	44	1	0.6	0.5	0.5
17	9.55 988	33	9.59 056	38	0.40 944	9.96 932	5	43	2	1.1	1.1	1.0
18	9.56 021	32	9.59 094	37	0.40 906	9.96 927	5	42	3	1.6	1.6	1.6
19	9.56 053	32	9.59 131	37	0.40 869	9.96 922	5	41	4	2.2	2.1	2.1
20	9.56 085	33	9.59 168	37	0.40 832	9.96 917	5	**40**	5	2.8	2.7	2.6
21	9.56 118	32	9.59 205	38	0.40 795	9.96 912	5	39	6	3.3	3.2	3.1
22	9.56 150	32	9.59 243	37	0.40 757	9.96 907	4	38	7	3.8	3.7	3.6
23	9.56 182	33	9.59 280	37	0.40 720	9.96 903	5	37	8	4.4	4.3	4.1
24	9.56 215	32	9.59 317	37	0.40 683	9.96 898	5	36	9	5.0	4.8	4.6
25	9.56 247	32	9.59 354	37	0.40 646	9.96 893	5	35	10	5.5	5.3	5.2
26	9.56 279	32	9.59 391	38	0.40 609	9.96 888	5	34	20	11.0	10.7	10.3
27	9.56 311	32	9.59 429	37	0.40 571	9.96 883	5	33	30	16.5	16.0	15.5
28	9.56 343	32	9.59 466	37	0.40 534	9.96 878	5	32	40	22.0	21.3	20.7
29	9.56 375	33	9.59 503	37	0.40 497	9.96 873	5	31	50	27.5	26.7	25.8
30	9.56 408	32	9.59 540	37	0.40 460	9.96 868	5	**30**	″	**6**	**5**	**4**
31	9.56 440	32	9.59 577	37	0.40 423	9.96 863	5	29	1	0.1	0.1	0.1
32	9.56 472	32	9.59 614	37	0.40 386	9.96 858	5	28	2	0.2	0.2	0.1
33	9.56 504	32	9.59 651	37	0.40 349	9.96 853	5	27	3	0.3	0.2	0.2
34	9.56 536	32	9.59 688	37	0.40 312	9.96 848	5	26	4	0.4	0.3	0.3
35	9.56 568	31	9.59 725	37	0.40 275	9.96 843	5	25	5	0.5	0.4	0.3
36	9.56 599	32	9.59 762	37	0.40 238	9.96 838	5	24	6	0.6	0.5	0.4
37	9.56 631	32	9.59 799	36	0.40 201	9.96 833	5	23	7	0.7	0.6	0.5
38	9.56 663	32	9.59 835	37	0.40 165	9.96 828	5	22	8	0.8	0.7	0.5
39	9.56 695	32	9.59 872	37	0.40 128	9.96 823	5	21	9	0.9	0.8	0.6
40	9.56 727	32	9.59 909	37	0.40 091	9.96 818	5	**20**	10	1.0	0.8	0.7
41	9.56 759	31	9.59 946	37	0.40 054	9.96 813	5	19	20	2.0	1.7	1.3
42	9.56 790	32	9.59 983	36	0.40 017	9.96 808	5	18	30	3.0	2.5	2.0
43	9.56 822	32	9.60 019	37	0.39 981	9.96 803	5	17	40	4.0	3.3	2.7
44	9.56 854	32	9.60 056	37	0.39 944	9.96 798	5	16	50	5.0	4.2	3.3
45	9.56 886	31	9.60 093	37	0.39 907	9.96 793	5	15		**6**	**5**	**5**
46	9.56 917	32	9.60 130	36	0.39 870	9.96 788	5	14		**37**	**38**	**37**
47	9.56 949	31	9.60 166	37	0.39 834	9.96 783	5	13	0			
48	9.56 980	32	9.60 203	37	0.39 797	9.96 778	6	12	1	3.1	3.8	3.7
49	9.57 012	32	9.60 240	36	0.39 760	9.96 772	5	11	2	9.2	11.4	11.1
									3	15.4	19.0	18.5
50	9.57 044	31	9.60 276	37	0.39 724	9.96 767	5	**10**	4	21.6	26.6	25.9
51	9.57 075	32	9.60 313	36	0.39 687	9.96 762	5	9	5	27.8	34.2	33.3
52	9.57 107	31	9.60 349	37	0.39 651	9.96 757	5	8	6	33.9	—	—
53	9.57 138	31	9.60 386	36	0.39 614	9.96 752	5	7				
54	9.57 169	32	9.60 422	37	0.39 578	9.96 747	5	6		**5**	**4**	**4**
55	9.57 201	31	9.60 459	36	0.39 541	9.96 742	5	5		**36**	**38**	**37**
56	9.57 232	32	9.60 495	37	0.39 505	9.96 737	5	4	0			
57	9.57 264	31	9.60 532	36	0.39 468	9.96 732	5	3	1	3.6	4.8	4.6
58	9.57 295	31	9.60 568	37	0.39 432	9.96 727	5	2	2	10.8	14.2	13.9
59	9.57 326	32	9.60 605	36	0.39 395	9.96 722	5	1	3	18.0	23.8	23.1
									4	25.2	33.2	32.4
60	9.57 358		9.60 641		0.39 359	9.96 717		**0**	5	32.4	—	—
′	L. Cos.	d.	L. Cot.	c.d.	L. Tan.	L. Sin.	d.	′	P. P.		

111° (291°)   (248°) **68°**

COMMON LOGARITHMS OF THE TRIGONOMETRIC
FUNCTIONS (Continued)

22° (202°)   **(337°) 157°**

′	L. Sin.	d.	L. Tan.	c.d.	L. Cot.	L. Cos.	d.	′
0	9.57 358	31	9.60 641	36	0.39 359	9.96 717	6	60
1	9.57 389	31	9.60 677	37	0.39 323	9.96 711	6	59
2	9.57 420	31	9.60 714	36	0.39 286	9.96 706	5	58
3	9.57 451	31	9.60 750	36	0.39 250	9.96 701	5	57
4	9.57 482	32	9.60 786	37	0.39 214	9.96 696	5	56
5	9.57 514	31	9.60 823	36	0.39 177	9.96 691	5	55
6	9.57 543	31	9.60 859	36	0.39 141	9.96 686	5	54
7	9.57 576	31	9.60 895	36	0.39 105	9.96 681	5	53
8	9.57 607	31	9.60 931	36	0.39 069	9.96 676	6	52
9	9.57 638	31	9.60 967	37	0.39 033	9.96 670	5	51
10	9.57 669	31	9.61 004	36	0.38 996	9.96 665	5	50
11	9.57 700	31	9.61 040	36	0.38 960	9.96 660	5	49
12	9.57 731	31	9.61 076	36	0.38 924	9.96 655	5	48
13	9.57 762	31	9.61 112	36	0.38 888	9.96 650	5	47
14	9.57 793	31	9.61 148	36	0.38 852	9.96 645	5	46
15	9.57 824	31	9.61 184	36	0.38 816	9.96 640	6	45
16	9.57 855	30	9.61 220	36	0.38 780	9.96 634	5	44
17	9.57 885	31	9.61 256	36	0.38 744	9.96 629	5	43
18	9.57 916	31	9.61 292	36	0.38 708	9.96 624	5	42
19	9.57 947	31	9.61 328	36	0.38 672	9.96 619	5	41
20	9.57 978	30	9.61 364	36	0.38 636	9.96 614	6	40
21	9.58 008	31	9.61 400	36	0.38 600	9.96 608	5	39
22	9.58 039	31	9.61 436	36	0.38 564	9.96 603	5	38
23	9.58 070	31	9.61 472	36	0.38 528	9.96 598	5	37
24	9.58 101	30	9.61 508	36	0.38 492	9.96 593	5	36
25	9.58 131	31	9.61 544	35	0.38 456	9.96 588	6	35
26	9.58 162	30	9.61 579	36	0.38 421	9.96 582	5	34
27	9.58 192	31	9.61 615	36	0.38 385	9.96 577	5	33
28	9.58 223	30	9.61 651	36	0.38 349	9.96 572	5	32
29	9.58 253	31	9.61 687	35	0.38 313	9.96 567	5	31
30	9.58 284	30	9.61 722	36	0.38 278	9.96 562	6	30
31	9.58 314	31	9.61 758	36	0.38 242	9.96 556	5	29
32	9.58 345	30	9.61 794	36	0.38 206	9.96 551	5	28
33	9.58 375	31	9.61 830	35	0.38 170	9.96 546	5	27
34	9.58 406	30	9.61 865	36	0.38 135	9.96 541	6	26
35	9.58 436	31	9.61 901	35	0.38 099	9.96 535	5	25
36	9.58 467	30	9.61 936	36	0.38 064	9.96 530	5	24
37	9.58 497	30	9.61 972	36	0.38 028	9.96 525	5	23
38	9.58 527	30	9.62 008	35	0.37 992	9.96 520	6	22
39	9.58 557	31	9.62 043	36	0.37 957	9.96 514	5	21
40	9.58 588	30	9.62 079	35	0.37 921	9.96 509	5	20
41	9.58 618	30	9.62 114	36	0.37 886	9.96 504	5	19
42	9.58 648	30	9.62 150	35	0.37 850	9.96 498	5	18
43	9.58 678	31	9.62 185	36	0.37 815	9.96 493	5	17
44	9.58 709	30	9.62 221	35	0.37 779	9.96 488	5	16
45	9.58 739	30	9.62 256	36	0.37 744	9.96 483	6	15
46	9.58 769	30	9.62 292	35	0.37 708	9.96 477	5	14
47	9.58 799	30	9.62 327	35	0.37 673	9.96 472	5	13
48	9.58 829	30	9.62 362	36	0.37 638	9.96 467	6	12
49	9.58 859	30	9.62 398	35	0.37 602	9.96 461	5	11
50	9.58 889	30	9.62 433	35	0.37 567	9.96 456	5	10
51	9.58 919	30	9.62 468	36	0.37 532	9.96 451	6	9
52	9.58 949	30	9.62 504	35	0.37 496	9.96 445	5	8
53	9.58 979	30	9.62 539	35	0.37 461	9.96 440	5	7
54	9.59 009	30	9.62 574	35	0.37 426	9.96 435	6	6
55	9.59 039	30	9.62 609	36	0.37 391	9.96 429	5	5
56	9.59 069	29	9.62 645	35	0.37 355	9.96 424	5	4
57	9.59 098	30	9.62 680	35	0.37 320	9.96 419	6	3
58	9.59 128	30	9.62 715	35	0.37 285	9.96 413	5	2
59	9.59 158	30	9.62 750	35	0.37 250	9.96 408	5	1
60	9.59 188		9.62 785		0.37 215	9.96 403		0
′	L. Cos.	d.	L. Cot.	c.d.	L. Tan.	L. Sin.	d.	′

P. P.

60 ″	37	36	35
1	0.6	0.6	0.6
2	1.2	1.2	1.2
3	1.8	1.8	1.8
4	2.5	2.4	2.3
5	3.1	3.0	2.9
6	3.7	3.6	3.5
7	4.3	4.2	4.1
8	4.9	4.8	4.7
9	5.6	5.4	5.2
10	6.2	6.0	5.8
20	12.3	12.0	11.7
30	18.5	18.0	17.5
40	24.7	24.0	23.3
50	30.8	30.0	29.2

″	32	31	30
1	0.5	0.5	0.5
2	1.1	1.0	1.0
3	1.6	1.6	1.5
4	2.1	2.1	2.0
5	2.7	2.6	2.5
6	3.2	3.1	3.0
7	3.7	3.6	3.5
8	4.3	4.1	4.0
9	4.8	4.6	4.5
10	5.3	5.2	5.0
20	10.7	10.3	10.0
30	16.0	15.5	15.0
40	21.3	20.7	20.0
50	26.7	25.8	25.0

″	29	6	5
1	0.5	0.1	0.1
2	1.0	0.2	0.2
3	1.4	0.3	0.2
4	1.9	0.4	0.3
5	2.4	0.5	0.4
6	2.9	0.6	0.5
7	3.4	0.7	0.6
8	3.9	0.8	0.7
9	4.4	0.9	0.8
10	4.8	1.0	0.8
20	9.7	2.0	1.7
30	14.5	3.0	2.5
40	19.3	4.0	3.3
50	24.2	5.0	4.2

	6	6
	36	35
0		
1		
2	3.0	2.9
3	9.0	8.8
4	15.0	14.6
5	21.0	20.4
6	27.0	26.2
	33.0	32.1

	5	5	5
	37	36	35
0			
1	3.7	3.6	3.5
2	11.1	10.8	10.5
3	18.5	18.0	17.5
4	25.9	25.2	24.5
5	33.3	32.4	31.5

112° (292°)   **(247°) 67°**

COMMON LOGARITHMS OF THE TRIGONOMETRIC
FUNCTIONS (Continued)

23° (203°)   (336°) **156°**

′	L. Sin.	d.	L. Tan.	c.d.	L. Cot.	L. Cos.	d.	′
0	9.59 188	30	9.62 785	35	0.37 215	9.96 403	6	60
1	9.59 218	29	9.62 820	35	0.37 180	9.96 397	5	59
2	9.59 247	30	9.62 855	35	0.37 145	9.96 392	5	58
3	9.59 277	30	9.62 890	36	0.37 110	9.96 387	6	57
4	9.59 307	29	9.62 926	35	0.37 074	9.96 381	5	56
5	9.59 336	30	9.62 961	35	0.37 039	9.96 376	6	55
6	9.59 366	30	9.62 996	35	0.37 004	9.96 370	6	54
7	9.59 396	29	9.63 031	35	0.36 969	9.96 365	5	53
8	9.59 425	30	9.63 066	35	0.36 934	9.96 360	6	52
9	9.59 455	29	9.63 101	34	0.36 899	9.96 354	5	51
10	9.59 484	30	9.63 135	35	0.36 865	9.96 349	6	50
11	9.59 514	29	9.63 170	35	0.36 830	9.96 343	5	49
12	9.59 543	30	9.63 205	35	0.36 795	9.96 338	5	48
13	9.59 573	29	9.63 240	35	0.36 760	9.96 333	6	47
14	9.59 602	30	9.63 275	35	0.36 725	9.96 327	5	46
15	9.59 632	29	9.63 310	35	0.36 690	9.96 322	6	45
16	9.59 661	29	9.63 345	34	0.36 655	9.96 316	5	44
17	9.59 690	30	9.63 379	35	0.36 621	9.96 311	6	43
18	9.59 720	29	9.63 414	35	0.36 586	9.96 305	5	42
19	9.59 749	29	9.63 449	35	0.36 551	9.96 300	6	41
20	9.59 778	30	9.63 484	35	0.36 516	9.96 294	5	40
21	9.59 808	29	9.63 519	34	0.36 481	9.96 289	5	39
22	9.59 837	29	9.63 553	35	0.36 447	9.96 284	6	38
23	9.59 866	29	9.63 588	35	0.36 412	9.96 278	5	37
24	9.59 895	29	9.63 623	34	0.36 377	9.96 273	6	36
25	9.59 924	30	9.63 657	35	0.36 343	9.96 267	5	35
26	9.59 954	29	9.63 692	34	0.36 308	9.96 262	6	34
27	9.59 983	29	9.63 726	35	0.36 274	9.96 256	5	33
28	9.60 012	29	9.63 761	35	0.36 239	9.96 251	6	32
29	9.60 041	29	9.63 796	34	0.36 204	9.96 245	5	31
30	9.60 070	29	9.63 830	35	0.36 170	9.96 240	6	30
31	9.60 099	29	9.63 865	34	0.36 135	9.96 234	5	29
32	9.60 128	29	9.63 899	35	0.36 101	9.96 229	6	28
33	9.60 157	29	9.63 934	34	0.36 066	9.96 223	5	27
34	9.60 186	29	9.63 968	35	0.36 032	9.96 218	6	26
35	9.60 215	29	9.64 003	34	0.35 997	9.96 212	5	25
36	9.60 244	29	9.64 037	35	0.35 963	9.96 207	6	24
37	9.60 273	29	9.64 072	34	0.35 928	9.96 201	5	23
38	9.60 302	29	9.64 106	34	0.35 894	9.96 196	6	22
39	9.60 331	28	9.64 140	35	0.35 860	9.96 190	5	21
40	9.60 359	29	9.64 175	34	0.35 825	9.96 185	6	20
41	9.60 388	29	9.64 209	34	0.35 791	9.96 179	5	19
42	9.60 417	29	9.64 243	35	0.35 757	9.96 174	6	18
43	9.60 446	28	9.64 278	34	0.35 722	9.96 168	6	17
44	9.60 474	29	9.64 312	34	0.35 688	9.96 162	5	16
45	9.60 503	29	9.64 346	35	0.35 654	9.96 157	6	15
46	9.60 532	29	9.64 381	34	0.35 619	9.96 151	5	14
47	9.60 561	28	9.64 415	34	0.35 585	9.96 146	6	13
48	9.60 589	29	9.64 449	34	0.35 551	9.96 140	5	12
49	9.60 618	28	9.64 483	34	0.35 517	9.96 135	6	11
50	9.60 646	29	9.64 517	35	0.35 483	9.96 129	6	10
51	9.60 675	29	9.64 552	34	0.35 448	9.96 123	5	9
52	9.60 704	28	9.64 586	34	0.35 414	9.96 118	6	8
53	9.60 732	29	9.64 620	34	0.35 380	9.96 112	5	7
54	9.60 761	28	9.64 654	34	0.35 346	9.96 107	6	6
55	9.60 789	29	9.64 688	34	0.35 312	9.96 101	6	5
56	9.60 818	28	9.64 722	34	0.35 278	9.96 095	5	4
57	9.60 846	29	9.64 756	34	0.35 244	9.96 090	5	3
58	9.60 875	28	9.64 790	34	0.35 210	9.96 084	5	2
59	9.60 903	28	9.64 824	34	0.35 176	9.96 079	6	1
60	9.60 931		9.64 858		0.35 142	9.96 073		0

′	L. Cos.	d.	L. Cot.	c.d.	L. Tan.	L. Sin.	d.	′

113° (293°)   (246°) **66°**

P. P.

″	36	35	34
1	0.6	0.6	0.6
2	1.2	1.2	1.1
3	1.8	1.8	1.7
4	2.4	2.3	2.3
5	3.0	2.9	2.8
6	3.6	3.5	3.4
7	4.2	4.1	4.0
8	4.8	4.7	4.5
9	5.4	5.2	5.1
10	6.0	5.8	5.7
20	12.0	11.7	11.3
30	18.0	17.5	17.0
40	24.0	23.3	22.7
50	30.0	29.2	28.3

″	30	29	28
1	0.5	0.5	0.5
2	1.0	1.0	0.9
3	1.5	1.4	1.4
4	2.0	1.9	1.9
5	2.5	2.4	2.3
6	3.0	2.9	2.8
7	3.5	3.4	3.3
8	4.0	3.9	3.7
9	4.5	4.4	4.2
10	5.0	4.8	4.7
20	10.0	9.7	9.3
30	15.0	14.5	14.0
40	20.0	19.3	18.7
50	25.0	24.2	23.3

″	6	5
1	0.1	0.1
2	0.2	0.2
3	0.3	0.2
4	0.4	0.3
5	0.5	0.4
6	0.6	0.5
7	0.7	0.6
8	0.8	0.7
9	0.9	0.8
10	1.0	0.8
20	2.0	1.7
30	3.0	2.5
40	4.0	3.3
50	5.0	4.2

	6	6	6
	36	35	34
0			
1	3.0	2.9	2.8
2	9.0	8.8	8.5
3	15.0	14.6	14.2
4	21.0	20.4	19.8
5	27.0	26.2	25.5
6	33.0	32.1	31.2

	5	5
	35	34
0		
1	3.5	3.4
2	10.5	10.2
3	17.5	17.0
4	24.5	23.8
5	31.5	30.6

COMMON LOGARITHMS OF THE TRIGONOMETRIC
FUNCTIONS (Continued)

24° (204°)　　　　　　　　　　　　　　　　　　　　(335°) **155°**

'	L. Sin.	d.	L. Tan.	c.d.	L. Cot.	L. Cos.	d.	'
0	9.60 931	29	9.64 858	34	0.35 142	9.96 073	6	60
1	9.60 960	28	9.64 892	34	0.35 108	9.96 067	5	59
2	9.60 988	28	9.64 926	34	0.35 074	9.96 062	6	58
3	9.61 016	29	9.64 960	34	0.35 040	9.96 056	6	57
4	9.61 045	28	9.64 994	34	0.35 006	9.96 050	5	56
5	9.61 073	28	9.65 028	34	0.34 972	9.96 045	6	55
6	9.61 101	28	9.65 062	34	0.34 938	9.96 039	5	54
7	9.61 129	29	9.65 096	34	0.34 904	9.96 034	6	53
8	9.61 158	28	9.65 130	34	0.34 870	9.96 028	6	52
9	9.61 186	28	9.65 164	33	0.34 836	9.96 022	5	51
10	9.61 214	28	9.65 197	34	0.34 803	9.96 017	6	50
11	9.61 242	28	9.65 231	34	0.34 769	9.96 011	6	49
12	9.61 270	28	9.65 265	34	0.34 735	9.96 005	5	48
13	9.61 298	28	9.65 299	34	0.34 701	9.96 000	6	47
14	9.61 326	28	9.65 333	33	0.34 667	9.95 994	6	46
15	9.61 354	28	9.65 366	34	0.34 634	9.95 988	6	45
16	9.61 382	29	9.65 400	34	0.34 600	9.95 982	5	44
17	9.61 411	27	9.65 434	33	0.34 566	9.95 977	6	43
18	9.61 438	28	9.65 467	34	0.34 533	9.95 971	6	42
19	9.61 466	28	9.65 501	34	0.34 499	9.95 965	5	41
20	9.61 494	28	9.65 535	33	0.34 465	9.95 960	6	40
21	9.61 522	28	9.65 568	34	0.34 432	9.95 954	6	39
22	9.61 550	28	9.65 602	34	0.34 398	9.95 948	6	38
23	9.61 578	28	9.65 636	33	0.34 364	9.95 942	5	37
24	9.61 606	28	9.65 669	34	0.34 331	9.95 937	6	36
25	9.61 634	28	9.65 703	33	0.34 297	9.95 931	6	35
26	9.61 662	27	9.65 736	34	0.34 264	9.95 925	5	34
27	9.61 689	28	9.65 770	33	0.34 230	9.95 920	6	33
28	9.61 717	28	9.65 803	34	0.34 197	9.95 914	6	32
29	9.61 745	28	9.65 837	33	0.34 163	9.95 908	6	31
30	9.61 773	27	9.65 870	34	0.34 130	9.95 902	5	30
31	9.61 800	28	9.65 904	33	0.34 096	9.95 897	6	29
32	9.61 828	28	9.65 937	34	0.34 063	9.95 891	6	28
33	9.61 856	27	9.65 971	33	0.34 029	9.95 885	6	27
34	9.61 883	28	9.66 004	34	0.33 996	9.95 879	6	26
35	9.61 911	28	9.66 038	33	0.33 962	9.95 873	5	25
36	9.61 939	27	9.66 071	33	0.33 929	9.95 868	6	24
37	9.61 966	28	9.66 104	34	0.33 896	9.95 862	6	23
38	9.61 994	27	9.66 138	33	0.33 862	9.95 856	6	22
39	9.62 021	28	9.66 171	33	0.33 829	9.95 850	6	21
40	9.62 049	27	9.66 204	34	0.33 796	9.95 844	5	20
41	9.62 076	28	9.66 238	33	0.33 762	9.95 839	6	19
42	9.62 104	27	9.66 271	33	0.33 729	9.95 833	6	18
43	9.62 131	28	9.66 304	33	0.33 696	9.95 827	6	17
44	9.62 159	27	9.66 337	34	0.33 663	9.95 821	6	16
45	9.62 186	28	9.66 371	33	0.33 629	9.95 815	5	15
46	9.62 214	27	9.66 404	33	0.33 596	9.95 810	6	14
47	9.62 241	27	9.66 437	33	0.33 563	9.95 804	6	13
48	9.62 268	28	9.66 470	33	0.33 530	9.95 798	6	12
49	9.62 296	27	9.66 503	34	0.33 497	9.95 792	6	11
50	9.62 323	27	9.66 537	33	0.33 463	9.95 786	6	10
51	9.62 350	27	9.66 570	33	0.33 430	9.95 780	5	9
52	9.62 377	28	9.66 603	33	0.33 397	9.95 775	6	8
53	9.62 405	27	9.66 636	33	0.33 364	9.95 769	6	7
54	9.62 432	27	9.66 669	33	0.33 331	9.95 763	6	6
55	9.62 459	27	9.66 702	33	0.33 298	9.95 757	6	5
56	9.62 486	27	9.66 735	33	0.33 265	9.95 751	6	4
57	9.62 513	28	9.66 768	33	0.33 232	9.95 745	6	3
58	9.62 541	27	9.66 801	33	0.33 199	9.95 739	6	2
59	9.62 568	27	9.66 834	33	0.33 166	9.95 733	5	1
60	9.62 595		9.66 867		0.33 133	9.95 728		0
'	L. Cos.	d.	L. Cot.	c.d.	L. Tan.	L. Sin.	d.	'

P. P.

"	34	33
1	0.6	0.6
2	1.1	1.1
3	1.7	1.6
4	2.3	2.2
5	2.8	2.8
6	3.4	3.3
7	4.0	3.8
8	4.5	4.4
9	5.1	5.0
10	5.7	5.5
20	11.3	11.0
30	17.0	16.5
40	22.7	22.0
50	28.3	27.5

"	29	28	27
1	0.5	0.5	0.4
2	1.0	0.9	0.9
3	1.4	1.4	1.4
4	1.9	1.9	1.8
5	2.4	2.3	2.2
6	2.9	2.8	2.7
7	3.4	3.3	3.2
8	3.9	3.7	3.6
9	4.4	4.2	4.0
10	4.8	4.7	4.5
20	9.7	9.3	9.0
30	14.5	14.0	13.5
40	19.3	18.7	18.0
50	24.2	23.3	22.5

"	6	5
1	0.1	0.1
2	0.2	0.2
3	0.3	0.2
4	0.4	0.3
5	0.5	0.4
6	0.6	0.5
7	0.7	0.6
8	0.8	0.7
9	0.9	0.8
10	1.0	0.8
20	2.0	1.7
30	3.0	2.5
40	4.0	3.3
50	5.0	4.2

	6	6	5
	34	33	34
0			
1	2.8	2.8	3.4
2	8.5	8.2	10.2
3	14.2	13.8	17.0
4	19.8	19.2	23.8
5	25.5	24.8	30.6
6	31.2	30.2	—

P. P.

COMMON LOGARITHMS OF THE TRIGONOMETRIC FUNCTIONS (Continued)

25° (205°)   (334°) **154°**

′	L. Sin.	d.	L. Tan.	c.d.	L. Cot.	L. Cos.	d	′
0	9.62 595	27	9.66 867	33	0.33 133	9.95 728	6	60
1	9.62 622	27	9.66 900	33	0.33 100	9.95 722	6	59
2	9.62 649	27	9.66 933	33	0.33 067	9.95 716	6	58
3	9.62 676	27	9.66 966	33	0.33 034	9.95 710	6	57
4	9.62 703	27	9.66 999	33	0.33 001	9.95 704	6	56
5	9.62 730	27	9.67 032	33	0.32 968	9.95 698	6	55
6	9.62 757	27	9.67 065	33	0.32 935	9.95 692	6	54
7	9.62 784	27	9.67 098	33	0.32 902	9.95 686	6	53
8	9.62 811	27	9.67 131	32	0.32 869	9.95 680	6	52
9	9.62 838	27	9.67 163	33	0.32 837	9.95 674	6	51
10	9.62 865	27	9.67 196	33	0.32 804	9.95 668	5	50
11	9.62 892	26	9.67 229	33	0.32 771	9.95 663	6	49
12	9.62 918	27	9.67 262	33	0.32 738	9.95 657	6	48
13	9.62 945	27	9.67 295	32	0.32 705	9.95 651	6	47
14	9.62 972	27	9.67 327	33	0.32 673	9.95 645	6	46
15	9.62 999	27	9.67 360	33	0.32 640	9.95 639	6	45
16	9.63 026	26	9.67 393	33	0.32 607	9.95 633	6	44
17	9.63 052	27	9.67 426	32	0.32 574	9.95 627	6	43
18	9.63 079	27	9.67 458	33	0.32 542	9.95 621	6	42
19	9.63 106	27	9.67 491	33	0.32 509	9.95 615	6	41
20	9.63 133	26	9.67 524	32	0.32 476	9.95 609	6	40
21	9.63 159	27	9.67 556	33	0.32 444	9.95 603	6	39
22	9.63 186	27	9.67 589	33	0.32 411	9.95 597	6	38
23	9.63 213	26	9.67 622	32	0.32 378	9.95 591	6	37
24	9.63 239	27	9.67 654	33	0.32 346	9.95 585	6	36
25	9.63 266	26	9.67 687	32	0.32 313	9.95 579	6	35
26	9.63 292	27	9.67 719	33	0.32 281	9.95 573	6	34
27	9.63 319	26	9.67 752	33	0.32 248	9.95 567	6	33
28	9.63 345	27	9.67 785	32	0.32 215	9.95 561	6	32
29	9.63 372	26	9.67 817	33	0.32 183	9.95 555	6	31
30	9.63 398	27	9.67 850	32	0.32 150	9.95 549	6	30
31	9.63 425	26	9.67 882	33	0.32 118	9.95 543	6	29
32	9.63 451	27	9.67 915	32	0.32 085	9.95 537	6	28
33	9.63 478	26	9.67 947	33	0.32 053	9.95 531	6	27
34	9.63 504	27	9.67 980	32	0.32 020	9.95 525	6	26
35	9.63 531	26	9.68 012	32	0.31 988	9.95 519	6	25
36	9.63 557	26	9.68 044	33	0.31 956	9.95 513	6	24
37	9.63 583	27	9.68 077	32	0.31 923	9.95 507	6	23
38	9.63 610	26	9.68 109	33	0.31 891	9.95 500	7	22
39	9.63 636	26	9.68 142	32	0.31 858	9.95 494	6	21
40	9.63 662	27	9.68 174	32	0.31 826	9.95 488	6	20
41	9.63 689	26	9.68 206	33	0.31 794	9.95 482	6	19
42	9.63 715	26	9.68 239	32	0.31 761	9.95 476	6	18
43	9.63 741	26	9.68 271	32	0.31 729	9.95 470	6	17
44	9.63 767	27	9.68 303	33	0.31 697	9.95 464	6	16
45	9.63 794	26	9.68 336	32	0.31 664	9.95 458	6	15
46	9.63 820	26	9.68 368	32	0.31 632	9.95 452	6	14
47	9.63 846	26	9.68 400	32	0.31 600	9.95 446	6	13
48	9.63 872	26	9.68 432	33	0.31 568	9.95 440	6	12
49	9.63 898	26	9.68 465	32	0.31 535	9.95 434	7	11
50	9.63 924	26	9.68 497	32	0.31 503	9.95 427	6	10
51	9.63 950	26	9.68 529	32	0.31 471	9.95 421	6	9
52	9.63 976	26	9.68 561	32	0.31 439	9.95 415	6	8
53	9.64 002	26	9.68 593	33	0.31 407	9.95 409	6	7
54	9.64 028	26	9.68 626	32	0.31 374	9.95 403	6	6
55	9.64 054	26	9.68 658	32	0.31 342	9.95 397	6	5
56	9.64 080	26	9.68 690	32	0.31 310	9.95 391	7	4
57	9.64 106	26	9.68 722	32	0.31 278	9.95 384	6	3
58	9.64 132	26	9.68 754	32	0.31 246	9.95 378	6	2
59	9.64 158	26	9.68 786	32	0.31 214	9.95 372	6	1
60	9.64 184		9.68 818		0.31 182	9.95 366		0

P. P.

″	33	32
1	0.6	0.5
2	1.1	1.1
3	1.6	1.6
4	2.2	2.1
5	2.8	2.7
6	3.3	3.2
7	3.8	3.7
8	4.4	4.3
9	5.0	4.8
10	5.5	5.3
20	11.0	10.7
30	16.5	16.0
40	22.0	21.3
50	27.5	26.7

″	27	26
1	0.4	0.4
2	0.9	0.9
3	1.4	1.3
4	1.8	1.7
5	2.2	2.2
6	2.7	2.6
7	3.2	3.0
8	3.6	3.5
9	4.0	3.9
10	4.5	4.3
20	9.0	8.7
30	13.5	13.0
40	18.0	17.3
50	22.5	21.7

″	7	6	5
1	0.1	0.1	0.1
2	0.2	0.2	0.2
3	0.4	0.3	0.2
4	0.5	0.4	0.3
5	0.6	0.5	0.4
6	0.7	0.6	0.5
7	0.8	0.7	0.6
8	0.9	0.8	0.7
9	1.0	0.9	0.8
10	1.2	1.0	0.8
20	2.3	2.0	1.7
30	3.5	3.0	2.5
40	4.7	4.0	3.3
50	5.8	5.0	4.2

	7	6	5
	32	32	33
0	2.3	2.7	3.3
1	6.9	8.0	9.9
2	11.4	13.3	16.5
3	16.0	18.7	23.1
4	20.6	24.0	29.7
5	25.1	29.3	—
6	29.7	—	—
7			

′	L. Cos.	d.	L. Cot.	c.d.	L. Tan.	L. Sin.	d.	′	P. P.

COMMON LOGARITHMS OF THE TRIGONOMETRIC
FUNCTIONS (Continued)

26° (206°)   (333°) **153°**

′	L. Sin.	d.	L. Tan.	c.d.	L. Cot.	L. Cos.	d.	′	P.P.
0	9.64 184	26	9.68 818	32	0.31 182	9.95 366	6	60	
1	9.64 210	26	9.68 850	32	0.31 150	9.95 360	6	59	″ 32 31
2	9.64 236	26	9.68 882	32	0.31 118	9.95 354	6	58	1 0.5 0.5
3	9.64 262	26	9.68 914	32	0.31 086	9.95 348	7	57	2 1.1 1.0
4	9.64 288	25	9.68 946	32	0.31 054	9.95 341	6	56	3 1.6 1.6
									4 2.1 2.1
5	9.64 313	26	9.68 978	32	0.31 022	9.95 335	6	55	
6	9.64 339	26	9.69 010	32	0.30 990	9.95 329	6	54	5 2.7 2.6
7	9.64 365	26	9.69 042	32	0.30 958	9.95 323	6	53	6 3.2 3.1
8	9.64 391	26	9.69 074	32	0.30 926	9.95 317	7	52	7 3.7 3.6
9	9.64 417	25	9.69 106	32	0.30 894	9.95 310	6	51	8 4.3 4.1
									9 4.8 4.6
10	9.64 442	26	9.69 138	32	0.30 862	9.95 304	6	50	
11	9.64 468	26	9.69 170	32	0.30 830	9.95 298	6	49	10 5.3 5.2
12	9.64 494	25	9.69 202	32	0.30 798	9.95 292	6	48	20 10.7 10.3
13	9.64 519	26	9.69 234	32	0.30 766	9.95 286	7	47	30 16.0 15.5
14	9.64 545	26	9.69 266	32	0.30 734	9.95 279	6	46	40 21.3 20.7
									50 26.7 25.8
15	9.64 571	25	9.69 298	31	0.30 702	9.95 273	6	45	
16	9.64 596	26	9.69 329	32	0.30 671	9.95 267	6	44	″ 26 25 24
17	9.64 622	25	9.69 361	32	0.30 639	9.95 261	7	43	1 0.4 0.4 0.4
18	9.64 647	26	9.69 393	32	0.30 607	9.95 254	6	42	2 0.9 0.8 0.8
19	9.64 673	25	9.69 425	32	0.30 575	9.95 248	6	41	3 1.3 1.2 1.2
									4 1.7 1.7 1.6
20	9.64 698	26	9.69 457	31	0.30 543	9.95 242	6	40	
21	9.64 724	25	9.69 488	32	0.30 512	9.95 236	7	39	5 2.2 2.1 2.0
22	9.64 749	26	9.69 520	32	0.30 480	9.95 229	6	38	6 2.6 2.5 2.4
23	9.64 775	25	9.69 552	32	0.30 448	9.95 223	6	37	7 3.0 2.9 2.8
24	9.64 800	26	9.69 584	31	0.30 416	9.95 217	6	36	8 3.5 3.3 3.2
									9 3.9 3.8 3.6
25	9.64 826	25	9.69 615	32	0.30 385	9.95 211	7	35	
26	9.64 851	26	9.69 647	32	0.30 353	9.95 204	6	34	10 4.3 4.2 4.0
27	9.64 877	25	9.69 679	31	0.30 321	9.95 198	6	33	20 8.7 8.3 8.0
28	9.64 902	25	9.69 710	32	0.30 290	9.95 192	7	32	30 13.0 12.5 12.0
29	9.64 927	26	9.69 742	32	0.30 258	9.95 185	6	31	40 17.3 16.7 16.0
									50 21.7 20.8 20.0
30	9.64 953	25	9.69 774	31	0.30 226	9.95 179	6	30	
31	9.64 978	25	9.69 805	32	0.30 195	9.95 173	6	29	″ 7 6
32	9.65 003	26	9.69 837	31	0.30 163	9.95 167	7	28	1 0.1 0.1
33	9.65 029	25	9.69 868	32	0.30 132	9.95 160	6	27	2 0.2 0.2
34	9.65 054	25	9.69 900	32	0.30 100	9.95 154	6	26	3 0.4 0.3
									4 0.5 0.4
35	9.65 079	25	9.69 932	31	0.30 068	9.95 148	7	25	
36	9.65 104	26	9.69 963	32	0.30 037	9.95 141	6	24	5 0.6 0.5
37	9.65 130	25	9.69 995	31	0.30 005	9.95 135	6	23	6 0.7 0.6
38	9.65 155	25	9.70 026	32	0.29 974	9.95 129	7	22	7 0.8 0.7
39	9.65 180	25	9.70 058	31	0.29 942	9.95 122	6	21	8 0.9 0.8
									9 1.0 0.9
40	9.65 205	25	9.70 089	32	0.29 911	9.95 116	6	20	
41	9.65 230	25	9.70 121	31	0.29 879	9.95 110	7	19	10 1.2 1.0
42	9.65 255	26	9.70 152	32	0.29 848	9.95 103	6	18	20 2.3 2.0
43	9.65 281	25	9.70 184	31	0.29 816	9.95 097	7	17	30 3.5 3.0
44	9.65 306	25	9.70 215	32	0.29 785	9.95 090	6	16	40 4.7 4.0
									50 5.8 5.0
45	9.65 331	25	9.70 247	31	0.29 753	9.95 084	6	15	
46	9.65 356	25	9.70 278	31	0.29 722	9.95 078	7	14	
47	9.65 381	25	9.70 309	32	0.29 691	9.95 071	6	13	
48	9.65 406	25	9.70 341	31	0.29 659	9.95 065	6	12	
49	9.65 431	25	9.70 372	32	0.29 628	9.95 059	7	11	7 7 6
50	9.65 456	25	9.70 404	31	0.29 596	9.95 052	6	10	32 31 32
51	9.65 481	25	9.70 435	31	0.29 565	9.95 046	7	9	
52	9.65 506	25	9.70 466	32	0.29 534	9.95 039	6	8	0
53	9.65 531	25	9.70 498	31	0.29 502	9.95 033	6	7	1 2.3 2.2 2.7
54	9.65 556	24	9.70 529	31	0.29 471	9.95 027	7	6	2 6.9 6.6 8.0
									3 11.4 11.1 13.3
55	9.65 580	25	9.70 560	32	0.29 440	9.95 020	6	5	4 16.0 15.5 18.7
56	9.65 605	25	9.70 592	31	0.29 408	9.95 014	7	4	5 20.6 19.9 24.0
57	9.65 630	25	9.70 623	31	0.29 377	9.95 007	6	3	6 25.1 24.4 29.3
58	9.65 655	25	9.70 654	31	0.29 346	9.95 001	6	2	7 29.7 28.8 —
59	9.65 680	25	9.70 685	32	0.29 315	9.94 995	7	1	
60	9.65 705		9.70 717		0.29 283	9.94 988		0	

| ′ | L. Cos. | d. | L. Cot. | c.d. | L. Tan. | L. Sin. | d. | ′ | P.P. |

116° (296°)   (243°) **63°**

COMMON LOGARITHMS OF THE TRIGONOMETRIC
FUNCTIONS (Continued)

27° (207°) (332°) **152°**

′	L. Sin.	d.	L. Tan.	c.d.	L. Cot.	L. Cos.	d.	′
0	9.65 705	24	9.70 717	31	0.29 283	9.94 988	6	60
1	9.65 729	25	9.70 748	31	0.29 252	9.94 982	7	59
2	9.65 754	25	9.70 779	31	0.29 221	9.94 975	6	58
3	9.65 779	25	9.70 810	31	0.29 190	9.94 969	7	57
4	9.65 804	24	9.70 841	32	0.29 159	9.94 962	6	56
5	9.65 828	25	9.70 873	31	0.29 127	9.94 956	7	55
6	9.65 853	25	9.70 904	31	0.29 096	9.94 949	6	54
7	9.65 878	24	9.70 935	31	0.29 065	9.94 943	7	53
8	9.65 902	25	9.70 966	31	0.29 034	9.94 936	6	52
9	9.65 927	25	9.70 997	31	0.29 003	9.94 930	7	51
10	9.65 952	24	9.71 028	31	0.28 972	9.94 923	6	50
11	9.65 976	25	9.71 059	31	0.28 941	9.94 917	6	49
12	9.66 001	24	9.71 090	31	0.28 910	9.94 911	7	48
13	9.66 025	25	9.71 121	32	0.28 879	9.94 904	6	47
14	9.66 050	25	9.71 153	31	0.28 847	9.94 898	7	46
15	9.66 075	24	9.71 184	31	0.28 816	9.94 891	6	45
16	9.66 099	24	9.71 215	31	0.28 785	9.94 885	7	44
17	9.66 124	24	9.71 246	31	0.28 754	9.94 878	7	43
18	9.66 148	25	9.71 277	31	0.28 723	9.94 871	6	42
19	9.66 173	24	9.71 308	31	0.28 692	9.94 865	7	41
20	9.66 197	24	9.71 339	31	0.28 661	9.94 858	6	40
21	9.66 221	25	9.71 370	31	0.28 630	9.94 852	7	39
22	9.66 246	24	9.71 401	30	0.28 599	9.94 845	6	38
23	9.66 270	25	9.71 431	31	0.28 569	9.94 839	7	37
24	9.66 295	24	9.71 462	31	0.28 538	9.94 832	6	36
25	9.66 319	24	9.71 493	31	0.28 507	9.94 826	7	35
26	9.66 343	25	9.71 524	31	0.28 476	9.94 819	6	34
27	9.66 368	24	9.71 555	31	0.28 445	9.94 813	7	33
28	9.66 392	24	9.71 586	31	0.28 414	9.94 806	7	32
29	9.66 416	25	9.71 617	31	0.28 383	9.94 799	6	31
30	9.66 441	24	9.71 648	31	0.28 352	9.94 793	7	30
31	9.66 465	24	9.71 679	30	0.28 321	9.94 786	6	29
32	9.66 489	24	9.71 709	31	0.28 291	9.94 780	7	28
33	9.66 513	24	9.71 740	31	0.28 260	9.94 773	6	27
34	9.66 537	25	9.71 771	31	0.28 229	9.94 767	7	26
35	9.66 562	24	9.71 802	31	0.28 198	9.94 760	7	25
36	9.66 586	24	9.71 833	30	0.28 167	9.94 753	6	24
37	9.66 610	24	9.71 863	31	0.28 137	9.94 747	7	23
38	9.66 634	24	9.71 894	31	0.28 106	9.94 740	6	22
39	9.66 658	24	9.71 925	30	0.28 075	9.94 734	7	21
40	9.66 682	24	9.71 955	31	0.28 045	9.94 727	7	20
41	9.66 706	25	9.71 986	31	0.28 014	9.94 720	6	19
42	9.66 731	24	9.72 017	31	0.27 983	9.94 714	7	18
43	9.66 755	24	9.72 048	30	0.27 952	9.94 707	7	17
44	9.66 779	24	9.72 078	31	0.27 922	9.94 700	6	16
45	9.66 803	24	9.72 109	31	0.27 891	9.94 694	7	15
46	9.66 827	24	9.72 140	30	0.27 860	9.94 687	7	14
47	9.66 851	24	9.72 170	31	0.27 830	9.94 680	6	13
48	9.66 875	24	9.72 201	30	0.27 799	9.94 674	7	12
49	9.66 899	23	9.72 231	31	0.27 769	9.94 667	7	11
50	9.66 922	24	9.72 262	31	0.27 738	9.94 660	6	10
51	9.66 946	24	9.72 293	30	0.27 707	9.94 654	7	9
52	9.66 970	24	9.72 323	31	0.27 677	9.94 647	7	8
53	9.66 994	24	9.72 354	30	0.27 646	9.94 640	6	7
54	9.67 018	24	9.72 384	31	0.27 616	9.94 634	7	6
55	9.67 042	24	9.72 415	30	0.27 585	9.94 627	7	5
56	9.67 066	24	9.72 445	31	0.27 555	9.94 620	6	4
57	9.67 090	23	9.72 476	30	0.27 524	9.94 614	7	3
58	9.67 113	24	9.72 506	31	0.27 494	9.94 607	7	2
59	9.67 137	24	9.72 537	30	0.27 463	9.94 600	7	1
60	9.67 161		9.72 567		0.27 433	9.94 593		0

′	L. Cos.	d.	L. Cot.	c.d.	L. Tan.	L. Sin.	d.	′

117° (297°) (242°) **62°**

P. P.

″	32	31	30
1	0.5	0.5	0.5
2	1.1	1.0	1.0
3	1.6	1.6	1.5
4	2.1	2.1	2.0
5	2.7	2.6	2.5
6	3.2	3.1	3.0
7	3.7	3.6	3.5
8	4.3	4.1	4.0
9	4.8	4.6	4.5
10	5.3	5.2	5.0
20	10.7	10.3	10.0
30	16.0	15.5	15.0
40	21.3	20.7	20.0
50	26.7	25.8	25.0

″	25	24	23
1	0.4	0.4	0.4
2	0.8	0.8	0.8
3	1.2	1.2	1.2
4	1.7	1.6	1.5
5	2.1	2.0	1.9
6	2.5	2.4	2.3
7	2.9	2.8	2.7
8	3.3	3.2	3.1
9	3.8	3.6	3.4
10	4.2	4.0	3.8
20	8.3	8.0	7.7
30	12.5	12.0	11.5
40	16.7	16.0	15.3
50	20.8	20.0	19.2

″	7	6
1	0.1	0.1
2	0.2	0.2
3	0.4	0.3
4	0.5	0.4
5	0.6	0.5
6	0.7	0.6
7	0.8	0.7
8	0.9	0.8
9	1.0	0.9
10	1.2	1.0
20	2.3	2.0
30	3.5	3.0
40	4.7	4.0
50	5.8	5.0

	7/30	6/31	6/30
0			
1	2.1	2.6	2.5
2	6.4	7.8	7.5
3	10.7	12.9	12.5
4	15.0	18.1	17.5
5	19.3	23.2	22.5
6	23.6	28.4	27.5
7	27.9	—	—

COMMON LOGARITHMS OF THE TRIGONOMETRIC
FUNCTIONS (Continued)

28° (208°)   (331°) **151°**

′	L. Sin.	d.	L. Tan.	c.d.	L. Cot.	L. Cos.	d.	′
0	9.67 161	24	9.72 567	31	0.27 433	9.94 593	6	60
1	9.67 185	23	9.72 598	30	0.27 402	9.94 587	7	59
2	9.67 208	24	9.72 628	31	0.27 372	9.94 580	7	58
3	9.67 232	24	9.72 659	30	0.27 341	9.94 573	6	57
4	9.67 256	24	9.72 689	31	0.27 311	9.94 567	7	56
5	9.67 280	23	9.72 720	30	0.27 280	9.94 560	7	55
6	9.67 303	24	9.72 750	30	0.27 250	9.94 553	7	54
7	9.67 327	23	9.72 780	31	0.27 220	9.94 546	6	53
8	9.67 350	24	9.72 811	30	0.27 189	9.94 540	7	52
9	9.67 374	24	9.72 841	31	0.27 159	9.94 533	7	51
10	9.67 398	23	9.72 872	30	0.27 128	9.94 526	7	50
11	9.67 421	24	9.72 902	30	0.27 098	9.94 519	6	49
12	9.67 445	23	9.72 932	31	0.27 068	9.94 513	7	48
13	9.67 468	24	9.72 963	30	0.27 037	9.94 506	7	47
14	9.67 492	23	9.72 993	30	0.27 007	9.94 499	7	46
15	9.67 515	24	9.73 023	31	0.26 977	9.94 492	7	45
16	9.67 539	23	9.73 054	30	0.26 946	9.94 485	6	44
17	9.67 562	24	9.73 084	30	0.26 916	9.94 479	7	43
18	9.67 586	23	9.73 114	30	0.26 886	9.94 472	7	42
19	9.67 609	24	9.73 144	31	0.26 856	9.94 465	7	41
20	9.67 633	23	9.73 175	30	0.26 825	9.94 458	7	40
21	9.67 656	24	9.73 205	30	0.26 795	9.94 451	6	39
22	9.67 680	23	9.73 235	30	0.26 765	9.94 445	7	38
23	9.67 703	23	9.73 265	30	0.26 735	9.94 438	7	37
24	9.67 726	24	9.73 295	31	0.26 705	9.94 431	7	36
25	9.67 750	23	9.73 326	30	0.26 674	9.94 424	7	35
26	9.67 773	23	9.73 356	30	0.26 644	9.94 417	7	34
27	9.67 796	24	9.73 386	30	0.26 614	9.94 410	6	33
28	9.67 820	23	9.73 416	30	0.26 584	9.94 404	7	32
29	9.67 843	23	9.73 446	30	0.26 554	9.94 397	7	31
30	9.67 866	24	9.73 476	31	0.26 524	9.94 390	7	30
31	9.67 890	23	9.73 507	30	0.26 493	9.94 383	7	29
32	9.67 913	23	9.73 537	30	0.26 463	9.94 376	7	28
33	9.67 936	23	9.73 567	30	0.26 433	9.94 369	7	27
34	9.67 959	23	9.73 597	30	0.26 403	9.94 362	7	26
35	9.67 982	24	9.73 627	30	0.26 373	9.94 355	6	25
36	9.68 006	23	9.73 657	30	0.26 343	9.94 349	7	24
37	9.68 029	23	9.73 687	30	0.26 313	9.94 342	7	23
38	9.68 052	23	9.73 717	30	0.26 283	9.94 335	7	22
39	9.68 075	23	9.73 747	30	0.26 253	9.94 328	7	21
40	9.68 098	23	9.73 777	30	0.26 223	9.94 321	7	20
41	9.68 121	23	9.73 807	30	0.26 193	9.94 314	7	19
42	9.68 144	23	9.73 837	30	0.26 163	9.94 307	7	18
43	9.68 167	23	9.73 867	30	0.26 133	9.94 300	7	17
44	9.68 190	23	9.73 897	30	0.26 103	9.94 293	7	16
45	9.68 213	24	9.73 927	30	0.26 073	9.94 286	7	15
46	9.68 237	23	9.73 957	30	0.26 043	9.94 279	6	14
47	9.68 260	23	9.73 987	30	0.26 013	9.94 273	7	13
48	9.68 283	22	9.74 017	30	0.25 983	9.94 266	7	12
49	9.68 305	23	9.74 047	30	0.25 953	9.94 259	7	11
50	9.68 328	23	9.74 077	30	0.25 923	9.94 252	7	10
51	9.68 351	23	9.74 107	30	0.25 893	9.94 245	7	9
52	9.68 374	23	9.74 137	29	0.25 863	9.94 238	7	8
53	9.68 397	23	9.74 166	30	0.25 834	9.94 231	7	7
54	9.68 420	23	9.74 196	30	0.25 804	9.94 224	7	6
55	9.68 443	23	9.74 226	30	0.25 774	9.94 217	7	5
56	9.68 466	23	9.74 256	30	0.25 744	9.94 210	7	4
57	9.68 489	23	9.74 286	30	0.25 714	9.94 203	7	3
58	9.68 512	22	9.74 316	29	0.25 684	9.94 196	7	2
59	9.68 534	23	9.74 345	30	0.25 655	9.94 189	7	1
60	9.68 557		9.74 375		0.25 625	9.94 182		0

P. P.

″	31	30	29
1	0.5	0.5	0.5
2	1.0	1.0	1.0
3	1.6	1.5	1.4
4	2.1	2.0	1.9
5	2.6	2.5	2.4
6	3.1	3.0	2.9
7	3.6	3.5	3.4
8	4.1	4.0	3.9
9	4.6	4.5	4.4
10	5.2	5.0	4.8
20	10.3	10.0	9.7
30	15.5	15.0	14.5
40	20.7	20.0	19.3
50	25.8	25.0	24.2

″	24	23	22
1	0.4	0.4	0.4
2	0.8	0.8	0.7
3	1.2	1.2	1.1
4	1.6	1.5	1.5
5	2.0	1.9	1.8
6	2.4	2.3	2.2
7	2.8	2.7	2.6
8	3.2	3.1	2.9
9	3.6	3.4	3.3
10	4.0	3.8	3.7
20	8.0	7.7	7.3
30	12.0	11.5	11.0
40	16.0	15.3	14.7
50	20.0	19.2	18.3

″	7	6
1	0.1	0.1
2	0.2	0.2
3	0.4	0.3
4	0.5	0.4
5	0.6	0.5
6	0.7	0.6
7	0.8	0.7
8	0.9	0.8
9	1.0	0.9
10	1.2	1.0
20	2.3	2.0
30	3.5	3.0
40	4.7	4.0
50	5.8	5.0

	7/31	6/31	6/30
0	2.2	2.6	2.5
1	6.6	7.8	7.5
2	11.1	12.9	12.5
3	15.5	18.1	17.5
4	19.9	23.2	22.5
5	24.4	28.4	27.5
6	28.8	—	—
7			

′	L. Cos.	d.	L. Cot.	c.d.	L. Tan.	L. Sin.	d.	′

P. P.

COMMON LOGARITHMS OF THE TRIGONOMETRIC FUNCTIONS (Continued)

29° (209°)   (330°) **150°**

′	L. Sin.	d.	L. Tan.	c.d.	L. Cot.	L. Cos.	d.	′		P. P.		
0	9.68 557	23	9.74 375	30	0.25 625	9.94 182	7	60	″	**30**	**29**	**23**
1	9.68 580	23	9.74 405	30	0.25 595	9.94 175	7	59	1	0.5	0.5	0.4
2	9.68 603	22	9.74 435	30	0.25 565	9.94 168	7	58	2	1.0	1.0	0.8
3	9.68 625	23	9.74 465	29	0.25 535	9.94 161	7	57	3	1.5	1.4	1.2
4	9.68 648	23	9.74 494	30	0.25 506	9.94 154	7	56	4	2.0	1.9	1.5
5	9.68 671	23	9.74 524	30	0.25 476	9.94 147	7	55				
6	9.68 694	22	9.74 554	29	0.25 446	9.94 140	7	54	5	2.5	2.4	1.9
7	9.68 716	23	9.74 583	30	0.25 417	9.94 133	7	53	6	3.0	2.9	2.3
8	9.68 739	23	9.74 613	30	0.25 387	9.94 126	7	52	7	3.5	3.4	2.7
9	9.68 762	22	9.74 643	30	0.25 357	9.94 119	7	51	8	4.0	3.9	3.1
									9	4.5	4.4	3.4
10	9.68 784	23	9.74 673	29	0.25 327	9.94 112	7	50				
11	9.68 807	22	9.74 702	30	0.25 298	9.94 105	7	49	10	5.0	4.8	3.8
12	9.68 829	23	9.74 732	30	0.25 268	9.94 098	8	48	20	10.0	9.7	7.7
13	9.68 852	23	9.74 762	29	0.25 238	9.94 090	7	47	30	15.0	14.5	11.5
14	9.68 875	22	9.74 791	30	0.25 209	9.94 083	7	46	40	20.0	19.3	15.3
									50	25.0	24.2	19.2
15	9.68 897	23	9.74 821	30	0.25 179	9.94 076	7	45				
16	9.68 920	22	9.74 851	29	0.25 149	9.94 069	7	44	″	**22**	**8**	**7**
17	9.68 942	23	9.74 880	30	0.25 120	9.94 062	7	43	1	0.4	0.1	0.1
18	9.68 965	22	9.74 910	30	0.25 090	9.94 055	7	42	2	0.7	0.3	0.2
19	9.68 987	23	9.74 939	30	0.25 061	9.94 048	7	41	3	1.1	0.4	0.4
									4	1.5	0.5	0.5
20	9.69 010	22	9.74 969	29	0.25 031	9.94 041	7	40				
21	9.69 032	23	9.74 998	30	0.25 002	9.94 034	7	39	5	1.8	0.7	0.6
22	9.69 055	22	9.75 028	30	0.24 972	9.94 027	7	38	6	2.2	0.8	0.7
23	9.69 077	23	9.75 058	29	0.24 942	9.94 020	8	37	7	2.6	0.9	0.8
24	9.69 100	22	9.75 087	30	0.24 913	9.94 012	7	36	8	2.9	1.1	0.9
									9	3.3	1.2	1.0
25	9.69 122	22	9.75 117	29	0.24 883	9.94 005	7	35				
26	9.69 144	23	9.75 146	30	0.24 854	9.93 998	7	34	10	3.7	1.3	1.2
27	9.69 167	22	9.75 176	29	0.24 824	9.93 991	7	33	20	7.3	2.7	2.3
28	9.69 189	23	9.75 205	30	0.24 795	9.93 984	7	32	30	11.0	4.0	3.5
29	9.69 212	22	9.75 235	29	0.24 765	9.93 977	7	31	40	14.7	5.3	4.7
									50	18.3	6.7	5.8
30	9.69 234	22	9.75 264	30	0.24 736	9.93 970	7	30				
31	9.69 256	23	9.75 294	29	0.24 706	9.93 963	8	29				
32	9.69 279	22	9.75 323	30	0.24 677	9.93 955	7	28				
33	9.69 301	22	9.75 353	29	0.24 647	9.93 948	7	27				
34	9.69 323	22	9.75 382	29	0.24 618	9.93 941	7	26				
35	9.69 345	23	9.75 411	30	0.24 589	9.93 934	7	25		**8**		**8**
36	9.69 368	22	9.75 441	29	0.24 559	9.93 927	7	24		**30**		**29**
37	9.69 390	22	9.75 470	30	0.24 530	9.93 920	8	23				
38	9.69 412	22	9.75 500	29	0.24 500	9.93 912	7	22	0			
39	9.69 434	22	9.75 529	29	0.24 471	9.93 905	7	21	1	1.9		1.8
									2	5.6		5.4
40	9.69 456	23	9.75 558	30	0.24 442	9.93 898	7	20	3	9.4		9.1
41	9.69 479	22	9.75 588	29	0.24 412	9.93 891	7	19	4	13.1		12.7
42	9.69 501	22	9.75 617	30	0.24 383	9.93 884	8	18	5	16.9		16.3
43	9.69 523	22	9.75 647	29	0.24 353	9.93 876	7	17	6	20.6		19.9
44	9.69 545	22	9.75 676	29	0.24 324	9.93 869	7	16	7	24.4		23.6
									8	28.1		27.2
45	9.69 567	22	9.75 705	30	0.24 295	9.93 862	7	15				
46	9.69 589	22	9.75 735	29	0.24 265	9.93 855	8	14				
47	9.69 611	22	9.75 764	29	0.24 236	9.93 847	7	13				
48	9.69 633	22	9.75 793	29	0.24 207	9.93 840	7	12				
49	9.69 655	22	9.75 822	30	0.24 178	9.93 833	7	11		**7**		**7**
50	9.69 677	22	9.75 852	29	0.24 148	9.93 826	7	10		**30**		**29**
51	9.69 699	22	9.75 881	29	0.24 119	9.93 819	8	9	0			
52	9.69 721	22	9.75 910	29	0.24 090	9.93 811	7	8	1	2.1		2.1
53	9.69 743	22	9.75 939	30	0.24 061	9.93 804	7	7	2	6.4		6.2
54	9.69 765	22	9.75 969	29	0.24 031	9.93 797	8	6	3	10.7		10.4
									4	15.0		14.5
55	9.69 787	22	9.75 998	29	0.24 002	9.93 789	7	5	5	19.3		18.6
56	9.69 809	22	9.76 027	29	0.23 973	9.93 782	7	4	6	23.6		22.8
57	9.69 831	22	9.76 056	30	0.23 944	9.93 775	7	3	7	27.9		26.9
58	9.69 853	22	9.76 086	29	0.23 914	9.93 768	8	2				
59	9.69 875	22	9.76 115	29	0.23 885	9.93 760	7	1				
60	9.69 897		9.76 144		0.23 856	9.93 753		0				
′	L. Cos.	d.	L. Cot.	c.d.	L. Tan.	L. Sin.	d.	′		P. P.		

COMMON LOGARITHMS OF THE TRIGONOMETRIC
FUNCTIONS (Continued)

30° (210°) (329°) 149°

'	L. Sin.	d.	L. Tan.	c.d.	L. Cot.	L. Cos.	d.	'
0	9.69 897	22	9.76 144	29	0.23 856	9.93 753	7	60
1	9.69 919	22	9.76 173	29	0.23 827	9.95 746	8	59
2	9.69 941	22	9.76 202	29	0.23 798	9.93 738	7	58
3	9.69 963	21	9.76 231	30	0.23 769	9.93 731	7	57
4	9.69 984	22	9.76 261	29	0.23 739	9.93 724	7	56
5	9.70 006	22	9.76 290	29	0.23 710	9.93 717	8	55
6	9.70 028	22	9.76 319	29	0.23 681	9.93 709	7	54
7	9.70 050	22	9.76 348	29	0.23 652	9.93 702	7	53
8	9.70 072	21	9.76 377	29	0.23 623	9.93 695	8	52
9	9.70 093	22	9.76 406	29	0.23 594	9.93 687	7	51
10	9.70 115	22	9.76 435	29	0.23 565	9.93 680	7	50
11	9.70 137	22	9.76 464	29	0.23 536	9.93 673	8	49
12	9.70 159	21	9.76 493	29	0.23 507	9.93 665	7	48
13	9.70 180	22	9.76 522	29	0.23 478	9.93 658	8	47
14	9.70 202	22	9.76 551	29	0.23 449	9.93 650	7	46
15	9.70 224	21	9.76 580	29	0.23 420	9.93 643	7	45
16	9.70 245	22	9.76 609	30	0.23 391	9.93 636	8	44
17	9.70 267	21	9.76 639	29	0.23 361	9.93 628	7	43
18	9.70 288	22	9.76 668	29	0.23 332	9.93 621	7	42
19	9.70 310	22	9.76 697	28	0.23 303	9.93 614	8	41
20	9.70 332	21	9.76 725	29	0.23 275	9.93 606	7	40
21	9.70 353	22	9.76 754	29	0.23 246	9.93 599	8	39
22	9.70 375	21	9.76 783	29	0.23 217	9.93 591	7	38
23	9.70 396	22	9.76 812	29	0.23 188	9.93 584	7	37
24	9.70 418	21	9.76 841	29	0.23 159	9.93 577	8	36
25	9.70 439	22	9.76 870	29	0.23 130	9.93 569	7	35
26	9.70 461	21	9.76 899	29	0.23 101	9.93 562	8	34
27	9.70 482	22	9.76 928	29	0.23 072	9.93 554	7	33
28	9.70 504	21	9.76 957	29	0.23 043	9.93 547	8	32
29	9.70 525	22	9.76 986	29	0.23 014	9.93 539	7	31
30	9.70 547	21	9.77 015	29	0.22 985	9.93 532	7	30
31	9.70 568	22	9.77 044	29	0.22 956	9.93 525	8	29
32	9.70 590	21	9.77 073	28	0.22 927	9.93 517	7	28
33	9.70 611	22	9.77 101	29	0.22 899	9.93 510	8	27
34	9.70 633	21	9.77 130	29	0.22 870	9.93 502	7	26
35	9.70 654	21	9.77 159	29	0.22 841	9.93 495	8	25
36	9.70 675	22	9.77 188	29	0.22 812	9.93 487	7	24
37	9.70 697	21	9.77 217	29	0.22 783	9.93 480	8	23
38	9.70 718	21	9.77 246	28	0.22 754	9.93 472	7	22
39	9.70 739	22	9.77 274	29	0.22 726	9.93 465	8	21
40	9.70 761	21	9.77 303	29	0.22 697	9.93 457	7	20
41	9.70 782	21	9.77 332	29	0.22 668	9.93 450	8	19
42	9.70 803	21	9.77 361	29	0.22 639	9.93 442	7	18
43	9.70 824	22	9.77 390	28	0.22 610	9.93 435	8	17
44	9.70 846	21	9.77 418	29	0.22 582	9.93 427	7	16
45	9.70 867	21	9.77 447	29	0.22 553	9.93 420	8	15
46	9.70 888	21	9.77 476	29	0.22 524	9.93 412	7	14
47	9.70 909	22	9.77 505	28	0.22 495	9.93 405	8	13
48	9.70 931	21	9.77 533	29	0.22 467	9.93 397	7	12
49	9.70 952	21	9.77 562	29	0.22 438	9.93 390	8	11
50	9.70 973	21	9.77 591	28	0.22 409	9.93 382	7	10
51	9.70 994	21	9.77 619	29	0.22 381	9.93 375	8	9
52	9.71 015	21	9.77 648	29	0.22 352	9.93 367	7	8
53	9.71 036	22	9.77 677	29	0.22 323	9.93 360	8	7
54	9.71 058	21	9.77 706	28	0.22 294	9.93 352	8	6
55	9.71 079	21	9.77 734	29	0.22 266	9.93 344	7	5
56	9.71 100	21	9.77 763	28	0.22 237	9.93 337	8	4
57	9.71 121	21	9.77 791	29	0.22 209	9.93 329	7	3
58	9.71 142	21	9.77 820	29	0.22 180	9.93 322	8	2
59	9.71 163	21	9.77 849	28	0.22 151	9.93 314	7	1
60	9.71 184		9.77 877		0.22 123	9.93 307		0
'	L. Cos.	d.	L. Cot.	c.d.	L. Tan.	L. Sin.	d.	'

120° (300°) (239°) 59°

P. P.

"	30	29	28
1	0.5	0.5	0.5
2	1.0	1.0	0.9
3	1.5	1.4	1.4
4	2.0	1.9	1.9
5	2.5	2.4	2.3
6	3.0	2.9	2.8
7	3.5	3.4	3.3
8	4.0	3.9	3.7
9	4.5	4.4	4.2
10	5.0	4.8	4.7
20	10.0	9.7	9.3
30	15.0	14.5	14.0
40	20.0	19.3	18.7
50	25.0	24.2	23.3

"	22	21
1	0.4	0.4
2	0.7	0.7
3	1.1	1.0
4	1.5	1.4
5	1.8	1.8
6	2.2	2.1
7	2.6	2.4
8	2.9	2.8
9	3.3	3.2
10	3.7	3.5
20	7.3	7.0
30	11.0	10.5
40	14.7	14.0
50	18.3	17.5

"	8	7
1	0.1	0.1
2	0.3	0.2
3	0.4	0.4
4	0.5	0.5
5	0.7	0.6
6	0.8	0.7
7	0.9	0.8
8	1.1	0.9
9	1.2	1.0
10	1.3	1.2
20	2.7	2.3
30	4.0	3.5
40	5.3	4.7
50	6.7	5.8

	7	7	7
	30	29	28
0			
1	2.1	2.1	2.0
2	6.4	6.2	6.0
3	10.7	10.4	10.0
4	15.0	14.5	14.0
5	19.3	18.6	18.0
6	23.6	22.8	22.0
7	27.9	26.9	26.0

P. P.

COMMON LOGARITHMS OF THE TRIGONOMETRIC
FUNCTIONS (Continued)

31° (211°) (328°) **148°**

′	L. Sin.	d.	L. Tan.	c.d.	L. Cot.	L. Cos.	d.	′	P. P.		
0	9.71 184	21	9.77 877	29	0.22 123	9.93 307	8	60		″ **29**	**28**
1	9.71 205	21	9.77 906	29	0.22 094	9.93 299	8	59			
2	9.71 226	21	9.77 935	28	0.22 065	9.93 291	8	58	1	0.5	0.5
3	9.71 247	21	9.77 963	29	0.22 037	9.93 284	7	57	2	1.0	0.9
4	9.71 268	21	9.77 992	28	0.22 008	9.93 276	8	56	3	1.4	1.4
							7		4	1.9	1.9
5	9.71 289	21	9.78 020	29	0.21 980	9.93 269	8	55			
6	9.71 310	21	9.78 049	28	0.21 951	9.93 261	8	54	5	2.4	2.3
7	9.71 331	21	9.78 077	29	0.21 923	9.93 253	7	53	6	2.9	2.8
8	9.71 352	21	9.78 106	29	0.21 894	9.93 246	8	52	7	3.4	3.3
9	9.71 373	20	9.78 135	28	0.21 865	9.93 238	8	51	8	3.9	3.7
									9	4.4	4.2
10	9.71 393	21	9.78 163	29	0.21 837	9.93 230	7	50			
11	9.71 414	21	9.78 192	28	0.21 808	9.93 223	8	49	10	4.8	4.7
12	9.71 435	21	9.78 220	29	0.21 780	9.93 215	8	48	20	9.7	9.3
13	9.71 456	21	9.78 249	28	0.21 751	9.93 207	7	47	30	14.5	14.0
14	9.71 477	21	9.78 277	29	0.21 723	9.93 200	8	46	40	19.3	18.7
									50	24.2	23.3
15	9.71 498	21	9.78 306	28	0.21 694	9.93 192	8	45			
16	9.71 519	20	9.78 334	29	0.21 666	9.93 184	7	44	″ **21**	**20**	
17	9.71 539	21	9.78 363	28	0.21 637	9.93 177	8	43	1	0.4	0.3
18	9.71 560	21	9.78 391	28	0.21 609	9.93 169	8	42	2	0.7	0.7
19	9.71 581	21	9.78 419	29	0.21 581	9.93 161	7	41	3	1.0	1.0
									4	1.4	1.3
20	9.71 602	20	9.78 448	28	0.21 552	9.93 154	8	40	5	1.8	1.7
21	9.71 622	21	9.78 476	29	0.21 524	9.93 146	8	39	6	2.1	2.0
22	9.71 643	21	9.78 505	28	0.21 495	9.93 138	7	38	7	2.4	2.3
23	9.71 664	21	9.78 533	29	0.21 467	9.93 131	8	37	8	2.8	2.7
24	9.71 685	20	9.78 562	28	0.21 438	9.93 123	8	36	9	3.2	3.0
25	9.71 705	21	9.78 590	28	0.21 410	9.93 115	7	35	10	3.5	3.3
26	9.71 726	21	9.78 618	29	0.21 382	9.93 108	8	34	20	7.0	6.7
27	9.71 747	20	9.78 647	28	0.21 353	9.93 100	8	33	30	10.5	10.0
28	9.71 767	21	9.78 675	29	0.21 325	9.93 092	8	32	40	14.0	13.3
29	9.71 788	21	9.78 704	28	0.21 296	9.93 084	7	31	50	17.5	16.7
30	9.71 809	20	9.78 732	28	0.21 268	9.93 077	8	30	″ **8**	**7**	
31	9.71 829	21	9.78 760	29	0.21 240	9.93 069	8	29	1	0.1	0.1
32	9.71 850	20	9.78 789	28	0.21 211	9.93 061	8	28	2	0.3	0.2
33	9.71 870	21	9.78 817	28	0.21 183	9.93 053	7	27	3	0.4	0.4
34	9.71 891	20	9.78 845	29	0.21 155	9.93 046	8	26	4	0.5	0.5
35	9.71 911	21	9.78 874	28	0.21 126	9.93 038	8	25	5	0.7	0.6
36	9.71 932	20	9.78 902	28	0.21 098	9.93 030	8	24	6	0.8	0.7
37	9.71 952	21	9.78 930	29	0.21 070	9.93 022	8	23	7	0.9	0.8
38	9.71 973	21	9.78 959	28	0.21 041	9.93 014	7	22	8	1.1	0.9
39	9.71 994	20	9.78 987	28	0.21 013	9.93 007	8	21	9	1.2	1.0
40	9.72 014	20	9.79 015	28	0.20 985	9.92 999	8	20	10	1.3	1.2
41	9.72 034	21	9.79 043	29	0.20 957	9.92 991	8	19	20	2.7	2.3
42	9.72 055	20	9.79 072	28	0.20 928	9.92 983	7	18	30	4.0	3.5
43	9.72 075	21	9.79 100	28	0.20 900	9.92 976	8	17	40	5.3	4.7
44	9.72 096	20	9.79 128	28	0.20 872	9.92 968	8	16	50	6.7	5.8
45	9.72 116	21	9.79 156	29	0.20 844	9.92 960	8	15			
46	9.72 137	20	9.79 185	28	0.20 815	9.92 952	8	14			
47	9.72 157	20	9.79 213	28	0.20 787	9.92 944	8	13			
48	9.72 177	21	9.79 241	28	0.20 759	9.92 936	7	12			
49	9.72 198	20	9.79 269	28	0.20 731	9.92 929	8	11	**8**	**8**	**8**
50	9.72 218	20	9.79 297	29	0.20 703	9.92 921	8	10	**30**	**29**	**28**
51	9.72 238	21	9.79 326	28	0.20 674	9.92 913	8	9			
52	9.72 259	20	9.79 354	28	0.20 646	9.92 905	8	8	0		
53	9.72 279	20	9.79 382	28	0.20 618	9.92 897	8	7	1	1.9 1.8	1.8
54	9.72 299	21	9.79 410	28	0.20 590	9.92 889	8	6	2	5.6 5.4	5.2
									3	9.4 9.1	8.8
55	9.72 320	20	9.79 438	28	0.20 562	9.92 881	7	5	4	13.1 12.7	12.2
56	9.72 340	20	9.79 466	29	0.20 534	9.92 874	8	4	5	16.9 16.3	15.8
57	9.72 360	21	9.79 495	28	0.20 505	9.92 866	8	3	6	20.6 19.9	19.2
58	9.72 381	20	9.79 523	28	0.20 477	9.92 858	8	2	7	24.4 23.6	22.8
59	9.72 401	20	9.79 551	28	0.20 449	9.92 850	8	1	8	28.1 27.2	26.2
60	9.72 421		9.79 579		0.20 421	9.92 842		0			

′	L. Cos.	d.	L. Cot.	c.d.	L. Tan.	L.Sin.	d.	′	P. P.		

121° (301°) (238°) **58°**

COMMON LOGARITHMS OF THE TRIGONOMETRIC
FUNCTIONS (Continued)

32° (212°)   (327°) **147°**

′	L. Sin.	d.	L. Tan.	c.d.	L. Cot.	L. Cos.	d.	′	P. P.		
0	9.72 421	20	9.79 579	28	0.20 421	9.92 842	8	**60**			
1	9.72 441	20	9.79 607	28	0.20 393	9.92 834	8	59	″	29	28	27
2	9.72 461	21	9.79 635	28	0.20 365	9.92 826	8	58	1	0.5	0.5	0.4
3	9.72 482	20	9.79 663	28	0.20 337	9.92 818	8	57	2	1.0	0.9	0.9
4	9.72 502	20	9.79 691	28	0.20 309	9.92 810	7	56	3	1.4	1.4	1.4
									4	1.9	1.9	1.8
5	9.72 522	20	9.79 719	28	0.20 281	9.92 803	8	55				
6	9.72 542	20	9.79 747	29	0.20 253	9.92 795	8	54	5	2.4	2.3	2.2
7	9.72 562	20	9.79 776	28	0.20 224	9.92 787	8	53	6	2.9	2.8	2.7
8	9.72 582	20	9.79 804	28	0.20 196	9.92 779	8	52	7	3.4	3.3	3.2
9	9.72 602	20	9.79 832	28	0.20 168	9.92 771	8	51	8	3.9	3.7	3.6
									9	4.4	4.2	4.0
10	9.72 622	21	9.79 860	28	0.20 140	9.92 763	8	**50**				
11	9.72 643	20	9.79 888	28	0.20 112	9.92 755	8	49	10	4.8	4.7	4.5
12	9.72 663	20	9.79 916	28	0.20 084	9.92 747	8	48	20	9.7	9.3	9.0
13	9.72 683	20	9.79 944	28	0.20 056	9.92 739	8	47	30	14.5	14.0	13.5
14	9.72 703	20	9.79 972	28	0.20 028	9.92 731	8	46	40	19.3	18.7	18.0
									50	24.2	23.3	22.5
15	9.72 723	20	9.80 000	28	0.20 000	9.92 723	8	**45**				
16	9.72 743	20	9.80 028	28	0.19 972	9.92 715	8	44	″	21	20	19
17	9.72 763	20	9.80 056	28	0.19 944	9.92 707	8	43	1	0.4	0.3	0.3
18	9.72 783	20	9.80 084	28	0.19 916	9.92 699	8	42	2	0.7	0.7	0.6
19	9.72 803	20	9.80 112	28	0.19 888	9.92 691	8	41	3	1.0	1.0	1.0
									4	1.4	1.3	1.3
20	9.72 823	20	9.80 140	28	0.19 860	9.92 683	8	**40**				
21	9.72 843	20	9.80 168	27	0.19 832	9.92 675	8	39	5	1.8	1.7	1.6
22	9.72 863	20	9.80 195	28	0.19 805	9.92 667	8	38	6	2.1	2.0	1.9
23	9.72 883	19	9.80 223	28	0.19 777	9.92 659	8	37	7	2.4	2.3	2.2
24	9.72 902	20	9.80 251	28	0.19 749	9.92 651	8	36	8	2.8	2.7	2.5
									9	3.2	3.0	2.8
25	9.72 922	20	9.80 279	28	0.19 721	9.92 643	8	**35**				
26	9.72 942	20	9.80 307	28	0.19 693	9.92 635	8	34	10	3.5	3.3	3.2
27	9.72 962	20	9.80 335	28	0.19 665	9.92 627	8	33	20	7.0	6.7	6.3
28	9.72 982	20	9.80 363	28	0.19 637	9.92 619	8	32	30	10.5	10.0	9.5
29	9.73 002	20	9.80 391	28	0.19 609	9.92 611	8	31	40	14.0	13.3	12.7
									50	17.5	16.7	15.8
30	9.73 022	19	9.80 419	28	0.19 581	9.92 603	8	**30**				
31	9.73 041	20	9.80 447	27	0.19 553	9.92 595	8	29	″	9	8	7
32	9.73 061	20	9.80 474	28	0.19 526	9.92 587	8	28	1	0.2	0.1	0.1
33	9.73 081	20	9.80 502	28	0.19 498	9.92 579	8	27	2	0.3	0.3	0.2
34	9.73 101	20	9.80 530	28	0.19 470	9.92 571	8	26	3	0.4	0.4	0.4
									4	0.6	0.5	0.5
35	9.73 121	19	9.80 558	28	0.19 442	9.92 563	8	**25**				
36	9.73 140	20	9.80 586	28	0.19 414	9.92 555	9	24	5	0.8	0.7	0.6
37	9.73 160	20	9.80 614	28	0.19 386	9.92 546	8	23	6	0.9	0.8	0.7
38	9.73 180	20	9.80 642	27	0.19 358	9.92 538	8	22	7	1.0	0.9	0.8
39	9.73 200	19	9.80 669	28	0.19 331	9.92 530	8	21	8	1.2	1.1	0.9
									9	1.4	1.2	1.0
40	9.73 219	20	9.80 697	28	0.19 303	9.92 522	8	**20**				
41	9.73 239	20	9.80 725	28	0.19 275	9.92 514	8	19	10	1.5	1.3	1.2
42	9.73 259	19	9.80 753	28	0.19 247	9.92 506	8	18	20	3.0	2.7	2.3
43	9.73 278	20	9.80 781	27	0.19 219	9.92 498	8	17	30	4.5	4.0	3.5
44	9.73 298	20	9.80 808	28	0.19 192	9.92 490	8	16	40	6.0	5.3	4.7
									50	7.5	6.7	5.8
45	9.73 318	19	9.80 836	28	0.19 164	9.92 482	9	**15**				
46	9.73 337	20	9.80 864	28	0.19 136	9.92 473	8	14				
47	9.73 357	20	9.80 892	27	0.19 108	9.92 465	8	13				
48	9.73 377	19	9.80 919	28	0.19 081	9.92 457	8	12		8	8	7
49	9.73 396	20	9.80 947	28	0.19 053	9.92 449	8	11		29	28	28
50	9.73 416	19	9.80 975	28	0.19 025	9.92 441	8	**10**				
51	9.73 435	20	9.81 003	27	0.18 997	9.92 433	8	9	0			
52	9.73 455	19	9.81 030	28	0.18 970	9.92 425	9	8	1	1.8	1.8	2.0
53	9.73 474	20	9.81 058	28	0.18 942	9.92 416	8	7	2	5.4	5.2	6.0
54	9.73 494	19	9.81 086	27	0.18 914	9.92 408	8	6	3	9.1	8.8	10.0
									4	12.7	12.2	14.0
55	9.73 513	20	9.81 113	28	0.18 887	9.92 400	8	**5**	5	16.3	15.8	18.0
56	9.73 533	19	9.81 141	28	0.18 859	9.92 392	8	4	6	19.9	19.2	22.0
57	9.73 552	20	9.81 169	27	0.18 831	9.92 384	8	3	7	23.6	22.8	26.0
58	9.73 572	19	9.81 196	28	0.18 804	9.92 376	9	2	8	27.2	26.2	—
59	9.73 591	20	9.81 224	28	0.18 776	9.92 367	8	1				
60	9.73 611		9.81 252		0.18 748	9.92 359		**0**				

′	L. Cos.	d.	L. Cot.	c.d.	L. Tan.	L. Sin.	d.	′	P. P.		

122° (302°)   (237°) **57°**

COMMON LOGARITHMS OF THE TRIGONOMETRIC FUNCTIONS (Continued)

33° (213°)   **(326°) 146°**

	L. Sin.	d.	L. Tan.	c.d.	L. Cot.	L. Cos.	d.	'
0	9.73 611	19	9.81 252	27	0.18 748	9.92 359	8	60
1	9.73 630	20	9.81 279	28	0.18 721	9.92 351	8	59
2	9.73 650	19	9.81 307	28	0.18 693	9.92 343	8	58
3	9.73 669	20	9.81 335	27	0.18 665	9.92 335	9	57
4	9.73 689	19	9.81 362	28	0.18 638	9.92 326	8	56
5	9.73 708	19	9.81 390	28	0.18 610	9.92 318	8	55
6	9.73 727	20	9.81 418	27	0.18 582	9.92 310	8	54
7	9.73 747	19	9.81 445	28	0.18 555	9.92 302	9	53
8	9.73 766	19	9.81 473	27	0.18 527	9.92 293	8	52
9	9.73 785	20	9.81 500	28	0.18 500	9.92 285	8	51
10	9.73 805	19	9.81 528	28	0.18 472	9.92 277	8	50
11	9.73 824	19	9.81 556	27	0.18 444	9.92 269	9	49
12	9.73 843	20	9.81 583	28	0.18 417	9.92 260	8	48
13	9.73 863	19	9.81 611	27	0.18 389	9.92 252	8	47
14	9.73 882	19	9.81 638	28	0.18 362	9.92 244	9	46
15	9.73 901	20	9.81 666	27	0.18 334	9.92 235	8	45
16	9.73 921	19	9.81 693	28	0.18 307	9.92 227	8	44
17	9.73 940	19	9.81 721	27	0.18 279	9.92 219	8	43
18	9.73 959	19	9.81 748	28	0.18 252	9.92 211	9	42
19	9.73 978	19	9.81 776	27	0.18 224	9.92 202	8	41
20	9.73 997	20	9.81 803	28	0.18 197	9.92 194	8	40
21	9.74 017	19	9.81 831	27	0.18 169	9.92 186	9	39
22	9.74 036	19	9.81 858	28	0.18 142	9.92 177	8	38
23	9.74 055	19	9.81 886	27	0.18 114	9.92 169	8	37
24	9.74 074	19	9.81 913	28	0.18 087	9.92 161	9	36
25	9.74 093	20	9.81 941	27	0.18 059	9.92 152	8	35
26	9.74 113	19	9.81 968	28	0.18 032	9.92 144	8	34
27	9.74 132	19	9.81 996	28	0.18 004	9.92 136	9	33
28	9.74 151	19	9.82 023	28	0.17 977	9.92 127	8	32
29	9.74 170	19	9.82 051	27	0.17 949	9.92 119	8	31
30	9.74 189	19	9.82 078	28	0.17 922	9.92 111	9	30
31	9.74 208	19	9.82 106	27	0.17 894	9.92 102	8	29
32	9.74 227	19	9.82 133	28	0.17 867	9.92 094	8	28
33	9.74 246	19	9.82 161	27	0.17 839	9.92 086	9	27
34	9.74 265	19	9.82 188	27	0.17 812	9.92 077	8	26
35	9.74 284	19	9.82 215	28	0.17 785	9.92 069	9	25
36	9.74 303	19	9.82 243	27	0.17 757	9.92 060	8	24
37	9.74 322	19	9.82 270	28	0.17 730	9.92 052	8	23
38	9.74 341	19	9.82 298	27	0.17 702	9.92 044	9	22
39	9.74 360	19	9.82 325	27	0.17 675	9.92 035	8	21
40	9.74 379	19	9.82 352	28	0.17 648	9.92 027	9	20
41	9.74 398	19	9.82 380	27	0.17 620	9.92 018	8	19
42	9.74 417	19	9.82 407	28	0.17 593	9.92 010	8	18
43	9.74 436	19	9.82 435	27	0.17 565	9.92 002	9	17
44	9.74 455	19	9.82 462	27	0.17 538	9.91 993	8	16
45	9.74 474	19	9.82 489	28	0.17 511	9.91 985	9	15
46	9.74 493	19	9.82 517	27	0.17 483	9.91 976	8	14
47	9.74 512	19	9.82 544	27	0.17 456	9.91 968	9	13
48	9.74 531	18	9.82 571	28	0.17 429	9.91 959	8	12
49	9.74 549	19	9.82 599	27	0.17 401	9.91 951	9	11
50	9.74 568	19	9.82 626	27	0.17 374	9.91 942	8	10
51	9.74 587	19	9.82 653	28	0.17 347	9.91 934	9	9
52	9.74 606	19	9.82 681	27	0.17 319	9.91 925	9	8
53	9.74 625	19	9.82 708	27	0.17 292	9.91 917	9	7
54	9.74 644	18	9.82 735	27	0.17 265	9.91 908	8	6
55	9.74 662	19	9.82 762	28	0.17 238	9.91 900	9	5
56	9.74 681	19	9.82 790	27	0.17 210	9.91 891	8	4
57	9.74 700	19	9.82 817	27	0.17 183	9.91 883	9	3
58	9.74 719	18	9.82 844	27	0.17 156	9.91 874	8	2
59	9.74 737	19	9.82 871	28	0.17 129	9.91 866	9	1
60	9.74 756		9.82 899		0.17 101	9.91 857		0
'	L. Cos.	d.	L. Cot.	c.d.	L. Tan.	L. Sin.	d.	'

P. P.

"	28	27
1	0.5	0.4
2	0.9	0.9
3	1.4	1.4
4	1.9	1.8
5	2.3	2.2
6	2.8	2.7
7	3.3	3.2
8	3.7	3.6
9	4.2	4.0
10	4.7	4.5
20	9.3	9.0
30	14.0	13.5
40	18.7	18.0
50	23.3	22.5

"	20	19	18
1	0.3	0.3	0.3
2	0.7	0.6	0.6
3	1.0	1.0	0.9
4	1.3	1.3	1.2
5	1.7	1.6	1.5
6	2.0	1.9	1.8
7	2.3	2.2	2.1
8	2.7	2.5	2.4
9	3.0	2.8	2.7
10	3.3	3.2	3.0
20	6.7	6.3	6.0
30	10.0	9.5	9.0
40	13.3	12.7	12.0
50	16.7	15.8	15.0

"	9	8
1	0.2	0.1
2	0.3	0.3
3	0.4	0.4
4	0.6	0.5
5	0.8	0.7
6	0.9	0.9
7	1.0	0.9
8	1.2	1.1
9	1.4	1.2
10	1.5	1.3
20	3.0	2.7
30	4.5	4.0
40	6.0	5.3
50	7.5	6.7

	9	9	8
	28	27	27
0			
1	1.6	1.5	1.7
2	4.7	4.5	5.1
3	7.8	7.5	8.4
4	10.9	10.5	11.8
5	14.0	13.5	15.2
6	17.1	16.5	18.6
7	20.2	19.5	21.9
8	23.3	22.5	25.3
9	26.4	25.5	—

123° (303°)   **(236°) 56°**

COMMON LOGARITHMS OF THE TRIGONOMETRIC FUNCTIONS (Continued)

34° (214°)   **(325°) 145°**

'	L. Sin.	d.	L. Tan.	c.d.	L. Cot.	L. Cos.	d.	'
0	9.74 756	19	9.82 899	27	0.17 101	9.91 857	8	60
1	9.74 775	19	9.82 926	27	0.17 074	9.91 849	8	59
2	9.74 794	18	9.82 953	27	0.17 047	9.91 840	8	58
3	9.74 812	19	9.82 980	28	0.17 020	9.91 832	9	57
4	9.74 831	19	9.83 008	27	0.16 992	9.91 823	8	56
5	9.74 850	18	9.83 035	27	0.16 965	9.91 815	9	55
6	9.74 868	19	9.83 062	27	0.16 938	9.91 806	8	54
7	9.74 887	19	9.83 089	28	0.16 911	9.91 798	9	53
8	9.74 906	18	9.83 117	27	0.16 883	9.91 789	8	52
9	9.74 924	19	9.83 144	27	0.16 856	9.91 781	9	51
10	9.74 943	18	9.83 171	27	0.16 829	9.91 772	9	50
11	9.74 961	19	9.83 198	27	0.16 802	9.91 763	8	49
12	9.74 980	19	9.83 225	27	0.16 775	9.91 755	9	48
13	9.74 999	18	9.83 252	28	0.16 748	9.91 746	8	47
14	9.75 017	19	9.83 280	27	0.16 720	9.91 738	9	46
15	9.75 036	18	9.83 307	27	0.16 693	9.91 729	9	45
16	9.75 054	19	9.83 334	27	0.16 666	9.91 720	8	44
17	9.75 073	18	9.83 361	27	0.16 639	9.91 712	9	43
18	9.75 091	19	9.83 388	27	0.16 612	9.91 703	8	42
19	9.75 110	18	9.83 415	27	0.16 585	9.91 695	9	41
20	9.75 128	19	9.83 442	28	0.16 558	9.91 686	9	40
21	9.75 147	18	9.83 470	27	0.16 530	9.91 677	8	39
22	9.75 165	19	9.83 497	27	0.16 503	9.91 669	9	38
23	9.75 184	18	9.83 524	27	0.16 476	9.91 660	9	37
24	9.75 202	19	9.83 551	27	0.16 449	9.91 651	8	36
25	9.75 221	18	9.83 578	27	0.16 422	9.91 643	9	35
26	9.75 239	19	9.83 605	27	0.16 395	9.91 634	9	34
27	9.75 258	18	9.83 632	27	0.16 368	9.91 625	8	33
28	9.75 276	18	9.83 659	27	0.16 341	9.91 617	9	32
29	9.75 294	19	9.83 686	27	0.16 314	9.91 608	9	31
30	9.75 313	18	9.83 713	27	0.16 287	9.91 599	8	30
31	9.75 331	19	9.83 740	28	0.16 260	9.91 591	9	29
32	9.75 350	18	9.83 768	27	0.16 232	9.91 582	9	28
33	9.75 368	18	9.83 795	27	0.16 205	9.91 573	8	27
34	9.75 386	19	9.83 822	27	0.16 178	9.91 565	9	26
35	9.75 405	18	9.83 849	27	0.16 151	9.91 556	9	25
36	9.75 423	18	9.83 876	27	0.16 124	9.91 547	9	24
37	9.75 441	18	9.83 903	27	0.16 097	9.91 538	8	23
38	9.75 459	19	9.83 930	27	0.16 070	9.91 530	9	22
39	9.75 478	18	9.83 957	27	0.16 043	9.91 521	9	21
40	9.75 496	18	9.83 984	27	0.16 016	9.91 512	8	20
41	9.75 514	19	9.84 011	27	0.15 989	9.91 504	9	19
42	9.75 533	18	9.84 038	27	0.15 962	9.91 495	9	18
43	9.75 551	18	9.84 065	27	0.15 935	9.91 486	9	17
44	9.75 569	18	9.84 092	27	0.15 908	9.91 477	8	16
45	9.75 587	18	9.84 119	27	0.15 881	9.91 469	9	15
46	9.75 605	19	9.84 146	27	0.15 854	9.91 460	9	14
47	9.75 624	18	9.84 173	27	0.15 827	9.91 451	9	13
48	9.75 642	18	9.84 200	27	0.15 800	9.91 442	9	12
49	9.75 660	18	9.84 227	27	0.15 773	9.91 433	8	11
50	9.75 678	18	9.84 254	26	0.15 746	9.91 425	9	10
51	9.75 696	18	9.84 280	27	0.15 720	9.91 416	9	9
52	9.75 714	19	9.84 307	27	0.15 693	9.91 407	9	8
53	9.75 733	18	9.84 334	27	0.15 666	9.91 398	9	7
54	9.75 751	18	9.84 361	27	0.15 639	9.91 389	8	6
55	9.75 769	18	9.84 388	27	0.15 612	9.91 381	9	5
56	9.75 787	18	9.84 415	27	0.15 585	9.91 372	9	4
57	9.75 805	18	9.84 442	27	0.15 558	9.91 363	9	3
58	9.75 823	18	9.84 469	27	0.15 531	9.91 354	9	2
59	9.75 841	18	9.84 496	27	0.15 504	9.91 345	9	1
60	9.75 859		9.84 523		0.15 477	9.91 336		0
'	L. Cos.	d.	L. Cot.	c.d.	L. Tan.	L. Sin.	d.	'

124° (304°)   **(235°) 55°**

P. P.

''	28	27	26
1	0.5	0.4	0.4
2	0.9	0.9	0.9
3	1.4	1.4	1.3
4	1.9	1.8	1.7
5	2.3	2.2	2.2
6	2.8	2.7	2.6
7	3.3	3.2	3.0
8	3.7	3.6	3.5
9	4.2	4.0	3.9
10	4.7	4.5	4.3
20	9.3	9.0	8.7
30	14.0	13.5	13.0
40	18.7	18.0	17.3
50	23.3	22.5	21.7

''	19	18
1	0.3	0.3
2	0.6	0.6
3	1.0	0.9
4	1.3	1.2
5	1.6	1.5
6	1.9	1.8
7	2.2	2.1
8	2.5	2.4
9	2.8	2.7
10	3.2	3.0
20	6.3	6.0
30	9.5	9.0
40	12.7	12.0
50	15.8	15.0

''	9	8
1	0.2	0.1
2	0.3	0.3
3	0.4	0.4
4	0.6	0.5
5	0.8	0.7
6	0.9	0.8
7	1.0	0.9
8	1.2	1.1
9	1.4	1.2
10	1.5	1.3
20	3.0	2.7
30	4.5	4.0
40	6.0	5.3
50	7.5	6.7

	9	8	8
	28	28	27
0			
1	1.6	1.8	1.7
2	4.7	5.2	5.1
3	7.8	8.8	8.4
4	10.9	12.2	11.8
5	14.0	15.8	15.2
6	17.1	19.2	18.6
7	20.2	22.8	21.9
8	23.3	26.2	25.3
9	26.4	—	—

COMMON LOGARITHMS OF THE TRIGONOMETRIC
FUNCTIONS (Continued)

35° (215°)   **(324°) 144°**

′	L. Sin.	d.	L. Tan.	c.d.	L. Cot.	L. Cos.	d.	′	P. P.		
0	9.75 859	18	9.84 523	27	0.15 477	9.91 336	8	60			
1	9.75 877	18	9.84 550	26	0.15 450	9.91 328	9	59	″	**27** **26** **18**	
2	9.75 895	18	9.84 576	27	0.15 424	9.91 319	9	58	1	0.4 0.4 0.3	
3	9.75 913	18	9.84 603	27	0.15 397	9.91 310	9	57	2	0.9 0.9 0.6	
4	9.75 931	18	9.84 630	27	0.15 370	9.91 301	9	56	3	1.4 1.3 0.9	
									4	1.8 1.7 1.2	
5	9.75 949	18	9.84 657	27	0.15 343	9.91 292	9	55			
6	9.75 967	18	9.84 684	27	0.15 316	9.91 283	9	54	5	2.2 2.2 1.5	
7	9.75 985	18	9.84 711	27	0.15 289	9.91 274	8	53	6	2.7 2.6 1.8	
8	9.76 003	18	9.84 738	26	0.15 262	9.91 266	9	52	7	3.2 3.0 2.1	
9	9.76 021	18	9.84 764	27	0.15 236	9.91 257	9	51	8	3.6 3.5 2.4	
									9	4.0 3.9 2.7	
10	9.76 039	18	9.84 791	27	0.15 209	9.91 248	9	50			
11	9.76 057	18	9.84 818	27	0.15 182	9.91 239	9	49	10	4.5 4.3 3.0	
12	9.76 075	18	9.84 845	27	0.15 155	9.91 230	9	48	20	9.0 8.7 6.0	
13	9.76 093	18	9.84 872	27	0.15 128	9.91 221	9	47	30	13.5 13.0 9.0	
14	9.76 111	18	9.84 899	26	0.15 101	9.91 212	9	46	40	18.0 17.3 12.0	
									50	22.5 21.7 15.0	
15	9.76 129	17	9.84 925	27	0.15 075	9.91 203	9	45			
16	9.76 146	18	9.84 952	27	0.15 048	9.91 194	9	44	″	**17** **10** **9** **8**	
17	9.76 164	18	9.84 979	27	0.15 021	9.91 185	9	43	1	0.3 0.2 0.2 0.1	
18	9.76 182	18	9.85 006	27	0.14 994	9.91 176	9	42	2	0.6 0.3 0.3 0.3	
19	9.76 200	18	9.85 033	26	0.14 967	9.91 167	9	41	3	0.8 0.5 0.4 0.4	
									4	1.1 0.7 0.6 0.5	
20	9.76 218	18	9.85 059	27	0.14 941	9.91 158	9	40			
21	9.76 236	17	9.85 086	27	0.14 914	9.91 149	8	39	5	1.4 0.8 0.8 0.7	
22	9.76 253	18	9.85 113	27	0.14 887	9.91 141	9	38	6	1.7 1.0 0.9 0.8	
23	9.76 271	18	9.85 140	26	0.14 860	9.91 132	9	37	7	2.0 1.2 1.0 0.9	
24	9.76 289	18	9.85 166	27	0.14 834	9.91 123	9	36	8	2.3 1.3 1.2 1.1	
									9	2.6 1.5 1.4 1.2	
25	9.76 307	17	9.85 193	27	0.14 807	9.91 114	9	35			
26	9.76 324	18	9.85 220	27	0.14 780	9.91 105	9	34	10	2.8 1.7 1.5 1.3	
27	9.76 342	18	9.85 247	26	0.14 753	9.91 096	9	33	20	5.7 3.3 3.0 2.7	
28	9.76 360	18	9.85 273	27	0.14 727	9.91 087	9	32	30	8.5 5.0 4.5 4.0	
29	9.76 378	17	9.85 300	27	0.14 700	9.91 078	9	31	40	11.3 6.7 6.0 5.3	
									50	14.2 8.3 7.5 6.7	
30	9.76 395	18	9.85 327	27	0.14 673	9.91 069	9	30			
31	9.76 413	18	9.85 354	26	0.14 646	9.91 060	9	29			
32	9.76 431	17	9.85 380	27	0.14 620	9.91 051	9	28			
33	9.76 448	18	9.85 407	27	0.14 593	9.91 042	9	27			
34	9.76 466	18	9.85 434	26	0.14 566	9.91 033	10	26			
										10 **10**	
35	9.76 484	17	9.85 460	27	0.14 540	9.91 023	9	25		**27** **26**	
36	9.76 501	18	9.85 487	27	0.14 513	9.91 014	9	24			
37	9.76 519	18	9.85 514	26	0.14 486	9.91 005	9	23	0		
38	9.76 537	17	9.85 540	27	0.14 460	9.90 996	9	22	1	1.4 1.3	
39	9.76 554	18	9.85 567	27	0.14 433	9.90 987	9	21	2	4.1 3.9	
									3	6.8 6.5	
40	9.76 572	18	9.85 594	26	0.14 406	9.90 978	9	20	4	9.4 9.1	
41	9.76 590	17	9.85 620	27	0.14 380	9.90 969	9	19	5	12.2 11.7	
42	9.76 607	18	9.85 647	27	0.14 353	9.90 960	9	18	6	14.8 14.3	
43	9.76 625	17	9.85 674	26	0.14 326	9.90 951	9	17	7	17.6 16.9	
44	9.76 642	18	9.85 700	27	0.14 300	9.90 942	9	16	8	20.2 19.5	
									9	22.9 22.1	
45	9.76 660	17	9.85 727	27	0.14 273	9.90 933	9	15	10	25.6 24.7	
46	9.76 677	18	9.85 754	26	0.14 246	9.90 924	9	14			
47	9.76 695	17	9.85 780	27	0.14 220	9.90 915	9	13			
48	9.76 712	18	9.85 807	27	0.14 193	9.90 906	10	12		**9** **9**	
49	9.76 730	17	9.85 834	26	0.14 166	9.90 896	9	11		**27** **26**	
50	9.76 747	18	9.85 860	27	0.14 140	9.90 887	9	10	0		
51	9.76 765	17	9.85 887	26	0.14 113	9.90 878	9	9	1	1.5 1.4	
52	9.76 782	18	9.85 913	27	0.14 087	9.90 869	9	8	2	4.5 4.3	
53	9.76 800	17	9.85 940	27	0.14 060	9.90 860	9	7	3	7.5 7.2	
54	9.76 817	18	9.85 967	26	0.14 033	9.90 851	9	6	4	10.5 10.1	
									5	13.5 13.0	
55	9.76 835	17	9.85 993	27	0.14 007	9.90 842	10	5	6	16.5 15.9	
56	9.76 852	18	9.86 020	26	0.13 980	9.90 832	9	4	7	19.5 18.8	
57	9.76 870	17	9.86 046	27	0.13 954	9.90 823	9	3	8	22.5 21.7	
58	9.76 887	17	9.86 073	27	0.13 927	9.90 814	9	2	9	25.5 24.6	
59	9.76 904	18	9.86 100	26	0.13 900	9.90 805	9	1			
60	9.76 922		9.86 126		0.13 874	9.90 796		0			

′	L. Cos.	d.	L. Cot.	c.d.	L. Tan.	L. Sin.	d.	′	P. P.		

COMMON LOGARITHMS OF THE TRIGONOMETRIC
FUNCTIONS (Continued)

36° (216°)   (323°) **143°**

′	L. Sin.	d.	L. Tan.	c.d.	L. Cot	L. Cos.	d.	′	P. P.
0	9.76 922	17	9.86 126	27	0.13 874	9.90 796	9	**60**	
1	9.76 939	18	9.86 153	26	0.13 847	9.90 787	10	59	″ **27** **26**
2	9.76 957	17	9.86 179	27	0.13 821	9.90 777	9	58	1 0.4 0.4
3	9.76 974	17	9.86 206	26	0.13 794	9.90 768	9	57	2 0.9 0.9
4	9.76 991	18	9.86 232	27	0.13 768	9.90 759	9	56	3 1.4 1.3
									4 1.8 1.7
5	9.77 009	17	9.86 259	26	0.13 741	9.90 750	9	**55**	
6	9.77 026	17	9.86 285	27	0.13 715	9.90 741	10	54	5 2.2 2.2
7	9.77 043	18	9.86 312	26	0.13 688	9.90 731	9	53	6 2.7 2.6
8	9.77 061	17	9.86 338	27	0.13 662	9.90 722	9	52	7 3.2 3.0
9	9.77 078	17	9.86 365	27	0.13 635	9.90 713	9	51	8 3.6 3.5
									9 4.0 3.9
10	9.77 095	17	9.86 392	26	0.13 608	9.90 704	10	**50**	
11	9.77 112	18	9.86 418	27	0.13 582	9.90 694	9	49	10 4.5 4.3
12	9.77 130	17	9.86 445	26	0.13 555	9.90 685	9	48	20 9.0 8.7
13	9.77 147	17	9.86 471	27	0.13 529	9.90 676	9	47	30 13.5 13.0
14	9.77 164	17	9.86 498	26	0.13 502	9.90 667	10	46	40 18.0 17.3
									50 22.5 21.7
15	9.77 181	18	9.86 524	27	0.13 476	9.90 657	9	**45**	
16	9.77 199	17	9.86 551	26	0.13 449	9.90 648	9	44	″ **18** **17** **16**
17	9.77 216	17	9.86 577	26	0.13 423	9.90 639	9	43	1 0.3 0.3 0.3
18	9.77 233	17	9.86 603	27	0.13 397	9.90 630	10	42	2 0.6 0.6 0.5
19	9.77 250	18	9.86 630	26	0.13 370	9.90 620	9	41	3 0.9 0.8 0.8
									4 1.2 1.1 1.1
20	9.77 268	17	9.86 656	27	0.13 344	9.90 611	9	**40**	
21	9.77 285	17	9.86 683	26	0.13 317	9.90 602	10	39	5 1.5 1.4 1.3
22	9.77 302	17	9.86 709	27	0.13 291	9.90 592	9	38	6 1.8 1.7 1.6
23	9.77 319	17	9.86 736	26	0.13 264	9.90 583	9	37	7 2.1 2.0 1.9
24	9.77 336	17	9.86 762	27	0.13 238	9.90 574	9	36	8 2.4 2.3 2.1
									9 2.7 2.6 2.4
25	9.77 353	17	9.86 789	26	0.13 211	9.90 565	10	**35**	
26	9.77 370	17	9.86 815	27	0.13 185	9.90 555	9	34	10 3.0 2.8 2.7
27	9.77 387	18	9.86 842	26	0.13 158	9.90 546	9	33	20 6.0 5.7 5.3
28	9.77 405	17	9.86 868	26	0.13 132	9.90 537	10	32	30 9.0 8.5 8.0
29	9.77 422	17	9.86 894	27	0.13 106	9.90 527	9	31	40 12.0 11.3 10.7
									50 15.0 14.2 13.3
30	9.77 439	17	9.86 921	26	0.13 079	9.90 518	9	**30**	
31	9.77 456	17	9.86 947	27	0.13 053	9.90 509	10	29	″ **10** **9**
32	9.77 473	17	9.86 974	26	0.13 026	9.90 499	9	28	1 0.2 0.2
33	9.77 490	17	9.87 000	27	0.13 000	9.90 490	10	27	2 0.3 0.3
34	9.77 507	17	9.87 027	26	0.12 973	9.90 480	9	26	3 0.5 0.4
									4 0.7 0.6
35	9.77 524	17	9.87 053	26	0.12 947	9.90 471	9	**25**	
36	9.77 541	17	9.87 079	27	0.12 921	9.90 462	10	24	5 0.8 0.8
37	9.77 558	17	9.87 106	26	0.12 894	9.90 452	9	23	6 1.0 0.9
38	9.77 575	17	9.87 132	26	0.12 868	9.90 443	9	22	7 1.2 1.0
39	9.77 592	17	9.87 158	27	0.12 842	9.90 434	10	21	8 1.3 1.2
									9 1.5 1.4
40	9.77 609	17	9.87 185	26	0.12 815	9.90 424	9	**20**	
41	9.77 626	17	9.87 211	27	0.12 789	9.90 415	10	19	10 1.7 1.5
42	9.77 643	17	9.87 238	26	0.12 762	9.90 405	9	18	20 3.3 3.0
43	9.77 660	17	9.87 264	26	0.12 736	9.90 396	10	17	30 5.0 4.5
44	9.77 677	17	9.87 290	27	0.12 710	9.90 386	9	16	40 6.7 6.0
									50 8.3 7.5
45	9.77 694	17	9.87 317	26	0.12 683	9.90 377	9	**15**	
46	9.77 711	17	9.87 343	26	0.12 657	9.90 368	10	14	
47	9.77 728	16	9.87 369	27	0.12 631	9.90 358	9	13	
48	9.77 744	17	9.87 396	26	0.12 604	9.90 349	10	12	
49	9.77 761	17	9.87 422	26	0.12 578	9.90 339	9	11	
50	9.77 778	17	9.87 448	27	0.12 552	9.90 330	10	**10**	**9** **9**
51	9.77 795	17	9.87 475	26	0.12 525	9.90 320	9	9	**27** **26**
52	9.77 812	17	9.87 501	26	0.12 499	9.90 311	10	8	
53	9.77 829	17	9.87 527	27	0.12 473	9.90 301	9	7	0
54	9.77 846	16	9.87 554	26	0.12 446	9.90 292	10	6	1 1.5 1.4
									2 4.5 4.3
55	9.77 862	17	9.87 580	26	0.12 420	9.90 282	9	**5**	3 7.5 7.2
56	9.77 879	17	9.87 606	27	0.12 394	9.90 273	10	4	4 10.5 10.1
57	9.77 896	17	9.87 633	26	0.12 367	9.90 263	9	3	5 13.5 13.0
58	9.77 913	17	9.87 659	26	0.12 341	9.90 254	10	2	6 16.5 15.9
59	9.77 930	16	9.87 685	26	0.12 315	9.90 244	9	1	7 19.5 18.8
									8 22.5 21.7
60	9.77 946		9.87 711		0.12 289	9.90 235		**0**	9 25.5 24.6
′	L. Cos.	d.	L. Cot.	c.d.	L. Tan.	L. Sin.	d.	′	P. P.

126° (306°)   (233°) **53°**

COMMON LOGARITHMS OF THE TRIGONOMETRIC
FUNCTIONS (Continued)

37° (217°) (322°) 142°

'	L. Sin.	d.	L. Tan.	c.d.	L. Cot.	L. Cos.	d.	'
0	9.77 946	17	9.87 711	27	0.12 289	9.90 235	10	60
1	9.77 963	17	9.87 738	26	0.12 262	9.90 225	9	59
2	9.77 980	17	9.87 764	26	0.12 236	9.90 216	9	58
3	9.77 997	16	9.87 790	27	0.12 210	9.90 206	10	57
4	9.78 013	17	9.87 817	26	0.12 183	9.90 197	9	56
5	9.78 030	17	9.87 843	26	0.12 157	9.90 187	10	55
6	9.78 047	16	9.87 869	26	0.12 131	9.90 178	9	54
7	9.78 063	17	9.87 895	27	0.12 105	9.90 168	9	53
8	9.78 080	17	9.87 922	26	0.12 078	9.90 159	10	52
9	9.78 097	16	9.87 948	26	0.12 052	9.90 149	10	51
10	9.78 113	17	9.87 974	26	0.12 026	9.90 139	9	50
11	9.78 130	17	9.88 000	27	0.12 000	9.90 130	10	49
12	9.78 147	16	9.88 027	26	0.11 973	9.90 120	9	48
13	9.78 163	17	9.88 053	26	0.11 947	9.90 111	10	47
14	9.78 180	17	9.88 079	26	0.11 921	9.90 101	10	46
15	9.78 197	16	9.88 105	26	0.11 895	9.90 091	9	45
16	9.78 213	17	9.88 131	27	0.11 869	9.90 082	10	44
17	9.78 230	16	9.88 158	26	0.11 842	9.90 072	9	43
18	9.78 246	17	9.88 184	26	0.11 816	9.90 063	10	42
19	9.78 263	17	9.88 210	26	0.11 790	9.90 053	10	41
20	9.78 280	16	9.88 236	26	0.11 764	9.90 043	10	40
21	9.78 296	17	9.88 262	27	0.11 738	9.90 034	10	39
22	9.78 313	16	9.88 289	26	0.11 711	9.90 024	10	38
23	9.78 329	17	9.88 315	26	0.11 685	9.90 014	10	37
24	9.78 346	16	9.88 341	26	0.11 659	9.90 005	10	36
25	9.78 362	17	9.88 367	26	0.11 633	9.89 995	10	35
26	9.78 379	16	9.88 393	27	0.11 607	9.89 985	9	34
27	9.78 395	17	9.88 420	25	0.11 580	9.89 976	10	33
28	9.78 412	16	9.88 446	26	0.11 554	9.89 966	10	32
29	9.78 428	17	9.88 472	26	0.11 528	9.89 956	9	31
30	9.78 445	16	9.88 498	26	0.11 502	9.89 947	10	30
31	9.78 461	17	9.88 524	25	0.11 476	9.89 937	10	29
32	9.78 478	16	9.88 550	27	0.11 450	9.89 927	9	28
33	9.78 494	16	9.88 577	26	0.11 423	9.89 918	10	27
34	9.78 510	17	9.88 603	26	0.11 397	9.89 908	10	26
35	9.78 527	16	9.88 629	26	0.11 371	9.89 898	10	25
36	9.78 543	17	9.88 655	26	0.11 345	9.89 888	9	24
37	9.78 560	16	9.88 681	26	0.11 319	9.89 879	10	23
38	9.78 576	16	9.88 707	26	0.11 293	9.89 869	10	22
39	9.78 592	17	9.88 733	26	0.11 267	9.89 859	10	21
40	9.78 609	16	9.88 759	27	0.11 241	9.89 849	9	20
41	9.78 625	17	9.88 786	26	0.11 214	9.89 840	10	19
42	9.78 642	16	9.88 812	26	0.11 188	9.89 830	10	18
43	9.78 658	16	9.88 838	26	0.11 162	9.89 820	10	17
44	9.78 674	17	9.88 864	26	0.11 136	9.89 810	9	16
45	9.78 691	16	9.88 890	26	0.11 110	9.89 801	10	15
46	9.78 707	16	9.88 916	26	0.11 084	9.89 791	10	14
47	9.78 723	16	9.88 942	26	0.11 058	9.89 781	10	13
48	9.78 739	17	9.88 968	26	0.11 032	9.89 771	10	12
49	9.78 756	16	9.88 994	26	0.11 006	9.89 761	9	11
50	9.78 772	16	9.89 020	26	0.10 980	9.89 752	10	10
51	9.78 788	17	9.89 046	27	0.10 954	9.89 742	10	9
52	9.78 805	16	9.89 073	26	0.10 927	9.89 732	10	8
53	9.78 821	16	9.89 099	26	0.10 901	9.89 722	10	7
54	9.78 837	16	9.89 125	26	0.10 875	9.89 712	10	6
55	9.78 853	16	9.89 151	26	0.10 849	9.89 702	9	5
56	9.78 869	17	9.89 177	26	0.10 823	9.89 693	10	4
57	9.78 886	16	9.89 203	26	0.10 797	9.89 683	10	3
58	9.78 902	16	9.89 229	26	0.10 771	9.89 673	10	2
59	9.78 918	16	9.89 255	26	0.10 745	9.89 663	10	1
60	9.78 934		9.89 281		0.10 719	9.89 653		0
'	L. Cos.	d.	L. Cot.	c.d.	L. Tan.	L. Sin.	d.	'

127° (307°) (232°) 52°

P. P.

"	27	26
1	0.4	0.4
2	0.9	0.9
3	1.4	1.3
4	1.8	1.7
5	2.2	2.2
6	2.7	2.6
7	3.2	3.0
8	3.6	3.5
9	4.0	3.9
10	4.5	4.3
20	9.0	8.7
30	13.5	13.0
40	18.0	17.3
50	22.5	21.7

"	17	16
1	0.3	0.3
2	0.6	0.5
3	0.8	0.8
4	1.1	1.1
5	1.4	1.3
6	1.7	1.6
7	2.0	1.9
8	2.3	2.1
9	2.6	2.4
10	2.8	2.7
20	5.7	5.3
30	8.5	8.0
40	11.3	10.7
50	14.2	13.3

"	10	9
1	0.2	0.2
2	0.3	0.3
3	0.5	0.4
4	0.7	0.6
5	0.8	0.8
6	1.0	0.9
7	1.2	1.0
8	1.3	1.2
9	1.5	1.4
10	1.7	1.5
20	3.3	3.0
30	5.0	4.5
40	6.7	6.0
50	8.3	7.5

	10	10
	27	26
0		
1	1.4	1.3
2	4.1	3.9
3	6.8	6.5
4	9.4	9.1
5	12.2	11.7
6	14.8	14.3
7	17.6	16.9
8	20.2	19.5
9	22.9	22.1
10	25.6	24.7

Tables for Use in Trigonometry

COMMON LOGARITHMS OF THE TRIGONOMETRIC
FUNCTIONS (Continued)

38° (218°)   **(321°) 141°**

′	L. Sin.	d.	L. Tan.	c.d.	L. Cot.	L. Cos.	d.	′
0	9.78 934	16	9.89 281	26	0.10 719	9.89 653	10	60
1	9.78 950	17	9.89 307	26	0.10 693	9.89 643	10	59
2	9.78 967	16	9.89 333	26	0.10 667	9.89 633	9	58
3	9.78 983	16	9.89 359	26	0.10 641	9.89 624	10	57
4	9.78 999	16	9.89 385	26	0.10 615	9.89 614	10	56
5	9.79 015	16	9.89 411	26	0.10 589	9.89 604	10	55
6	9.79 031	16	9.89 437	26	0.10 563	9.89 594	10	54
7	9.79 047	16	9.89 463	26	0.10 537	9.89 584	10	53
8	9.79 063	16	9.89 489	26	0.10 511	9.89 574	10	52
9	9.79 079	16	9.89 515	26	0.10 485	9.89 564	10	51
10	9.79 095	16	9.89 541	26	0.10 459	9.89 554	10	50
11	9.79 111	17	9.89 567	26	0.10 433	9.89 544	10	49
12	9.79 128	16	9.89 593	26	0.10 407	9.89 534	10	48
13	9.79 144	16	9.89 619	26	0.10 381	9.89 524	10	47
14	9.79 160	16	9.89 645	26	0.10 355	9.89 514	10	46
15	9.79 176	16	9.89 671	26	0.10 329	9.89 504	9	45
16	9.79 192	16	9.89 697	26	0.10 303	9.89 495	10	44
17	9.79 208	16	9.89 723	26	0.10 277	9.89 485	10	43
18	9.79 224	16	9.89 749	26	0.10 251	9.89 475	10	42
19	9.79 240	16	9.89 775	26	0.10 225	9.89 465	10	41
20	9.79 256	16	9.89 801	26	0.10 199	9.89 455	10	40
21	9.79 272	16	9.89 827	26	0.10 173	9.89 445	10	39
22	9.79 288	16	9.89 853	26	0.10 147	9.89 435	10	38
23	9.79 304	15	9.89 879	26	0.10 121	9.89 425	10	37
24	9.79 319	16	9.89 905	26	0.10 095	9.89 415	10	36
25	9.79 335	16	9.89 931	26	0.10 069	9.89 405	10	35
26	9.79 351	16	9.89 957	26	0.10 043	9.89 395	10	34
27	9.79 367	16	9.89 983	26	0.10 017	9.89 385	10	33
28	9.79 383	16	9.90 009	26	0.09 991	9.89 375	11	32
29	9.79 399	16	9.90 035	26	0.09 965	9.89 364	10	31
30	9.79 415	16	9.90 061	25	0.09 939	9.89 354	10	30
31	9.79 431	16	9.90 086	26	0.09 914	9.89 344	10	29
32	9.79 447	16	9.90 112	26	0.09 888	9.89 334	10	28
33	9.79 463	15	9.90 138	26	0.09 862	9.89 324	10	27
34	9.79 478	16	9.90 164	26	0.09 836	9.89 314	10	26
35	9.79 494	16	9.90 190	26	0.09 810	9.89 304	10	25
36	9.79 510	16	9.90 216	26	0.09 784	9.89 294	10	24
37	9.79 526	16	9.90 242	26	0.09 758	9.89 284	10	23
38	9.79 542	16	9.90 268	26	0.09 732	9.89 274	10	22
39	9.79 558	15	9.90 294	26	0.09 706	9.89 264	10	21
40	9.79 573	16	9.90 320	26	0.09 680	9.89 254	10	20
41	9.79 589	16	9.90 346	25	0.09 654	9.89 244	11	19
42	9.79 605	16	9.90 371	26	0.09 629	9.89 233	10	18
43	9.79 621	15	9.90 397	26	0.09 603	9.89 223	10	17
44	9.79 636	16	9.90 423	26	0.09 577	9.89 213	10	16
45	9.79 652	16	9.90 449	26	0.09 551	9.89 203	10	15
46	9.79 668	16	9.90 475	26	0.09 525	9.89 193	10	14
47	9.79 684	15	9.90 501	26	0.09 499	9.89 183	10	13
48	9.79 699	16	9.90 527	26	0.09 473	9.89 173	11	12
49	9.79 715	16	9.90 553	25	0.09 447	9.89 162	10	11
50	9.79 731	15	9.90 578	26	0.09 422	9.89 152	10	10
51	9.79 746	16	9.90 604	26	0.09 396	9.89 142	10	9
52	9.79 762	16	9.90 630	26	0.09 370	9.89 132	10	8
53	9.79 778	15	9.90 656	26	0.09 344	9.89 122	10	7
54	9.79 793	16	9.90 682	26	0.09 318	9.89 112	11	6
55	9.79 809	16	9.90 708	26	0.09 292	9.89 101	10	5
56	9.79 825	15	9.90 734	25	0.09 266	9.89 091	10	4
57	9.79 840	16	9.90 759	26	0.09 241	9.89 081	10	3
58	9.79 856	16	9.90 785	26	0.09 215	9.89 071	11	2
59	9.79 872	15	9.90 811	26	0.09 189	9.89 060	10	1
60	9.79 887		9.90 837		0.09 163	9.89 050		0

′	L. Cos.	d.	L. Cot.	c.d.	L. Tan.	L. Sin.	d.	′

128° (308°)   **(231°) 51°**

P. P.

″	26	25
1	0.4	0.4
2	0.9	0.8
3	1.3	1.2
4	1.7	1.7
5	2.2	2.1
6	2.6	2.5
7	3.0	2.9
8	3.5	3.3
9	3.9	3.8
10	4.3	4.2
20	8.7	8.3
30	13.0	12.5
40	17.3	16.7
50	21.7	20.8

″	17	16	15
1	0.3	0.3	0.2
2	0.6	0.5	0.5
3	0.8	0.8	0.8
4	1.1	1.1	1.0
5	1.4	1.3	1.2
6	1.7	1.6	1.5
7	2.0	1.9	1.8
8	2.3	2.1	2.0
9	2.6	2.4	2.2
10	2.8	2.7	2.5
20	5.7	5.3	5.0
30	8.5	8.0	7.5
40	11.3	10.7	10.0
50	14.2	13.3	12.5

″	11	10	9
1	0.2	0.2	0.2
2	0.4	0.3	0.3
3	0.6	0.5	0.4
4	0.7	0.7	0.6
5	0.9	0.8	0.8
6	1.1	1.0	0.9
7	1.3	1.2	1.0
8	1.5	1.3	1.2
9	1.6	1.5	1.4
10	1.8	1.7	1.5
20	3.7	3.3	3.0
30	5.5	5.0	4.5
40	7.3	6.7	6.0
50	9.2	8.3	7.5

	10	10	9
	26	25	26
0	1.3	1.2	1.4
1	3.9	3.8	4.3
2	6.5	6.2	7.2
3	9.1	8.8	10.1
4	11.7	11.2	13.0
5	14.3	13.8	15.9
6	16.9	16.2	18.8
7	19.5	18.8	21.7
8	22.1	21.2	24.6
9	24.7	23.8	—
10			

COMMON LOGARITHMS OF THE TRIGONOMETRIC FUNCTIONS (Continued)

39° (219°)   (320°) **140°**

'	L. Sin.	d.	L. Tan.	c.d.	L. Cot.	L. Cos.	d.	'
0	9.79 887	16	9.90 837	26	0.09 163	9.89 050	10	60
1	9.79 903	15	9.90 863	26	0.09 137	9.89 040	10	59
2	9.79 918	16	9.90 889	25	0.09 111	9.89 030	10	58
3	9.79 934	16	9.90 914	26	0.09 086	9.89 020	11	57
4	9.79 950	15	9.90 940	26	0.09 060	9.89 009	10	56
5	9.79 965	16	9.90 966	26	0.09 034	9.88 999	10	55
6	9.79 981	15	9.90 992	26	0.09 008	9.88 989	11	54
7	9.79 996	16	9.91 018	25	0.08 982	9.88 978	10	53
8	9.80 012	15	9.91 043	26	0.08 957	9.88 968	10	52
9	9.80 027	16	9.91 069	26	0.08 931	9.88 958	10	51
10	9.80 043	15	9.91 095	26	0.08 905	9.88 948	11	50
11	9.80 058	16	9.91 121	26	0.08 879	9.88 937	10	49
12	9.80 074	15	9.91 147	25	0.08 853	9.88 927	10	48
13	9.80 089	16	9.91 172	26	0.08 828	9.88 917	11	47
14	9.80 105	15	9.91 198	26	0.08 802	9.88 906	10	46
15	9.80 120	16	9.91 224	26	0.08 776	9.88 896	10	45
16	9.80 136	15	9.91 250	26	0.08 750	9.88 886	11	44
17	9.80 151	15	9.91 276	25	0.08 724	9.88 875	10	43
18	9.80 166	16	9.91 301	26	0.08 699	9.88 865	10	42
19	9.80 182	15	9.91 327	26	0.08 673	9.88 855	11	41
20	9.80 197	16	9.91 353	26	0.08 647	9.88 844	10	40
21	9.80 213	15	9.91 379	25	0.08 621	9.88 834	10	39
22	9.80 228	16	9.91 404	26	0.08 596	9.88 824	11	38
23	9.80 244	15	9.91 430	26	0.08 570	9.88 813	10	37
24	9.80 259	15	9.91 456	26	0.08 544	9.88 803	10	36
25	9.80 274	16	9.91 482	25	0.08 518	9.88 793	11	35
26	9.80 290	15	9.91 507	26	0.08 493	9.88 782	10	34
27	9.80 305	15	9.91 533	26	0.08 467	9.88 772	11	33
28	9.80 320	16	9.91 559	26	0.08 441	9.88 761	10	32
29	9.80 336	15	9.91 585	25	0.08 415	9.88 751	10	31
30	9.80 351	15	9.91 610	26	0.08 390	9.88 741	11	30
31	9.80 366	16	9.91 636	26	0.08 364	9.88 730	10	29
32	9.80 382	15	9.91 662	26	0.08 338	9.88 720	11	28
33	9.80 397	15	9.91 688	25	0.08 312	9.88 709	10	27
34	9.80 412	16	9.91 713	26	0.08 287	9.88 699	11	26
35	9.80 428	15	9.91 739	26	0.08 261	9.88 688	10	25
36	9.80 443	15	9.91 765	26	0.08 235	9.88 678	10	24
37	9.80 458	15	9.91 791	25	0.08 209	9.88 668	11	23
38	9.80 473	16	9.91 816	26	0.08 184	9.88 657	10	22
39	9.80 489	15	9.91 842	26	0.08 158	9.88 647	11	21
40	9.80 504	15	9.91 868	25	0.08 132	9.88 636	10	20
41	9.80 519	15	9.91 893	26	0.08 107	9.88 626	11	19
42	9.80 534	16	9.91 919	26	0.08 081	9.88 615	10	18
43	9.80 550	15	9.91 945	26	0.08 055	9.88 605	11	17
44	9.80 565	15	9.91 971	25	0.08 029	9.88 594	10	16
45	9.80 580	15	9.91 996	26	0.08 004	9.88 584	11	15
46	9.80 595	15	9.92 022	26	0.07 978	9.88 573	10	14
47	9.80 610	15	9.92 048	25	0.07 952	9.88 563	11	13
48	9.80 625	16	9.92 073	26	0.07 927	9.88 552	10	12
49	9.80 641	15	9.92 099	26	0.07 901	9.88 542	11	11
50	9.80 656	15	9.92 125	25	0.07 875	9.88 531	10	10
51	9.80 671	15	9.92 150	26	0.07 850	9.88 521	11	9
52	9.80 686	15	9.92 176	26	0.07 824	9.88 510	11	8
53	9.80 701	15	9.92 202	25	0.07 798	9.88 499	10	7
54	9.80 716	15	9.92 227	26	0.07 773	9.88 489	11	6
55	9.80 731	15	9.92 253	26	0.07 747	9.88 478	10	5
56	9.80 746	16	9.92 279	25	0.07 721	9.88 468	11	4
57	9.80 762	15	9.92 304	26	0.07 696	9.88 457	10	3
58	9.80 777	15	9.92 330	26	0.07 670	9.88 447	11	2
59	9.80 792	15	9.92 356	25	0.07 644	9.88 436	11	1
60	9.80 807		9.92 381		0.07 619	9.88 425		0

'	L. Cos.	d.	L. Cot.	c.d.	L. Tan.	L. Sin.	d.	'

129° (309°)   (230°) **50°**

P. P.

"	26	25
1	0.4	0.4
2	0.9	0.8
3	1.3	1.2
4	1.7	1.7
5	2.2	2.1
6	2.6	2.5
7	3.0	2.9
8	3.5	3.3
9	3.9	3.8
10	4.3	4.2
20	8.7	8.3
30	13.0	12.5
40	17.3	16.7
50	21.7	20.8

"	16	15
1	0.3	0.2
2	0.5	0.5
3	0.8	0.8
4	1.1	1.0
5	1.3	1.2
6	1.6	1.5
7	1.9	1.8
8	2.1	2.0
9	2.4	2.2
10	2.7	2.5
20	5.3	5.0
30	8.0	7.5
40	10.7	10.0
50	13.3	12.5

"	11	10
1	0.2	0.2
2	0.4	0.3
3	0.6	0.5
4	0.7	0.7
5	0.9	0.8
6	1.1	1.0
7	1.3	1.2
8	1.5	1.3
9	1.6	1.5
10	1.8	1.7
20	3.7	3.3
30	5.5	5.0
40	7.3	6.7
50	9.2	8.3

	11	11
	26	25
0		
1	1.2	1.1
2	3.5	3.4
3	5.9	5.7
4	8.3	7.9
5	10.6	10.2
6	13.0	12.5
7	15.4	14.8
8	17.7	17.1
9	20.1	19.3
10	22.5	21.6
11	24.8	23.9

COMMON LOGARITHMS OF THE TRIGONOMETRIC
FUNCTIONS (Continued)

40° (220°)　　　　　　　　　　　　　　　　(319°) **139°**

′	L. Sin.	d.	L. Tan.	c.d.	L. Cot.	L. Cos.	d.	′
0	9.80 807	15	9.92 381	26	0.07 619	9.88 425	10	60
1	9.80 822	15	9.92 407	26	0.07 593	9.88 415	11	59
2	9.80 837	15	9.92 433	25	0.07 567	9.88 404	10	58
3	9.80 852	15	9.92 458	26	0.07 542	9.88 394	11	57
4	9.80 867	15	9.92 484	26	0.07 516	9.88 383	11	56
5	9.80 882	15	9.92 510	25	0.07 490	9.88 372	10	55
6	9.80 897	15	9.92 535	26	0.07 465	9.88 362	11	54
7	9.80 912	15	9.92 561	26	0.07 439	9.88 351	11	53
8	9.80 927	15	9.92 587	25	0.07 413	9.88 340	10	52
9	9.80 942	15	9.92 612	26	0.07 388	9.88 330	11	51
10	9.80 957	15	9.92 638	25	0.07 362	9.88 319	11	50
11	9.80 972	15	9.92 663	26	0.07 337	9.88 308	10	49
12	9.80 987	15	9.92 689	26	0.07 311	9.88 298	11	48
13	9.81 002	15	9.92 713	25	0.07 285	9.88 287	11	47
14	9.81 017	15	9.92 740	26	0.07 260	9.88 276	10	46
15	9.81 032	15	9.92 766	26	0.07 234	9.88 266	11	45
16	9.81 047	14	9.92 792	25	0.07 208	9.88 255	11	44
17	9.81 061	15	9.92 817	26	0.07 183	9.88 244	10	43
18	9.81 076	15	9.92 843	25	0.07 157	9.88 234	11	42
19	9.81 091	15	9.92 868	26	0.07 132	9.88 223	11	41
20	9.81 106	15	9.92 894	26	0.07 106	9.88 212	11	40
21	9.81 121	15	9.92 920	25	0.07 080	9.88 201	10	39
22	9.81 136	15	9.92 945	26	0.07 055	9.88 191	11	38
23	9.81 151	15	9.92 971	25	0.07 029	9.88 180	11	37
24	9.81 166	14	9.92 996	26	0.07 004	9.88 169	11	36
25	9.81 180	15	9.93 022	26	0.06 978	9.88 158	10	35
26	9.81 195	15	9.93 048	25	0.06 952	9.88 148	11	34
27	9.81 210	15	9.93 073	26	0.06 927	9.88 137	11	33
28	9.81 225	15	9.93 099	25	0.06 901	9.88 126	11	32
29	9.81 240	14	9.93 124	26	0.06 876	9.88 115	10	31
30	9.81 254	15	9.93 150	25	0.06 850	9.88 105	11	30
31	9.81 269	15	9.93 175	26	0.06 825	9.88 094	11	29
32	9.81 284	15	9.93 201	26	0.06 799	9.88 083	11	28
33	9.81 299	15	9.93 227	25	0.06 773	9.88 072	11	27
34	9.81 314	14	9.93 252	26	0.06 748	9.88 061	10	26
35	9.81 328	15	9.93 278	25	0.06 722	9.88 051	11	25
36	9.81 343	15	9.93 303	26	0.06 697	9.88 040	11	24
37	9.81 358	14	9.93 329	25	0.06 671	9.88 029	11	23
38	9.81 372	15	9.93 354	26	0.06 646	9.88 018	11	22
39	9.81 387	15	9.93 380	26	0.06 620	9.88 007	11	21
40	9.81 402	15	9.93 406	25	0.06 594	9.87 996	11	20
41	9.81 417	14	9.93 431	26	0.06 569	9.87 985	10	19
42	9.81 431	15	9.93 457	25	0.06 543	9.87 975	11	18
43	9.81 446	15	9.93 482	26	0.06 518	9.87 964	11	17
44	9.81 461	14	9.93 508	25	0.06 492	9.87 953	11	16
45	9.81 475	15	9.93 533	26	0.06 467	9.87 942	11	15
46	9.81 490	15	9.93 559	25	0.06 441	9.87 931	11	14
47	9.81 505	14	9.93 584	26	0.06 416	9.87 920	11	13
48	9.81 519	15	9.93 610	26	0.06 390	9.87 909	11	12
49	9.81 534	15	9.93 636	25	0.06 364	9.87 898	11	11
50	9.81 549	14	9.93 661	26	0.06 339	9.87 887	10	10
51	9.81 563	15	9.93 687	25	0.06 313	9.87 877	11	9
52	9.81 578	14	9.93 712	26	0.06 288	9.87 866	11	8
53	9.81 592	15	9.93 738	25	0.06 262	9.87 855	11	7
54	9.81 607	15	9.93 763	26	0.06 237	9.87 844	11	6
55	9.81 622	14	9.93 789	25	0.06 211	9.87 833	11	5
56	9.81 636	15	9.93 814	26	0.06 186	9.87 822	11	4
57	9.81 651	14	9.93 840	25	0.06 160	9.87 811	11	3
58	9.81 665	15	9.93 865	26	0.06 135	9.87 800	11	2
59	9.81 680	14	9.93 891	25	0.06 109	9.87 789	11	1
60	9.81 694		9.93 916		0.06 084	9.87 778		0

P. P.

″	26	25
1	0.4	0.4
2	0.9	0.8
3	1.3	1.2
4	1.7	1.7
5	2.2	2.1
6	2.6	2.5
7	3.0	2.9
8	3.5	3.3
9	3.9	3.8
10	4.3	4.2
20	8.7	8.3
30	13.0	12.5
40	17.3	16.7
50	21.7	20.8

″	15	14
1	0.2	0.2
2	0.5	0.5
3	0.8	0.7
4	1.0	0.9
5	1.2	1.2
6	1.5	1.4
7	1.8	1.6
8	2.0	1.9
9	2.2	2.1
10	2.5	2.3
20	5.0	4.7
30	7.5	7.0
40	10.0	9.3
50	12.5	11.7

″	11	10
1	0.2	0.2
2	0.4	0.3
3	0.6	0.5
4	0.7	0.7
5	0.9	0.8
6	1.1	1.0
7	1.3	1.2
8	1.5	1.3
9	1.6	1.5
10	1.8	1.7
20	3.7	3.3
30	5.5	5.0
40	7.3	6.7
50	9.2	8.3

	11	10	10
	26	26	25
0	1.2	1.3	1.2
1	3.5	3.9	3.8
2	5.9	6.5	6.2
3	8.3	9.1	8.8
4	10.6	11.7	11.2
5	13.0	14.3	13.8
6	15.4	16.9	16.2
7	17.7	19.5	18.8
8	20.1	22.1	21.2
9	22.5	24.7	23.8
10	24.8	—	—
11			

′	L. Cos.	d.	L. Cot.	c.d.	L. Tan.	L. Sin.	d.	′	P. P.

130° (310°)　　　　　　　　　　　　　　　　(229°) **49°**

COMMON LOGARITHMS OF THE TRIGONOMETRIC FUNCTIONS (Continued)

41° (221°)   (318°) **138°**

'	L. Sin.	d.	L. Tan.	c.d.	L. Cot.	L. Cos.	d.	'
0	9.81 694	15	9.93 916	26	0.06 084	9.87 778	11	60
1	9.81 709	14	9.93 942	25	0.06 058	9.87 767	11	59
2	9.81 723	15	9.93 967	26	0.06 033	9.87 756	11	58
3	9.81 738	14	9.93 993	25	0.06 007	9.87 745	11	57
4	9.81 752	15	9.94 018	26	0.05 982	9.87 734	11	56
5	9.81 767	14	9.94 044	25	0.05 956	9.87 723	11	55
6	9.81 781	15	9.94 069	26	0.05 931	9.87 712	11	54
7	9.81 796	14	9.94 095	25	0.05 905	9.87 701	11	53
8	9.81 810	15	9.94 120	26	0.05 880	9.87 690	11	52
9	9.81 825	14	9.94 146	25	0.05 854	9.87 679	11	51
10	9.81 839	15	9.94 171	26	0.05 829	9.87 668	11	50
11	9.81 854	14	9.94 197	25	0.05 803	9.87 657	11	49
12	9.81 868	14	9.94 222	26	0.05 778	9.87 646	11	48
13	9.81 882	15	9.94 248	25	0.05 752	9.87 635	11	47
14	9.81 897	14	9.94 273	26	0.05 727	9.87 624	11	46
15	9.81 911	15	9.94 299	25	0.05 701	9.87 613	12	45
16	9.81 926	14	9.94 324	26	0.05 676	9.87 601	11	44
17	9.81 940	15	9.94 350	25	0.05 650	9.87 590	11	43
18	9.81 955	14	9.94 375	26	0.05 625	9.87 579	11	42
19	9.81 969	14	9.94 401	25	0.05 599	9.87 568	11	41
20	9.81 983	15	9.94 426	26	0.05 574	9.87 557	11	40
21	9.81 998	14	9.94 452	25	0.05 548	9.87 546	11	39
22	9.82 012	14	9.94 477	26	0.05 523	9.87 535	11	38
23	9.82 026	15	9.94 503	25	0.05 497	9.87 524	11	37
24	9.82 041	14	9.94 528	26	0.05 472	9.87 513	12	36
25	9.82 055	14	9.94 554	25	0.05 446	9.87 501	11	35
26	9.82 069	15	9.94 579	25	0.05 421	9.87 490	11	34
27	9.82 084	14	9.94 604	26	0.05 396	9.87 479	11	33
28	9.82 098	14	9.94 630	25	0.05 370	9.87 468	11	32
29	9.82 112	14	9.94 655	26	0.05 345	9.87 457	11	31
30	9.82 126	15	9.94 681	25	0.05 319	9.87 446	12	30
31	9.82 141	14	9.94 706	26	0.05 294	9.87 434	11	29
32	9.82 155	14	9.94 732	25	0.05 268	9.87 423	11	28
33	9.82 169	15	9.94 757	26	0.05 243	9.87 412	11	27
34	9.82 184	14	9.94 783	25	0.05 217	9.87 401	11	26
35	9.82 198	14	9.94 808	26	0.05 192	9.87 390	12	25
36	9.82 212	14	9.94 834	25	0.05 166	9.87 378	11	24
37	9.82 226	14	9.94 859	25	0.05 141	9.87 367	11	23
38	9.82 240	15	9.94 884	26	0.05 116	9.87 356	11	22
39	9.82 255	14	9.94 910	25	0.05 090	9.87 345	11	21
40	9.82 269	14	9.94 935	26	0.05 065	9.87 334	12	20
41	9.82 283	14	9.94 961	25	0.05 039	9.87 322	11	19
42	9.82 297	14	9.94 986	26	0.05 014	9.87 311	11	18
43	9.82 311	15	9.95 012	25	0.04 988	9.87 300	12	17
44	9.82 326	14	9.95 037	25	0.04 963	9.87 288	11	16
45	9.82 340	14	9.95 062	26	0.04 938	9.87 277	11	15
46	9.82 354	14	9.95 088	25	0.04 912	9.87 266	11	14
47	9.82 368	14	9.95 113	26	0.04 887	9.87 255	12	13
48	9.82 382	14	9.95 139	25	0.04 861	9.87 243	11	12
49	9.82 396	14	9.95 164	26	0.04 836	9.87 232	11	11
50	9.82 410	14	9.95 190	25	0.04 810	9.87 221	12	10
51	9.82 424	15	9.95 215	25	0.04 785	9.87 209	11	9
52	9.82 439	14	9.95 240	26	0.04 760	9.87 198	11	8
53	9.82 453	14	9.95 266	25	0.04 734	9.87 187	11	7
54	9.82 467	14	9.95 291	26	0.04 709	9.87 175	11	6
55	9.82 481	14	9.95 317	25	0.04 683	9.87 164	11	5
56	9.82 495	14	9.95 342	26	0.04 658	9.87 153	12	4
57	9.82 509	14	9.95 368	25	0.04 632	9.87 141	11	3
58	9.82 523	14	9.95 393	26	0.04 607	9.87 130	11	2
59	9.82 537	14	9.95 418	25	0.04 582	9.87 119	12	1
60	9.82 551		9.95 444		0.04 556	9.87 107		0

P. P.

"	26	25
1	0.4	0.4
2	0.9	0.8
3	1.3	1.2
4	1.7	1.7
5	2.2	2.1
6	2.6	2.5
7	3.0	2.9
8	3.5	3.3
9	3.9	3.8
10	4.3	4.2
20	8.7	8.3
30	13.0	12.5
40	17.3	16.7
50	21.7	20.8

"	15	14
1	0.2	0.2
2	0.5	0.5
3	0.8	0.7
4	1.0	0.9
5	1.2	1.2
6	1.5	1.4
7	1.8	1.6
8	2.0	1.9
9	2.2	2.1
10	2.5	2.3
20	5.0	4.7
30	7.5	7.0
40	10.0	9.3
50	12.5	11.7

"	12	11
1	0.2	0.2
2	0.4	0.4
3	0.6	0.6
4	0.8	0.7
5	1.0	0.9
6	1.2	1.1
7	1.4	1.3
8	1.6	1.5
9	1.8	1.6
10	2.0	1.8
20	4.0	3.7
30	6.0	5.5
40	8.0	7.3
50	10.0	9.2

	12	12	11
	26	25	25
0	1.1	1.1	1.1
1	3.2	3.1	3.4
2	5.4	5.2	5.7
3	7.6	7.3	7.9
4	9.8	9.4	10.2
5	11.9	11.5	12.5
6	14.1	13.5	14.8
7	16.2	15.6	17.1
8	18.4	17.7	19.3
9	20.6	19.8	21.6
10	22.8	21.9	23.9
11	24.9	23.9	—
12			

Tables for Use in Trigonometry

COMMON LOGARITHMS OF THE TRIGONOMETRIC
FUNCTIONS (Continued)

42° (222°)   (317°) **137°**

′	L. Sin.	d.	L. Tan.	c.d.	L. Cot.	L. Cos.	d.	′	P. P.
0	9.82 551	14	9.95 444	25	0.04 556	9.87 107	11	60	
1	9.82 565	14	9.95 469	26	0.04 531	9.87 096	11	59	″ **26** **25**
2	9.82 579	14	9.95 495	25	0.04 505	9.87 085	12	58	1 0.4 0.4
3	9.82 593	14	9.95 520	25	0.04 480	9.87 073	11	57	2 0.9 0.8
4	9.82 607	14	9.95 545	26	0.04 455	9.87 062	12	56	3 1.3 1.2
									4 1.7 1.7
5	9.82 621	14	9.95 571	25	0.04 429	9.87 050	11	55	
6	9.82 635	14	9.95 596	26	0.04 404	9.87 039	11	54	5 2.2 2.1
7	9.82 649	14	9.95 622	25	0.04 378	9.87 028	11	53	6 2.6 2.5
8	9.82 663	14	9.95 647	25	0.04 353	9.87 016	11	52	7 3.0 2.9
9	9.82 677	14	9.95 672	26	0.04 328	9.87 005	12	51	8 3.5 3.3
									9 3.9 3.8
10	9.82 691	14	9.95 698	25	0.04 302	9.86 993	11	50	
11	9.82 705	14	9.95 723	25	0.04 277	9.86 982	12	49	10 4.3 4.2
12	9.82 719	14	9.95 748	26	0.04 252	9.86 970	11	48	20 8.7 8.3
13	9.82 733	14	9.95 774	25	0.04 226	9.86 959	12	47	30 13.0 12.5
14	9.82 747	14	9.95 799	26	0.04 201	9.86 947	11	46	40 17.3 16.7
									50 21.7 20.8
15	9.82 761	14	9.95 825	25	0.04 175	9.86 936	12	45	
16	9.82 775	13	9.95 850	25	0.04 150	9.86 924	11	44	″ **14** **13**
17	9.82 788	14	9.95 875	26	0.04 125	9.86 913	11	43	1 0.2 0.2
18	9.82 802	14	9.95 901	25	0.04 099	9.86 902	12	42	2 0.5 0.4
19	9.82 816	14	9.95 926	26	0.04 074	9.86 890	11	41	3 0.7 0.6
									4 0.9 0.9
20	9.82 830	14	9.95 952	25	0.04 048	9.86 879	12	40	
21	9.82 844	14	9.95 977	25	0.04 023	9.86 867	12	39	5 1.2 1.1
22	9.82 858	14	9.96 002	26	0.03 998	9.86 855	11	38	6 1.4 1.3
23	9.82 872	13	9.96 028	25	0.03 972	9.86 844	12	37	7 1.6 1.5
24	9.82 885	14	9.96 053	25	0.03 947	9.86 832	11	36	8 1.9 1.7
									9 2.1 2.0
25	9.82 899	14	9.96 078	26	0.03 922	9.86 821	12	35	
26	9.82 913	14	9.96 104	25	0.03 896	9.86 809	11	34	10 2.3 2.2
27	9.82 927	14	9.96 129	26	0.03 871	9.86 798	12	33	20 4.7 4.3
28	9.82 941	14	9.96 155	25	0.03 845	9.86 786	11	32	30 7.0 6.5
29	9.82 955	13	9.96 180	25	0.03 820	9.86 775	12	31	40 9.3 8.7
									50 11.7 10.8
30	9.82 968	14	9.96 205	26	0.03 795	9.86 763	11	30	
31	9.82 982	14	9.96 231	25	0.03 769	9.86 752	12	29	″ **12** **11**
32	9.82 996	14	9.96 256	25	0.03 744	9.86 740	12	28	1 0.2 0.2
33	9.83 010	13	9.96 281	26	0.03 719	9.86 728	12	27	2 0.4 0.4
34	9.83 023	14	9.96 307	25	0.03 693	9.86 717	12	26	3 0.6 0.6
									4 0.8 0.7
35	9.83 037	14	9.96 332	25	0.03 668	9.86 705	11	25	
36	9.83 051	14	9.96 357	26	0.03 643	9.86 694	12	24	5 1.0 0.9
37	9.83 065	13	9.96 383	25	0.03 617	9.86 682	12	23	6 1.2 1.1
38	9.83 078	14	9.96 408	25	0.03 592	9.86 670	11	22	7 1.4 1.3
39	9.83 092	14	9.96 433	26	0.03 567	9.86 659	12	21	8 1.6 1.5
									9 1.8 1.6
40	9.83 106	14	9.96 459	25	0.03 541	9.86 647	12	20	
41	9.83 120	13	9.96 484	26	0.03 516	9.86 635	11	19	10 2.0 1.8
42	9.83 133	14	9.96 510	25	0.03 490	9.86 624	12	18	20 4.0 3.7
43	9.83 147	14	9.96 535	25	0.03 465	9.86 612	12	17	30 6.0 5.5
44	9.83 161	13	9.96 560	26	0.03 440	9.86 600	11	16	40 8.0 7.3
									50 10.0 9.2
45	9.83 174	14	9.96 586	25	0.03 414	9.86 589	12	15	
46	9.83 188	14	9.96 611	25	0.03 389	9.86 577	12	14	
47	9.83 202	13	9.96 636	26	0.03 364	9.86 565	11	13	**12** **11** **11**
48	9.83 215	14	9.96 662	25	0.03 338	9.86 554	12	12	— — —
49	9.83 229	13	9.96 687	25	0.03 313	9.86 542	12	11	**26** **26** **25**
50	9.83 242	14	9.96 712	26	0.03 288	9.86 530	12	10	0
51	9.83 256	14	9.96 738	25	0.03 262	9.86 518	11	9	1 1.1 1.2 1.1
52	9.83 270	13	9.96 763	25	0.03 237	9.86 507	12	8	2 3.2 3.5 3.4
53	9.83 283	14	9.96 788	26	0.03 212	9.86 495	12	7	3 5.4 5.9 5.7
54	9.83 297	13	9.96 814	25	0.03 186	9.86 483	11	6	4 7.6 8.3 7.9
									5 9.8 10.6 10.2
55	9.83 310	14	9.96 839	25	0.03 161	9.86 472	12	5	6 11.9 13.0 12.5
56	9.83 324	14	9.96 864	26	0.03 136	9.86 460	12	4	7 14.1 15.4 14.8
57	9.83 338	13	9.96 890	25	0.03 110	9.86 448	12	3	8 16.2 17.7 17.1
58	9.83 351	14	9.96 915	25	0.03 085	9.86 436	11	2	9 18.4 20.1 19.3
59	9.83 365	13	9.96 940	26	0.03 060	9.86 425	12	1	10 20.6 22.5 21.6
									11 22.8 24.8 23.9
60	9.83 378		9.96 966		0.03 034	9.86 413		0	12 24.9 — —
′	L. Cos.	d.	L. Cot.	c.d.	L. Tan.	L. Sin.	d.	′	P. P.

132° (312°)   (227°) **47°**

COMMON LOGARITHMS OF THE TRIGONOMETRIC FUNCTIONS (Continued)

43° (223°)   (316°) **136°**

′	L. Sin.	d.	L. Tan.	c.d.	L. Cot.	L. Cos.	d.	′
0	9.83 378	14	9.96 966	25	0.03 034	9.86 413	12	60
1	9.83 392	13	9.96 991	25	0.03 009	9.86 401	12	59
2	9.83 405	14	9.97 016	26	0.02 984	9.86 389	12	58
3	9.83 419	13	9.97 042	25	0.02 958	9.86 377	11	57
4	9.83 432	14	9.97 067	25	0.02 933	9.86 366	12	56
5	9.83 446	13	9.97 092	26	0.02 908	9.86 354	12	55
6	9.83 459	14	9.97 118	25	0.02 882	9.86 342	12	54
7	9.83 473	13	9.97 143	25	0.02 857	9.86 330	12	53
8	9.83 486	14	9.97 168	25	0.02 832	9.86 318	12	52
9	9.83 500	13	9.97 193	26	0.02 807	9.86 306	11	51
10	9.83 513	14	9.97 219	25	0.02 781	9.86 295	12	50
11	9.83 527	13	9.97 244	25	0.02 756	9.86 283	12	49
12	9.83 540	14	9.97 269	26	0.02 731	9.86 271	12	48
13	9.83 554	13	9.97 295	25	0.02 705	9.86 259	12	47
14	9.83 567	14	9.97 320	25	0.02 680	9.86 247	12	46
15	9.83 581	13	9.97 345	26	0.02 655	9.86 235	12	45
16	9.83 594	14	9.97 371	25	0.02 629	9.86 223	12	44
17	9.83 608	13	9.97 396	25	0.02 604	9.86 211	11	43
18	9.83 621	13	9.97 421	26	0.02 579	9.86 200	12	42
19	9.83 634	14	9.97 447	25	0.02 553	9.86 188	12	41
20	9.83 648	13	9.97 472	25	0.02 528	9.86 176	12	40
21	9.83 661	13	9.97 497	26	0.02 503	9.86 164	12	39
22	9.83 674	14	9.97 523	25	0.02 477	9.86 152	12	38
23	9.83 688	13	9.97 548	25	0.02 452	9.86 140	12	37
24	9.83 701	14	9.97 573	25	0.02 427	9.86 128	12	36
25	9.83 715	13	9.97 598	26	0.02 402	9.86 116	12	35
26	9.83 728	13	9.97 624	25	0.02 376	9.86 104	12	34
27	9.83 741	14	9.97 649	25	0.02 351	9.86 092	12	33
28	9.83 755	13	9.97 674	26	0.02 326	9.86 080	12	32
29	9.83 768	13	9.97 700	25	0.02 300	9.86 068	12	31
30	9.83 781	14	9.97 725	25	0.02 275	9.86 056	12	30
31	9.83 795	13	9.97 750	26	0.02 250	9.86 044	12	29
32	9.83 808	13	9.97 776	25	0.02 224	9.86 032	12	28
33	9.83 821	13	9.97 801	25	0.02 199	9.86 020	12	27
34	9.83 834	14	9.97 826	25	0.02 174	9.86 008	12	26
35	9.83 848	13	9.97 851	26	0.02 149	9.85 996	12	25
36	9.83 861	13	9.97 877	25	0.02 123	9.85 984	12	24
37	9.83 874	13	9.97 902	25	0.02 098	9.85 972	12	23
38	9.83 887	14	9.97 927	26	0.02 073	9.85 960	12	22
39	9.83 901	13	9.97 953	25	0.02 047	9.85 948	12	21
40	9.83 914	13	9.97 978	25	0.02 022	9.85 936	12	20
41	9.83 927	13	9.98 003	26	0.01 997	9.85 924	12	19
42	9.83 940	14	9.98 029	25	0.01 971	9.85 912	12	18
43	9.83 954	13	9.98 054	25	0.01 946	9.85 900	12	17
44	9.83 967	13	9.98 079	25	0.01 921	9.85 888	12	16
45	9.83 980	13	9.98 104	26	0.01 896	9.85 876	12	15
46	9.83 993	13	9.98 130	25	0.01 870	9.85 864	13	14
47	9.84 006	14	9.98 155	25	0.01 845	9.85 851	12	13
48	9.84 020	13	9.98 180	26	0.01 820	9.85 839	12	12
49	9.84 033	13	9.98 206	25	0.01 794	9.85 827	12	11
50	9.84 046	13	9.98 231	25	0.01 769	9.85 815	12	10
51	9.84 059	13	9.98 256	25	0.01 744	9.85 803	12	9
52	9.84 072	13	9.98 281	26	0.01 719	9.85 791	12	8
53	9.84 085	13	9.98 307	25	0.01 693	9.85 779	13	7
54	9.84 098	14	9.98 332	25	0.01 668	9.85 766	12	6
55	9.84 112	13	9.98 357	26	0.01 643	9.85 754	12	5
56	9.84 125	13	9.98 383	25	0.01 617	9.85 742	12	4
57	9.84 138	13	9.98 408	25	0.01 592	9.85 730	12	3
58	9.84 151	13	9.98 433	25	0.01 567	9.85 718	12	2
59	9.84 164	13	9.98 458	26	0.01 542	9.85 706	13	1
60	9.84 177		9.98 484		0.01 516	9.85 693		0

P. P.

″	26	25
1	0.4	0.4
2	0.9	0.8
3	1.3	1.2
4	1.7	1.7
5	2.2	2.1
6	2.6	2.5
7	3.0	2.9
8	3.5	3.3
9	3.9	3.8
10	4.3	4.2
20	8.7	8.3
30	13.0	12.5
40	17.3	16.7
50	21.7	20.8

″	14	13
1	0.2	0.2
2	0.5	0.4
3	0.7	0.6
4	0.9	0.9
5	1.2	1.1
6	1.4	1.3
7	1.6	1.5
8	1.9	1.7
9	2.1	2.0
10	2.3	2.2
20	4.7	4.3
30	7.0	6.5
40	9.3	8.7
50	11.7	10.8

″	12	11
1	0.2	0.2
2	0.4	0.4
3	0.6	0.6
4	0.8	0.7
5	1.0	0.9
6	1.2	1.1
7	1.4	1.3
8	1.6	1.5
9	1.8	1.6
10	2.0	1.8
20	4.0	3.7
30	6.0	5.5
40	8.0	7.3
50	10.0	9.2

	13	13	12
	26	25	25
1	1.0	0.9	1.1
2	3.0	2.9	3.1
3	5.0	4.8	5.2
4	7.0	6.7	7.3
5	9.0	8.7	9.4
6	11.0	10.6	11.5
7	13.0	12.5	13.5
8	15.0	14.4	15.6
9	17.0	16.3	17.7
10	19.0	18.3	19.8
11	21.0	20.2	21.9
12	23.0	22.1	23.9
13	25.0	24.1	—

′	L. Cos.	d.	L. Cot.	c.d.	L. Tan.	L. Sin.	d.	′

133° (313°)   (226°) **46°**

COMMON LOGARITHMS OF THE TRIGONOMETRIC
FUNCTIONS (Continued)

44° (224°)   **(315°) 135°**

'	L. Sin.	d.	L. Tan.	c.d.	L. Cot.	L. Cos.	d.	'	P. P.
0	9.84 177		9.98 484		0.01 516	9.85 693	12	60	
1	9.84 190	13	9.98 509	25	0.01 491	9.85 681	12	59	**" 26 25**
2	9.84 203	13	9.98 534	25	0.01 466	9.85 669	12	58	1 0.4 0.4
3	9.84 216	13	9.98 560	26	0.01 440	9.85 657	12	57	2 0.9 0.8
4	9.84 229	13	9.98 585	25	0.01 415	9.85 645	12	56	3 1.3 1.2
		13		25			13		4 1.7 1.7
5	9.84 242		9.98 610		0.01 390	9.85 632		55	
6	9.84 255	13	9.98 635	25	0.01 365	9.85 620	12	54	5 2.2 2.1
7	9.84 269	14	9.98 661	26	0.01 339	9.85 608	12	53	6 2.6 2.5
8	9.84 282	13	9.98 686	25	0.01 314	9.85 596	12	52	7 3.0 2.9
9	9.84 295	13	9.98 711	25	0.01 289	9.85 583	13	51	8 3.5 3.3
		13		26			12		9 3.9 3.8
10	9.84 308		9.98 737		0.01 263	9.85 571		50	
11	9.84 321	13	9.98 762	25	0.01 238	9.85 559	12	49	10 4.3 4.2
12	9.84 334	13	9.98 787	25	0.01 213	9.85 547	12	48	20 8.7 8.3
13	9.84 347	13	9.98 812	25	0.01 188	9.85 534	13	47	30 13.0 12.5
14	9.84 360	13	9.98 838	26	0.01 162	9.85 522	12	46	40 17.3 16.7
		13		25			12		50 21.7 20.8
15	9.84 373		9.98 863		0.01 137	9.85 510		45	
16	9.84 385	12	9.98 888	25	0.01 112	9.85 497	13	44	**" 14 13 12**
17	9.84 398	13	9.98 913	25	0.01 087	9.85 485	12	43	1 0.2 0.2 0.2
18	9.84 411	13	9.98 939	26	0.01 061	9.85 473	12	42	2 0.5 0.4 0.4
19	9.84 424	13	9.98 964	25	0.01 036	9.85 460	13	41	3 0.7 0.6 0.6
		13		25			12		4 0.9 0.9 0.8
20	9.84 437		9.98 989		0.01 011	9.85 448		40	
21	9.84 450	13	9.99 015	26	0.00 985	9.85 436	12	39	5 1.2 1.1 1.0
22	9.84 463	13	9.99 040	25	0.00 960	9.85 423	13	38	6 1.4 1.3 1.2
23	9.84 476	13	9.99 065	25	0.00 935	9.85 411	13	37	7 1.6 1.5 1.4
24	9.84 489	13	9.99 090	25	0.00 910	9.85 399	12	36	8 1.9 1.7 1.6
		13		26			13		9 2.1 2.0 1.8
25	9.84 502		9.99 116		0.00 884	9.85 386		35	
26	9.84 515	13	9.99 141	25	0.00 859	9.85 374	12	34	10 2.3 2.2 2.0
27	9.84 528	13	9.99 166	25	0.00 834	9.85 361	13	33	20 4.7 4.3 4.0
28	9.84 540	12	9.99 191	25	0.00 809	9.85 349	12	32	30 7.0 6.5 6.0
29	9.84 553	13	9.99 217	26	0.00 783	9.85 337	12	31	40 9.3 8.7 8.0
		13		25			13		50 11.7 10.8 10.0
30	9.84 566		9.99 242		0.00 758	9.85 324		30	
31	9.84 579	13	9.99 267	25	0.00 733	9.85 312	12	29	
32	9.84 592	13	9.99 293	26	0.00 707	9.85 299	13	28	**13 13**
33	9.84 605	13	9.99 318	25	0.00 682	9.85 287	12	27	**26 25**
34	9.84 618	13	9.99 343	25	0.00 657	9.85 274	13	26	
		12		25			12		0 1.0 0.9
35	9.84 630		9.99 368		0.00 632	9.85 262		25	1 3.0 2.9
36	9.84 643	13	9.99 394	26	0.00 606	9.85 250	12	24	2 5.0 4.8
37	9.84 656	13	9.99 419	25	0.00 581	9.85 237	13	23	3 7.0 6.7
38	9.84 669	13	9.99 444	25	0.00 556	9.85 225	12	22	4 9.0 8.7
39	9.84 682	13	9.99 469	25	0.00 531	9.85 212	13	21	5 11.0 10.6
		12		26			12		6 13.0 12.5
40	9.84 694		9.99 495		0.00 505	9.85 200		20	7 15.0 14.4
41	9.84 707	13	9.99 520	25	0.00 480	9.85 187	13	19	8 17.0 16.3
42	9.84 720	13	9.99 545	25	0.00 455	9.85 175	12	18	9 19.0 18.3
43	9.84 733	13	9.99 570	25	0.00 430	9.85 162	13	17	10 21.0 20.2
44	9.84 745	12	9.99 596	26	0.00 404	9.85 150	12	16	11 23.0 22.1
		13		25			13		12 25.0 24.1
45	9.84 758		9.99 621		0.00 379	9.85 137		15	13
46	9.84 771	13	9.99 646	25	0.00 354	9.85 125	12	14	
47	9.84 784	13	9.99 672	26	0.00 328	9.85 112	13	13	**12 12**
48	9.84 796	12	9.99 697	25	0.00 303	9.85 100	12	12	**26 25**
49	9.84 809	13	9.99 722	25	0.00 278	9.85 087	13	11	
		13		25			13		0 1.1 1.1
50	9.84 822		9.99 747		0.00 253	9.85 074		10	1 3.2 3.1
51	9.84 835	13	9.99 773	26	0.00 227	9.85 062	12	9	2 5.4 5.2
52	9.84 847	12	9.99 798	25	0.00 202	9.85 049	13	8	3 7.6 7.3
53	9.84 860	13	9.99 823	25	0.00 177	9.85 037	12	7	4 9.8 9.4
54	9.84 873	13	9.99 848	25	0.00 152	9.85 024	13	6	5 11.9 11.5
		12		26			12		6 14.1 13.5
55	9.84 885		9.99 874		0.00 126	9.85 012		5	7 16.2 15.6
56	9.84 898	13	9.99 899	25	0.00 101	9.84 999	13	4	8 18.4 17.7
57	9.84 911	13	9.99 924	25	0.00 076	9.84 986	13	3	9 20.6 19.8
58	9.84 923	12	9.99 949	25	0.00 051	9.84 974	12	2	10 22.8 21.9
59	9.84 936	13	9.99 975	26	0.00 025	9.84 961	13	1	11 24.9 23.9
		13		25			12		12
60	9.84 949		0.00 000		0.00 000	9.84 949		0	
'	L. Cos.	d.	L. Cot.	c.d.	L. Tan.	L. Sin.	d.	'	P. P.

134° (314°)   **(225°) 45°**

COMMON LOGARITHMS OF THE TRIGONOMETRIC FUNCTIONS FOR ANGLES IN DEGREES AND DECIMALS

The table that follows gives the common logarithms of the functions sine, cosine, tangent and cotangent for each tenth of a degree from 0° to 90°. Linear interpolation may be used to obtain functional values for angles expressed in hundredths of a degree, except where the values of the functions are rapidly changing.

For argument values found in the left column, use the column headings at the top of the columns. For argument values found in the right column, use the column headings at the bottom of the columns.

The quantity − 10 is to be appended to the logarithm of all sines and cosines, and to logarithms of tangents from 0° to 45°, and cotangents from 45° to 90°.

COMMON LOGARITHMS OF THE TRIGONOMETRIC FUNCTIONS FOR ANGLES IN DEGREES AND DECIMALS

Deg.	L. Sin	*L. Tan	*L. Cot	L. Cos	
0.0	− ∞	− ∞	∞	0.00000	**90.0**
.1	7.24188	7.24188	2.75812	0.00000	89.9
.2	7.54291	7.54291	2.45709	0.00000	.8
.3	7.71900	7.71900	2.28100	9.99999	.7
.4	7.84393	7.84394	2.15606	9.99999	.6
.5	7.94084	7.94086	2.05914	9.99998	.5
.6	8.02002	8.02004	1.97996	9.99998	.4
.7	8.08696	8.08700	1.91300	9.99997	.3
.8	8.14495	8.14500	1.85500	9.99996	.2
.9	8.19610	8.19616	1.80384	9.99995	89.1
1.0	8.24186	8.24192	1.75808	9.99993	**89.9**
.1	8.28324	8.28332	1.71668	9.99992	88.9
.2	8.32103	8.32112	1.67888	9.99990	.8
.3	8.35578	8.35590	1.64410	9.99989	.7
.4	8.38796	8.38809	1.61191	9.99987	.6
.5	8.41792	8.41807	1.58193	9.99985	.5
.6	8.44594	8.44611	1.55389	9.99983	.4
.7	8.47226	8.47245	1.52755	9.99981	.3
.8	8.49708	8.49729	1.50271	9.99979	.2
.9	8.52055	8.52079	1.47921	9 99976	88.1
2.0	8.54282	8.54308	1.45692	9.99974	**88.0**
.1	8.56400	8.56429	1.43571	9.99971	87.9
.2	8.58419	8.58451	1.41549	9.99969	.8
.3	8.60349	8.60384	1.39616	9.99965	.7
.4	8.62196	8.62234	1.37766	9.99962	.6
.5	8.63968	8.64009	1.35991	9.99959	.5
.6	8.65670	8.65715	1.34285	9.99955	.4
.7	8.67308	8.67356	1.32644	9.99952	.3
.8	8.68886	8.68938	1.31062	9.99948	.2
.9	8.70409	8.70465	1.29535	9.99944	87.1
3.0	8.71880	8.71940	1.28060	9.99940	**87.0**
.1	8.73303	8.73366	1.26634	9.99936	86.9
.2	8.74680	8.74748	1.25252	9.99932	.8
.3	8.76015	8.76087	1.23913	9.99928	.7
.4	8.77310	8.77387	1.22613	9.99923	.6
.5	8.78568	8.78649	1.21351	9.99919	.5
.6	8.79789	8.79875	1.20125	9.99914	.4
.7	8.80978	8.81068	1.18932	9.99909	.3
.8	8.82134	8.82230	1.17770	9.99904	.2
.9	8.83261	8.83361	1.16639	9.99899	86.1
4.0	8.84358	8.84464	1.15536	9.99894	**86.0**
.1	8.85429	8.85540	1.14460	9.99889	85.9
.2	8.86474	8.86591	1.13409	9.99883	.8
.3	8.87494	8.87616	1.12384	9.99878	.7
.4	8.88490	8.88618	1.11382	9.99872	.6
.5	8.89464	8.89598	1.10402	9.99866	.5
.6	8.90417	8.90557	1.09443	9.99860	.4
.7	8.91349	8.91495	1.08505	9.99854	.3
.8	8.92261	8.92414	1.07586	9.99847	.2
.9	8.93154	8.93313	1.06687	9.99841	85.1
5.0	8.94030	8.94195	1.05805	9.99834	**85.0**
.1	8.94887	8 95060	1.04940	9.99828	84.9
.2	8.95728	8.95908	1.04092	9.99821	.8
.3	8.96553	8.96739	1.03261	9.99814	.7
.4	8.97363	8.97556	1.02444	9.99807	.6
.5	8.98157	8.98358	1.01642	9.99800	.5
.6	8.98937	8.99145	1.00855	9.99792	.4
.7	8.99704	8.99919	1.00081	9.99785	.3
.8	9.00456	9.00679	0.99321	9.99777	.2
.9	9.01196	9.01427	0.98573	9.99769	84.1
6.0	9.01923	9.02162	0.97838	9.99761	**84.0**
	L. Cos	*L. Cot	*L. Tan	L. Sin	Deg.

Deg.	L. Sin	L. Tan	L. Cot	L. Cos	
6.0	9.01923	9.02162	0.97838	9.99761	**84.0**
.1	9.02639	9.02885	0.97115	9.99753	83.9
.2	9.03342	9.03597	0.96403	9.99745	.8
.3	9 04034	9.04297	0.95703	9.99737	.7
.4	9.04715	9.04987	0.95013	9.99728	.6
.5	9.05386	9.05666	0.94334	9.99720	.5
.6	9.06046	9.06335	0.93665	9.99711	.4
.7	9.06696	9.06994	0.93006	9.99702	.3
.8	9.07337	9.07643	0.92357	9.99693	.2
.9	9.07968	9.08283	0.91717	9.99684	83.1
7.0	9.08589	9.08914	0.91086	9.99675	**83.0**
.1	9.09202	9.09537	0.90463	9.99666	82.9
.2	9.09807	9.10150	0.89850	9.99656	.8
.3	9.10402	9.10756	0.89244	9.99647	.7
.4	9.10990	9.11353	0.88647	9.99637	.6
.5	9.11570	9.11943	0.88057	9.99627	.5
.6	9.12142	9.12525	0.87475	9.99617	.4
7	9.12706	9.13099	0.86901	9.99607	.3
8	9.13263	9.13667	0.86333	9.99596	.2
.9	9.13813	9.14227	0.85773	9.99586	82.1
8.0	9.14356	9.14780	0.85220	9.99575	**82.0**
.1	9.14891	9.15327	0.84673	9.99565	81.9
2	9.15421	9.15867	0.84133	9.99554	.8
.3	9.15944	9.16401	0.83599	9.99543	.7
.4	9.16460	9.16928	0.83072	9.99532	.6
.5	9.16970	9.17450	0.82550	9.99520	.5
.6	9.17474	9.17965	0.82035	9.99509	.4
.7	9.17973	9.18475	0.81525	9.99497	.3
.8	9.18465	9.18979	0.81021	9.99486	.2
.9	9.18952	9.19478	0.80522	9.99474	81.1
9.0	9.19433	9.19971	0.80029	9.99462	**81.0**
.1	9.19909	9.20459	0.79541	9.99450	80.9
.2	9.20380	9.20942	0.79058	9.99438	.8
.3	9.20845	9.21420	0.78580	9.99425	.7
.4	9.21306	9.21893	0.78107	9.99413	.6
.5	9.21761	9.22361	0.77639	9.99400	.5
6	9.22211	9.22824	0.77176	9.99388	.4
.7	9.22657	9.23283	0.76717	9.99375	.3
.8	9.23098	9.23737	0.76263	9.99362	.2
.9	9.23535	9.24186	0.75814	9.99348	80.1
10.0	9.23967	9.24632	0.75368	9.99335	**80.0**
.1	9.24395	9.25073	0.74927	9.99322	79.9
2	9.24818	9.25510	0.74490	9.99308	.8
3	9.25237	9.25943	0.74057	9.99294	.7
.4	9.25652	9.26372	0.73628	9.99281	.6
.5	9.26063	9.26797	0.73203	9.99267	.5
.6	9.26470	9.27218	0.72782	9.99252	.4
.7	9.26873	9.27635	0.72365	9.99238	.3
8	9.27273	9.28049	0.71951	9.99224	.2
.9	9.27668	9.28459	0.71541	9.99209	79.1
11.0	9.28060	9.28865	0.71135	9.99195	**79.0**
1	9.28448	9.29268	0.70732	9.99180	78.9
.2	9.28833	9.29668	0.70332	9.99165	.8
.3	9.29214	9.30064	0.69936	9.99150	.7
.4	9.29591	9.30457	0.69543	9.99135	.6
.5	9.29966	9.30846	0.69154	9.99119	.5
.6	9.30336	9.31233	0.68767	9.99104	.4
.7	9.30704	9.31616	0.68384	9.99088	.3
.8	9.31068	9.31996	0.68004	9.99072	.2
.9	9.31430	9.32373	0.67627	9.99056	78.1
12.0	9.31788	9.32747	0 67253	9.99040	**78.0**
	L. Cos	L. Cot	L. Tan	L. Sin	Deg.

*Linear interpolation in this section of the table is inaccurate.

COMMON LOGARITHMS OF THE TRIGONOMETRIC FUNCTIONS FOR ANGLES IN DEGREES AND DECIMALS (Continued)

Deg.	L. Sin	L. Tan	L. Cot	L. Cos	
12.0	9.31788	9.32747	0.67253	9.99040	**78.0**
.1	9.32143	9.33119	0.66881	9.99024	77.9
.2	9.32495	9.33487	0.66513	9.99008	.8
.3	9.32844	9.33853	0.66147	9.98991	.7
.4	9.33190	9.34215	0.65785	9.98975	.6
.5	9.33534	9.34576	0.65424	9.98958	.5
.6	9.33874	9.34933	0.65067	9.98941	.4
.7	9.34212	9.35288	0.64712	9.98924	.3
.8	9.34547	9.35640	0.64360	9.98907	.2
.9	9.34879	9.35989	0.64011	9.98890	77.1
13.0	9.35209	9.36336	0.63664	9.98872	**77.0**
.1	9.35536	9.36681	0.63319	9.98855	76.9
.2	9.35860	9.37023	0.62977	9.98837	.8
.3	9.36182	9.37363	0.62637	9.98819	.7
.4	9.36502	9.37700	0.62300	9.98801	.6
.5	9.36819	9.38035	0.61965	6.98783	.5
.6	9.37133	9.38368	0.61632	9.98765	.4
.7	9.37445	9.38699	0.61301	9.98746	.3
.8	9.37755	9.39027	0.60973	9.98728	.2
.9	9.38062	9.39353	0.60647	9.98709	76.1
14.0	9.38368	9.39677	0.60323	9.98690	**76.0**
.1	9.38670	9.39999	0.60001	9.98671	75.9
.2	9.38971	9.40319	0.59681	9.98652	.8
.3	9.39270	9.40636	0.59364	9.98633	.7
.4	9.39566	9.40952	0.59048	9.98614	.6
.5	9.39860	9.41266	0.58734	9.98594	.5
.6	9.40152	9.41578	0.58422	9.98574	.4
.7	9.40442	9.41887	0.58113	9.98555	.3
.8	9.40730	9.42195	0.57805	9.98535	.2
.9	9.41016	9.42501	0.57499	9.98515	75.1
15.0	9.41300	9.42805	0.57195	9.98494	**75.0**
.1	9.41582	9.43108	0.56892	9.98474	74.9
.2	9.41861	9.43408	0.56592	9.98453	.8
.3	9.42140	9.43707	0.56293	9.98433	.7
.4	9.42416	9.44004	0.55996	9.98412	.6
.5	9.42690	9.44299	0.55701	9.98391	.5
.6	9.42962	9.44592	0.55408	9.98370	.4
.7	9.43233	9.44884	0.55116	9.98349	.3
.8	9.43502	9.45174	0.54826	9.98327	.2
.9	9.43769	9.45463	0.54537	9.98306	74.1
16.0	9.44034	9.45750	0.54250	9.98284	**74.0**
.1	9.44297	9.46035	0.53965	9.98262	73.9
.2	9.44559	9.46319	0.53681	9.98240	.8
.3	9.44819	9.46601	0.53399	9.98218	.7
.4	9.45077	9.46881	0.53119	9.98196	.6
.5	9.45334	9.47160	0.52840	9.98174	.5
.6	9.45589	9.47438	0.52562	9.98151	.4
.7	9.45843	9.47714	0.52286	9.98129	.3
.8	9.46095	9.47989	0.52011	9.98106	.2
.9	9.46345	9.48262	0.51738	9.98083	73.1
17.0	9.46594	9.48534	0.51466	9.98060	**73.0**
.1	9.46841	9.48804	0.51196	9·98036	72.9
.2	9.47086	9.49073	0.50927	9.98013	.8
.3	9.47330	9.49341	0.50659	9.97989	.7
.4	9.47573	9.49607	0.50393	9.97966	.6
.5	9.47814	9.49872	0.50128	9.97942	.5
.6	9.48054	9.50136	0.49864	9.97918	.4
.7	9.48292	9.50398	0.49602	9.97894	.3
.8	9.48529	9.50659	0.49341	9.97870	.2
.9	9.48764	9.50919	0.49081	9.97845	72.1
18.0	9.48998	9.51178	0.48822	9.97821	**72.0**
	L. Cos	L. Cot	L. Tan	L. Sin	Deg.

Deg.	L. Sin	L. Tan	L. Cot	L. Cos	
18.0	9.48998	9.51178	0.48822	9.97821	**72.0**
.1	9.49231	9.51435	0.48565	9.97795	71.9
.2	9.49462	9.51691	0.48309	9.97771	.8
.3	9.49692	9.51946	0.48054	9.97746	.7
.4	9.49920	9.52200	0.47801	9.97721	.6
.5	9.50148	9.52452	0.47548	9.97696	.5
.6	9.50374	9.52703	0.47297	9.97670	.4
.7	9.50598	9.52953	0.47047	9.97645	.3
.8	9.50821	9.53202	0.46798	9.97619	.2
.9	9.51043	9.53450	0.46550	9.97593	71.1
19.0	9 51264	9.53697	0.46303	9.97567	**71.0**
.1	9.51484	9.53943	0.46057	9.97541	70.9
.2	9.51702	9.54187	0.45813	9.97515	.8
.3	9.51919	9.54431	0.45569	9.97488	.7
.4	9 52135	9.54673	0.45327	9.97461	.6
.5	9.52350	9.54915	0.45085	9.97435	.5
.6	9.52563	9.55155	0.44845	9.97408	.4
.7	9.52775	9.55395	0.44605	9.97381	.3
.8	9.52986	9.55633	0.44367	9.97353	.2
.9	9.53196	9.55870	0.44130	9.97326	70.1
20.0	9.53405	9.56107	0.43893	9.97299	**70.0**
.1	9.53613	9.56342	0.43658	9.97271	69.9
.2	9.53819	9.56576	0.43424	9.97243	.8
.3	9.54025	9.56810	0.43190	9.97215	.7
.4	9.54229	9.57042	0.42958	9.97187	.6
.5	9.54433	9.57274	0.42726	9.97159	.5
.6	9.54635	9.57504	0.42496	9.97130	.4
.7	9.54836	9.57734	0.42266	9.97102	.3
.8	9.55036	9.57963	0.42037	9.97073	.2
.9	9.55235	9.58191	0.41809	9.97044	69.1
21.0	9.55433	9.58418	0.41582	9.97015	**69.0**
.1	9.55630	9.58644	0.41356	9.96986	68.9
.2	9.55826	9.58869	0.41131	9.96957	.8
.3	9.56021	9.59094	0.40906	9.96927	.7
.4	9.56215	9.59317	0.40683	9.96898	.6
.5	9.56407	9.59540	0.40460	9.96868	.5
.6	9.56599	9.59762	0.40238	9.96838	.4
.7	9.56790	9.59983	0.40017	9.96808	.3
.8	9.56980	9.60203	0.39797	9.96778	.2
.9	9.57169	9.60422	0.39578	9.96747	68.1
22.0	9.57358	9.60641	0.39359	9.96717	**68.0**
.1	9.57545	9.60859	0.39141	9.96686	67.9
.2	9.57731	9.61076	0.38924	9.96655	.8
.3	9.57916	9.61292	0.38708	9.96624	.7
.4	9.58101	9.61508	0.38492	9.96593	.6
.5	9.58284	9.61722	0.38278	9.96562	.5
.6	9.58467	9.61936	0.38064	9.96530	.4
.7	9.58648	9.62150	0.37850	9.96498	.3
.8	9.58829	9.62362	0.37638	9.96467	.2
.9	9.59009	9.62574	0.37426	9.96435	67.1
23.0	9.59188	9.62785	0.37215	9.96403	**67.0**
.1	9.59366	9.62996	0.37004	9.96370	66.9
.2	9.59543	9.63205	0.36794	9.96338	.8
.3	9.59720	9.63414	0.36586	9.96305	.7
.4	9.59895	9.63623	0.36377	9.96273	.6
.5	9.60070	9.63830	0.36170	9.96240	.5
.6	9.60244	9.64037	0.35963	9.96207	.4
.7	9.60417	9·64243	0.35757	9.96174	.3
.8	9.60589	9.64449	0.35551	9.96140	.2
.9	9.60761	9.64654	0.35346	9.96107	66.1
24.0	9.60931	9.64858	0.35142	9.96073	**66.0**
	L. Cos	L. Cot	L. Tan	L. Sin	Deg.

COMMON LOGARITHMS OF THE TRIGONOMETRIC FUNCTIONS FOR ANGLES IN DEGREES AND DECIMALS (Continued)

Deg.	L. Sin	L. Tan	L. Cot	L. Cos		Deg.	L. Sin	L. Tan	L. Cot	L. Cos	
24.0	9.60931	9.64858	0.35142	9.96073	**66.0**	**30.0**	9.69897	9.76144	0.23856	9.93753	**60.0**
.1	9.61101	9.65062	0.34938	9.96039	65.9	.1	9.70028	9.76319	0.23681	9.93709	59.9
.2	9.61270	9.65265	0.34735	9.96005	.8	.2	9.70159	9.76493	0.23507	9.93665	.8
.3	9.61438	9.65467	0.34533	9.95971	.7	.3	9.70288	9.76668	0.23332	9.93621	.7
.4	9.61606	9.65669	0.34331	9.95937	.6	.4	9.70418	9.76841	0.23159	9.93577	.6
.5	9.61773	9.65870	0.34130	9.95902	.5	.5	9.70547	9.77015	0.22985	9.93532	.5
.6	9.61939	9.66071	0.33929	9.95868	.4	.6	9.70675	9.77188	0.22812	9.93487	.4
.7	9.62104	9.66271	0.33729	9.95833	.3	.7	9.70803	9.77361	0.22639	9.93442	.3
.8	9.62268	9.66470	0.33530	9.95798	.2	.8	9.70931	9.77533	0.22467	9.93397	.2
.9	9.62432	9.66669	0.33331	9.95763	65.1	.9	9.71057	9.77706	0.22294	9.93352	59.1
25.0	9.62595	9.66867	0.33133	9.95728	**65.0**	**31.0**	9.71184	9.77877	0.22123	9.93307	**59.0**
.1	9.62757	9.67065	0.32935	9.95692	64.9	.1	9.71310	9.78049	0.21951	9.93261	58.9
.2	9.62918	9.67262	0.32738	9.95657	.8	.2	9.71435	9.78220	0.21780	9.93215	.8
.3	9.63079	9.67458	0.32542	9.95621	.7	.3	9.71560	9.78391	0.21609	9.93169	.7
.4	9.63239	9.67654	0.32346	9.95585	.6	.4	9.71685	9.78562	0.21438	9.93123	.6
.5	9.63398	9.67850	0.32150	9.95549	.5	.5	9.71809	9.78732	0.21268	9.93077	.5
.6	9.63557	9.68044	0.31956	9.95513	.4	.6	9.71932	9.78902	0.21098	9.93030	.4
.7	9.63715	9.68239	0.31761	9.95476	.3	.7	9.72055	9.79072	0.20928	9.92983	.3
.8	9.63872	9.68432	0.31568	9.95440	.2	.8	9.72177	9.79241	0.20759	9.92936	.2
.9	9.64028	9.68626	0.31374	9.95403	64.1	.9	9.72299	9.79410	0.20590	9.92889	58.1
26.0	9.64184	9.68818	0.31182	9.95366	**64.0**	**32.0**	9.72421	9.79579	0.20421	9.92842	**58.0**
.1	9.64339	9.69010	0.30990	9.95329	63.9	.1	9.72542	9.79747	0.20253	9.92795	57.9
.2	9.64494	9.69202	0.30798	9.95292	.8	.2	9.72663	9.79916	0.20084	9.92747	.8
.3	9.64647	9.69392	0.30607	9.95254	.7	.3	9.72783	9.80084	0.19916	9.92699	.7
.4	9.64800	9.69584	0.30416	9.95217	.6	.4	9.72902	9.80251	0.19749	9.92651	.6
.5	9.64953	9.69774	0.30226	9.95179	.5	.5	9.73022	9.80419	0.19581	9.92603	.5
.6	9.65104	9.69963	0.30037	9.95141	.4	.6	9.73140	9.80586	0.19414	9.92555	.4
.7	9.65255	9.70152	0.29848	9.95103	.3	.7	9.73259	9.80753	0.19247	9.92506	.3
.8	9.65406	9.70341	0.29659	9.95065	.2	.8	9.73376	9.80919	0.19081	9.92457	.2
.9	9.65556	9.70529	0.29471	9.95027	63.1	.9	9.73494	9.81086	0.18914	9.92408	57.1
27.0	9.65705	9.70717	0.29283	9.94988	**63.0**	**33.0**	9.73611	9.81252	0.18748	9.92359	**57.0**
.1	9.65853	9.70904	0.29096	9.94949	62.9	.1	9.73727	9.81418	0.18582	9.92310	56.9
.2	9.66001	9.71090	0.28910	9.94911	.8	.2	9.73843	9.81583	0.18417	9.92260	.8
.3	9.66148	9.71277	0.28723	9.94871	.7	.3	9.73959	9.81748	0.18252	9.92211	.7
.4	9.66295	9.71462	0.28538	9.94832	.6	.4	9.74074	9.81913	0.18087	9.92161	.6
.5	9.66441	9.71648	0.28352	9.94792	.5	.5	9.74189	9.82078	0.17922	9.92111	.5
.6	9.66586	9.71833	0.28167	9.94753	.4	.6	9.74303	9.82243	0.17757	9.92060	.4
.7	9.66731	9.72017	0.27983	9.94714	.3	.7	9.74417	9.82407	0.17593	9.92010	.3
.8	9.66875	9.72201	0.27799	9.94674	.2	.8	9.74531	9.82571	0.17429	9.91959	.2
.9	9.67018	9.72384	0.27616	9.94634	62.1	.9	9.74644	9.82735	0.17265	9.91908	56.1
28.0	9.67161	9.72567	0.27433	9.94593	**62.0**	**34.0**	9.74756	9.82899	0.17101	9.91857	**56.0**
.1	9.67303	9.72750	0.27250	9.94553	61.9	.1	9.74868	9.83062	0.16938	9.91806	55.9
.2	9.67445	9.72932	0.27068	9.94513	.8	.2	9.74980	9.83225	0.16775	9.91755	.8
.3	9.67586	9.73114	0.26886	9.94472	.7	.3	9.75091	9.83388	0.16612	9.91703	.7
.4	9.67726	9.73295	0.26705	9.94431	.6	.4	9.75202	9.83551	0.16449	9.91651	.6
.5	9.67866	9.73476	0.26524	9.94390	.5	.5	9.75313	9.83713	0.16287	9.91599	.5
.6	9.68006	9.73657	0.26343	9.94349	.4	.6	9.75423	9.83876	0.16124	9.91547	.4
.7	9.68144	9.73837	0.26163	9.94307	.3	.7	9.75533	9.84038	0.15962	9.91495	.3
.8	9.68283	9.74017	0.25983	9.94266	.2	.8	9.75642	9.84200	0.15800	9.91442	.2
.9	9.68420	9.74196	0.25804	9.94224	61.1	.9	9.75751	9.84361	0.15639	9.91389	55.1
29.0	9.68557	9.74375	0.25625	9.94182	**61.0**	**35.0**	9.75859	9.84523	0.15477	9.91336	**55.0**
.1	9.68694	9.74554	0.25446	9.94140	60.9	.1	9.75967	9.84684	0.15316	9.91283	54.9
.2	9.68829	9.74732	0.25268	9.94098	.8	.2	9.76075	9.84845	0.15155	9.91230	.8
.3	9.68965	9.74910	0.25090	9.94055	.7	.3	9.76182	9.85006	0.14994	9.91176	.7
.4	9.69100	9.75087	0.24913	9.94012	.6	.4	9.76289	9.85166	0.14834	9.91123	.6
.5	9.69234	9.75264	0.24736	9.93970	.5	.5	9.76395	9.85327	0.14673	9.91069	.5
.6	9.69368	9.75441	0.24559	9.93927	.4	.6	9.76501	9.85487	0.14513	9.91014	.4
.7	9.69501	9.75617	0.24383	9.93884	.3	.7	9.76607	9.85647	0.14353	9.90960	.3
.8	9.69633	9.75793	0.24207	9.93840	.2	.8	9.76712	9.85807	0.14193	9.90906	.2
.9	9.69765	9.75969	0.24031	9.93797	60.1	.9	9.76817	9.85967	0.14033	9.90851	54.1
30.0	9.69897	9.76144	0.23856	9.93753	**60.0**	**36.0**	9.76922	9.86126	0.13874	9.90796	**54.0**
	L. Cos	L. Cot	L. Tan	L. Sin	Deg.		L. Cos	L. Cot	L. Tan	L. Sin	Deg.

COMMON LOGARITHMS OF THE TRIGONOMETRIC FUNCTIONS FOR ANGLES IN DEGREES AND DECIMALS (Continued)

Deg.	L. Sin	L. Tan	L. Cot	L. Cos	
36.0	9 76922	9.86126	0.13874	9.90796	**54.0**
.1	9.77026	9.86285	0.13715	9.90741	53.9
.2	9.77130	9.86445	0.13555	9.90685	.8
.3	9.77233	9.86603	0.13397	9.90630	.7
.4	9.77336	9.86762	0.13238	9.90574	.6
.5	9.77439	9.86921	0.13079	9.90518	.5
.6	9.77541	9.87079	0.12921	9.90462	.4
.7	9.77643	9.87238	0.12762	9.90405	.3
.8	9.77744	9.87396	0.12604	9.90349	.2
.9	9.77846	9.87554	0.12446	9.90292	53.1
37.0	9.77946	9 87711	0.12289	9.90235	**53.0**
.1	9.78047	9.87869	0.12131	9.90178	52.9
.2	9.78147	9 88027	0.11973	9 90120	.8
.3	9.78246	9 88184	0.11816	9.90063	.7
.4	9.78346	9.88341	0.11659	9 90005	.6
.5	9.78445	9.88498	0.11502	9.89947	.5
.6	9 78543	9.88655	0.11345	9.89888	.4
.7	9.78642	9 88812	0.11188	9 89830	.3
.8	9.78739	9.88968	0.11032	9.89771	.2
.9	9.78837	9.89125	0.10875	9 89712	52.1
38.0	9.78934	9 89281	0.10719	9.89653	**52.0**
.1	9.79031	9.89437	0.10563	9.89594	51.9
.2	9.79128	9 89593	0.10407	9.89534	.8
.3	9.79224	9.89749	0.10251	9.89475	.7
.4	9.79319	9 89905	0.10095	9.89415	.6
.5	9.79415	9.90061	0.09939	9.89354	.5
.6	9.79510	9.90216	0.09784	9.89294	.4
.7	9.79605	9.90371	0.09629	9.89233	.3
.8	9.79699	9.90527	0.09473	9.89173	.2
.9	9.79793	9.90682	0.09318	9.89112	51.1
39.0	9 79887	9.90837	0.09163	9.89050	**51.0**
.1	9 79981	9.90992	0.09008	9.88989	50.9
.2	9.80074	9 91147	0 08853	9.88927	.8
.3	9.80166	9.91301	0.08699	9.88865	.7
.4	9.80259	9.91456	0 08544	9.88803	.6
.5	9 80351	9.91610	0.08390	9.88741	.5
.6	9 80443	9.91765	0 08235	9.88678	.4
.7	9.80534	9 91919	0 08081	9 88615	.3
.8	9 80625	9.92073	0.07927	9.88552	.2
.9	9.80716	9.92227	0.07773	9.88489	50.1
40.0	9 80807	9.92381	0.07619	9 88425	**50.0**
.1	9.80897	9.92535	0.07465	9.88362	49.9
.2	9.80987	9.92689	0.07311	9.88298	.8
.3	9 81076	9.92843	0.07157	9.88234	.7
.4	9.81166	9.92996	0.07004	9 88169	.6
.5	9.81254	9.93150	0.06850	9.88105	.5
.6	9 81343	9.93303	0.06697	9.88040	.4
.7	9.81431	9.93457	0.06543	9 87975	.3
.8	9.81519	9.93610	0.06390	9.87909	.2
.9	9.81607	9.93763	0.06237	9.87844	49.1
41.0	9.81694	9.93916	0.06084	9.87778	**49.0**
	L. Cos	L. Cot	L. Tan	L. Sin	Deg.

Deg.	D Sin	L. Tan	L. Cot	L. Cos	
41.0	9.81694	9.93916	0.06084	9.87778	**49.0**
.1	9.81781	9.94069	0.05931	9.87712	48.9
.2	9 81868	9.94222	0.05778	9.87646	.8
.3	9.81955	9.94375	0.05625	9.87579	.7
.4	9.82041	9.94528	0.05472	9.87513	.6
.5	9 82126	9.94681	0.05319	9.87446	.5
.6	9.82212	9.94834	0 05166	9.87378	.4
.7	9.82297	9.94986	0.05014	9.87311	.3
.8	9.82382	9.95139	0.04861	9.87243	.2
.9	9.82467	9.95291	0.04709	9.87175	48.1
42.0	9 82551	9.95444	0.04556	9.87107	**48.0**
.1	9.82635	9.95596	0.04404	9.87039	47.9
.2	9 82719	9.95748	0.04252	9 86970	.8
.3	9.82802	9 95901	0.04099	9 86902	.7
.4	9.82885	9.96053	0.03947	9 86832	.6
.5	9.82968	9.96205	0 03795	9.86763	.5
.6	9 83051	9.96357	0 03643	9 86694	.4
.7	9.83133	9.96510	0 03490	9.86624	.3
.8	9 83215	9.96662	0.03338	9 86554	.2
.9	9.83297	9.96814	0.03186	9 86483	47.1
43.0	9.83378	9.96966	0.03034	9 86413	**47.0**
.1	9 83459	9.97118	0.02882	9.86342	46.9
.2	9.83540	9.97269	0.02731	9 86271	.8
.3	9 83621	9.97421	0.02579	9 86200	7
.4	9.83701	9 97573	0.02427	9 86128	.6
.5	9.83781	9.97725	0.02275	9.86056	.5
.6	9.83861	9 97877	0 02123	9.85984	.4
.7	9.83940	9.98029	0.01971	9.85912	.3
.8	9.84020	9.98180	0.01820	9.85839	.2
.9	9.84098	9.98332	0.01668	9.85766	46.1
44.0	9.84177	9 98484	0.01516	9.85693	**46.0**
.1	9.84255	9.98635	0 01365	9.85620	45.9
.2	9 84334	9.98787	0 01213	9.85547	.8
.3	9 84411	9.98939	0 01061	9.85473	.7
.4	9.84489	9.99090	0 00910	9.85399	.6
.5	9.84566	9.99242	0.00758	9.85324	.5
.6	9 84643	9.99394	0 00606	9.85250	.4
.7	9.84720	9.99545	0.00455	9 85175	.3
.8	9.84796	9.99697	0 00303	9.85100	.2
.9	9.84873	9.99848	0.00152	9.85024	45.1
45.0	9.84949	0.00000	0.00000	9.84949	**45.0**
	L. Cos	L. Cot	L. Tan	L. Sin	Deg.

COMMON LOGARITHMS OF THE
TRIGONOMETRIC FUNCTIONS FOR
ANGLES IN RADIANS

The table that follows gives the common logarithms of the functions sine, cosine, tangent and cotangent for each hundredth of a radian from 0 to 2.

The quantity − 10 is to be appended to all logarithms of the sine and cosine, to logarithms of the tangent from 0 to .78, and of the cotangent from .79 to 2.

Rad.	L. Sin	L. Tan	L. Cot	L. Cos		Rad.	L. Sin	L. Tan	L. Cot	L. Cos
.00	− ∞	− ∞	∞	0.00000		**.50**	9.68072	9.73743	0.26257	9.94329
.01	7.99999	8.00001	1.99999	9.99998		.51	9.68858	9.74769	0.25231	9.94089
.02	8.30100	8.30109	1.69891	9.99991		.52	9.69625	9.75782	0.24218	9.93843
.03	8.47706	8.47725	1.52275	9.99980		.53	9.70375	9.76784	0.23216	9.93591
.04	8.60194	8.60229	1.39771	9.99965		.54	9.71108	9.77774	0.22226	9.93334
.05	8.69879	8.69933	1.30067	9.99946		.55	9.71824	9.78754	0.21246	9.93071
.06	8.77789	8.77867	1.22133	9.99922		.56	9.72525	9.79723	0.20277	9.92801
.07	8.84474	8.84581	1.15419	9.99894		.57	9.73210	9.80684	0.19316	9.92526
.08	8.90263	8.90402	1.09598	9.99861		.58	9.73880	9.81635	0.18365	9.92245
.09	8.95366	8.95542	1.04458	9.99824		.59	9.74536	9.82579	0.17421	9.91957
.10	8.99928	9.00145	0.99855	9.99782		**.60**	9.75177	9.83514	0.16486	9.91663
.11	9.04052	9.04315	0.95685	9.99737		.61	9.75805	9.84443	0.15557	9.91363
.12	9.07814	9.08127	0.91873	9.99687		.62	9.76420	9.85364	0.14636	9.91056
.13	9.11272	9.11640	0.88360	9.99632		.63	9.77022	9.86280	0.13720	9.90743
.14	9.14471	9.14898	0.85102	9.99573		.64	9.77612	9.87189	0.12811	9.90423
.15	9.17446	9.17937	0.82063	9.99510		.65	9.78189	9.88093	0.11907	9.90096
.16	9.20227	9.20785	0.79215	9.99442		.66	9.78754	9.88992	0.11008	9.89762
.17	9.22836	9.23466	0.76534	9.99369		.67	9.79308	9.89886	0.10114	9.89422
.18	9.25292	9.26000	0.74000	9.99293		.68	9.79851	9.90777	0.09223	9.89074
.19	9.27614	9.28402	0.71598	9.99211		.69	9.80382	9.91663	0.08337	9.88719
.20	9.29813	9.30688	0.69312	9.99126		**.70**	9.80903	9.92546	0.07454	9.88357
.21	9.31902	9.32867	0.67133	9.99035		.71	9.81414	9.93426	0.06574	9.87988
.22	9.33891	9.34951	0.65049	9.98940		.72	9.81914	9.94303	0.05697	9.87611
.23	9.35789	9.36948	0.63052	9.98841		.73	9.82404	9.95178	0.04822	9.87226
.24	9.37603	9.38866	0.61134	9.98737		.74	9.82885	9.96051	0.03949	9.86833
.25	9.39341	9.40712	0.59288	9.98628		.75	9.83355	9.96923	0.03077	9.86433
.26	9.41007	9.42492	0.57508	9.98515		.76	9.83817	9.97793	0.02207	9.86024
.27	9.42607	9.44210	0.55790	9.98397		.77	9.84269	9.98662	0.01338	9.85607
.28	9.44147	9.45872	0.54128	9.98275		.78	9.84713	9.99531	0.00469	9.85182
.29	9.45629	9.47482	0.52518	9.98148		.79	9.85147	0.00400	9.99600	9.84748
.30	9.47059	9.49043	0.50957	9.98016		**.80**	9.85573	0.01268	9.98732	9.84305
.31	9.48438	9.50559	0.49441	9.97879		.81	9.85991	0.02138	9.97862	9.83853
.32	9.49771	9.52034	0.47966	9.97737		.82	9.86400	0.03008	9.96992	9.83393
.33	9.51060	9.53469	0.46531	9.97591		.83	9.86802	0.03879	9.96121	9.82922
.34	9.52308	9.54868	0.45132	9.97440		.84	9.87195	0.04752	9.95248	9.82443
.35	9.53516	9.56233	0.43767	9.97284		.85	9.87580	0.05627	9.94373	9.81953
.36	9.54688	9.57565	0.42435	9.97123		.86	9.87958	0.06504	9.93496	9.81454
.37	9.55825	9.58868	0.41132	9.96957		.87	9.88328	0.07384	9.92616	9.80944
.38	9.56928	9.60142	0.39858	9.96786		.88	9.88691	0.08266	9.91734	9.80424
.39	9.58000	9.61390	0.38610	9.96610		.89	9.89046	0.09153	9.90847	9.79894
.40	9.59042	9.62613	0.37387	9.96429		**.90**	9.89394	0.10043	9.89957	9.79352
.41	9.60055	9.63812	0.36188	9.96243		.91	9.89735	0.10937	9.89063	9.78799
.42	9.61041	9.64989	0.35011	9.96051		.92	9.90070	0.11835	9.88165	9.78234
.43	9.62000	9.66145	0.33855	9.95855		.93	9.90397	0.12739	9.87261	9.77658
.44	9.62935	9.67282	0.32718	9.95653		.94	9.90717	0.13648	9.86352	9.77070
.45	9.63845	9.68400	0.31600	9.95446		.95	9.91031	0.14563	9.85437	9.76469
.46	9.64733	9.69500	0.30500	9.95233		.96	9.91339	0.15484	9.84516	9.75855
.47	9.65599	9.70583	0.29417	9.95015		.97	9.91639	0.16412	9.83588	9.75228
.48	9.66443	9.71651	0.28349	9.94792		.98	9.91934	0.17347	9.82653	9.74587
.49	9.67268	9.72704	0.27296	9.94563		.99	9.92222	0.18289	9.81711	9.73933
.50	9.68072	9.73743	0.26257	9.94329		**1.00**	9.92504	0.19240	9.80760	9.73264
Rad.	L. Sin	L. Tan	L. Cot	L. Cos		Rad.	L. Sin	L. Tan	L. Cot	L. Cos

COMMON LOGARITHMS OF THE
TRIGONOMETRIC FUNCTIONS FOR
ANGLES IN RADIANS (Continued)

Rad.	L. Sin	L. Tan	L. Cot	L. Cos	Rad.	L. Sin	L. Tan	L. Cot	L. Cos
1.00	9.92504	0.19240	9.80760	9.73264	**1.50**	9.99891	1.14926	8.85074	8.84965
1.01	9.92780	0.20200	9.79800	9.72580	1.51	9.99920	1.21559	8.78441	8.78361
1.02	9.93049	0.21169	9.78831	9.71881	1.52	9.99944	1.29379	8.70621	8.70565
1.03	9.93313	0.22148	9.77852	9.71165	1.53	9.99964	1.38914	8.61086	8.61050
1.04	9.93571	0.23137	9.76863	9.70434	1.54	9.99979	1.51136	8.48864	8.48843
1.05	9.93823	0.24138	9.75862	9.69686	1.55	9.99991	1.68195	8.31805	8.31796
1.06	9.94069	0.25150	9.74850	9.68920	1.56	9.99997	1.96671	8.03329	8.03327
1.07	9.94310	0.26175	9.73825	9.68135	1.57	0.00000	3.09891	6.90109	6.90109
1.08	9.94545	0.27212	9.72788	9.67332	1.58	9.99998	2.03603*	7.96397*	7.96396*
1.09	9.94774	0.28264	9.71736	9.66510	1.59	9.99992	1.71656	8.28344	8.28336
1.10	9.94998	0.29331	9.70669	9.65667	**1.60**	9.99981	1.53444	8.46556	8.46538
1.11	9.95216	0.30413	9.69587	9.64803	1.61	9.99967	1.40645	8.59355	8.59323
1.12	9.95429	0.31512	9.68488	9.63917	1.62	9.99947	1.30765	8.69235	8.69182
1.13	9.95637	0.32628	9.67372	9.63008	1.63	9.99924	1.22714	8.77286	8.77209
1.14	9.95839	0.33763	9.66237	9.62075	1.64	9.99896	1.15918	8.84082	8.83978
1.15	9.96036	0.34918	9.65082	9.61118	1.65	9.99864	1.10035	8.89965	8.89829
1.16	9.96228	0.36093	9.63907	9.60134	1.66	9.99827	1.04847	8.95154	8.94981
1.17	9.96414	0.37291	9.62709	9.59123	1.67	9.99786	1.00204	8.99796	8.99582
1.18	9.96596	0.38512	9.61488	9.58084	1.68	9.99741	0.96003	9.03997	9.03737
1.19	9.96772	0.39757	9.60243	9.57015	1.69	9.99691	0.92165	9.07835	9.07526
1.20	9.96943	0.41030	9.58970	9.55914	**1.70**	9.99636	0.88630	9.11370	9.11007
1.21	9.97110	0.42330	9.57670	9.54780	1.71	9.99578	0.85353	9.14647	9.14225
1.22	9.97271	0.43660	9.56340	9.53611	1.72	9.99515	0.82298	9.17702	9.17217
1.23	9.97428	0.45022	9.54978	9.52406	1.73	9.99447	0.79436	9.20564	9.20012
1.24	9.97579	0.46418	9.53582	9.51161	1.74	9.99375	0.76742	9.23258	9.22634
1.25	9.97726	0.47850	9.52150	9.49875	1.75	9.99299	0.74197	9.25803	9.25102
1.26	9.97868	0.49322	9.50678	9.48546	1.76	9.99218	0.71784	9.28216	9.27434
1.27	9.98005	0.50835	9.49165	9.47170	1.77	9.99133	0.69490	9.30510	9.29642
1.28	9.98137	0.52392	9.47608	9.45745	1.78	9.99043	0.67303	9.32697	9.31740
1.29	9.98265	0.53998	9.46002	9.44267	1.79	9.98948	0.65212	9.34788	9.33736
1.30	9.98388	0.55656	9.44344	9.42732	**1.80**	9.98849	0.63208	9.36792	9.35641
1.31	9.98506	0.57369	9.42631	9.41137	1.81	9.98745	0.61284	9.38716	9.37462
1.32	9.98620	0.59144	9.40856	9.39476	1.82	9.98637	0.59432	9.40568	9.39205
1.33	9.98729	0.60984	9.39016	9.37744	1.83	9.98524	0.57648	9.42352	9.40877
1.34	9.98833	0.62896	9.37104	9.35937	1.84	9.98407	0.55925	9.44075	9.42482
1.35	9.98933	0.64887	9.35113	9.34046	1.85	9.98285	0.54258	9.45742	9.44026
1.36	9.99028	0.66964	9.33036	9.32064	1.86	9.98158	0.52645	9.47355	9.45513
1.37	9.99119	0.69135	9.30865	9.29983	1.87	9.98026	0.51080	9.48920	9.46947
1.38	9.99205	0.71411	9.28589	9.27793	1.88	9.97890	0.49560	9.50440	9.48330
1.39	9.99286	0.73804	9.26196	9.25482	1.89	9.97749	0.48082	9.51918	9.49667
1.40	9.99363	0.76327	9.23673	9.23036	**1.90**	9.97603	0.46644	9.53356	9.50959
1.41	9.99436	0.78996	9.21004	9.20440	1.91	9.97452	0.45242	9.54758	9.52210
1.42	9.99504	0.81830	9.18170	9.17674	1.92	9.97296	0.43875	9.56125	9.53422
1.43	9.99568	0.84853	9.15147	9.14716	1.93	9.97136	0.42540	9.57460	9.54597
1.44	9.99627	0.88092	9.11908	9.11536	1.94	9.96970	0.41235	9.58765	9.55735
1.45	9.99682	0.91583	9.08417	9.08100	1.95	9.96800	0.39958	9.60042	9.56841
1.46	9.99733	0.95369	9.04631	9.04364	1.96	9.96624	0.38708	9.61292	9.57916
1.47	9.99779	0.99508	9.00492	9.00271	1.97	9.96443	0.37484	9.62516	9.58960
1.48	9.99821	1.04074	8.95926	8.95747	1.98	9.96258	0.36283	9.63717	9.59975
1.49	9.99858	1.09166	8.90834	8.90692	1.99	9.96067	0.35104	9.64896	9.60963
1.50	9.99891	1.14926	8.85074	8.84965	**2.00**	9.95871	0.33946	9.66054	9.61925
Rad.	L. Sin	L. Tan	L. Cot	L. Cos	Rad.	L. Sin	L. Tan	L. Cot	L. Cos

* Values of the cosine, tangent and cotangent for angles in the table, 1.58 radians and above, are negative. As a consequence the logarithms of the functions involved are for their absolute values. For example log |cos 1.90| = 9.50959 − 10.

SINE AND COSINE FUNCTIONS FOR SPECIAL MULTIPLES OF π RADIANS

k	$\sin\dfrac{2\pi k}{m}$	$\cos\dfrac{2\pi k}{m}$	$\sin\dfrac{2\pi k}{m}$	$\cos\dfrac{2\pi k}{m}$	$\sin\dfrac{2\pi k}{m}$	$\cos\dfrac{2\pi k}{m}$
	$m=3$		$m=4$		$m=5$	
1	0.86603	-0.50000	1.00000	$+0.00000$	0.95106	$+0.30902$
2			0.00000	-1.00000	0.58779	-0.80902
	$m=6$		$m=7$		$m=8$	
1	0.86603	$+0.50000$	0.78183	$+0.62349$	0.70711	0.70711
2	0.86603	-0.50000	0.97493	-0.22252	1.00000	$+0.00000$
3	0.00000	-1.00000	0.43388	-0.90097	0.70711	$+0.70711$
4					0.00000	-1.00000
	$m=9$		$m=10$		$m=11$	
1	0.64279	0.76604	0.58779	0.80902	0.54064	0.84125
2	0.98481	$+0.17365$	0.95106	$+0.30902$	0.90963	$+0.41542$
3	0.86603	-0.50000	0.95106	-0.30902	0.98982	-0.14231
4	0.34202	-0.93969	0.58779	-1.80902	0.75575	-0.65486
5			0.00000	-1.00000	0.28173	-0.95949
	$m=12$		$m=13$		$m=14$	
1	0.50000	0.86603	0.46472	0.88546	0.43388	0.90097
2	0.86603	0.50000	0.82289	0.56806	0.78183	0.62349
3	1.00000	$+0.00000$	0.99271	$+0.12054$	0.97493	$+0.22252$
4	0.86603	-0.50000	0.93502	-0.35460	0.97493	-0.22252
5	0.50000	-0.86603	0.66312	-0.74851	0.78183	-0.62349
6	0.00000	-1.00000	0.23932	-0.97904	0.43388	-0.90097
7					0.00000	-1.00000
	$m=15$		$m=16$		$m=17$	
1	0.40674	0.91353	0.38268	0.92388	0.36124	0.93247
2	0.74314	0.66913	0.70711	0.70711	0.67370	0.73901
3	0.95106	$+0.30902$	0.92388	0.38268	0.89516	0.44574
4	0.99452	-0.10453	1.00000	$+0.00000$	0.99573	$+0.09227$
5	0.86603	-0.50000	0.92388	-0.38268	0.96183	-0.27366
6	0.58779	-0.80902	0.70711	-0.70711	0.79802	-0.60263
7	0.20791	-0.97815	0.38268	-0.92388	0.52643	-0.85022
8			0.00000	-1.00000	0.18375	-0.98297
	$m=18$		$m=19$		$m=20$	
1	0.34202	0.93969	0.32470	0.94582	0.30902	0.95106
2	0.64279	0.76604	0.61421	0.78914	0.58779	0.80902
3	0.86603	0.50000	0.83717	0.54695	0.80902	0.58779
4	0.98481	$+0.17365$	0.96940	$+0.24549$	0.95106	0.30902
5	0.98481	-0.17365	0.99658	-0.08258	1.00000	$+0.00000$
6	0.86603	-0.50000	0.91577	-0.40170	0.95106	-0.30902
7	0.64279	-0.76604	0.73572	-0.67728	0.80902	-0.58779
8	0.34202	-0.93969	0.47595	-0.87947	0.58779	-0.80902
9	0.00000	-1.00000	0.16459	-0.98636	0.30902	-0.95106
10					0.00000	-1.00000
	$m=21$		$m=22$		$m=23$	
1	0.29476	0.95557	0.28173	0.95949	0.26980	0.96292
2	0.56332	0.82624	0.54064	0.84125	0.51958	0.85442
3	0.78183	0.62349	0.75575	0.65486	0.73084	0.68255
4	0.93087	0.36534	0.90963	0.41542	0.88789	0.46007
5	0.99720	$+0.07473$	0.98982	$+0.14231$	0.97908	$+0.20346$
6	0.97493	-0.22252	0.98982	-0.14231	0.99767	-0.06824
7	0.86603	-0.50000	0.90963	-0.41542	0.94226	-0.33488
8	0.68017	-0.73305	0.75575	-0.65486	0.81697	-0.57668
9	0.43388	-0.90097	0.54064	-0.84125	0.63109	-0.77571
10	0.14904	-0.98883	0.28173	-0.95949	0.39840	-0.91721
11			0.00000	-1.00000	0.13617	-0.99069
	$m=24$		$m=25$			
1	0.25882	0.96593	0.24869	0.96858		
2	0.50000	0.86603	0.48175	0.87631		
3	0.70711	0.70711	0.68455	0.72897		
4	0.86603	0.50000	0.84433	0.53583		
5	0.96593	0.25832	0.95106	0.30902		
6	1.00000	$+0.00000$	0.99803	$+0.06279$		
7	0.96593	-0.25882	0.98229	-0.18738		
8	0.86603	-0.50000	0.90483	-0.42578		
9	0.70711	-0.70711	0.77051	-0.63742		
10	0.50000	-0.86603	0.58779	-0.80902		
11	0.25882	-0.96593	0.36812	-0.92978		
12	0.00000	-1.00000	0.12533	-0.99211		

SQUARE OF THE SINE AND
COSINE AND THEIR PRODUCT

The table that follows gives the squares of the sine and cosine and their product for each minute from 0 to 360.

For angles at the top of the page, use the column headings at the top of the page. For angles at the bottom of the page, use the column headings at the bottom of the page.

For degrees on the left, use the minute column on the left. For degrees on the right, use the minute column on the right.

For angles in the second and fourth quadrants, the product of the sine and cosine is negative.

If $\sin^2 \theta \cos^2 \theta$ is desired, it can be obtained by using the identity

$$\sin^2 \theta \cos^2 \theta = \tfrac{1}{4} \sin^2 2\theta.$$

Thus

$$\sin^2 10° \cos^2 10° = \tfrac{1}{4} \sin^2 20° = \frac{0.11698}{4} = 0.02924.$$

SQUARE OF THE SINE AND COSINE
AND THEIR PRODUCT

Compiled by Niel F. Beardsley.

0° (180°)   (359°) **179°**

′	Sin²	Sin · Cos	Cos²	′
0	.00000	.00000	1.00000	**60**
1	.00000	.00029	1.00000	59
2	.00000	.00058	1.00000	58
3	.00000	.00087	1.00000	57
4	.00000	.00116	1.00000	56
5	.00000	.00145	1.00000	**55**
6	.00000	.00175	1.00000	54
7	.00000	.00204	1.00000	53
8	.00001	.00233	.99999	52
9	.00001	.00262	.99999	51
10	.00001	.00291	.99999	**50**
11	.00001	.00320	.99999	49
12	.00001	.00349	.99999	48
13	.00001	.00378	.99999	47
14	.00002	.00407	.99998	46
15	.00002	.00436	.99998	**45**
16	.00002	.00465	.99998	44
17	.00002	.00495	.99998	43
18	.00003	.00524	.99997	42
19	.00003	.00553	.99997	41
20	.00003	.00582	.99997	**40**
21	.00004	.00611	.99996	39
22	.00004	.00640	.99996	38
23	.00004	.00669	.99996	37
24	.00005	.00698	.99995	36
25	.00005	.00727	.99995	**35**
26	.00006	.00756	.99994	34
27	.00006	.00785	.99994	33
28	.00007	.00814	.99993	32
29	.00007	.00844	.99993	31
30	.00008	.00873	.99992	**30**
31	.00008	.00902	.99992	29
32	.00009	.00931	.99991	28
33	.00009	.00960	.99991	27
34	.00010	.00989	.99990	26
35	.00010	.01018	.99990	**25**
36	.00011	.01047	.99989	24
37	.00012	.01076	.99988	23
38	.00012	.01105	.99988	22
39	.00013	.01134	.99987	21
40	.00014	.01163	.99986	**20**
41	.00014	.01193	.99986	19
42	.00015	.01222	.99985	18
43	.00016	.01251	.99984	17
44	.00016	.01280	.99984	16
45	.00017	.01309	.99983	**15**
46	.00018	.01338	.99982	14
47	.00019	.01367	.99981	13
48	.00019	.01396	.99981	12
49	.00020	.01425	.99980	11
50	.00021	.01454	.99979	**10**
51	.00022	.01483	.99978	9
52	.00023	.01512	.99977	8
53	.00024	.01541	.99976	7
54	.00025	.01571	.99975	6
55	.00026	.01600	.99974	**5**
56	.00027	.01629	.99973	4
57	.00027	.01658	.99973	3
58	.00028	.01687	.99972	2
59	.00029	.01716	.99971	1
60	.00030	.01745	.99970	**0**
′	Cos²	Sin · Cos	Sin²	′

90° (270°)   (269°) **89°**

1° (181°)   (358°) **178°**

′	Sin²	Sin · Cos	Cos²	′
0	.00030	.01745	.99970	**60**
1	.00031	.01774	.99969	59
2	.00033	.01803	.99967	58
3	.00034	.01832	.99966	57
4	.00035	.01861	.99965	56
5	.00036	.01890	.99964	**55**
6	.00037	.01919	.99963	54
7	.00038	.01948	.99962	53
8	.00039	.01978	.99961	52
9	.00040	.02007	.99960	51
10	.00041	.02036	.99959	**50**
11	.00043	.02065	.99957	49
12	.00044	.02094	.99956	48
13	.00045	.02123	.99955	47
14	.00046	.02152	.99954	46
15	.00048	.02181	.99952	**45**
16	.00049	.02210	.99951	44
17	.00050	.02239	.99950	43
18	.00051	.02268	.99949	42
19	.00053	.02297	.99947	41
20	.00054	.02326	.99946	**40**
21	.00056	.02355	.99944	39
22	.00057	.02384	.99943	38
23	.00058	.02413	.99942	37
24	.00060	.02442	.99940	36
25	.00061	.02472	.99939	**35**
26	.00063	.02501	.99937	34
27	.00064	.02530	.99936	33
28	.00066	.02559	.99934	32
29	.00067	.02588	.99933	31
30	.00069	.02617	.99931	**30**
31	.00070	.02646	.99930	29
32	.00072	.02675	.99928	28
33	.00073	.02704	.99927	27
34	.00075	.02733	.99925	26
35	.00076	.02762	.99924	**25**
36	.00078	.02791	.99922	24
37	.00080	.02820	.99920	23
38	.00081	.02849	.99919	22
39	.00083	.02878	.99917	21
40	.00085	.02907	.99915	**20**
41	.00086	.02936	.99914	19
42	.00088	.02965	.99912	18
43	.00090	.02994	.99910	17
44	.00091	.03023	.99909	16
45	.00093	.03052	.99907	**15**
46	.00095	.03081	.99905	14
47	.00097	.03110	.99903	13
48	.00099	.03140	.99901	12
49	.00100	.03169	.99900	11
50	.00102	.03198	.99898	**10**
51	.00104	.03227	.99896	9
52	.00106	.03256	.99894	8
53	.00108	.03285	.99892	7
54	.00110	.03314	.99890	6
55	.00112	.03343	.99888	**5**
56	.00114	.03372	.99886	4
57	.00116	.03401	.99884	3
58	.00118	.03430	.99882	2
59	.00120	.03459	.99880	1
60	.00122	.03488	.99878	**0**
′	Cos²	Sin · Cos	Sin²	′

91° (271°)   (268°) **88°**

SQUARE OF THE SINE AND COSINE
AND THEIR PRODUCT (Continued)

2° (182°) (357°) **177°**   **3°** (183°) (356°) **176°**

′	Sin²	Sin · Cos	Cos²	′	′	Sin²	Sin · Cos	Cos²	′
0	.00122	.03488	.99878	**60**	**0**	.00274	.05226	.99726	**60**
1	.00124	.03517	.99876	59	1	.00277	.05255	.99723	59
2	.00126	.03546	.99874	58	2	.00280	.05284	.99720	58
3	.00128	.03575	.99872	57	3	.00283	.05313	.99717	57
4	.00130	.03604	.99870	56	4	.00286	.05342	.99714	56
5	.00132	.03633	.99868	**55**	**5**	.00289	.05371	.99711	**55**
6	.00134	.03662	.99866	54	6	.00292	.05400	.99708	54
7	.00136	.03691	.99864	53	7	.00296	.05429	.99704	53
8	.00139	.03720	.99861	52	8	.00299	.05458	.99701	52
9	.00141	.03749	.99859	51	9	.00302	.05487	.99698	51
10	.00143	.03778	.99857	**50**	**10**	.00305	.05516	.99695	**50**
11	.00145	.03807	.99855	49	11	.00308	.05545	.99692	49
12	.00147	.03836	.99853	48	12	.00312	.05573	.99688	48
13	.00150	.03865	.99850	47	13	.00315	.05602	.99685	47
14	.00152	.03894	.99848	46	14	.00318	.05631	.99682	46
15	.00154	.03923	.99846	**45**	**15**	.00321	.05660	.99679	**45**
16	.00156	.03952	.99844	44	16	.00325	.05689	.99675	44
17	.00159	.03981	.99841	43	17	.00328	.05718	.99672	43
18	.00161	.04010	.99839	42	18	.00331	.05747	.99669	42
19	.00163	.04039	.99837	41	19	.00335	.05776	.99665	41
20	.00166	.04068	.99834	**40**	**20**	.00338	.05805	.99662	**40**
21	.00168	.04097	.99832	39	21	.00341	.05834	.99659	39
22	.00171	.04126	.99829	38	22	.00345	.05862	.99655	38
23	.00173	.04155	.99827	37	23	.00348	.05891	.99652	37
24	.00175	.04184	.99825	36	24	.00352	.05920	.99648	36
25	.00178	.04213	.99822	**35**	**25**	.00355	.05949	.99645	**35**
26	.00180	.04242	.99820	34	26	.00359	.05978	.99641	34
27	.00183	.04271	.99817	33	27	.00362	.06007	.99638	33
28	.00185	.04300	.99815	32	28	.00366	.06036	.99634	32
29	.00188	.04329	.99812	31	29	.00369	.06065	.99631	31
30	.00190	.04358	.99810	**30**	**30**	.00373	.06093	.99627	**30**
31	.00193	.04387	.99807	29	31	.00376	.06122	.99624	29
32	.00195	.04416	.99805	28	32	.00380	.06151	.99620	28
33	.00198	.04445	.99802	27	33	.00383	.06180	.99617	27
34	.00201	.04474	.99799	26	34	.00387	.06209	.99613	26
35	.00203	.04503	.99797	**25**	**35**	.00391	.06238	.99609	**25**
36	.00206	.04532	.99794	24	36	.00394	.06267	.99606	24
37	.00208	.04561	.99792	23	37	.00398	.06296	.99602	23
38	.00211	.04590	.99789	22	38	.00402	.06324	.99598	22
39	.00214	.04619	.99786	21	39	.00405	.06353	.99595	21
40	.00216	.04647	.99784	**20**	**40**	.00409	.06382	.99591	**20**
41	.00219	.04676	.99781	19	41	.00413	.06411	.99587	19
42	.00222	.04705	.99778	18	42	.00416	.06440	.99584	18
43	.00225	.04734	.99775	17	43	.00420	.06469	.99580	17
44	.00227	.04763	.99773	16	44	.00424	.06497	.99576	16
45	.00230	.04792	.99770	**15**	**45**	.00428	.06526	.99572	**15**
46	.00233	.04821	.99767	14	46	.00432	.06555	.99568	14
47	.00236	.04850	.99764	13	47	.00435	.06584	.99565	13
48	.00239	.04879	.99761	12	48	.00439	.06613	.99561	12
49	.00241	.04908	.99759	11	49	.00443	.06642	.99557	11
50	.00244	.04937	.99756	**10**	**50**	.00447	.06670	.99553	**10**
51	.00247	.04966	.99753	9	51	.00451	.06699	.99549	9
52	.00250	.04995	.99750	8	52	.00455	.06728	.99545	8
53	.00253	.05024	.99747	7	53	.00459	.06757	.99541	7
54	.00256	.05053	.99744	6	54	.00463	.06786	.99537	6
55	.00259	.05082	.99741	**5**	**55**	.00467	.06815	.99533	**5**
56	.00262	.05111	.99738	4	56	.00471	.06843	.99529	4
57	.00265	.05140	.99735	3	57	.00475	.06872	.99525	3
58	.00268	.05169	.99732	2	58	.00479	.06901	.99521	2
59	.00271	.05197	.99729	1	59	.00483	.06930	.99517	1
60	.00274	.05226	.99726	**0**	**60**	.00487	.06959	.99513	**0**
′	Cos²	Sin · Cos	Sin²	′	′	Cos²	Sin · Cos	Sin²	′

92° (272°) (267°) **87°**   **93°** (273°) (266°) **86°**

SQUARE OF THE SINE AND COSINE
AND THEIR PRODUCT (Continued)

4° (184°)   (355°) **175°**   5° (185°)   (354°) (**174°**)

′	Sin²	Sin · Cos	Cos²	′		′	Sin²	Sin · Cos	Cos²	′
0	.00487	.06959	.99513	**60**		**0**	.00760	.08682	.99240	**60**
1	.00491	.06987	.99509	59		1	.00765	.08711	.99235	59
2	.00495	.07016	.99505	58		2	.00770	.08740	.99230	58
3	.00499	.07045	.99501	57		3	.00775	.08768	.99225	57
4	.00503	.07074	.99497	56		4	.00780	.08797	.99220	56
5	.00507	.07103	.99493	**55**		**5**	.00785	.08826	.99215	**55**
6	.00511	.07131	.99489	54		6	.00790	.08854	.99210	54
7	.00515	.07160	.99485	53		7	.00795	.08883	.99205	53
8	.00520	.07189	.99480	52		**8**	.00801	.08911	.99199	52
9	.00524	.07218	.99476	51		9	.00806	.08940	.99194	51
10	.00528	.07247	.99472	**50**		**10**	.00811	.08969	.99189	**50**
11	.00532	.07275	.99468	49		11	.00816	.08997	.99184	49
12	.00536	.07304	.99464	48		12	.00821	.09026	.99179	48
13	.00541	.07333	.99459	47		13	.00827	.09055	.99173	47
14	.00545	.07362	.99455	46		14	.00832	.09083	.99168	46
15	.00549	.07390	.99451	**45**		**15**	.00837	.09112	.99163	**45**
16	.00554	.07419	.99446	44		16	.00843	.09140	.99157	44
17	.00558	.07448	.99442	43		17	.00848	.09169	.99152	43
18	.00562	.07477	.99438	42		18	.00853	.09198	.99147	42
19	.00567	.07506	.99433	41		19	.00859	.09226	.99141	41
20	.00571	.07534	.99429	**40**		**20**	.00864	.09255	.99136	**40**
21	.00575	.07563	.99425	39		21	.00869	.09283	.99131	39
22	.00580	.07592	.99420	38		22	.00875	.09312	.99125	38
23	.00584	.07621	.99416	37		23	.00880	.09340	.99120	37
24	.00589	.07649	.99411	36		24	.00886	.09369	.99114	36
25	.00593	.07678	.99407	**35**		**25**	.00891	.09398	.99109	**35**
26	.00598	.07707	.99402	34		26	.00897	.09426	.99103	34
27	.00602	.07736	.99398	33		27	.00902	.09455	.99098	33
28	.00607	.07764	.99393	32		28	.00908	.09483	.99092	32
29	.00611	.07793	.99389	31		29	.00913	.09512	.99087	31
30	.00616	.07822	.99384	**30**		**30**	.00919	.09540	.99081	**30**
31	.00620	.07850	.99380	29		31	.00924	.09569	.99076	29
32	.00625	.07879	.99375	28		32	.00930	.09598	.99070	28
33	.00629	.07908	.99371	27		33	.00935	.09626	.99065	27
34	.00634	.07937	.99366	26		34	.00941	.09655	.99059	26
35	.00639	.07965	.99361	**25**		**35**	.00947	.09683	.99053	**25**
36	.00643	.07994	.99357	24		36	.00952	.09712	.99048	24
37	.00648	.08023	.99352	23		37	.00958	.09740	.99042	23
38	.00653	.08051	.99347	22		38	.00964	.09769	.99036	22
39	.00657	.08080	.99343	21		39	.00969	.09797	.99031	21
40	.00662	.08109	.99338	**20**		**40**	.00975	.09826	.99025	**20**
41	.00667	.08138	.99333	19		41	.00981	.09854	.99019	19
42	.00671	.08166	.99329	18		42	.00986	.09883	.99014	18
43	.00676	.08195	.99324	17		43	.00992	.09911	.99008	17
44	.00681	.08224	.99319	16		44	.00998	.09940	.99002	16
45	.00686	.08252	.99314	**15**		**45**	.01004	.09968	.98996	**15**
46	.00691	.08281	.99309	14		46	.01010	.09997	.98990	14
47	.00695	.08310	.99305	13		47	.01015	.10025	.98985	13
48	.00700	.08338	.99300	12		48	.01021	.10054	.98979	12
49	.00705	.08367	.99295	11		49	.01027	.10082	.98973	11
50	.00710	.08396	.99290	**10**		**50**	.01033	.10111	.98967	**10**
51	.00715	.08424	.99285	9		51	.01039	.10139	.98961	9
52	.00720	.08453	.99280	8		52	.01045	.10168	.98955	8
53	.00725	.08482	.99275	7		53	.01051	.10196	.98949	7
54	.00730	.08510	.99270	6		54	.01057	.10225	.98943	6
55	.00735	.08539	.99265	**5**		**55**	.01063	.10253	.98937	**5**
56	.00740	.08568	.99260	4		56	.01069	.10282	.98931	4
57	.00745	.08596	.99255	3		57	.01075	.10310	.98925	3
58	.00750	.08625	.99250	2		58	.01081	.10339	.98919	2
59	.00755	.08654	.99245	1		59	.01087	.10367	.98913	1
60	.00760	.08682	.99240	**0**		**60**	.01093	.10396	.98907	**0**
′	Cos²	Sin · Cos	Sin²	′		′	Cos²	Sin · Cos	Sin²	′

SQUARE OF THE SINE AND COSINE
AND THEIR PRODUCT (Continued)

6° (186°)   (353°) 173°   7° (187°)   (352°) 172°

′	Sin²	Sin·Cos	Cos²	′	′	Sin²	Sin·Cos	Cos²	′
0	.01093	.10396	.98907	60	0	.01485	.12096	.98515	60
1	.01099	.10424	.98901	59	1	.01492	.12124	.98508	59
2	.01105	.10452	.98895	58	2	.01499	.12153	.98501	58
3	.01111	.10481	.98889	57	3	.01506	.12181	.98494	57
4	.01117	.10509	.98883	56	4	.01513	.12209	.98487	56
5	.01123	.10538	.98877	55	5	.01521	.12237	.98479	55
6	.01129	.10566	.98871	54	6	.01528	.12265	.98472	54
7	.01135	.10595	.98865	53	7	.01535	.12294	.98465	53
8	.01142	.10623	.98858	52	8	.01542	.12322	.98458	52
9	.01148	.10652	.98852	51	9	.01549	.12350	.98451	51
10	.01154	.10680	.98846	50	10	.01556	.12378	.98444	50
11	.01160	.10708	.98840	49	11	.01564	.12406	.98436	49
12	.01166	.10737	.98834	48	12	.01571	.12434	.98429	48
13	.01173	.10765	.98827	47	13	.01578	.12463	.98422	47
14	.01179	.10794	.98821	46	14	.01585	.12491	.98415	46
15	.01185	.10822	.98815	45	15	.01593	.12519	.98407	45
16	.01192	.10850	.98808	44	16	.01600	.12547	.98400	44
17	.01198	.10879	.98802	43	17	.01607	.12575	.98393	43
18	.01204	.10907	.98796	42	18	.01615	.12603	.98385	42
19	.01211	.10936	.98789	41	19	.01622	.12632	.98378	41
20	.01217	.10964	.98783	40	20	.01629	.12660	.98371	40
21	.01223	.10992	.98777	39	21	.01637	.12688	.98363	39
22	.01230	.11021	.98770	38	22	.01644	.12716	.98356	38
23	.01236	.11049	.98764	37	23	.01651	.12744	.98349	37
24	.01243	.11077	.98757	36	24	.01659	.12772	.98341	36
25	.01249	.11106	.98751	35	25	.01666	.12800	.98334	35
26	.01255	.11134	.98745	34	26	.01674	.12829	.98326	34
27	.01262	.11163	.98738	33	27	.01681	.12857	.98319	33
28	.01268	.11191	.98732	32	28	.01689	.12885	.98311	32
29	.01275	.11219	.98725	31	29	.01696	.12913	.98304	31
30	.01281	.11248	.98719	30	30	.01704	.12941	.98296	30
31	.01288	.11276	.98712	29	31	.01711	.12969	.98289	29
32	.01295	.11304	.98705	28	32	.01719	.12997	.98281	28
33	.01301	.11333	.98699	27	33	.01726	.13025	.98274	27
34	.01308	.11361	.98692	26	34	.01734	.13053	.98266	26
35	.01314	.11389	.98686	25	35	.01742	.13081	.98258	25
36	.01321	.11418	.98679	24	36	.01749	.13109	.98251	24
37	.01328	.11446	.98672	23	37	.01757	.13138	.98243	23
38	.01334	.11474	.98666	22	38	.01764	.13166	.98236	22
39	.01341	.11502	.98659	21	39	.01772	.13194	.98228	21
40	.01348	.11531	.98652	20	40	.01780	.13222	.98220	20
41	.01354	.11559	.98646	19	41	.01788	.13250	.98212	19
42	.01361	.11587	.98639	18	42	.01795	.13278	.98205	18
43	.01368	.11616	.98632	17	43	.01803	.13306	.98197	17
44	.01375	.11644	.98625	16	44	.01811	.13334	.98189	16
45	.01382	.11672	.98618	15	45	.01818	.13362	.98182	15
46	.01388	.11701	.98612	14	46	.01826	.13390	.98174	14
47	.01395	.11729	.98605	13	47	.01834	.13418	.98166	13
48	.01402	.11757	.98598	12	48	.01842	.13446	.98158	12
49	.01409	.11785	.98591	11	49	.01850	.13474	.98150	11
50	.01416	.11814	.98584	10	50	.01858	.13502	.98142	10
51	.01423	.11842	.98577	9	51	.01865	.13530	.98135	9
52	.01429	.11870	.98571	8	52	.01873	.13558	.98127	8
53	.01436	.11898	.98564	7	53	.01881	.13586	.98119	7
54	.01443	.11927	.98557	6	54	.01889	.13614	.98111	6
55	.01450	.11955	98550	5	55	.01897	.13642	.98103	5
56	.01457	.11983	.98543	4	56	.01905	.13670	.98095	4
57	.01464	.12011	.98536	3	57	.01913	.13698	.98087	3
58	.01471	.12040	.98529	2	58	.01921	.13726	.98079	2
59	.01478	.12068	.98522	1	59	.01929	.13754	.98071	1
60	.01485	.12096	.98515	0	60	.01937	.13782	.98063	0
′	Cos²	Sin·Cos	Sin²	′	′	Cos²	Sin·Cos	Sin²	′

96° (276°)   (263°) 83°   97° (277°)   (262°) 82°

SQUARE OF THE SINE AND COSINE
AND THEIR PRODUCT (Continued)

8° (188°)   (351°) **171°**   9° (189°)   (350°) **170°**

′	Sin²	Sin · Cos	Cos²	′		′	Sin²	Sin · Cos	Cos²	′
0	.01937	.13782	.98063	**60**		**0**	.02447	.15451	.97553	**60**
1	.01945	.13810	.98055	59		1	.02456	.15479	.97544	59
2	.01953	.13838	.98047	58		2	.02465	.15506	.97535	58
3	.01961	.13866	.98039	57		3	.02474	.15534	.97526	57
4	.01969	.13894	.98031	56		4	.02483	.15561	.97517	56
5	.01977	.13922	.98023	**55**		**5**	.02492	.15589	.97508	**55**
6	.01985	.13950	.98015	54		6	.02501	.15617	.97499	54
7	.01993	.13977	.98007	53		7	.02510	.15644	.97490	53
8	.02002	.14005	.97998	52		8	.02520	.15672	.97480	52
9	.02010	.14033	.97990	51		9	.02529	.15700	.97471	51
10	.02018	.14061	.97982	**50**		**10**	.02538	.15727	.97462	**50**
11	.02026	.14089	.97974	49		11	.02547	.15755	.97453	49
12	.02034	.14117	.97966	48		12	.02556	.15782	.97444	48
13	.02043	.14145	.97957	47		13	.02565	.15810	.97435	47
14	.02051	.14173	.97949	46		14	.02575	.15838	.97425	46
15	.02059	.14201	.97941	**45**		**15**	.02584	.15865	.97416	**45**
16	.02067	.14229	.97933	44		16	.02593	.15893	.97407	44
17	.02076	.14257	.97924	43		17	.02602	.15920	.97398	43
18	.02084	.14284	.97916	42		18	.02612	.15948	.97388	42
19	.02092	.14312	.97908	41		19	.02621	.15976	.97379	41
20	.02101	.14340	.97899	**40**		**20**	.02630	.16003	.97370	**40**
21	.02109	.14368	.97891	39		21	.02639	.16031	.97361	39
22	.02117	.14396	.97883	38		22	.02649	.16058	.97351	38
23	.02126	.14424	.97874	37		23	.02658	.16086	.97342	37
24	.02134	.14452	.97866	36		24	.02668	.16113	.97332	36
25	.02142	.14479	.97858	**35**		**25**	.02677	.16141	.97323	**35**
26	.02151	.14507	.97849	34		26	.02686	.16168	.97314	34
27	.02159	.14535	.97841	33		27	.02696	.16196	.97304	33
28	.02168	.14563	.97832	32		28	.02705	.16223	.97295	32
29	.02176	.14591	.97824	31		29	.02715	.16251	.97285	31
30	.02185	.14619	.97815	**30**		**30**	.02724	.16278	.97276	**30**
31	.02193	.14646	.97807	29		31	.02734	.16306	.97266	29
32	.02202	.14674	.97798	28		32	.02743	.16333	.97257	28
33	.02210	.14702	.97790	27		33	.02753	.16361	.97247	27
34	.02219	.14730	.97781	26		34	.02762	.16388	.97238	26
35	.02227	.14758	.97773	**25**		**35**	.02772	.16416	.97228	**25**
36	.02236	.14785	.97764	24		36	.02781	.16443	.97219	24
37	.02245	.14813	.97755	23		37	.02791	.16471	.97209	23
38	.02253	.14841	.97747	22		38	.02800	.16498	.97200	22
39	.02262	.14869	.97738	21		39	.02810	.16526	.97190	21
40	.02271	.14897	.97729	**20**		**40**	.02820	.16553	.97180	**20**
41	.02279	.14924	.97721	19		41	.02829	.16581	.97171	19
42	.02288	.14952	.97712	18		42	.02839	.16608	.97161	18
43	.02297	.14980	.97703	17		43	.02849	.16635	.97151	17
44	.02305	.15008	.97695	16		44	.02858	.16663	.97142	16
45	.02314	.15035	.97686	**15**		**45**	.02868	.16690	.97132	**15**
46	.02323	.15063	.97677	14		46	.02878	.16718	.97122	14
47	.02332	.15091	.97668	13		47	.02887	.16745	.97113	13
48	.02340	.15118	.97660	12		48	.02897	.16773	.97103	12
49	.02349	.15146	.97651	11		49	.02907	.16800	.97093	11
50	.02358	.15174	.97642	**10**		**50**	.02917	.16827	.97083	**10**
51	.02367	.15202	.97633	9		51	.02926	.16855	.97074	9
52	.02376	.15229	.97624	8		52	.02936	.16882	.97064	8
53	.02385	.15257	.97615	7		53	.02946	.16910	.97054	7
54	.02394	.15285	.97606	6		54	.02956	.16937	.97044	6
55	.02402	.15312	.97598	**5**		**55**	.02966	.16964	.97034	**5**
56	.02411	.15340	.97589	4		56	.02976	.16992	.97024	4
57	.02420	.15368	.97580	3		57	.02986	.17019	.97014	3
58	.02429	.15396	.97571	2		58	.02996	.17046	.97004	2
59	.02438	.15423	.97562	1		59	.03005	.17074	.96995	1
60	.02447	.15451	.97553	**0**		**60**	.03015	.17101	.96985	**0**
′	Cos²	Sin · Cos	Sin²	′		′	Cos²	Sin · Cos	Sin²	′

98° (278°)   (261°) **81°**   99° (279°)   (260°) **80°**

SQUARE OF THE SINE AND COSINE
AND THEIR PRODUCT (Continued)

10° (190°)   (349°) **169°**   **11° (191°)**   (348°) **168°**

′	Sin²	Sin · Cos	Cos²	′	′	Sin²	Sin · Cos	Cos²	′
0	.03015	.17101	.96985	60	0	.03641	.18730	.96359	60
1	.03025	.17128	.96975	59	1	.03652	.18757	.96348	59
2	.03035	.17156	.96965	58	2	.03663	.18784	.96337	58
3	.03045	.17183	.96955	57	3	.03674	.18811	.96326	57
4	.03055	.17210	.96945	56	4	.03685	.18838	.96315	56
5	.03065	.17238	.96935	55	5	.03695	.18865	.96305	55
6	.03075	.17265	.96925	54	6	.03706	.18892	.96294	54
7	.03085	.17292	.96915	53	7	.03717	.18919	.96283	53
8	.03095	.17319	.96905	52	8	.03728	.18946	.96272	52
9	.03106	.17347	.96894	51	9	.03740	.18973	.96260	51
10	.03116	.17374	.96884	50	10	.03751	.19000	.96249	50
11	.03126	.17401	.96874	49	11	.03762	.19027	.96238	49
12	.03136	.17429	.96864	48	12	.03773	.19054	.96227	48
13	.03146	.17456	.96854	47	13	.03784	.19080	.96216	47
14	.03156	.17483	.96844	46	14	.03795	.19107	.96205	46
15	.03166	.17510	.96834	45	15	.03806	.19134	.96194	45
16	.03177	.17538	.96823	44	16	.03817	.19161	.96183	44
17	.03187	.17565	.96813	43	17	.03828	.19188	.96172	43
18	.03197	.17592	.96803	42	18	.03839	.19215	.96161	42
19	.03207	.17619	.96793	41	19	.03851	.19242	.96149	41
20	.03218	.17647	.96782	40	20	.03862	.19268	.96138	40
21	.03228	.17674	.96772	39	21	.03873	.19295	.96127	39
22	.03238	.17701	.96762	38	22	.03884	.19322	.96116	38
23	.03248	.17728	.96752	37	23	.03896	.19349	.96104	37
24	.03259	.17755	.96741	36	24	.03907	.19376	.96093	36
25	.03269	.17783	.96731	35	25	.03918	.19403	.96082	35
26	.03279	.17810	.96721	34	26	.03929	.19429	.96071	34
27	.03290	.17837	.96710	33	27	.03941	.19456	.96059	33
28	.03300	.17864	.96700	32	28	.03952	.19483	.96048	32
29	.03311	.17891	.96689	31	29	.03963	.19510	.96037	31
30	.03321	.17918	.96679	30	30	.03975	.19537	.96025	30
31	.03331	.17946	.96669	29	31	.03986	.19563	.96014	29
32	.03342	.17973	.96658	28	32	.03998	.19590	.96002	28
33	.03352	.18000	.96648	27	33	.04009	.19617	.95991	27
34	.03363	.18027	.96637	26	34	.04020	.19644	.95980	26
35	.03373	.18054	.96627	25	35	.04032	.19670	.95968	25
36	.03384	.18081	.96616	24	36	.04043	.19697	.95957	24
37	.03394	.18108	.96606	23	37	.04055	.19724	.95945	23
38	.03405	.18135	.96595	22	38	.04066	.19751	.95934	22
39	.03415	.18163	.96585	21	39	.04078	.19777	.95922	21
40	.03426	.18190	.96574	20	40	.04089	.19804	.95911	20
41	.03437	.18217	.96563	19	41	.04101	.19831	.95899	19
42	.03447	.18244	.96553	18	42	.04112	.19857	.95888	18
43	.03458	.18271	.96542	17	43	.04124	.19884	.95876	17
44	.03468	.18298	.96532	16	44	.04135	.19911	.95865	16
45	.03479	.18325	.96521	15	45	.04147	.19937	.95853	15
46	.03490	.18352	.96510	14	46	.04159	.19964	.95841	14
47	.03500	.18379	.96500	13	47	.04170	.19991	.95830	13
48	.03511	.18406	.96489	12	48	.04182	.20017	.95818	12
49	.03522	.18433	.96478	11	49	.04194	.20044	.95806	11
50	.03533	.18460	.96467	10	50	.04205	.20071	.95795	10
51	.03543	.18487	.96457	9	51	.04217	.20097	.95783	9
52	.03554	.18514	.96446	8	52	.04229	.20124	.95771	8
53	.03565	.18541	.96435	7	53	.04240	.20151	.95760	7
54	.03576	.18568	.96424	6	54	.04252	.20177	.95748	6
55	.03587	.18595	.96413	5	55	.04264	.20204	.95736	5
56	.03597	.18622	.96403	4	56	.04276	.20230	.95724	4
57	.03608	.18649	.96392	3	57	.04287	.20257	.95713	3
58	.03619	.18676	.96381	2	58	.04299	.20284	.95701	2
59	.03630	.18703	.96370	1	59	.04311	.20310	.95689	1
60	.03641	.18730	.96359	0	60	.04323	.20337	.95677	0
′	Cos²	Sin · Cos	Sin²	′	′	Cos²	Sin · Cos	Sin²	′

100° (280°)   (259°) **79°**   **101° (281°)**   (258°) **78°**

SQUARE OF THE SINE AND COSINE
AND THEIR PRODUCT (Continued)

12° (192°)   (347°) **167°**   **13° (193°)**   (346°) **166°**

′	Sin²	Sin · Cos	Cos²	′		′	Sin²	Sin · Cos	Cos²	′
0	.04323	.20337	.95677	60		0	.05060	.21919	.94940	60
1	.04335	.20363	.95665	59		1	.05073	.21945	.94927	59
2	.04346	.20390	.95654	58		2	.05086	.21971	.94914	58
3	.04358	.20417	.95642	57		3	.05099	.21997	.94901	57
4	.04370	.20443	.95630	56		4	.05111	.22023	.94889	56
5	.04382	.20470	.95618	55		5	.05124	.22049	.94876	55
6	.04394	.20496	.95606	54		6	.05137	.22075	.94863	54
7	.04406	.20523	.95594	53		7	.05150	.22101	.94850	53
8	.04418	.20549	.95582	52		8	.05163	.22127	.94837	52
9	.04430	.20576	.95570	51		9	.05176	.22154	.94824	51
10	.04442	.20602	.95558	50		10	.05189	.22180	.94811	50
11	.04454	.20629	.95546	49		11	.05201	.22206	.94799	49
12	.04466	.20655	.95534	48		12	.05214	.22232	.94786	48
13	.04478	.20682	.95522	47		13	.05227	.22258	.94773	47
14	.04490	.20708	.95510	46		14	.05240	.22284	.94760	46
15	.04502	.20735	.95498	45		15	.05253	.22310	.94747	45
16	.04514	.20761	.95486	44		16	.05266	.22336	.94734	44
17	.04526	.20788	.95474	43		17	.05279	.22362	.94721	43
18	.04538	.20814	.95462	42		18	.05292	.22388	.94708	42
19	.04550	.20840	.95450	41		19	.05305	.22414	.94695	41
20	.04562	.20867	.95438	40		20	.05318	.22440	.94682	40
21	.04575	.20893	.95425	39		21	.05331	.22466	.94669	39
22	.04587	.20920	.95413	38		22	.05345	.22492	.94655	38
23	.04599	.20946	.95401	37		23	.05358	.22518	.94642	37
24	.04611	.20973	.95389	36		24	.05371	.22544	.94629	36
25	.04623	.20999	.95377	35		25	.05384	.22570	.94616	35
26	.04636	.21025	.95364	34		26	.05397	.22596	.94603	34
27	.04648	.21052	.95352	33		27	.05410	.22622	.94590	33
28	.04660	.21078	.95340	32		28	.05423	.22648	.94577	32
29	.04672	.21105	.95328	31		29	.05436	.22674	.94564	31
30	.04685	.21131	.95315	30		30	.05450	.22700	.94550	30
31	.04697	.21157	.95303	29		31	.05463	.22725	.94537	29
32	.04709	.21184	.95291	28		32	.05476	.22751	.94524	28
33	.04722	.21210	.95278	27		33	.05489	.22777	.94511	27
34	.04734	.21236	.95266	26		34	.05503	.22803	.94497	26
35	.04746	.21263	.95254	25		35	.05516	.22829	.94484	25
36	.04759	.21289	.95241	24		36	.05529	.22855	.94471	24
37	.04771	.21315	.95229	23		37	.05542	.22881	.94458	23
38	.04783	.21342	.95217	22		38	.05556	.22907	.94444	22
39	.04796	.21368	.95204	21		39	.05569	.22932	.94431	21
40	.04808	.21394	.95192	20		40	.05582	.22958	.94418	20
41	.04821	.21420	.95179	19		41	.05596	.22984	.94404	19
42	.04833	.21447	.95167	18		42	.05609	.23010	.94391	18
43	.04846	.21473	.95154	17		43	.05623	.23036	.94377	17
44	.04858	.21499	.95142	16		44	.05636	.23062	.94364	16
45	.04871	.21526	.95129	15		45	.05649	.23087	.94351	15
46	.04883	.21552	.95117	14		46	.05663	.23113	.94337	14
47	.04896	.21578	.95104	13		47	.05676	.23139	.94324	13
48	.04908	.21604	.95092	12		48	.05690	.23165	.94310	12
49	.04921	.21631	.95079	11		49	.05703	.23191	.94297	11
50	.04934	.21657	.95066	10		50	.05717	.23216	.94283	10
51	.04946	.21683	.95054	9		51	.05730	.23242	.94270	9
52	.04959	.21709	.95041	8		52	.05744	.23268	.94256	8
53	.04971	.21735	.95029	7		53	.05757	.23294	.94243	7
54	.04984	.21762	.95016	6		54	.05771	.23319	.94229	6
55	.04997	.21788	.95003	5		55	.05785	.23345	.94215	5
56	.05009	.21814	.94991	4		56	.05798	.23371	.94202	4
57	.05022	.21840	.94978	3		57	.05812	.23396	.94188	3
58	.05035	.21866	.94965	2		58	.05825	.23422	.94175	2
59	.05048	.21892	.94952	1		59	.05839	.23448	.94161	1
60	.05060	.21919	.94940	0		60	.05853	.23474	.94147	0
′	Cos²	Sin · Cos	Sin²	′		′	Cos²	Sin · Cos	Sin²	′

SQUARE OF THE SINE AND COSINE
AND THEIR PRODUCT (Continued)

14° (194°)　　　　　　　　(345°) **165°**　　**15° (195°)**　　　　　　(344°) **164°**

′	Sin²	Sin · Cos	Cos²	′		′	Sin²	Sin · Cos	Cos²	′
0	.05853	.23474	.94147	60		0	.06699	.25000	.93301	60
1	.05866	.23499	.94134	59		1	.06713	.25025	.93287	59
2	.05880	.23525	.94120	58		2	.06728	.25050	.93272	58
3	.05894	.23551	.94106	57		3	.06742	.25076	.93258	57
4	.05907	.23576	.94093	56		4	.06757	.25101	.93243	56
5	.05921	.23602	.94079	55		5	.06772	.25126	.93228	55
6	.05935	.23628	.94065	54		6	.06786	.25151	.93214	54
7	.05949	.23653	.94051	53		7	.06801	.25176	.93199	53
8	.05962	.23679	.94038	52		8	.06816	.25201	.93184	52
9	.05976	.23704	.94024	51		9	.06830	.25226	.93170	51
10	.05990	.23730	.94010	50		10	.06845	.25251	.93155	50
11	.06004	.23756	.93996	49		11	.06860	.25277	.93140	49
12	.06018	.23781	.93982	48		12	.06874	.25302	.93126	48
13	.06031	.23807	.93969	47		13	.06889	.25327	.93111	47
14	.06045	.23832	.93955	46		14	.06904	.25352	.93096	46
15	.06059	.23858	.93941	45		15	.06919	.25377	.93081	45
16	.06073	.23883	.93927	44		16	.06933	.25402	.93067	44
17	.06087	.23909	.93913	43		17	.06948	.25427	.93052	43
18	.06101	.23935	.93899	42		18	.06963	.25452	.93037	42
19	.06115	.23960	.93885	41		19	.06978	.25477	.93022	41
20	.06129	.23986	.93871	40		20	.06993	.25502	.93007	40
21	.06143	.24011	.93857	39		21	.07007	.25527	.92993	39
22	.06157	.24037	.93843	38		22	.07022	.25552	.92978	38
23	.06171	.24062	.93829	37		23	.07037	.25577	.92963	37
24	.06185	.24088	.93815	36		24	.07052	.25602	.92948	36
25	.06199	.24113	.93801	35		25	.07067	.25627	.92933	35
26	.06213	.24139	.93787	34		26	.07082	.25652	.92918	34
27	.06227	.24164	.93773	33		27	.07097	.25677	.92903	33
28	.06241	.24190	.93759	32		28	.07112	.25702	.92888	32
29	.06255	.24215	.93745	31		29	.07127	.25727	.92873	31
30	.06269	.24240	.93731	30		30	.07142	.25752	.92858	30
31	.06283	.24266	.93717	29		31	.07157	.25777	.92843	29
32	.06297	.24291	.93703	28		32	.07172	.25802	.92828	28
33	.06311	.24317	.93689	27		33	.07187	.25827	.92813	27
34	.06326	.24342	.93674	26		34	.07202	.25852	.92798	26
35	.06340	.24368	.93660	25		35	.07217	.25876	.92783	25
36	.06354	.24393	.93646	24		36	.07232	.25901	.92768	24
37	.06368	.24418	.93632	23		37	.07247	.25926	.92753	23
38	.06382	.24444	.93618	22		38	.07262	.25951	.92738	22
39	.06397	.24469	.93603	21		39	.07277	.25976	.92723	21
40	.06411	.24494	.93589	20		40	.07292	.26001	.92708	20
41	.06425	.24520	.93575	19		41	.07307	.26026	.92693	19
42	.06439	.24545	.93561	18		42	.07322	.26050	.92678	18
43	.06454	.24571	.93546	17		43	.07338	.26075	.92662	17
44	.06468	.24596	.93532	16		44	.07353	.26100	.92647	16
45	.06482	.24621	.93518	15		45	.07368	.26125	.92632	15
46	.06497	.24646	.93503	14		46	.07383	.26150	.92617	14
47	.06511	.24672	.93489	13		47	.07398	.26175	.92602	13
48	.06525	.24697	.93475	12		48	.07414	.26199	.92586	12
49	.06540	.24722	.93460	11		49	.07429	.26224	.92571	11
50	.06554	.24748	.93446	10		50	.07444	.26249	.92556	10
51	.06568	.24773	.93432	9		51	.07459	.26274	.92541	9
52	.06583	.24798	.93417	8		52	.07475	.26298	.92525	8
53	.06597	.24823	.93403	7		53	.07490	.26323	.92510	7
54	.06612	.24849	.93388	6		54	.07505	.26348	.92495	6
55	.06626	.24874	.93374	5		55	.07521	.26373	.92479	5
56	.06641	.24899	.93359	4		56	.07536	.26397	.92464	4
57	.06655	.24924	.93345	3		57	.07551	.26422	.92449	3
58	.06670	.24950	.93330	2		58	.07567	.26447	.92433	2
59	.06684	.24975	.93316	1		59	.07582	.26471	.92418	1
60	.06699	.25000	.93301	0		60	.07598	.26496	.92402	0
′	Cos²	Sin · Cos	Sin²	′		′	Cos²	Sin · Cos	Sin²	′

104° (284°)　　　　　　(255°) **75°**　　**105° (285°)**　　　　　(254°) **74°**

SQUARE OF THE SINE AND COSINE
AND THEIR PRODUCT (Continued)

16° (196°)   **(343°) 163°**   **17° (197°)**   **(342°) 162°**

′	Sin²	Sin · Cos	Cos²	′		′	Sin²	Sin · Cos	Cos²	′
0	.07598	.26494	.92402	60		0	.08548	.27960	.91452	60
1	.07613	.26521	.92387	59		1	.08564	.27984	.91436	59
2	.07628	.26545	.92372	58		2	.08581	.28008	.91419	58
3	.07644	.26570	.92356	57		3	.08597	.28032	.91403	57
4	.07659	.26595	.92341	56		4	.08613	.28056	.91387	56
5	.07675	.26619	.92325	55		5	.08630	.28080	.91370	55
6	.07690	.26644	.92310	54		6	.08646	.28104	.91354	54
7	.07706	.26668	.92294	53		7	.08662	.28128	.91338	53
8	.07721	.26693	.92279	52		8	.08679	.28152	.91321	52
9	.07737	.26718	.92263	51		9	.08695	.28176	.91305	51
10	.07752	.26742	.92248	50		10	.08711	.28200	.91289	50
11	.07768	.26767	.92232	49		11	.08728	.28224	.91272	49
12	.07784	.26791	.92216	48		12	.08744	.28248	.91256	48
13	.07799	.26816	.92201	47		13	.08761	.28272	.91239	47
14	.07815	.26840	.92185	46		14	.08777	.28296	.91223	46
15	.07830	.26865	.92170	45		15	.08794	.28320	.91206	45
16	.07846	.26890	.92154	44		16	.08810	.28344	.91190	44
17	.07862	.26914	.92138	43		17	.08827	.28368	.91173	43
18	.07877	.26939	.92123	42		18	.08843	.28392	.91157	42
19	.07893	.26963	.92107	41		19	.08860	.28416	.91140	41
20	.07909	.26988	.92091	40		20	.08876	.28440	.91124	40
21	.07924	.27012	.92076	39		21	.08893	.28464	.91107	39
22	.07940	.27036	.92060	38		22	.08909	.28488	.91091	38
23	.07956	.27061	.92044	37		23	.08926	.28512	.91074	37
24	.07972	.27085	.92028	36		24	.08943	.28536	.91057	36
25	.07987	.27110	.92013	35		25	.08959	.28560	.91041	35
26	.08003	.27134	.91997	34		26	.08976	.28583	.91024	34
27	.08019	.27159	.91981	33		27	.08992	.28607	.91008	33
28	.08035	.27183	.91965	32		28	.09009	.28631	.90991	32
29	.08051	.27208	.91949	31		29	.09026	.28655	.90974	31
30	.08066	.27232	.91934	30		30	.09042	.28679	.90958	30
31	.08082	.27256	.91918	29		31	.09059	.28703	.90941	29
32	.08098	.27281	.91902	28		32	.09076	.28726	.90924	28
33	.08114	.27305	.91886	27		33	.09093	.28750	.90907	27
34	.08130	.27329	.91870	26		34	.09109	.28774	.90891	26
35	.08146	.27354	.91854	25		35	.09126	.28798	.90874	25
36	.08162	.27378	.91838	24		36	.09143	.28822	.90857	24
37	.08178	.27402	.91822	23		37	.09160	.28845	.90840	23
38	.08194	.27427	.91806	22		38	.09176	.28869	.90824	22
39	.08210	.27451	.91790	21		39	.09193	.28893	.90807	21
40	.08226	.27475	.91774	20		40	.09210	.28917	.90790	20
41	.08242	.27500	.91758	19		41	.09227	.28940	.90773	19
42	.08258	.27524	.91742	18		42	.09244	.28964	.90756	18
43	.08274	.27548	.91726	17		43	.09260	.28988	.90740	17
44	.08290	.27573	.91710	16		44	.09277	.29011	.90723	16
45	.08306	.27597	.91694	15		45	.09294	.29035	.90706	15
46	.08322	.27621	.91678	14		46	.09311	.29059	.90689	14
47	.08338	.27645	.91662	13		47	.09328	.29082	.90672	13
48	.08354	.27670	.91646	12		48	.09345	.29106	.90655	12
49	.08370	.27694	.91630	11		49	.09362	.29130	.90638	11
50	.08386	.27718	.91614	10		50	.09379	.29153	.90621	10
51	.08402	.27742	.91598	9		51	.09396	.29177	.90604	9
52	.08418	.27766	.91582	8		52	.09413	.29201	.90587	8
53	.08435	.27791	.91565	7		53	.09430	.29224	.90570	7
54	.08451	.27815	.91549	6		54	.09447	.29248	.90553	6
55	.08467	.27839	.91533	5		55	.09464	.29271	.90536	5
56	.08483	.27863	.91517	4		56	.09481	.29295	.90519	4
57	.08499	.27887	.91501	3		57	.09498	.29319	.90502	3
58	.08516	.27911	.91484	2		58	.09515	.29342	.90485	2
59	.08532	.27936	.91468	1		59	.09532	.29366	.90468	1
60	.08548	.27960	.91452	0		60	.09549	.29389	.90451	0
′	Cos²	Sin · Cos	Sin²	′		′	Cos²	Sin · Cos	Sin²	′

SQUARE OF THE SINE AND COSINE
AND THEIR PRODUCT (Continued)

18° (198°)   (341°) **161°**

′	Sin²	Sin · Cos	Cos²	′
0	.09549	.29389	.90451	60
1	.09566	.29413	.90434	59
2	.09583	.29436	.90417	58
3	.09601	.29460	.90399	57
4	.09618	.29483	.90382	56
5	.09635	.29507	.90365	55
6	.09652	.29530	.90348	54
7	.09669	.29554	.90331	53
8	.09686	.29577	.90314	52
9	.09704	.29601	.90296	51
10	.09721	.29624	.90279	50
11	.09738	.29648	.90262	49
12	.09755	.29671	.90245	48
13	.09773	.29694	.90227	47
14	.09790	.29718	.90210	46
15	.09807	.29741	.90193	45
16	.09824	.29765	.90176	44
17	.09842	.29788	.90158	43
18	.09859	.29811	.90141	42
19	.09876	.29835	.90124	41
20	.09894	.29858	.90106	40
21	.09911	.29881	.90089	39
22	.09929	.29905	.90071	38
23	.09946	.29928	.90054	37
24	.09963	.29951	.90037	36
25	.09981	.29974	.90019	35
26	.09998	.29998	.90002	34
27	.10016	.30021	.89984	33
28	.10033	.30044	.89967	32
29	.10051	.30068	.89949	31
30	.10068	.30091	.89932	30
31	.10086	.30114	.89914	29
32	.10103	.30137	.89897	28
33	.10121	.30160	.89879	27
34	.10138	.30184	.89862	26
35	.10156	.30207	.89844	25
36	.10174	.30230	.89826	24
37	.10191	.30253	.89809	23
38	.10209	.30276	.89791	22
39	.10226	.30299	.89774	21
40	.10244	.30323	.89756	20
41	.10262	.30346	.89738	19
42	.10279	.30369	.89721	18
43	.10297	.30392	.89703	17
44	.10315	.30415	.89685	16
45	.10332	.30438	.89668	15
46	.10350	.30461	.89650	14
47	.10368	.30484	.89632	13
48	.10386	.30507	.89614	12
49	.10403	.30530	.89597	11
50	.10421	.30553	.89579	10
51	.10439	.30576	.89561	9
52	.10457	.30599	.89543	8
53	.10474	.30622	.89526	7
54	.10492	.30645	.89508	6
55	.10510	.30668	.89490	5
56	.10528	.30691	.89472	4
57	.10546	.30714	.89454	3
58	.10564	.30737	.89436	2
59	.10582	.30760	.89418	1
60	.10599	.30783	.89401	0
′	Cos²	Sin · Cos	Sin²	′

108° (288°)   (251°) **71°**

19° (199°)   (340°) **160°**

′	Sin²	Sin · Cos	Cos²	′
0	.10599	.30783	.89401	60
1	.10617	.30806	.89383	59
2	.10635	.30829	.89365	58
3	.10653	.30852	.89347	57
4	.10671	.30875	.89329	56
5	.10689	.30898	.89311	55
6	.10707	.30920	.89293	54
7	.10725	.30943	.89275	53
8	.10743	.30966	.89257	52
9	.10761	.30989	.89239	51
10	.10779	.31012	.89221	50
11	.10797	.31035	.89203	49
12	.10815	.31057	.89185	48
13	.10833	.31080	.89167	47
14	.10851	.31103	.89149	46
15	.10870	.31126	.89130	45
16	.10888	.31148	.89112	44
17	.10906	.31171	.89094	43
18	.10924	.31194	.89076	42
19	.10942	.31217	.89058	41
20	.10960	.31239	.89040	40
21	.10978	.31262	.89022	39
22	.10997	.31285	.89003	38
23	.11015	.31308	.88985	37
24	.11033	.31330	.88967	36
25	.11051	.31353	.88949	35
26	.11070	.31376	.88930	34
27	.11088	.31398	.88912	33
28	.11106	.31421	.88894	32
29	.11124	.31443	.88876	31
30	.11143	.31466	.88857	30
31	.11161	.31489	.88839	29
32	.11179	.31511	.88821	28
33	.11198	.31534	.88802	27
34	.11216	.31556	.88784	26
35	.11234	.31579	.88766	25
36	.11253	.31601	.88747	24
37	.11271	.31624	.88729	23
38	.11290	.31647	.88710	22
39	.11308	.31669	.88692	21
40	.11326	.31692	.88674	20
41	.11345	.31714	.88655	19
42	.11363	.31737	.88637	18
43	.11382	.31759	.88618	17
44	.11400	.31781	.88600	16
45	.11419	.31804	.88581	15
46	.11437	.31826	.88563	14
47	.11456	.31849	.88544	13
48	.11474	.31871	.88526	12
49	.11493	.31894	.88507	11
50	.11511	.31916	.88489	10
51	.11530	.31938	.88470	9
52	.11549	.31961	.88451	8
53	.11567	.31983	.88433	7
54	.11586	.32005	.88414	6
55	.11604	.32028	.88396	5
56	.11623	.32050	.88377	4
57	.11642	.32072	.88358	3
58	.11660	.32095	.88340	2
59	.11679	.32117	.88321	1
60	.11698	.32139	.88302	0
′	Cos²	Sin · Cos	Sin²	′

109° (289°)   (250°) **70°**

SQUARE OF THE SINE AND COSINE
AND THEIR PRODUCT (Continued)

′	Sin²	Sin · Cos	Cos²	′	′	Sin²	Sin · Cos	Cos²	′
0	.11698	.32139	.88302	60	0	.12843	.33457	.87157	60
1	.11716	.32162	.88284	59	1	.12862	.33478	.87138	59
2	.11735	.32184	.88265	58	2	.12882	.33500	.87118	58
3	.11754	.32206	.88246	57	3	.12901	.33521	.87099	57
4	.11773	.32228	.88227	56	4	.12921	.33543	.87079	56
5	.11791	.32251	.88209	55	5	.12940	.33564	.87060	55
6	.11810	.32273	.88190	54	6	.12960	.33586	.87040	54
7	.11829	.32295	.88171	53	7	.12979	.33608	.87021	53
8	.11848	.32317	.88152	52	8	.12999	.33629	.87001	52
9	.11867	.32339	.88133	51	9	.13018	.33651	.86982	51
10	.11885	.32362	.88115	50	10	.13038	.33672	.86962	50
11	.11904	.32384	.88096	49	11	.13058	.33694	.86942	49
12	.11923	.32406	.88077	48	12	.13077	.33715	.86923	48
13	.11942	.32428	.88058	47	13	.13097	.33737	.86903	47
14	.11961	.32450	.88039	46	14	.13116	.33758	.86884	46
15	.11980	.32472	.88020	45	15	.13136	.33780	.86864	45
16	.11999	.32495	.88001	44	16	.13156	.33801	.86844	44
17	.12018	.32517	.87982	43	17	.13175	.33822	.86825	43
18	.12036	.32539	.87964	42	18	.13195	.33844	.86805	42
19	.12055	.32561	.87945	41	19	.13215	.33865	.86785	41
20	.12074	.32583	.87926	40	20	.13235	.33887	.86765	40
21	.12093	.32605	.87907	39	21	.13254	.33908	.86746	39
22	.12112	.32627	.87888	38	22	.13274	.33929	.86726	38
23	.12131	.32649	.87869	37	23	.13294	.33951	.86706	37
24	.12150	.32671	.87850	36	24	.13314	.33972	.86686	36
25	.12169	.32693	.87831	35	25	.13333	.33993	.86667	35
26	.12188	.32715	.87812	34	26	.13353	.34015	.86647	34
27	.12207	.32737	.87793	33	27	.13373	.34036	.86627	33
28	.12226	.32759	.87774	32	28	.13393	.34057	.86607	32
29	.12245	.32781	.87755	31	29	.13412	.34079	.86588	31
30	.12265	.32803	.87735	30	30	.13432	.34100	.86568	30
31	.12284	.32825	.87716	29	31	.13452	.34121	.86548	29
32	.12303	.32847	.87697	28	32	.13472	.34142	.86528	28
33	.12322	.32869	.87678	27	33	.13492	.34164	.86508	27
34	.12341	.32891	.87659	26	34	.13512	.34185	.86488	26
35	.12360	.32913	.87640	25	35	.13532	.34206	.86468	25
36	.12379	.32934	.87621	24	36	.13552	.34227	.86448	24
37	.12398	.32956	.87602	23	37	.13571	.34249	.86429	23
38	.12418	.32978	.87582	22	38	.13591	.34270	.86409	22
39	.12437	.33000	.87563	21	39	.13611	.34291	.86389	21
40	.12456	.33022	.87544	20	40	.13631	.34312	.86369	20
41	.12475	.33044	.87525	19	41	.13651	.34333	.86349	19
42	.12494	.33066	.87506	18	42	.13671	.34354	.86329	18
43	.12514	.33087	.87486	17	43	.13691	.34376	.86309	17
44	.12533	.33109	.87467	16	44	.13711	.34397	.86289	16
45	.12552	.33131	.87448	15	45	.13731	.34418	.86269	15
46	.12571	.33153	.87429	14	46	.13751	.34439	.86249	14
47	.12591	.33175	.87409	13	47	.13771	.34460	.86229	13
48	.12610	.33196	.87390	12	48	.13791	.34481	.86209	12
49	.12629	.33218	.87371	11	49	.13811	.34502	.86189	11
50	.12649	.33240	.87351	10	50	.13832	.34523	.86168	10
51	.12668	.33262	.87332	9	51	.13852	.34544	.86148	9
52	.12687	.33283	.87313	8	52	.13872	.34565	.86128	8
53	.12707	.33305	.87293	7	53	.13892	.34586	.86108	7
54	.12726	.33327	.87274	6	54	.13912	.34607	.86088	6
55	.12746	.33348	.87254	5	55	.13932	.34628	.86068	5
56	.12765	.33370	.87235	4	56	.13952	.34649	.86048	4
57	.12784	.33392	.87216	3	57	.13972	.34670	.86028	3
58	.12804	.33413	.87196	2	58	.13993	.34691	.86007	2
59	.12823	.33435	.87177	1	59	.14013	.34712	.85987	1
60	.12843	33457	.87157	0	60	.14033	.34733	.85967	0
′	Cos²	Sin · Cos	Sin²	′	′	Cos²	Sin · Cos	Sin²	′

SQUARE OF THE SINE AND COSINE
AND THEIR PRODUCT (Continued)

22° (202°)   (337°) **157°**

′	Sin²	Sin · Cos	Cos²	′
0	.14033	.34733	.85967	**60**
1	.14053	.34754	.85947	59
2	.14073	.34775	.85927	58
3	.14094	.34796	.85906	57
4	.14114	.34817	.85886	56
5	.14134	.34837	.85866	**55**
6	.14154	.34858	.85846	54
7	.14175	.34879	.85825	53
8	.14195	.34900	.85805	52
9	.14215	.34921	.85785	51
10	.14236	.34942	.85764	**50**
11	.14256	.34962	.85744	49
12	.14276	.34983	.85724	48
13	.14297	.35004	.85703	47
14	.14317	.35025	.85683	46
15	.14337	.35045	.85663	**45**
16	.14358	.35066	.85642	44
17	.14378	.35087	.85622	43
18	.14399	.35108	.85601	42
19	.14419	.35128	.85581	41
20	.14440	.35149	.85560	**40**
21	.14460	.35170	.85540	39
22	.14480	.35190	.85520	38
23	.14501	.35211	.85499	37
24	.14521	.35232	.85479	36
25	.14542	.35252	.85458	**35**
26	.14562	.35273	.85438	34
27	.14583	.35294	.85417	33
28	.14604	.35314	.85396	32
29	.14624	.35335	.85376	31
30	.14645	.35355	.85355	**30**
31	.14665	.35376	.85335	29
32	.14686	.35396	.85314	28
33	.14706	.35417	.85294	27
34	.14727	.35438	.85273	26
35	.14748	.35458	.85252	**25**
36	.14768	.35479	.85232	24
37	.14789	.35499	.85211	23
38	.14810	.35520	.85190	22
39	.14830	.35540	.85170	21
40	.14851	.35560	.85149	**20**
41	.14872	.35581	.85128	19
42	.14892	.35601	.85108	18
43	.14913	.35622	.85087	17
44	.14934	.35642	.85066	16
45	.14955	.35663	.85045	**15**
46	.14975	.35683	.85025	14
47	.14996	.35703	.85004	13
48	.15017	.35724	.84983	12
49	.15038	.35744	.84962	11
50	.15058	.35764	.84942	**10**
51	.15079	.35785	.84921	9
52	.15100	.35805	.84900	8
53	.15121	.35825	.84879	7
54	.15142	.35846	.84858	6
55	.15163	.35866	.84837	**5**
56	.15183	.35886	.84817	4
57	.15204	.35906	.84796	3
58	.15225	.35927	.84775	2
59	.15246	.35947	.84754	1
60	.15267	.35967	.84733	**0**
′	Cos²	Sin · Cos	Sin²	′

112° (292°)   (247°) **67°**

23° (203°)   (336°) **156°**

′	Sin²	Sin · Cos	Cos²	′
0	.15267	.35967	.84733	**60**
1	.15288	.35987	.84712	59
2	.15309	.36007	.84691	58
3	.15330	.36028	.84670	57
4	.15351	.36048	.84649	56
5	.15372	.36068	.84628	**55**
6	.15393	.36088	.84607	54
7	.15414	.36108	.84586	53
8	.15435	.36128	.84565	52
9	.15456	.36148	.84544	51
10	.15477	.36168	.84523	**50**
11	.15498	.36189	.84502	49
12	.15519	.36209	.84481	48
13	.15540	.36229	.84460	47
14	.15561	.36249	.84439	46
15	.15582	.36269	.84418	**45**
16	.15603	.36289	.84397	44
17	.15624	.36309	.84376	43
18	.15646	.36329	.84354	42
19	.15667	.36349	.84333	41
20	.15688	.36369	.84312	**40**
21	.15709	.36389	.84291	39
22	.15730	.36409	.84270	38
23	.15751	.36429	.84249	37
24	.15773	.36448	.84227	36
25	.15794	.36468	.84206	**35**
26	.15815	.36488	.84185	34
27	.15836	.36508	.84164	33
28	.15858	.36528	.84142	32
29	.15879	.36548	.84121	31
30	.15900	.36568	.84100	**30**
31	.15921	.36588	.84079	29
32	.15943	.36607	.84057	28
33	.15964	.36627	.84036	27
34	.15985	.36647	.84015	26
35	.16007	.36667	.83993	**25**
36	.16028	.36686	.83972	24
37	.16049	.36706	.83951	23
38	.16071	.36726	.83929	22
39	.16092	.36746	.83908	21
40	.16113	.36765	.83887	**20**
41	.16135	.36785	.83865	19
42	.16156	.36805	.83844	18
43	.16178	.36825	.83822	17
44	.16199	.36844	.83801	16
45	.16220	.36864	.83780	**15**
46	.16242	.36884	.83758	14
47	.16263	.36903	.83737	13
48	.16285	.36923	.83715	12
49	.16306	.36942	.83694	11
50	.16328	.36962	.83672	**10**
51	.16349	.36982	.83651	9
52	.16371	.37001	.83629	8
53	.16392	.37021	.83608	7
54	.16414	.37040	.83586	6
55	.16436	.37060	.83564	**5**
56	.16457	.37079	.83543	4
57	.16479	.37099	.83521	3
58	.16500	.37118	.83500	2
59	.16522	.37138	.83478	1
60	.16543	.37157	.83457	**0**
′	Cos²	Sin · Cos	Sin²	′

113° (293°)   (246°) **66°**

SQUARE OF THE SINE AND COSINE
AND THEIR PRODUCT (Continued)

24° (204°)   (335°) **155°**   **25° (205°)**   (334°) **154°**

′	Sin²	Sin · Cos	Cos²	′		′	Sin²	Sin · Cos	Cos²	′
0	.16543	.37157	.83457	60		0	.17861	.38302	.82139	60
1	.16565	.37177	.83435	59		1	.17883	.38321	.82117	59
2	.16587	.37196	.83413	58		2	.17905	.38340	.82095	58
3	.16608	.37216	.83392	57		3	.17928	.38358	.82072	57
4	.16630	.37235	.83370	56		4	.17950	.38377	.82050	56
5	.16652	.37254	.83348	55		5	.17972	.38396	.82028	55
6	.16673	.37274	.83327	54		6	.17995	.38414	.82005	54
7	.16695	.37293	.83305	53		7	.18017	.38433	.81983	53
8	.16717	.37313	.83283	52		8	.18039	.38451	.81961	52
9	.16738	.37332	.83262	51		9	.18062	.38470	.81938	51
10	.16760	.37351	.83240	50		10	.18084	.38489	.81916	50
11	.16782	.37371	.83218	49		11	.18106	.38507	.81894	49
12	.16804	.37390	.83196	48		12	.18129	.38526	.81871	48
13	.16825	.37409	.83175	47		13	.18151	.38544	.81849	47
14	.16847	.37429	.83153	46		14	.18174	.38563	.81826	46
15	.16869	.37448	.83131	45		15	.18196	.38581	.81804	45
16	.16891	.37467	.83109	44		16	.18219	.38600	.81781	44
17	.16913	.37486	.83087	43		17	.18241	.38618	.81759	43
18	.16934	.37506	.83066	42		18	.18263	.38637	.81737	42
19	.16956	.37525	.83044	41		19	.18286	.38655	.81714	41
20	.16978	.37544	.83022	40		20	.18308	.38674	.81692	40
21	.17000	.37563	.83000	39		21	.18331	.38692	.81669	39
22	.17022	.37582	.82978	38		22	.18353	.38710	.81647	38
23	.17044	.37602	.82956	37		23	.18376	.38729	.81624	37
24	.17066	.37621	.82934	36		24	.18399	.38747	.81601	36
25	.17087	.37640	.82913	35		25	.18421	.38766	.81579	35
26	.17109	.37659	.82891	34		26	.18444	.38784	.81556	34
27	.17131	.37678	.82869	33		27	.18466	.38802	.81534	33
28	.17153	.37697	.82847	32		28	.18489	.38821	.81511	32
29	.17175	.37716	.82825	31		29	.18511	.38839	.81489	31
30	.17197	.37735	.82803	30		30	.18534	.38857	.81466	30
31	.17219	.37755	.82781	29		31	.18557	.38876	.81443	29
32	.17241	.37774	.82759	28		32	.18579	.38894	.81421	28
33	.17263	.37793	.82737	27		33	.18602	.38912	.81398	27
34	.17285	.37812	.82715	26		34	.18624	.38930	.81376	26
35	.17307	.37831	.82693	25		35	.18647	.38949	.81353	25
36	.17329	.37850	.82671	24		36	.18670	.38967	.81330	24
37	.17351	.37869	.82649	23		37	.18692	.38985	.81308	23
38	.17373	.37888	.82627	22		38	.18715	.39003	.81285	22
39	.17395	.37907	.82605	21		39	.18738	.39022	.81262	21
40	.17417	.37926	.82583	20		40	.18761	.39040	.81239	20
41	.17439	.37945	.82561	19		41	.18783	.39058	.81217	19
42	.17461	.37964	.82539	18		42	.18806	.39076	.81194	18
43	.17483	.37982	.82517	17		43	.18829	.39094	.81171	17
44	.17505	.38001	.82495	16		44	.18852	.39112	.81148	16
45	.17528	.38020	.82472	15		45	.18874	.39130	.81126	15
46	.17550	.38039	.82450	14		46	.18897	.39149	.81103	14
47	.17572	.38058	.82428	13		47	.18920	.39167	.81080	13
48	.17594	.38077	.82406	12		48	.18943	.39185	.81057	12
49	.17616	.38096	.82384	11		49	.18965	.39203	.81035	11
50	.17638	.38115	.82362	10		50	.18988	.39221	.81012	10
51	.17661	.38133	.82339	9		51	.19011	.39239	.80989	9
52	.17683	.38152	.82317	8		52	.19034	.39257	.80966	8
53	.17705	.38171	.82295	7		53	.19057	.39275	.80943	7
54	.17727	.38190	.82273	6		54	.19080	.39293	.80920	6
55	.17749	.38209	.82251	5		55	.19102	.39311	.80898	5
56	.17772	.38227	.82228	4		56	.19125	.39329	.80875	4
57	.17794	.38246	.82206	3		57	.19148	.39347	.80852	3
58	.17816	.38265	.82184	2		58	.19171	.39365	.80829	2
59	.17838	.38284	.82162	1		59	.19194	.39383	.80806	1
60	.17861	.38302	.82139	0		60	.19217	.39401	.80783	0
′	Cos²	Sin · Cos	Sin²	′		′	Cos²	Sin · Cos	Sin²	′

114° (294°)   (245°) **65°**   **115° (295°)**   (244°) **64°**

SQUARE OF THE SINE AND COSINE
AND THEIR PRODUCT (Continued)

26° (206°)   (333°) **153°**   **27° (207°)**   (332°) **152°**

′	Sin²	Sin · Cos	Cos²	′		′	Sin²	Sin · Cos	Cos²	′
0	.19217	.39401	.80783	60		0	.20611	.40451	.79389	60
1	.19240	.39418	.80760	59		1	.20634	.40468	.79366	59
2	.19263	.39436	.80737	58		2	.20658	.40485	.79342	58
3	.19286	.39454	.80714	57		3	.20681	.40502	.79319	57
4	.19309	.39472	.80691	56		4	.20705	.40519	.79295	56
5	.19332	.39490	.80668	55		5	.20729	.40536	.79271	55
6	.19355	.39508	.80645	54		6	.20752	.40553	.79248	54
7	.19378	.39526	.80622	53		7	.20776	.40570	.79224	53
8	.19401	.39543	.80599	52		8	.20799	.40587	.79201	52
9	.19424	.39561	.80576	51		9	.20823	.40604	.79177	51
10	.19447	.39579	.80553	50		10	.20847	.40621	.79153	50
11	.19470	.39597	.80530	49		11	.20870	.40638	.79130	49
12	.19493	.39614	.80507	48		12	.20894	.40655	.79106	48
13	.19516	.39632	.80484	47		13	.20918	.40672	.79082	47
14	.19539	.39650	.80461	46		14	.20941	.40689	.79059	46
15	.19562	.39668	.80438	45		15	.20965	.40706	.79035	45
16	.19585	.39685	.80415	44		16	.20989	.40723	.79011	44
17	.19608	.39703	.80392	43		17	.21012	.40740	.78988	43
18	.19631	.39721	.80369	42		18	.21036	.40756	.78964	42
19	.19654	.39738	.80346	41		19	.21060	.40773	.78940	41
20	.19677	.39756	.80323	40		20	.21083	.40790	.78917	40
21	.19701	.39774	.80299	39		21	.21107	.40807	.78893	39
22	.19724	.39791	.80276	38		22	.21131	.40824	.78869	38
23	.19747	.39809	.80253	37		23	.21155	.40840	.78845	37
24	.19770	.39826	.80230	36		24	.21178	.40857	.78822	36
25	.19793	.39844	.80207	35		25	.21202	.40874	.78798	35
26	.19816	.39862	.80184	34		26	.21226	.40891	.78774	34
27	.19840	.39879	.80160	33		27	.21250	.40907	.78750	33
28	.19863	.39897	.80137	32		28	.21274	.40924	.78726	32
29	.19886	.39914	.80114	31		29	.21297	.40941	.78703	31
30	.19909	.39932	.80091	30		30	.21321	.40958	.78679	30
31	.19932	.39949	.80068	29		31	.21345	.40974	.78655	29
32	.19956	.39967	.80044	28		32	.21369	.40991	.78631	28
33	.19979	.39984	.80021	27		33	.21393	.41008	.78607	27
34	.20002	.40002	.79998	26		34	.21417	.41024	.78583	26
35	.20026	.40019	.79974	25		35	.21440	.41041	.78560	25
36	.20049	.40037	.79951	24		36	.21464	.41057	.78536	24
37	.20072	.40054	.79928	23		37	.21488	.41074	.78512	23
38	.20095	.40071	.79905	22		38	.21512	.41091	.78488	22
39	.20119	.40089	.79881	21		39	.21536	.41107	.78464	21
40	.20142	.40106	.79858	20		40	.21560	.41124	.78440	20
41	.20165	.40124	.79835	19		41	.21584	.41140	.78416	19
42	.20189	.40141	.79811	18		42	.21608	.41157	.78392	18
43	.20212	.40158	.79788	17		43	.21632	.41173	.78368	17
44	.20235	.40176	.79765	16		44	.21656	.41190	.78344	16
45	.20259	.40193	.79741	15		45	.21680	.41206	.78320	15
46	.20282	.40210	.79718	14		46	.21704	.41223	.78296	14
47	.20306	.40227	.79694	13		47	.21728	.41239	.78272	13
48	.20329	.40245	.79671	12		48	.21752	.41256	.78248	12
49	.20352	.40262	.79648	11		49	.21776	.41272	.78224	11
50	.20376	.40279	.79624	10		50	.21800	.41289	.78200	10
51	.20399	.40296	.79601	9		51	.21824	.41305	.78176	9
52	.20423	.40314	.79577	8		52	.21848	.41321	.78152	8
53	.20446	.40331	.79554	7		53	.21872	.41338	.78128	7
54	.20470	.40348	.79530	6		54	.21896	.41354	.78104	6
55	.20493	.40365	.79507	5		55	.21920	.41370	.78080	5
56	.20517	.40382	.79483	4		56	.21944	.41387	.78056	4
57	.20540	.40399	.79460	3		57	.21968	.41403	.78032	3
58	.20564	.40417	.79436	2		58	.21992	.41419	.78008	2
59	.20587	.40434	.79413	1		59	.22016	.41436	.77984	1
60	.20611	.40451	.79389	0		60	.22040	.41452	.77960	0
′	Cos²	Sin · Cos	Sin²	′		′	Cos²	Sin · Cos	Sin²	′

116° (296°)   (243°) **63°**   **117° (297°)**   (242°) **62°**

SQUARE OF THE SINE AND COSINE
AND THEIR PRODUCT (Continued)

28° (208°)   (331°) 151°

′	Sin²	Sin · Cos	Cos²	′
0	.22040	.41452	.77960	60
1	.22064	.41468	.77936	59
2	.22089	.41484	.77911	58
3	.22113	.41501	.77887	57
4	.22137	.41517	.77863	56
5	.22161	.41533	.77839	55
6	.22185	.41549	.77815	54
7	.22209	.41565	.77791	53
8	.22234	.41582	.77766	52
9	.22258	.41598	.77742	51
10	.22282	.41614	.77718	50
11	.22306	.41630	.77694	49
12	.22330	.41646	.77670	48
13	.22355	.41662	.77645	47
14	.22379	.41678	.77621	46
15	.22403	.41694	.77597	45
16	.22427	.41710	.77573	44
17	.22452	.41726	.77548	43
18	.22476	.41742	.77524	42
19	.22500	.41758	.77500	41
20	.22525	.41774	.77475	40
21	.22549	.41790	.77451	39
22	.22573	.41806	.77427	38
23	.22598	.41822	.77402	37
24	.22622	.41838	.77378	36
25	.22646	.41854	.77354	35
26	.22671	.41870	.77329	34
27	.22695	.41886	.77305	33
28	.22719	.41902	.77281	32
29	.22744	.41918	.77256	31
30	.22768	.41934	.77232	30
31	.22792	.41949	.77208	29
32	.22817	.41965	.77183	28
33	.22841	.41981	.77159	27
34	.22866	.41997	.77134	26
35	.22890	.42013	.77110	25
36	.22915	.42028	.77085	24
37	.22939	.42044	.77061	23
38	.22964	.42060	.77036	22
39	.22988	.42076	.77012	21
40	.23012	.42091	.76988	20
41	.23037	.42107	.76963	19
42	.23061	.42123	.76939	18
43	.23086	.42138	.76914	17
44	.23110	.42154	.76890	16
45	.23135	.42170	.76865	15
46	.23160	.42185	.76840	14
47	.23184	.42201	.76816	13
48	.23209	.42216	.76791	12
49	.23233	.42232	.76767	11
50	.23258	.42248	.76742	10
51	.23282	.42263	.76718	9
52	.23307	.42279	.76693	8
53	.23332	.42294	.76668	7
54	.23356	.42310	.76644	6
55	.23381	.42325	.76619	5
56	.23405	.42341	.76595	4
57	.23430	.42356	.76570	3
58	.23455	.42372	.76545	2
59	.23479	.42387	.76521	1
60	.23504	.42402	.76496	0
′	Cos²	Sin · Cos	Sin²	′

29° (209°)   (330°) 150°

′	Sin²	Sin · Cos	Cos²	′
0	.23504	.42402	.76496	60
1	.23529	.42418	.76471	59
2	.23553	.42433	.76447	58
3	.23578	.42449	.76422	57
4	.23603	.42464	.76397	56
5	.23627	.42479	.76373	55
6	.23652	.42495	.76348	54
7	.23677	.42510	.76323	53
8	.23702	.42525	.76298	52
9	.23726	.42541	.76274	51
10	.23751	.42556	.76249	50
11	.23776	.42571	.76224	49
12	.23801	.42586	.76199	48
13	.23825	.42602	.76175	47
14	.23850	.42617	.76150	46
15	.23875	.42632	.76125	45
16	.23900	.42647	.76100	44
17	.23925	.42662	.76075	43
18	.23950	.42678	.76050	42
19	.23974	.42693	.76026	41
20	.23999	.42708	.76001	40
21	.24024	.42723	.75976	39
22	.24049	.42738	.75951	38
23	.24074	.42753	.75926	37
24	.24099	.42768	.75901	36
25	.24124	.42783	.75876	35
26	.24148	.42798	.75852	34
27	.24173	.42813	.75827	33
28	.24198	.42828	.75802	32
29	.24223	.42843	.75777	31
30	.24248	.42858	.75752	30
31	.24273	.42873	.75727	29
32	.24298	.42888	.75702	28
33	.24323	.42903	.75677	27
34	.24348	.42918	.75652	26
35	.24373	.42933	.75627	25
36	.24398	.42948	.75602	24
37	.24423	.42963	.75577	23
38	.24448	.42978	.75552	22
39	.24473	.42993	.75527	21
40	.24498	.43007	.75502	20
41	.24523	.43022	.75477	19
42	.24548	.43037	.75452	18
43	.24573	.43052	.75427	17
44	.24598	.43067	.75402	16
45	.24623	.43081	.75377	15
46	.24648	.43096	.75352	14
47	.24673	.43111	.75327	13
48	.24698	.43126	.75302	12
49	.24723	.43140	.75277	11
50	.24749	.43155	.75251	10
51	.24774	.43170	.75226	9
52	.24799	.43184	.75201	8
53	.24824	.43199	.75176	7
54	.24849	.43214	.75151	6
55	.24874	.43228	.75126	5
56	.24899	.43243	.75101	4
57	.24924	.43258	.75076	3
58	.24950	.43272	.75050	2
59	.24975	.43287	.75025	1
60	.25000	.43301	.75000	0
′	Cos²	Sin · Cos	Sin²	′

SQUARE OF THE SINE AND COSINE
AND THEIR PRODUCT (Continued)

30° (210°)   (329°) **149°**   31° (211°)   (328°) **148°**

′	Sin²	Sin · Cos	Cos²	′		′	Sin²	Sin · Cos	Cos²	′
0	.25000	.43501	.75000	**60**		**0**	.26526	.44147	.73474	**60**
1	.25025	.43316	.74975	59		1	.26552	.44161	.73448	59
2	.25050	.43330	.74950	58		2	.26578	.44175	.73422	58
3	.25076	.43345	.74924	57		3	.26604	.44188	.73396	57
4	.25101	.43359	.74899	56		4	.26629	.44202	.73371	56
5	.25126	.43374	.74874	**55**		**5**	.26655	.44215	.73345	**55**
6	.25151	.43388	.74849	54		6	.26681	.44229	.73319	54
7	.25177	.43403	.74823	53		7	.26706	.44243	.73294	53
8	.25202	.43417	.74798	52		8	.26732	.44256	.73268	52
9	.25227	.43432	.74773	51		9	.26758	.44270	.73242	51
10	.25252	.43446	.74748	**50**		**10**	.26784	.44283	.73216	**50**
11	.25278	.43460	.74722	49		11	.26809	.44297	.73191	49
12	.25303	.43475	.74697	48		12	.26835	.44310	.73165	48
13	.25328	.43489	.74672	47		13	.26861	.44324	.73139	47
14	.25354	.43503	.74646	46		14	.26887	.44337	.73113	46
15	.25379	.43518	.74621	**45**		**15**	.26913	.44351	.73087	**45**
16	.25404	.43532	.74596	44		16	.26938	.44364	.73062	44
17	.25429	.43546	.74571	43		17	.26964	.44377	.73036	43
18	.25455	.43561	.74545	42		18	.26990	.44391	.73010	42
19	.25480	.43575	.74520	41		19	.27016	.44404	.72984	41
20	.25506	.43589	.74494	**40**		**20**	.27042	.44418	.72958	**40**
21	.25531	.43603	.74469	39		21	.27068	.44431	.72932	39
22	.25556	.43618	.74444	38		22	.27093	.44444	.72907	38
23	.25582	.43632	.74418	37		23	.27119	.44458	.72881	37
24	.25607	.43646	.74393	36		24	.27145	.44471	.72855	36
25	.25632	.43660	.74368	**35**		**25**	.27171	.44484	.72829	**35**
26	.25658	.43674	.74342	34		26	.27197	.44497	.72803	34
27	.25683	.43689	.74317	33		27	.27223	.44511	.72777	33
28	.25709	.43703	.74291	32		28	.27249	.44524	.72751	32
29	.25734	.43717	.74266	31		29	.27275	.44537	.72725	31
30	.25760	.43731	.74240	**30**		**30**	.27300	.44550	.72700	**30**
31	.25785	.43745	.74215	29		31	.27326	.44564	.72674	29
32	.25810	.43759	.74190	28		32	.27352	.44577	.72648	28
33	.25836	.43773	.74164	27		33	.27378	.44590	.72622	27
34	.25861	.43787	.74139	26		34	.27404	.44603	.72596	26
35	.25887	.43801	.74113	**25**		**35**	.27430	.44616	.72570	**25**
36	.25912	.43815	.74088	24		36	.27456	.44629	.72544	24
37	.25938	.43829	.74062	23		37	.27482	.44642	.72518	23
38	.25963	.43843	.74037	22		38	.27508	.44655	.72492	22
39	.25989	.43857	.74011	21		39	.27534	.44669	.72466	21
40	.26014	.43871	.73986	**20**		**40**	.27560	.44682	.72440	**20**
41	.26040	.43885	.73960	19		41	.27586	.44695	.72414	19
42	.26065	.43899	.73935	18		42	.27612	.44708	.72388	18
43	.26091	.43913	.73909	17		43	.27638	.44721	.72362	17
44	.26117	.43927	.73883	16		44	.27664	.44734	.72336	16
45	.26142	.43941	.73858	**15**		**45**	.27690	.44747	.72310	**15**
46	.26168	.43955	.73832	14		46	.27716	.44760	.72284	14
47	.26193	.43969	.73807	13		47	.27742	.44773	.72258	13
48	.26219	.43982	.73781	12		48	.27768	.44786	.72232	12
49	.26244	.43996	.73756	11		49	.27794	.44799	.72206	11
50	.26270	.44010	.73730	**10**		**50**	.27820	.44811	.72180	**10**
51	.26296	.44024	.73704	9		51	.27846	.44824	.72154	9
52	.26321	.44038	.73679	8		52	.27873	.44837	.72127	8
53	.26347	.44051	.73653	7		53	.27899	.44850	.72101	7
54	.26372	.44065	.73628	6		54	.27925	.44863	.72075	6
55	.26398	.44079	.73602	**5**		**55**	.27951	.44876	.72049	**5**
56	.26424	.44093	.73576	4		56	.27977	.44889	.72023	4
57	.26449	.44106	.73551	3		57	.28003	.44901	.71997	3
58	.26475	.44120	.73525	2		58	.28029	.44914	.71971	2
59	.26501	.44134	.73499	1		59	.28055	.44927	.71945	1
60	.26526	.44147	.73474	**0**		**60**	.28081	.44940	.71919	**0**
′	Cos²	Sin · Cos	Sin²	′		′	Cos²	Sin · Cos	Sin²	′

120° (300°)   (239°) **59°**   121° (301°)   (238°) **58°**

SQUARE OF THE SINE AND COSINE
AND THEIR PRODUCT (Continued)

32° (212°)   (327°) **147°**

′	Sin²	Sin · Cos	Cos²	′
0	.28081	.44940	.71919	**60**
1	.28108	.44952	.71892	59
2	.28134	.44965	.71866	58
3	.28160	.44978	.71840	57
4	.28186	.44991	.71814	56
5	.28212	.45003	.71788	**55**
6	.28228	.45016	.71762	54
7	.28265	.45029	.71735	53
8	.28291	.45041	.71709	52
9	.28317	.45054	.71683	51
10	.28343	.45066	.71657	**50**
11	.28369	.45079	.71631	49
12	.28396	.45092	.71604	48
13	.28422	.45104	.71578	47
14	.28448	.45117	.71552	46
15	.28474	.45129	.71526	**45**
16	.28501	.45142	.71499	44
17	.28527	.45154	.71473	43
18	.28553	.45167	.71447	42
19	.28580	.45179	.71420	41
20	.28606	.45192	.71394	**40**
21	.28632	.45204	.71368	39
22	.28658	.45217	.71342	38
23	.28685	.45229	.71315	37
24	.28711	.45241	.71289	36
25	.28737	.45254	.71263	**35**
26	.28764	.45266	.71236	34
27	.28790	.45278	.71210	33
28	.28816	.45291	.71184	32
29	.28843	.45303	.71157	31
30	.28869	.45315	.71131	**30**
31	.28895	.45328	.71105	29
32	.28922	.45340	.71078	28
33	.28948	.45352	.71052	27
34	.28975	.45364	.71025	26
35	.29001	.45377	.70999	**25**
36	.29027	.45389	.70973	24
37	.29054	.45401	.70946	23
38	.29080	.45413	.70920	22
39	.29107	.45425	.70893	21
40	.29133	.45438	.70867	**20**
41	.29160	.45450	.70840	19
42	.29186	.45462	.70814	18
43	.29212	.45474	.70788	17
44	.29239	.45486	.70761	16
45	.29265	.45498	.70735	**15**
46	.29292	.45510	.70708	14
47	.29318	.45522	.70682	13
48	.29345	.45534	.70655	12
49	.29371	.45546	.70629	11
50	.29398	.45558	.70602	**10**
51	.29424	.45570	.70576	9
52	.29451	.45582	.70549	8
53	.29477	.45594	.70523	7
54	.29504	.45606	.70496	6
55	.29530	.45618	.70470	**5**
56	.29557	.45630	.70443	4
57	.29583	.45642	.70417	3
58	.29610	.45654	.70390	2
59	.29637	.45665	.70363	1
60	.29663	.45677	.70337	**0**
′	Cos²	Sin · Cos	Sin²	′

122° (302°)   (237°) **57°**

33° (213°)   (326°) **146°**

′	Sin²	Sin · Cos	Cos²	′
0	.29663	.45677	.70337	**60**
1	.29690	.45689	.70310	59
2	.29716	.45701	.70284	58
3	.29743	.45713	.70257	57
4	.29770	.45724	.70230	56
5	.29796	.45736	.70204	**55**
6	.29823	.45748	.70177	54
7	.29849	.45760	.70151	53
8	.29876	.45771	.70124	52
9	.29903	.45783	.70097	51
10	.29929	.45795	.70071	**50**
11	.29956	.45806	.70044	49
12	.29983	.45818	.70017	48
13	.30009	.45830	.69991	47
14	.30036	.45841	.69964	46
15	.30063	.45853	.69937	**45**
16	.30089	.45865	.69911	44
17	.30116	.45876	.69884	43
18	.30143	.45888	.69857	42
19	.30169	.45899	.69831	41
20	.30196	.45911	.69804	**40**
21	.30223	.45922	.69777	39
22	.30249	.45934	.69751	38
23	.30276	.45945	.69724	37
24	.30303	.45957	.69697	36
25	.30330	.45968	.69670	**35**
26	.30356	.45980	.69644	34
27	.30383	.45991	.69617	33
28	.30410	.46002	.69590	32
29	.30437	.46014	.69563	31
30	.30463	.46025	.69537	**30**
31	.30490	.46037	.69510	29
32	.30517	.46048	.69483	28
33	.30544	.46059	.69456	27
34	.30571	.46071	.69429	26
35	.30597	.46082	.69403	**25**
36	.30624	.46093	.69376	24
37	.30651	.46104	.69349	23
38	.30678	.46116	.69322	22
39	.30705	.46127	.69295	21
40	.30732	.46138	.69268	**20**
41	.30758	.46149	.69242	19
42	.30785	.46161	.69215	18
43	.30812	.46172	.69188	17
44	.30839	.46183	.69161	16
45	.30866	.46194	.69134	**15**
46	.30893	.46205	.69107	14
47	.30920	.46216	.69080	13
48	.30946	.46227	.69054	12
49	.30973	.46238	.69027	11
50	.31000	.46249	.69000	**10**
51	.31027	.46260	.68973	9
52	.31054	.46272	.68946	8
53	.31081	.46283	.68919	7
54	.31108	.46294	.68892	6
55	.31135	.46305	.68865	**5**
56	.31162	.46315	.68838	4
57	.31189	.46326	.68811	3
58	.31216	.46337	.68784	2
59	.31243	.46348	.68757	1
60	.31270	.46359	.68730	**0**
′	Cos²	Sin · Cos	Sin²	′

123° (303°)   (236°) **56°**

SQUARE OF THE SINE AND COSINE
AND THEIR PRODUCT (Continued)

34° (214°) (325°) **145°**

'	Sin²	Sin · Cos	Cos²	'
0	.31270	.46359	.68730	60
1	.31297	.46370	.68703	59
2	.31324	.46381	.68676	58
3	.31351	.46392	.68649	57
4	.31378	.46403	.68622	56
5	.31405	.46413	.68595	55
6	.31432	.46424	.68568	54
7	.31459	.46435	.68541	53
8	.31486	.46446	.68514	52
9	.31513	.46457	.68487	51
10	.31540	.46467	.68460	50
11	.31567	.46478	.68433	49
12	.31594	.46489	.68406	48
13	.31621	.46500	.68379	47
14	.31648	.46510	.68352	46
15	.31675	.46521	.68325	45
16	.31702	.46532	.68298	44
17	.31729	.46542	.68271	43
18	.31756	.46553	.68244	42
19	.31783	.46563	.68217	41
20	.31810	.46574	.68190	40
21	.31837	.46585	.68163	39
22	.31865	.46595	.68135	38
23	.31892	.46606	.68108	37
24	.31919	.46616	.68081	36
25	.31946	.46627	.68054	35
26	.31973	.46637	.68027	34
27	.32000	.46648	.68000	33
28	.32027	.46658	.67973	32
29	.32054	.46669	.67946	31
30	.32082	.46679	.67918	30
31	.32109	.46689	.67891	29
32	.32136	.46700	.67864	28
33	.32163	.46710	.67837	27
34	.32190	.46721	.67810	26
35	.32217	.46731	.67783	25
36	.32245	.46741	.67755	24
37	.32272	.46752	.67728	23
38	.32299	.46762	.67701	22
39	.32326	.46772	.67674	21
40	.32353	.46782	.67647	20
41	.32381	.46793	.67619	19
42	.32408	.46803	.67592	18
43	.32435	.46813	.67565	17
44	.32462	.46823	.67538	16
45	.32490	.46834	.67510	15
46	.32517	.46844	.67483	14
47	.32544	.46854	.67456	13
48	.32571	.46864	.67429	12
49	.32599	.46874	.67401	11
50	.32626	.46884	.67374	10
51	.32653	.46894	.67347	9
52	.32681	.46905	.67319	8
53	.32708	.46915	.67292	7
54	.32735	.46925	.67265	6
55	.32762	.46935	.67238	5
56	.32790	.46945	.67210	4
57	.32817	.46955	.67183	3
58	.32844	.46965	.67156	2
59	.32872	.46975	.67128	1
60	.32899	.46985	.67101	0
'	Cos²	Sin · Cos	Sin²	'

124° (304°) (235°) **55°**

35° (215°) (324°) **144°**

'	Sin²	Sin · Cos	Cos²	'
0	.32899	.46985	.67101	60
1	.32926	.46995	.67074	59
2	.32954	.47004	.67046	58
3	.32981	.47014	.67019	57
4	.33008	.47024	.66992	56
5	.33036	.47034	.66964	55
6	.33063	.47044	.66937	54
7	.33090	.47054	.66910	53
8	.33118	.47064	.66882	52
9	.33145	.47074	.66855	51
10	.33173	.47083	.66827	50
11	.33200	.47093	.66800	49
12	.33227	.47103	.66773	48
13	.33255	.47113	.66745	47
14	.33282	.47122	.66718	46
15	.33310	.47132	.66690	45
16	.33337	.47142	.66663	44
17	.33365	.47151	.66635	43
18	.33392	.47161	.66608	42
19	.33419	.47171	.66581	41
20	.33447	.47180	.66553	40
21	.33474	.47190	.66526	39
22	.33502	.47200	.66498	38
23	.33529	.47209	.66471	37
24	.33557	.47219	.66443	36
25	.33584	.47228	.66416	35
26	.33612	.47238	.66388	34
27	.33639	.47247	.66361	33
28	.33667	.47257	.66333	32
29	.33694	.47266	.66306	31
30	.33722	.47276	.66278	30
31	.33749	.47285	.66251	29
32	.33777	.47295	.66223	28
33	.33804	.47304	.66196	27
34	.33832	.47314	.66168	26
35	.33859	.47323	.66141	25
36	.33887	.47332	.66113	24
37	.33914	.47342	.66086	23
38	.33942	.47351	.66058	22
39	.33969	.47361	.66031	21
40	.33997	.47370	.66003	20
41	.34024	.47379	.65976	19
42	.34052	.47388	.65948	18
43	.34080	.47398	.65920	17
44	.34107	.47407	.65893	16
45	.34135	.47416	.65865	15
46	.34162	.47425	.65838	14
47	.34190	.47435	.65810	13
48	.34218	.47444	.65782	12
49	.34245	.47453	.65755	11
50	.34273	.47462	.65727	10
51	.34300	.47471	.65700	9
52	.34328	.47480	.65672	8
53	.34356	.47490	.65644	7
54	.34383	.47499	.65617	6
55	.34411	.47508	.65589	5
56	.34439	.47517	.65561	4
57	.34466	.47526	.65534	3
58	.34494	.47535	.65506	2
59	.34521	.47544	.65479	1
60	.34549	.47553	.65451	0
'	Cos²	Sin · Cos	Sin²	'

125° (305°) (234°) **54°**

SQUARE OF THE SINE AND COSINE
AND THEIR PRODUCT (Continued)

36° (216°)   (323°) **143°**   **37° (217°)**   (322°) **142°**

′	Sin²	Sin · Cos	Cos²	′		′	Sin²	Sin · Cos	Cos²	′
0	.34549	.47553	.65451	60		0	.36218	.48063	.63782	60
1	.34577	.47562	.65423	59		1	.36246	.48071	.63754	59
2	.34604	.47571	.65396	58		2	.36274	.48079	.63726	58
3	.34632	.47580	.65368	57		3	.36302	.48087	.63698	57
4	.34660	.47589	.65340	56		4	.36330	.48095	.63670	56
5	.34688	.47598	.65312	55		5	.36358	.48103	.63642	55
6	.34715	.47606	.65285	54		6	.36386	.48111	.63614	54
7	.34743	.47615	.65257	53		7	.36414	.48119	.63586	53
8	.34771	.47624	.65229	52		8	.36442	.48127	.63558	52
9	.34798	.47633	.65202	51		9	.36470	.48135	.63530	51
10	.34826	.47642	.65174	50		10	.36498	.48142	.63502	50
11	.34854	.47651	.65146	49		11	.36526	.48150	.63474	49
12	.34882	.47660	.65118	48		12	.36554	.48158	.63446	48
13	.34909	.47668	.65091	47		13	.36582	.48166	.63418	47
14	.34937	.47677	.65063	46		14	.36610	.48174	.63390	46
15	.34965	.47686	.65035	45		15	.36638	.48182	.63362	45
16	.34992	.47695	.65008	44		16	.36666	.48189	.63334	44
17	.35020	.47703	.64980	43		17	.36694	.48197	.63306	43
18	.35048	.47712	.64952	42		18	.36722	.48205	.63278	42
19	.35076	.47721	.64924	41		19	.36750	.48212	.63250	41
20	.35103	.47729	.64897	40		20	.36778	.48220	.63222	40
21	.35131	.47738	.64869	39		21	.36806	.48228	.63194	39
22	.35159	.47747	.64841	38		22	.36834	.48236	.63166	38
23	.35187	.47755	.64813	37		23	.36862	.48243	.63138	37
24	.35215	.47764	.64785	36		24	.36891	.48251	.63109	36
25	.35242	.47773	.64758	35		25	.36919	.48258	.63081	35
26	.35270	.47781	.64730	34		26	.36947	.48266	.63053	34
27	.35298	.47790	.64702	33		27	.36975	.48274	.63025	33
28	.35326	.47798	.64674	32		28	.37003	.48281	.62997	32
29	.35354	.47807	.64646	31		29	.37031	.48289	.62969	31
30	.35381	.47815	.64619	30		30	.37059	.48296	.62941	30
31	.35409	.47824	.64591	29		31	.37087	.48304	.62913	29
32	.35437	.47832	.64563	28		32	.37115	.48311	.62885	28
33	.35465	.47841	.64535	27		33	.37143	.48319	.62857	27
34	.35493	.47849	.64507	26		34	.37171	.48326	.62829	26
35	.35521	.47858	.64479	25		35	.37200	.48334	.62800	25
36	.35548	.47866	.64452	24		36	.37228	.48341	.62772	24
37	.35576	.47874	.64424	23		37	.37256	.48349	.62744	23
38	.35604	.47883	.64396	22		38	.37284	.48356	.62716	22
39	.35632	.47891	.64368	21		39	.37312	.48363	.62688	21
40	.35660	.47899	.64340	20		40	.37340	.48371	.62660	20
41	.35688	.47908	.64312	19		41	.37368	.48378	.62632	19
42	.35716	.47916	.64284	18		42	.37397	.48385	.62603	18
43	.35743	.47924	.64257	17		43	.37425	.48393	.62575	17
44	.35771	.47933	.64229	16		44	.37453	.48400	.62547	16
45	.35799	.47941	.64201	15		45	.37481	.48407	.62519	15
46	.35827	.47949	.64173	14		46	.37509	.48415	.62491	14
47	.35855	.47957	.64145	13		47	.37537	.48422	.62463	13
48	.35883	.47966	.64117	12		48	.37566	.48429	.62434	12
49	.35911	.47974	.64089	11		49	.37594	.48436	.62406	11
50	.35939	.47982	.64061	10		50	.37622	.48444	.62378	10
51	.35967	.47990	.64033	9		51	.37650	.48451	.62350	9
52	.35995	.47998	.64005	8		52	.37678	.48458	.62322	8
53	.36023	.48007	.63977	7		53	.37706	.48465	.62294	7
54	.36050	.48015	.63950	6		54	.37735	.48472	.62265	6
55	.36078	.48023	.63922	5		55	.37763	.48479	.62237	5
56	.36106	.48031	.63894	4		56	.37791	.48487	.62209	4
57	.36134	.48039	.63866	3		57	.37819	.48494	.62181	3
58	.36162	.48047	.63838	2		58	.37847	.48501	.62153	2
59	.36190	.48055	.63810	1		59	.37876	.48508	.62124	1
60	.36218	.48063	.63782	0		60	.37904	.48515	.62096	0
′	Cos²	Sin · Cos	Sin²	′		′	Cos²	Sin · Cos	Sin²	′

126° (306°)   (233°) **53°**   **127° (307°)**   (232°) **52°**

SQUARE OF THE SINE AND COSINE
AND THEIR PRODUCT (Continued)

38° (218°)   **(321°) 141°**

'	Sin²	Sin · Cos	Cos²	'
0	.37904	.48515	.62096	60
1	.37932	.48522	.62068	59
2	.37960	.48529	.62040	58
3	.37989	.48536	.62011	57
4	.38017	.48543	.61983	56
5	.38045	.48550	.61955	55
6	.38073	.48557	.61927	54
7	.38102	.48564	.61898	53
8	.38130	.48571	.61870	52
9	.38158	.48577	.61842	51
10	.38186	.48584	.61814	50
11	.38215	.48591	.61785	49
12	.38243	.48598	.61757	48
13	.38271	.48605	.61729	47
14	.38299	.48612	.61701	46
15	.38328	.48618	.61672	45
16	.38356	.48625	.61644	44
17	.38384	.48632	.61616	43
18	.38413	.48639	.61587	42
19	.38441	.48646	.61559	41
20	.38469	.48652	.61531	40
21	.38498	.48659	.61502	39
22	.38526	.48666	.61474	38
23	.38554	.48672	.61446	37
24	.38582	.48679	.61418	36
25	.38611	.48686	.61389	35
26	.38639	.48692	.61361	34
27	.38667	.48699	.61333	33
28	.38696	.48705	.61304	32
29	.38724	.48712	.61276	31
30	.38752	.48719	.61248	30
31	.38781	.48725	.61219	29
32	.38809	.48732	.61191	28
33	.38837	.48738	.61163	27
34	.38866	.48745	.61134	26
35	.38894	.48751	.61106	25
36	.38923	.48757	.61077	24
37	.38951	.48764	.61049	23
38	.38979	.48770	.61021	22
39	.39008	.48777	.60992	21
40	.39036	.48783	.60964	20
41	.39064	.48789	.60936	19
42	.39093	.48796	.60907	18
43	.39121	.48802	.60879	17
44	.39150	.48808	.60850	16
45	.39178	.48815	.60822	15
46	.39206	.48821	.60794	14
47	.39235	.48827	.60765	13
48	.39263	.48834	.60737	12
49	.39292	.48840	.60708	11
50	.39320	.48846	.60680	10
51	.39348	.48852	.60652	9
52	.39377	.48858	.60623	8
53	.39405	.48865	.60595	7
54	.39434	.48871	.60566	6
55	.39462	.48877	.60538	5
56	.39491	.48883	.60509	4
57	.39519	.48889	.60481	3
58	.39548	.48895	.60452	2
59	.39576	.48901	.60424	1
60	.39604	.48907	.60396	0
'	Cos²	Sin · Cos	Sin²	'

128° (308°)   **(231°) 51°**

39° (219°)   **(320°) 140°**

'	Sin²	Sin · Cos	Cos²	'
0	.39604	.48907	.60396	60
1	.39633	.48913	.60367	59
2	.39661	.48919	.60339	58
3	.39690	.48925	.60310	57
4	.39718	.48931	.60282	56
5	.39747	.48937	.60253	55
6	.39775	.48943	.60225	54
7	.39804	.48949	.60196	53
8	.39832	.48955	.60168	52
9	.39861	.48961	.60139	51
10	.39889	.48967	.60111	50
11	.39918	.48973	.60082	49
12	.39946	.48979	.60054	48
13	.39975	.48985	.60025	47
14	.40003	.48990	.59997	46
15	.40032	.48996	.59968	45
16	.40060	.49002	.59940	44
17	.40089	.49008	.59911	43
18	.40117	.49014	.59883	42
19	.40146	.49019	.59854	41
20	.40174	.49025	.59826	40
21	.40203	.49031	.59797	39
22	.40231	.49036	.59769	38
23	.40260	.49042	.59740	37
24	.40288	.49048	.59712	36
25	.40317	.49053	.59683	35
26	.40345	.49059	.59655	34
27	.40374	.49065	.59626	33
28	.40402	.49070	.59598	32
29	.40431	.49076	.59569	31
30	.40460	.49081	.59540	30
31	.40488	.49087	.59512	29
32	.40517	.49092	.59483	28
33	.40545	.49098	.59455	27
34	.40574	.49103	.59426	26
35	.40602	.49109	.59398	25
36	.40631	.49114	.59369	24
37	.40660	.49120	.59340	23
38	.40688	.49125	.59312	22
39	.40717	.49131	.59283	21
40	.40745	.49136	.59255	20
41	.40774	.49141	.59226	19
42	.40802	.49147	.59198	18
43	.40831	.49152	.59169	17
44	.40860	.49157	.59140	16
45	.40888	.49163	.59112	15
46	.40917	.49168	.59083	14
47	.40945	.49173	.59055	13
48	.40974	.49179	.59026	12
49	.41003	.49184	.58997	11
50	.41031	.49189	.58969	10
51	.41060	.49194	.58940	9
52	.41089	.49199	.58911	8
53	.41117	.49205	.58883	7
54	.41146	.49210	.58854	6
55	.41174	.49215	.58826	5
56	.41203	.49220	.58797	4
57	.41232	.49225	.58768	3
58	.41260	.49230	.58740	2
59	.41289	.49235	.58711	1
60	.41318	.49240	.58682	0
'	Cos²	Sin · Cos	Sin²	'

129° (309°)   **(230°) 50°**

SQUARE OF THE SINE AND COSINE
AND THEIR PRODUCT (Continued)

40° (220°)   (319°) 139°   41° (221°)   (318°) 138°

′	Sin²	Sin · Cos	Cos²	′	′	Sin²	Sin · Cos	Cos²	′
0	.41318	.49240	.58682	60	0	.43041	.49513	.56959	60
1	.41346	.49245	.58654	59	1	.43070	.49517	.56930	59
2	.41375	.49250	.58625	58	2	.43099	.49521	.56901	58
3	.41404	.49255	.58596	57	3	.43128	.49525	.56872	57
4	.41432	.49260	.58568	56	4	.43157	.49529	.56843	56
5	.41461	.49265	.58539	55	5	.43185	.49533	.56815	55
6	.41490	.49270	.58510	54	6	.43214	.49537	.56786	54
7	.41518	.49275	.58482	53	7	.43243	.49541	.56757	53
8	.41547	.49280	.58453	52	8	.43272	.49545	.56728	52
9	.41576	.49285	.58424	51	9	.43301	.49549	.56699	51
10	.41604	.49290	.58396	50	10	.43330	.49553	.56670	50
11	.41633	.49295	.58367	49	11	.43358	.49557	.56642	49
12	.41662	.49300	.58338	48	12	.43387	.49561	.56613	48
13	.41690	.49305	.58310	47	13	.43416	.49565	.56584	47
14	.41719	.49309	.58281	46	14	.43445	.49568	.56555	46
15	.41748	.49314	.58252	45	15	.43474	.49572	.56526	45
16	.41776	.49319	.58224	44	16	.43503	.49576	.56497	44
17	.41805	.49324	.58195	43	17	.43531	.49580	.56469	43
18	.41834	.49329	.58166	42	18	.43560	.49584	.56440	42
19	.41862	.49333	.58138	41	19	.43589	.49587	.56411	41
20	.41891	.49338	.58109	40	20	.43618	.49591	.56382	40
21	.41920	.49343	.58080	39	21	.43647	.49595	.56353	39
22	.41949	.49347	.58051	38	22	.43676	.49598	.56324	38
23	.41977	.49352	.58023	37	23	.43704	.49602	.56296	37
24	.42006	.49357	.57994	36	24	.43733	.49606	.56267	36
25	.42035	.49361	.57965	35	25	.43762	.49609	.56238	35
26	.42063	.49366	.57937	34	26	.43791	.49613	.56209	34
27	.42092	.49371	.57908	33	27	.43820	.49617	.56180	33
28	.42121	.49375	.57879	32	28	.43849	.49620	.56151	32
29	.42150	.49380	.57850	31	29	.43878	.49624	.56122	31
30	.42178	.49384	.57822	30	30	.43907	.49627	.56093	30
31	.42207	.49389	.57793	29	31	.43935	.49631	.56065	29
32	.42236	.49393	.57764	28	32	.43964	.49634	.56036	28
33	.42264	.49398	.57736	27	33	.43993	.49638	.56007	27
34	.42293	.49402	.57707	26	34	.44022	.49641	.55978	26
35	.42322	.49407	.57678	25	35	.44051	.49645	.55949	25
36	.42351	.49411	.57649	24	36	.44080	.49648	.55920	24
37	.42379	.49416	.57621	23	37	.44109	.49652	.55891	23
38	.42408	.49420	.57592	22	38	.44138	.49655	.55862	22
39	.42437	.49425	.57563	21	39	.44166	.49659	.55834	21
40	.42466	.49429	.57534	20	40	.44195	.49662	.55805	20
41	.42494	.49433	.57506	19	41	.44224	.49665	.55776	19
42	.42523	.49438	.57477	18	42	.44253	.49669	.55747	18
43	.42552	.49442	.57448	17	43	.44282	.49672	.55718	17
44	.42581	.49446	.57419	16	44	.44311	.49675	.55689	16
45	.42610	.49451	.57390	15	45	.44340	.49679	.55660	15
46	.42638	.49455	.57362	14	46	.44369	.49682	.55631	14
47	.42667	.49459	.57333	13	47	.44398	.49685	.55602	13
48	.42696	.49464	.57304	12	48	.44427	.49688	.55573	12
49	.42725	.49468	.57275	11	49	.44455	.49692	.55545	11
50	.42753	.49472	.57247	10	50	.44484	.49695	.55516	10
51	.42782	.49476	.57218	9	51	.44513	.49698	.55487	9
52	.42811	.49480	.57189	8	52	.44542	.49701	.55458	8
53	.42840	.49485	.57160	7	53	.44571	.49704	.55429	7
54	.42869	.49489	.57131	6	54	.44600	.49708	.55400	6
55	.42897	.49493	.57103	5	55	.44629	.49711	.55371	5
56	.42926	.49497	.57074	4	56	.44658	.49714	.55342	4
57	.42955	.49501	.57045	3	57	.44687	.49717	.55313	3
58	.42984	.49505	.57016	2	58	.44716	.49720	.55284	2
59	.43013	.49509	.56987	1	59	.44745	.49723	.55255	1
60	.43041	.49513	.56959	0	60	.44774	.49726	.55226	0
′	Cos²	Sin · Cos	Sin²	′	′	Cos²	Sin · Cos	Sin²	′

130° (310°)   (229°) 49°   131° (311°)   (228°) 48°

SQUARE OF THE SINE AND COSINE
AND THEIR PRODUCT (Continued)

42° (222°)   (317°) **137°**   **43° (223°)**   (316°) **136°**

′	Sin²	Sin · Cos	Cos²	′		′	Sin²	Sin · Cos	Cos²	′
0	.44774	.49726	.55226	60		0	.46512	.49878	.53488	60
1	.44803	.49729	.55197	59		1	.46541	.49880	.53459	59
2	.44831	.49732	.55169	58		2	.46570	.49882	.53430	58
3	.44860	.49735	.55140	57		3	.46599	.49884	.53401	57
4	.44889	.49738	.55111	56		4	.46628	.49886	.53372	56
5	.44918	.49741	.55082	55		5	.46657	.49888	.53343	55
6	.44947	.49744	.55053	54		6	.46686	.49890	.53314	54
7	.44976	.49747	.55024	53		7	.46715	.49892	.53285	53
8	.45005	.49750	.54995	52		8	.46744	.49894	.53256	52
9	.45034	.49753	.54966	51		9	.46773	.49896	.53227	51
10	.45063	.49756	.54937	50		10	.46802	.49898	.53198	50
11	.45092	.49759	.54908	49		11	.46831	.49900	.53169	49
12	.45121	.49761	.54879	48		12	.46860	.49901	.53140	48
13	.45150	.49764	.54850	47		13	.46890	.49903	.53110	47
14	.45179	.49767	.54821	46		14	.46919	.49905	.53081	46
15	.45208	.49770	.54792	45		15	.46948	.49907	.53052	45
16	.45237	.49773	.54763	44		16	.46977	.49909	.53023	44
17	.45266	.49775	.54734	43		17	.47006	.49910	.52994	43
18	.45295	.49778	.54705	42		18	.47035	.49912	.52965	42
19	.45324	.49781	.54676	41		19	.47064	.49914	.52936	41
20	.45353	.49784	.54647	40		20	.47093	.49915	.52907	40
21	.45381	.49786	.54619	39		21	.47122	.49917	.52878	39
22	.45410	.49789	.54590	38		22	.47151	.49919	.52849	38
23	.45439	.49792	.54561	37		23	.47180	.49920	.52820	37
24	.45468	.49794	.54532	36		24	.47209	.49922	.52791	36
25	.45497	.49797	.54503	35		25	.47238	.49924	.52762	35
26	.45526	.49799	.54474	34		26	.47267	.49925	.52733	34
27	.45555	.49802	.54445	33		27	.47296	.49927	.52704	33
28	.45584	.49805	.54416	32		28	.47325	.49928	.52675	32
29	.45613	.49807	.54387	31		29	.47354	.49930	.52646	31
30	.45642	.49810	.54358	30		30	.47383	.49931	.52617	30
31	.45671	.49812	.54329	29		31	.47412	.49933	.52588	29
32	.45700	.49815	.54300	28		32	.47441	.49934	.52559	28
33	.45729	.49817	.54271	27		33	.47470	.49936	.52530	27
34	.45758	.49820	.54242	26		34	.47499	.49937	.52501	26
35	.45787	.49822	.54213	25		35	.47528	.49939	.52472	25
36	.45816	.49825	.54184	24		36	.47558	.49940	.52442	24
37	.45845	.49827	.54155	23		37	.47587	.49942	.52413	23
38	.45874	.49829	.54126	22		38	.47616	.49943	.52384	22
39	.45903	.49832	.54097	21		39	.47645	.49944	.52355	21
40	.45932	.49834	.54068	20		40	.47674	.49946	.52326	20
41	.45961	.49837	.54039	19		41	.47703	.49947	.52297	19
42	.45990	.49839	.54010	18		42	.47732	.49949	.52268	18
43	.46019	.49841	.53981	17		43	.47761	.49950	.52239	17
44	.46048	.49844	.53952	16		44	.47790	.49951	.52210	16
45	.46077	.49846	.53923	15		45	.47819	.49952	.52181	15
46	.46106	.49848	.53894	14		46	.47848	.49954	.52152	14
47	.46135	.49850	.53865	13		47	.47877	.49955	.52123	13
48	.46164	.49853	.53836	12		48	.47906	.49956	.52094	12
49	.46193	.49855	.53807	11		49	.47935	.49957	.52065	11
50	.46222	.49857	.53778	10		50	.47964	.49959	.52036	10
51	.46251	.49859	.53749	9		51	.47993	.49960	.52007	9
52	.46280	.49861	.53720	8		52	.48022	.49961	.51978	8
53	.46309	.49864	.53691	7		53	.48052	.49962	.51948	7
54	.46338	.49866	.53662	6		54	.48081	.49963	.51919	6
55	.46367	.49868	.53633	5		55	.48110	.49964	.51890	5
56	.46396	.49870	.53604	4		56	.48139	.49965	.51861	4
57	.46425	.49872	.53575	3		57	.48168	.49966	.51832	3
58	.46454	.49874	.53546	2		58	.48197	.49967	.51803	2
59	.46483	.49876	.53517	1		59	.48226	.49969	.51774	1
60	.46512	.49878	.53488	0		60	.48255	.49970	.51745	0
′	Cos²	Sin · Cos	Sin²	′		′	Cos²	Sin · Cos	Sin²	′

132° (312°)   (227°) **47°**   **133° (313°)**   (226°) **46°**

SQUARE OF THE SINE AND COSINE
AND THEIR PRODUCT (Continued)

44° (224°)   (315°) 135°

′	Sin²	Sin · Cos	Cos²	′
0	.48255	.49970	.51745	**60**
1	.48284	.49971	.51716	59
2	.48313	.49972	.51687	58
3	.48342	.49973	.51658	57
4	.48371	.49973	.51629	56
5	.48400	.49974	.51600	**55**
6	.48429	.49975	.51571	54
7	.48459	.49976	.51541	53
8	.48488	.49977	.51512	52
9	.48517	.49978	.51483	51
10	.48546	.49979	.51454	**50**
11	.48575	.49980	.51425	49
12	.48604	.49981	.51396	48
13	.48633	.49981	.51367	47
14	.48662	.49982	.51338	46
15	.48691	.49983	.51309	**45**
16	.48720	.49984	.51280	44
17	.48749	.49984	.51251	43
18	.48778	.49985	.51222	42
19	.48807	.49986	.51193	41
20	.48837	.49986	.51163	**40**
21	.48866	.49987	.51134	39
22	.48895	.49988	.51105	38
23	.48924	.49988	.51076	37
24	.48953	.49989	.51047	36
25	.48982	.49990	.51018	**35**
26	.49011	.49990	.50989	34
27	.49040	.49991	.50960	33
28	.49069	.49991	.50931	32
29	.49098	.49992	.50902	31
30	.49127	.49992	.50873	**30**
31	.49156	.49993	.50844	29
32	.49186	.49993	.50814	28
33	.49215	.49994	.50785	27
34	.49244	.49994	50756	26
35	.49273	.49995	.50727	**25**
36	.49302	.49995	.50698	24
37	.49331	.49996	.50669	23
38	.49360	.49996	.50640	22
39	.49389	.49996	.50611	21
40	.49418	.49997	.50582	**20**
41	.49447	.49997	.50553	19
42	.49476	.49997	.50524	18
43	.49505	.49998	.50495	17
44	.49535	.49998	.50465	16
45	.49564	.49998	.50436	**15**
46	.49593	.49998	.50407	14
47	.49622	.49999	.50378	13
48	.49651	.49999	.50349	12
49	.49680	.49999	.50320	11
50	.49709	.49999	.50291	**10**
51	.49738	.49999	.50262	9
52	.49767	.49999	.50233	8
53	.49796	.50000	.50204	7
54	.49825	.50000	.50175	6
55	.49855	.50000	.50145	**5**
56	.49884	.50000	.50116	4
57	.49913	.50000	.50087	3
58	.49942	.50000	.50058	2
59	.49971	.50000	.50029	1
60	.50000	.50000	.50000	**0**
′	Cos²	Sin · Cos	Sin²	′

134° (314°)   (225°) 45°

HAVERSINES

The table that follows gives −values of $\frac{1}{2}(1 - \cos\theta)$ for angles between 0 and 180° are given to five significant figures. The five-place mantissas of the logarithms of the haversines are also given. The correct characteristic must be provided in each case.

The listed values of the haversines were derived from values which were computed to seven significant figures. The logarithms were independently derived from the more exact value of the haversines and are, therefore, in many cases not the exact value of the logarithm of the haversine as listed. This is notably true at the beginning of the table where the logarithm can be given with more exactness than the function.

Tables for Use in Trigonometry

HAVERSINES

hav $\theta = \frac{1}{2}$ vers $\theta = \frac{1}{2}(1 - \cos \theta) = \sin^2 \frac{1}{2}\theta$
hav $(-\theta) = $ hav θ
hav $(180° - \theta) = $ hav $(180° + \theta) = 1 - $ hav θ
Characteristics of the logarithms are omitted.

θ°	0' Value	Log	10' Value	Log	20' Value	Log	30' Value	Log	40' Value	Log	50' Value	Log
0	.00000	—	.00000	6.32539	.00001	6.92745	.00002	.27963	.00003	.52951	.00005	.72332
1	.00008	.88168	.00010	.01557	.00014	.13155	.00017	.23385	.00021	.32536	.00026	.40814
2	.00030	.48371	.00036	.55323	.00041	.61759	.00048	.67551	.00054	.73355	.00061	.78620
3	.00069	.83584	.00076	.88279	.00085	.92733	.00093	.96970	.00102	.01009	.00112	.04869
4	.00122	.08564	.00132	.12108	.00143	.15513	.00154	.18790	.00166	.21947	.00178	.24993
5	.00190	.27936	.00203	.30782	.00216	.33538	.00230	.36209	.00244	.38800	.00259	.41315
6	.00274	.43760	.00289	.46138	.00305	.48452	.00321	.50706	.00338	.52902	.00355	.55044
7	.00373	.57135	.00391	.59176	.00409	.61170	.00428	.63120	.00447	.65026	.00467	.66891
8	.00487	.68717	.00507	.70505	.00528	.72257	.00549	.73974	.00571	.75657	.00593	.77308
9	.00616	.78929	.00639	.80519	.00662	.82081	.00686	.83615	.00710	.85122	.00735	.86603
10	.00760	.88059	.00785	.89491	.00811	.90900	.00837	.92286	.00864	.93650	.00891	.94993
11	.00919	.96315	.00947	.97617	.00975	.98899	.01004	.00163	.01033	.01409	.01063	.02636
12	.01093	.03847	.01123	.05041	.01154	.06218	.01185	.07379	.01217	.08525	.01249	.09656
13	.01281	.10772	.01314	.11873	.01348	.12961	.01382	.14035	.01416	.15096	.01450	.16144
14	.01485	.17179	.01521	.18202	.01556	.19212	.01593	.20211	.01629	.21198	.01666	.22175
15	.01704	.23140	.01742	.24094	.01780	.25037	.01818	.25971	.01858	.26894	.01897	.27807
16	.01937	.28711	.01977	.29605	.02018	.30490	.02059	.31366	.02101	.32233	.02142	.33091
17	.02185	.33940	.02227	.34782	.02271	.35614	.02314	.36439	.02358	.37256	.02402	.38065
18	.02447	.38867	.02492	.39660	.02538	.40447	.02584	.41226	.02630	.41998	.02677	.42764
19	.02724	.43522	.02772	.44273	.02820	.45018	.02868	.45757	.02917	.46489	.02966	.47215
20	.03015	.47934	.03065	.48647	.03116	.49355	.03166	.50056	.03218	.50752	.03269	.51442
21	.03321	.52127	.03373	.52805	.03426	.53479	.03479	.54147	.03533	.54810	.03587	.55467
22	.03641	.56120	.03695	.56767	.03751	.57410	.03806	.58047	.03862	.58680	.03918	.59308
23	.03975	.59931	.04032	.60550	.04089	.61164	.04147	.61773	.04205	.62379	.04264	.62979
24	.04323	.63576	.04382	.64168	.04442	.64756	.04502	.65340	.04562	.65920	.04623	.66496
25	.04685	.67067	.04746	.67635	.04808	.68199	.04871	.68759	.04934	.69316	.04997	.69869
26	.05060	.70418	.05124	.70963	.05189	.71505	.05253	.72043	.05318	.72578	.05384	.73109
27	.05450	.73637	.05516	.74162	.05582	.74683	.05649	.75201	.05717	.75715	.05785	.76227
28	.05853	.76735	.05921	.77240	.05990	.77742	.06059	.78241	.06129	.78737	.06199	.79230
29	.06269	.79720	.06340	.80207	.06411	.80691	.06482	.81172	.06554	.81651	.06626	.82126
30	.06699	.82599	.06772	.83069	.06845	.83537	.06919	.84001	.06993	.84464	.07067	.84923
31	.07142	.85380	.07217	.85834	.07292	.86286	.07368	.86735	.07444	.87182	.07521	.87626
32	.07598	.88068	.07675	.88507	.07752	.88944	.07830	.89379	.07909	.89811	.07987	.90241
33	.08066	.90668	.08146	.91094	.08226	.91517	.08306	.91938	.08386	.92356	.08467	.92773
34	.08548	.93187	.08630	.93599	.08711	.94009	.08794	.94417	.08876	.94823	.08959	.95227
35	.09042	.95628	.09126	.96028	.09210	.96426	.09294	.96821	.09379	.97215	.09464	.97607
36	.09549	.97996	.09635	.98384	.09721	.98770	.09807	.99154	.09894	.99536	.09981	.99917
37	.10068	.00295	.10156	.00672	.10244	.01047	.10332	.01420	.10421	.01791	.10510	.02161
38	.10599	.02528	.10689	.02894	.10779	.03259	.10870	.03621	.10960	.03982	.11051	.04341
39	.11143	.04699	.11234	.05055	.11326	.05409	.11419	.05762	.11511	.06113	.11604	.06462
40	.11698	.06810	.11791	.07157	.11885	.07501	.11980	.07845	.12074	.08186	.12169	.08526
41	.12265	.08865	.12360	.09202	.12456	.09538	.12552	.09872	.12649	.10205	.12746	.10536
42	.12843	.10866	.12940	.11194	.13038	.11521	.13136	.11847	.13235	.12171	.13333	.12494
43	.13432	.12815	.13532	.13135	.13631	.13454	.13731	.13771	.13832	.14087	.13932	.14402
44	.14033	.14715	.14134	.15027	.14236	.15338	.14337	.15647	.14440	.15955	.14542	.16262
45	.14645	.16568	.14748	.16872	.14851	.17175	.14955	.17477	.15058	.17778	.15163	.18077
46	.15267	.18376	.15372	.18673	.15477	.18968	.15582	.19263	.15688	.19557	.15794	.19849
47	.15900	.20140	.16007	.20430	.16113	.20719	.16220	.21006	.16328	.21293	.16436	.21578
48	.16543	.21863	.16652	.22146	.16760	.22428	.16869	.22709	.16978	.22989	.17087	.23268
49	.17197	.23545	.17307	.23822	.17417	.24098	.17528	.24372	.17638	.24646	.17749	.24918
50	.17861	.25190	.17972	.25460	.18084	.25729	.18196	.25998	.18308	.26265	.18421	.26532
51	.18534	.26797	.18647	.27061	.18761	.27325	.18874	.27587	.18988	.27848	.19102	.28109
52	.19217	.28368	.19332	.28627	.19447	.28885	.19562	.29141	.19677	.29397	.19793	.29652
53	.19909	.29905	.20026	.30158	.20142	.30410	.20259	.30662	.20376	.30912	.20493	.31161
54	.20611	.31409	.20729	.31657	.20847	.31903	.20965	.32149	.21083	.32394	.21202	.32638
55	.21321	.32881	.21440	.33123	.21560	.33365	.21680	.33605	.21800	.33845	.21920	.34084
56	.22040	.34322	.22161	.34559	.22282	.34795	.22403	.35031	.22525	.35266	.22646	.35499
57	.22768	.35733	.22890	.35965	.23012	.36196	.23135	.36427	.23258	.36657	.23381	.36886
58	.23504	.37114	.23627	.37342	.23751	.37569	.23875	.37794	.23999	.38020	.24124	.38244
59	.24248	.38468	.24373	.38691	.24498	.38913	.24623	.39134	.24749	.39355	.24874	.39575
60	.25000	.39794	.25126	.40012	.25252	.40230	.25379	.40447	.25506	.40663	.25632	.40879

HAVERSINES (Continued)

Characteristics of the logarithms are omitted.

θ°	0' Value	Log	10' Value	Log	20' Value	Log	30' Value	Log	40' Value	Log	50' Value	Log
60	.25000	.39794	.25126	.40012	.25252	.40230	.25379	.40447	.25506	.40663	.25632	.40879
61	.25760	.41094	.25887	.41308	.26014	.41521	.26142	.41734	.26270	.41946	.26398	.42157
62	.26526	.42368	.26655	.42578	.26784	.42787	.26913	.42996	.27042	.43203	.27171	.43411
63	.27300	.43617	.27430	.43823	.27560	.44028	.27690	.44232	.27820	.44436	.27951	.44639
64	.28081	.44842	.28212	.45044	.28343	.45245	.28474	.45446	.28606	.45645	.28737	.45845
65	.28869	.46043	.29001	.46241	.29133	.46439	.29265	.46635	.29398	.46831	.29530	.47027
66	.29663	.47222	.29796	.47416	.29929	.47610	.30063	.47802	.30196	.47995	.30330	.48187
67	.30463	.48378	.30597	.48568	.30732	.48758	.30866	.48948	.31000	.49137	.31135	.49325
68	.31270	.49512	.31405	.49699	.31540	.49886	.31675	.50072	.31810	.50257	.31946	.50442
69	.32082	.50625	.32217	.50809	.32353	.50992	.32490	.51174	.32626	.51356	.32762	.51538
70	.32899	.51718	.33036	.51898	.33173	.52078	.33310	.52257	.33447	.52435	.33584	.52613
71	.33722	.52791	.33859	.52968	.33997	.53144	.34135	.53320	.34273	.53495	.34411	.53670
72	.34549	.53844	.34688	.54017	.34826	.54190	.34965	.54363	.35103	.54535	.35242	.54707
73	.35381	.54878	.35521	.55048	.35660	.55218	.35799	.55387	.35939	.55556	.36078	.55725
74	.36218	.55893	.36358	.56060	.36498	.56227	.36638	.56393	.36778	.56559	.36919	.56725
75	.37059	.56889	.37200	.57054	.37340	.57218	.37481	.57381	.37622	.57544	.37763	.57706
76	.37904	.57868	.38045	.58030	.38186	.58191	.38328	.58351	.38469	.58511	.38611	.58671
77	.38752	.58830	.38894	.58988	.39036	.59147	.39178	.59304	.39320	.59461	.39462	.59618
78	.39604	.59774	.39747	.59929	.39889	.60085	.40032	.60240	.40174	.60395	.40317	.60549
79	.40460	.60702	.40602	.60855	.40745	.61008	.40888	.61160	.41031	.61311	.41174	.61463
80	.41318	.61613	.41461	.61764	.41604	.61914	.41748	.62063	.41891	.62212	.42035	.62361
81	.42178	.62509	.42322	.62657	.42466	.62804	.42610	.62951	.42753	.63097	.42897	.63243
82	.43041	.63389	.43185	.63534	.43330	.63678	.43474	.63823	.43618	.63966	.43762	.64110
83	.43907	.64253	.44051	.64395	.44195	.64538	.44340	.64679	.44484	.64821	.44629	.64962
84	.44774	.65102	.44918	.65242	.45063	.65382	.45208	.65521	.45353	.65660	.45497	.65799
85	.45642	.65937	.45787	.66074	.45932	.66212	.46077	.66348	.46222	.66485	.46367	.66621
86	.46512	.66757	.46657	.66892	.46802	.67027	.46948	.67161	.47093	.67295	.47238	.67429
87	.47383	.67562	.47528	.67695	.47674	.67828	.47819	.67960	.47964	.68092	.48110	.68223
88	.48255	.68354	.48400	.68485	.48546	.68615	.48691	.68745	.48837	.68874	.48982	.69004
89	.49127	.69132	.49273	.69261	.49418	.69389	.49564	.69516	.49709	.69644	.49855	.69770
90	.50000	.69897	.50145	.70023	.50291	.70149	.50436	.70274	.50582	.70399	.50727	.70524
91	.50873	.70648	.51018	.70772	.51163	.70896	.51309	.71019	.51454	.71142	.51600	.71265
92	.51745	.71387	.51890	.71509	.52036	.71630	.52181	.71751	.52326	.71872	.52472	.71992
93	.52617	.72112	.52762	.72232	.52907	.72352	.53052	.72471	.53198	.72589	.53343	.72708
94	.53488	.72825	.53633	.72943	.53778	.73060	.53923	.73177	.54068	.73294	.54213	.73410
95	.54358	.73526	.54503	.73642	.54647	.73757	.54792	.73872	.54937	.73987	.55082	.74101
96	.55226	.74215	.55371	.74328	.55516	.74442	.55660	.74554	.55805	.74667	.55949	.74779
97	.56093	.74891	.56238	.75003	.56382	.75114	.56526	.75225	.56670	.75336	.56815	.75446
98	.56959	.75556	.57103	.75666	.57247	.75775	.57390	.75884	.57534	.75993	.57678	.76101
99	.57822	.76209	.57965	.76317	.58109	.76424	.58252	.76531	.58396	.76638	.58539	.76745
100	.58682	.76851	.58826	.76957	.58969	.77062	.59112	.77167	.59255	.77272	.59398	.77377
101	.59540	.77481	.59683	.77585	.59826	.77689	.59968	.77792	.60111	.77895	.60253	.77998
102	.60396	.78101	.60538	.78203	.60680	.78305	.60822	.78406	.60964	.78507	.61106	.78608
103	.61248	.78709	.61389	.78809	.61531	.78909	.61672	.79009	.61814	.79108	.61955	.79208
104	.62096	.79306	.62237	.79405	.62378	.79503	.62519	.79601	.62660	.79699	.62800	.79796
105	.62941	.79893	.63081	.79990	.63222	.80087	.63362	.80183	.63502	.80279	.63642	.80374
106	.63782	.80470	.63922	.80565	.64061	.80660	.64201	.80754	.64340	.80848	.64479	.80942
107	.64619	.81036	.64758	.81129	.64897	.81222	.65035	.81315	.65174	.81407	.65312	.81500
108	.65451	.81592	.65589	.81683	.65727	.81775	.65865	.81866	.66003	.81956	.66141	.82047
109	.66278	.82137	.66416	.82227	.66553	.82317	.66690	.82406	.66827	.82495	.66964	.82584
110	.67101	.82673	.67238	.82761	.67374	.82849	.67510	.82937	.67647	.83025	.67783	.83112
111	.67918	.83199	.68054	.83285	.68190	.83372	.68325	.83458	.68460	.83544	.68595	.83629
112	.68730	.83715	.68865	.83800	.69000	.83885	.69134	.83969	.69268	.84054	.69403	.84138
113	.69537	.84221	.69670	.84305	.69804	.84388	.69937	.84471	.70071	.84554	.70204	.84636
114	.70337	.84718	.70470	.84800	.70602	.84882	.70735	.84963	.70867	.85044	.70999	.85125
115	.71131	.85206	.71263	.85286	.71394	.85366	.71526	.85446	.71657	.85526	.71788	.85605
116	.71919	.85684	.72049	.85763	.72180	.85841	.72310	.85920	.72440	.85998	.72570	.86076
117	.72700	.86153	.72829	.86230	.72958	.86307	.73087	.86384	.73216	.86461	.73345	.86537
118	.73474	.86613	.73602	.86689	.73730	.86764	.73858	.86840	.73986	.86915	.74113	.86990
119	.74240	.87064	.74368	.87138	.74494	.87212	.74621	.87286	.74748	.87360	.74874	.87433
120	.75000	.87506	.75126	.87579	.75251	.87652	.75377	.87724	.75502	.87796	.75627	.87868

HAVERSINES (Continued)

Characteristics of the logarithms are omitted.

$\theta°$	0' Value	Log	10' Value	Log	20' Value	Log	30' Value	Log	40' Value	Log	50' Value	Log
120	.75000	.87506	.75126	.87579	.75251	.87652	.75377	.87724	.75502	.87796	.75627	.87868
121	.75752	.87939	.75876	.88011	.76001	.88082	.76125	.88153	.76249	.88223	.76373	.88294
122	.76496	.88364	.76619	.88434	.76742	.88503	.76865	.88573	.76988	.88642	.77110	.88711
123	.77232	.88780	.77354	.88848	.77475	.88916	.77597	.88984	.77718	.89052	.77839	.89120
124	.77960	.89187	.78080	.89254	.78200	.89321	.78320	.89387	.78440	.89454	.78560	.89520
125	.78679	.89586	.78798	.89651	.78917	.89717	.79035	.89782	.79153	.89847	.79271	.89912
126	.79389	.89976	.79507	.90040	.79624	.90104	.79741	.90168	.79858	.90232	.79974	.90295
127	.80091	.90358	.80207	.90421	.80323	.90484	.80438	.90546	.80553	.90608	.80668	.90670
128	.80783	.90732	.80898	.90794	.81012	.90855	.81126	.90916	.81239	.90977	.81353	.91037
129	.81466	.91098	.81579	.91158	.81692	.91218	.81804	.91277	.81916	.91337	.82028	.91396
130	.82139	.91455	.82251	.91514	.82362	.91573	.82472	.91631	.82583	.91689	.82693	.91747
131	.82803	.91805	.82913	.91862	.83022	.91919	.83131	.91976	.83240	.92033	.83348	.92090
132	.83457	.92146	.83564	.92202	.83672	.92258	.83780	.92314	.83887	.92369	.83993	.92425
133	.84100	.92480	.84206	.92534	.84312	.92589	.84418	.92643	.84523	.92698	.84628	.92751
134	.84733	.92805	.84837	.92859	.84942	.92912	.85045	.92965	.85149	.93018	.85252	.93071
135	.85355	.93123	.85458	.93175	.85560	.93227	.85663	.93279	.85764	.93331	.85866	.93382
136	.85967	.93433	.86068	.93484	.86168	.93535	.86269	.93585	.86369	.93636	.86468	.93686
137	.86568	.93736	.86667	.93785	.86765	.93835	.86864	.93884	.86962	.93933	.87060	.93982
138	.87157	.94030	.87254	.94079	.87351	.94127	.87448	.94175	.87544	.94223	.87640	.94270
139	.87735	.94318	.87831	.94365	.87926	.94412	.88020	.94458	.88115	.94505	.88209	.94551
140	.88302	.94597	.88396	.94643	.88489	.94689	.88581	.94734	.88674	.94779	.88766	.94824
141	.88857	.94869	.88949	.94914	.89040	.94958	.89130	.95003	.89221	.95047	.89311	.95091
142	.89401	.95134	.89490	.95177	.89579	.95221	.89668	.95264	.89756	.95306	.89844	.95349
143	.89932	.95391	.90019	.95433	.90106	.95475	.90193	.95517	.90279	.95559	.90365	.95600
144	.90451	.95641	.90536	.95682	.90621	.95723	.90706	.95763	.90790	.95804	.90874	.95844
145	.90958	.95884	.91041	.95924	.91124	.95963	.91206	.96002	.91289	.96042	.91370	.96081
146	.91452	.96119	.91533	.96158	.91614	.96196	.91694	.96234	.91774	.96272	.91854	.96310
147	.91934	.96347	.92013	.96385	.92091	.96422	.92170	.96459	.92248	.96495	.92325	.96532
148	.92402	.96568	.92479	.96604	.92556	.96640	.92632	.96676	.92708	.96712	.92783	.96747
149	.92858	.96782	.92933	.96817	.93007	.96852	.93081	.96886	.93155	.96921	.93228	.96955
150	.93301	.96989	.93374	.97023	.93446	.97056	.93518	.97089	.93589	.97123	.93660	.97156
151	.93731	.97188	.93801	.97221	.93871	.97253	.93941	.97285	.94010	.97317	.94079	.97349
152	.94147	.97381	.94215	.97412	.94283	.97443	.94351	.97475	.94418	.97505	.94484	.97536
153	.94550	.97566	.94616	.97597	.94682	.97627	.94747	.97656	.94811	.97686	.94876	.97716
154	.94940	.97745	.95003	.97774	.95066	.97803	.95129	.97831	.95194	.97861	.95254	.97888
155	.95315	.97916	.95377	.97944	.95438	.97972	.95498	.97999	.95558	.98027	.95618	.98054
156	.95677	.98081	.95736	.98107	.95795	.98134	.95853	.98161	.95911	.98187	.95968	.98213
157	.96025	.98239	.96082	.98264	.96138	.98290	.96194	.98315	.96249	.98340	.96305	.98365
158	.96359	.98389	.96413	.98414	.96467	.98438	.96521	.98462	.96574	.98486	.96627	.98510
159	.96679	.98533	.96731	.98557	.96782	.98580	.96834	.98603	.96884	.98625	.96935	.98648
160	.96985	.98670	.97034	.98692	.97083	.98714	.97132	.98736	.97180	.98758	.97228	.98779
161	.97276	.98801	.97323	.98822	.97370	.98842	.97416	.98863	.97462	.98884	.97508	.98904
162	.97553	.98924	.97598	.98944	.97642	.98964	.97686	.98983	.97729	.99003	.97773	.99022
163	.97815	.99041	.97858	.99059	.97899	.99078	.97941	.99096	.97982	.99115	.98023	.99133
164	.98063	.99151	.98103	.99168	.98142	.99186	.98182	.99203	.98220	.99220	.98258	.99237
165	.98296	.99254	.98334	.99270	.98371	.99287	.98407	.99303	.98444	.99319	.98479	.99335
166	.98515	.99350	.98550	.99366	.98584	.99381	.98618	.99396	.98652	.99411	.98686	.99425
167	.98719	.99440	.98751	.99454	.98783	.99468	.98815	.99482	.98846	.99496	.98877	.99509
168	.98907	.99523	.98937	.99536	.98967	.99549	.98996	.99562	.99025	.99574	.99053	.99587
169	.99081	.99599	.99109	.99611	.99136	.99623	.99163	.99635	.99189	.99646	.99215	.99658
170	.99240	.99669	.99265	.99680	.99290	.99691	.99314	.99701	.99338	.99712	.99361	.99722
171	.99384	.99732	.99407	.99742	.99429	.99751	.99451	.99761	.99472	.99770	.99493	.99779
172	.99513	.99788	.99533	.99797	.99553	.99805	.99572	.99814	.99591	.99822	.99609	.99830
173	.99627	.99838	.99645	.99845	.99662	.99853	.99679	.99860	.99695	.99867	.99711	.99874
174	.99726	.99881	.99741	.99887	.99756	.99894	.99770	.99900	.99784	.99906	.99797	.99912
175	.99810	.99917	.99822	.99923	.99834	.99928	.99846	.99933	.99857	.99938	.99868	.99943
176	.99878	.99947	.99888	.99951	.99898	.99956	.99907	.99959	.99915	.99963	.99924	.99967
177	.99931	.99970	.99939	.99973	.99946	.99976	.99952	.99979	.99959	.99982	.99964	.99984
178	.99970	.99987	.99974	.99989	.99979	.99991	.99983	.99993	.99986	.99994	.99990	.99995
179	.99992	.99997	.99995	.99998	.99997	.99999	.99998	.99999	.99999	.00000	1.00000	.00000
180	1.00000	.00000										

HYPERBOLIC FUNCTIONS AND THEIR COMMON LOGARITHMS

The logarithms given below show the mantissa only. The proper characteristic must be added.

x	Sinh x		Cosh x		Tanh x		Coth x	
	Value	$\log_{10}$	Value	$\log_{10}$	Value	$\log_{10}$	Value	$\log_{10}$
0.00	0.00000	$-\infty$	1.00000	.00000	0.00000	$-\infty$	∞	∞
0.01	.01000	.00001	1.00005	.00002	.01000	.99999	100.003	.00001
0.02	.02000	.30106	1.00020	.00009	.02000	.30097	50.007	.69903
0.03	.03000	.47719	1.00045	.00020	.02999	.47699	33.343	.52301
0.04	.04001	.60218	1.00080	.00035	.03998	.60183	25.013	.39817
0.05	0.05002	.69915	1.00125	.00054	0.04996	.69861	20.017	.30139
0.06	.06004	.77841	1.00180	.00078	.05993	.77763	16.687	.22237
0.07	.07006	.84545	1.00245	.00106	.06989	.84439	14.309	.15561
0.08	.08009	.90355	1.00320	.00139	.07983	.90216	12.527	.09784
0.09	.09012	.95483	1.00405	.00176	.08976	.95307	11.141	.04693
0.10	0.10017	.00072	1.00500	.00217	0.09967	.99856	10.0333	.00144
0.11	.11022	.04227	1.00606	.00262	.10956	.03965	9.1275	.96035
0.12	.12029	.08022	1.00721	.00312	.11943	.07710	8.3733	.92290
0.13	.13037	.11517	1.00846	.00366	.12927	.11151	7.7356	.88849
0.14	.14046	.14755	1.00982	.00424	.13909	.14330	7.1895	.85670
0.15	0.15056	.17772	1.01127	.00487	0.14889	.17285	6.7166	.82715
0.16	.16068	.20597	1.01283	.00554	.15865	.20044	6.3032	.79956
0.17	.17082	.23254	1.01448	.00625	.16838	.22629	5.9389	.77371
0.18	.18097	.25762	1.01624	.00700	.17808	.25062	5.6154	.74938
0.19	.19115	.28136	1.01810	.00779	.18775	.27357	5.3263	.72643
0.20	0.20134	.30392	1.02007	.00863	0.19738	.29529	5.0665	.70471
0.21	.21155	.32541	1.02213	.00951	.20697	.31590	4.8317	.68410
0.22	.22178	.34592	1.02430	.01043	.21652	.33549	4.6186	.66451
0.23	.23203	.36555	1.02657	.01139	.22603	.35416	4.4242	.64584
0.24	.24231	.38437	1.02894	.01239	.23550	.37198	4.2464	.62802
0.25	0.25261	.40245	1.03141	.01343	0.24492	.38902	4.0830	.61098
0.26	.26294	.41986	1.03399	.01452	.25430	.40534	3.9324	.59466
0.27	.27329	.43663	1.03667	.01564	.26362	.42099	3.7933	.57901
0.28	.28367	.45282	1.03946	.01681	.27291	.43601	3.6643	.56399
0.29	.29408	.46847	1.04235	.01801	.28213	.45046	3.5444	.54954
0.30	0.30452	.48362	1.04534	.01926	0.29131	.46436	3.4327	.53564
0.31	.31499	.49830	1.04844	.02054	.30044	.47775	3.3285	.52225
0.32	.32549	.51254	1.05164	.02187	.30951	.49067	3.2309	.50933
0.33	.33602	.52637	1.05495	.02323	.31852	.50314	3.1395	.49686
0.34	.34659	.53981	1.05836	.02463	.32748	.51518	3.0536	.48482
0.35	0.35719	.55290	1.06188	.02607	0.33638	.52682	2.9729	.47318
0.36	.36783	.56564	1.06550	.02755	.34521	.53809	2.8968	.46191
0.37	.37850	.57807	1.06923	.02907	.35399	.54899	2.8249	.45101
0.38	.38921	.59019	1.07307	.03063	.36271	.55956	2.7570	.44044
0.39	.39996	.60202	1.07702	.03222	.37136	.56980	2.6928	.43020
0.40	0.41075	.61358	1.08107	.03385	0.37995	.57973	2.6319	.42027
0.41	.42158	.62488	1.08523	.03552	.38847	.58936	2.5742	.41064
0.42	.43246	.63594	1.08950	.03723	.39693	.59871	2.5193	.40129
0.43	.44337	.64677	1.09388	.03897	.40532	.60780	2.4672	.39220
0.44	.45434	.65738	1.09837	.04075	.41364	.61663	2.4175	.38337
0.45	0.46534	.66777	1.10297	.04256	0.42190	.62521	2.3702	.37479
0.46	.47640	.67797	1.10768	.04441	.43008	.63355	2.3251	.36645
0.47	.48750	.68797	1.11250	.04630	.43820	.64167	2.2821	.35833
0.48	.49865	.69779	1.11743	.04822	.44624	.64957	2.2409	.35043
0.49	.50984	.70744	1.12247	.05018	.45422	.65726	2.2016	.34274

HYPERBOLIC FUNCTIONS AND THEIR COMMON LOGARITHMS (Continued)

x	Sinh x		Cosh x		Tanh x		Coth x	
	Value	$\log_{10}$	Value	$\log_{10}$	Value	$\log_{10}$	Value	$\log_{10}$
0.50	0.52110	.71692	1.12763	.05217	0.46212	.66475	2.1640	.33525
0.51	.53240	.72624	1.13289	.05419	.46995	.67205	2.1279	.32795
0.52	.54375	.73540	1.13827	.05625	.47770	.67916	2.0934	.32084
0.53	.55516	.74442	1.14377	.05834	.48538	.68608	2.0602	.31392
0.54	.56663	.75330	1.14938	.06046	.49299	.69284	2.0284	.30716
0.55	0.57815	.76204	1.15510	.06262	0.50052	.69942	1.9979	.30058
0.56	.58973	.77065	1.16094	.06481	.50798	.70584	1.9686	.29416
0.57	.60137	.77914	1.16690	.06703	.51536	.71211	1.9404	.28789
0.58	.61307	.78751	1.17297	.06929	.52267	.71822	1.9133	.28178
0.59	.62483	.79576	1.17916	.07157	.52990	.72419	1.8872	.27581
0.60	0.63665	.80390	1.18547	.07389	0.53705	.73001	1.8620	.26999
0.61	.64854	.81194	1.19189	.07624	.54413	.73570	1.8378	.26430
0.62	.66049	.81987	1.19844	.07861	.55113	.74125	1.8145	.25875
0.63	.67251	.82770	1.20510	.08102	.55805	.74667	1.7919	.25333
0.64	.68459	.83543	1.21189	.08346	.56490	.75197	1.7702	.24803
0.65	0.69675	.84308	1.21879	.08593	0.57167	.75715	1.7493	.24285
0.66	.70897	.85063	1.22582	.08843	.57836	.76220	1.7290	.23780
0.67	.72126	.85809	1.23297	.09095	.58498	.76714	1.7095	.23286
0.68	.73363	.86548	1.24025	.09351	.59152	.77197	1.6906	.22803
0.69	.74607	.87278	1.24765	.09609	.59798	.77669	1.6723	.22331
0.70	0.75858	.88000	1.25517	.09870	0.60437	.78130	1.6546	.21870
0.71	.77117	.88715	1.26282	.10134	.61068	.78581	1.6375	.21419
0.72	.78384	.89423	1.27059	.10401	.61691	.79022	1.6210	.20978
0.73	.79659	.90123	1.27849	.10670	.62307	.79453	1.6050	.20547
0.74	.80941	.90817	1.28652	.10942	.62915	.79875	1.5895	.20125
0.75	0.82232	.91504	1.29468	.11216	0.63515	.80288	1.5744	.19712
0.76	.83530	.92185	1.30297	.11493	.64108	.80691	1.5599	.19309
0.77	.84838	.92859	1.31139	.11773	.64693	.81086	1.5458	.18914
0.78	.86153	.93527	1.31994	.12055	.65271	.81472	1.5321	.18528
0.79	.87478	.94190	1.32862	.12340	.65841	.81850	1.5188	.18150
0.80	0.88811	.94846	1.33743	.12627	0.66404	.82219	1.5059	.17781
0.81	.90152	.95498	1.34638	.12917	.66959	.82581	1.4935	.17419
0.82	.91503	.96144	1.35547	.13209	.67507	.82935	1.4813	.17065
0.83	.92863	.96784	1.36468	.13503	.68048	.83281	1.4696	.16719
0.84	.94233	.97420	1.37404	.13800	.68581	.83620	1.4581	.16380
0.85	0.95612	.98051	1.38353	.14099	0.69107	.83952	1.4470	.16048
0.86	.97000	.98677	1.39316	.14400	.69626	.84277	1.4362	.15723
0.87	.98398	.99299	1.40293	.14704	.70137	.84595	1.4258	.15405
0.88	.99806	.99916	1.41284	.15009	.70642	.84906	1.4156	.15094
0.89	1.01224	.00528	1.42289	.15317	.71139	.85211	1.4057	.14789
0.90	1.02652	.01137	1.43309	.15627	0.71630	.85509	1.3961	.14491
0.91	1.04090	.01741	1.44342	.15939	.72113	.85801	1.3867	.14199
0.92	1.05539	.02341	1.45390	.16254	.72590	.86088	1.3776	.13912
0.93	1.06998	.02937	1.46453	.16570	.73059	.86368	1.3687	.13632
0.94	1.08468	.03530	1.47530	.16888	.73522	.86642	1.3601	.13358
0.95	1.09948	.04119	1.48623	.17208	0.73978	.86910	1.3517	.13090
0.96	1.11440	.04704	1.49729	.17531	.74428	.87173	1.3436	.12827
0.97	1.12943	.05286	1.50851	.17855	.74870	.87431	1.3356	.12569
0.98	1.14457	.05864	1.51988	.18181	.75307	.87683	1.3279	.12317
0.99	1.15983	.06439	1.53141	.18509	.75736	.87930	1.3204	.12070

HYPERBOLIC FUNCTIONS AND THEIR COMMON LOGARITHMS (Continued)

x	Sinh x		Cosh x		Tanh x		Coth x	
	Value	$\log_{10}$	Value	$\log_{10}$	Value	$\log_{10}$	Value	$\log_{10}$
1.00	1.17520	.07011	1.54308	.18839	0.76159	.88172	1.3130	.11828
1.01	1.19069	.07580	1.55491	.19171	.76576	.88409	1.3059	.11591
1.02	1.20630	.08146	1.56689	.19504	.76987	.88642	1.2989	.11358
1.03	1.22203	.08708	1.57904	.19839	.77391	.88869	1.2921	.11131
1.04	1.23788	.09268	1.59134	.20176	.77789	.89092	1.2855	.10908
1.05	1.25386	.09825	1.60379	.20515	0.78181	.89310	1.2791	.10690
1.06	1.26996	.10379	1.61641	.20855	.78566	.89524	1.2728	.10476
1.07	1.28619	.10930	1.62919	.21197	.78946	.89733	1.2667	.10267
1.08	1.30254	.11479	1.64214	.21541	.79320	.89938	1.2607	.10062
1.09	1.31903	.12025	1.65525	.21886	.79688	.90139	1.2549	.09861
1.10	1.33565	.12569	1.66852	.22233	0.80050	.90336	1.2492	.09664
1.11	1.35240	.13111	1.68196	.22582	.80406	.90529	1.2437	.09471
1.12	1.36929	.13649	1.69557	.22931	.80757	.90718	1.2383	.09282
1.13	1.38631	.14186	1.70934	.23283	.81102	.90903	1.2330	.09097
1.14	1.40347	.14720	1.72329	.23636	.81441	.91085	1.2279	.08915
1.15	1.42078	.15253	1.73741	.23990	0.81775	.91262	1.2229	.08738
1.16	1.43822	.15783	1.75171	.24346	.82104	.91436	1.2180	.08564
1.17	1.45581	.16311	1.76618	.24703	.82427	.91607	1.2132	.08393
1.18	1.47355	.16836	1.78083	.25062	.82745	.91774	1.2085	.08226
1.19	1.49143	.17360	1.79565	.25422	.83058	.91938	1.2040	.08062
1.20	1.50946	.17882	1.81066	.25784	0.83365	.92099	1.1995	.07901
1.21	1.52764	.18402	1.82584	.26146	.83668	.92256	1.1952	.07744
1.22	1.54598	.18920	1.84121	.26510	.83965	.92410	1.1910	.07590
1.23	1.56447	.19437	1.85676	.26876	.84258	.92561	1.1868	.07439
1.24	1.58311	.19951	1.87250	.27242	.84546	.92709	1.1828	.07291
1.25	1.60192	.20464	1.88842	.27610	0.84828	.92854	1.1789	.07146
1.26	1.62088	.20975	1.90454	.27979	.85106	.92996	1.1750	.07004
1.27	1.64001	.21485	1.92084	.28349	.85380	.93135	1.1712	.06865
1.28	1.65930	.21993	1.93734	.28721	.85648	.93272	1.1676	.06728
1.29	1.67876	.22499	1.95403	.29093	.85913	.93406	1.1640	.06594
1.30	1.69838	.23004	1.97091	.29467	0.86172	.93537	1.1605	.06463
1.31	1.71818	.23507	1.98800	.29842	.86428	.93665	1.1570	.06335
1.32	1.73814	.24009	2.00528	.30217	.86678	.93791	1.1537	.06209
1.33	1.75828	.24509	2.02276	.30594	.86925	.93914	1.1504	.06086
1.34	1.77860	.25008	2.04044	.30972	.87167	.94035	1.1472	.05965
1.35	1.79909	.25505	2.05833	.31352	0.87405	.94154	1.1441	.05846
1.36	1.81977	.26002	2.07643	.31732	.87639	.94270	1.1410	.05730
1.37	1.84062	.26496	2.09473	.32113	.87869	.94384	1.1381	.05616
1.38	1.86166	.26990	2.11324	.32495	.88095	.94495	1.1351	.05505
1.39	1.88289	.27482	2.13196	.32878	.88317	.94604	1.1323	.05396
1.40	1.90430	.27974	2.15090	.33262	0.88535	.94712	1.1295	.05288
1.41	1.92591	.28464	2.17005	.33647	.88749	.94817	1.1268	.05183
1.42	1.94770	.28952	2.18942	.34033	.88960	.94919	1.1241	.05081
1.43	1.96970	.29440	2.20900	.34420	.89167	.95020	1.1215	.04980
1.44	1.99188	.29926	2.22881	.34807	.89370	.95119	1.1189	.04881
1.45	2.01427	.30412	2.24884	.35196	0.89569	.95216	1.1165	.04784
1.46	2.03686	.30896	2.26910	.35585	.89765	.95311	1.1140	.04689
1.47	2.05965	.31379	2.28958	.35976	.89958	.95404	1.1116	.04596
1.48	2.08265	.31862	2.31029	.36367	.90147	.95495	1.1093	.04505
1.49	2.10586	.32343	2.33123	.36759	.90332	.95584	1.1070	.04416

HYPERBOLIC FUNCTIONS AND THEIR COMMON LOGARITHMS (Continued)

x	Sinh x		Cosh x		Tanh x		Coth x	
	Value	$\log_{10}$	Value	$\log_{10}$	Value	$\log_{10}$	Value	$\log_{10}$
1.50	2.12928	.32823	2.35241	.37151	0.90515	.95672	1.1048	.04328
1.51	2.15291	.33303	2.37382	.37545	.90694	.95758	1.1026	.04242
1.52	2.17676	.33781	2.39547	.37939	.90870	.95842	1.1005	.04158
1.53	2.20082	.34258	2.41736	.38334	.91042	.95924	1.0984	.04076
1.54	2.22510	.34735	2.43949	.38730	.91212	.96005	1.0963	.03995
1.55	2.24961	.35211	2.46186	.39126	0.91379	.96084	1.0943	.03916
1.56	2.27434	.35686	2.48448	.39524	.91542	.96162	1.0924	.03838
1.57	2.29930	.36160	2.50735	.39921	.91703	.96238	1.0905	.03762
1.58	2.32449	.36633	2.53047	.40320	.91860	.96313	1.0886	.03687
1.59	2.34991	.37105	2.55384	.40719	.92015	.96386	1.0868	.03614
1.60	2.37557	.37577	2.57746	.41119	0.92167	.96457	1.0850	.03543
1.61	2.40146	.38048	2.60135	.41520	.92316	.96528	1.0832	.03472
1.62	2.42760	.38518	2.62549	.41921	.92462	.96597	1.0815	.03403
1.63	2.45397	.38987	2.64990	.42323	.92606	.96664	1.0798	.03336
1.64	2.48059	.39456	2.67457	.42725	.92747	.96730	1.0782	.03270
1.65	2.50746	.39923	2.69951	.43129	0.92886	.96795	1.0766	.03205
1.66	2.53459	.40391	2.72472	.43532	.93022	.96858	1.0750	.03142
1.67	2.56196	.40857	2.75021	.43937	.93155	.96921	1.0735	.03079
1.68	2.58959	.41323	2.77596	.44341	.93286	.96982	1.0720	.03018
1.69	2.61748	.41788	2.80200	.44747	.93415	.97042	1.0705	.02958
1.70	2.64563	.42253	2.82832	.45153	.93541	.97100	1.0691	.02900
1.71	2.67405	.42717	2.85491	.45559	.93665	.97158	1.0676	.02842
1.72	2.70273	.43180	2.88180	.45966	.93786	.97214	1.0663	.02786
1.73	2.73168	.43643	2.90897	.46374	.93906	.97269	1.0649	.02731
1.74	2.76091	.44105	2.93643	.46782	.94023	.97323	1.0636	.02677
1.75	2.79041	.44567	2.96419	.47191	0.94138	.97376	1.0623	.02624
1.76	2.82020	.45028	2.99224	.47600	.94250	.97428	1.0610	.02572
1.77	2.85026	.45488	3.02059	.48009	.94361	.97479	1.0598	.02521
1.78	2.88061	.45948	3.04925	.48419	.94470	.97529	1.0585	.02471
1.79	2.91125	.46408	3.07821	.48830	.94576	.97578	1.0574	.02422
1.80	2.94217	.46867	3.10747	.49241	0.94681	.97626	1.0562	.02374
1.81	2.97340	.47325	3.13705	.49652	.94783	.97673	1.0550	.02327
1.82	3.00492	.47783	3.16694	.50064	.94884	.97719	1.0539	.02281
1.83	3.03674	.48241	3.19715	.50476	.94983	.97764	1.0528	.02236
1.84	3.06886	.48698	3.22768	.50889	.95080	.97809	1.0518	.02191
1.85	3.10129	.49154	3.25853	.51302	0.95175	.97852	1.0507	.02148
1.86	3.13403	.49610	3.28970	.51716	.95268	.97895	1.0497	.02105
1.87	3.16709	.50066	3.32121	.52130	.95359	.97936	1.0487	.02064
1.88	3.20046	.50521	3.35305	.52544	.95449	.97977	1.0477	.02023
1.89	3.23415	.50976	3.38522	.52959	.95537	.98017	1.0467	.01983
1.90	3.26816	.51430	3.41773	.53374	0.95624	.98057	1.0458	.01943
1.91	3.30250	.51884	3.45058	.53789	.95709	.98095	1.0448	.01905
1.92	3.33718	.52338	3.48378	.54205	.95792	.98133	1.0439	.01867
1.93	3.37218	.52791	3.51733	.54621	.95873	.98170	1.0430	.01830
1.94	3.40752	.53244	3.55123	.55038	.95953	.98206	1.0422	.01794
1.95	3.44321	.53696	3.58548	.55455	0.96032	.98242	1.0413	.01758
1.96	3.47923	.54148	3.62009	.55872	.96109	.98276	1.0405	.01724
1.97	3.51561	.54600	3.65507	.56290	.96185	.98311	1.0397	.01689
1.98	3.55234	.55051	3.69041	.56707	.96259	.98344	1.0389	.01656
1.99	3.58942	.55502	3.72611	.57126	.96331	.98377	1.0381	.01623

HYPERBOLIC FUNCTIONS AND THEIR COMMON LOGARITHMS (Continued)

x	Sinh x Value	$\log_{10}$	Cosh x Value	$\log_{10}$	Tanh x Value	$\log_{10}$	Coth x Value	$\log_{10}$
2.00	3.62686	.55953	3.76220	.57544	0.96403	.98409	1.0373	.01591
2.01	3.66466	.56403	3.79865	.57963	.96473	.98440	1.0366	.01560
2.02	3.70283	.56853	3.83549	.58382	.96541	.98471	1.0358	.01529
2.03	3.74138	.57303	3.87271	.58802	.96609	.98502	1.0351	.01498
2.04	3.78029	.57753	3.91032	.59221	.96675	.98531	1.0344	.01469
2.05	3.81958	.58202	3.94832	.59641	0.96740	.98560	1.0337	.01440
2.06	3.85926	.58650	3.98671	.60061	.96803	.98589	1.0330	.01411
2.07	3.89932	.59099	4.02550	.60482	.96865	.98617	1.0324	.01383
2.08	3.93977	.59547	4.06470	.60903	.96926	.98644	1.0317	.01356
2.09	3.98061	.59995	4.10430	.61324	.96986	.98671	1.0311	.01329
2.10	4.02186	.60443	4.14431	.61745	0.97045	.98697	1.0304	.01303
2.11	4.06350	.60890	4.18474	.62167	.97103	.98723	1.0298	.01277
2.12	4.10555	.61337	4.22558	.62589	.97159	.98748	1.0292	.01252
2.13	4.14801	.61784	4.26685	.63011	.97215	.98773	1.0286	.01227
2.14	4.19089	.62231	4.30855	.63433	.97269	.98798	1.0281	.01202
2.15	4.23419	.62677	4.35067	.63856	0.97323	.98821	1.0275	.01179
2.16	4.27791	.63123	4.39323	.64278	.97375	.98845	1.0270	.01155
2.17	4.32205	.63569	4.43623	.64701	.97426	.98868	1.0264	.01132
2.18	4.36663	.64015	4.47967	.65125	.97477	.98890	1.0259	.01110
2.19	4.41165	.64460	4.52356	.65548	.97526	.98912	1.0254	.01088
2.20	4.45711	.64905	4.56791	.65972	0.97574	.98934	1.0249	.01066
2.21	4.50301	.65350	4.61271	.66396	.97622	.98955	1.0244	.01045
2.22	4.54936	.65795	4.65797	.66820	.97668	.98975	1.0239	.01025
2.23	4.59617	.66240	4.70370	.67244	.97714	.98996	1.0234	.01004
2.24	4.64344	.66684	4.74989	.67668	.97759	.99016	1.0229	.00984
2.25	4.69117	.67128	4.79657	.68093	0.97803	.99035	1.0225	.00965
2.26	4.73937	.67572	4.84372	.68518	.97846	.99054	1.0220	.00946
2.27	4.78804	.68016	4.89136	.68943	.97888	.99073	1.0216	.00927
2.28	4.83720	.68459	4.93948	.69368	.97929	.99091	1.0211	.00909
2.29	4.88684	.68903	4.98810	.69794	.97970	.99109	1.0207	.00891
2.30	4.93696	.69346	5.03722	.70219	0.98010	.99127	1.0203	.00873
2.31	4.98758	.69789	5.08684	.70645	.98049	.99144	1.0199	.00856
2.32	5.03870	.70232	5.13697	.71071	.98087	.99161	1.0195	00839
2.33	5.09032	.70675	5.18762	.71497	.98124	.99178	1.0191	.00822
2.34	5.14245	.71117	5.23878	.71923	.98161	.99194	1.0187	.00806
2.35	5.19510	.71559	5.29047	.72349	0.98197	.99210	1.0184	.00790
2.36	5.24827	.72002	5.34269	.72776	.98233	.99226	1.0180	.00774
2.37	5.30196	.72444	5.39544	.73203	.98267	.99241	1.0176	.00759
2.38	5.35618	.72885	5.44873	.73630	.98301	.99256	1.0173	.00744
2.39	5.41093	.73327	5.50256	.74056	.98335	.99271	1.0169	.00729
2.40	5.46623	.73769	5.55695	.74484	0.98367	.99285	1.0166	.00715
2.41	5.52207	.74210	5.61189	.74911	.98400	.99299	1.0163	.00701
2.42	5.57847	.74652	5.66739	.75338	.98431	.99313	1.0159	.00687
2.43	5.63542	.75093	5.72346	.75766	.98462	.99327	1.0156	.00673
2.44	5.69294	.75534	5.78010	.76194	.98492	.99340	1.0153	.00660
2.45	5.75103	.75975	5.83732	.76621	0.98522	.99353	1.0150	.00647
2.46	5.80969	.75415	5.89512	.77049	.98551	.99366	1.0147	.00634
2.47	5.86893	.76856	5.95352	.77477	.98579	.99379	1.0144	.00621
2.48	5.92876	.77296	6.01250	.77906	.98607	.99391	1.0141	.00609
2.49	5.98918	.77737	6.07209	.78334	.98635	.99403	1.0138	.00597

HYPERBOLIC FUNCTIONS AND THEIR COMMON LOGARITHMS (Continued)

x	Sinh x		Cosh x		Tanh x		Coth x	
	Value	$\log_{10}$	Value	$\log_{10}$	Value	$\log_{10}$	Value	$\log_{10}$
2.50	6.05020	.78177	6.13229	.78762	0.98661	.99415	1.0136	.00585
2.51	6.11183	.78617	6.19310	.79191	.98688	.99426	1.0133	.00574
2.52	6.17407	.79057	6.25453	.79619	.98714	.99438	1.0130	.00562
2.53	6.23692	.79497	6.31658	.80048	.98739	.99449	1.0128	.00551
2.54	6.30040	.79937	6.37927	.80477	.98764	.99460	1.0125	.00540
2.55	6.36451	.80377	6.44259	.80906	0.98788	.99470	1.0123	.00530
2.56	6.42926	.80816	6.50656	.81335	.98812	.99481	1.0120	.00519
2.57	6.49464	.81256	6.57118	.81764	.98835	.99491	1.0118	.00509
2.58	6.56068	.81695	6.63646	.82194	.98858	.99501	1.0115	.00499
2.59	6.62738	.82134	6.70240	.82623	.98881	.99511	1.0113	.00489
2.60	6.69473	.82573	6.76901	.83052	0.98903	.99521	1.0111	.00479
2.61	6.76276	.83012	6.83629	.83482	.98924	.99530	1.0109	.00470
2.62	6.83146	.83451	6.90426	.83912	.98946	.99540	1.0107	.00460
2.63	6.90085	.83890	6.97292	.84341	.98966	.99549	1.0104	.00451
2.64	6.97092	.84329	7.04228	.84771	.98987	.99558	1.0102	.00442
2.65	7.04169	.84768	7.11234	.85201	0.99007	.99566	1.0100	.00434
2.66	7.11317	.85206	7.18312	.85631	.99026	.99575	1.0098	.00425
2.67	7.18536	.85645	7.25461	.86061	.99045	.99583	1.0096	.00417
2.68	7.25827	.86083	7.32683	.86492	.99064	.99592	1.0094	.00408
2.69	7.33190	.86522	7.39978	.86922	.99083	.99600	1.0093	.00400
2.70	7.40626	.86960	7.47347	.87352	0.99101	.99608	1.0091	.00392
2.71	7.48137	.87398	7.54791	.87783	.99118	.99615	1.0089	.00385
2.72	7.55722	.87836	7.62310	.88213	.99136	.99623	1.0087	.00377
2.73	7.63383	.88274	7.69905	.88644	.99153	.99631	1.0085	.00369
2.74	7.71121	.88712	7.77578	.89074	.99170	.99638	1.0084	.00362
2.75	7.78935	.89150	7.85328	.89505	0.99186	.99645	1.0082	.00355
2.76	7.86828	.89588	7.93157	.89936	.99202	.99652	1.0080	.00348
2.77	7.94799	.90026	8.01065	.90367	.99218	.99659	1.0079	.00341
2.78	8.02849	.90463	8.09053	.90798	.99233	.99666	1.0077	.00334
2.79	8.10980	.90901	8.17122	.91229	.99248	.99672	1.0076	.00328
2.80	8.19192	.91339	8.25273	.91660	0.99263	.99679	1.0074	.00321
2.81	8.27486	.91776	8.33506	.92091	.99278	.99685	1.0073	.00315
2.82	8.35862	.92213	8.41823	.92522	.99292	.99691	1.0071	.00309
2.83	8.44322	.92651	8.50224	.92953	.99306	.99698	1.0070	.00302
2.84	8.52867	.93088	8.58710	.93385	.99320	.99704	1.0069	.00296
2.85	8.61497	.93525	8.67281	.93816	0.99333	.99709	1.0067	.00291
2.86	8.70213	.93963	8.75940	.94247	.99346	.99715	1.0066	.00285
2.87	8.79016	.94400	8.84686	.94679	.99359	.99721	1.0065	.00279
2.88	8.87907	.94837	8.93520	.95110	.99372	.99726	1.0063	.00274
2.89	8.96887	.95274	9.02444	.95542	.99384	.99732	1.0062	.00268
2.90	9.05956	.95711	9.11458	.95974	0.99396	.99737	1.0061	.00263
2.91	9.15116	.96148	9.20564	.96405	.99408	.99742	1.0060	.00258
2.92	9.24368	.96584	9.29761	.96837	.99420	.99747	1.0058	.00253
2.93	9.33712	.97021	9.39051	.97269	.99431	.99752	1.0057	.00248
2.94	9.43149	.97458	9.48436	.97701	.99443	.99757	1.0056	.00243
2.95	9.52681	.97895	9.57915	.98133	0.99454	.99762	1.0055	.00238
2.96	9.62308	.98331	9.67490	.98565	.99464	.99767	1.0054	.00233
2.97	9.72031	.98768	9.77161	.98997	.99475	.99771	1.0053	.00229
2.98	9.81851	.99205	9.86930	.99429	.99485	.99776	1.0052	.00224
2.99	9.91770	.99641	9.96798	.99861	.99496	.99780	1.0051	.00220

HYPERBOLIC FUNCTIONS AND THEIR COMMON LOGARITHMS (Continued)

x	Sinh x		Cosh x		Tanh x		Coth x	
	Value	$\log_{10}$	Value	$\log_{10}$	Value	$\log_{10}$	Value	$\log_{10}$
3.0	10.0179	.00078	10.0677	.00293	0.99505	.99785	1.0050	.00215
3.1	11.0765	.04440	11.1215	.04616	.99595	.99824	1.0041	.00176
3.2	12.2459	.08799	12.2866	.08943	.99668	.99856	1.0033	.00144
3.3	13.5379	.13155	13.5748	.13273	.99728	.99882	1.0027	.00118
3.4	14.9654	.17509	14.9987	.17605	.99777	.99903	1.0022	.00097
3.5	16.5426	.21860	16.5728	.21940	0.99818	.99921	1.0018	.00079
3.6	18.2855	.26211	18.3128	.26275	.99851	.99935	1.0015	.00065
3.7	20.2113	.30559	20.2360	.30612	.99878	.99947	1.0012	.00053
3.8	22.3394	.34907	22.3618	.34951	.99900	.99957	1.0010	.00043
3.9	24.6911	.39254	24.7113	.39290	.99918	.99964	1.0008	.00036
4.0	27.2899	.43600	27.3082	.43629	0.99933	.99971	1.0007	.00029
4.1	30.1619	.47946	30.1784	.47970	.99945	.99976	1.0005	.00024
4.2	33.3357	.52291	33.3507	.52310	.99955	.99980	1.0004	.00020
4.3	36.8431	.56636	36.8567	.56652	.99963	.99984	1.0004	.00016
4.4	40.7193	.60980	40.7316	.60993	.99970	.99987	1.0003	.00013
4.5	45.0030	.65324	45.0141	.65335	0.99975	.99989	1.0002	.00011
4.6	49.7371	.69668	49.7472	.69677	.99980	.99991	1.0002	.00009
4.7	54.9690	.74012	54.9781	.74019	.99983	.99993	1.0002	.00007
4.8	60.7511	.78355	60.7593	.78361	.99986	.99994	1.0001	.00006
4.9	67.1412	.82699	67.1486	.82704	.99989	.99995	1.0001	.00005
5.0	74.2032	.87042	74.2099	.87046	0.99991	.99996	1.0001	.00004
5.1	82.008	.91386	82.014	.91389	.99993	.99997	1.0001	.00003
5.2	90.633	.95729	90.639	.95731	.99994	.99997	1.0001	.00003
5.3	100.17	.00072	100.17	.00074	.99995	.99998	1.0000	.00002
5.4	110.70	.04415	110.71	.04417	.99996	.99998	1.0000	.00002
5.5	122.34	.08758	122.35	.08760	0.99997	.99999	1.0000	.00001
5.6	135.21	.13101	135.22	.13103	.99997	.99999	1.0000	.00001
5.7	149.43	.17444	149.44	.17445	.99998	.99999	1.0000	.00001
5.8	165.15	.21787	165.15	.21788	.99998	.99999	1.0000	.00001
5.9	182.52	.26130	182.52	.26131	.99998	.99999	1.0000	.00001
6.0	201.71	.30473	201.72	.30474	0.99999	.00000	1.0000	.00000
6.1	222.93	.34817	222.93	.34817	.99999	.00000	1.0000	.00000
6.2	246.37	.39159	246.38	.39161	.99999	.00000	1.0000	.00000
6.3	272.29	.43503	272.29	.43503	.99999	.00000	1.0000	.00000
6.4	300.92	.47845	300.92	.47845	.99999	.00000	1.0000	.00000
6.5	332.57	.52188	332.57	.52188	1.0000	.00000	1.0000	.00000
6.6	367.55	.56532	367.55	.56532	1.0000	.00000	1.0000	.00000
6.7	406.20	.60874	406.20	.60874	1.0000	.00000	1.0000	.00000
6.8	448.92	.65217	448.92	.65217	1.0000	.00000	1.0000	.00000
6.9	496.14	.69560	496.14	.69560	1.0000	.00000	1.0000	.00000
7.0	548.32	.73903	548.32	.73903	1.0000	.00000	1.0000	.00000
7.1	605.98	.78246	605.98	.78246	1.0000	.00000	1.0000	.00000
7.2	669.72	.82589	669.72	.82589	1.0000	.00000	1.0000	.00000
7.3	740.15	.86932	740.15	.86932	1.0000	.00000	1.0000	.00000
7.4	817.99	.91275	817.99	.91275	1.0000	.00000	1.0000	.00000
7.5	904.02	.95618	904.02	.95618	1.0000	.00000	1.0000	.00000
7.6	999.10	.99961	999.10	.99961	1.0000	.00000	1.0000	.00000
7.7	1104.2	.04305	1104.2	.04305	1.0000	.00000	1.0000	.00000
7.8	1220.3	.08647	1220.3	.08647	1.0000	.00000	1.0000	.00000
7.9	1348.6	.12988	1348.6	.12988	1.0000	.00000	1.0000	.00000

HYPERBOLIC FUNCTIONS AND THEIR COMMON LOGARITHMS (Continued)

x	Sinh x		Cosh x		Tanh x		Coth x	
	Value	$\log_{10}$	Value	$\log_{10}$	Value	$\log_{10}$	Value	$\log_{10}$
8.0	1490.5	.17333	1490.5	.17333	1.0000	.00000	1.0000	.00000
8.1	1647.2	.21675	1647.2	.21675	1.0000	.00000	1.0000	.00000
8.2	1820.5	.26019	1820.5	.26019	1.0000	.00000	1.0000	.00000
8.3	2011.9	.30360	2011.9	.30360	1.0000	.00000	1.0000	.00000
8.4	2223.5	.34704	2223.5	.34704	1.0000	.00000	1.0000	.00000
8.5	2457.4	.39048	2457.4	.39048	1.0000	.00000	1.0000	.00000
8.6	2715.8	.43390	2715.8	.43390	1.0000	.00000	1.0000	.00000
8.7	3001.5	.47734	3001.5	.47734	1.0000	.00000	1.0000	.00000
8.8	3317.1	.52076	3317.1	.52076	1.0000	.00000	1.0000	.00000
8.9	3666.0	.56419	3666.0	.56419	1.0000	.00000	1.0000	.00000
9.0	4051.5	.60762	4051.5	.60762	1.0000	.00000	1.0000	.00000
9.1	4477.6	.65105	4477.6	.65105	1.0000	.00000	1.0000	.00000
9.2	4948.6	.69448	4948.6	.69448	1.0000	.00000	1.0000	.00000
9.3	5469.0	.73791	5469.0	.73791	1.0000	.00000	1.0000	.00000
9.4	6044.2	.78134	6044.2	.78134	1.0000	.00000	1.0000	.00000
9.5	6679.9	.82477	6679.9	.82477	1.0000	.00000	1.0000	.00000
9.6	7382.4	.86820	7382.4	.86820	1.0000	.00000	1.0000	.00000
9.7	8158.8	.91163	8158.8	.91163	1.0000	.00000	1.0000	.00000
9.8	9016.9	.95506	9016.9	.95506	1.0000	.00000	1.0000	.00000
9.9	9965.2	.99849	9965.2	.99849	1.0000	.00000	1.0000	.00000
10.0	11013.2	.04191	11013.2	.04191	1.0000	.00000	1.0000	.00000

EXPONENTIAL AND HYPERBOLIC FUNCTIONS FOR πx

x	$e^{\pi x}$	$e^{-\pi x}$	$\sinh \pi x$	$\cosh \pi x$	$\tanh \pi x$
0.00	1.00000	1.00000	0.00000	1.00000	0.00000
0.01	1.03191	0.96907	0.03142	1.00049	0.03141
0.02	1.06485	0.93910	0.06287	1.00197	0.06275
0.03	1.09883	0.91006	0.09439	1.00444	0.09397
0.04	1.13390	0.88191	0.12599	1.00791	0.12501
0.05	1.17009	0.85464	0.15773	1.01236	0.15580
0.06	1.20743	0.82820	0.18961	1.01782	0.18629
0.07	1.24597	0.80259	0.22169	1.02428	0.21643
0.08	1.28573	0.77777	0.25398	1.03175	0.24617
0.09	1.32676	0.75371	0.28653	1.04024	0.27544
0.10	1.36911	0.73040	0.31935	1.04976	0.30422
0.11	1.41280	0.70781	0.35249	1.06031	0.33245
0.12	1.45789	0.68592	0.38598	1.07191	0.36009
0.13	1.50442	0.66471	0.41986	1.08456	0.38712
0.14	1.55243	0.64415	0.45414	1.09829	0.41350
0.15	1.60198	0.62423	0.48887	1.11310	0.43920
0.16	1.65310	0.60492	0.52409	1.12901	0.46420
0.17	1.70586	0.58621	0.55982	1.14604	0.48849
0.18	1.76030	0.56808	0.59611	1.16419	0.51204
0.19	1.81648	0.55051	0.63298	1.18350	0.53484
0.20	1.87446	0.53349	0.67048	1.20397	0.55689
0.21	1.93428	0.51699	0.70865	1.22563	0.57819
0.22	1.99601	0.50100	0.74751	1.24850	0.59872
0.23	2.05971	0.48550	0.78710	1.27261	0.61850
0.24	2.12545	0.47049	0.82748	1.29797	0.63752
0.25	2.19328	0.45594	0.86867	1.32461	0.65579
0.26	2.26328	0.44184	0.91072	1.35256	0.67333
0.27	2.33551	0.42817	0.95367	1.38184	0.69014
0.28	2.41005	0.41493	0.99756	1.41249	0.70624
0.29	2.48696	0.40210	1.04243	1.44453	0.72164
0.30	2.56633	0.38966	1.08834	1.47800	0.73636
0.31	2.64824	0.37761	1.13531	1.51292	0.75041
0.32	2.73275	0.36593	1.18341	1.54934	0.76382
0.33	2.81997	0.35461	1.23268	1.58729	0.77659
0.34	2.90997	0.34365	1.28316	1.62681	0.78876
0.35	3.00284	0.33302	1.33491	1.66793	0.80034
0.36	3.09867	0.32272	1.38798	1.71070	0.81135
0.37	3.19756	0.31274	1.44241	1.75515	0.82182
0.38	3.29961	0.30307	1.49827	1.80134	0.83176
0.39	3.40492	0.29369	1.55561	1.84931	0.84119
0.40	3.51359	0.28461	1.61449	1.89910	0.85013
0.41	3.62572	0.27581	1.67496	1.95076	0.85862
0.42	3.74143	0.26728	1.73708	2.00436	0.86665
0.43	3.86084	0.25901	1.80091	2.05993	0.87426
0.44	3.98406	0.25100	1.86653	2.11753	0.88147
0.45	4.11121	0.24324	1.93398	2.17722	0.88828
0.46	4.24241	0.23571	2.00335	2.23906	0.89473
0.47	4.37781	0.22842	2.07469	2.30312	0.90082
0.48	4.51753	0.22136	2.14808	2.36944	0.90658
0.49	4.66170	0.21451	2.22359	2.43811	0.91202
0.50	4.81048	0.20788	2.30130	2.50918	0.91715
0.51	4.96400	0.20145	2.38128	2.58273	0.92200
0.52	5.12243	0.19522	2.46360	2.65882	0.92658
0.53	5.28591	0.18918	2.54836	2.73754	0.93089
0.54	5.45460	0.18333	2.63564	2.81897	0.93497

EXPONENTIAL, HYPERBOLIC FUNCTIONS FOR πx (Continued)

x	$e^{\pi x}$	$e^{-\pi x}$	πx	$\cosh \pi x$	$\tanh \pi x$
0.55	5.62869	0.17766	2.72551	2.90317	0.93880
0.56	5.80832	0.17217	2.81808	2.99024	0.94242
0.57	5.99369	0.16684	2.91343	3.08027	0.94584
0.58	6.18498	0.16168	3.01165	3.17333	0.94905
0.59	6.38237	0.15668	3.11284	3.26953	0.95208
0.60	6.58606	0.15184	3.21711	3.36895	0.95493
0.61	6.79625	0.14714	3.32456	3.47170	0.95762
0.62	7.01315	0.14259	3.43528	3.57787	0.96015
0.63	7.23698	0.13818	3.54940	3.68758	0.96253
0.64	7.46794	0.13391	3.66702	3.80092	0.96477
0.65	7.70628	0.12976	3.78826	3.91802	0.96688
0.66	7.95222	0.12575	3.91323	4.03899	0.96887
0.67	8.20601	0.12186	4.04208	4.16394	0.97073
0.68	8.46790	0.11809	4.17491	4.29300	0.97249
0.69	8.73815	0.11444	4.31186	4.42630	0.97415
0.70	9.01703	0.11090	4.45306	4.56396	0.97570
0.71	9.30480	0.10747	4.59867	4.70614	0.97716
0.72	9.60176	0.10415	4.74881	4.85295	0.97854
0.73	9.90820	0.10093	4.90364	5.00456	0.97983
0.74	10.22442	0.09781	5.06331	5.16111	0.98105
0.75	10.55072	0.09478	5.22797	5.32275	0.98219
0.76	10.88745	0.09185	5.39780	5.48965	0.98327
0.77	11.23492	0.08901	5.57295	5.66196	0.98428
0.78	11.59347	0.08626	5.75361	5.83986	0.98523
0.79	11.96347	0.08359	5.93994	6.02353	0.98612
0.80	12.34528	0.08100	6.13214	6.21314	0.98696
0.81	12.73928	0.07850	6.33039	6.40889	0.98775
0.82	13.14585	0.07607	6.53489	6.61096	0.98849
0.83	13.56539	0.07372	6.74584	6.81955	0.98919
0.84	13.99833	0.07144	6.96344	7.03488	0.98985
0.85	14.44508	0.06923	7.18792	7.25715	0.99046
0.86	14.90609	0.06709	7.41950	7.48659	0.99104
0.87	15.38181	0.06501	7.65840	7.72341	0.99158
0.88	15.87271	0.06300	7.90486	7.96786	0.99209
0.89	16.37929	0.06105	8.15912	8.22017	0.99257
0.90	16.90202	0.05916	8.41243	8.48059	0.99302
0.91	17.44145	0.05733	8.69205	8.74939	0.99345
0.92	17.99808	0.05556	8.97126	9.02682	0.99384
0.93	18.57248	0.05384	9.25932	9.31316	0.99422
0.94	19.16522	0.05218	9.55652	9.60870	0.99457
0.95	19.77687	0.05056	9.86315	9.91372	0.99490
0.96	20.40804	0.04900	10.17952	10.22852	0.99521
0.97	21.05935	0.04748	10.50594	10.55342	0.99550
0.98	21.73146	0.04602	10.84272	10.88874	0.99577
0.99	22.42501	0.04459	11.19021	11.23480	0.99603
1.00	23.14069	0.04321	11.54874	11.59195	0.99627

ANALYTIC GEOMETRY

Dr. Howard Eves

RECTANGULAR COORDINATES IN A PLANE

Rectangular (Cartesian) Coordinates

Let $X'X$ (called the *x-axis*) and $Y'Y$ (called the *y-axis*) be two perpendicular lines (here taken horizontally and vertically, respectively) intersecting in point O (called the *origin*). Then any point P in the plane of the axes is located by the distance x (called the *abscissa*) and the distance y (called the *ordinate*) from $Y'Y$ and $X'X$, respectively, to P, where x is taken as positive to the right and negative to the left of $Y'Y$, and y is taken as positive above and negative below $X'X$. The ordered pair of numbers, (x,y), are called *rectangular coordinates* of the point P.

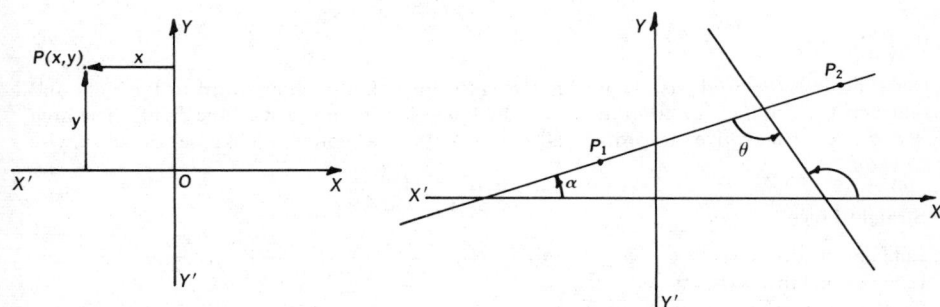

Points, Slopes, Angles

Let $P_1(x_1,y_1)$ and $P_2(x_2,y_2)$ be any two points and let α be the angle measured counterclockwise from $X'X$ to P_1P_2.

Distance between P_1 and P_2: $\sqrt{(x_2 - x_1)^2 + (y_2 - y_1)^2}$

Point dividing P_1P_2 in ratio $\dfrac{r}{s}$: $\left(\dfrac{rx_2 + sx_1}{r + s}, \dfrac{ry_2 + sy_1}{r + s}\right)$

Midpoint of P_1P_2: $\left(\dfrac{x_1 + x_2}{2}, \dfrac{y_1 + y_2}{2}\right)$

Slope m of P_1P_2: $m = \tan \alpha = \dfrac{y_2 - y_1}{x_2 - x_1}$

Angle θ between two lines of slopes m_1 and m_2: $\tan \theta = \dfrac{m_2 - m_1}{1 + m_1m_2}$

For parallel lines: $m_1 = m_2$

For perpendicular lines: $m_1m_2 = -1$

Points P_1, P_2, P_3 are collinear if and only if $\begin{vmatrix} x_1 & y_1 & 1 \\ x_2 & y_2 & 1 \\ x_3 & y_3 & 1 \end{vmatrix} = 0.$

Polygonal Areas

Area of triangle $P_1 P_2 P_3$:

$$\frac{1}{2}\begin{vmatrix} x_1 & y_1 & 1 \\ x_2 & y_2 & 1 \\ x_3 & y_3 & 1 \end{vmatrix} = \frac{1}{2}(x_1 y_2 + x_2 y_3 + x_3 y_1 - y_1 x_2 - y_2 x_3 - y_3 x_1)$$

Area of polygon $P_1 P_2 \cdots P_n$:

$$\tfrac{1}{2}(x_1 y_2 + x_2 y_3 + \cdots + x_{n-1} y_n + x_n y_1 - y_1 x_2 - y_2 x_3 - \cdots - y_{n-1} x_n - y_n x_1)$$

Note. The parenthesis in the last formula is remembered by the device

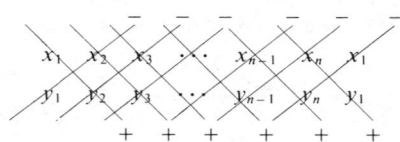

Here one adds the products of coordinates on the lines slanting downward to the right and subtracts the products of coordinates on the lines slanting upward to the right. The area is positive or negative according as $P_1 P_2 \cdots P_n$ is a counterclockwise or clockwise polygon.

Straight Lines

Line parallel to y-axis: $x = a$
Line parallel to x-axis: $y = b$
Slope y-intercept form: $y = mx + b$

Intercept form: $\dfrac{x}{a} + \dfrac{y}{b} = 1$

Point-slope form: $y - y_1 = m(x - x_1)$

Two-point form: $\dfrac{y - y_1}{x - x_1} = \dfrac{y_2 - y_1}{x_2 - x_1}$

or

$$\begin{vmatrix} x & y & 1 \\ x_1 & y_1 & 1 \\ x_2 & y_2 & 1 \end{vmatrix} = 0$$

Normal form: $x \cos \omega + y \sin \omega = p$
General form: $Ax + By + C = 0$

Slope: $m = -\dfrac{A}{B}$

Intercepts: $a = -\dfrac{C}{A}, \quad b = -\dfrac{C}{B}$

To reduce $Ax + By + C = 0$ to normal form, divide by $\pm \sqrt{A^2 + B^2}$, where the sign of the radical is chosen opposite to the sign of C when $C \neq 0$ and the same as the sign of B when $C = 0$.

Distance from $Ax + By + C = 0$ to P_1: $\dfrac{Ax_1 + By_1 + C}{\pm \sqrt{A^2 + B^2}}$

Angle θ between lines $A_1x + B_1y + C_1 = 0$
and $A_2x + B_2y + C_2 = 0$

$$\tan\theta = \frac{A_1B_2 - A_2B_1}{A_1A_2 + B_1B_2}$$

Lines parallel: $\qquad A_1B_2 = A_2B_1$

Lines perpendicular: $\qquad A_1A_2 = -B_1B_2$

Lines $A_1x + B_1y + C_1 = 0$, $A_2x + B_2y + C_2 = 0$, $A_3x + B_3y + C_3 = 0$ are concurrent if and only if

$$\begin{vmatrix} A_1 & B_1 & C_1 \\ A_2 & B_2 & C_2 \\ A_3 & B_3 & C_3 \end{vmatrix} = 0.$$

Line of Best Fit

In seeking the straight line which best fits a given set of n points $P_1(x_1,y_1)$, $P_2(x_2,y_2)$, $\cdots$, $P_n(x_n,y_n)$, calculate

$$\bar{x} = \frac{x_1 + x_2 + \cdots + x_n}{n}, \quad \bar{y} = \frac{y_1 + y_2 + \cdots + y_n}{n},$$

$$m = \frac{(x_1y_1 + x_2y_2 + \cdots + x_ny_n) - n\bar{x}\bar{y}}{(x_1^2 + x_2^2 + \cdots + x_n^2) - n\bar{x}^2}.$$

Then the sought line is given by

$$y - \bar{y} = m(x - \bar{x}).$$

Circles

Center at origin, radius r: $\qquad x^2 + y^2 = r^2$

Center at (h,k), radius r: $\qquad (x - h)^2 + (y - k)^2 = r^2$

General form: $\qquad \begin{cases} Ax^2 + Ay^2 + Dx + Ey + F = 0, A \neq 0 \\ x^2 + y^2 + 2dx + 2ey + f = 0 \end{cases}$

Center: $\qquad (-d, -e)$

Radius: $\qquad r = \sqrt{d^2 + e^2 - f}$

Circle on P_1P_2 as diameter: $\qquad (x - x_1)(x - x_2) + (y - y_1)(y - y_2) = 0$

Three-point form: $\qquad \begin{vmatrix} x^2 + y^2 & x & y & 1 \\ x_1^2 + y_1^2 & x_1 & y_1 & 1 \\ x_2^2 + y_2^2 & x_2 & y_2 & 1 \\ x_3^2 + y_3^2 & x_3 & y_3 & 1 \end{vmatrix} = 0.$

Conic Sections

A *conic section* is the locus of a point P that moves in the plane of a fixed point F (called a *focus*) and a fixed line d (called a *directrix*), F not on d, such that the ratio of the distance of P from F to its distance from d is a constant e (called the *eccentricity*).

If $e = 1$, the conic is a *parabola*; if $e < 1$, an *ellipse*; if $e > 1$, a *hyperbola*.

Focus, $(0,0)$; directrix, $x = -a$: $\quad x^2 + y^2 = e^2(x + a)^2$

Parabolas (e = 1)

Let p = distance from the vertex to the focus, e = eccentricity.

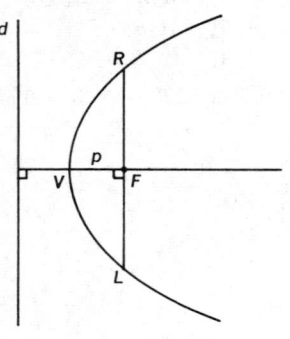

V: vertex
F: focus
d: directrix
LR: latus rectum
line VF: axis

Latus rectum:	$4p$
Distance from vertex to directrix:	p
Vertex at origin, focus at $(p,0)$:	$y^2 = 4px$
Vertex at origin, focus at $(-p,0)$:	$y^2 = -4px$
Vertex at origin, focus at $(0,p)$:	$x^2 = 4py$
Vertex at origin, focus at $(0,-p)$:	$x^2 = -4py$
Vertex, (h,k); focus, $(h + p,k)$:	$(y - k)^2 = 4p(x - h)$
Vertex, (h,k); focus, $(h - p,k)$:	$(y - k)^2 = -4p(x - h)$
Vertex, (h,k); focus, $(h,k + p)$:	$(x - h)^2 = 4p(y - k)$
Vertex, (h,k); focus, $(h,k - p)$:	$(x - h)^2 = -4p(y - k)$
General form, axis parallel to $X'X$:	$Cy^2 + Dx + Ey + F = 0$
General form, axis parallel to $Y'Y$:	$\begin{cases} Ax^2 + Dx + Ey + F = 0 \\ y = ax^2 + bx + c \end{cases}$
General form, axis oblique to coordinate axes:	$Ax^2 + Bxy + Cy^2 + Dx + Ey + F = 0,$ $B^2 - 4AC = 0$

Ellipses (e < 1)

Let $2a$ = major axis, $2b$ = minor axis, e = eccentricity.

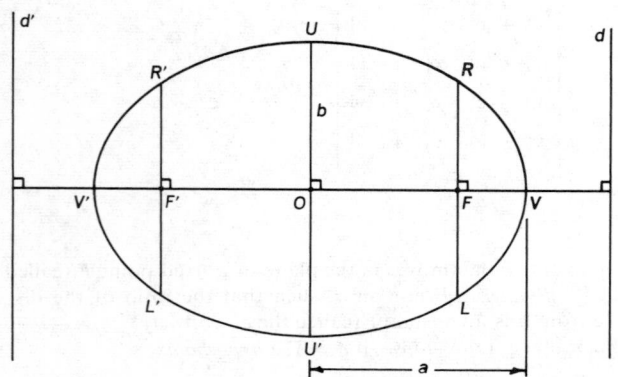

O: center
V, V': vertices
$V'V$: major axis $= 2a$
$U'U$: minor axis $= 2b$
F, F': foci
d, d': directrices
$LR, L'R'$: latera recta

Eccentricity:	$e = \dfrac{\sqrt{a^2 - b^2}}{a}$
Latus rectum:	$\dfrac{2b^2}{a}$
Distance from center to either focus:	$\sqrt{a^2 - b^2}$
Distance from center to either directrix:	$\dfrac{a}{e}$
Sum of distances from any point on ellipse to the foci:	$2a$
Center at origin, foci on $X'X$:	$\dfrac{x^2}{a^2} + \dfrac{y^2}{b^2} = 1$
Center at origin, foci on $Y'Y$:	$\dfrac{x^2}{b^2} + \dfrac{y^2}{a^2} = 1$
Center at (h,k), major axis parallel to $X'X$:	$\dfrac{(x - h)^2}{a^2} + \dfrac{(y - k)^2}{b^2} = 1$
Center at (h,k), major axis parallel to $Y'Y$:	$\dfrac{(x - h)^2}{b^2} + \dfrac{(y - k)^2}{a^2} = 1$
General form, axes parallel to coordinate axes:	$Ax^2 + Cy^2 + Dx + Ey + F = 0, AC > 0$
General form, axes oblique to coordinate axes:	$Ax^2 + Bxy + Cy^2 + Dx + Ey + F = 0,$ $B^2 - 4AC < 0$

For a *circle*: $a = b$, $e = 0$, foci coincide at the center of the circle, directrices are at infinity.

Hyperbolas ($e > 1$)

Let $2a$ = transverse axis, $2b$ = conjugate axis, e = eccentricity.

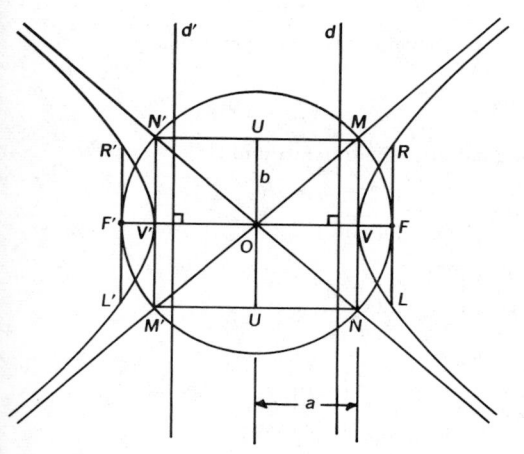

O: center
V, V': vertices
$V'V$: transverse axis = $2a$
$U'U$: conjugate axis = $2b$
F, F': foci
d, d': directrices
$LR, L'R'$: latera recta
lines $M'M$ and $N'N$: asymptotes

Eccentricity:	$e = \dfrac{\sqrt{a^2 + b^2}}{a}$
Latus rectum:	$\dfrac{2b^2}{a}$
Distance from center to either focus:	$\sqrt{a^2 + b^2}$
Distance from center to either directrix:	$\dfrac{a}{e}$
Difference of distances of any point on hyperbola from foci:	$2a$
Center at origin, foci on $X'X$:	$\dfrac{x^2}{a^2} - \dfrac{y^2}{b^2} = 1$
Slopes of asymptotes:	$\pm \dfrac{b}{a}$
Center at origin, foci on $Y'Y$:	$\dfrac{y^2}{a^2} - \dfrac{x^2}{b^2} = 1$
Slopes of asymptotes:	$\pm \dfrac{a}{b}$
Center at (h,k), transverse axis parallel to $X'X$:	$\dfrac{(x - h)^2}{a^2} - \dfrac{(y - k)^2}{b^2} = 1$
Slopes of asymptotes:	$\pm \dfrac{b}{a}$
Center at (h, k), transverse axis parallel to $Y'Y$:	$\dfrac{(y - k)^2}{a^2} - \dfrac{(x - h)^2}{b^2} = 1$
Slopes of asymptotes:	$\pm \dfrac{a}{b}$
Center at origin, $X'X$ and $Y'Y$ for asymptotes:	$xy = c$
Center at (h,k), asymptotes parallel to $X'X$ and $Y'Y$:	$(x - h)(y - k) = c$
General form, axes parallel to coordinate axes:	$Ax^2 + Cy^2 + Dx + Ey + F = 0, AC < 0$
General form, axes oblique to coordinate axes:	$Ax^2 + Bxy + Cy^2 + Dx + Ey + F = 0,$ $B^2 - 4AC > 0$

For a *rectangular hyperbola*: $a = b$, $e = \sqrt{2}$, asymptotes are perpendicular.

General Equation of Second Degree

The nature of the graph of the general quadratic equation in x and y,

$$ax^2 + 2hxy + by^2 + 2gx + 2fy + c = 0,$$

is described in the following table in terms of the values of

$$\triangle = \begin{vmatrix} a & h & g \\ h & b & f \\ g & f & c \end{vmatrix}, \quad J = \begin{vmatrix} a & h \\ h & b \end{vmatrix},$$

$$I = a + b, \quad K = \begin{vmatrix} a & g \\ g & c \end{vmatrix} + \begin{vmatrix} b & f \\ f & c \end{vmatrix}.$$

Case	$\triangle$	J	$\triangle/I$	K	Conic
1	$\neq 0$	> 0	< 0		real ellipse
2	$\neq 0$	> 0	> 0		imaginary ellipse
3	$\neq 0$	< 0			hyperbola
4	$\neq 0$	0			parabola
5	0	< 0			real intersecting lines
6	0	> 0			conjugate complex intersecting lines
7	0	0		< 0	real distinct parallel lines
8	0	0		> 0	conjugate complex parallel lines
9	0	0		0	coincident lines

In cases 1, 2, and 3, the center (x_0, y_0) of the conic is given by the simultaneous solution of the equations

$$ax + hy + g = 0, \quad hx + by + f = 0.$$

The equations of the axes of the conic are

$$y - y_0 = m(x - x_0), \quad y - y_0 = -\frac{1}{m}(x - x_0),$$

where m is the positive root of

$$hm^2 + (a - b)m - h = 0.$$

Transformation of Coordinates

To transform an equation of a curve from an old system of rectangular coordinates (x, y) to a new system of rectangular coordinates (x', y'), substitute for each old variable in the equation of the curve its expression in terms of the new variables.

Translation:
$$\begin{cases} x = x' + h \\ y = y' + k \end{cases}$$
The new axes are parallel to the old axes and the coordinates of the new origin in terms of the old system are (h, k).

Rotation:
$$\begin{cases} x = x' \cos\theta - y' \sin\theta \\ y = x' \sin\theta + y' \cos\theta \end{cases}$$
The new origin is coincident with the old origin and the new axes make an angle θ with the old axes.

To remove the xy-term from the equation

$$ax^2 + 2hxy + by^2 + 2gx + 2fy + c = 0,$$

rotate the coordinate axes about the origin through the acute angle $\theta = \arctan m$, where m is the positive root of

$$hm^2 + (a - b)m - h = 0.$$

OBLIQUE COORDINATES IN A PLANE

Oblique (Cartesian) Coordinates

Let $X'X$ (called the *x-axis*, here taken horizontally) and $Y'Y$ (called the *y-axis*) be two lines intersecting in point O (called the *origin*), and denote by ω the counterclockwise angle from $X'X$ to $Y'Y$. Then any point P in the plane of the axes is located by the distance x (called the *abscissa*) measured parallel to the x-axis and the distance y (called the *ordinate*) measured parallel to the y-axis from $Y'Y$ and $X'X$, respectively, to P, where x is taken as positive to the right and negative to the left of $Y'Y$, and y is taken as positive above and negative below $X'X$. The ordered pair of numbers, (x,y), are called *oblique co-ordinates* of the point P. If $\omega = 90°$, this coordinate system becomes a rectangular (Cartesian) coordinate system.

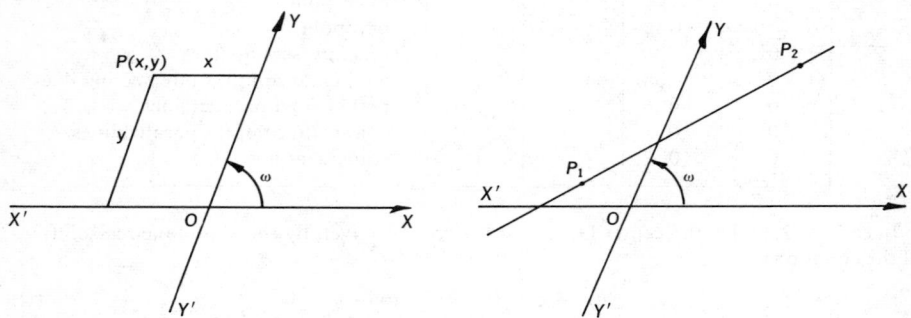

Points

Let $P_1(x_1,y_1)$ and $P_2(x_2,y_2)$ be any two points.
Distance between P_1 and P_2:

$$\sqrt{(x_2 - x_1)^2 + (y_2 - y_1)^2 + 2(x_2 - x_1)(y_2 - y_1)\cos \omega}$$

Point dividing $P_1 P_2$ in ratio $\dfrac{r}{s}$:　　　$\left(\dfrac{rx_2 + sx_1}{r + s}, \dfrac{ry_2 + sy_1}{r + s}\right)$

Midpoint of $P_1 P_2$:　　　$\left(\dfrac{x_1 + x_2}{2}, \dfrac{y_1 + y_2}{2}\right)$

Points P_1, P_2, P_3 are collinear if and only if $\begin{vmatrix} x_1 & y_1 & 1 \\ x_2 & y_2 & 1 \\ x_3 & y_3 & 1 \end{vmatrix} = 0.$

Polygonal Areas

Area of triangle $P_1 P_2 P_3$:

$$\sin \omega \begin{vmatrix} x_1 & y_1 & 1 \\ x_2 & y_2 & 1 \\ x_3 & y_3 & 1 \end{vmatrix} = \tfrac{1}{2} \sin \omega (x_1 y_2 + x_2 y_3 + x_3 y_1 - y_1 x_2 - y_2 x_3 - y_2 x_1)$$

Area of polygon $P_1 P_2 \cdots P_n$:

$$\tfrac{1}{2} \sin \omega (x_1 y_2 + x_2 y_3 + \cdots + x_{n-1} y_n + x_n y_1 - y_1 x_2 - y_2 x_3 - \cdots - y_{n-1} x_n - y_n x_1)$$

The area is positive or negative according as $P_1 P_2 \cdots P_n$ is a counterclockwise or clockwise polygon.

Straight Lines

Line parallel to y-axis:　　　$x = a$

Line parallel to x-axis:　　　$y = b$

Intercept form:
$$\frac{x}{a} + \frac{y}{b} = 1$$

Two-point form:
$$\frac{y - y_1}{x - x_1} = \frac{y_2 - y_1}{x_2 - x_1}, \quad \text{or} \quad \begin{vmatrix} x & y & 1 \\ x_1 & y_1 & 1 \\ x_2 & y_2 & 1 \end{vmatrix} = 0$$

General form:
$$Ax + By + C = 0$$

Intercepts:
$$a = -\frac{C}{A}, \quad b = -\frac{C}{B}$$

Distance from $Ax + By + C = 0$ to P_1:
$$\frac{(Ax_1 + By_1 + C) \sin \omega}{\pm \sqrt{A^2 + B^2 - 2AB \cos \omega}}$$

Angle θ between lines $A_1 x + B_1 y + C_1 = 0$
and $A_2 x + B_2 y + C_2 = 0$:
$$\tan \theta = \frac{(A_1 B_2 - A_2 B_1) \sin \omega}{A_1 A_2 + B_1 B_2 - (A_1 B_2 + A_2 B_1) \cos \omega}$$

Lines parallel:
$$A_1 B_2 = A_2 B_1$$

Lines perpendicular:
$$A_1 A_2 + B_1 B_2 = (A_1 B_2 + A_2 B_1) \cos \omega$$

Lines $A_1 x + B_1 y + C_1 = 0$, $A_2 x + B_2 y + C_2 = 0$, $A_3 x + B_3 y + C_3 = 0$ are concurrent if and only if

$$\begin{vmatrix} A_1 & B_1 & C_1 \\ A_2 & B_2 & C_2 \\ A_3 & B_3 & C_3 \end{vmatrix} = 0.$$

Circles

Center at (h, k), radius r: $(x - h)^2 + (y - k)^2 + 2(x - h)(y - k) \cos \omega = r^2$

Transformation of Coordinates

Translation:
$$\begin{cases} x = x' + h \\ y = y' + k \end{cases}$$
The new axes are parallel to the old axes and the coordinates of the new origin in terms of the old system are (h, k).

From one oblique system to another, origin fixed:
$$\begin{cases} x = \dfrac{x' \sin (\omega - \theta) + y' \sin (\omega - \omega' - \theta)}{\sin \omega} \\ y = \dfrac{x' \sin \theta + y' \sin (\omega' + \theta)}{\sin \omega} \end{cases}$$

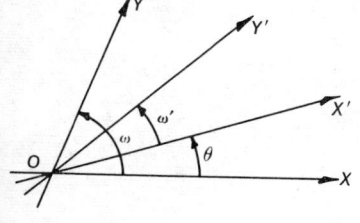

The old and new origins coincide; the old axes intersect at angle ω; the new axes intersect at angle ω'; the counterclockwise angle from x-axis to x'-axis is θ.

POLAR COORDINATES IN A PLANE

Polar Coordinates

In a plane, let OX (called the *initial line*) be a fixed ray radiating from point O (called the *pole* or *origin*). Then any point P, other than O, in the plane is located by angle θ (called the *vectorial angle*) measured from OX to the line determined by O and P and the distance r (called the *radius vector*) from O to P, where θ is taken as positive if measured counterclockwise and negative if measured clockwise, and r is taken as positive if measured along the terminal side of angle θ and negative if measured along the terminal side of θ produced through the pole. Such an ordered pair of numbers, (r, θ), are called *polar coordinates* of the point P. The polar coordinates of the pole O are taken as $(0, \theta)$, where θ is arbitrary. It follows that, for a given initial line and pole, each point of the plane has infinitely many polar coordinates.

Example

Some polar coordinates of P are: $(2, 60°)$, $(2, 420°)$, $(2, -300°)$, $(-2, 240°)$, $(-2, -120°)$.

Points

Distance between P_1 and P_2: $\quad \sqrt{r_1^2 + r_2^2 - 2r_1 r_2 \cos(\theta_1 - \theta_2)}$

Points P_1, P_2, P_3 are collinear if and only if

$$r_2 r_3 \sin(\theta_3 - \theta_2) + r_3 r_1 \sin(\theta_1 - \theta_3) + r_1 r_2 \sin(\theta_2 - \theta_1) = 0.$$

Polygonal Areas

Area of triangle $P_1 P_2 P_3$:

$$\tfrac{1}{2}[r_1 r_2 \sin(\theta_2 - \theta_1) + r_2 r_3 \sin(\theta_3 - \theta_2) + r_3 r_1 \sin(\theta_1 - \theta_3)]$$

Area of polygon $P_1 P_2 \cdots P_n$:

$$\tfrac{1}{2}[r_1 r_2 \sin(\theta_2 - \theta_1) + r_2 r_3 \sin(\theta_3 - \theta_2) + \cdots + r_{n-1} r_n \sin(\theta_n - \theta_{n-1}) + r_n r_1 \sin(\theta_1 - \theta_n)]$$

The area is positive or negative according as $P_1 P_2 \cdots P_n$ is a counterclockwise or clockwise polygon.

Straight Lines

Let p = distance of line from O, ω = counterclockwise angle from OX to the perpendicular through O to the line.

Normal form: $r \cos(\theta - \omega) = p$

Two-point form: $r[r_1 \sin(\theta - \theta_1) + r_2 \sin(\theta - \theta_2)] = r_1 r_2 \sin(\theta_2 - \theta_1)$

Circles

Center at pole, radius a: $r = a$

Center at $(a, 0)$ and passing
 through the pole: $r = 2a \cos \theta$

Center at $\left(a, \dfrac{\pi}{2}\right)$ and passing

through the pole: $\qquad\qquad\qquad r = 2a \sin \theta$

Center (h, α), radius a: $\qquad\quad r^2 - 2hr \cos (\theta - \alpha) + h^2 - a^2 = 0$

Conics

Let $2p$ = distance from directrix to focus, e = eccentricity.

Focus at pole, directrix to left of pole: $\qquad r = \dfrac{2ep}{1 - e \cos \theta}$

Focus at pole, directrix to right of pole: $\qquad r = \dfrac{2ep}{1 + e \cos \theta}$

Focus at pole, directrix below pole: $\qquad r = \dfrac{2ep}{1 - e \sin \theta}$

Focus at pole, directrix above pole: $\qquad r = \dfrac{2ep}{1 + e \sin \theta}$

Parabola with vertex at pole,
directrix to left of pole: $\qquad\qquad r = \dfrac{4p \cos \theta}{\sin^2 \theta}$

Ellipse with center at pole, semiaxes a and
b horizontal and vertical, respectively: $\qquad r^2 = \dfrac{a^2 b^2}{a^2 \sin^2 \theta + b^2 \cos^2 \theta}$

Hyperbola with center at pole, semiaxes a
and b horizontal and vertical, respectively: $\qquad r^2 = \dfrac{a^2 b^2}{a^2 \sin^2 \theta - b^2 \cos^2 \theta}$

Relations Between Rectangular and Polar Coordinates

Let the positive x-axis coincide with the initial line and let r be nonnegative.

$$x = r \cos \theta, \quad y = r \sin \theta,$$

$$r = \sqrt{x^2 + y^2}, \quad \theta = \arctan \frac{y}{x},$$

$$\sin \theta = \frac{y}{\sqrt{x^2 + y^2}}, \quad \cos \theta = \frac{x}{\sqrt{x^2 + y^2}}$$

RECTANGULAR COORDINATES IN SPACE

Rectangular (Cartesian) Coordinates

Let $X'X$, $Y'Y$, $Z'Z$ (called the *x-axis*, the *y-axis*, and the *z-axis*, respectively) be three mutually perpendicular lines in space intersecting in a point O (called the *origin*), forming in this way three mutually perpendicular planes XOY, XOZ, YOZ (called the *xy-*

plane, the *xz-plane*, and the *yz-plane*, respectively). Then any point P of space is located by its signed distances x, y, z from the *yz*-plane, the *xz*-plane, and the *xy*-plane, respectively, where x and y are the rectangular coordinates with respect to the axes $X'X$ and $Y'Y$ of the orthogonal projection P' of P on the *xy*-plane (here taken horizontally) and z is taken as positive above and negative below the *xy*-plane. The ordered triple of numbers, (x, y, z), are called *rectangular coordinates* of the point P.

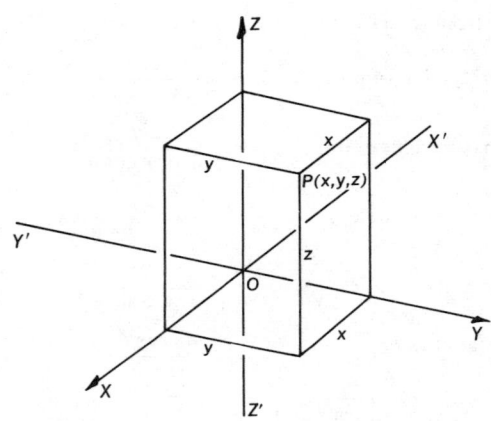

Points

Let $P_1(x_1, y_1, z_1)$ and $P_2(x_2, y_2, z_2)$ be any two points.

Distance between P_1 and P_2: $\qquad \sqrt{(x_2 - x_1)^2 + (y_2 - y_1)^2 + (z_2 - z_1)^2}$

Point dividing P_1P_2 in ratio $\dfrac{r}{s}$: $\qquad \left(\dfrac{rx_2 + sx_1}{r + s}, \dfrac{ry_2 + sy_1}{r + s}, \dfrac{rz_2 + sz_1}{r + s} \right)$

Midpoint of P_1P_2: $\qquad \left(\dfrac{x_1 + x_2}{2}, \dfrac{y_1 + y_2}{2}, \dfrac{z_1 + z_2}{2} \right)$

Points P_1, P_2, P_3 are collinear if and only if

$$x_2 - x_1 : y_2 - y_1 : z_2 - z_1 = x_3 - x_1 : y_3 - y_1 : z_3 - z_1.$$

Points P_1, P_2, P_3, P_4 are coplanar if and only if $\qquad \begin{vmatrix} x_1 & y_1 & z_1 & 1 \\ x_2 & y_2 & z_2 & 1 \\ x_3 & y_3 & z_3 & 1 \\ x_4 & y_4 & z_4 & 1 \end{vmatrix} = 0.$

Area of triangle $P_1P_2P_3$:

$$\frac{1}{2} \sqrt{ \begin{vmatrix} y_1 & z_1 & 1 \\ y_2 & z_2 & 1 \\ y_3 & z_3 & 1 \end{vmatrix}^2 + \begin{vmatrix} z_1 & x_1 & 1 \\ z_2 & x_2 & 1 \\ z_3 & x_3 & 1 \end{vmatrix}^2 + \begin{vmatrix} x_1 & y_1 & 1 \\ x_2 & y_2 & 1 \\ x_3 & y_3 & 1 \end{vmatrix}^2 }$$

Volume of tetrahedron $P_1 P_2 P_3 P_4$: $\quad \frac{1}{6} \begin{vmatrix} x_1 & y_1 & z_1 & 1 \\ x_2 & y_2 & z_2 & 1 \\ x_3 & y_3 & z_3 & 1 \\ x_4 & y_4 & z_4 & 1 \end{vmatrix}$

Direction Numbers and Direction Cosines

Let α, β, γ (called *direction angles*) be the angles that $P_1 P_2$, or any line parallel to $P_1 P_2$, makes with the x-, y-, and z-axis, respectively. Let d = distance between P_1 and P_2.

Direction cosines of $P_1 P_2$:

$$\cos \alpha = \frac{x_2 - x_1}{d}, \quad \cos \beta = \frac{y_2 - y_1}{d}, \quad \cos \gamma = \frac{z_2 - z_1}{d}$$

$$\cos^2 \alpha + \cos^2 \beta + \cos^2 \gamma = 1$$

If a, b, c are direction numbers of $P_1 P_2$, then:

$$a : b : c = x_2 - x_1 : y_2 - y_1 : z_2 - z_1$$
$$= \cos \alpha : \cos \beta : \cos \gamma$$

$$\cos \alpha = \frac{a}{\pm \sqrt{a^2 + b^2 + c^2}}, \quad \cos \beta = \frac{b}{\pm \sqrt{a^2 + b^2 + c^2}},$$

$$\cos \gamma = \frac{c}{\pm \sqrt{a^2 + b^2 + c^2}}$$

Angle between two lines with direction angles α_1, β_1, γ_1 and α_2, β_2, γ_2:

$$\cos \theta = \cos \alpha_1 \cos \alpha_2 + \cos \beta_1 \cos \beta_2 + \cos \gamma_1 \cos \gamma_2$$

For parallel lines: $\quad \alpha_1 = \alpha_2, \quad \beta_1 = \beta_2, \quad \gamma_1 = \gamma_2$

For perpendicular lines:

$$\cos \alpha_1 \cos \alpha_2 + \cos \beta_1 \cos \beta_2 + \cos \gamma_1 \cos \gamma_2 = 0$$

Angle between two lines with directions (a_1, b_1, c_1) and (a_2, b_2, c_2):

$$\cos \theta = \frac{a_1 a_2 + b_1 b_2 + c_1 c_2}{\sqrt{a_1^2 + b_1^2 + c_1^2} \sqrt{a_2^2 + b_2^2 + c_2^2}}$$

$$\sin \theta = \frac{\sqrt{(b_1 c_2 - c_1 b_2)^2 + (c_1 a_2 - a_1 c_2)^2 + (a_1 b_2 - b_1 a_2)^2}}{\sqrt{a_1^2 + b_1^2 + c_1^2} \sqrt{a_2^2 + b_2^2 + c_2^2}}$$

For parallel lines: $\quad a_1 : b_1 : c_1 = a_2 : b_2 : c_2$

For perpendicular lines: $\quad a_1 a_2 + b_1 b_2 + c_1 c_2 = 0$

The direction

$$(b_1 c_2 - c_1 b_2, c_1 a_2 - a_1 c_2, a_1 b_2 - b_1 a_2)$$

is perpendicular to both directions (a_1, b_1, c_1) and (a_2, b_2, c_2).

The directions (a_1, b_1, c_1), (a_2, b_2, c_2), (a_3, b_3, c_3) are parallel to a common plane if and only if

$$\begin{vmatrix} a_1 & b_1 & c_1 \\ a_2 & b_2 & c_2 \\ a_3 & b_3 & c_3 \end{vmatrix} = 0.$$

Straight Lines

Point-direction form:
$$\frac{x - x_1}{a} = \frac{y - y_1}{b} = \frac{z - z_1}{c}$$

Two-point form:
$$\frac{x - x_1}{x_2 - x_1} = \frac{y - y_1}{y_2 - y_1} = \frac{z - z_1}{z_2 - z_1}$$

Parametric form: $x = x_1 + ta, \ y = y_1 + tb, \ z = z_1 + tc$

General form:
$$\begin{cases} A_1 x + B_1 y + C_1 z + D_1 = 0 \\ A_2 x + B_2 y + C_2 z + D_2 = 0 \end{cases}$$

Direction of line: $(B_1 C_2 - C_1 B_2, C_1 A_2 - A_1 C_2, A_1 B_2 - B_1 A_2)$

Projection of segment $P_1 P_2$ on direction (a, b, c):
$$\frac{(x_2 - x_1)a + (y_2 - y_1)b + (z_2 - z_1)c}{\sqrt{a^2 + b^2 + c^2}}$$

Distance from point P_0 to line through P_1 in direction (a, b, c):
$$\sqrt{\frac{\begin{vmatrix} y_0 - y_1 & z_0 - z_1 \\ b & c \end{vmatrix}^2 + \begin{vmatrix} z_0 - z_1 & x_0 - x_1 \\ c & a \end{vmatrix}^2 + \begin{vmatrix} x_0 - x_1 & y_0 - y_1 \\ a & b \end{vmatrix}^2}{a^2 + b^2 + c^2}}$$

Distance between line through P_1 in direction (a_1, b_1, c_1) and line through P_2 in direction (a_2, b_2, c_2):

$$\pm \frac{\begin{vmatrix} x_2 - x_1 & y_2 - y_1 & z_2 - z_1 \\ a_1 & b_1 & c_1 \\ a_2 & b_2 & c_2 \end{vmatrix}}{\sqrt{\begin{vmatrix} b_1 & c_1 \\ b_2 & c_2 \end{vmatrix}^2 + \begin{vmatrix} c_1 & a_1 \\ c_2 & a_2 \end{vmatrix}^2 + \begin{vmatrix} a_1 & b_1 \\ a_2 & b_2 \end{vmatrix}^2}}$$

The line through P_1 in direction (a_1, b_1, c_1) and the line through P_2 in direction (a_2, b_2, c_2) intersect if and only if

$$\begin{vmatrix} x_2 - x_1 & y_2 - y_1 & z_2 - z_1 \\ a_1 & b_1 & c_1 \\ a_2 & b_2 & c_2 \end{vmatrix} = 0.$$

Planes

General form: $Ax + By + Cz + D = 0$

  Direction of normal: (A, B, C)

Perpendicular to yz-plane: $By + Cz + D = 0$

Perpendicular to xz-plane: $Ax + Cz + D = 0$

Perpendicular to xy-plane: $Ax + By + D = 0$

Perpendicular to x-axis: $Ax + D = 0$

Perpendicular to y-axis: $By + D = 0$

Perpendicular to z-axis: $Cz + D = 0$

Intercept form:
$$\frac{x}{a} + \frac{y}{b} + \frac{z}{c} = 1$$

Plane through point P_1 and perpendicular to direction (a, b, c):
$$a(x - x_1) + b(y - y_1) + c(z - z_1) = 0$$

Plane through point P_1 and parallel to directions (a_1,b_1,c_1) and (a_2,b_2,c_2):

$$\begin{vmatrix} x - x_1 & y - y_1 & z - z_1 \\ a_1 & b_1 & c_1 \\ a_2 & b_2 & c_2 \end{vmatrix} = 0$$

Plane through points P_1 and P_2 parallel to direction (a,b,c):

$$\begin{vmatrix} x - x_1 & y - y_1 & z - z_1 \\ x_2 - x_1 & y_2 - y_1 & z_2 - z_1 \\ a & b & c \end{vmatrix} = 0$$

Three-point form:

$$\begin{vmatrix} x & y & z & 1 \\ x_1 & y_1 & z_1 & 1 \\ x_2 & y_2 & z_2 & 1 \\ x_3 & y_3 & z_3 & 1 \end{vmatrix} = 0 \quad \text{or} \quad \begin{vmatrix} x - x_1 & y - y_1 & z - z_1 \\ x_2 - x_1 & y_2 - y_1 & z_2 - z_1 \\ x_3 - x_1 & y_3 - y_1 & z_3 - z_1 \end{vmatrix} = 0$$

Normal form (p = distance from origin to plane; α, β, γ are direction angles of perpendicular to plane from origin):

$$x \cos \alpha + y \cos \beta + z \cos \gamma = p$$

To reduce $Ax + By + Cz + D = 0$ to normal form, divide by $\pm \sqrt{A^2 + B^2 + C^2}$, where the sign of the radical is chosen opposite to the sign of D when $D \neq 0$, the same as the sign of C when $D = 0$ and $C \neq 0$, the same as the sign of B when $C = D = 0$.
Distance from point P_1 to plane $Ax + By + Cz + D = 0$:

$$\frac{Ax_1 + By_1 + Cz_1 + D}{\pm \sqrt{A^2 + B^2 + C^2}}$$

Angle θ between planes $A_1x + B_1y + C_1z + D_1 = 0$ and $A_2x + B_2y + C_2z + D_2 = 0$:

$$\cos \theta = \frac{A_1A_2 + B_1B_2 + C_1C_2}{\sqrt{A_1^2 + B_1^2 + C_1^2} \sqrt{A_2^2 + B_2^2 + C_2^2}}$$

Planes parallel: $\quad A_1 : B_1 : C_1 = A_2 : B_2 : C_2$

Planes perpendicular: $\quad A_1A_2 + B_1B_2 + C_1C_2 = 0$

Spheres

Center at origin, radius r: $\quad x^2 + y^2 + z^2 = r^2$

Center at (g,h,k), radius r: $\quad (x - g)^2 + (y - h)^2 + (z - k)^2 = r^2$

General form: $\quad \begin{cases} Ax^2 + Ay^2 + Az^2 + Dx + Ey + Fz + M = 0, & A \neq 0 \\ x^2 + y^2 + z^2 + 2dx + 2ey + 2fz + m = 0 \end{cases}$

Center: $\quad (-d, -e, -f)$

Radius: $\quad r = \sqrt{d^2 + e^2 + f^2 - m}$

Sphere on $P_1 P_2$ as diameter:

$$(x - x_1)(x - x_2) + (y - y_1)(y - y_2) + (z - z_1)(z - z_2) = 0$$

Four-point form:

$$\begin{vmatrix} x^2 + y^2 + z^2 & x & y & z & 1 \\ x_1^2 + y_1^2 + z_1^2 & x_1 & y_1 & z_1 & 1 \\ x_2^2 + y_2^2 + z_2^2 & x_2 & y_2 & z_2 & 1 \\ x_3^2 + y_3^2 + z_3^2 & x_3 & y_3 & z_3 & 1 \\ x_4^2 + y_4^2 + z_4^2 & x_4 & y_4 & z_4 & 1 \end{vmatrix} = 0$$

The Seventeen Quadric Surfaces in Standard Form

1. Real ellipsoid: $x^2/a^2 + y^2/b^2 + z^2/c^2 = 1$
2. Imaginary ellipsoid: $x^2/a^2 + y^2/b^2 + z^2/c^2 = -1$
3. Hyperboloid of one sheet: $x^2/a^2 + y^2/b^2 - z^2/c^2 = 1$
4. Hyperboloid of two sheets: $x^2/a^2 + y^2/b^2 - z^2/c^2 = -1$
5. Real quadric cone: $x^2/a^2 + y^2/b^2 - z^2/c^2 = 0$
6. Imaginary quadric cone: $x^2/a^2 + y^2/b^2 + z^2/c^2 = 0$
7. Elliptic paraboloid: $x^2/a^2 + y^2/b^2 + 2z = 0$
8. Hyperbolic paraboloid: $x^2/a^2 - y^2/b^2 + 2z = 0$
9. Real elliptic cylinder: $x^2/a^2 + y^2/b^2 = 1$
10. Imaginary elliptic cylinder: $x^2/a^2 + y^2/b^2 = -1$
11. Hyperbolic cylinder: $x^2/a^2 - y^2/b^2 = -1$
12. Real intersecting planes: $x^2/a^2 - y^2/b^2 = 0$
13. Imaginary intersecting planes: $x^2/a^2 + y^2/b^2 = 0$
14. Parabolic cylinder: $x^2 + 2rz = 0$
15. Real parallel planes: $x^2 = a^2$
16. Imaginary parallel planes: $x^2 = -a^2$
17. Coincident planes: $x^2 = 0$

General Equation of Second Degree

The nature of the graph of the general quadratic equation in x, y, z,

$$ax^2 + by^2 + cz^2 + 2fyz + 2gzx + 2hxy + 2px + 2qy + 2rz + d = 0,$$

is described in the following table in terms of $\rho_3, \rho_4, \Delta, k_1, k_2, k_3$, where

$$e = \begin{bmatrix} a & h & g \\ h & b & f \\ g & f & c \end{bmatrix}, \quad E = \begin{bmatrix} a & h & g & p \\ h & b & f & q \\ g & f & c & r \\ p & q & r & d \end{bmatrix},$$

$$\rho_3 = \text{rank } e, \quad \rho_4 = \text{rank } E,$$

$$\Delta = \text{determinant of } E,$$

k_1, k_2, k_3 are the roots of $\begin{vmatrix} a - x & h & g \\ h & b - x & f \\ g & f & c - x \end{vmatrix} = 0.$

Case	ρ_3	ρ_4	Sign of Δ	Nonzero k's same sign?	Quadric Surface
1	3	4	−	yes	Real ellipsoid
2	3	4	+	yes	Imaginary ellipsoid
3	3	4	+	no	Hyperboloid of one sheet
4	3	4	−	no	Hyperboloid of two sheets
5	3	3		no	Real quadric cone
6	3	3		yes	Imaginary quadric cone
7	2	4	−	yes	Elliptic paraboloid
8	2	4	+	no	Hyperbolic paraboloid
9	2	3		yes	Real elliptic cylinder
10	2	3		yes	Imaginary elliptic cylinder
11	2	3		no	Hyperbolic cylinder
12	2	2		no	Real intersecting planes
13	2	2		yes	Imaginary intersecting planes
14	1	3			Parabolic cylinder
15	1	2			Real parallel planes
16	1	2			Imaginary parallel planes
17	1	1			Coincident planes

Cylindrical and Conical Surfaces

Any equation in just two of the variables x, y, z represents a *cylindrical surface* whose elements are parallel to the axis of the missing variable.

Any equation homogeneous in the variables x, y, z represents a *conical surface* whose vertex is at the origin.

Transformation of Coordinates

To transform an equation of a surface from an old system of rectangular coordinates (x, y, z) to a new system of rectangular coordinates (x', y', z'), substitute for each old variable in the equation of the surface its expression in terms of the new variables.

Translation:

$x = x' + h$ The new axes are parallel to the old axes and the coordinates of
$y = y' + k$ the new origin in terms of the old system are (h, k, l).
$z = z' + l$

Rotation about the origin:

$x = \lambda_1 x' + \lambda_2 y' + \lambda_3 z'$ The new origin is coincident with the old origin and
$y = \mu_1 x' + \mu_2 y' + \mu_3 z'$ the x'-axis, y'-axis, z'-axis have direction cosines
$z = \nu_1 x' + \nu_2 y' + \nu_3 z'$ $(\lambda_1, \mu_1, \nu_1), (\lambda_2, \mu_2, \nu_2), (\lambda_3, \mu_3, \nu_3)$, respectively, with respect to the old system of axes.

$x' = \lambda_1 x + \mu_1 y + \nu_1 z$
$y' = \lambda_2 x + \mu_2 y + \nu_2 z$
$z' = \lambda_3 x + \mu_3 y + \nu_3 z$

Cylindrical Coordinates

If (r, θ, z) are the cylindrical co-ordinates and (x, y, z) the rectangular coordinates of a point P, then

$$x = r \cos \theta, \quad r = \sqrt{x^2 + y^2},$$

$$y = r \sin \theta, \quad \theta = \arctan \frac{y}{x},$$

$$z = z, \qquad z = z.$$

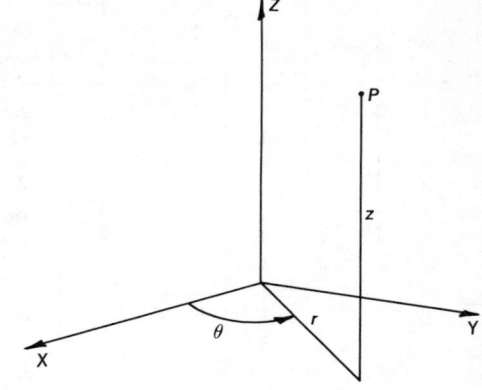

Spherical Coordinates

If (r, θ, ϕ) are the spherical co-ordinates and (x, y, z) the rectangular coordinates of a point P, then

$$x = r \sin \theta \cos \phi,$$
$$y = r \sin \theta \sin \phi,$$
$$z = r \cos \theta,$$
$$r = \sqrt{x^2 + y^2 + z^2},$$
$$\theta = \arccos \frac{z}{\sqrt{x^2 + y^2 + z^2}},$$
$$\phi = \arctan \frac{y}{x}.$$

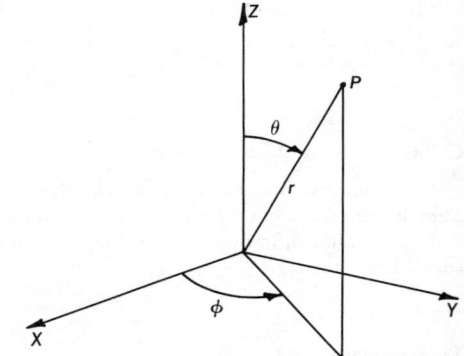

CURVES AND SURFACES

The curves and surfaces collected here for reference appear frequently in mathematical literature. The equations most generally associated with each figure are given. The equation of a plane curve when placed otherwise on the coordinate frame of reference may often be found from the given equation by the following rules.

RECTANGULAR COORDINATES

1. If a given curve is reflected in the x-axis, the new equation is obtained from the old by replacing y by $-y$.

2. If a given curve is reflected in the y-axis, the new equation is obtained from the old by replacing x by $-x$.

3. If a given curve is reflected in the origin, the new equation is obtained from the old by replacing x by $-x$ and y by $-y$.

4. If a given curve is reflected in the line $y = x$, the new equation is obtained from the old by interchanging x and y.

5. If a given curve is rotated about the origin through 90°, the new equation is obtained from the old by replacing x by y and y by $-x$.

6. If a given curve is rotated about the origin through $-90°$, the new equation is obtained from the old by replacing x by $-y$ and y by x.

7. If a given curve is translated a distance h in the x-direction, the new equation is obtained from the old by replacing x by $x - h$.

8. If a given curve is translated a distance k in the y-direction, the new equation is obtained from the old by replacing y by $y - k$.

9. If a given curve is altered by multiplying all the abscissas by a, the new equation is obtained from the old by replacing x by x/a.

10. If a given curve is altered by multiplying all the ordinates by b, the new equation is obtained from the old by replacing y by y/b.

POLAR COORDINATES

1. If a given curve is reflected in the polar axis, the new equation is obtained from the old by replacing θ by $-\theta$, or by replacing r by $-r$ and θ by $\pi - \theta$.

2. If a given curve is reflected in the 90° axis, the new equation is obtained from the old by replacing θ by $\pi - \theta$, or by replacing r by $-r$ and θ by $-\theta$.

3. If a given curve is reflected in the pole, the new equation is obtained from the old by replacing θ by $\pi + \theta$, or by replacing r by $-r$.

4. If a given curve is rotated about the pole through an angle α, the new equation is obtained from the old by replacing θ by $\theta - \alpha$.

PLANE CURVES

Archimedean spiral
 See: Spiral of Archimedes

Astroid
 See: Hypocycloid of four cusps

Bifolium

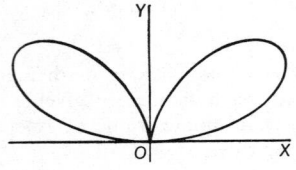

$$(x^2 + y^2)^2 = ax^2 y$$
$$r = a \sin \theta \cos^2 \theta$$

Cardioid

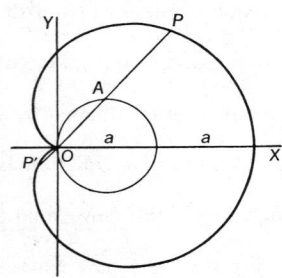

$$(x^2 + y^2 - ax)^2 = a^2(x^2 + y^2)$$
$$r = a(\cos \theta + 1)$$
or
$$r = a(\cos \theta - 1)$$
$$[P'A = AP = a]$$

Cassinian curves
  See: Ovals of Cassini

Catenary, Hyperbolic cosine

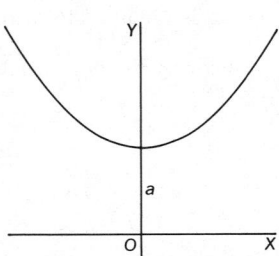

$$y = \frac{x}{a}(e^{x/a} + e^{-x/a}) = a \cosh \frac{x}{a}$$

Circle
(a)

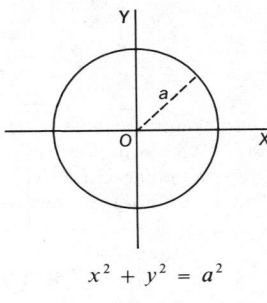

$$x^2 + y^2 = a^2$$
$$r = a$$

(b)

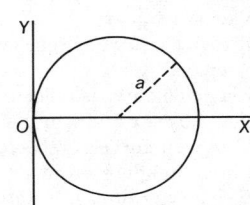

$$x^2 + y^2 = 2ax$$
$$r = 2a \cos \theta$$

(c)

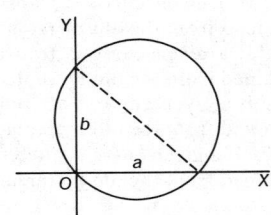

$$x^2 + y^2 = ax + by$$
$$r = a \cos \theta + b \sin \theta$$

Cissoid of Diocles

$$y^2(a - x) = x^3$$
$$r = a \sin \theta \tan \theta$$
$$[OP = AB]$$

Cochleoid, Oui-ja board curve

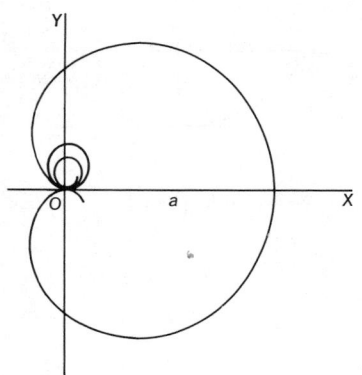

$$(x^2 + y^2)\tan^{-1}(y/x) = ay$$
$$r\theta = a\sin\theta$$

Companion to the cycloid

$$\begin{cases} x = a\phi \\ y = a(1 - \cos\phi) \end{cases}$$
$$[OB = \widehat{AB}]$$
(This is a sinusoid)

Conchoid of Nicomedes
(a) $a < b$

(b) $a > b$

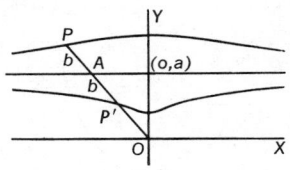

$$(y - a)^2(x^2 + y^2) = b^2y^2$$
$$r = a\csc\theta \pm b$$
$$[P'A = AP = b]$$

Conic sections
See: Circle; Ellipse; Hyperbola; Parabola

Cosecant curve

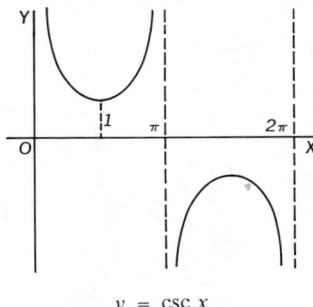

$$y = \csc x$$

Cosine curve

$$y = \cos x$$

Cotangent curve

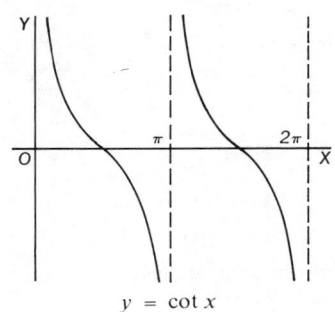

$$y = \cot x$$

Cubical parabola (special)

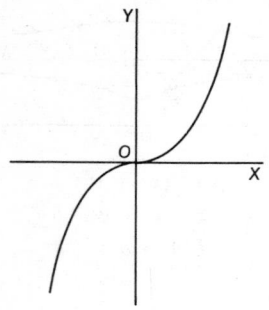

$$y = ax^3, \quad a > 0$$

$$r^2 = \frac{1}{a} \sec^2 \theta \tan \theta, \quad a > 0$$

Cubical parabola (general)

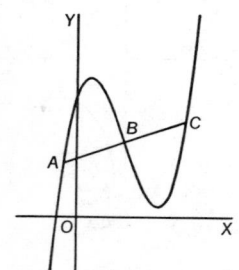

$$y = ax^3 + bx^2 + cx + d, \quad a > 0$$

$$[AB = BC]$$

(abscissa of $B = -b/3a$)

Curtate cycloid
   See: Cycloid, curtate

Cycloid (cusp at origin)

$$x = a \arccos \frac{a - y}{a} \mp \sqrt{2ay - y^2}$$

$$\begin{cases} x = a(\phi - \sin \phi) \\ y = a(1 - \cos \phi) \end{cases}$$

(For one arch: arc length = $8a$; area = $3\pi a^2$)

Cycloid (vertex at origin)

$$x = 2a \arcsin \sqrt{y/2a} + \sqrt{2ay - y^2}$$

$$\begin{cases} x = a(\phi + \sin \phi) \\ y = a(1 - \cos \phi) \end{cases}$$

Cycloid, curtate

$$\begin{cases} x = a\phi - b \sin \phi \\ y = a - b \cos \phi \end{cases}$$

$$a > b$$

Cycloid, prolate

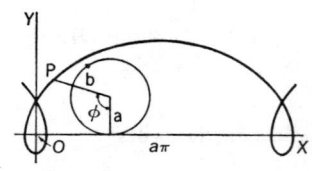

$$\begin{cases} x = a\phi - b \sin \phi \\ y = a - b \cos \phi \end{cases}$$

$$a < b$$

Deltoid
   See: Hypocycloid of three cusps

Ellipse

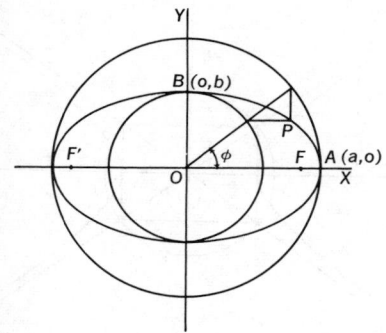

$$x^2/a^2 + y^2/b^2 = 1$$

$$\begin{cases} x = a \cos \phi \\ y = b \sin \phi \end{cases}$$

$$[BF' = BF = a, \quad PF' + PF = 2a]$$

Evolute of ellipse

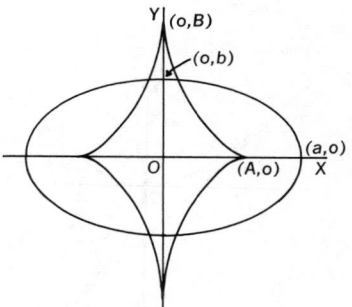

$$(ax)^{2/3} + (by)^{2/3} = (a^2 - b^2)^{2/3}$$

$$\begin{cases} x = A \cos^3 \phi \\ y = B \sin^3 \phi \end{cases}$$

$$[A = (a^2 - b^2)/a, \quad B = (a^2 - b^2)/b]$$

Exponential curve

(1) $a > 0$

Epicycloid

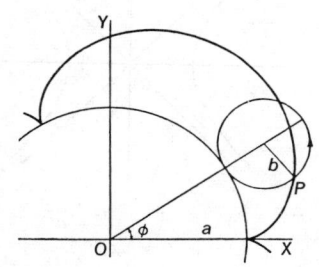

$$\begin{cases} x = (a + b) \cos \phi - b \cos\left(\dfrac{a + b}{b} \phi\right) \\ y = (a + b) \sin \phi - b \sin\left(\dfrac{a + b}{b} \phi\right) \end{cases}$$

(2) $a < 0$

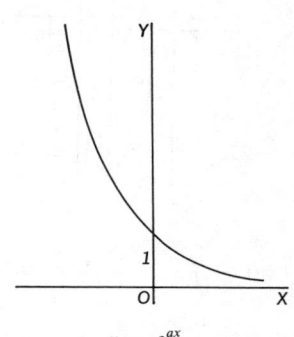

$$y = e^{ax}$$

Equiangular spiral

See: Spiral, logarithmic or equiangular

Equilateral hyperbola

See: Hyperbola, equilateral or rectangular

Folium of Descartes

$$x^3 + y^3 - 3axy = 0$$
$$\begin{cases} x = 3a\phi/(1 + \phi^3) \\ y = 3a\phi^2/(1 + \phi^3) \end{cases}$$
$$r = \frac{3a \sin\theta \cos\theta}{\sin^3\theta + \cos^3\theta}$$

[asymptote: $x + y + a = 0$]

Gamma function

$$\Gamma(n) = \int_0^\infty x^{n-1} e^{-x} dx \quad (n > 0)$$

$$\Gamma(n) = \frac{\Gamma(n+1)}{n} \quad (0 > n \neq -1, -2, -3, \ldots)$$

Hyperbola

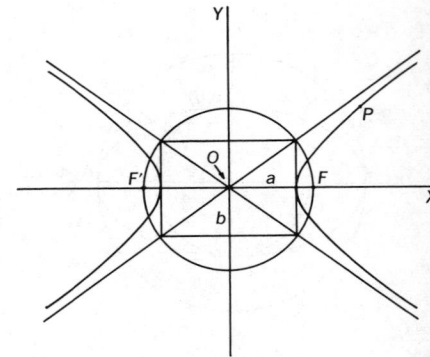

$$x^2/a^2 - y^2/b^2 = 1$$
$$[F'P - FP = 2a]$$

Hyperbola, equilateral or rectangular
(1)

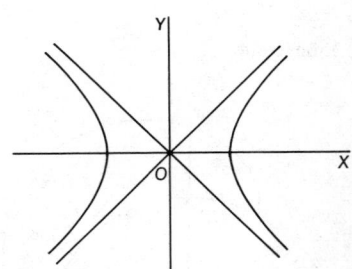

$$x^2 - y^2 = a^2$$

(2)

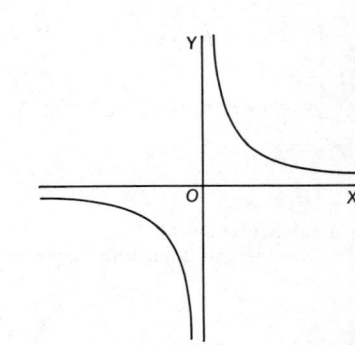

$$xy = k, \quad k > 0$$

(3)

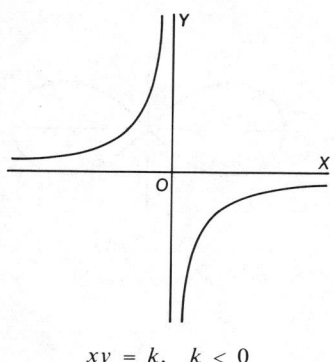

$$xy = k, \quad k < 0$$

Hyperbolic functions

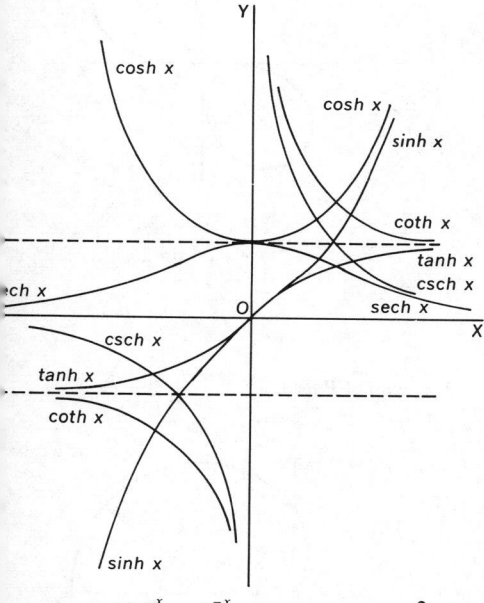

$$\sinh x = \frac{e^x - e^{-x}}{2} \qquad \operatorname{csch} x = \frac{2}{e^x - e^{-x}}$$

$$\cosh x = \frac{e^x + e^{-x}}{2} \qquad \operatorname{sech} x = \frac{2}{e^x + e^{-x}}$$

$$\tanh x = \frac{e^x - e^{-x}}{e^x + e^{-x}} \qquad \coth x = \frac{e^x + e^{-x}}{e^x - e^{-x}}$$

Hyperbolic spiral

See: Spiral, hyperbolic or reciprocal

Hypocycloid of three cusps, Deltoid

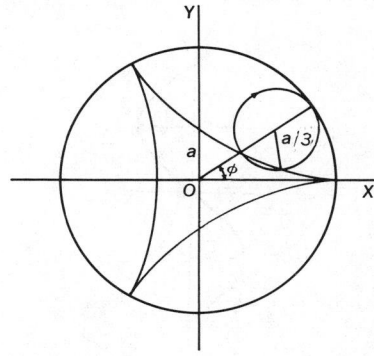

$$\begin{cases} x = 2a \cos \phi + a \cos 2\phi \\ y = 2a \sin \phi - a \sin 2\phi \end{cases}$$

Hypocycloid of four cusps, Astroid

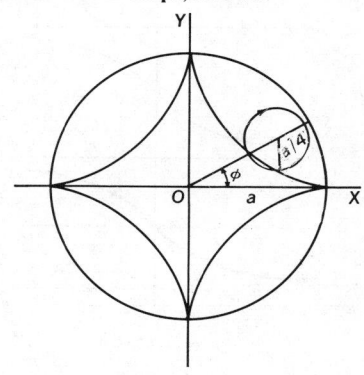

$$x^{2/3} + y^{2/3} = a^{2/3}$$
$$\begin{cases} x = a \cos^3 \phi \\ y = a \sin^3 \phi \end{cases}$$

Inverse cosine curve

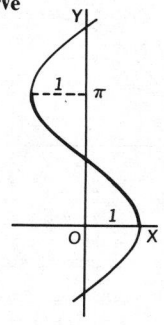

$$y = \arccos x$$

Inverse sine curve

$$y = \arcsin x$$

Inverse tangent curve

$$y = \arctan x$$

Involute of circle

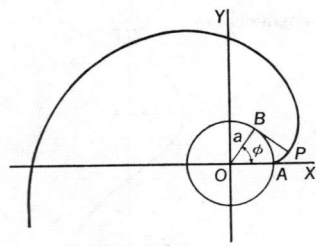

$$\begin{cases} x = a \cos \phi + a\phi \sin \phi \\ y = a \sin \phi - a\phi \cos \phi \end{cases}$$

$$[BP = \widehat{BA}]$$

Lemniscate of Bernoulli, Two-leaved rose

(a)

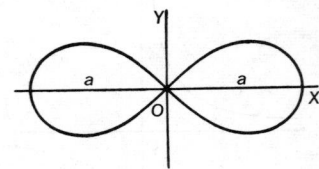

$$(x^2 + y^2)^2 = a^2(x^2 - y^2)$$
$$r^2 = a^2 \cos 2\theta$$

(b)

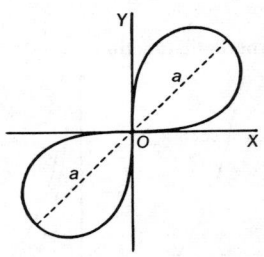

$$(x^2 + y^2)^2 = 2a^2 xy$$
$$r^2 = a^2 \sin 2\theta$$

Limaçon of Pascal

(1) $a > b$

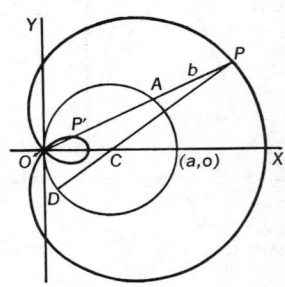

[If $a = 2b$, the curve is called the *trisectrix*, since then $\measuredangle OPD = \frac{1}{3} \measuredangle OCD$.]

(2) $a = b$
  See: Cardioid

(3) $a < b$

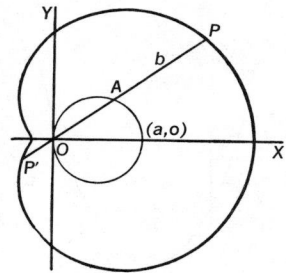

$$(x^2 + y^2 - ax)^2 = b^2(x^2 + y^2)$$
$$r = b + a \cos \theta$$
$$[P'A = AP = b]$$

Lituus

$$r^2 \theta = a^2$$

Logarithmic curve
(1) $a > 1$

(2) $0 < a < 1$

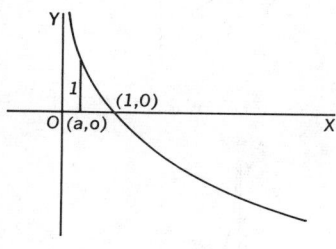

$$y = \log_a x$$

Logarithmic spiral
See: Spiral, logarithmic or equiangular

Nephroid

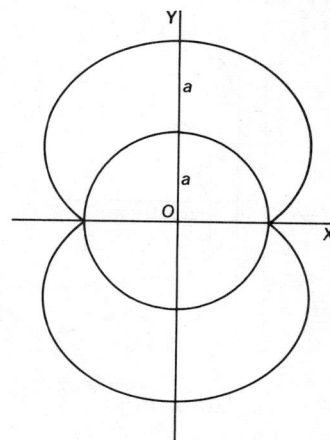

$$\begin{cases} x = \frac{1}{2}a(3 \cos \phi - \cos 3\phi) \\ y = \frac{1}{2}a(3 \sin \phi - \sin 3\phi) \end{cases}$$

[The nephroid is a 2-cusped epicycloid.]

Oui-ja board curve
See: Cochleoid

Ovals of Cassini
(1) $b > k$

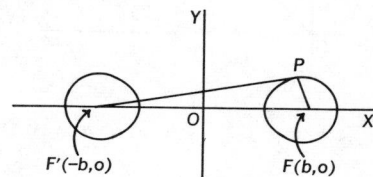

(2) $b = k$
See: Lemniscate of Bernoulli
(3) $b < k$

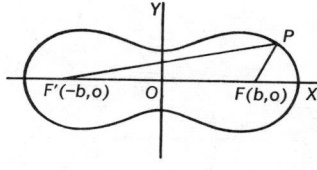

$$(x^2 + y^2 + b^2)^2 - 4b^2x^2 = k^4$$
$$r^4 + b^4 - 2r^2b^2 \cos 2\theta = k^4$$
$$[F'P \cdot FP = k^2]$$

[These curves are sections of a torus on planes parallel to the axis of the torus.]

Parabola

(1)

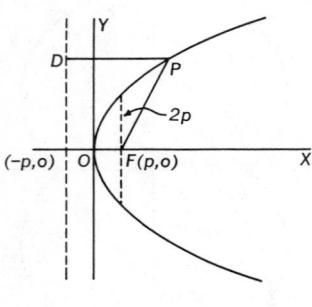

$$y^2 = 4px$$
$$[DP = FP]$$

(2)

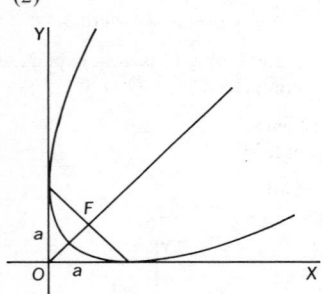

$$\pm x^{1/2} \pm y^{1/2} = a^{1/2}$$
$$(x - y)^2 - 2a(x + y) + a^2 = 0$$

(3)

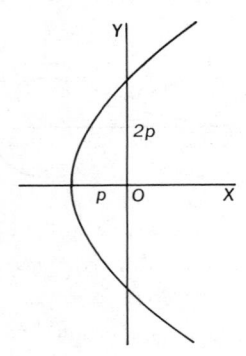

$$r = 2p/(1 - \cos \theta)$$

(4)

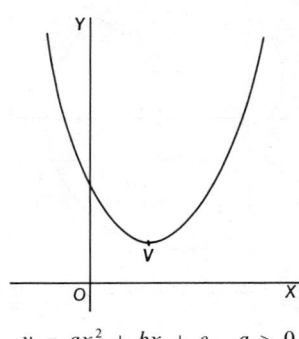

$$y = ax^2 + bx + c, \quad a > 0$$
$$[\text{abscissa of vertex} = -b/2a]$$

Parabolic spiral
   See: Spiral, parabolic

Power functions
   (1)

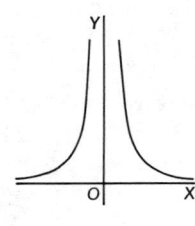

$$y = x^{-2}$$

(2) Equilateral hyperbola

$$y = x^{-1}$$

(3)

$$y = x^{-1/2}$$

(4) Cubical parabola

$$y = x^{1/3}$$

(5) Half of a parabola

$$y = x^{1/2}$$

(6) Semicubical parabola

$$y = x^{2/3}$$

(7) Half of semicubical parabola

$$y = x^{3/2}$$

(8) Parabola

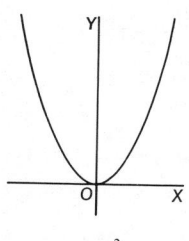

$$y = x^{2}$$

(9) Cubical parabola

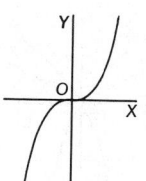

$$y = x^{3}$$

Probability curve

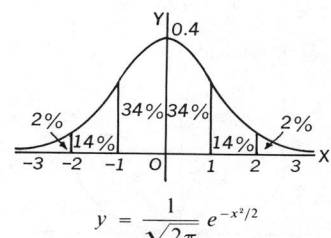

$$y = \frac{1}{\sqrt{2\pi}} e^{-x^2/2}$$

Prolate cycloid
   See: Cycloid, prolate

Pursuit curve
   See: Tractrix

Quadratrix of Hippias

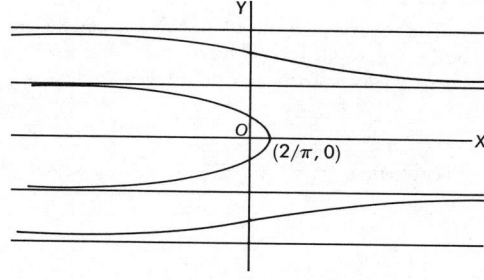

$$y = x \tan (\pi y/2)$$

Reciprocal spiral
   See: Spiral, hyperbolic or reciprocal

Rectangular hyperbola
   See: Hyperbola, equilateral or rectangular

Rose curves
   (1) Two-leaved
      See: Lemniscate of Bernoulli, Two-
      leaved rose

(2) Three-leaved   (3) Three-leaved

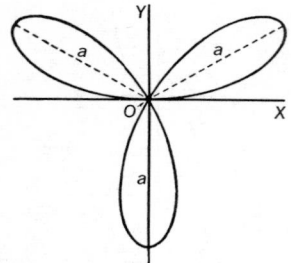

$r = a \sin 3\theta$

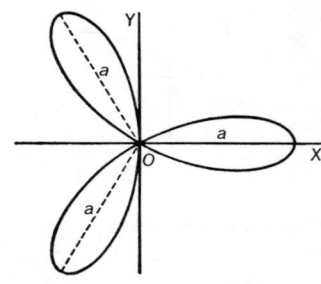

$r = a \cos 3\theta$

(4) Four-leaved   (5) Four-leaved

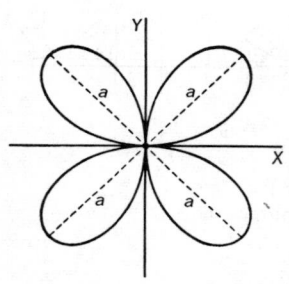

$r = a \sin 2\theta$

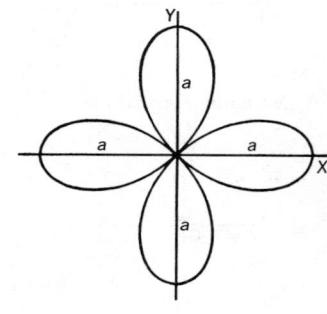

$r = a \cos 2\theta$

(6) *n*-leaved

The roses $r = a \sin n\theta$ and $r = a \cos n\theta$, have, for *n* an even integer, $2n$ leaves; for *n* an odd integer, *n* leaves. The roses $r^2 = a \sin n\theta$ and $r^2 = a \cos n\theta$, have, for *n* an even integer, *n* leaves; for *n* an odd integer, $2n$ leaves.

Secant curve   **Semicubical parabola**

$y = \sec x$

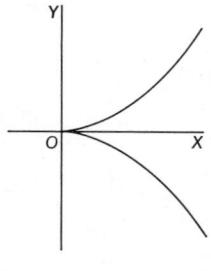

$$y^2 = ax^3$$

$$r = \frac{1}{a} \tan^2 \theta \sec \theta$$

Serpentine curve

$$(a^2 + x^2)y = abx$$

$$\begin{cases} x = a \cot \phi \\ y = b \sin \phi \cos \phi \end{cases}$$

Sine curve

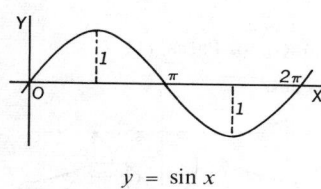

$$y = \sin x$$

Sinusoid

$$y = a \sin (bx + c)$$

Spiral of Archimedes

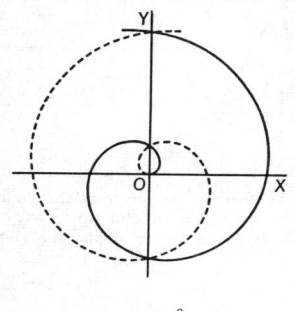

$$r = a\theta$$

Spiral, hyperbolic or reciprocal

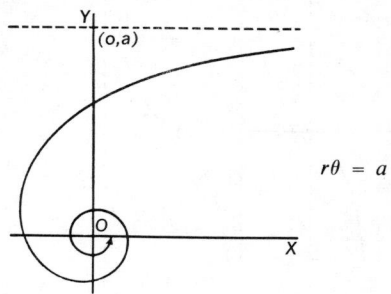

$$r\theta = a$$

Spiral, logarithmic or equiangular

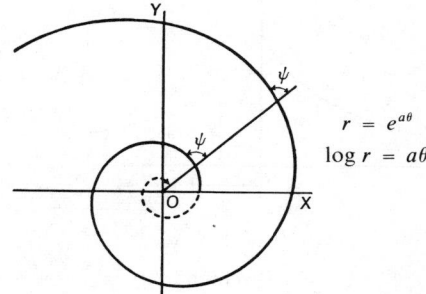

$$r = e^{a\theta}$$
$$\log r = a\theta$$

Spiral, parabolic

$$(r - a)^2 = 4ak\theta$$

Strophoid

$$y^2 = x^2 \frac{a - x}{a + x}$$

$$r = a \cos 2\theta \sec \theta$$

$$[P'A = AP = OA]$$

Tangent curve

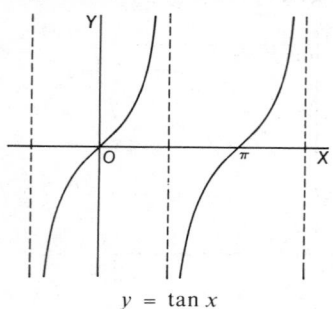

$$y = \tan x$$

Tractrix, Pursuit curve

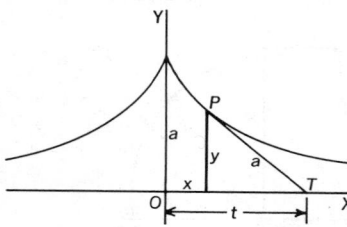

$$x = a \operatorname{sech}^{-1}(y/a) - \sqrt{a^2 - y^2}$$

$$\begin{cases} x = t - a \tanh(t/a) \\ y = a \operatorname{sech}(t/a) \end{cases}$$

$$[PT = a]$$

Trajectory (a parabola)

$$y = x \tan \alpha - gx^2/(2v_0^2 \cos^2 \alpha)$$
$$x = (v_0 \cos \alpha) t$$
$$y = (v_0 \sin \alpha) t - gt^2/2$$

Trigonometric functions

See: Cosecant curve; Cosine curve; Cotangent curve; Secant curve; Sine curve; Tangent curve

Trisectrix

See: Limaçon of Pascal (1)

Witch of Agnesi

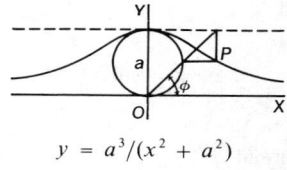

$$y = a^3/(x^2 + a^2)$$

$$\begin{cases} x = a \cot \phi \\ y = a \sin^2 \phi \end{cases}$$

*QUADRIC SURFACES

Ellipsoid

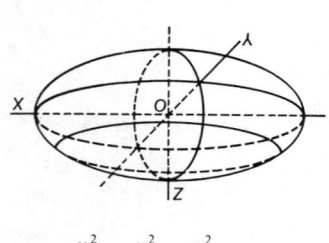

$$\frac{x^2}{a^2} + \frac{y^2}{b^2} + \frac{z^2}{c^2} = 1$$

Elliptic cone

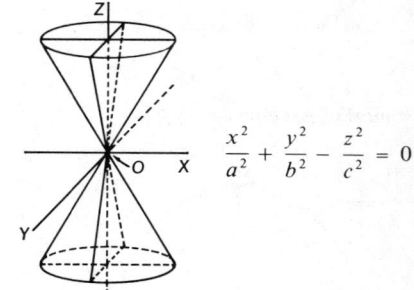

$$\frac{x^2}{a^2} + \frac{y^2}{b^2} - \frac{z^2}{c^2} = 0$$

*Each of the equations is given for the case where the origin is located at $(0,0,0)$, the center of the quadric surface. If, however, the center of the surface is at (h, k, l), replace x by $x - h$, y by $y - k$, and z by $z - l$, and the particular standardized form will be that of the surface with center at (h, k, l). For example, the elliptic paraboloid would be

$$\frac{(x - h)^2}{a^2} - \frac{(y - k)^2}{b^2} = c(z - l).$$

Elliptic cylinder

$$\frac{x^2}{a^2} + \frac{y^2}{b^2} = 1$$

Hyperboloid of one sheet

$$\frac{x^2}{a^2} + \frac{y^2}{b^2} - \frac{z^2}{c^2} = 1$$

Elliptic paraboloid

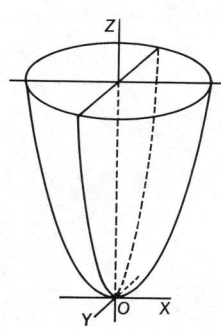

$$\frac{x^2}{a^2} + \frac{y^2}{b^2} = cz$$

Hyperboloid of two sheets

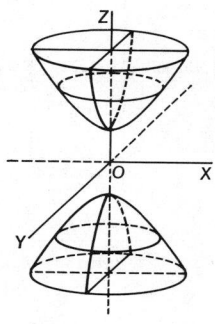

$$\frac{z^2}{c^2} - \frac{x^2}{a^2} - \frac{y^2}{b^2} = 1$$

Hyperbolic paraboloid

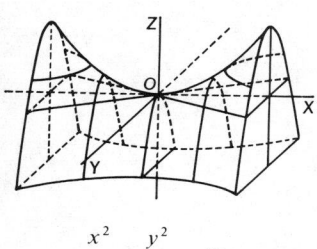

$$\frac{x^2}{a^2} - \frac{y^2}{b^2} = cz$$

Sphere

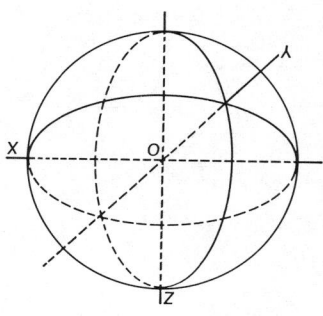

$$x^2 + y^2 + z^2 = a^2$$

PATTERNS OF REGULAR POLYHEDRA

Tetrahedron

Octahedron

Hexahedron, or **Cube**

Icosahedron

Dodecahedron

*Derivatives

In the following formulas u, v, w represent functions of x, while a, c, n represent fixed real numbers. All arguments in the trigonometric functions are measured in radians, and all inverse trigonometric and hyperbolic functions represent principal values.

1. $\dfrac{d}{dx}(a) = 0$

2. $\dfrac{d}{dx}(x) = 1$

3. $\dfrac{d}{dx}(au) = a\dfrac{du}{dx}$

4. $\dfrac{d}{dx}(u + v - w) = \dfrac{du}{dx} + \dfrac{dv}{dx} - \dfrac{dw}{dx}$

5. $\dfrac{d}{dx}(uv) = u\dfrac{dv}{dx} + v\dfrac{du}{dx}$

6. $\dfrac{d}{dx}(uvw) = uv\dfrac{dw}{dx} + vw\dfrac{du}{dx} + uw\dfrac{dv}{dx}$

7. $\dfrac{d}{dx}\left(\dfrac{u}{v}\right) = \dfrac{v\dfrac{du}{dx} - u\dfrac{dv}{dx}}{v^2} = \dfrac{1}{v}\dfrac{du}{dx} - \dfrac{u}{v^2}\dfrac{dv}{dx}$

8. $\dfrac{d}{dx}(u^n) = nu^{n-1}\dfrac{du}{dx}$

9. $\dfrac{d}{dx}(\sqrt{u}) = \dfrac{1}{2\sqrt{u}}\dfrac{du}{dx}$

10. $\dfrac{d}{dx}\left(\dfrac{1}{u}\right) = -\dfrac{1}{u^2}\dfrac{du}{dx}$

11. $\dfrac{d}{dx}\left(\dfrac{1}{u^n}\right) = -\dfrac{n}{u^{n+1}}\dfrac{du}{dx}$

12. $\dfrac{d}{dx}\left(\dfrac{u^n}{v^m}\right) = \dfrac{u^{n-1}}{v^{m+1}}\left(nv\dfrac{du}{dx} - mu\dfrac{dv}{dx}\right)$

13. $\dfrac{d}{dx}(u^n v^m) = u^{n-1}v^{m-1}\left(nv\dfrac{du}{dx} + mu\dfrac{dv}{dx}\right)$

14. $\dfrac{d}{dx}[f(u)] = \dfrac{d}{du}[f(u)] \cdot \dfrac{du}{dx}$

* Let $y = f(x)$ and $\dfrac{dy}{dx} = \dfrac{d[f(x)]}{dx} = f'(x)$ define respectively a function and its derivative for any value x in their common domain. The differential for the function at such a value x is accordingly defined as

$$dy = d[f(x)] = \dfrac{dy}{dx}dx = \dfrac{d[f(x)]}{dx}dx = f'(x)\,dx$$

Each derivative formula has an associated differential formula. For example, formula 6 above has the differential formula

$$d(uvw) = uv\,dw + vw\,du + uw\,dv$$

395

DERIVATIVES (Continued)

15. $\dfrac{d^2}{dx^2}[f(u)] = \dfrac{df(u)}{du} \cdot \dfrac{d^2u}{dx^2} + \dfrac{d^2f(u)}{du^2} \cdot \left(\dfrac{du}{dx}\right)^2$

16. $\dfrac{d^n}{dx^n}[uv] = \binom{n}{0}v\dfrac{d^nu}{dx^n} + \binom{n}{1}\dfrac{dv}{dx}\dfrac{d^{n-1}u}{dx^{n-1}} + \binom{n}{2}\dfrac{d^2v}{dx^2}\dfrac{d^{n-2}u}{dx^{n-2}}$

$$+ \cdots + \binom{n}{k}\dfrac{d^kv}{dx^k}\dfrac{d^{n-k}u}{dx^{n-k}} + \cdots + \binom{n}{n}u\dfrac{d^nv}{dx^n}$$

where $\dbinom{n}{r} = \dfrac{n!}{r!(n-r)!}$ the binomial coefficient, n non-negative integer and $\dbinom{n}{0} = 1$.

17. $\dfrac{du}{dx} = \dfrac{1}{\dfrac{dx}{du}} \qquad \text{if } \dfrac{dx}{du} \neq 0$

18. $\dfrac{d}{dx}(\log_a u) = (\log_a e)\dfrac{1}{u}\dfrac{du}{dx}$

19. $\dfrac{d}{dx}(\log_e u) = \dfrac{1}{u}\dfrac{du}{dx}$

20. $\dfrac{d}{dx}(a^u) = a^u(\log_e a)\dfrac{du}{dx}$

21. $\dfrac{d}{dx}(e^u) = e^u\dfrac{du}{dx}$

22. $\dfrac{d}{dx}(u^v) = vu^{v-1}\dfrac{du}{dx} + (\log_e u)u^v\dfrac{dv}{dx}$

23. $\dfrac{d}{dx}(\sin u) = \dfrac{du}{dx}(\cos u)$

24. $\dfrac{d}{dx}(\cos u) = -\dfrac{du}{dx}(\sin u)$

25. $\dfrac{d}{dx}(\tan u) = \dfrac{du}{dx}(\sec^2 u)$

26. $\dfrac{d}{dx}(\cot u) = -\dfrac{du}{dx}(\csc^2 u)$

27. $\dfrac{d}{dx}(\sec u) = \dfrac{du}{dx}\sec u \cdot \tan u$

28. $\dfrac{d}{dx}(\csc u) = -\dfrac{du}{dx}\csc u \cdot \cot u$

29. $\dfrac{d}{dx}(\text{vers } u) = \dfrac{du}{dx}\sin u$

30. $\dfrac{d}{dx}(\text{arc sin } u) = \dfrac{1}{\sqrt{1-u^2}}\dfrac{du}{dx}, \qquad \left(-\dfrac{\pi}{2} \leq \text{arc sin } u \leq \dfrac{\pi}{2}\right)$

DERIVATIVES (Continued)

31. $\dfrac{d}{dx}(\arccos u) = -\dfrac{1}{\sqrt{1-u^2}}\dfrac{du}{dx}$, $\quad (0 \le \arccos u \le \pi)$

32. $\dfrac{d}{dx}(\arctan u) = \dfrac{1}{1+u^2}\dfrac{du}{dx}$, $\quad \left(-\dfrac{\pi}{2} < \arctan u < \dfrac{\pi}{2}\right)$

33. $\dfrac{d}{dx}(\operatorname{arc cot} u) = -\dfrac{1}{1+u^2}\dfrac{du}{dx}$, $\quad (0 \le \operatorname{arc cot} u \le \pi)$

34. $\dfrac{d}{dx}(\operatorname{arc sec} u) = \dfrac{1}{u\sqrt{u^2-1}}\dfrac{du}{dx}$, $\quad \left(0 \le \operatorname{arc sec} u < \dfrac{\pi}{2}, -\pi \le \operatorname{arc sec} u < -\dfrac{\pi}{2}\right)$

35. $\dfrac{d}{dx}(\operatorname{arc csc} u) = -\dfrac{1}{u\sqrt{u^2-1}}\dfrac{du}{dx}$, $\quad \left(0 < \operatorname{arc csc} u \le \dfrac{\pi}{2}, -\pi < \operatorname{arc csc} u \le -\dfrac{\pi}{2}\right)$

36. $\dfrac{d}{dx}(\operatorname{arc vers} u) = \dfrac{1}{\sqrt{2u-u^2}}\dfrac{du}{dx}$, $\quad (0 \le \operatorname{arc vers} u \le \pi)$

37. $\dfrac{d}{dx}(\sinh u) = \dfrac{du}{dx}(\cosh u)$

38. $\dfrac{d}{dx}(\cosh u) = \dfrac{du}{dx}(\sinh u)$

39. $\dfrac{d}{dx}(\tanh u) = \dfrac{du}{dx}(\operatorname{sech}^2 u)$

40. $\dfrac{d}{dx}(\coth u) = -\dfrac{du}{dx}(\operatorname{csch}^2 u)$

41. $\dfrac{d}{dx}(\operatorname{sech} u) = -\dfrac{du}{dx}(\operatorname{sech} u \cdot \tanh u)$

42. $\dfrac{d}{dx}(\operatorname{csch} u) = -\dfrac{du}{dx}(\operatorname{csch} u \cdot \coth u)$

43. $\dfrac{d}{dx}(\sinh^{-1} u) = \dfrac{d}{dx}[\log(u + \sqrt{u^2+1})] = \dfrac{1}{\sqrt{u^2+1}}\dfrac{du}{dx}$

44. $\dfrac{d}{dx}(\cosh^{-1} u) = \dfrac{d}{dx}[\log(u + \sqrt{u^2-1})] = \dfrac{1}{\sqrt{u^2-1}}\dfrac{du}{dx}$, $\quad (u > 1, \cosh^{-1} u > 0)$

45. $\dfrac{d}{dx}(\tanh^{-1} u) = \dfrac{d}{dx}\left[\dfrac{1}{2}\log\dfrac{1+u}{1-u}\right] = \dfrac{1}{1-u^2}\dfrac{du}{dx}$, $\quad (u^2 < 1)$

46. $\dfrac{d}{dx}(\coth^{-1} u) = \dfrac{d}{dx}\left[\dfrac{1}{2}\log\dfrac{u+1}{u-1}\right] = \dfrac{1}{1-u^2}\dfrac{du}{dx}$, $\quad (u^2 > 1)$

47. $\dfrac{d}{dx}(\operatorname{sech}^{-1} u) = \dfrac{d}{dx}\left[\log\dfrac{1+\sqrt{1-u^2}}{u}\right] = -\dfrac{1}{u\sqrt{1-u^2}}\dfrac{du}{dx}$, $\quad (0 < u < 1, \operatorname{sech}^{-1} u > 0)$

48. $\dfrac{d}{dx}(\operatorname{csch}^{-1} u) = \dfrac{d}{dx}\left[\log\dfrac{1+\sqrt{1+u^2}}{u}\right] = -\dfrac{1}{|u|\sqrt{1+u^2}}\dfrac{du}{dx}$

49. $\dfrac{d}{dq} \displaystyle\int_p^q f(x)\,dx = f(q),$ 　　　[p constant]

50. $\dfrac{d}{dp} \displaystyle\int_p^q f(x)\,dx = -f(p),$ 　　　[q constant]

51. $\dfrac{d}{da} \displaystyle\int_p^q f(x,a)\,dx = \displaystyle\int_p^q \dfrac{\partial}{\partial a}[f(x,a)]\,dx + f(q,a)\dfrac{dq}{da} - f(p,a)\dfrac{dp}{da}$

INTEGRATION

The following is a brief discussion of some integration techniques. A more complete discussion can be found in a number of good text books. However, the purpose of this introduction is simply to discuss a few of the important techniques which may be used, in conjunction with the integral table which follows, to integrate particular functions.

No matter how extensive the integral table, it is a fairly uncommon occurrence to find in the table the exact integral desired. Usually some form of transformation will have to be made. The simplest type of transformation, and yet the most general, is substitution. Simple forms of substitution, such as $y = ax$, are employed almost unconsciously by experienced users of integral tables. Other substitutions may require more thought. In some sections of the tables, appropriate substitutions are suggested for integrals which are similar to, but not exactly like, integrals in the table. Finding the right substitution is largely a matter of intuition and experience.

Several precautions must be observed when using substitutions:

1. Be sure to make the substitution in the dx term, as well as everywhere else in the integral.
2. Be sure that the function substituted is one-to-one and continuous. If this is not the case, the integral must be restricted in such a way as to make it true. See the example following.
3. With definite integrals, the limits should also be expressed in terms of the new dependent variable. With indefinite integrals, it is necessary to perform the reverse substitution to obtain the answer in terms of the original independent variable. This may also be done for definite integrals, but it is usually easier to change the limits.

Example:

$$\int \frac{x^4}{\sqrt{a^2 - x^2}} \, dx$$

Here we make the substitution $x = |a| \sin \theta$. Then $dx = |a| \cos \theta \, d\theta$, and

$$\sqrt{a^2 - x^2} = \sqrt{a^2 - a^2 \sin^2 \theta} = |a|\sqrt{1 - \sin^2 \theta} = |a \cos \theta|$$

Notice the absolute value signs. It is very important to keep in mind that a square root radical always denotes the positive square root, and to assure the sign is always kept positive. Thus $\sqrt{x^2} = |x|$. Failure to observe this is a common cause of errors in integration.

Notice also that the indicated substitution is not a one-to-one function, that is, it does not have a unique inverse. Thus we must restrict the range of θ in such a way as to make the function one-to-one. Fortunately, this is easily done by solving for θ

$$\theta = \sin^{-1} \frac{x}{|a|}$$

and restricting the inverse sine to the principal values, $-\frac{\pi}{2} \le \theta \le \frac{\pi}{2}$.

Thus the integral becomes

$$\int \frac{a^4 \sin^4 \theta |a| \cos \theta \, d\theta}{|a| |\cos \theta|}$$

Now, however, in the range of values chosen for θ, $\cos \theta$ is always positive. Thus we may remove the absolute value signs from $\cos \theta$ in the denominator. (This is one of the reasons that the principal values of the inverse trigonometric functions are defined as they are.)

Then the cos θ terms cancel, and the integral becomes

$$a^4 \int \sin^4 \theta \, d\theta$$

By application of integral formulas 299 and 296, we integrate this to

$$-a^4 \frac{\sin^3 \theta \cos \theta}{4} - \frac{3a^4}{8} \cos \theta \sin \theta + \frac{3a^4}{8}\theta + C$$

We now must perform the inverse substitution to get the result in terms of x. We have

$$\theta = \sin^{-1} \frac{x}{|a|}$$

$$\sin \theta = \frac{x}{|a|}$$

Then

$$\cos \theta = \pm\sqrt{1 - \sin^2 \theta} = \pm\sqrt{1 - \frac{x^2}{a^2}} = \pm\frac{\sqrt{a^2 - x^2}}{|a|}.$$

Because of the previously mentioned fact that cos θ is positive, we may omit the $\pm$ sign. The reverse substitution then produces the final answer

$$\int \frac{x^4}{\sqrt{a^2 - x^2}} \, dx = -\tfrac{1}{4}x^3\sqrt{a^2 - x^2} - \tfrac{3}{8}a^2x\sqrt{a^2 - x^2} + \frac{3a^4}{8} \sin^{-1} \frac{x}{|a|} + C.$$

Any rational function of x may be integrated, if the denominator is factored into linear and irreducible quadratic factors. The function may then be broken into partial fractions, and the individual partial fractions integrated by use of the appropriate formula from the integral table. See the section on partial fractions for further information.

Many integrals may be reduced to rational functions by proper substitutions. For example,

$$z = \tan \frac{x}{2}$$

will reduce any rational function of the six trigonometric functions of x to a rational function of z. (Frequently there are other substitutions which are simpler to use, but this one will always work. See integral formula number 484.)

Any rational function of x and $\sqrt{ax + b}$ may be reduced to a rational function of z by making the substitution

$$z = \sqrt{ax + b}.$$

Other likely substitutions will be suggested by looking at the form of the integrand.

The other main method of transforming integrals is integration by parts. This involves applying formula number 5 or 6 in the accompanying integral table. The critical factor in this method is the choice of the functions u and v. In order for the method to be successful, $v = \int dv$ and $\int v \, du$ must be easier to integrate than the original integral. Again, this choice is largely a matter of intuition and experience.

Example:

$$\int x \sin x \, dx$$

Two obvious choices are $u = x$, $dv = \sin x \, dx$, or $u = \sin x$, $dv = x \, dx$. Since a preliminary mental calculation indicates that $\int v \, du$ in the second choice would be more, rather than less, complicated than the original integral (it would contain x^2), we use the first choice.

$$u = x \qquad\qquad du = dx$$
$$dv = \sin x \, dx \qquad\qquad v = -\cos x$$
$$\int x \sin x \, dx = \int u \, dv = uv - \int v \, du = -x \cos x + \int \cos x \, dx$$
$$= \sin x - x \cos x$$

Of course, this result could have been obtained directly from the integral table, but it provides a simple example of the method. In more complicated examples the choice of u and v may not be so obvious, and several different choices may have to be tried. Of course, there is no guarantee that any of them will work.

Integration by parts may be applied more than once, or combined with substitution. A fairly common case is illustrated by the following example.

Example:

$$\int e^x \sin x \, dx$$

Let

$$u = e^x \qquad \text{Then} \quad du = e^x \, dx$$
$$dv = \sin x \, dx \qquad\qquad v = -\cos x$$
$$\int e^x \sin x \, dx = \int u \, dv = uv - \int v \, du = -e^x \cos x + \int e^x \cos x \, dx$$

In this latter integral,

$$\text{let} \quad u = e^x \qquad \text{Then} \quad du = e^x \, dx$$
$$dv = \cos x \, dx \qquad\qquad v = \sin x$$
$$\int e^x \sin x \, dx = -e^x \cos x + \int e^x \cos x \, dx = -e^x \cos x + \int u \, dv$$
$$= -e^x \cos x + uv - \int v \, du$$
$$= -e^x \cos x + e^x \sin x - \int e^x \sin x \, dx$$

This looks as if a circular transformation has taken place, since we are back at the same integral we started from. However, the above equation can be solved algebraically for the required integral:

$$\int e^x \sin x \, dx = \tfrac{1}{2}(e^x \sin x - e^x \cos x)$$

In the second integration by parts, if the parts had been chosen as $u = \cos x$, $dv = e^x \, dx$, we would indeed have made a circular transformation, and returned to the starting place. In general, when doing repeated integration by parts, one should never choose the function u at any stage to be the same as the function v at the previous stage, or a constant times the previous v.

The following rule is called the extended rule for integration by parts. It is the result of $n + 1$ successive applications of integration by parts.

If

$$g_1(x) = \int g(x)\, dx, \qquad g_2(x) = \int g_1(x)\, dx,$$

$$g_3(x) = \int g_2(x)\, dx, \ldots, g_m(x) = \int g_{m-1}(x)\, dx, \ldots,$$

then

$$\int f(x) \cdot g(x)\, dx = f(x) \cdot g_1(x) - f'(x) \cdot g_2(x) + f''(x) \cdot g_3(x) - + \cdots$$

$$+ (-1)^n f^{(n)}(x) g_{n+1}(x) + (-1)^{n+1} \int f^{(n+1)}(x) g_{n+1}(x)\, dx.$$

A useful special case of the above rule is when $f(x)$ is a polynomial of degree n. Then $f^{(n+1)}(x) = 0$, and

$$\int f(x) \cdot g(x)\, dx = f(x) \cdot g_1(x) - f'(x) \cdot g_2(x) + f''(x) \cdot g_3(x) - + \cdots + (-1)^n f^{(n)}(x) g_{n+1}(x) + C$$

Example:
If $f(x) = x^2, g(x) = \sin x$

$$\int x^2 \sin x\, dx = -x^2 \cos x + 2x \sin x + 2 \cos x + C$$

Another application of this formula occurs if

$$f''(x) = af(x) \quad \text{and} \quad g''(x) = bg(x),$$

where a and b are unequal constants. In this case, by a process similar to that used in the above example for $\int e^x \sin x\, dx$, we get the formula

$$\int f(x)g(x)\, dx = \frac{f(x) \cdot g'(x) - f'(x) \cdot g(x)}{b - a} + C$$

This formula could have been used in the example mentioned. Here is another example.

Example:
If $f(x) = e^{2x}, g(x) = \sin 3x$, then $a = 4, b = -9$, and

$$\int e^{2x} \sin 3x\, dx = \frac{3 e^{2x} \cos 3x - 2 e^{2x} \sin 3x}{-9 - 4} + C = \frac{e^{2x}}{13}(2 \sin 3x - 3 \cos 3x) + C$$

The following additional points should be observed when using this table.

1. A constant of integration is to be supplied with the answers for indefinite integrals.
2. Logarithmic expressions are to base $e = 2.71828\ldots$, unless otherwise specified, and are to be evaluated for the absolute value of the arguments involved therein.
3. All angles are measured in radians, and inverse trigonometric and hyperbolic functions represent principal values, unless otherwise indicated.
4. If the application of a formula produces either a zero denominator or the square root of a negative number in the result, there is usually available another form of the answer which avoids this difficulty. In many of the results, the excluded values are specified, but when such are omitted it is presumed that one can tell what these should be, especially when difficulties of the type herein mentioned are obtained.
5. When inverse trigonometric functions occur in the integrals, be sure that any replacements made for them are strictly in accordance with the rules for such functions. This causes

little difficulty when the argument of the inverse trigonometric function is positive, since then all angles involved are in the first quadrant. However, if the argument is negative, special care must be used. Thus if $u > 0$,

$$\sin^{-1} u = \cos^{-1}\sqrt{1 - u^2} = \csc^{-1}\frac{1}{u}, \text{ etc.}$$

However, if $u < 0$,

$$\sin^{-1} u = -\cos^{-1}\sqrt{1 - u^2} = -\pi - \csc^{-1}\frac{1}{u}, \text{ etc.}$$

See the section on inverse trigonometric functions for a full treatment of the allowable substitutions.

6. In integrals 340–345 and some others, the right side includes expressions of the form

$$A \tan^{-1}[B + C \tan f(x)].$$

In these formulas, the $\tan^{-1}$ does not necessarily represent the principal value. Instead of always employing the principal branch of the inverse tangent function, one must instead use that branch of the inverse tangent function upon which $f(x)$ lies for any particular choice of x.

Example:

Using Integral Formula 340.

$$\int_0^{4\pi} \frac{dx}{2 + \sin x} = \frac{2}{\sqrt{3}}\tan^{-1}\frac{2\tan\frac{x}{2} + 1}{\sqrt{3}}\Bigg]_0^{4\pi}$$

$$= \frac{2}{\sqrt{3}}\left[\tan^{-1}\frac{2\tan 2\pi + 1}{\sqrt{3}} - \tan^{-1}\frac{2\tan 0 + 1}{\sqrt{3}}\right]$$

$$= \frac{2}{\sqrt{3}}\left[\frac{13\pi}{6} - \frac{\pi}{6}\right] = \frac{4\pi}{\sqrt{3}} = \frac{4\sqrt{3}\pi}{3}$$

Here

$$\tan^{-1}\frac{2\tan 2\pi + 1}{\sqrt{3}} = \tan^{-1}\frac{1}{\sqrt{3}} = \frac{13\pi}{6},$$

since $f(x) = 2\pi$; and

$$\tan^{-1}\frac{2\tan 0 + 1}{\sqrt{3}} = \tan^{-1}\frac{1}{\sqrt{3}} = \frac{\pi}{6},$$

since $f(x) = 0$.

INTEGRALS

ELEMENTARY FORMS

1. $\int a\,dx = ax$

2. $\int a \cdot f(x)\,dx = a \int f(x)\,dx$

3. $\int \phi(y)\,dx = \int \dfrac{\phi(y)}{y'}\,dy,$ where $y' = \dfrac{dy}{dx}$

4. $\int (u + v)\,dx = \int u\,dx + \int v\,dx,$ where u and v are any functions of x

5. $\int u\,dv = u \int dv - \int v\,du = uv - \int v\,du$

6. $\int u\dfrac{dv}{dx}\,dx = uv - \int v\dfrac{du}{dx}\,dx$

7. $\int x^n\,dx = \dfrac{x^{n+1}}{n+1},$ except $n = -1$

8. $\int \dfrac{f'(x)\,dx}{f(x)} = \log f(x),$ $(df(x) = f'(x)\,dx)$

9. $\int \dfrac{dx}{x} = \log x$

10. $\int \dfrac{f'(x)\,dx}{2\sqrt{f(x)}} = \sqrt{f(x)},$ $(df(x) = f'(x)\,dx)$

11. $\int e^x\,dx = e^x$

12. $\int e^{ax}\,dx = e^{ax}/a$

13. $\int b^{ax}\,dx = \dfrac{b^{ax}}{a\log b},$ $(b > 0)$

14. $\int \log x\,dx = x \log x - x$

15. $\int a^x \log a\,dx = a^x,$ $(a > 0)$

16. $\int \dfrac{dx}{a^2 + x^2} = \dfrac{1}{a}\tan^{-1}\dfrac{x}{a}$

INTEGRALS (Continued)

17. $\displaystyle\int \frac{dx}{a^2 - x^2} = \begin{cases} \dfrac{1}{a}\tanh^{-1}\dfrac{x}{a} \\ \quad\text{or} \\ \dfrac{1}{2a}\log\dfrac{a + x}{a - x}, \quad (a^2 > x^2) \end{cases}$

18. $\displaystyle\int \frac{dx}{x^2 - a^2} = \begin{cases} -\dfrac{1}{a}\coth^{-1}\dfrac{x}{a} \\ \quad\text{or} \\ \dfrac{1}{2a}\log\dfrac{x - a}{x + a}, \quad (x^2 > a^2) \end{cases}$

19. $\displaystyle\int \frac{dx}{\sqrt{a^2 - x^2}} = \begin{cases} \sin^{-1}\dfrac{x}{|a|} \\ \quad\text{or} \\ -\cos^{-1}\dfrac{x}{|a|}, \quad (a^2 > x^2) \end{cases}$

20. $\displaystyle\int \frac{dx}{\sqrt{x^2 \pm a^2}} = \log\left(x + \sqrt{x^2 \pm a^2}\right)$

21. $\displaystyle\int \frac{dx}{x\sqrt{x^2 - a^2}} = \frac{1}{|a|}\sec^{-1}\frac{x}{a}$

22. $\displaystyle\int \frac{dx}{x\sqrt{a^2 \pm x^2}} = -\frac{1}{a}\log\left(\frac{a + \sqrt{a^2 \pm x^2}}{x}\right)$

FORMS CONTAINING $(a + bx)$

For forms containing $a + bx$, but not listed in the table, the substitution $u = \dfrac{a + bx}{x}$ may prove helpful.

23. $\displaystyle\int (a + bx)^n \, dx = \frac{(a + bx)^{n+1}}{(n + 1)b}, \quad (n \neq -1)$

24. $\displaystyle\int x(a + bx)^n \, dx$

$$= \frac{1}{b^2(n + 2)}(a + bx)^{n+2} - \frac{a}{b^2(n + 1)}(a + bx)^{n+1}, \quad (n \neq -1, -2)$$

25. $\displaystyle\int x^2(a + bx)^n \, dx = \frac{1}{b^3}\left[\frac{(a + bx)^{n+3}}{n + 3} - 2a\frac{(a + bx)^{n+2}}{n + 2} + a^2\frac{(a + bx)^{n+1}}{n + 1}\right]$

INTEGRALS (Continued)

26. $\displaystyle\int x^m(a + bx)^n \, dx = \begin{cases} \dfrac{x^{m+1}(a + bx)^n}{m + n + 1} + \dfrac{an}{m + n + 1}\displaystyle\int x^m(a + bx)^{n-1} \, dx \\[4pt] \text{or} \\[4pt] \dfrac{1}{a(n + 1)}\left[-x^{m+1}(a + bx)^{n+1} \right. \\[8pt] \qquad\qquad \left. + (m + n + 2)\displaystyle\int x^m(a + bx)^{n+1} \, dx\right] \\[4pt] \text{or} \\[4pt] \dfrac{1}{b(m + n + 1)}\left[x^m(a + bx)^{n+1} - ma\displaystyle\int x^{m-1}(a + bx)^n \, dx\right] \end{cases}$

27. $\displaystyle\int \frac{dx}{a + bx} = \frac{1}{b}\log(a + bx)$

28. $\displaystyle\int \frac{dx}{(a + bx)^2} = -\frac{1}{b(a + bx)}$

29. $\displaystyle\int \frac{dx}{(a + bx)^3} = -\frac{1}{2b(a + bx)^2}$

30. $\displaystyle\int \frac{x \, dx}{a + bx} = \begin{cases} \dfrac{1}{b^2}[a + bx - a\log(a + bx)] \\[4pt] \text{or} \\[4pt] \dfrac{x}{b} - \dfrac{a}{b^2}\log(a + bx) \end{cases}$

31. $\displaystyle\int \frac{x \, dx}{(a + bx)^2} = \frac{1}{b^2}\left[\log(a + bx) + \frac{a}{a + bx}\right]$

32. $\displaystyle\int \frac{x \, dx}{(a + bx)^n} = \frac{1}{b^2}\left[\frac{-1}{(n - 2)(a + bx)^{n-2}} + \frac{a}{(n - 1)(a + bx)^{n-1}}\right], \qquad n \neq 1, 2$

33. $\displaystyle\int \frac{x^2 \, dx}{a + bx} = \frac{1}{b^3}\left[\frac{1}{2}(a + bx)^2 - 2a(a + bx) + a^2\log(a + bx)\right]$

34. $\displaystyle\int \frac{x^2 \, dx}{(a + bx)^2} = \frac{1}{b^3}\left[a + bx - 2a\log(a + bx) - \frac{a^2}{a + bx}\right]$

35. $\displaystyle\int \frac{x^2 \, dx}{(a + bx)^3} = \frac{1}{b^3}\left[\log(a + bx) + \frac{2a}{a + bx} - \frac{a^2}{2(a + bx)^2}\right]$

36. $\displaystyle\int \frac{x^2 \, dx}{(a + bx)^n} = \frac{1}{b^3}\left[\frac{-1}{(n - 3)(a + bx)^{n-3}}\right.$

$\left. + \frac{2a}{(n - 2)(a + bx)^{n-2}} - \frac{a^2}{(n - 1)(a + bx)^{n-1}}\right], \qquad n \neq 1, 2, 3$

INTEGRALS (Continued)

37. $\int \dfrac{dx}{x(a + bx)} = -\dfrac{1}{a} \log \dfrac{a + bx}{x}$

38. $\int \dfrac{dx}{x(a + bx)^2} = \dfrac{1}{a(a + bx)} - \dfrac{1}{a^2} \log \dfrac{a + bx}{x}$

39. $\int \dfrac{dx}{x(a + bx)^3} = \dfrac{1}{a^3}\left[\dfrac{1}{2}\left(\dfrac{2a + bx}{a + bx} \right)^2 + \log \dfrac{x}{a + bx} \right]$

40. $\int \dfrac{dx}{x^2(a + bx)} = -\dfrac{1}{ax} + \dfrac{b}{a^2} \log \dfrac{a + bx}{x}$

41. $\int \dfrac{dx}{x^3(a + bx)} = \dfrac{2bx - a}{2a^2 x^2} + \dfrac{b^2}{a^3} \log \dfrac{x}{a + bx}$

42. $\int \dfrac{dx}{x^2(a + bx)^2} = -\dfrac{a + 2bx}{a^2 x(a + bx)} + \dfrac{2b}{a^3} \log \dfrac{a + bx}{x}$

FORMS CONTAINING $c^2 \pm x^2$, $x^2 - c^2$

43. $\int \dfrac{dx}{c^2 + x^2} = \dfrac{1}{c} \tan^{-1} \dfrac{x}{c}$

44. $\int \dfrac{dx}{c^2 - x^2} = \dfrac{1}{2c} \log \dfrac{c + x}{c - x}, \qquad (c^2 > x^2)$

45. $\int \dfrac{dx}{x^2 - c^2} = \dfrac{1}{2c} \log \dfrac{x - c}{x + c}, \qquad (x^2 > c^2)$

46. $\int \dfrac{x\,dx}{c^2 \pm x^2} = \pm \dfrac{1}{2} \log (c^2 \pm x^2)$

47. $\int \dfrac{x\,dx}{(c^2 \pm x^2)^{n+1}} = \mp \dfrac{1}{2n(c^2 \pm x^2)^n}$

48. $\int \dfrac{dx}{(c^2 \pm x^2)^n} = \dfrac{1}{2c^2(n - 1)}\left[\dfrac{x}{(c^2 \pm x^2)^{n-1}} + (2n - 3) \int \dfrac{dx}{(c^2 \pm x^2)^{n-1}} \right]$

49. $\int \dfrac{dx}{(x^2 - c^2)^n} = \dfrac{1}{2c^2(n - 1)}\left[-\dfrac{x}{(x^2 - c^2)^{n-1}} - (2n - 3) \int \dfrac{dx}{(x^2 - c^2)^{n-1}} \right]$

50. $\int \dfrac{x\,dx}{x^2 - c^2} = \dfrac{1}{2} \log (x^2 - c^2)$

51. $\int \dfrac{x\,dx}{(x^2 - c^2)^{n+1}} = -\dfrac{1}{2n(x^2 - c^2)^n}$

FORMS CONTAINING $a + bx$ and $c + dx$

$$u = a + bx, \qquad v = c + dx, \qquad k = ad - bc$$

If $k = 0$, then $v = \dfrac{c}{a}u$

52. $\displaystyle\int \frac{dx}{u \cdot v} = \frac{1}{k} \cdot \log\left(\frac{v}{u}\right)$

53. $\displaystyle\int \frac{x\,dx}{u \cdot v} = \frac{1}{k}\left[\frac{a}{b}\log(u) - \frac{c}{d}\log(v)\right]$

54. $\displaystyle\int \frac{dx}{u^2 \cdot v} = \frac{1}{k}\left(\frac{1}{u} + \frac{d}{k}\log\frac{v}{u}\right)$

55. $\displaystyle\int \frac{x\,dx}{u^2 \cdot v} = \frac{-a}{bku} - \frac{c}{k^2}\log\frac{v}{u}$

56. $\displaystyle\int \frac{x^2\,dx}{u^2 \cdot v} = \frac{a^2}{b^2 ku} + \frac{1}{k^2}\left[\frac{c^2}{d}\log(v) + \frac{a(k - bc)}{b^2}\log(u)\right]$

57. $\displaystyle\int \frac{dx}{u^n \cdot v^m} = \frac{1}{k(m-1)}\left[\frac{-1}{u^{n-1} \cdot v^{m-1}} - (m + n - 2)b\int \frac{dx}{u^n \cdot v^{m-1}}\right]$

58. $\displaystyle\int \frac{u}{v}\,dx = \frac{bx}{d} + \frac{k}{d^2}\log(v)$

59. $\displaystyle\int \frac{u^m\,dx}{v^n} = \begin{cases} \dfrac{-1}{k(n-1)}\left[\dfrac{u^{m+1}}{v^{n-1}} + b(n - m - 2)\displaystyle\int \dfrac{u^m}{v^{n-1}}\,dx\right] \\ \qquad\qquad\text{or} \\ \dfrac{-1}{d(n - m - 1)}\left[\dfrac{u^m}{v^{n-1}} + mk\displaystyle\int \dfrac{u^{m-1}}{v^n}\,dx\right] \\ \qquad\qquad\text{or} \\ \dfrac{-1}{d(n-1)}\left[\dfrac{u^m}{v^{n-1}} - mb\displaystyle\int \dfrac{u^{m-1}}{v^{n-1}}\,dx\right] \end{cases}$

FORMS CONTAINING $(a + bx^n)$

60. $\displaystyle\int \frac{dx}{a + bx^2} = \frac{1}{\sqrt{ab}}\tan^{-1}\frac{x\sqrt{ab}}{a}, \qquad (ab > 0)$

61. $\displaystyle\int \frac{dx}{a + bx^2} = \begin{cases} \dfrac{1}{2\sqrt{-ab}}\log\dfrac{a + x\sqrt{-ab}}{a - x\sqrt{-ab}}, \qquad (ab < 0) \\ \qquad\qquad\text{or} \\ \dfrac{1}{\sqrt{-ab}}\tanh^{-1}\dfrac{x\sqrt{-ab}}{a}, \qquad (ab < 0) \end{cases}$

INTEGRALS (Continued)

62. $\displaystyle\int \frac{dx}{a^2 + b^2 x^2} = \frac{1}{ab} \tan^{-1} \frac{bx}{a}$

63. $\displaystyle\int \frac{x\,dx}{a + bx^2} = \frac{1}{2b} \log(a + bx^2)$

64. $\displaystyle\int \frac{x^2\,dx}{a + bx^2} = \frac{x}{b} - \frac{a}{b} \int \frac{dx}{a + bx^2}$

65. $\displaystyle\int \frac{dx}{(a + bx^2)^2} = \frac{x}{2a(a + bx^2)} + \frac{1}{2a} \int \frac{dx}{a + bx^2}$

66. $\displaystyle\int \frac{dx}{a^2 - b^2 x^2} = \frac{1}{2ab} \log \frac{a + bx}{a - bx}$

67. $\displaystyle\int \frac{dx}{(a + bx^2)^{m+1}} = \begin{cases} \dfrac{1}{2ma} \dfrac{x}{(a + bx^2)^m} + \dfrac{2m - 1}{2ma} \displaystyle\int \dfrac{dx}{(a + bx^2)^m} \\[2ex] \qquad\qquad \text{or} \\[1ex] \dfrac{(2m)!}{(m!)^2} \left[\dfrac{x}{2a} \displaystyle\sum_{r=1}^{m} \dfrac{r!(r-1)!}{(4a)^{m-r}(2r)!(a + bx^2)^r} + \dfrac{1}{(4a)^m} \displaystyle\int \dfrac{dx}{a + bx^2} \right] \end{cases}$

68. $\displaystyle\int \frac{x\,dx}{(a + bx^2)^{m+1}} = -\frac{1}{2bm(a + bx^2)^m}$

69. $\displaystyle\int \frac{x^2\,dx}{(a + bx^2)^{m+1}} = \frac{-x}{2mb(a + bx^2)^m} + \frac{1}{2mb} \int \frac{dx}{(a + bx^2)^m}$

70. $\displaystyle\int \frac{dx}{x(a + bx^2)} = \frac{1}{2a} \log \frac{x^2}{a + bx^2}$

71. $\displaystyle\int \frac{dx}{x^2(a + bx^2)} = -\frac{1}{ax} - \frac{b}{a} \int \frac{dx}{a + bx^2}$

72. $\displaystyle\int \frac{dx}{x(a + bx^2)^{m+1}} = \begin{cases} \dfrac{1}{2am(a + bx^2)^m} + \dfrac{1}{a} \displaystyle\int \dfrac{dx}{x(a + bx^2)^m} \\[2ex] \qquad\qquad \text{or} \\[1ex] \dfrac{1}{2a^{m+1}} \left[\displaystyle\sum_{r=1}^{m} \dfrac{a^r}{r(a + bx^2)^r} + \log \dfrac{x^2}{a + bx^2} \right] \end{cases}$

73. $\displaystyle\int \frac{dx}{x^2(a + bx^2)^{m+1}} = \frac{1}{a} \int \frac{dx}{x^2(a + bx^2)^m} - \frac{b}{a} \int \frac{dx}{(a + bx^2)^{m+1}}$

74. $\displaystyle\int \frac{dx}{a + bx^3} = \frac{k}{3a} \left[\frac{1}{2} \log \frac{(k + x)^3}{a + bx^3} + \sqrt{3} \tan^{-1} \frac{2x - k}{k\sqrt{3}} \right], \qquad \left(k = \sqrt[3]{\frac{a}{b}} \right)$

75. $\displaystyle\int \frac{x\,dx}{a + bx^3} = \frac{1}{3bk} \left[\frac{1}{2} \log \frac{a + bx^3}{(k + x)^3} + \sqrt{3} \tan^{-1} \frac{2x - k}{k\sqrt{3}} \right], \qquad \left(k = \sqrt[3]{\frac{a}{b}} \right)$

76. $\displaystyle \int \frac{x^2\, dx}{a + bx^3} = \frac{1}{3b} \log (a + bx^3)$

77. $\displaystyle \int \frac{dx}{a + bx^4} = \frac{k}{2a} \left[\frac{1}{2} \log \frac{x^2 + 2kx + 2k^2}{x^2 - 2kx + 2k^2} + \tan^{-1} \frac{2kx}{2k^2 - x^2} \right],$

$$\left(ab > 0,\, k = \sqrt[4]{\frac{a}{4b}} \right)$$

78. $\displaystyle \int \frac{dx}{a + bx^4} = \frac{k}{2a} \left[\frac{1}{2} \log \frac{x + k}{x - k} + \tan^{-1} \frac{x}{k} \right], \qquad \left(ab < 0,\, k = \sqrt[4]{-\frac{a}{b}} \right)$

79. $\displaystyle \int \frac{x\, dx}{a + bx^4} = \frac{1}{2bk} \tan^{-1} \frac{x^2}{k}, \qquad \left(ab > 0,\, k = \sqrt{\frac{a}{b}} \right)$

80. $\displaystyle \int \frac{x\, dx}{a + bx^4} = \frac{1}{4bk} \log \frac{x^2 - k}{x^2 + k}, \qquad \left(ab < 0,\, k = \sqrt{-\frac{a}{b}} \right)$

81. $\displaystyle \int \frac{x^2\, dx}{a + bx^4} = \frac{1}{4bk} \left[\frac{1}{2} \log \frac{x^2 - 2kx + 2k^2}{x^2 + 2kx + 2k^2} + \tan^{-1} \frac{2kx}{2k^2 - x^2} \right],$

$$\left(ab > 0,\, k = \sqrt[4]{\frac{a}{4b}} \right)$$

82. $\displaystyle \int \frac{x^2\, dx}{a + bx^4} = \frac{1}{4bk} \left[\log \frac{x - k}{x + k} + 2 \tan^{-1} \frac{x}{k} \right], \qquad \left(ab < 0,\, k = \sqrt[4]{-\frac{a}{b}} \right)$

83. $\displaystyle \int \frac{x^3\, dx}{a + bx^4} = \frac{1}{4b} \log (a + bx^4)$

84. $\displaystyle \int \frac{dx}{x(a + bx^n)} = \frac{1}{an} \log \frac{x^n}{a + bx^n}$

85. $\displaystyle \int \frac{dx}{(a + bx^n)^{m+1}} = \frac{1}{a} \int \frac{dx}{(a + bx^n)^m} - \frac{b}{a} \int \frac{x^n\, dx}{(a + bx^n)^{m+1}}$

86. $\displaystyle \int \frac{x^m\, dx}{(a + bx^n)^{p+1}} = \frac{1}{b} \int \frac{x^{m-n}\, dx}{(a + bx^n)^p} - \frac{a}{b} \int \frac{x^{m-n}\, dx}{(a + bx^n)^{p+1}}$

87. $\displaystyle \int \frac{dx}{x^m(a + bx^n)^{p+1}} = \frac{1}{a} \int \frac{dx}{x^m(a + bx^n)^p} - \frac{b}{a} \int \frac{dx}{x^{m-n}(a + bx^n)^{p+1}}$

INTEGRALS (Continued)

88. $\displaystyle \int x^m(a + bx^n)^p \, dx = \begin{cases} \end{cases}$

$$\frac{1}{b(np + m + 1)}\left[x^{m-n+1}(a + bx^n)^{p+1} \right.$$

$$\left. - a(m - n + 1)\int x^{m-n}(a + bx^n)^p \, dx \right]$$

or

$$\frac{1}{np + m + 1}\left[x^{m+1}(a + bx^n)^p \right.$$

$$\left. + anp \int x^m(a + bx^n)^{p-1} \, dx \right]$$

or

$$\frac{1}{a(m + 1)}\left[x^{m+1}(a + bx^n)^{p+1} \right.$$

$$\left. - (m + 1 + np + n)b \int x^{m+n}(a + bx^n)^p \, dx \right]$$

or

$$\frac{1}{an(p + 1)}\left[-x^{m+1}(a + bx^n)^{p+1} \right.$$

$$\left. + (m + 1 + np + n) \int x^m(a + bx^n)^{p+1} \, dx \right]$$

FORMS CONTAINING $c^3 \pm x^3$

89. $\displaystyle \int \frac{dx}{c^3 \pm x^3} = \pm \frac{1}{6c^2} \log \frac{(c \pm x)^3}{c^3 \pm x^3} + \frac{1}{c^2\sqrt{3}} \tan^{-1} \frac{2x \mp c}{c\sqrt{3}}$

90. $\displaystyle \int \frac{dx}{(c^3 \pm x^3)^2} = \frac{x}{3c^3(c^3 \pm x^3)} + \frac{2}{3c^3}\int \frac{dx}{c^3 \pm x^3}$

91. $\displaystyle \int \frac{dx}{(c^3 \pm x^3)^{n+1}} = \frac{1}{3nc^3}\left[\frac{x}{(c^3 \pm x^3)^n} + (3n - 1)\int \frac{dx}{(c^3 \pm x^3)^n} \right]$

92. $\displaystyle \int \frac{x \, dx}{c^3 \pm x^3} = \frac{1}{6c} \log \frac{c^3 \pm x^3}{(c \pm x)^3} \pm \frac{1}{c\sqrt{3}} \tan^{-1} \frac{2x \mp c}{c\sqrt{3}}$

93. $\displaystyle \int \frac{x \, dx}{(c^3 \pm x^3)^2} = \frac{x^2}{3c^3(c^3 \pm x^3)} + \frac{1}{3c^3}\int \frac{x \, dx}{c^3 \pm x^3}$

94. $\displaystyle \int \frac{x \, dx}{(c^3 \pm x^3)^{n+1}} = \frac{1}{3nc^3}\left[\frac{x^2}{(c^3 \pm x^3)^n} + (3n - 2)\int \frac{x \, dx}{(c^3 \pm x^3)^n} \right]$

95. $\displaystyle \int \frac{x^2 \, dx}{c^3 \pm x^3} = \pm \frac{1}{3} \log (c^3 \pm x^3)$

INTEGRALS (Continued)

96. $\displaystyle\int \frac{x^2\,dx}{(c^3 \pm x^3)^{n+1}} = \mp\frac{1}{3n(c^3 \pm x^3)^n}$

97. $\displaystyle\int \frac{dx}{x(c^3 \pm x^3)} = \frac{1}{3c^3}\log\frac{x^3}{c^3 \pm x^3}$

98. $\displaystyle\int \frac{dx}{x(c^3 \pm x^3)^2} = \frac{1}{3c^3(c^3 \pm x^3)} + \frac{1}{3c^6}\log\frac{x^3}{c^3 \pm x^3}$

99. $\displaystyle\int \frac{dx}{x(c^3 \pm x^3)^{n+1}} = \frac{1}{3nc^3(c^3 \pm x^3)^n} + \frac{1}{c^3}\int \frac{dx}{x(c^3 \pm x^3)^n}$

100. $\displaystyle\int \frac{dx}{x^2(c^3 \pm x^3)} = -\frac{1}{c^3 x} \mp \frac{1}{c^3}\int \frac{x\,dx}{c^3 \pm x^3}$

101. $\displaystyle\int \frac{dx}{x^2(c^3 \pm x^3)^{n+1}} = \frac{1}{c^3}\int \frac{dx}{x^2(c^3 \pm x^3)^n} \mp \frac{1}{c^3}\int \frac{x\,dx}{(c^3 \pm x^3)^{n+1}}$

FORMS CONTAINING $c^4 \pm x^4$

102. $\displaystyle\int \frac{dx}{c^4 + x^4} = \frac{1}{2c^3\sqrt{2}}\left[\frac{1}{2}\log\frac{x^2 + cx\sqrt{2} + c^2}{x^2 - cx\sqrt{2} + c^2} + \tan^{-1}\frac{cx\sqrt{2}}{c^2 - x^2}\right]$

103. $\displaystyle\int \frac{dx}{c^4 - x^4} = \frac{1}{2c^3}\left[\frac{1}{2}\log\frac{c + x}{c - x} + \tan^{-1}\frac{x}{c}\right]$

104. $\displaystyle\int \frac{x\,dx}{c^4 + x^4} = \frac{1}{2c^2}\tan^{-1}\frac{x^2}{c^2}$

105. $\displaystyle\int \frac{x\,dx}{c^4 - x^4} = \frac{1}{4c^2}\log\frac{c^2 + x^2}{c^2 - x^2}$

106. $\displaystyle\int \frac{x^2\,dx}{c^4 + x^4} = \frac{1}{2c\sqrt{2}}\left[\frac{1}{2}\log\frac{x^2 - cx\sqrt{2} + c^2}{x^2 + cx\sqrt{2} + c^2} + \tan^{-1}\frac{cx\sqrt{2}}{c^2 - x^2}\right]$

107. $\displaystyle\int \frac{x^2\,dx}{c^4 - x^4} = \frac{1}{2c}\left[\frac{1}{2}\log\frac{c + x}{c - x} - \tan^{-1}\frac{x}{c}\right]$

108. $\displaystyle\int \frac{x^3\,dx}{c^4 \pm x^4} = \pm\frac{1}{4}\log(c^4 \pm x^4)$

FORMS CONTAINING $(a + bx + cx^2)$

$$X = a + bx + cx^2 \text{ and } q = 4ac - b^2$$

If $q = 0$, then $X = c\left(x + \dfrac{b}{2c}\right)^2$, and formulas starting with 23 should be used in place of these.

109. $\displaystyle\int \frac{dx}{X} = \frac{2}{\sqrt{q}}\tan^{-1}\frac{2cx + b}{\sqrt{q}}, \qquad (q > 0)$

INTEGRALS (Continued)

110. $\displaystyle\int \frac{dx}{X} = \begin{cases} \dfrac{-2}{\sqrt{-q}}\tanh^{-1}\dfrac{2cx+b}{\sqrt{-q}} \\[4mm] \qquad\text{or} \\[4mm] \dfrac{1}{\sqrt{-q}}\log\dfrac{2cx+b-\sqrt{-q}}{2cx+b+\sqrt{-q}}, \qquad (q<0) \end{cases}$

111. $\displaystyle\int \frac{dx}{X^2} = \frac{2cx+b}{qX} + \frac{2c}{q}\int\frac{dx}{X}$

112. $\displaystyle\int \frac{dx}{X^3} = \frac{2cx+b}{q}\left(\frac{1}{2X^2}+\frac{3c}{qX}\right) + \frac{6c^2}{q^2}\int\frac{dx}{X}$

113. $\displaystyle\int \frac{dx}{X^{n+1}} = \begin{cases} \dfrac{2cx+b}{nqX^n} + \dfrac{2(2n-1)c}{qn}\displaystyle\int\dfrac{dx}{X^n} \\[4mm] \qquad\text{or} \\[4mm] \dfrac{(2n)!}{(n!)^2}\left(\dfrac{c}{q}\right)^n\left[\dfrac{2cx+b}{q}\displaystyle\sum_{r=1}^{n}\left(\dfrac{q}{cX}\right)^r\left(\dfrac{(r-1)!r!}{(2r)!}\right) + \displaystyle\int\dfrac{dx}{X}\right] \end{cases}$

114. $\displaystyle\int \frac{x\,dx}{X} = \frac{1}{2c}\log X - \frac{b}{2c}\int\frac{dx}{X}$

115. $\displaystyle\int \frac{x\,dx}{X^2} = -\frac{bx+2a}{qX} - \frac{b}{q}\int\frac{dx}{X}$

116. $\displaystyle\int \frac{x\,dx}{X^{n+1}} = -\frac{2a+bx}{nqX^n} - \frac{b(2n-1)}{nq}\int\frac{dx}{X^n}$

117. $\displaystyle\int \frac{x^2}{X}\,dx = \frac{x}{c} - \frac{b}{2c^2}\log X + \frac{b^2-2ac}{2c^2}\int\frac{dx}{X}$

118. $\displaystyle\int \frac{x^2}{X^2}\,dx = \frac{(b^2-2ac)x+ab}{cqX} + \frac{2a}{q}\int\frac{dx}{X}$

119. $\displaystyle\int \frac{x^m\,dx}{X^{n+1}} = -\frac{x^{m-1}}{(2n-m+1)cX^n} - \frac{n-m+1}{2n-m+1}\cdot\frac{b}{c}\int\frac{x^{m-1}\,dx}{X^{n+1}}$
$$+ \frac{m-1}{2n-m+1}\cdot\frac{a}{c}\int\frac{x^{m-2}\,dx}{X^{n+1}}$$

120. $\displaystyle\int \frac{dx}{xX} = \frac{1}{2a}\log\frac{x^2}{X} - \frac{b}{2a}\int\frac{dx}{X}$

121. $\displaystyle\int \frac{dx}{x^2X} = \frac{b}{2a^2}\log\frac{X}{x^2} - \frac{1}{ax} + \left(\frac{b^2}{2a^2}-\frac{c}{a}\right)\int\frac{dx}{X}$

122. $\displaystyle\int \frac{dx}{xX^n} = \frac{1}{2a(n-1)X^{n-1}} - \frac{b}{2a}\int\frac{dx}{X^n} + \frac{1}{a}\int\frac{dx}{xX^{n-1}}$

INTEGRALS (Continued)

123. $\int \dfrac{dx}{x^m X^{n+1}} = -\dfrac{1}{(m-1)ax^{m-1}X^n} - \dfrac{n+m-1}{m-1} \cdot \dfrac{b}{a} \int \dfrac{dx}{x^{m-1}X^{n+1}}$

$$- \dfrac{2n+m-1}{m-1} \cdot \dfrac{c}{a} \int \dfrac{dx}{x^{m-2}X^{n+1}}$$

FORMS CONTAINING $\sqrt{a + bx}$

124. $\int \sqrt{a + bx}\, dx = \dfrac{2}{3b}\sqrt{(a+bx)^3}$

125. $\int x\sqrt{a + bx}\, dx = -\dfrac{2(2a - 3bx)\sqrt{(a+bx)^3}}{15b^2}$

126. $\int x^2\sqrt{a + bx}\, dx = \dfrac{2(8a^2 - 12abx + 15b^2x^2)\sqrt{(a+bx)^3}}{105b^3}$

127. $\int x^m\sqrt{a + bx}\, dx = \begin{cases} \dfrac{2}{b(2m+3)}\left[x^m\sqrt{(a+bx)^3} - ma\int x^{m-1}\sqrt{a + bx}\, dx \right] \\[2mm] \text{or} \\[2mm] \dfrac{2}{b^{m+1}}\sqrt{a + bx}\ \sum\limits_{r=0}^{m} \dfrac{m!(-a)^{m-r}}{r!(m-r)!(2r+3)}(a+bx)^{r+1} \end{cases}$

128. $\int \dfrac{\sqrt{a + bx}}{x}\, dx = 2\sqrt{a + bx} + a\int \dfrac{dx}{x\sqrt{a + bx}}$

129. $\int \dfrac{\sqrt{a + bx}}{x^2}\, dx = -\dfrac{\sqrt{a + bx}}{x} + \dfrac{b}{2}\int \dfrac{dx}{x\sqrt{a + bx}}$

130. $\int \dfrac{\sqrt{a + bx}}{x^m}\, dx = -\dfrac{1}{(m-1)a}\left[\dfrac{\sqrt{(a+bx)^3}}{x^{m-1}} + \dfrac{(2m-5)b}{2}\int \dfrac{\sqrt{a + bx}}{x^{m-1}}\, dx \right]$

131. $\int \dfrac{dx}{\sqrt{a + bx}} = \dfrac{2\sqrt{a + bx}}{b}$

132. $\int \dfrac{x\, dx}{\sqrt{a + bx}} = -\dfrac{2(2a - bx)}{3b^2}\sqrt{a + bx}$

133. $\int \dfrac{x^2\, dx}{\sqrt{a + bx}} = \dfrac{2(8a^2 - 4abx + 3b^2x^2)}{15b^3}\sqrt{a + bx}$

INTEGRALS (Continued)

134. $\displaystyle\int \frac{x^m\,dx}{\sqrt{a + bx}} = \begin{cases} \dfrac{2}{(2m + 1)b}\left[x^m\sqrt{a + bx} - ma\displaystyle\int \dfrac{x^{m-1}\,dx}{\sqrt{a + bx}}\right] \\[2mm] \text{or} \\[2mm] \dfrac{2(-a)^m\sqrt{a + bx}}{b^{m+1}}\displaystyle\sum_{r=0}^{m}\dfrac{(-1)^r m!(a + bx)^r}{(2r + 1)r!(m - r)!a^r} \end{cases}$

135. $\displaystyle\int \frac{dx}{x\sqrt{a + bx}} = \frac{1}{\sqrt{a}}\log\left(\frac{\sqrt{a + bx} - \sqrt{a}}{\sqrt{a + bx} + \sqrt{a}}\right), \qquad (a > 0)$

136. $\displaystyle\int \frac{dx}{x\sqrt{a + bx}} = \frac{2}{\sqrt{-a}}\tan^{-1}\sqrt{\frac{a + bx}{a}}, \qquad (a < 0)$

137. $\displaystyle\int \frac{dx}{x^2\sqrt{a + bx}} = -\frac{\sqrt{a + bx}}{ax} - \frac{b}{2a}\int \frac{dx}{x\sqrt{a + bx}}$

138. $\displaystyle\int \frac{dx}{x^n\sqrt{a + bx}} = \begin{cases} -\dfrac{\sqrt{a + bx}}{(n - 1)ax^{n-1}} - \dfrac{(2n - 3)b}{(2n - 2)a}\displaystyle\int \dfrac{dx}{x^{n-1}\sqrt{a + bx}} \\[2mm] \text{or} \\[2mm] \dfrac{(2n - 2)!}{[(n - 1)!]^2}\left[-\dfrac{\sqrt{a + bx}}{a}\displaystyle\sum_{r=1}^{n-1}\dfrac{r!(r - 1)!}{x^r(2r)!}\left(-\dfrac{b}{4a}\right)^{n-r-1}\right. \\[2mm] \left. \qquad\qquad + \left(-\dfrac{b}{4a}\right)^{n-1}\displaystyle\int \dfrac{dx}{x\sqrt{a + bx}}\right] \end{cases}$

139. $\displaystyle\int (a + bx)^{\pm\frac{n}{2}}\,dx = \frac{2(a + bx)^{\frac{2\pm n}{2}}}{b(2 \pm n)}$

140. $\displaystyle\int x(a + bx)^{\pm\frac{n}{2}}\,dx = \frac{2}{b^2}\left[\frac{(a + bx)^{\frac{4\pm n}{2}}}{4 \pm n} - \frac{a(a + bx)^{\frac{2\pm n}{2}}}{2 \pm n}\right]$

141. $\displaystyle\int \frac{dx}{x(a + bx)^{\frac{m}{2}}} = \frac{1}{a}\int \frac{dx}{x(a + bx)^{\frac{m-2}{2}}} - \frac{b}{a}\int \frac{dx}{(a + bx)^{\frac{m}{2}}}$

142. $\displaystyle\int \frac{(a + bx)^{\frac{n}{2}}\,dx}{x} = b\int (a + bx)^{\frac{n-2}{2}}\,dx + a\int \frac{(a + bx)^{\frac{n-2}{2}}}{x}\,dx$

143. $\displaystyle\int f(x, \sqrt{a + bx})\,dx = \frac{2}{b}\int f\left(\frac{z^2 - a}{b}, z\right)z\,dz, \qquad (z = \sqrt{a + bx})$

INTEGRALS (Continued)

FORMS CONTAINING $\sqrt{a + bx}$ and $\sqrt{c + dx}$

$$u = a + bx \qquad v = c + dx \qquad k = ad - bc$$

If $k = 0$, then $v = \dfrac{c}{a}u$, and formulas starting with 124 should be used in place of these.

144. $\displaystyle\int \frac{dx}{\sqrt{uv}} = \begin{cases} \dfrac{2}{\sqrt{bd}} \tanh^{-1} \dfrac{\sqrt{bduv}}{bv} \\[2ex] \text{or} \\[1ex] \dfrac{1}{\sqrt{bd}} \log \dfrac{bv + \sqrt{bduv}}{bv - \sqrt{bduv}} \\[2ex] \text{or} \\[1ex] \dfrac{1}{\sqrt{bd}} \log \dfrac{(bv + \sqrt{bduv})^2}{v}, \qquad (bd > 0) \end{cases}$

145. $\displaystyle\int \frac{dx}{\sqrt{uv}} = \begin{cases} \dfrac{2}{\sqrt{-bd}} \tan^{-1} \dfrac{\sqrt{-bduv}}{bv} \\[2ex] \text{or} \\[1ex] -\dfrac{1}{\sqrt{-bd}} \sin^{-1} \left(\dfrac{2bdx + ad + bc}{|k|} \right), \qquad (bd < 0) \end{cases}$

146. $\displaystyle\int \sqrt{uv}\, dx = \frac{k + 2bv}{4bd} \sqrt{uv} - \frac{k^2}{8bd} \int \frac{dx}{\sqrt{uv}}$

147. $\displaystyle\int \frac{dx}{v\sqrt{u}} = \begin{cases} \dfrac{1}{\sqrt{kd}} \log \dfrac{d\sqrt{u} - \sqrt{kd}}{d\sqrt{u} + \sqrt{kd}} \\[2ex] \text{or} \\[1ex] \dfrac{1}{\sqrt{kd}} \log \dfrac{(d\sqrt{u} - \sqrt{kd})^2}{v}, \qquad (kd > 0) \end{cases}$

148. $\displaystyle\int \frac{dx}{v\sqrt{u}} = \frac{2}{\sqrt{-kd}} \tan^{-1} \frac{d\sqrt{u}}{\sqrt{-kd}}, \qquad (kd < 0)$

149. $\displaystyle\int \frac{x\, dx}{\sqrt{uv}} = \frac{\sqrt{uv}}{bd} - \frac{ad + bc}{2bd} \int \frac{dx}{\sqrt{uv}}$

150. $\displaystyle\int \frac{dx}{v\sqrt{uv}} = \frac{-2\sqrt{uv}}{kv}$

INTEGRALS (Continued)

151. $\displaystyle\int \frac{v\,dx}{\sqrt{uv}} = \frac{\sqrt{uv}}{b} - \frac{k}{2b}\int \frac{dx}{\sqrt{uv}}$

152. $\displaystyle\int \sqrt{\frac{v}{u}}\,dx = \frac{v}{|v|}\int \frac{v\,dx}{\sqrt{uv}}$

153. $\displaystyle\int v^m \sqrt{u}\,dx = \frac{1}{(2m+3)d}\left(2v^{m+1}\sqrt{u} + k\int \frac{v^m\,dx}{\sqrt{u}}\right)$

154. $\displaystyle\int \frac{dx}{v^m\sqrt{u}} = -\frac{1}{(m-1)k}\left(\frac{\sqrt{u}}{v^{m-1}} + \left(m - \frac{3}{2}\right)b\int \frac{dx}{v^{m-1}\sqrt{u}}\right)$

155. $\displaystyle\int \frac{v^m\,dx}{\sqrt{u}} = \begin{cases} \dfrac{2}{b(2m+1)}\left[v^m\sqrt{u} - mk\int \dfrac{v^{m-1}}{\sqrt{u}}\,dx\right] \\[2mm] \qquad\qquad\text{or} \\[2mm] \dfrac{2(m!)^2\sqrt{u}}{b(2m+1)!}\displaystyle\sum_{r=0}^{m}\left(-\frac{4k}{b}\right)^{m-r}\frac{(2r)!}{(r!)^2}v^r \end{cases}$

FORMS CONTAINING $\sqrt{x^2 \pm a^2}$

156. $\displaystyle\int \sqrt{x^2 \pm a^2}\,dx = \tfrac{1}{2}[x\sqrt{x^2 \pm a^2} \pm a^2 \log(x + \sqrt{x^2 \pm a^2})]$

157. $\displaystyle\int \frac{dx}{\sqrt{x^2 \pm a^2}} = \log(x + \sqrt{x^2 \pm a^2})$

158. $\displaystyle\int \frac{dx}{x\sqrt{x^2 - a^2}} = \frac{1}{|a|}\sec^{-1}\frac{x}{a}$

159. $\displaystyle\int \frac{dx}{x\sqrt{x^2 + a^2}} = -\frac{1}{a}\log\left(\frac{a + \sqrt{x^2 + a^2}}{x}\right)$

160. $\displaystyle\int \frac{\sqrt{x^2 + a^2}}{x}\,dx = \sqrt{x^2 + a^2} - a\log\left(\frac{a + \sqrt{x^2 + a^2}}{x}\right)$

161. $\displaystyle\int \frac{\sqrt{x^2 - a^2}}{x}\,dx = \sqrt{x^2 - a^2} - |a|\sec^{-1}\frac{x}{a}$

162. $\displaystyle\int \frac{x\,dx}{\sqrt{x^2 \pm a^2}} = \sqrt{x^2 \pm a^2}$

163. $\displaystyle\int x\sqrt{x^2 \pm a^2}\,dx = \tfrac{1}{3}\sqrt{(x^2 \pm a^2)^3}$

INTEGRALS (Continued)

164. $\int \sqrt{(x^2 \pm a^2)^3}\, dx = \dfrac{1}{4}\bigg[x\sqrt{(x^2 \pm a^2)^3} \pm \dfrac{3a^2 x}{2}\sqrt{x^2 \pm a^2}$
$$+ \dfrac{3a^4}{2} \log\left(x + \sqrt{x^2 \pm a^2}\right)\bigg]$$

165. $\int \dfrac{dx}{\sqrt{(x^2 \pm a^2)^3}} = \dfrac{\pm x}{a^2\sqrt{x^2 \pm a^2}}$

166. $\int \dfrac{x\, dx}{\sqrt{(x^2 \pm a^2)^3}} = \dfrac{-1}{\sqrt{x^2 \pm a^2}}$

167. $\int x\sqrt{(x^2 \pm a^2)^3}\, dx = \tfrac{1}{5}\sqrt{(x^2 \pm a^2)^5}$

168. $\int x^2\sqrt{x^2 \pm a^2}\, dx = \dfrac{x}{4}\sqrt{(x^2 \pm a^2)^3} \mp \dfrac{a^2}{8} x\sqrt{x^2 \pm a^2} - \dfrac{a^4}{8}\log\left(x + \sqrt{x^2 \pm a^2}\right)$

169. $\int x^3\sqrt{x^2 + a^2}\, dx = (\tfrac{1}{5}x^2 - \tfrac{2}{15}a^2)\sqrt{(a^2 + x^2)^3}$

170. $\int x^3\sqrt{x^2 - a^2}\, dx = \dfrac{1}{5}\sqrt{(x^2 - a^2)^5} + \dfrac{a^2}{3}\sqrt{(x^2 - a^2)^3}$

171. $\int \dfrac{x^2\, dx}{\sqrt{x^2 \pm a^2}} = \dfrac{x}{2}\sqrt{x^2 \pm a^2} \mp \dfrac{a^2}{2}\log\left(x + \sqrt{x^2 \pm a^2}\right)$

172. $\int \dfrac{x^3\, dx}{\sqrt{x^2 \pm a^2}} = \dfrac{1}{3}\sqrt{(x^2 \pm a^2)^3} \mp a^2\sqrt{x^2 \pm a^2}$

173. $\int \dfrac{dx}{x^2\sqrt{x^2 \pm a^2}} = \mp \dfrac{\sqrt{x^2 \pm a^2}}{a^2 x}$

174. $\int \dfrac{dx}{x^3\sqrt{x^2 + a^2}} = -\dfrac{\sqrt{x^2 + a^2}}{2a^2 x^2} + \dfrac{1}{2a^3}\log\dfrac{a + \sqrt{x^2 + a^2}}{x}$

175. $\int \dfrac{dx}{x^3\sqrt{x^2 - a^2}} = \dfrac{\sqrt{x^2 - a^2}}{2a^2 x^2} + \dfrac{1}{2|a^3|}\sec^{-1}\dfrac{x}{a}$

176. $\int x^2\sqrt{(x^2 \pm a^2)^3}\, dx = \dfrac{x}{6}\sqrt{(x^2 \pm a^2)^5} \mp \dfrac{a^2 x}{24}\sqrt{(x^2 \pm a^2)^3} - \dfrac{a^4 x}{16}\sqrt{x^2 \pm a^2}$
$$\mp \dfrac{a^6}{16}\log\left(x + \sqrt{x^2 \pm a^2}\right)$$

177. $\int x^3\sqrt{(x^2 \pm a^2)^3}\, dx = \dfrac{1}{7}\sqrt{(x^2 \pm a^2)^7} \mp \dfrac{a^2}{5}\sqrt{(x^2 \pm a^2)^5}$

INTEGRALS (Continued)

178. $\displaystyle\int \frac{\sqrt{x^2 \pm a^2}\; dx}{x^2} = -\frac{\sqrt{x^2 \pm a^2}}{x} + \log(x + \sqrt{x^2 \pm a^2})$

179. $\displaystyle\int \frac{\sqrt{x^2 + a^2}}{x^3}\, dx = -\frac{\sqrt{x^2 + a^2}}{2x^2} - \frac{1}{2a}\log\frac{a + \sqrt{x^2 + a^2}}{x}$

180. $\displaystyle\int \frac{\sqrt{x^2 - a^2}}{x^3}\, dx = -\frac{\sqrt{x^2 - a^2}}{2x^2} + \frac{1}{2|a|}\sec^{-1}\frac{x}{a}$

181. $\displaystyle\int \frac{\sqrt{x^2 \pm a^2}}{x^4}\, dx = \mp \frac{\sqrt{(x^2 \pm a^2)^3}}{3a^2 x^3}$

182. $\displaystyle\int \frac{x^2\, dx}{\sqrt{(x^2 \pm a^2)^3}} = \frac{-x}{\sqrt{x^2 \pm a^2}} + \log(x + \sqrt{x^2 \pm a^2})$

183. $\displaystyle\int \frac{x^3\, dx}{\sqrt{(x^2 \pm a^2)^3}} = \sqrt{x^2 \pm a^2} \pm \frac{a^2}{\sqrt{x^2 \pm a^2}}$

184. $\displaystyle\int \frac{dx}{x\sqrt{(x^2 + a^2)^3}} = \frac{1}{a^2\sqrt{x^2 + a^2}} - \frac{1}{a^3}\log\frac{a + \sqrt{x^2 + a^2}}{x}$

185. $\displaystyle\int \frac{dx}{x\sqrt{(x^2 - a^2)^3}} = -\frac{1}{a^2\sqrt{x^2 - a^2}} - \frac{1}{|a^3|}\sec^{-1}\frac{x}{a}$

186. $\displaystyle\int \frac{dx}{x^2\sqrt{(x^2 \pm a^2)^3}} = -\frac{1}{a^4}\left[\frac{\sqrt{x^2 \pm a^2}}{x} + \frac{x}{\sqrt{x^2 \pm a^2}}\right]$

187. $\displaystyle\int \frac{dx}{x^3\sqrt{(x^2 + a^2)^3}} = -\frac{1}{2a^2 x^2 \sqrt{x^2 + a^2}} - \frac{3}{2a^4\sqrt{x^2 + a^2}}$

$$+ \frac{3}{2a^5}\log\frac{a + \sqrt{x^2 + a^2}}{x}$$

188. $\displaystyle\int \frac{dx}{x^3\sqrt{(x^2 - a^2)^3}} = \frac{1}{2a^2 x^2\sqrt{x^2 - a^2}} - \frac{3}{2a^4\sqrt{x^2 - a^2}} - \frac{3}{2|a^5|}\sec^{-1}\frac{x}{a}$

189. $\displaystyle\int \frac{x^m}{\sqrt{x^2 \pm a^2}}\, dx = \frac{1}{m}x^{m-1}\sqrt{x^2 \pm a^2} \mp \frac{m-1}{m}a^2 \int \frac{x^{m-2}}{\sqrt{x^2 \pm a^2}}\, dx$

190. $\displaystyle\int \frac{x^{2m}}{\sqrt{x^2 \pm a^2}}\, dx = \frac{(2m)!}{2^{2m}(m!)^2}\left[\sqrt{x^2 \pm a^2}\sum_{r=1}^{m}\frac{r!(r-1)!}{(2r)!}(\mp a^2)^{m-r}(2x)^{2r-1}\right.$

$$\left. + (\mp a^2)^m \log(x + \sqrt{x^2 \pm a^2})\right]$$

191. $\displaystyle\int \frac{x^{2m+1}}{\sqrt{x^2 \pm a^2}}\, dx = \sqrt{x^2 \pm a^2}\sum_{r=0}^{m}\frac{(2r)!(m!)^2}{(2m+1)!(r!)^2}(\mp 4a^2)^{m-r}x^{2r}$

INTEGRALS (Continued)

192. $\displaystyle\int \frac{dx}{x^m\sqrt{x^2 \pm a^2}} = \mp\frac{\sqrt{x^2 \pm a^2}}{(m-1)a^2 x^{m-1}} \mp \frac{(m-2)}{(m-1)a^2}\int \frac{dx}{x^{m-2}\sqrt{x^2 \pm a^2}}$

193. $\displaystyle\int \frac{dx}{x^{2m}\sqrt{x^2 \pm a^2}} = \sqrt{x^2 \pm a^2}\sum_{r=0}^{m-1}\frac{(m-1)!\,m!\,(2r)!\,2^{2m-2r-1}}{(r!)^2(2m)!(\mp a^2)^{m-r}x^{2r+1}}$

194. $\displaystyle\int \frac{dx}{x^{2m+1}\sqrt{x^2 + a^2}} = \frac{(2m)!}{(m!)^2}\left[\frac{\sqrt{x^2 + a^2}}{a^2}\sum_{r=1}^{m}(-1)^{m-r+1}\frac{r!(r-1)!}{2(2r)!(4a^2)^{m-r}x^{2r}}\right.$

$$\left. + \frac{(-1)^{m+1}}{2^{2m}a^{2m+1}}\log\frac{\sqrt{x^2 + a^2} + a}{x}\right]$$

195. $\displaystyle\int \frac{dx}{x^{2m+1}\sqrt{x^2 - a^2}} = \frac{(2m)!}{(m!)^2}\left[\frac{\sqrt{x^2 - a^2}}{a^2}\sum_{r=1}^{m}\frac{r!(r-1)!}{2(2r)!(4a^2)^{m-r}x^{2r}}\right.$

$$\left. + \frac{1}{2^{2m}|a|^{2m+1}}\sec^{-1}\frac{x}{a}\right]$$

196. $\displaystyle\int \frac{dx}{(x-a)\sqrt{x^2 - a^2}} = -\frac{\sqrt{x^2 - a^2}}{a(x-a)}$

197. $\displaystyle\int \frac{dx}{(x+a)\sqrt{x^2 - a^2}} = \frac{\sqrt{x^2 - a^2}}{a(x+a)}$

198. $\displaystyle\int f(x, \sqrt{x^2 + a^2})\,dx = a\int f(a\tan u, a\sec u)\sec^2 u\,du, \qquad \left(u = \tan^{-1}\frac{x}{a}, a > 0\right)$

199. $\displaystyle\int f(x, \sqrt{x^2 - a^2})\,dx = a\int f(a\sec u, a\tan u)\sec u\tan u\,du, \qquad \left(u = \sec^{-1}\frac{x}{a},\right.$

$$\left. a > 0\right)$$

FORMS CONTAINING $\sqrt{a^2 - x^2}$

200. $\displaystyle\int \sqrt{a^2 - x^2}\,dx = \frac{1}{2}\left[x\sqrt{a^2 - x^2} + a^2\sin^{-1}\frac{x}{|a|}\right]$

201. $\displaystyle\int \frac{dx}{\sqrt{a^2 - x^2}} = \begin{cases} \sin^{-1}\dfrac{x}{|a|} \\[2mm] \text{or} \\[2mm] -\cos^{-1}\dfrac{x}{|a|} \end{cases}$

202. $\displaystyle\int \frac{dx}{x\sqrt{a^2 - x^2}} = -\frac{1}{a}\log\left(\frac{a + \sqrt{a^2 - x^2}}{x}\right)$

INTEGRALS (Continued)

203. $\displaystyle\int \frac{\sqrt{a^2 - x^2}}{x}\, dx = \sqrt{a^2 - x^2} - a \log\left(\frac{a + \sqrt{a^2 - x^2}}{x}\right)$

204. $\displaystyle\int \frac{x\, dx}{\sqrt{a^2 - x^2}} = -\sqrt{a^2 - x^2}$

205. $\displaystyle\int x\sqrt{a^2 - x^2}\, dx = -\tfrac{1}{3}\sqrt{(a^2 - x^2)^3}$

206. $\displaystyle\int \sqrt{(a^2 - x^2)^3}\, dx = \frac{1}{4}\left[x\sqrt{(a^2 - x^2)^3} + \frac{3a^2 x}{2}\sqrt{a^2 - x^2} + \frac{3a^4}{2}\sin^{-1}\frac{x}{|a|}\right]$

207. $\displaystyle\int \frac{dx}{\sqrt{(a^2 - x^2)^3}} = \frac{x}{a^2\sqrt{a^2 - x^2}}$

208. $\displaystyle\int \frac{x\, dx}{\sqrt{(a^2 - x^2)^3}} = \frac{1}{\sqrt{a^2 - x^2}}$

209. $\displaystyle\int x\sqrt{(a^2 - x^2)^3}\, dx = -\tfrac{1}{5}\sqrt{(a^2 - x^2)^5}$

210. $\displaystyle\int x^2\sqrt{a^2 - x^2}\, dx = -\frac{x}{4}\sqrt{(a^2 - x^2)^3} + \frac{a^2}{8}\left(x\sqrt{a^2 - x^2} + a^2\sin^{-1}\frac{x}{|a|}\right)$

211. $\displaystyle\int x^3\sqrt{a^2 - x^2}\, dx = (-\tfrac{1}{5}x^2 - \tfrac{2}{15}a^2)\sqrt{(a^2 - x^2)^3}$

212. $\displaystyle\int x^2\sqrt{(a^2 - x^2)^3}\, dx = -\frac{1}{6}x\sqrt{(a^2 - x^2)^5} + \frac{a^2 x}{24}\sqrt{(a^2 - x^2)^3}$

$$+ \frac{a^4 x}{16}\sqrt{a^2 - x^2} + \frac{a^6}{16}\sin^{-1}\frac{x}{|a|}$$

213. $\displaystyle\int x^3\sqrt{(a^2 - x^2)^3}\, dx = \frac{1}{7}\sqrt{(a^2 - x^2)^7} - \frac{a^2}{5}\sqrt{(a^2 - x^2)^5}$

214. $\displaystyle\int \frac{x^2\, dx}{\sqrt{a^2 - x^2}} = -\frac{x}{2}\sqrt{a^2 - x^2} + \frac{a^2}{2}\sin^{-1}\frac{x}{|a|}$

215. $\displaystyle\int \frac{dx}{x^2\sqrt{a^2 - x^2}} = -\frac{\sqrt{a^2 - x^2}}{a^2 x}$

216. $\displaystyle\int \frac{\sqrt{a^2 - x^2}}{x^2}\, dx = -\frac{\sqrt{a^2 - x^2}}{x} - \sin^{-1}\frac{x}{|a|}$

217. $\displaystyle\int \frac{\sqrt{a^2 - x^2}}{x^3}\, dx = -\frac{\sqrt{a^2 - x^2}}{2x^2} + \frac{1}{2a}\log\frac{a + \sqrt{a^2 - x^2}}{x}$

218. $\displaystyle\int \frac{\sqrt{a^2 - x^2}}{x^4}\, dx = -\frac{\sqrt{(a^2 - x^2)^3}}{3a^2 x^3}$

INTEGRALS (Continued)

219. $\displaystyle \int \frac{x^2\,dx}{\sqrt{(a^2-x^2)^3}} = \frac{x}{\sqrt{a^2-x^2}} - \sin^{-1}\frac{x}{|a|}$

220. $\displaystyle \int \frac{x^3\,dx}{\sqrt{a^2-x^2}} = -\frac{2}{3}(a^2-x^2)^{\frac{3}{2}} - x^2(a^2-x^2)^{\frac{1}{2}} - \frac{1}{3}\sqrt{a^2-x^2}(x^2+2a^2)$

221. $\displaystyle \int \frac{x^3\,dx}{\sqrt{(a^2-x^2)^3}} = 2(a^2-x^2)^{\frac{1}{2}} + \frac{x^2}{(a^2-x^2)^{\frac{1}{2}}} = \frac{a^2}{\sqrt{a^2-x^2}} + \sqrt{a^2-x^2}$

222. $\displaystyle \int \frac{dx}{x^3\sqrt{a^2-x^2}} = -\frac{\sqrt{a^2-x^2}}{2a^2x^2} - \frac{1}{2a^3}\log\frac{a+\sqrt{a^2-x^2}}{x}$

223. $\displaystyle \int \frac{dx}{x\sqrt{(a^2-x^2)^3}} = \frac{1}{a^2\sqrt{a^2-x^2}} - \frac{1}{a^3}\log\frac{a+\sqrt{a^2-x^2}}{x}$

224. $\displaystyle \int \frac{dx}{x^2\sqrt{(a^2-x^2)^3}} = \frac{1}{a^4}\left[-\frac{\sqrt{a^2-x^2}}{x} + \frac{x}{\sqrt{a^2-x^2}}\right]$

225. $\displaystyle \int \frac{dx}{x^3\sqrt{(a^2-x^2)^3}} = -\frac{1}{2a^2x^2\sqrt{a^2-x^2}} + \frac{3}{2a^4\sqrt{a^2-x^2}}$

$$-\frac{3}{2a^5}\log\frac{a+\sqrt{a^2-x^2}}{x}$$

226. $\displaystyle \int \frac{x^m}{\sqrt{a^2-x^2}}\,dx = -\frac{x^{m-1}\sqrt{a^2-x^2}}{m} + \frac{(m-1)a^2}{m}\int \frac{x^{m-2}}{\sqrt{a^2-x^2}}\,dx$

227. $\displaystyle \int \frac{x^{2m}}{\sqrt{a^2-x^2}}\,dx = \frac{(2m)!}{(m!)^2}\left[-\sqrt{a^2-x^2}\sum_{r=1}^{m}\frac{r!(r-1)!}{2^{2m-2r+1}(2r)!}a^{2m-2r}x^{2r-1}\right.$

$$\left. + \frac{a^{2m}}{2^{2m}}\sin^{-1}\frac{x}{|a|}\right]$$

228. $\displaystyle \int \frac{x^{2m+1}}{\sqrt{a^2-x^2}}\,dx = -\sqrt{a^2-x^2}\sum_{r=0}^{m}\frac{(2r)!(m!)^2}{(2m+1)!(r!)^2}(4a^2)^{m-r}x^{2r}$

229. $\displaystyle \int \frac{dx}{x^m\sqrt{a^2-x^2}} = -\frac{\sqrt{a^2-x^2}}{(m-1)a^2x^{m-1}} + \frac{m-2}{(m-1)a^2}\int \frac{dx}{x^{m-2}\sqrt{a^2-x^2}}$

230. $\displaystyle \int \frac{dx}{x^{2m}\sqrt{a^2-x^2}} = -\sqrt{a^2-x^2}\sum_{r=0}^{m-1}\frac{(m-1)!\,m!\,(2r)!\,2^{2m-2r-1}}{(r!)^2(2m)!\,a^{2m-2r}x^{2r+1}}$

231. $\displaystyle \int \frac{dx}{x^{2m+1}\sqrt{a^2-x^2}} = \frac{(2m)!}{(m!)^2}\left[-\frac{\sqrt{a^2-x^2}}{a^2}\sum_{r=1}^{m}\frac{r!(r-1)!}{2(2r)!(4a^2)^{m-r}x^{2r}}\right.$

$$\left. + \frac{1}{2^{2m}a^{2m+1}}\log\frac{a-\sqrt{a^2-x^2}}{x}\right]$$

INTEGRALS (Continued)

232. $\displaystyle\int \frac{dx}{(b^2 - x^2)\sqrt{a^2 - x^2}} = \frac{1}{2b\sqrt{a^2 - b^2}} \log \frac{(b\sqrt{a^2 - x^2} + x\sqrt{a^2 - b^2})^2}{b^2 - x^2},$

$$(a^2 > b^2)$$

233. $\displaystyle\int \frac{dx}{(b^2 - x^2)\sqrt{a^2 - x^2}} = \frac{1}{b\sqrt{b^2 - a^2}} \tan^{-1} \frac{x\sqrt{b^2 - a^2}}{b\sqrt{a^2 - x^2}}, \qquad (b^2 > a^2)$

234. $\displaystyle\int \frac{dx}{(b^2 + x^2)\sqrt{a^2 - x^2}} = \frac{1}{b\sqrt{a^2 + b^2}} \tan^{-1} \frac{x\sqrt{a^2 + b^2}}{b\sqrt{a^2 - x^2}}$

235. $\displaystyle\int \frac{\sqrt{a^2 - x^2}}{b^2 + x^2} dx = \frac{\sqrt{a^2 + b^2}}{|b|} \sin^{-1} \frac{x\sqrt{a^2 + b^2}}{|a|\sqrt{x^2 + b^2}} - \sin^{-1} \frac{x}{|a|}$

236. $\displaystyle\int f(x, \sqrt{a^2 - x^2})\, dx = a \int f(a \sin u, a \cos u) \cos u\, du, \qquad \left(u = \sin^{-1} \frac{x}{a}, a > 0\right)$

FORMS CONTAINING $\sqrt{a + bx + cx^2}$

$$X = a + bx + cx^2, q = 4ac - b^2, \text{and } k = \frac{4c}{q}$$

If $q = 0$, then $\sqrt{X} = \sqrt{c} \left| x + \dfrac{b}{2c} \right|$

237. $\displaystyle\int \frac{dx}{\sqrt{X}} = \begin{cases} \dfrac{1}{\sqrt{c}} \log\left(2\sqrt{cX} + 2cx + b\right) \\ \quad\text{or} \\ \dfrac{1}{\sqrt{c}} \sinh^{-1} \dfrac{2cx + b}{\sqrt{q}}, \qquad (c > 0) \end{cases}$

238. $\displaystyle\int \frac{dx}{\sqrt{X}} = -\frac{1}{\sqrt{-c}} \sin^{-1} \frac{2cx + b}{\sqrt{-q}}, \qquad (c < 0)$

239. $\displaystyle\int \frac{dx}{X\sqrt{X}} = \frac{2(2cx + b)}{q\sqrt{X}}$

240. $\displaystyle\int \frac{dx}{X^2\sqrt{X}} = \frac{2(2cx + b)}{3q\sqrt{X}} \left(\frac{1}{X} + 2k\right)$

241. $\displaystyle\int \frac{dx}{X^n\sqrt{X}} = \begin{cases} \dfrac{2(2cx + b)\sqrt{X}}{(2n - 1)qX^n} + \dfrac{2k(n - 1)}{2n - 1} \displaystyle\int \frac{dx}{X^{n-1}\sqrt{X}} \\ \quad\text{or} \\ \dfrac{(2cx + b)(n!)(n - 1)!4^n k^{n-1}}{q[(2n)!]\sqrt{X}} \displaystyle\sum_{r=0}^{n-1} \frac{(2r)!}{(4kX)^r(r!)^2} \end{cases}$

INTEGRALS (Continued)

242. $\int \sqrt{X}\, dx = \dfrac{(2cx + b)\sqrt{X}}{4c} + \dfrac{1}{2k}\int \dfrac{dx}{\sqrt{X}}$

243. $\int X\sqrt{X}\, dx = \dfrac{(2cx + b)\sqrt{X}}{8c}\left(X + \dfrac{3}{2k}\right) + \dfrac{3}{8k^2}\int \dfrac{dx}{\sqrt{X}}$

244. $\int X^2\sqrt{X}\, dx = \dfrac{(2cx + b)\sqrt{X}}{12c}\left(X^2 + \dfrac{5X}{4k} + \dfrac{15}{8k^2}\right) + \dfrac{5}{16k^3}\int \dfrac{dx}{\sqrt{X}}$

245. $\int X^n\sqrt{X}\, dx = \begin{cases} \dfrac{(2cx + b)X^n\sqrt{X}}{4(n + 1)c} + \dfrac{2n + 1}{2(n + 1)k}\int X^{n-1}\sqrt{X}\, dx \\ \text{or} \\ \dfrac{(2n + 2)!}{[(n + 1)!]^2(4k)^{n+1}}\left[\dfrac{k(2cx + b)\sqrt{X}}{c}\displaystyle\sum_{r=0}^{n}\dfrac{r!(r + 1)!(4kX)^r}{(2r + 2)!} + \int \dfrac{dx}{\sqrt{X}}\right] \end{cases}$

246. $\int \dfrac{x\, dx}{\sqrt{X}} = \dfrac{\sqrt{X}}{c} - \dfrac{b}{2c}\int \dfrac{dx}{\sqrt{X}}$

247. $\int \dfrac{x\, dx}{X\sqrt{X}} = -\dfrac{2(bx + 2a)}{q\sqrt{X}}$

248. $\int \dfrac{x\, dx}{X^n\sqrt{X}} = -\dfrac{\sqrt{X}}{(2n - 1)cX^n} - \dfrac{b}{2c}\int \dfrac{dx}{X^n\sqrt{X}}$

249. $\int \dfrac{x^2\, dx}{\sqrt{X}} = \left(\dfrac{x}{2c} - \dfrac{3b}{4c^2}\right)\sqrt{X} + \dfrac{3b^2 - 4ac}{8c^2}\int \dfrac{dx}{\sqrt{X}}$

250. $\int \dfrac{x^2\, dx}{X\sqrt{X}} = \dfrac{(2b^2 - 4ac)x + 2ab}{cq\sqrt{X}} + \dfrac{1}{c}\int \dfrac{dx}{\sqrt{X}}$

251. $\int \dfrac{x^2\, dx}{X^n\sqrt{X}} = \dfrac{(2b^2 - 4ac)x + 2ab}{(2n - 1)cqX^{n-1}\sqrt{X}} + \dfrac{4ac + (2n - 3)b^2}{(2n - 1)cq}\int \dfrac{dx}{X^{n-1}\sqrt{X}}$

252. $\int \dfrac{x^3\, dx}{\sqrt{X}} = \left(\dfrac{x^2}{3c} - \dfrac{5bx}{12c^2} + \dfrac{5b^2}{8c^3} - \dfrac{2a}{3c^2}\right)\sqrt{X} + \left(\dfrac{3ab}{4c^2} - \dfrac{5b^3}{16c^3}\right)\int \dfrac{dx}{\sqrt{X}}$

253. $\int \dfrac{x^n\, dx}{\sqrt{X}} = \dfrac{1}{nc}x^{n-1}\sqrt{X} - \dfrac{(2n - 1)b}{2nc}\int \dfrac{x^{n-1}\, dx}{\sqrt{X}} - \dfrac{(n - 1)a}{nc}\int \dfrac{x^{n-2}\, dx}{\sqrt{X}}$

INTEGRALS (Continued)

254. $\displaystyle \int x\sqrt{X}\,dx = \frac{X\sqrt{X}}{3c} - \frac{b(2cx+b)}{8c^2}\sqrt{X} - \frac{b}{4ck}\int \frac{dx}{\sqrt{X}}$

255. $\displaystyle \int xX\sqrt{X}\,dx = \frac{X^2\sqrt{X}}{5c} - \frac{b}{2c}\int X\sqrt{X}\,dx$

256. $\displaystyle \int xX^n\sqrt{X}\,dx = \frac{X^{n+1}\sqrt{X}}{(2n+3)c} - \frac{b}{2c}\int X^n\sqrt{X}\,dx$

257. $\displaystyle \int x^2\sqrt{X}\,dx = \left(x - \frac{5b}{6c}\right)\frac{X\sqrt{X}}{4c} + \frac{5b^2 - 4ac}{16c^2}\int \sqrt{X}\,dx$

258. $\displaystyle \int \frac{dx}{x\sqrt{X}} = -\frac{1}{\sqrt{a}}\log \frac{2\sqrt{aX} + bx + 2a}{x}, \qquad (a > 0)$

259. $\displaystyle \int \frac{dx}{x\sqrt{X}} = \frac{1}{\sqrt{-a}}\sin^{-1}\left(\frac{bx + 2a}{|x|\sqrt{-q}}\right), \qquad (a < 0)$

260. $\displaystyle \int \frac{dx}{x\sqrt{X}} = -\frac{2\sqrt{X}}{bx}, \qquad (a = 0)$

261. $\displaystyle \int \frac{dx}{x^2\sqrt{X}} = -\frac{\sqrt{X}}{ax} - \frac{b}{2a}\int \frac{dx}{x\sqrt{X}}$

262. $\displaystyle \int \frac{\sqrt{X}\,dx}{x} = \sqrt{X} + \frac{b}{2}\int \frac{dx}{\sqrt{X}} + a\int \frac{dx}{x\sqrt{X}}$

263. $\displaystyle \int \frac{\sqrt{X}\,dx}{x^2} = -\frac{\sqrt{X}}{x} + \frac{b}{2}\int \frac{dx}{x\sqrt{X}} + c\int \frac{dx}{\sqrt{X}}$

FORMS INVOLVING $\sqrt{2ax - x^2}$

264. $\displaystyle \int \sqrt{2ax - x^2}\,dx = \frac{1}{2}\left[(x-a)\sqrt{2ax - x^2} + a^2\sin^{-1}\frac{x-a}{|a|}\right]$

265. $\displaystyle \int \frac{dx}{\sqrt{2ax - x^2}} = \begin{cases} \cos^{-1}\dfrac{a-x}{|a|} \\ \quad \text{or} \\ \sin^{-1}\dfrac{x-a}{|a|} \end{cases}$

266. $\displaystyle\int x^n\sqrt{2ax - x^2}\,dx = \begin{cases} -\dfrac{x^{n-1}(2ax - x^2)^{\frac{3}{2}}}{n + 2} + \dfrac{(2n + 1)a}{n + 2}\displaystyle\int x^{n-1}\sqrt{2ax - x^2}\,dx \\[2mm] \text{or} \\[2mm] \sqrt{2ax - x^2}\left[\dfrac{x^{n+1}}{n + 2} - \displaystyle\sum_{r=0}^{n}\dfrac{(2n + 1)!(r!)^2 a^{n-r+1}}{2^{n-r}(2r + 1)!(n + 2)!n!}x^r\right] \\[2mm] \qquad\qquad + \dfrac{(2n + 1)!a^{n+2}}{2^n n!(n + 2)!}\sin^{-1}\dfrac{x - a}{|a|} \end{cases}$

267. $\displaystyle\int\frac{\sqrt{2ax - x^2}}{x^n}\,dx = \frac{(2ax - x^2)^{\frac{3}{2}}}{(3 - 2n)ax^n} + \frac{n - 3}{(2n - 3)a}\int\frac{\sqrt{2ax - x^2}}{x^{n-1}}\,dx$

268. $\displaystyle\int\frac{x^n\,dx}{\sqrt{2ax - x^2}} = \begin{cases} \dfrac{-x^{n-1}\sqrt{2ax - x^2}}{n} + \dfrac{a(2n - 1)}{n}\displaystyle\int\frac{x^{n-1}}{\sqrt{2ax - x^2}}\,dx \\[2mm] \text{or} \\[2mm] -\sqrt{2ax - x^2}\displaystyle\sum_{r=1}^{n}\dfrac{(2n)!r!(r - 1)!a^{n-r}}{2^{n-r}(2r)!(n!)^2}x^{r-1} \\[2mm] \qquad\qquad + \dfrac{(2n)!a^n}{2^n(n!)^2}\sin^{-1}\dfrac{x - a}{|a|} \end{cases}$

269. $\displaystyle\int\frac{dx}{x^n\sqrt{2ax - x^2}} = \begin{cases} \dfrac{\sqrt{2ax - x^2}}{a(1 - 2n)x^n} + \dfrac{n - 1}{(2n - 1)a}\displaystyle\int\frac{dx}{x^{n-1}\sqrt{2ax - x^2}} \\[2mm] \text{or} \\[2mm] -\sqrt{2ax - x^2}\displaystyle\sum_{r=0}^{n-1}\dfrac{2^{n-r}(n - 1)!n!(2r)!}{(2n)!(r!)^2 a^{n-r}x^{r+1}} \end{cases}$

270. $\displaystyle\int\frac{dx}{(2ax - x^2)^{\frac{3}{2}}} = \frac{x - a}{a^2\sqrt{2ax - x^2}}$

271. $\displaystyle\int\frac{x\,dx}{(2ax - x^2)^{\frac{3}{2}}} = \frac{x}{a\sqrt{2ax - x^2}}$

MISCELLANEOUS ALGEBRAIC FORMS

272. $\displaystyle\int\frac{dx}{\sqrt{2ax + x^2}} = \log(x + a + \sqrt{2ax + x^2})$

273. $\displaystyle\int\sqrt{ax^2 + c}\,dx = \frac{x}{2}\sqrt{ax^2 + c} + \frac{c}{2\sqrt{a}}\log(x\sqrt{a} + \sqrt{ax^2 + c}), \qquad (a > 0)$

274. $\displaystyle\int\sqrt{ax^2 + c}\,dx = \frac{x}{2}\sqrt{ax^2 + c} + \frac{c}{2\sqrt{-a}}\sin^{-1}\left(x\sqrt{-\frac{a}{c}}\right), \qquad (a < 0)$

INTEGRALS (Continued)

275. $\displaystyle\int \sqrt{\frac{1+x}{1-x}}\, dx = \sin^{-1} x - \sqrt{1-x^2}$

276. $\displaystyle\int \frac{dx}{x\sqrt{ax^n + c}} = \begin{cases} \dfrac{1}{n\sqrt{c}} \log \dfrac{\sqrt{ax^n + c} - \sqrt{c}}{\sqrt{ax^n + c} + \sqrt{c}} \\[2ex] \qquad\text{or} \\[1ex] \dfrac{2}{n\sqrt{c}} \log \dfrac{\sqrt{ax^n + c} - \sqrt{c}}{\sqrt{x^n}}, \qquad (c > 0) \end{cases}$

277. $\displaystyle\int \frac{dx}{x\sqrt{ax^n + c}} = \frac{2}{n\sqrt{-c}} \sec^{-1}\sqrt{-\frac{ax^n}{c}}, \qquad (c < 0)$

278. $\displaystyle\int \frac{dx}{\sqrt{ax^2 + c}} = \frac{1}{\sqrt{a}} \log(x\sqrt{a} + \sqrt{ax^2 + c}), \qquad (a > 0)$

279. $\displaystyle\int \frac{dx}{\sqrt{ax^2 + c}} = \frac{1}{\sqrt{-a}} \sin^{-1}\left(x\sqrt{-\frac{a}{c}}\right), \qquad (a < 0)$

280. $\displaystyle\int (ax^2 + c)^{m+\frac{1}{2}}\, dx = \begin{cases} \dfrac{x(ax^2 + c)^{m+\frac{1}{2}}}{2(m+1)} + \dfrac{(2m+1)c}{2(m+1)} \displaystyle\int (ax^2 + c)^{m-\frac{1}{2}}\, dx \\[2ex] \qquad\text{or} \\[1ex] x\sqrt{ax^2 + c} \displaystyle\sum_{r=0}^{m} \dfrac{(2m+1)!(r!)^2 c^{m-r}}{2^{2m-2r+1} m!(m+1)!(2r+1)!}(ax^2 + c)^r \\[2ex] \qquad + \dfrac{(2m+1)!c^{m+1}}{2^{2m+1} m!(m+1)!} \displaystyle\int \dfrac{dx}{\sqrt{ax^2 + c}} \end{cases}$

281. $\displaystyle\int x(ax^2 + c)^{m+\frac{1}{2}}\, dx = \frac{(ax^2 + c)^{m+\frac{3}{2}}}{(2m+3)a}$

282. $\displaystyle\int \frac{(ax^2 + c)^{m+\frac{1}{2}}}{x}\, dx = \begin{cases} \dfrac{(ax^2 + c)^{m+\frac{1}{2}}}{2m+1} + c \displaystyle\int \dfrac{(ax^2 + c)^{m-\frac{1}{2}}}{x}\, dx \\[2ex] \qquad\text{or} \\[1ex] \sqrt{ax^2 + c} \displaystyle\sum_{r=0}^{m} \dfrac{c^{m-r}(ax^2 + c)^r}{2r+1} + c^{m+1} \displaystyle\int \dfrac{dx}{x\sqrt{ax^2 + c}} \end{cases}$

283. $\displaystyle\int \frac{dx}{(ax^2 + c)^{m+\frac{1}{2}}} = \begin{cases} \dfrac{x}{(2m-1)c(ax^2 + c)^{m-\frac{1}{2}}} + \dfrac{2m-2}{(2m-1)c} \displaystyle\int \dfrac{dx}{(ax^2 + c)^{m-\frac{1}{2}}} \\[2ex] \qquad\text{or} \\[1ex] \dfrac{x}{\sqrt{ax^2 + c}} \displaystyle\sum_{r=0}^{m-1} \dfrac{2^{2m-2r-1}(m-1)!m!(2r)!}{(2m)!(r!)^2 c^{m-r}(ax^2 + c)^r} \end{cases}$

284. $\displaystyle\int \frac{dx}{x^m\sqrt{ax^2+c}} = -\frac{\sqrt{ax^2+c}}{(m-1)cx^{m-1}} - \frac{(m-2)a}{(m-1)c}\int \frac{dx}{x^{m-2}\sqrt{ax^2+c}}$

285. $\displaystyle\int \frac{1+x^2}{(1-x^2)\sqrt{1+x^4}}\,dx = \frac{1}{\sqrt{2}}\log \frac{x\sqrt{2}+\sqrt{1+x^4}}{1-x^2}$

286. $\displaystyle\int \frac{1-x^2}{(1+x^2)\sqrt{1+x^4}}\,dx = \frac{1}{\sqrt{2}}\tan^{-1}\frac{x\sqrt{2}}{\sqrt{1+x^4}}$

287. $\displaystyle\int \frac{dx}{x\sqrt{x^n+a^2}} = -\frac{2}{na}\log \frac{a+\sqrt{x^n+a^2}}{\sqrt{x^n}}$

288. $\displaystyle\int \frac{dx}{x\sqrt{x^n-a^2}} = -\frac{2}{na}\sin^{-1}\frac{a}{\sqrt{x^n}}$

289. $\displaystyle\int \sqrt{\frac{x}{a^3-x^3}}\,dx = \frac{2}{3}\sin^{-1}\left(\frac{x}{a}\right)^{\frac{3}{2}}$

FORMS INVOLVING TRIGONOMETRIC FUNCTIONS

290. $\displaystyle\int (\sin ax)\,dx = -\frac{1}{a}\cos ax$

291. $\displaystyle\int (\cos ax)\,dx = \frac{1}{a}\sin ax$

292. $\displaystyle\int (\tan ax)\,dx = -\frac{1}{a}\log\cos ax = \frac{1}{a}\log\sec ax$

293. $\displaystyle\int (\cot ax)\,dx = \frac{1}{a}\log\sin ax = -\frac{1}{a}\log\csc ax$

294. $\displaystyle\int (\sec ax)\,dx = \frac{1}{a}\log(\sec ax + \tan ax) = \frac{1}{a}\log\tan\left(\frac{\pi}{4}+\frac{ax}{2}\right)$

295. $\displaystyle\int (\csc ax)\,dx = \frac{1}{a}\log(\csc ax - \cot ax) = \frac{1}{a}\log\tan\frac{ax}{2}$

296. $\displaystyle\int (\sin^2 ax)\,dx = -\frac{1}{2a}\cos ax\sin ax + \frac{1}{2}x = \frac{1}{2}x - \frac{1}{4a}\sin 2ax$

297. $\displaystyle\int (\sin^3 ax)\,dx = -\frac{1}{3a}(\cos ax)(\sin^2 ax + 2)$

298. $\displaystyle\int (\sin^4 ax)\,dx = \frac{3x}{8} - \frac{\sin 2ax}{4a} + \frac{\sin 4ax}{32a}$

299. $\displaystyle\int (\sin^n ax)\,dx = -\frac{\sin^{n-1} ax\cos ax}{na} + \frac{n-1}{n}\int (\sin^{n-2} ax)\,dx$

INTEGRALS (Continued)

300. $\int (\sin^{2m} ax)\, dx = -\dfrac{\cos ax}{a} \sum\limits_{r=0}^{m-1} \dfrac{(2m)!(r!)^2}{2^{2m-2r}(2r+1)!(m!)^2} \sin^{2r+1} ax + \dfrac{(2m)!}{2^{2m}(m!)^2} x$

301. $\int (\sin^{2m+1} ax)\, dx = -\dfrac{\cos ax}{a} \sum\limits_{r=0}^{m} \dfrac{2^{2m-2r}(m!)^2(2r)!}{(2m+1)!(r!)^2} \sin^{2r} ax$

302. $\int (\cos^2 ax)\, dx = \dfrac{1}{2a}\sin ax \cos ax + \dfrac{1}{2}x = \dfrac{1}{2}x + \dfrac{1}{4a}\sin 2ax$

303. $\int (\cos^3 ax)\, dx = \dfrac{1}{3a}(\sin ax)(\cos^2 ax + 2)$

304. $\int (\cos^4 ax)\, dx = \dfrac{3x}{8} + \dfrac{\sin 2ax}{4a} + \dfrac{\sin 4ax}{32a}$

305. $\int (\cos^n ax)\, dx = \dfrac{1}{na}\cos^{n-1} ax \sin ax + \dfrac{n-1}{n}\int (\cos^{n-2} ax)\, dx$

306. $\int (\cos^{2m} ax)\, dx = \dfrac{\sin ax}{a} \sum\limits_{r=0}^{m-1} \dfrac{(2m)!(r!)^2}{2^{2m-2r}(2r+1)!(m!)^2} \cos^{2r+1} ax + \dfrac{(2m)!}{2^{2m}(m!)^2} x$

307. $\int (\cos^{2m+1} ax)\, dx = \dfrac{\sin ax}{a} \sum\limits_{r=0}^{m} \dfrac{2^{2m-2r}(m!)^2(2r)!}{(2m+1)!(r!)^2} \cos^{2r} ax$

308. $\int \dfrac{dx}{\sin^2 ax} = \int (\csc^2 ax)\, dx = -\dfrac{1}{a}\cot ax$

309. $\int \dfrac{dx}{\sin^m ax} = \int (\csc^m ax)\, dx = -\dfrac{1}{(m-1)a}\cdot\dfrac{\cos ax}{\sin^{m-1} ax} + \dfrac{m-2}{m-1}\int \dfrac{dx}{\sin^{m-2} ax}$

310. $\int \dfrac{dx}{\sin^{2m} ax} = \int (\csc^{2m} ax)\, dx = -\dfrac{1}{a}\cos ax \sum\limits_{r=0}^{m-1} \dfrac{2^{2m-2r-1}(m-1)!\,m!(2r)!}{(2m)!(r!)^2 \sin^{2r+1} ax}$

311. $\int \dfrac{dx}{\sin^{2m+1} ax} = \int (\csc^{2m+1} ax)\, dx =$

$\quad -\dfrac{1}{a}\cos ax \sum\limits_{r=0}^{m-1} \dfrac{(2m)!(r!)^2}{2^{2m-2r}(m!)^2(2r+1)! \sin^{2r+2} ax} + \dfrac{1}{a}\cdot\dfrac{(2m)!}{2^{2m}(m!)^2}\log\tan\dfrac{ax}{2}$

312. $\int \dfrac{dx}{\cos^2 ax} = \int (\sec^2 ax)\, dx = \dfrac{1}{a}\tan ax$

313. $\int \dfrac{dx}{\cos^n ax} = \int (\sec^n ax)\, dx = \dfrac{1}{(n-1)a}\cdot\dfrac{\sin ax}{\cos^{n-1} ax} + \dfrac{n-2}{n-1}\int \dfrac{dx}{\cos^{n-2} ax}$

314. $\int \dfrac{dx}{\cos^{2m} ax} = \int (\sec^{2m} ax)\, dx = \dfrac{1}{a}\sin ax \sum\limits_{r=0}^{m-1} \dfrac{2^{2m-2r-1}(m-1)!\,m!(2r)!}{(2m)!(r!)^2 \cos^{2r+1} ax}$

INTEGRALS (Continued)

315. $\displaystyle\int \frac{dx}{\cos^{2m+1} ax} = \int (\sec^{2m+1} ax)\, dx =$

$$\frac{1}{a} \sin ax \sum_{r=0}^{m-1} \frac{(2m)!\,(r!)^2}{2^{2m-2r}(m!)^2(2r+1)!\cos^{2r+2} ax}$$

$$+ \frac{1}{a} \cdot \frac{(2m)!}{2^{2m}(m!)^2} \log (\sec ax + \tan ax)$$

316. $\displaystyle\int (\sin mx)(\sin nx)\, dx = \frac{\sin(m-n)x}{2(m-n)} - \frac{\sin(m+n)x}{2(m+n)}, \qquad (m^2 \neq n^2)$

317. $\displaystyle\int (\cos mx)(\cos nx)\, dx = \frac{\sin(m-n)x}{2(m-n)} + \frac{\sin(m+n)x}{2(m+n)}, \qquad (m^2 \neq n^2)$

318. $\displaystyle\int (\sin ax)(\cos ax)\, dx = \frac{1}{2a} \sin^2 ax$

319. $\displaystyle\int (\sin mx)(\cos nx)\, dx = -\frac{\cos(m-n)x}{2(m-n)} - \frac{\cos(m+n)x}{2(m+n)}, \qquad (m^2 \neq n^2)$

320. $\displaystyle\int (\sin^2 ax)(\cos^2 ax)\, dx = -\frac{1}{32a} \sin 4ax + \frac{x}{8}$

321. $\displaystyle\int (\sin ax)(\cos^m ax)\, dx = -\frac{\cos^{m+1} ax}{(m+1)a}$

322. $\displaystyle\int (\sin^m ax)(\cos ax)\, dx = \frac{\sin^{m+1} ax}{(m+1)a}$

323. $\displaystyle\int (\cos^m ax)(\sin^n ax)\, dx = \begin{cases} \dfrac{\cos^{m-1} ax \sin^{n+1} ax}{(m+n)a} \\[2ex] \qquad + \dfrac{m-1}{m+n} \displaystyle\int (\cos^{m-2} ax)(\sin^n ax)\, dx \\[2ex] \text{or} \\[2ex] -\dfrac{\sin^{n-1} ax \cos^{m+1} ax}{(m+n)a} \\[2ex] \qquad + \dfrac{n-1}{m+n} \displaystyle\int (\cos^m ax)(\sin^{n-2} ax)\, dx \end{cases}$

324. $\displaystyle\int \frac{\cos^m ax}{\sin^n ax}\, dx = \begin{cases} -\dfrac{\cos^{m+1} ax}{(n-1)a \sin^{n-1} ax} - \dfrac{m-n+2}{n-1} \displaystyle\int \dfrac{\cos^m ax}{\sin^{n-2} ax}\, dx \\[2ex] \text{or} \\[2ex] \dfrac{\cos^{m-1} ax}{a(m-n) \sin^{n-1} ax} + \dfrac{m-1}{m-n} \displaystyle\int \dfrac{\cos^{m-2} ax}{\sin^n ax}\, dx \end{cases}$

INTEGRALS (Continued)

325. $\displaystyle\int \frac{\sin^m ax}{\cos^n ax}\,dx = \begin{cases} \dfrac{\sin^{m+1} ax}{a(n-1)\cos^{n-1} ax} + \dfrac{m-n+2}{n-1}\displaystyle\int \dfrac{\sin^m ax}{\cos^{n-2} ax}\,dx \\[2mm] \text{or} \\[2mm] -\dfrac{\sin^{m-1} ax}{a(m-n)\cos^{n-1} ax} - \dfrac{m-1}{m-n}\displaystyle\int \dfrac{\sin^{m-2} ax}{\cos^n ax}\,dx \end{cases}$

326. $\displaystyle\int \frac{\sin ax}{\cos^2 ax}\,dx = \frac{1}{a\cos ax} = \frac{\sec ax}{a}$

327. $\displaystyle\int \frac{\sin^2 ax}{\cos ax}\,dx = -\frac{1}{a}\sin ax + \frac{1}{a}\log\tan\left(\frac{\pi}{4} + \frac{ax}{2}\right)$

328. $\displaystyle\int \frac{\cos ax}{\sin^2 ax}\,dx = -\frac{1}{a\sin ax} = -\frac{\csc ax}{a}$

329. $\displaystyle\int \frac{dx}{(\sin ax)(\cos ax)} = \frac{1}{a}\log\tan ax$

330. $\displaystyle\int \frac{dx}{(\sin ax)(\cos^2 ax)} = \frac{1}{a}\left(\sec ax + \log\tan\frac{ax}{2}\right)$

331. $\displaystyle\int \frac{dx}{(\sin ax)(\cos^n ax)} = \frac{1}{a(n-1)\cos^{n-1} ax} + \int \frac{dx}{(\sin ax)(\cos^{n-2} ax)}$

332. $\displaystyle\int \frac{dx}{(\sin^2 ax)(\cos ax)} = -\frac{1}{a}\csc ax + \frac{1}{a}\log\tan\left(\frac{\pi}{4} + \frac{ax}{2}\right)$

333. $\displaystyle\int \frac{dx}{(\sin^2 ax)(\cos^2 ax)} = -\frac{2}{a}\cot 2ax$

334. $\displaystyle\int \frac{dx}{\sin^m ax \cos^n ax} = \begin{cases} -\dfrac{1}{a(m-1)(\sin^{m-1} ax)(\cos^{n-1} ax)} \\[3mm] \qquad + \dfrac{m+n-2}{m-1}\displaystyle\int \dfrac{dx}{(\sin^{m-2} ax)(\cos^n ax)} \\[3mm] \text{or} \\[3mm] \dfrac{1}{a(n-1)\sin^{m-1} ax \cos^{n-1} ax} \\[3mm] \qquad - \dfrac{m+n-2}{n-1}\displaystyle\int \dfrac{dx}{\sin^m ax \cos^{n-2} ax} \end{cases}$

335. $\displaystyle\int \sin(a+bx)\,dx = -\frac{1}{b}\cos(a+bx)$

336. $\displaystyle\int \cos(a+bx)\,dx = \frac{1}{b}\sin(a+bx)$

337. $\displaystyle\int \frac{dx}{1 \pm \sin ax} = \mp\frac{1}{a}\tan\left(\frac{\pi}{4} \mp \frac{ax}{2}\right)$

INTEGRALS (Continued)

338. $\displaystyle\int \frac{dx}{1 + \cos ax} = \frac{1}{a} \tan \frac{ax}{2}$

339. $\displaystyle\int \frac{dx}{1 - \cos ax} = -\frac{1}{a} \cot \frac{ax}{2}$

*340. $\displaystyle\int \frac{dx}{a + b \sin x} = \begin{cases} \dfrac{2}{\sqrt{a^2 - b^2}} \tan^{-1} \dfrac{a \tan \frac{x}{2} + b}{\sqrt{a^2 - b^2}} \\[2ex] \text{or} \\[2ex] \dfrac{1}{\sqrt{b^2 - a^2}} \log \dfrac{a \tan \frac{x}{2} + b - \sqrt{b^2 - a^2}}{a \tan \frac{x}{2} + b + \sqrt{b^2 - a^2}} \end{cases}$

*341. $\displaystyle\int \frac{dx}{a + b \cos x} = \begin{cases} \dfrac{2}{\sqrt{a^2 - b^2}} \tan^{-1} \dfrac{\sqrt{a^2 - b^2}\, \tan \frac{x}{2}}{a + b} \\[2ex] \text{or} \\[2ex] \dfrac{1}{\sqrt{b^2 - a^2}} \log \left(\dfrac{\sqrt{b^2 - a^2}\, \tan \frac{x}{2} + a + b}{\sqrt{b^2 - a^2}\, \tan \frac{x}{2} - a - b} \right) \end{cases}$

*342. $\displaystyle\int \frac{dx}{a + b \sin x + c \cos x}$

$= \begin{cases} \dfrac{1}{\sqrt{b^2 + c^2 - a^2}} \log \dfrac{b - \sqrt{b^2 + c^2 - a^2} + (a - c) \tan \frac{x}{2}}{b + \sqrt{b^2 + c^2 - a^2} + (a - c) \tan \frac{x}{2}}, & \text{if } a^2 < b^2 + c^2, a \neq c \\[3ex] \text{or} \\[2ex] \dfrac{2}{\sqrt{a^2 - b^2 - c^2}} \tan^{-1} \dfrac{b + (a - c) \tan \frac{x}{2}}{\sqrt{a^2 - b^2 - c^2}}, & \text{if } a^2 > b^2 + c^2 \\[3ex] \text{or} \\[2ex] \dfrac{1}{a} \left[\dfrac{a - (b + c) \cos x - (b - c) \sin x}{a - (b - c) \cos x + (b + c) \sin x} \right], & \text{if } a^2 = b^2 + c^2, a \neq c. \end{cases}$

*343. $\displaystyle\int \frac{\sin^2 x \, dx}{a + b \cos^2 x} = \frac{1}{b} \sqrt{\frac{a + b}{a}} \tan^{-1} \left(\sqrt{\frac{a}{a + b}} \tan x \right) - \frac{x}{b}, \qquad (ab > 0, \text{ or } |a| > |b|)$

* See note p. 403

INTEGRALS (Continued)

*344. $\displaystyle \int \frac{dx}{a^2 \cos^2 x + b^2 \sin^2 x} = \frac{1}{ab} \tan^{-1}\left(\frac{b \tan x}{a}\right)$

*345. $\displaystyle \int \frac{\cos^2 cx}{a^2 + b^2 \sin^2 cx} dx = \frac{\sqrt{a^2 + b^2}}{ab^2 c} \tan^{-1}\frac{\sqrt{a^2 + b^2} \tan cx}{a} - \frac{x}{b^2}$

346. $\displaystyle \int \frac{\sin cx \cos cx}{a \cos^2 cx + b \sin^2 cx} dx = \frac{1}{2c(b - a)} \log (a \cos^2 cx + b \sin^2 cx)$

347. $\displaystyle \int \frac{\cos cx}{a \cos cx + b \sin cx} dx = \int \frac{dx}{a + b \tan cx} =$

$$\frac{1}{c(a^2 + b^2)}[acx + b \log (a \cos cx + b \sin cx)]$$

348. $\displaystyle \int \frac{\sin cx}{a \sin cx + b \cos cx} dx = \int \frac{dx}{a + b \cot cx} =$

$$\frac{1}{c(a^2 + b^2)}[acx - b \log (a \sin cx + b \cos cx)]$$

*349. $\displaystyle \int \frac{dx}{a \cos^2 x + 2b \cos x \sin x + c \sin^2 x} = \begin{cases} \dfrac{1}{2\sqrt{b^2 - ac}} \log \dfrac{c \tan x + b - \sqrt{b^2 - ac}}{c \tan x + b + \sqrt{b^2 - ac}}, \\ \hspace{4cm} (b^2 > ac) \\ \text{or} \\ \dfrac{1}{\sqrt{ac - b^2}} \tan^{-1}\dfrac{c \tan x + b}{\sqrt{ac - b^2}}, \quad (b^2 < ac) \\ \text{or} \\ -\dfrac{1}{c \tan x + b}, \hspace{1.5cm} (b^2 = ac) \end{cases}$

350. $\displaystyle \int \frac{\sin ax}{1 \pm \sin ax} dx = \pm x + \frac{1}{a} \tan\left(\frac{\pi}{4} \mp \frac{ax}{2}\right)$

351. $\displaystyle \int \frac{dx}{(\sin ax)(1 \pm \sin ax)} = \frac{1}{a} \tan\left(\frac{\pi}{4} \mp \frac{ax}{2}\right) + \frac{1}{a} \log \tan \frac{ax}{2}$

352. $\displaystyle \int \frac{dx}{(1 + \sin ax)^2} = -\frac{1}{2a} \tan\left(\frac{\pi}{4} - \frac{ax}{2}\right) - \frac{1}{6a} \tan^3\left(\frac{\pi}{4} - \frac{ax}{2}\right)$

353. $\displaystyle \int \frac{dx}{(1 - \sin ax)^2} = \frac{1}{2a} \cot\left(\frac{\pi}{4} - \frac{ax}{2}\right) + \frac{1}{6a} \cot^3\left(\frac{\pi}{4} - \frac{ax}{2}\right)$

354. $\displaystyle \int \frac{\sin ax}{(1 + \sin ax)^2} dx = -\frac{1}{2a} \tan\left(\frac{\pi}{4} - \frac{ax}{2}\right) + \frac{1}{6a} \tan^3\left(\frac{\pi}{4} - \frac{ax}{2}\right)$

* See note p. 403.

INTEGRALS (Continued)

355. $\int \dfrac{\sin ax}{(1 - \sin ax)^2}\, dx = -\dfrac{1}{2a} \cot\left(\dfrac{\pi}{4} - \dfrac{ax}{2}\right) + \dfrac{1}{6a} \cot^3\left(\dfrac{\pi}{4} - \dfrac{ax}{2}\right)$

356. $\int \dfrac{\sin x\, dx}{a + b \sin x} = \dfrac{x}{b} - \dfrac{a}{b} \int \dfrac{dx}{a + b \sin x}$

357. $\int \dfrac{dx}{(\sin x)(a + b \sin x)} = \dfrac{1}{a} \log \tan \dfrac{x}{2} - \dfrac{b}{a} \int \dfrac{dx}{a + b \sin x}$

358. $\int \dfrac{dx}{(a + b \sin x)^2} = \dfrac{b \cos x}{(a^2 - b^2)(a + b \sin x)} + \dfrac{a}{a^2 - b^2} \int \dfrac{dx}{a + b \sin x}$

359. $\int \dfrac{\sin x\, dx}{(a + b \sin x)^2} = \dfrac{a \cos x}{(b^2 - a^2)(a + b \sin x)} + \dfrac{b}{b^2 - a^2} \int \dfrac{dx}{a + b \sin x}$

*360. $\int \dfrac{dx}{a^2 + b^2 \sin^2 cx} = \dfrac{1}{ac\sqrt{a^2 + b^2}} \tan^{-1} \dfrac{\sqrt{a^2 + b^2}\, \tan cx}{a}$

*361. $\int \dfrac{dx}{a^2 - b^2 \sin^2 cx} = \begin{cases} \dfrac{1}{ac\sqrt{a^2 - b^2}} \tan^{-1} \dfrac{\sqrt{a^2 - b^2}\, \tan cx}{a}, & (a^2 > b^2) \\[2ex] \text{or} \\[1ex] \dfrac{1}{2ac\sqrt{b^2 - a^2}} \log \dfrac{\sqrt{b^2 - a^2}\, \tan cx + a}{\sqrt{b^2 - a^2}\, \tan cx - a}, & (a^2 < b^2) \end{cases}$

362. $\int \dfrac{\cos ax}{1 + \cos ax}\, dx = x - \dfrac{1}{a} \tan \dfrac{ax}{2}$

363. $\int \dfrac{\cos ax}{1 - \cos ax}\, dx = -x - \dfrac{1}{a} \cot \dfrac{ax}{2}$

364. $\int \dfrac{dx}{(\cos ax)(1 + \cos ax)} = \dfrac{1}{a} \log \tan \left(\dfrac{\pi}{4} + \dfrac{ax}{2}\right) - \dfrac{1}{a} \tan \dfrac{ax}{2}$

365. $\int \dfrac{dx}{(\cos ax)(1 - \cos ax)} = \dfrac{1}{a} \log \tan \left(\dfrac{\pi}{4} + \dfrac{ax}{2}\right) - \dfrac{1}{a} \cot \dfrac{ax}{2}$

366. $\int \dfrac{dx}{(1 + \cos ax)^2} = \dfrac{1}{2a} \tan \dfrac{ax}{2} + \dfrac{1}{6a} \tan^3 \dfrac{ax}{2}$

367. $\int \dfrac{dx}{(1 - \cos ax)^2} = -\dfrac{1}{2a} \cot \dfrac{ax}{2} - \dfrac{1}{6a} \cot^3 \dfrac{ax}{2}$

368. $\int \dfrac{\cos ax}{(1 + \cos ax)^2}\, dx = \dfrac{1}{2a} \tan \dfrac{ax}{2} - \dfrac{1}{6a} \tan^3 \dfrac{ax}{2}$

369. $\int \dfrac{\cos ax}{(1 - \cos ax)^2}\, dx = \dfrac{1}{2a} \cot \dfrac{ax}{2} - \dfrac{1}{6a} \cot^3 \dfrac{ax}{2}$

* See note p. 403.

INTEGRALS (Continued)

370. $\displaystyle \int \frac{\cos x \, dx}{a + b \cos x} = \frac{x}{b} - \frac{a}{b} \int \frac{dx}{a + b \cos x}$

371. $\displaystyle \int \frac{dx}{(\cos x)(a + b \cos x)} = \frac{1}{a} \log \tan \left(\frac{x}{2} + \frac{\pi}{4} \right) - \frac{b}{a} \int \frac{dx}{a + b \cos x}$

372. $\displaystyle \int \frac{dx}{(a + b \cos x)^2} = \frac{b \sin x}{(b^2 - a^2)(a + b \cos x)} - \frac{a}{b^2 - a^2} \int \frac{dx}{a + b \cos x}$

373. $\displaystyle \int \frac{\cos x}{(a + b \cos x)^2} \, dx = \frac{a \sin x}{(a^2 - b^2)(a + b \cos x)} - \frac{b}{a^2 - b^2} \int \frac{dx}{a + b \cos x}$

*374. $\displaystyle \int \frac{dx}{a^2 + b^2 - 2ab \cos cx} = \frac{2}{c(a^2 - b^2)} \tan^{-1} \left(\frac{a + b}{a - b} \tan \frac{cx}{2} \right)$

*375. $\displaystyle \int \frac{dx}{a^2 + b^2 \cos^2 cx} = \frac{1}{ac\sqrt{a^2 + b^2}} \tan^{-1} \frac{a \tan cx}{\sqrt{a^2 + b^2}}$

*376. $\displaystyle \int \frac{dx}{a^2 - b^2 \cos^2 cx} = \begin{cases} \dfrac{1}{ac\sqrt{a^2 - b^2}} \tan^{-1} \dfrac{a \tan cx}{\sqrt{a^2 - b^2}}, & (a^2 > b^2) \\[2mm] \text{or} \\[2mm] \dfrac{1}{2ac\sqrt{b^2 - a^2}} \log \dfrac{a \tan cx - \sqrt{b^2 - a^2}}{a \tan cx + \sqrt{b^2 - a^2}}, & (b^2 > a^2) \end{cases}$

377. $\displaystyle \int \frac{\sin ax}{1 \pm \cos ax} \, dx = \mp \frac{1}{a} \log (1 \pm \cos ax)$

378. $\displaystyle \int \frac{\cos ax}{1 \pm \sin ax} \, dx = \pm \frac{1}{a} \log (1 \pm \sin ax)$

379. $\displaystyle \int \frac{dx}{(\sin ax)(1 \pm \cos ax)} = \pm \frac{1}{2a(1 \pm \cos ax)} + \frac{1}{2a} \log \tan \frac{ax}{2}$

380. $\displaystyle \int \frac{dx}{(\cos ax)(1 \pm \sin ax)} = \mp \frac{1}{2a(1 \pm \sin ax)} + \frac{1}{2a} \log \tan \left(\frac{\pi}{4} + \frac{ax}{2} \right)$

381. $\displaystyle \int \frac{\sin ax}{(\cos ax)(1 \pm \cos ax)} \, dx = \frac{1}{a} \log (\sec ax \pm 1)$

382. $\displaystyle \int \frac{\cos ax}{(\sin ax)(1 \pm \sin ax)} \, dx = -\frac{1}{a} \log (\csc ax \pm 1)$

383. $\displaystyle \int \frac{\sin ax}{(\cos ax)(1 \pm \sin ax)} \, dx = \frac{1}{2a(1 \pm \sin ax)} \pm \frac{1}{2a} \log \tan \left(\frac{\pi}{4} + \frac{ax}{2} \right)$

384. $\displaystyle \int \frac{\cos ax}{(\sin ax)(1 \pm \cos ax)} \, dx = -\frac{1}{2a(1 \pm \cos ax)} \pm \frac{1}{2a} \log \tan \frac{ax}{2}$

* See note p. 403.

INTEGRALS (Continued)

385. $\displaystyle\int \frac{dx}{\sin ax \pm \cos ax} = \frac{1}{a\sqrt{2}} \log \tan\left(\frac{ax}{2} \pm \frac{\pi}{8}\right)$

386. $\displaystyle\int \frac{dx}{(\sin ax \pm \cos ax)^2} = \frac{1}{2a} \tan\left(ax \mp \frac{\pi}{4}\right)$

387. $\displaystyle\int \frac{dx}{1 + \cos ax \pm \sin ax} = \pm \frac{1}{a} \log\left(1 \pm \tan\frac{ax}{2}\right)$

388. $\displaystyle\int \frac{dx}{a^2 \cos^2 cx - b^2 \sin^2 cx} = \frac{1}{2abc} \log \frac{b \tan cx + a}{b \tan cx - a}$

389. $\displaystyle\int x(\sin ax)\, dx = \frac{1}{a^2} \sin ax - \frac{x}{a} \cos ax$

390. $\displaystyle\int x^2(\sin ax)\, dx = \frac{2x}{a^2} \sin ax - \frac{a^2x^2 - 2}{a^3} \cos ax$

391. $\displaystyle\int x^3(\sin ax)\, dx = \frac{3a^2x^2 - 6}{a^4} \sin ax - \frac{a^2x^3 - 6x}{a^3} \cos ax$

392. $\displaystyle\int x^m \sin ax\, dx =$
$$\begin{cases} -\dfrac{1}{a}x^m \cos ax + \dfrac{m}{a} \displaystyle\int x^{m-1} \cos ax\, dx \\[2mm] \qquad\qquad \text{or} \\[2mm] \cos ax \displaystyle\sum_{r=0}^{\left[\frac{m}{2}\right]} (-1)^{r+1} \frac{m!}{(m-2r)!} \cdot \frac{x^{m-2r}}{a^{2r+1}} \\[4mm] + \sin ax \displaystyle\sum_{r=0}^{\left[\frac{m-1}{2}\right]} (-1)^r \frac{m!}{(m-2r-1)!} \cdot \frac{x^{m-2r-1}}{a^{2r+2}} \end{cases}$$

Note: $[s]$ means greatest integer $\leq s$; $[3\frac{1}{2}] = 3$, $[\frac{1}{2}] = 0$, etc.

393. $\displaystyle\int x(\cos ax)\, dx = \frac{1}{a^2} \cos ax + \frac{x}{a} \sin ax$

394. $\displaystyle\int x^2(\cos ax)\, dx = \frac{2x \cos ax}{a^2} + \frac{a^2x^2 - 2}{a^3} \sin ax$

395. $\displaystyle\int x^3(\cos ax)\, dx = \frac{3a^2x^2 - 6}{a^4} \cos ax + \frac{a^2x^3 - 6x}{a^3} \sin ax$

396. $\displaystyle\int x^m(\cos ax)\, dx =$
$$\begin{cases} \dfrac{x^m \sin ax}{a} - \dfrac{m}{a} \displaystyle\int x^{m-1} \sin ax\, dx \\[2mm] \qquad\qquad \text{or} \\[2mm] \sin ax \displaystyle\sum_{r=0}^{\left[\frac{m}{2}\right]} (-1)^r \frac{m!}{(m-2r)!} \cdot \frac{x^{m-2r}}{a^{2r+1}} \\[4mm] + \cos ax \displaystyle\sum_{r=0}^{\left[\frac{m-1}{2}\right]} (-1)^r \frac{m!}{(m-2r-1)!} \cdot \frac{x^{m-2r-1}}{a^{2r+2}} \end{cases}$$

See note integral 392.

INTEGRALS (Continued)

397. $\displaystyle \int \frac{\sin ax}{x}\,dx = \sum_{n=0}^{\infty}(-1)^n \frac{(ax)^{2n+1}}{(2n+1)(2n+1)!}$

398. $\displaystyle \int \frac{\cos ax}{x}\,dx = \log x + \sum_{n=1}^{\infty}(-1)^n \frac{(ax)^{2n}}{2n(2n)!}$

399. $\displaystyle \int x(\sin^2 ax)\,dx = \frac{x^2}{4} - \frac{x\sin 2ax}{4a} - \frac{\cos 2ax}{8a^2}$

400. $\displaystyle \int x^2(\sin^2 ax)\,dx = \frac{x^3}{6} - \left(\frac{x^2}{4a} - \frac{1}{8a^3}\right)\sin 2ax - \frac{x\cos 2ax}{4a^2}$

401. $\displaystyle \int x(\sin^3 ax)\,dx = \frac{x\cos 3ax}{12a} - \frac{\sin 3ax}{36a^2} - \frac{3x\cos ax}{4a} + \frac{3\sin ax}{4a^2}$

402. $\displaystyle \int x(\cos^2 ax)\,dx = \frac{x^2}{4} + \frac{x\sin 2ax}{4a} + \frac{\cos 2ax}{8a^2}$

403. $\displaystyle \int x^2(\cos^2 ax)\,dx = \frac{x^3}{6} + \left(\frac{x^2}{4a} - \frac{1}{8a^3}\right)\sin 2ax + \frac{x\cos 2ax}{4a^2}$

404. $\displaystyle \int x(\cos^3 ax)\,dx = \frac{x\sin 3ax}{12a} + \frac{\cos 3ax}{36a^2} + \frac{3x\sin ax}{4a} + \frac{3\cos ax}{4a^2}$

405. $\displaystyle \int \frac{\sin ax}{x^m}\,dx = -\frac{\sin ax}{(m-1)x^{m-1}} + \frac{a}{m-1}\int \frac{\cos ax}{x^{m-1}}\,dx$

406. $\displaystyle \int \frac{\cos ax}{x^m}\,dx = -\frac{\cos ax}{(m-1)x^{m-1}} - \frac{a}{m-1}\int \frac{\sin ax}{x^{m-1}}\,dx$

407. $\displaystyle \int \frac{x}{1 \pm \sin ax}\,dx = \mp\frac{x\cos ax}{a(1 \pm \sin ax)} + \frac{1}{a^2}\log(1 \pm \sin ax)$

408. $\displaystyle \int \frac{x}{1 + \cos ax}\,dx = \frac{x}{a}\tan\frac{ax}{2} + \frac{2}{a^2}\log\cos\frac{ax}{2}$

409. $\displaystyle \int \frac{x}{1 - \cos ax}\,dx = -\frac{x}{a}\cot\frac{ax}{2} + \frac{2}{a^2}\log\sin\frac{ax}{2}$

410. $\displaystyle \int \frac{x + \sin x}{1 + \cos x}\,dx = x\tan\frac{x}{2}$

411. $\displaystyle \int \frac{x - \sin x}{1 - \cos x}\,dx = -x\cot\frac{x}{2}$

412. $\displaystyle \int \sqrt{1 - \cos ax}\,dx = -\frac{2\sin ax}{a\sqrt{1 - \cos ax}}$

413. $\displaystyle \int \sqrt{1 + \cos ax}\,dx = \frac{2\sin ax}{a\sqrt{1 + \cos ax}}$

INTEGRALS (Continued)

414. $\int \sqrt{1 + \sin x}\, dx = \pm 2\left(\sin\dfrac{x}{2} - \cos\dfrac{x}{2}\right),$

[use $+$ if $(8k - 1)\dfrac{\pi}{2} < x \le (8k + 3)\dfrac{\pi}{2}$, otherwise $-$; k an integer]

415. $\int \sqrt{1 - \sin x}\, dx = \pm 2\left(\sin\dfrac{x}{2} + \cos\dfrac{x}{2}\right),$

[use $+$ if $(8k - 3)\dfrac{\pi}{2} < x \le (8k + 1)\dfrac{\pi}{2}$, otherwise $-$; k an integer]

416. $\int \dfrac{dx}{\sqrt{1 - \cos x}} = \pm \sqrt{2} \log \tan \dfrac{x}{4},$

[use $+$ if $4k\pi < x < (4k + 2)\pi$, otherwise $-$; k an integer]

417. $\int \dfrac{dx}{\sqrt{1 + \cos x}} = \pm \sqrt{2} \log \tan \left(\dfrac{x + \pi}{4}\right),$

[use $+$ if $(4k - 1)\pi < x < (4k + 1)\pi$, otherwise $-$; k an integer]

418. $\int \dfrac{dx}{\sqrt{1 - \sin x}} = \pm \sqrt{2} \log \tan \left(\dfrac{x}{4} - \dfrac{\pi}{8}\right),$

[use $+$ if $(8k + 1)\dfrac{\pi}{2} < x < (8k + 5)\dfrac{\pi}{2}$, otherwise $-$; k an integer]

419. $\int \dfrac{dx}{\sqrt{1 + \sin x}} = \pm \sqrt{2} \log \tan \left(\dfrac{x}{4} + \dfrac{\pi}{8}\right),$

[use $+$ if $(8k - 1)\dfrac{\pi}{2} < x < (8k + 3)\dfrac{\pi}{2}$, otherwise $-$; k an integer]

420. $\int (\tan^2 ax)\, dx = \dfrac{1}{a} \tan ax - x$

421. $\int (\tan^3 ax)\, dx = \dfrac{1}{2a} \tan^2 ax + \dfrac{1}{a} \log \cos ax$

422. $\int (\tan^4 ax)\, dx = \dfrac{\tan^3 ax}{3a} - \dfrac{1}{a} \tan x + x$

423. $\int (\tan^n ax)\, dx = \dfrac{\tan^{n-1} ax}{a(n - 1)} - \int (\tan^{n-2} ax)\, dx$

424. $\int (\cot^2 ax)\, dx = -\dfrac{1}{a} \cot ax - x$

425. $\int (\cot^3 ax)\, dx = -\dfrac{1}{2a} \cot^2 ax - \dfrac{1}{a} \log \sin ax$

426. $\int (\cot^4 ax)\, dx = -\dfrac{1}{3a} \cot^3 ax + \dfrac{1}{a} \cot ax + x$

INTEGRALS (Continued)

427. $\int (\cot^n ax)\, dx = -\dfrac{\cot^{n-1} ax}{a(n-1)} - \int (\cot^{n-2} ax)\, dx$

428. $\int \dfrac{x}{\sin^2 ax}\, dx = \int x(\csc^2 ax)\, dx = -\dfrac{x \cot ax}{a} + \dfrac{1}{a^2} \log \sin ax$

429. $\int \dfrac{x}{\sin^n ax}\, dx = \int x(\csc^n ax)\, dx = -\dfrac{x \cos ax}{a(n-1) \sin^{n-1} ax}$

$$- \dfrac{1}{a^2(n-1)(n-2) \sin^{n-2} ax} + \dfrac{(n-2)}{(n-1)} \int \dfrac{x}{\sin^{n-2} ax}\, dx$$

430. $\int \dfrac{x}{\cos^2 ax}\, dx = \int x(\sec^2 ax)\, dx = \dfrac{1}{a} x \tan ax + \dfrac{1}{a^2} \log \cos ax$

431. $\int \dfrac{x}{\cos^n ax}\, dx = \int x(\sec^n ax)\, dx = \dfrac{x \sin ax}{a(n-1) \cos^{n-1} ax}$

$$- \dfrac{1}{a^2(n-1)(n-2) \cos^{n-2} ax} + \dfrac{n-2}{n-1} \int \dfrac{x}{\cos^{n-2} ax}\, dx$$

432. $\int \dfrac{\sin ax}{\sqrt{1 + b^2 \sin^2 ax}}\, dx = -\dfrac{1}{ab} \sin^{-1} \dfrac{b \cos ax}{\sqrt{1 + b^2}}$

433. $\int \dfrac{\sin ax}{\sqrt{1 - b^2 \sin^2 ax}}\, dx = -\dfrac{1}{ab} \log (b \cos ax + \sqrt{1 - b^2 \sin^2 ax})$

434. $\int (\sin ax)\sqrt{1 + b^2 \sin^2 ax}\, dx = -\dfrac{\cos ax}{2a} \sqrt{1 + b^2 \sin^2 ax}$

$$- \dfrac{1 + b^2}{2ab} \sin^{-1} \dfrac{b \cos ax}{\sqrt{1 + b^2}}$$

435. $\int (\sin ax)\sqrt{1 - b^2 \sin^2 ax}\, dx = -\dfrac{\cos ax}{2a} \sqrt{1 - b^2 \sin^2 ax}$

$$- \dfrac{1 - b^2}{2ab} \log (b \cos ax + \sqrt{1 - b^2 \sin^2 ax})$$

436. $\int \dfrac{\cos ax}{\sqrt{1 + b^2 \sin^2 ax}}\, dx = \dfrac{1}{ab} \log (b \sin ax + \sqrt{1 + b^2 \sin^2 ax})$

437. $\int \dfrac{\cos ax}{\sqrt{1 - b^2 \sin^2 ax}}\, dx = \dfrac{1}{ab} \sin^{-1} (b \sin ax)$

438. $\int (\cos ax) \sqrt{1 + b^2 \sin^2 ax}\, dx = \dfrac{\sin ax}{2a} \sqrt{1 + b^2 \sin^2 ax}$

$$+ \dfrac{1}{2ab} \log (b \sin ax + \sqrt{1 + b^2 \sin^2 ax})$$

INTEGRALS (Continued)

439. $\int (\cos ax) \sqrt{1 - b^2 \sin^2 ax}\, dx = \dfrac{\sin ax}{2a} \sqrt{1 - b^2 \sin^2 ax} + \dfrac{1}{2ab} \sin^{-1}(b \sin ax)$

440. $\int \dfrac{dx}{\sqrt{a + b \tan^2 cx}} = \dfrac{\pm 1}{c\sqrt{a - b}} \sin^{-1}\left(\sqrt{\dfrac{a - b}{a}} \sin cx\right), \qquad (a > |b|)$

[use + if $(2k - 1)\dfrac{\pi}{2} < x \le (2k + 1)\dfrac{\pi}{2}$, otherwise $-$; k an integer]

FORMS INVOLVING INVERSE TRIGONOMETRIC FUNCTIONS

441. $\int (\sin^{-1} ax)\, dx = x \sin^{-1} ax + \dfrac{\sqrt{1 - a^2 x^2}}{a}$

442. $\int (\cos^{-1} ax)\, dx = x \cos^{-1} ax - \dfrac{\sqrt{1 - a^2 x^2}}{a}$

443. $\int (\tan^{-1} ax)\, dx = x \tan^{-1} ax - \dfrac{1}{2a} \log (1 + a^2 x^2)$

444. $\int (\cot^{-1} ax)\, dx = x \cot^{-1} ax + \dfrac{1}{2a} \log (1 + a^2 x^2)$

445. $\int (\sec^{-1} ax)\, dx = x \sec^{-1} ax - \dfrac{1}{a} \log (ax + \sqrt{a^2 x^2 - 1})$

446. $\int (\csc^{-1} ax)\, dx = x \csc^{-1} ax + \dfrac{1}{a} \log (ax + \sqrt{a^2 x^2 - 1})$

447. $\int \left(\sin^{-1} \dfrac{x}{a}\right) dx = x \sin^{-1} \dfrac{x}{a} + \sqrt{a^2 - x^2}, \qquad (a > 0)$

448. $\int \left(\cos^{-1} \dfrac{x}{a}\right) dx = x \cos^{-1} \dfrac{x}{a} - \sqrt{a^2 - x^2}, \qquad (a > 0)$

449. $\int \left(\tan^{-1} \dfrac{x}{a}\right) dx = x \tan^{-1} \dfrac{x}{a} - \dfrac{a}{2} \log (a^2 + x^2)$

450. $\int \left(\cot^{-1} \dfrac{x}{a}\right) dx = x \cot^{-1} \dfrac{x}{a} + \dfrac{a}{2} \log (a^2 + x^2)$

451. $\int x[\sin^{-1}(ax)]\, dx = \dfrac{1}{4a^2}[(2a^2 x^2 - 1) \sin^{-1}(ax) + ax\sqrt{1 - a^2 x^2}]$

452. $\int x[\cos^{-1}(ax)]\, dx = \dfrac{1}{4a^2}[(2a^2 x^2 - 1) \cos^{-1}(ax) - ax\sqrt{1 - a^2 x^2}]$

INTEGRALS (Continued)

453. $\int x^n[\sin^{-1}(ax)]\,dx = \dfrac{x^{n+1}}{n+1}\sin^{-1}(ax) - \dfrac{a}{n+1}\int \dfrac{x^{n+1}\,dx}{\sqrt{1-a^2x^2}},$ $\qquad (n \neq -1)$

454. $\int x^n[\cos^{-1}(ax)]\,dx = \dfrac{x^{n+1}}{n+1}\cos^{-1}(ax) + \dfrac{a}{n+1}\int \dfrac{x^{n+1}\,dx}{\sqrt{1-a^2x^2}},$ $\qquad (n \neq -1)$

455. $\int x(\tan^{-1}ax)\,dx = \dfrac{1+a^2x^2}{2a^2}\tan^{-1}ax - \dfrac{x}{2a}$

456. $\int x^n(\tan^{-1}ax)\,dx = \dfrac{x^{n+1}}{n+1}\tan^{-1}ax - \dfrac{a}{n+1}\int \dfrac{x^{n+1}}{1+a^2x^2}\,dx$

457. $\int x(\cot^{-1}ax)\,dx = \dfrac{1+a^2x^2}{2a^2}\cot^{-1}ax + \dfrac{x}{2a}$

458. $\int x^n(\cot^{-1}ax)\,dx = \dfrac{x^{n+1}}{n+1}\cot^{-1}ax + \dfrac{a}{n+1}\int \dfrac{x^{n+1}}{1+a^2x^2}\,dx$

459. $\int \dfrac{\sin^{-1}(ax)}{x^2}\,dx = a\log\left(\dfrac{1-\sqrt{1-a^2x^2}}{x}\right) - \dfrac{\sin^{-1}(ax)}{x}$

460. $\int \dfrac{\cos^{-1}(ax)\,dx}{x^2} = -\dfrac{1}{x}\cos^{-1}(ax) + a\log\dfrac{1+\sqrt{1-a^2x^2}}{x}$

461. $\int \dfrac{\tan^{-1}(ax)\,dx}{x^2} = -\dfrac{1}{x}\tan^{-1}(ax) - \dfrac{a}{2}\log\dfrac{1+a^2x^2}{x^2}$

462. $\int \dfrac{\cot^{-1}ax}{x^2}\,dx = -\dfrac{1}{x}\cot^{-1}ax - \dfrac{a}{2}\log\dfrac{x^2}{a^2x^2+1}$

463. $\int (\sin^{-1}ax)^2\,dx = x(\sin^{-1}ax)^2 - 2x + \dfrac{2\sqrt{1-a^2x^2}}{a}\sin^{-1}ax$

464. $\int (\cos^{-1}ax)^2\,dx = x(\cos^{-1}ax)^2 - 2x - \dfrac{2\sqrt{1-a^2x^2}}{a}\cos^{-1}ax$

465. $\int (\sin^{-1}ax)^n\,dx = \begin{cases} x(\sin^{-1}ax)^n + \dfrac{n\sqrt{1-a^2x^2}}{a}(\sin^{-1}ax)^{n-1} \\ \qquad\qquad\qquad\qquad -n(n-1)\int(\sin^{-1}ax)^{n-2}\,dx \\ \qquad\qquad \text{or} \\ \displaystyle\sum_{r=0}^{\left[\frac{n}{2}\right]} (-1)^r\dfrac{n!}{(n-2r)!}x(\sin^{-1}ax)^{n-2r} \\ \qquad + \displaystyle\sum_{r=0}^{\left[\frac{n-1}{2}\right]} (-1)^r\dfrac{n!\sqrt{1-a^2x^2}}{(n-2r-1)!a}(\sin^{-1}ax)^{n-2r-1} \end{cases}$

Note : [s] means greatest integer $\leq s$. Thus [3.5] means 3 ; [5] = 5, [$\tfrac{1}{2}$] = 0.

INTEGRALS (Continued)

466. $\displaystyle\int (\cos^{-1} ax)^n \, dx =$

$$\begin{cases} x(\cos^{-1} ax)^n - \dfrac{n\sqrt{1 - a^2 x^2}}{a} (\cos^{-1} ax)^{n-1} \\ \qquad\qquad\qquad - n(n-1) \displaystyle\int (\cos^{-1} ax)^{n-2} \, dx \\ \qquad\qquad\qquad \text{or} \\ \displaystyle\sum_{r=0}^{\left[\frac{n}{2}\right]} (-1)^r \dfrac{n!}{(n - 2r)!} x(\cos^{-1} ax)^{n - 2r} \\ \qquad - \displaystyle\sum_{r=0}^{\left[\frac{n-1}{2}\right]} (-1)^r \dfrac{n!\sqrt{1 - a^2 x^2}}{(n - 2r - 1)!a} (\cos^{-1} ax)^{n - 2r - 1} \end{cases}$$

467. $\displaystyle\int \frac{1}{\sqrt{1 - a^2 x^2}}(\sin^{-1} ax) \, dx = \frac{1}{2a}(\sin^{-1} ax)^2$

468. $\displaystyle\int \frac{x^n}{\sqrt{1 - a^2 x^2}}(\sin^{-1} ax) \, dx = -\frac{x^{n-1}}{na^2}\sqrt{1 - a^2 x^2}\,\sin^{-1} ax + \frac{x^n}{n^2 a}$

$$+ \frac{n-1}{na^2} \int \frac{x^{n-2}}{\sqrt{1 - a^2 x^2}} \sin^{-1} ax \, dx$$

469. $\displaystyle\int \frac{1}{\sqrt{1 - a^2 x^2}}(\cos^{-1} ax) \, dx = -\frac{1}{2a}(\cos^{-1} ax)^2$

470. $\displaystyle\int \frac{x^n}{\sqrt{1 - a^2 x^2}}(\cos^{-1} ax) \, dx = -\frac{x^{n-1}}{na^2}\sqrt{1 - a^2 x^2}\,\cos^{-1} ax - \frac{x^n}{n^2 a}$

$$+ \frac{n-1}{na^2} \int \frac{x^{n-2}}{\sqrt{1 - a^2 x^2}} \cos^{-1} ax \, dx$$

471. $\displaystyle\int \frac{\tan^{-1} ax}{a^2 x^2 + 1} \, dx = \frac{1}{2a}(\tan^{-1} ax)^2$

472. $\displaystyle\int \frac{\cot^{-1} ax}{a^2 x^2 + 1} \, dx = -\frac{1}{2a}(\cot^{-1} ax)^2$

473. $\displaystyle\int x \sec^{-1} ax \, dx = \frac{x^2}{2} \sec^{-1} ax - \frac{1}{2a^2}\sqrt{a^2 x^2 - 1}$

474. $\displaystyle\int x^n \sec^{-1} ax \, dx = \frac{x^{n+1}}{n + 1} \sec^{-1} ax - \frac{1}{n + 1}\int \frac{x^n \, dx}{\sqrt{a^2 x^2 - 1}}$

475. $\displaystyle\int \frac{\sec^{-1} ax}{x^2} \, dx = -\frac{\sec^{-1} ax}{x} + \frac{\sqrt{a^2 x^2 - 1}}{x}$

476. $\displaystyle\int x \csc^{-1} ax \, dx = \frac{x^2}{2} \csc^{-1} ax + \frac{1}{2a^2}\sqrt{a^2 x^2 - 1}$

477. $\displaystyle\int x^n \csc^{-1} ax \, dx = \frac{x^{n+1}}{n + 1} \csc^{-1} ax + \frac{1}{n + 1}\int \frac{x^n \, dx}{\sqrt{a^2 x^2 - 1}}$

INTEGRALS (Continued)

478. $\displaystyle\int \frac{\csc^{-1} ax}{x^2}\, dx = -\frac{\csc^{-1} ax}{x} - \frac{\sqrt{a^2 x^2 - 1}}{x}$

FORMS INVOLVING TRIGONOMETRIC SUBSTITUTIONS

479. $\displaystyle\int f(\sin x)\, dx = 2\int f\left(\frac{2z}{1 + z^2}\right) \frac{dz}{1 + z^2}, \qquad \left(z = \tan \frac{x}{2}\right)$

480. $\displaystyle\int f(\cos x)\, dx = 2\int f\left(\frac{1 - z^2}{1 + z^2}\right) \frac{dz}{1 + z^2}, \qquad \left(z = \tan \frac{x}{2}\right)$

*481. $\displaystyle\int f(\sin x)\, dx = \int f(u)\frac{du}{\sqrt{1 - u^2}}, \qquad (u = \sin x)$

*482. $\displaystyle\int f(\cos x)\, dx = -\int f(u)\frac{du}{\sqrt{1 - u^2}}, \qquad (u = \cos x)$

*483. $\displaystyle\int f(\sin x, \cos x)\, dx = \int f(u, \sqrt{1 - u^2})\frac{du}{\sqrt{1 - u^2}}, \qquad (u = \sin x)$

484. $\displaystyle\int f(\sin x, \cos x)\, dx = 2\int f\left(\frac{2z}{1 + z^2}, \frac{1 - z^2}{1 + z^2}\right)\frac{dz}{1 + z^2}, \qquad \left(z = \tan \frac{x}{2}\right)$

LOGARITHMIC FORMS

485. $\displaystyle\int (\log x)\, dx = x \log x - x$

486. $\displaystyle\int x(\log x)\, dx = \frac{x^2}{2} \log x - \frac{x^2}{4}$

487. $\displaystyle\int x^2(\log x)\, dx = \frac{x^3}{3} \log x - \frac{x^3}{9}$

488. $\displaystyle\int x^n(\log ax)\, dx = \frac{x^{n+1}}{n + 1} \log ax - \frac{x^{n+1}}{(n + 1)^2}$

489. $\displaystyle\int (\log x)^2\, dx = x(\log x)^2 - 2x \log x + 2x$

490. $\displaystyle\int (\log x)^n\, dx = \begin{cases} x(\log x)^n - n\displaystyle\int (\log x)^{n-1}\, dx, \qquad (n \neq -1) \\[2mm] \quad\text{or} \\[2mm] (-1)^n n!\, x \displaystyle\sum_{r=0}^{n} \frac{(-\log x)^r}{r!} \end{cases}$

---

* The square roots appearing in these formulas may be plus or minus, depending on the quadrant of x. Care must be used to give them the proper sign.

INTEGRALS (Continued)

491. $\displaystyle \int \frac{(\log x)^n}{x}\,dx = \frac{1}{n+1}(\log x)^{n+1}$

492. $\displaystyle \int \frac{dx}{\log x} = \log(\log x) + \log x + \frac{(\log x)^2}{2\cdot 2!} + \frac{(\log x)^3}{3\cdot 3!} + \cdots$

493. $\displaystyle \int \frac{dx}{x\log x} = \log(\log x)$

494. $\displaystyle \int \frac{dx}{x(\log x)^n} = -\frac{1}{(n-1)(\log x)^{n-1}}$

495. $\displaystyle \int \frac{x^m\,dx}{(\log x)^n} = -\frac{x^{m+1}}{(n-1)(\log x)^{n-1}} + \frac{m+1}{n-1}\int \frac{x^m\,dx}{(\log x)^{n-1}}$

496. $\displaystyle \int x^m(\log x)^n\,dx = \begin{cases} \dfrac{x^{m+1}(\log x)^n}{m+1} - \dfrac{n}{m+1}\displaystyle\int x^m(\log x)^{n-1}\,dx \\[2ex] \text{or} \\[1ex] (-1)^n\dfrac{n!}{m+1}x^{m+1}\displaystyle\sum_{r=0}^{n}\dfrac{(-\log x)^r}{r!(m+1)^{n-r}} \end{cases}$

497. $\displaystyle \int \sin(\log x)\,dx = \tfrac{1}{2}x\sin(\log x) - \tfrac{1}{2}x\cos(\log x)$

498. $\displaystyle \int \cos(\log x)\,dx = \tfrac{1}{2}x\sin(\log x) + \tfrac{1}{2}x\cos(\log x)$

499. $\displaystyle \int [\log(ax+b)]\,dx = \frac{ax+b}{a}\log(ax+b) - x$

500. $\displaystyle \int \frac{\log(ax+b)}{x^2}\,dx = \frac{a}{b}\log x - \frac{ax+b}{bx}\log(ax+b)$

501. $\displaystyle \int x^m[\log(ax+b)]\,dx = \frac{1}{m+1}\left[x^{m+1} - \left(-\frac{b}{a}\right)^{m+1}\right]\log(ax+b)$

$$-\frac{1}{m+1}\left(-\frac{b}{a}\right)^{m+1}\sum_{r=1}^{m+1}\frac{1}{r}\left(-\frac{ax}{b}\right)^r$$

502. $\displaystyle \int \frac{\log(ax+b)}{x^m}\,dx = -\frac{1}{m-1}\frac{\log(ax+b)}{x^{m-1}} + \frac{1}{m-1}\left(-\frac{a}{b}\right)^{m-1}\log\frac{ax+b}{x}$

$$+\frac{1}{m-1}\left(-\frac{a}{b}\right)^{m-1}\sum_{r=1}^{m-2}\frac{1}{r}\left(-\frac{b}{ax}\right)^r,\ (m>2)$$

503. $\displaystyle \int \left[\log\frac{x+a}{x-a}\right]dx = (x+a)\log(x+a) - (x-a)\log(x-a)$

504. $\displaystyle \int x^m\left[\log\frac{x+a}{x-a}\right]dx = \frac{x^{m+1} - (-a)^{m+1}}{m+1}\log(x+a) - \frac{x^{m+1} - a^{m+1}}{m+1}\log(x-a)$

$$+\frac{2a^{m+1}}{m+1}\sum_{r=1}^{\left[\frac{m+1}{2}\right]}\frac{1}{m-2r+2}\left(\frac{x}{a}\right)^{m-2r+2}$$

INTEGRALS (Continued)

505. $\displaystyle\int \frac{1}{x^2}\left[\log\frac{x+a}{x-a}\right]dx = \frac{1}{x}\log\frac{x-a}{x+a} - \frac{1}{a}\log\frac{x^2-a^2}{x^2}$

506. $\displaystyle\int (\log X)\,dx = \begin{cases} \left(x+\dfrac{b}{2c}\right)\log X - 2x + \dfrac{\sqrt{4ac-b^2}}{c}\tan^{-1}\dfrac{2cx+b}{\sqrt{4ac-b^2}}, \\ \hspace{7cm}(b^2-4ac<0) \\[0.3cm] \text{or} \\[0.3cm] \left(x+\dfrac{b}{2c}\right)\log X - 2x + \dfrac{\sqrt{b^2-4ac}}{c}\tanh^{-1}\dfrac{2cx+b}{\sqrt{b^2-4ac}}, \\ \hspace{7cm}(b^2-4ac>0) \\[0.3cm] \text{where} \\ X = a+bx+cx^2 \end{cases}$

507. $\displaystyle\int x^n(\log X)\,dx = \frac{x^{n+1}}{n+1}\log X - \frac{2c}{n+1}\int\frac{x^{n+2}}{X}\,dx - \frac{b}{n+1}\int\frac{x^{n+1}}{X}\,dx$

$$\text{where } X = a+bx+cx^2$$

508. $\displaystyle\int [\log(x^2+a^2)]\,dx = x\log(x^2+a^2) - 2x + 2a\tan^{-1}\frac{x}{a}$

509. $\displaystyle\int [\log(x^2-a^2)]\,dx = x\log(x^2-a^2) - 2x + a\log\frac{x+a}{x-a}$

510. $\displaystyle\int x[\log(x^2\pm a^2)]\,dx = \tfrac{1}{2}(x^2\pm a^2)\log(x^2\pm a^2) - \tfrac{1}{2}x^2$

511. $\displaystyle\int [\log(x+\sqrt{x^2\pm a^2})]\,dx = x\log(x+\sqrt{x^2\pm a^2}) - \sqrt{x^2\pm a^2}$

512. $\displaystyle\int x[\log(x+\sqrt{x^2\pm a^2})]\,dx = \left(\frac{x^2}{2}\pm\frac{a^2}{4}\right)\log(x+\sqrt{x^2\pm a^2}) - \frac{x\sqrt{x^2\pm a^2}}{4}$

513. $\displaystyle\int x^m[\log(x+\sqrt{x^2\pm a^2})]\,dx = \frac{x^{m+1}}{m+1}\log(x+\sqrt{x^2\pm a^2})$

$$-\frac{1}{m+1}\int\frac{x^{m+1}}{\sqrt{x^2\pm a^2}}\,dx$$

514. $\displaystyle\int\frac{\log(x+\sqrt{x^2+a^2})}{x^2}\,dx = -\frac{\log(x+\sqrt{x^2+a^2})}{x} - \frac{1}{a}\log\frac{a+\sqrt{x^2+a^2}}{x}$

515. $\displaystyle\int\frac{\log(x+\sqrt{x^2-a^2})}{x^2}\,dx = -\frac{\log(x+\sqrt{x^2-a^2})}{x} + \frac{1}{|a|}\sec^{-1}\frac{x}{a}$

INTEGRALS (Continued)

516. $\displaystyle\int x^n \log(x^2 - a^2)\,dx = \frac{1}{n+1}\bigg[x^{n+1}\log(x^2 - a^2) - a^{n+1}\log(x - a)$

$$-(-a)^{n+1}\log(x + a) - 2\sum_{r=0}^{\left[\frac{n}{2}\right]} \frac{a^{2r}x^{n-2r+1}}{n - 2r + 1}\bigg]$$

EXPONENTIAL FORMS

517. $\displaystyle\int e^x\,dx = e^x$

518. $\displaystyle\int e^{-x}\,dx = -e^{-x}$

519. $\displaystyle\int e^{ax}\,dx = \frac{e^{ax}}{a}$

520. $\displaystyle\int x\,e^{ax}\,dx = \frac{e^{ax}}{a^2}(ax - 1)$

521. $\displaystyle\int x^m e^{ax}\,dx = \begin{cases} \dfrac{x^m e^{ax}}{a} - \dfrac{m}{a}\displaystyle\int x^{m-1}e^{ax}\,dx \\[2mm] \qquad\qquad \text{or} \\[2mm] e^{ax}\displaystyle\sum_{r=0}^{m}(-1)^r\dfrac{m!\,x^{m-r}}{(m-r)!\,a^{r+1}} \end{cases}$

522. $\displaystyle\int \frac{e^{ax}\,dx}{x} = \log x + \frac{ax}{1!} + \frac{a^2 x^2}{2\cdot 2!} + \frac{a^3 x^3}{3\cdot 3!} + \cdots$

523. $\displaystyle\int \frac{e^{ax}}{x^m}\,dx = -\frac{1}{m-1}\frac{e^{ax}}{x^{m-1}} + \frac{a}{m-1}\int\frac{e^{ax}}{x^{m-1}}\,dx$

524. $\displaystyle\int e^{ax}\log x\,dx = \frac{e^{ax}\log x}{a} - \frac{1}{a}\int\frac{e^{ax}}{x}\,dx$

525. $\displaystyle\int \frac{dx}{1 + e^x} = x - \log(1 + e^x) = \log\frac{e^x}{1 + e^x}$

526. $\displaystyle\int \frac{dx}{a + be^{px}} = \frac{x}{a} - \frac{1}{ap}\log(a + be^{px})$

527. $\displaystyle\int \frac{dx}{ae^{mx} + be^{-mx}} = \frac{1}{m\sqrt{ab}}\tan^{-1}\left(e^{mx}\sqrt{\frac{a}{b}}\right), \qquad (a > 0, b > 0)$

528. $\displaystyle\int \frac{dx}{ae^{mx} - be^{-mx}} = \begin{cases} \dfrac{1}{2m\sqrt{ab}}\log\dfrac{\sqrt{a}\,e^{mx} - \sqrt{b}}{\sqrt{a}\,e^{mx} + \sqrt{b}} \\[3mm] \qquad\qquad \text{or} \\[3mm] \dfrac{-1}{m\sqrt{ab}}\tanh^{-1}\left(\sqrt{\dfrac{a}{b}}\,e^{mx}\right), \qquad (a > 0, b > 0) \end{cases}$

INTEGRALS (Continued)

529. $\displaystyle\int (a^x - a^{-x})\,dx = \frac{a^x + a^{-x}}{\log a}$

530. $\displaystyle\int \frac{e^{ax}}{b + ce^{ax}}\,dx = \frac{1}{ac}\log(b + ce^{ax})$

531. $\displaystyle\int \frac{x\,e^{ax}}{(1 + ax)^2}\,dx = \frac{e^{ax}}{a^2(1 + ax)}$

532. $\displaystyle\int x\,e^{-x^2}\,dx = -\tfrac{1}{2}e^{-x^2}$

533. $\displaystyle\int e^{ax}[\sin(bx)]\,dx = \frac{e^{ax}[a\sin(bx) - b\cos(bx)]}{a^2 + b^2}$

534. $\displaystyle\int e^{ax}[\sin(bx)][\sin(cx)]\,dx = \frac{e^{ax}[(b - c)\sin(b - c)x + a\cos(b - c)x]}{2[a^2 + (b - c)^2]}$

$$- \frac{e^{ax}[(b + c)\sin(b + c)x + a\cos(b + c)x]}{2[a^2 + (b + c)^2]}$$

$$\begin{cases} \dfrac{e^{ax}[a\sin(b - c)x - (b - c)\cos(b - c)x]}{2[a^2 + (b - c)^2]} \\[2ex] + \dfrac{e^{ax}[a\sin(b + c)x - (b + c)\cos(b + c)x]}{2[a^2 + (b + c)^2]} \\[2ex] \qquad\qquad \text{or} \end{cases}$$

535. $\displaystyle\int e^{ax}[\sin(bx)][\cos(cx)]\,dx = \begin{cases} \dfrac{e^{ax}}{\rho}[(a\sin bx - b\cos bx)[\cos(cx - \alpha)] \\[2ex] \qquad\qquad - c(\sin bx)\sin(cx - \alpha)] \\[1ex] \text{where} \\[1ex] \rho = \sqrt{(a^2 + b^2 - c^2)^2 + 4a^2c^2}, \\[1ex] \rho\cos\alpha = a^2 + b^2 - c^2, \qquad \rho\sin\alpha = 2ac \end{cases}$

536. $\displaystyle\int e^{ax}[\sin(bx)][\sin(bx + c)]\,dx$

$$= \frac{e^{ax}\cos c}{2a} - \frac{e^{ax}[a\cos(2bx + c) + 2b\sin(2bx + c)]}{2(a^2 + 4b^2)}$$

537. $\displaystyle\int e^{ax}[\sin(bx)][\cos(bx + c)]\,dx$

$$= \frac{-e^{ax}\sin c}{2a} + \frac{e^{ax}[a\sin(2bx + c) - 2b\cos(2bx + c)]}{2(a^2 + 4b^2)}$$

538. $\displaystyle\int e^{ax}[\cos(bx)]\,dx = \frac{e^{ax}}{a^2 + b^2}[a\cos(bx) + b\sin(bx)]$

INTEGRALS (Continued)

539. $\int e^{ax}[\cos(bx)][\cos(cx)]\,dx = \dfrac{e^{ax}[(b-c)\sin(b-c)x + a\cos(b-c)x]}{2[a^2 + (b-c)^2]}$

$$+ \dfrac{e^{ax}[(b+c)\sin(b+c)x + a\cos(b+c)x]}{2[a^2 + (b+c)^2]}$$

540. $\int e^{ax}[\cos(bx)][\cos(bx+c)]\,dx$

$$= \dfrac{e^{ax}\cos c}{2a} + \dfrac{e^{ax}[a\cos(2bx+c) + 2b\sin(2bx+c)]}{2(a^2 + 4b^2)}$$

541. $\int e^{ax}[\cos(bx)][\sin(bx+c)]\,dx$

$$= \dfrac{e^{ax}\sin c}{2a} + \dfrac{e^{ax}[a\sin(2bx+c) - 2b\cos(2bx+c)]}{2(a^2 + 4b^2)}$$

542. $\int e^{ax}[\sin^n bx]\,dx = \dfrac{1}{a^2 + n^2b^2}\Bigg[(a\sin bx - nb\cos bx)\,e^{ax}\sin^{n-1} bx$

$$+ n(n-1)b^2 \int e^{ax}[\sin^{n-2} bx]\,dx \Bigg]$$

543. $\int e^{ax}[\cos^n bx]\,dx = \dfrac{1}{a^2 + n^2b^2}\Bigg[(a\cos bx + nb\sin bx)\,e^{ax}\cos^{n-1} bx$

$$+ n(n-1)b^2 \int e^{ax}[\cos^{n-2} bx]\,dx \Bigg]$$

544. $\int x^m e^x \sin x\,dx = \dfrac{1}{2}x^m e^x(\sin x - \cos x) - \dfrac{m}{2}\int x^{m-1} e^x \sin x\,dx$

$$+ \dfrac{m}{2}\int x^{m-1} e^x \cos x\,dx$$

545. $\int x^m e^{ax}[\sin bx]\,dx = \begin{cases} x^m e^{ax}\dfrac{a\sin bx - b\cos bx}{a^2 + b^2} \\[2mm] \qquad - \dfrac{m}{a^2 + b^2}\int x^{m-1} e^{ax}(a\sin bx - b\cos bx)\,dx \\[2mm] \qquad\qquad \text{or} \\[2mm] e^{ax}\displaystyle\sum_{r=0}^{m} \dfrac{(-1)^r m!\,x^{m-r}}{\rho^{r+1}(m-r)!}\sin[bx - (r+1)\alpha] \\[2mm] \qquad\qquad \text{where} \\[2mm] \rho = \sqrt{a^2 + b^2}, \qquad \rho\cos\alpha = a, \qquad \rho\sin\alpha = b \end{cases}$

546. $\int x^m e^x \cos x\,dx = \dfrac{1}{2}x^m e^x(\sin x + \cos x)$

$$- \dfrac{m}{2}\int x^{m-1} e^x \sin x\,dx - \dfrac{m}{2}\int x^{m-1} e^x \cos x\,dx$$

INTEGRALS (Continued)

547. $\displaystyle\int x^m e^{ax} \cos bx \, dx =$

$$\begin{cases} x^m e^{ax} \dfrac{a \cos bx + b \sin bx}{a^2 + b^2} \\[2ex] \qquad -\dfrac{m}{a^2 + b^2} \displaystyle\int x^{m-1} e^{ax}(a \cos bx + b \sin bx)\, dx \\[2ex] \text{or} \\[1ex] e^{ax} \displaystyle\sum_{r=0}^{m} \dfrac{(-1)^r m! x^{m-r}}{\rho^{r+1}(m-r)!} \cos[bx - (r+1)\alpha] \\[2ex] \qquad \text{where} \\[1ex] \rho = \sqrt{a^2 + b^2}, \qquad \rho \cos \alpha = a, \qquad \rho \sin \alpha = b \end{cases}$$

548. $\displaystyle\int e^{ax}(\cos^m x)(\sin^n x)\, dx =$

$$\begin{cases} \dfrac{e^{ax} \cos^{m-1} x \sin^n x [a \cos x + (m+n)\sin x]}{(m+n)^2 + a^2} \\[2ex] \qquad -\dfrac{na}{(m+n)^2 + a^2} \displaystyle\int e^{ax}(\cos^{m-1} x)(\sin^{n-1} x)\, dx \\[2ex] \qquad +\dfrac{(m-1)(m+n)}{(m+n)^2 + a^2} \displaystyle\int e^{ax}(\cos^{m-2} x)(\sin^n x)\, dx \\[2ex] \text{or} \\[1ex] \dfrac{e^{ax} \cos^m x \sin^{n-1} x [a \sin x - (m+n)\cos x]}{(m+n)^2 + a^2} \\[2ex] \qquad +\dfrac{ma}{(m+n)^2 + a^2} \displaystyle\int e^{ax}(\cos^{m-1} x)(\sin^{n-1} x)\, dx \\[2ex] \qquad +\dfrac{(n-1)(m+n)}{(m+n)^2 + a^2} \displaystyle\int e^{ax}(\cos^m x)(\sin^{n-2} x)\, dx \\[2ex] \text{or} \\[1ex] \dfrac{e^{ax}(\cos^{m-1} x)(\sin^{n-1} x)(a \sin x \cos x + m \sin^2 x - n \cos^2 x)}{(m+n)^2 + a^2} \\[2ex] \qquad +\dfrac{m(m-1)}{(m+n)^2 + a^2} \displaystyle\int e^{ax}(\cos^{m-2} x)(\sin^n x)\, dx \\[2ex] \qquad +\dfrac{n(n-1)}{(m+n)^2 + a^2} \displaystyle\int e^{ax}(\cos^m x)(\sin^{n-2} x)\, dx \\[2ex] \text{or} \\[1ex] \dfrac{e^{ax}(\cos^{m-1} x)(\sin^{n-1} x)(a \cos x \sin x + m \sin^2 x - n \cos^2 x)}{(m+n)^2 + a^2} \\[2ex] \qquad +\dfrac{m(m-1)}{(m+n)^2 + a^2} \displaystyle\int e^{ax}(\cos^{m-2} x)(\sin^{n-2} x)\, dx \\[2ex] \qquad +\dfrac{(n-m)(n+m-1)}{(m+n)^2 + a^2} \displaystyle\int e^{ax}(\cos^m x)(\sin^{n-2} x)\, dx \end{cases}$$

INTEGRALS (Continued)

549. $\displaystyle \int x\, e^{ax}(\sin bx)\, dx = \frac{x\, e^{ax}}{a^2 + b^2}(a \sin bx - b \cos bx)$

$$- \frac{e^{ax}}{(a^2 + b^2)^2}[(a^2 - b^2)\sin bx - 2ab \cos bx]$$

550. $\displaystyle \int x\, e^{ax}(\cos bx)\, dx = \frac{x\, e^{ax}}{a^2 + b^2}(a \cos bx + b \sin bx)$

$$- \frac{e^{ax}}{(a^2 + b^2)^2}[(a^2 - b^2)\cos bx + 2ab \sin bx]$$

551. $\displaystyle \int \frac{e^{ax}}{\sin^n x}\, dx = -\frac{e^{ax}[a \sin x + (n-2)\cos x]}{(n-1)(n-2)\sin^{n-1} x} + \frac{a^2 + (n-2)^2}{(n-1)(n-2)}\int \frac{e^{ax}}{\sin^{n-2} x}\, dx$

552. $\displaystyle \int \frac{e^{ax}}{\cos^n x}\, dx = -\frac{e^{ax}[a \cos x - (n-2)\sin x]}{(n-1)(n-2)\cos^{n-1} x} + \frac{a^2 + (n-2)^2}{(n-1)(n-2)}\int \frac{e^{ax}}{\cos^{n-2} x}\, dx$

553. $\displaystyle \int e^{ax}\tan^n x\, dx = e^{ax}\frac{\tan^{n-1} x}{n-1} - \frac{a}{n-1}\int e^{ax}\tan^{n-1} x\, dx - \int e^{ax}\tan^{n-2} x\, dx$

HYPERBOLIC FORMS

554. $\displaystyle \int (\sinh x)\, dx = \cosh x$

555. $\displaystyle \int (\cosh x)\, dx = \sinh x$

556. $\displaystyle \int (\tanh x)\, dx = \log \cosh x$

557. $\displaystyle \int (\coth x)\, dx = \log \sinh x$

558. $\displaystyle \int (\operatorname{sech} x)\, dx = \tan^{-1}(\sinh x)$

559. $\displaystyle \int \operatorname{csch} x\, dx = \log \tanh \left(\frac{x}{2}\right)$

560. $\displaystyle \int x(\sinh x)\, dx = x \cosh x - \sinh x$

561. $\displaystyle \int x^n(\sinh x)\, dx = x^n \cosh x - n\int x^{n-1}(\cosh x)\, dx$

562. $\displaystyle \int x(\cosh x)\, dx = x \sinh x - \cosh x$

563. $\displaystyle \int x^n(\cosh x)\, dx = x^n \sinh x - n\int x^{n-1}(\sinh x)\, dx$

INTEGRALS (Continued)

564. $\displaystyle\int (\text{sech } x)(\tanh x)\, dx = -\text{sech } x$

565. $\displaystyle\int (\text{csch } x)(\coth x)\, dx = -\text{csch } x$

566. $\displaystyle\int (\sinh^2 x)\, dx = \frac{\sinh 2x}{4} - \frac{x}{2}$

567. $\displaystyle\int (\sinh^m x)(\cosh^n x)\, dx = \begin{cases} \dfrac{1}{m+n}(\sinh^{m+1} x)(\cosh^{n-1} x) \\[2mm] \qquad + \dfrac{n-1}{m+n}\displaystyle\int (\sinh^m x)(\cosh^{n-2} x)\, dx \\[2mm] \text{or} \\[2mm] \dfrac{1}{m+n}\sinh^{m-1} x \cosh^{n+1} x \\[2mm] \qquad - \dfrac{m-1}{m+n}\displaystyle\int (\sinh^{m-2} x)(\cosh^n x)\, dx, \quad (m+n \neq 0) \end{cases}$

568. $\displaystyle\int \frac{dx}{(\sinh^m x)(\cosh^n x)} = \begin{cases} -\dfrac{1}{(m-1)(\sinh^{m-1} x)(\cosh^{n-1} x)} \\[2mm] \qquad - \dfrac{m+n-2}{m-1}\displaystyle\int \dfrac{dx}{(\sinh^{m-2} x)(\cosh^n x)}, \quad (m \neq 1) \\[2mm] \text{or} \\[2mm] \dfrac{1}{(n-1)\sinh^{m-1} x \cosh^{n-1} x} \\[2mm] \qquad + \dfrac{m+n-2}{n-1}\displaystyle\int \dfrac{dx}{(\sinh^m x)(\cosh^{n-2} x)}, \quad (n \neq 1) \end{cases}$

569. $\displaystyle\int (\tanh^2 x)\, dx = x - \tanh x$

570. $\displaystyle\int (\tanh^n x)\, dx = -\frac{\tanh^{n-1} x}{n-1} + \int (\tanh^{n-2} x)\, dx, \quad (n \neq 1)$

571. $\displaystyle\int (\text{sech}^2 x)\, dx = \tanh x$

572. $\displaystyle\int (\cosh^2 x)\, dx = \frac{\sinh 2x}{4} + \frac{x}{2}$

573. $\displaystyle\int (\coth^2 x)\, dx = x - \coth x$

574. $\displaystyle\int (\coth^n x)\, dx = -\frac{\coth^{n-1} x}{n-1} + \int \coth^{n-2} x\, dx, \quad (n \neq 1)$

INTEGRALS (Continued)

575. $\displaystyle\int (\text{csch}^2\, x)\, dx = -\text{ctnh}\, x$

576. $\displaystyle\int (\sinh mx)(\sinh nx)\, dx = \frac{\sinh (m+n)x}{2(m+n)} - \frac{\sinh (m-n)x}{2(m-n)}, \qquad (m^2 \neq n^2)$

577. $\displaystyle\int (\cosh mx)(\cosh nx)\, dx = \frac{\sinh (m+n)x}{2(m+n)} + \frac{\sinh (m-n)x}{2(m-n)}, \qquad (m^2 \neq n^2)$

578. $\displaystyle\int (\sinh mx)(\cosh nx)\, dx = \frac{\cosh (m+n)x}{2(m+n)} + \frac{\cosh (m-n)x}{2(m-n)}, \qquad (m^2 \neq n^2)$

579. $\displaystyle\int \left(\sinh^{-1}\frac{x}{a}\right) dx = x \sinh^{-1}\frac{x}{a} - \sqrt{x^2 + a^2}, \qquad (a > 0)$

580. $\displaystyle\int x\left(\sinh^{-1}\frac{x}{a}\right) dx = \left(\frac{x^2}{2} + \frac{a^2}{4}\right)\sinh^{-1}\frac{x}{a} - \frac{x}{4}\sqrt{x^2 + a^2}, \qquad (a > 0)$

581. $\displaystyle\int x^n(\sinh^{-1}\, x)\, dx = \frac{x^{n+1}}{n+1}\sinh^{-1}\, x - \frac{1}{n+1}\int \frac{x^{n+1}}{(1+x^2)^{\frac{1}{2}}}\, dx, \qquad (n \neq -1)$

582. $\displaystyle\int \left(\cosh^{-1}\frac{x}{a}\right) dx = \begin{cases} x \cosh^{-1}\dfrac{x}{a} - \sqrt{x^2 - a^2}, & \left(\cosh^{-1}\dfrac{x}{a} > 0\right) \\[2mm] \qquad\text{or} \\[2mm] x \cosh^{-1}\dfrac{x}{a} + \sqrt{x^2 - a^2}, & \left(\cosh^{-1}\dfrac{x}{a} < 0\right), \end{cases} \qquad (a > 0)$

583. $\displaystyle\int x\left(\cosh^{-1}\frac{x}{a}\right) dx = \frac{2x^2 - a^2}{4}\cosh^{-1}\frac{x}{a} - \frac{x}{4}(x^2 - a^2)^{\frac{1}{2}}$

584. $\displaystyle\int x^n(\cosh^{-1}\, x)\, dx = \frac{x^{n+1}}{n+1}\cosh^{-1}\, x - \frac{1}{n+1}\int \frac{x^{n+1}}{(x^2 - 1)^{\frac{1}{2}}}\, dx, \qquad (n \neq -1)$

585. $\displaystyle\int \left(\tanh^{-1}\frac{x}{a}\right) dx = x \tanh^{-1}\frac{x}{a} + \frac{a}{2}\log (a^2 - x^2), \qquad \left(\left|\frac{x}{a}\right| < 1\right)$

586. $\displaystyle\int \left(\coth^{-1}\frac{x}{a}\right) dx = x \coth^{-1}\frac{x}{a} + \frac{a}{2}\log (x^2 - a^2), \qquad \left(\left|\frac{x}{a}\right| > 1\right)$

587. $\displaystyle\int x\left(\tanh^{-1}\frac{x}{a}\right) dx = \frac{x^2 - a^2}{2}\tanh^{-1}\frac{x}{a} + \frac{ax}{2}, \qquad \left(\left|\frac{x}{a}\right| < 1\right)$

588. $\displaystyle\int x^n\left(\tanh^{-1}\, x\right) dx = \frac{x^{n+1}}{n+1}\tanh^{-1}\, x - \frac{1}{n+1}\int \frac{x^{n+1}}{1 - x^2}\, dx, \qquad (n \neq -1)$

589. $\displaystyle\int x\left(\coth^{-1}\frac{x}{a}\right) dx = \frac{x^2 - a^2}{2}\coth^{-1}\frac{x}{a} + \frac{ax}{2}, \qquad \left(\left|\frac{x}{a}\right| > 1\right)$

590. $\displaystyle\int x^n(\coth^{-1}\, x)\, dx = \frac{x^{n+1}}{n+1}\coth^{-1}\, x + \frac{1}{n+1}\int \frac{x^{n+1}}{x^2 - 1}\, dx, \qquad (n \neq -1)$

DEFINITE INTEGRALS

591. $\int (\operatorname{sech}^{-1} x)\, dx = x \operatorname{sech}^{-1} x + \sin^{-1} x$

592. $\int x \operatorname{sech}^{-1} x\, dx = \dfrac{x^2}{2} \operatorname{sech}^{-1} x - \dfrac{1}{2}(1 - x^2)$

593. $\int x^n \operatorname{sech}^{-1} x\, dx = \dfrac{x^{n+1}}{n+1} \operatorname{sech}^{-1} x + \dfrac{1}{n+1} \int \dfrac{x^n}{(1 - x^2)^{\frac{1}{2}}}\, dx,\qquad (n \neq -1)$

594. $\int \operatorname{csch}^{-1} x\, dx = x \operatorname{csch}^{-1} x + \dfrac{x}{|x|} \sinh^{-1} x$

595. $\int x \operatorname{csch}^{-1} x\, dx = \dfrac{x^2}{2} \operatorname{csch}^{-1} x + \dfrac{1}{2} \dfrac{x}{|x|} \sqrt{1 + x^2}$

596. $\int x^n \operatorname{csch}^{-1} x\, dx = \dfrac{x^{n+1}}{n+1} \operatorname{csch}^{-1} x + \dfrac{1}{n+1} \dfrac{x}{|x|} \int \dfrac{x^n}{(x^2 + 1)^{\frac{1}{2}}}\, dx,\qquad (n \neq -1)$

DEFINITE INTEGRALS

597. $\displaystyle\int_0^\infty x^{n-1} e^{-x}\, dx = \int_0^1 \left(\log \dfrac{1}{x}\right)^{n-1} dx = \dfrac{1}{n} \prod_{m=1}^\infty \dfrac{\left(1 + \dfrac{1}{m}\right)^n}{1 + \dfrac{n}{m}}$

$$= \Gamma(n),\ n \neq 0, -1, -2, -3, \ldots \qquad \text{(Gamma Function)}$$

598. $\displaystyle\int_0^\infty t^n p^{-t}\, dt = \dfrac{n!}{(\log p)^{n+1}},\qquad (n = 0, 1, 2, 3, \ldots \text{ and } p > 0)$

599. $\displaystyle\int_0^\infty t^{n-1} e^{-(a+1)t}\, dt = \dfrac{\Gamma(n)}{(a+1)^n},\qquad (n > 0, a > -1)$

600. $\displaystyle\int_0^1 x^m \left(\log \dfrac{1}{x}\right)^n dx = \dfrac{\Gamma(n+1)}{(m+1)^{n+1}},\qquad (m > -1, n > -1)$

601. $\Gamma(n)$ is finite if $n > 0$, $\Gamma(n+1) = n\Gamma(n)$

602. $\Gamma(n) \cdot \Gamma(1 - n) = \dfrac{\pi}{\sin n\pi}$

603. $\Gamma(n) = (n - 1)!$ if $n = $ integer > 0

604. $\Gamma(\frac{1}{2}) = 2 \displaystyle\int_0^\infty e^{-t^2}\, dt = \sqrt{\pi} = 1.7724538509 \cdots = (-\frac{1}{2})!$

605. $\Gamma(n + \frac{1}{2}) = \dfrac{1 \cdot 3 \cdot 5 \ldots (2n - 1)}{2^n} \sqrt{\pi} \qquad n = 1, 2, 3, \ldots$

606. $\Gamma(-n + \frac{1}{2}) = \dfrac{(-1)^n 2^n \sqrt{\pi}}{1 \cdot 3 \cdot 5 \ldots (2n - 1)} \qquad n = 1, 2, 3, \ldots$

DEFINITE INTEGRALS (Continued)

607. $\displaystyle\int_0^1 x^{m-1}(1-x)^{n-1}\,dx = \int_0^\infty \frac{x^{m-1}}{(1+x)^{m+n}}\,dx = \frac{\Gamma(m)\Gamma(n)}{\Gamma(m+n)} = B(m,n)$

(Beta function)

608. $\displaystyle B(m,n) = B(n,m) = \frac{\Gamma(m)\Gamma(n)}{\Gamma(m+n)}$, where m and n are any positive real numbers.

609. $\displaystyle\int_a^b (x-a)^m(b-x)^n\,dx = (b-a)^{m+n+1}\frac{\Gamma(m+1)\cdot\Gamma(n+1)}{\Gamma(m+n+2)},$

$(m > -1, n > -1, b > a)$

610. $\displaystyle\int_1^\infty \frac{dx}{x^m} = \frac{1}{m-1}, \qquad [m > 1]$

611. $\displaystyle\int_0^\infty \frac{dx}{(1+x)x^p} = \pi\csc p\pi, \qquad [p < 1]$

612. $\displaystyle\int_0^\infty \frac{dx}{(1-x)x^p} = -\pi\cot p\pi, \qquad [p < 1]$

613. $\displaystyle\int_0^\infty \frac{x^{p-1}\,dx}{1+x} = \frac{\pi}{\sin p\pi}$

$\qquad\qquad = B(p, 1-p) = \Gamma(p)\Gamma(1-p), \quad [0 < p < 1]$

614. $\displaystyle\int_0^\infty \frac{x^{m-1}\,dx}{1+x^n} = \frac{\pi}{n\sin\dfrac{m\pi}{n}}, \qquad [0 < m < n]$

615. $\displaystyle\int_0^\infty \frac{x^a\,dx}{(m+x^b)^c} = \frac{m(a+1)-bc}{b^2}\cdot\frac{\Gamma\left(\dfrac{a+1}{b}\right)\Gamma\left(c-\dfrac{a+1}{b}\right)}{\Gamma(c)},$

$\left(a > -1, b > 0, m > 0, c > \dfrac{a+1}{b}\right)$

616. $\displaystyle\int_0^\infty \frac{dx}{(1+x)\sqrt{x}} = \pi$

617. $\displaystyle\int_0^\infty \frac{a\,dx}{a^2+x^2} = \frac{\pi}{2},$ if $a > 0$; 0, if $a = 0$; $-\dfrac{\pi}{2}$, if $a < 0$

618. $\displaystyle\int_0^a (a^2-x^2)^{\frac{n}{2}}\,dx = \frac{1}{2}\int_{-a}^a (a^2-x^2)^{\frac{n}{2}}\,dx = \frac{1\cdot3\cdot5\ldots n}{2\cdot4\cdot6\ldots(n+1)}\cdot\frac{\pi}{2}\cdot a^{n+1}$ (n odd)

619. $\displaystyle\int_0^a x^m(a^2-x^2)^{\frac{n}{2}}\,dx = \begin{cases} \dfrac{1}{2}a^{m+n+1}B\left(\dfrac{m+1}{2},\dfrac{n+2}{2}\right) \\[2mm] \text{or} \\[2mm] \dfrac{1}{2}a^{m+n+1}\dfrac{\Gamma\left(\dfrac{m+1}{2}\right)\Gamma\left(\dfrac{n+2}{2}\right)}{\Gamma\left(\dfrac{m+n+3}{2}\right)} \end{cases}$

DEFINITE INTEGRALS (Continued)

620. $\displaystyle\int_0^{\pi/2} (\sin^n x)\, dx = \begin{cases} \displaystyle\int_0^{\pi/2} (\cos^n x)\, dx \\[4pt] \text{or} \\[4pt] \dfrac{1\cdot 3\cdot 5\cdot 7 \ldots (n-1)}{2\cdot 4\cdot 6\cdot 8 \ldots (n)}\,\dfrac{\pi}{2}, \qquad (n \text{ an even integer, } n \neq 0) \\[10pt] \text{or} \\[4pt] \dfrac{2\cdot 4\cdot 6\cdot 8 \ldots (n-1)}{1\cdot 3\cdot 5\cdot 7 \ldots (n)}, \qquad (n \text{ an odd integer, } n \neq 1) \\[10pt] \text{or} \\[4pt] \dfrac{\sqrt{\pi}}{2}\,\dfrac{\Gamma\left(\dfrac{n+1}{2}\right)}{\Gamma\left(\dfrac{n}{2}+1\right)}, \qquad (n > -1) \end{cases}$

621. $\displaystyle\int_0^{\infty} \frac{\sin mx\, dx}{x} = \frac{\pi}{2}, \text{ if } m > 0;\ 0, \text{ if } m = 0;\ -\frac{\pi}{2}, \text{ if } m < 0$

622. $\displaystyle\int_0^{\infty} \frac{\cos x\, dx}{x} = \infty$

623. $\displaystyle\int_0^{\infty} \frac{\tan x\, dx}{x} = \frac{\pi}{2}$

624. $\displaystyle\int_0^{\pi} \sin ax \cdot \sin bx\, dx = \int_0^{\pi} \cos ax \cdot \cos bx\, dx = 0, \qquad (a \neq b;\ a, b \text{ integers})$

625. $\displaystyle\int_0^{\pi/a} [\sin (ax)][\cos (ax)]\, dx = \int_0^{\pi} [\sin (ax)][\cos (ax)]\, dx = 0$

626. $\displaystyle\int_0^{\pi} [\sin (ax)][\cos (bx)]\, dx = \frac{2a}{a^2 - b^2}, \text{ if } a - b \text{ is odd, or } 0 \text{ if } a - b \text{ is even}$

627. $\displaystyle\int_0^{\infty} \frac{\sin x \cos mx\, dx}{x}$

$$= 0, \text{ if } m < -1 \text{ or } m > 1;\ \frac{\pi}{4}, \text{ if } m = \pm 1;\ \frac{\pi}{2}, \text{ if } m^2 < 1$$

628. $\displaystyle\int_0^{\infty} \frac{\sin ax \sin bx}{x^2}\, dx = \frac{\pi a}{2}, \qquad (a \leq b)$

629. $\displaystyle\int_0^{\pi} \sin^2 mx\, dx = \int_0^{\pi} \cos^2 mx\, dx = \frac{\pi}{2}$

630. $\displaystyle\int_0^{\infty} \frac{\sin^2 (px)}{x^2}\, dx = \frac{\pi p}{2}$

DEFINITE INTEGRALS (Continued)

631. $\displaystyle\int_0^\infty \frac{\sin x}{x^p}\,dx = \frac{\pi}{2\Gamma(p)\sin(p\pi/2)}, \qquad 0 < p < 1$

632. $\displaystyle\int_0^\infty \frac{\cos x}{x^p}\,dx = \frac{\pi}{2\Gamma(p)\cos(p\pi/2)}, \qquad 0 < p < 1$

633. $\displaystyle\int_0^\infty \frac{1 - \cos px}{x^2}\,dx = \frac{\pi p}{2}$

634. $\displaystyle\int_0^\infty \frac{\sin px \cos qx}{x}\,dx = \left\{0,\quad q > p > 0;\quad \frac{\pi}{2},\ p > q > 0;\quad \frac{\pi}{4},\ p = q > 0\right\}$

635. $\displaystyle\int_0^\infty \frac{\cos(mx)}{x^2 + a^2}\,dx = \frac{\pi}{2a}\,e^{-|m|a}, \qquad (a > 0)$

636. $\displaystyle\int_0^\infty \cos(x^2)\,dx = \int_0^\infty \sin(x^2)\,dx = \frac{1}{2}\sqrt{\frac{\pi}{2}}$

637. $\displaystyle\int_0^\infty \sin ax^n\,dx = \frac{1}{na^{1/n}}\,\Gamma(1/n)\sin\frac{\pi}{2n}, \qquad n > 1$

638. $\displaystyle\int_0^\infty \cos ax^n\,dx = \frac{1}{na^{1/n}}\,\Gamma(1/n)\cos\frac{\pi}{2n}, \qquad n > 1$

639. $\displaystyle\int_0^\infty \frac{\sin x}{\sqrt{x}}\,dx = \int_0^\infty \frac{\cos x}{\sqrt{x}}\,dx = \sqrt{\frac{\pi}{2}}$

640. $\displaystyle\int_0^\infty \frac{\sin^3 x}{x^2}\,dx = \frac{3}{4}\log 3$

641. $\displaystyle\int_0^\infty \frac{\sin^3 x}{x^3}\,dx = \frac{3\pi}{8}$

642. $\displaystyle\int_0^\infty \frac{\sin^4 x}{x^4}\,dx = \frac{\pi}{3}$

643. $\displaystyle\int_0^{\pi/2} \frac{dx}{1 + a\cos x} = \frac{\cos^{-1} a}{\sqrt{1 - a^2}}, \qquad (a < 1)$

644. $\displaystyle\int_0^\pi \frac{dx}{a + b\cos x} = \frac{\pi}{\sqrt{a^2 - b^2}}, \qquad (a > b \geq 0)$

645. $\displaystyle\int_0^{2\pi} \frac{dx}{1 + a\cos x} = \frac{2\pi}{\sqrt{1 - a^2}}, \qquad (a^2 < 1)$

646. $\displaystyle\int_0^\infty \frac{\cos ax - \cos bx}{x}\,dx = \log\frac{b}{a}$

647. $\displaystyle\int_0^{\pi/2} \frac{dx}{a^2\sin^2 x + b^2\cos^2 x} = \frac{\pi}{2ab}$

DEFINITE INTEGRALS (Continued)

648. $\displaystyle\int_0^{\pi/2} \frac{dx}{(a^2 \sin^2 x + b^2 \cos^2 x)^2} = \frac{\pi(a^2 + b^2)}{4a^3 b^3}$, $\qquad (a, b > 0)$

649. $\displaystyle\int_0^{\pi/2} \sin^{n-1} x \cos^{m-1} x \, dx = \frac{1}{2} B\left(\frac{n}{2}, \frac{m}{2}\right)$, $\qquad m$ and n positive integers

650. $\displaystyle\int_0^{\pi/2} (\sin^{2n+1} \theta) \, d\theta = \frac{2 \cdot 4 \cdot 6 \ldots (2n)}{1 \cdot 3 \cdot 5 \ldots (2n+1)}$, $\qquad (n = 1, 2, 3 \ldots)$

651. $\displaystyle\int_0^{\pi/2} (\sin^{2n} \theta) \, d\theta = \frac{1 \cdot 3 \cdot 5 \ldots (2n-1)}{2 \cdot 4 \ldots (2n)} \left(\frac{\pi}{2}\right)$, $\qquad (n = 1, 2, 3 \ldots)$

652. $\displaystyle\int_0^{\pi/2} \frac{x}{\sin x} \, dx = 2\left\{\frac{1}{1^2} - \frac{1}{3^2} + \frac{1}{5^2} - \frac{1}{7^2} + \cdots\right\}$

653. $\displaystyle\int_0^{\pi/2} \frac{dx}{1 + \tan^m x} = \frac{\pi}{4}$

654. $\displaystyle\int_0^{\pi/2} \sqrt{\cos \theta} \, d\theta = \frac{(2\pi)^{\frac{3}{2}}}{[\Gamma(\frac{1}{4})]^2}$

655. $\displaystyle\int_0^{\pi/2} (\tan^h \theta) \, d\theta = \frac{\pi}{2 \cos\left(\dfrac{h\pi}{2}\right)}$, $\qquad (0 < h < 1)$

656. $\displaystyle\int_0^\infty \frac{\tan^{-1}(ax) - \tan^{-1}(bx)}{x} \, dx = \frac{\pi}{2} \log \frac{a}{b}$, $\qquad (a, b > 0)$

657. The area enclosed by a curve defined through the equation $x^{\frac{b}{c}} + y^{\frac{b}{c}} = a^{\frac{b}{c}}$ where $a > 0$, c a positive odd integer and b a positive even integer is given by

$$\frac{\left[\Gamma\left(\dfrac{c}{b}\right)\right]^2}{\Gamma\left(\dfrac{2c}{b}\right)} \left(\frac{2ca^2}{b}\right)$$

658. $I = \displaystyle\iiint_R x^{h-1} y^{m-1} z^{n-1} \, dv$, where R denotes the region of space bounded by

the co-ordinate planes and that portion of the surface $\left(\dfrac{x}{a}\right)^p + \left(\dfrac{y}{b}\right)^q + \left(\dfrac{z}{c}\right)^k = 1$,

which lies in the first octant and where $h, m, n, p, q, k, a, b, c$, denote positive real numbers is given by

$$\int_0^a x^{h-1} \, dx \int_0^{b\left[1-\left(\frac{x}{a}\right)^p\right]^{\frac{1}{q}}} y^m \, dy \int_0^{c\left[1-\left(\frac{x}{a}\right)^p-\left(\frac{y}{b}\right)^q\right]^{\frac{1}{k}}} z^{n-1} \, dz$$

$$= \frac{a^h b^m c^n}{pqk} \frac{\Gamma\left(\dfrac{h}{p}\right)\Gamma\left(\dfrac{m}{q}\right)\Gamma\left(\dfrac{n}{k}\right)}{\Gamma\left(\dfrac{h}{p} + \dfrac{m}{q} + \dfrac{n}{k} + 1\right)}$$

DEFINITE INTEGRALS (Continued)

659. $\displaystyle\int_0^\infty e^{-ax}\,dx = \frac{1}{a}, \quad (a > 0)$

660. $\displaystyle\int_0^\infty \frac{e^{-ax} - e^{-bx}}{x}\,dx = \log\frac{b}{a}, \quad (a, b > 0)$

661. $\displaystyle\int_0^\infty x^n e^{-ax}\,dx = \begin{cases} \dfrac{\Gamma(n+1)}{a^{n+1}}, & (n > -1, a > 0) \\ \quad\text{or} \\ \dfrac{n!}{a^{n+1}}, & (a > 0, n \text{ positive integer}) \end{cases}$

662. $\displaystyle\int_0^\infty x^n \exp(-ax^p)\,dx = \frac{\Gamma(k)}{pa^k}, \quad \left(n > -1, p > 0, a > 0, k = \frac{n+1}{p}\right)$

663. $\displaystyle\int_0^\infty e^{-a^2 x^2}\,dx = \frac{1}{2a}\sqrt{\pi} = \frac{1}{2a}\Gamma\!\left(\frac{1}{2}\right), \quad (a > 0)$

664. $\displaystyle\int_0^\infty x e^{-x^2}\,dx = \frac{1}{2}$

665. $\displaystyle\int_0^\infty x^2 e^{-x^2}\,dx = \frac{\sqrt{\pi}}{4}$

666. $\displaystyle\int_0^\infty x^{2n} e^{-ax^2}\,dx = \frac{1\cdot 3\cdot 5\ldots(2n-1)}{2^{n+1}a^n}\sqrt{\frac{\pi}{a}}$

667. $\displaystyle\int_0^\infty x^{2n+1} e^{-ax^2}\,dx = \frac{n!}{2a^{n+1}}, \quad (a > 0)$

668. $\displaystyle\int_0^1 x^m e^{-ax}\,dx = \frac{m!}{a^{m+1}}\left[1 - e^{-a}\sum_{r=0}^m \frac{a^r}{r!}\right]$

669. $\displaystyle\int_0^\infty e^{\left(-x^2 - \frac{a^2}{x^2}\right)}\,dx = \frac{e^{-2a}\sqrt{\pi}}{2}, \quad (a \geq 0)$

670. $\displaystyle\int_0^\infty e^{-nx}\sqrt{x}\,dx = \frac{1}{2n}\sqrt{\frac{\pi}{n}}$

671. $\displaystyle\int_0^\infty \frac{e^{-nx}}{\sqrt{x}}\,dx = \sqrt{\frac{\pi}{n}}$

672. $\displaystyle\int_0^\infty e^{-ax}(\cos mx)\,dx = \frac{a}{a^2 + m^2}, \quad (a > 0)$

673. $\displaystyle\int_0^\infty e^{-ax}(\sin mx)\,dx = \frac{m}{a^2 + m^2}, \quad (a > 0)$

DEFINITE INTEGRALS (Continued)

674. $\displaystyle\int_0^\infty x\,e^{-ax}[\sin(bx)]\,dx = \frac{2ab}{(a^2+b^2)^2}, \qquad (a>0)$

675. $\displaystyle\int_0^\infty x\,e^{-ax}[\cos(bx)]\,dx = \frac{a^2-b^2}{(a^2+b^2)^2}, \qquad (a>0)$

676. $\displaystyle\int_0^\infty x^n\,e^{-ax}[\sin(bx)]\,dx = \frac{n![(a-ib)^{n+1}-(a+ib)^{n+1}]}{2(a^2+b^2)^{n+1}}, \qquad (i^2=-1, a>0)$

677. $\displaystyle\int_0^\infty x^n\,e^{-ax}[\cos(bx)]\,dx = \frac{n![(a-ib)^{n+1}+(a+ib)^{n+1}]}{2(a^2+b^2)^{n+1}}, \qquad (i^2=-1, a>0)$

678. $\displaystyle\int_0^\infty \frac{e^{-ax}\sin x}{x}\,dx = \cot^{-1}a, \qquad (a>0)$

679. $\displaystyle\int_0^\infty e^{-a^2x^2}\cos bx\,dx = \frac{\sqrt{\pi}}{2a}\exp\left(-\frac{b^2}{4a^2}\right), \qquad (ab \neq 0)$

680. $\displaystyle\int_0^\infty e^{-t\cos\phi}\,t^{b-1}\sin(t\sin\phi)\,dt = [\Gamma(b)]\sin(b\phi), \qquad \left(b>0, -\frac{\pi}{2}<\phi<\frac{\pi}{2}\right)$

681. $\displaystyle\int_0^\infty e^{-t\cos\phi}\,t^{b-1}[\cos(t\sin\phi)]\,dt = [\Gamma(b)]\cos(b\phi), \qquad \left(b>0, -\frac{\pi}{2}<\phi<\frac{\pi}{2}\right)$

682. $\displaystyle\int_0^\infty t^{b-1}\cos t\,dt = [\Gamma(b)]\cos\left(\frac{b\pi}{2}\right), \qquad (0<b<1)$

683. $\displaystyle\int_0^\infty t^{b-1}(\sin t)\,dt = [\Gamma(b)]\sin\left(\frac{b\pi}{2}\right), \qquad (0<b<1)$

684. $\displaystyle\int_0^1 (\log x)^n\,dx = (-1)^n\cdot n!$

685. $\displaystyle\int_0^1 \left(\log\frac{1}{x}\right)^{\frac{1}{2}}\,dx = \frac{\sqrt{\pi}}{2}$

686. $\displaystyle\int_0^1 \left(\log\frac{1}{x}\right)^{-\frac{1}{2}}\,dx = \sqrt{\pi}$

687. $\displaystyle\int_0^1 \left(\log\frac{1}{x}\right)^n\,dx = n!$

688. $\displaystyle\int_0^1 x\log(1-x)\,dx = -\frac{3}{4}$

689. $\displaystyle\int_0^1 x\log(1+x)\,dx = \frac{1}{4}$

690. $\displaystyle\int_0^1 x^m(\log x)^n\,dx = \frac{(-1)^n n!}{(m+1)^{n+1}}, \qquad m>-1, n=0,1,2,\ldots$

If $n \neq 0,1,2,\ldots$ replace $n!$ by $\Gamma(n+1)$.

DEFINITE INTEGRALS (Continued)

691. $\displaystyle\int_0^1 \frac{\log x}{1 + x}\, dx = -\frac{\pi^2}{12}$

692. $\displaystyle\int_0^1 \frac{\log x}{1 - x}\, dx = -\frac{\pi^2}{6}$

693. $\displaystyle\int_0^1 \frac{\log (1 + x)}{x}\, dx = \frac{\pi^2}{12}$

694. $\displaystyle\int_0^1 \frac{\log (1 - x)}{x}\, dx = -\frac{\pi^2}{6}$

695. $\displaystyle\int_0^1 (\log x)[\log (1 + x)]\, dx = 2 - 2 \log 2 - \frac{\pi^2}{12}$

696. $\displaystyle\int_0^1 (\log x)[\log (1 - x)]\, dx = 2 - \frac{\pi^2}{6}$

697. $\displaystyle\int_0^1 \frac{\log x}{1 - x^2}\, dx = -\frac{\pi^2}{8}$

698. $\displaystyle\int_0^1 \log\left(\frac{1 + x}{1 - x}\right) \cdot \frac{dx}{x} = \frac{\pi^2}{4}$

699. $\displaystyle\int_0^1 \frac{\log x\, dx}{\sqrt{1 - x^2}} = -\frac{\pi}{2} \log 2$

700. $\displaystyle\int_0^1 x^m \left[\log\left(\frac{1}{x}\right)\right]^n dx = \frac{\Gamma(n + 1)}{(m + 1)^{n+1}}, \qquad \text{if } m + 1 > 0, n + 1 > 0$

701. $\displaystyle\int_0^1 \frac{(x^p - x^q)\, dx}{\log x} = \log\left(\frac{p + 1}{q + 1}\right), \qquad (p + 1 > 0, q + 1 > 0)$

702. $\displaystyle\int_0^1 \frac{dx}{\sqrt{\log\left(\frac{1}{x}\right)}} = \sqrt{\pi}$

703. $\displaystyle\int_0^\infty \log\left(\frac{e^x + 1}{e^x - 1}\right) dx = \frac{\pi^2}{4}$

704. $\displaystyle\int_0^{\pi/2} (\log \sin x)\, dx = \int_0^{\pi/2} \log \cos x\, dx = -\frac{\pi}{2} \log 2$

705. $\displaystyle\int_0^{\pi/2} (\log \sec x)\, dx = \int_0^{\pi/2} \log \csc x\, dx = \frac{\pi}{2} \log 2$

706. $\displaystyle\int_0^\pi x(\log \sin x)\, dx = -\frac{\pi^2}{2} \log 2$

707. $\displaystyle\int_0^{\pi/2} (\sin x)(\log \sin x)\, dx = \log 2 - 1$

DEFINITE INTEGRALS (Continued)

708. $\displaystyle\int_0^{\pi/2} (\log \tan x)\, dx = 0$

709. $\displaystyle\int_0^{\pi} \log (a \pm b \cos x)\, dx = \pi \log \left(\frac{a + \sqrt{a^2 - b^2}}{2} \right), \qquad (a \geq b)$

710. $\displaystyle\int_0^{\pi} \log (a^2 - 2ab \cos x + b^2)\, dx = \begin{cases} 2\pi \log a, & a \geq b > 0 \\ 2\pi \log b, & b \geq a > 0 \end{cases}$

711. $\displaystyle\int_0^{\infty} \frac{\sin ax}{\sinh bx}\, dx = \frac{\pi}{2b} \tanh \frac{a\pi}{2b}$

712. $\displaystyle\int_0^{\infty} \frac{\cos ax}{\cosh bx}\, dx = \frac{\pi}{2b} \operatorname{sech} \frac{a\pi}{2b}$

713. $\displaystyle\int_0^{\infty} \frac{dx}{\cosh ax} = \frac{\pi}{2a}$

714. $\displaystyle\int_0^{\infty} \frac{x\, dx}{\sinh ax} = \frac{\pi^2}{4a^2}$

715. $\displaystyle\int_0^{\infty} e^{-ax}(\cosh bx)\, dx = \frac{a}{a^2 - b^2}, \qquad (0 \leq |b| < a)$

716. $\displaystyle\int_0^{\infty} e^{-ax}(\sinh bx)\, dx = \frac{b}{a^2 - b^2}, \qquad (0 \leq |b| < a)$

717. $\displaystyle\int_0^{\infty} \frac{\sinh ax}{e^{bx} + 1}\, dx = \frac{\pi}{2b} \csc \frac{a\pi}{b} - \frac{1}{2a}$

718. $\displaystyle\int_0^{\infty} \frac{\sinh ax}{e^{bx} - 1}\, dx = \frac{1}{2a} - \frac{\pi}{2b} \cot \frac{a\pi}{b}$

719. $\displaystyle\int_0^{\pi/2} \frac{dx}{\sqrt{1 - k^2 \sin^2 x}} = \frac{\pi}{2}\left[1 + \left(\frac{1}{2}\right)^2 k^2 + \left(\frac{1\cdot 3}{2\cdot 4}\right)^2 k^4 \right.$

$$\left. + \left(\frac{1\cdot 3\cdot 5}{2\cdot 4\cdot 6}\right)^2 k^6 + \cdots \right], \text{ if } k^2 < 1$$

720. $\displaystyle\int_0^{\pi/2} \sqrt{1 - k^2 \sin^2 x}\, dx = \frac{\pi}{2}\left[1 - \left(\frac{1}{2}\right)^2 k^2 - \left(\frac{1\cdot 3}{2\cdot 4}\right)^2 \frac{k^4}{3} \right.$

$$\left. - \left(\frac{1\cdot 3\cdot 5}{2\cdot 4\cdot 6}\right)^2 \frac{k^6}{5} - \cdots \right], \text{ if } k^2 < 1$$

721. $\displaystyle\int_0^{\infty} e^{-x} \log x\, dx = -\gamma = -0.5772157\ldots$

722. $\displaystyle\int_0^{\infty} e^{-x^2} \log x\, dx = -\frac{\sqrt{\pi}}{4}(\gamma + 2 \log 2)$

DEFINITE INTEGRALS (Continued)

723. $\displaystyle\int_0^\infty \log\left(\frac{e^x + 1}{e^x - 1}\right) dx = \frac{\pi^2}{4}$

724. $\displaystyle\int_0^\infty \left(\frac{1}{1 - e^{-x}} - \frac{1}{x}\right) e^{-x}\, dx = \gamma = 0.5772157\ldots$ [Euler's Constant]

725. $\displaystyle\int_0^\infty \frac{1}{x}\left(\frac{1}{1 + x} - e^{-x}\right) dx = \gamma = 0.5772157\ldots$

SERIES

The expression in parentheses following certain of the series indicates the region of convergence. If not otherwise indicated it is to be understood that the series converges for all finite values of x.

BINOMIAL

$$(x + y)^n = x^n + nx^{n-1}y + \frac{n(n-1)}{2!} x^{n-2}y^2$$

$$+ \frac{n(n-1)(n-2)}{3!} x^{n-3}y^3 + \cdots \quad (y^2 < x^2)$$

$$(1 \pm x)^n = 1 \pm nx + \frac{n(n-1)x^2}{2!} \pm \frac{n(n-1)(n-2)x^3}{3!} + \cdots \text{ etc.} \quad (x^2 < 1)$$

$$(1 \pm x)^{-n} = 1 \mp nx + \frac{n(n+1)x^2}{2!} \mp \frac{n(n+1)(n+2)x^3}{3!} + \cdots \text{ etc.} \quad (x^2 < 1)$$

$$(1 \pm x)^{-1} = 1 \mp x + x^2 \mp x^3 + x^4 \mp x^5 + \cdots \qquad (x^2 < 1)$$
$$(1 \pm x)^{-2} = 1 \mp 2x + 3x^2 \mp 4x^3 + 5x^4 \mp 6x^5 + \cdots \qquad (x^2 < 1)$$

REVERSION OF SERIES

Let a series be represented by

$$y = a_1 x + a_2 x^2 + a_3 x^3 + a_4 x^4 + a_5 x^5 + a_6 x^6 + \cdots \quad (a_1 \neq 0)$$

to find the coefficients of the series

$$x = A_1 y + A_2 y^2 + A_3 y^3 + A_4 y^4 + \cdots$$

$$A_1 = \frac{1}{a_1} \qquad A_2 = -\frac{a_2}{a_1^3} \qquad A_3 = \frac{1}{a_1^5}(2a_2^2 - a_1 a_3)$$

$$A_4 = \frac{1}{a_1^7}(5a_1 a_2 a_3 - a_1^2 a_4 - 5a_2^3)$$

$$A_5 = \frac{1}{a_1^9}(6a_1^2 a_2 a_4 + 3a_1^2 a_3^2 + 14a_2^4 - a_1^3 a_5 - 21a_1 a_2^2 a_3)$$

$$A_6 = \frac{1}{a_1^{11}}(7a_1^3 a_2 a_5 + 7a_1^3 a_3 a_4 + 84a_1 a_2^3 a_3 - a_1^4 a_6 - 28a_1^2 a_2^2 a_4 - 28a_1^2 a_2 a_3^2 - 42a_2^5)$$

$$A_7 = \frac{1}{a_1^{13}}(8a_1^4 a_2 a_6 + 8a_1^4 a_3 a_5 + 4a_1^4 a_4^2 + 120a_1^2 a_2^3 a_4$$

$$+ 180a_1^2 a_2^2 a_3^2 + 132a_2^6 - a_1^5 a_7$$
$$- 36a_1^3 a_2^2 a_5 - 72a_1^3 a_2 a_3 a_4 - 12a_1^3 a_3^3 - 330a_1 a_2^4 a_3)$$

TAYLOR

1. $f(x) = f(a) + (x - a)f'(a) + \dfrac{(x-a)^2}{2!} f''(a) + \dfrac{(x-a)^3}{3!} f'''(a)$

$$+ \cdots + \frac{(x-a)^n}{n!} f^{(n)}(a) + \cdots \quad \text{(Taylor's Series)}$$

(Increment form)

2. $f(x + h) = f(x) + hf'(x) + \dfrac{h^2}{2!} f''(x) + \dfrac{h^3}{3!} f'''(x) + \cdots$

$$= f(h) + xf'(h) + \dfrac{x^3}{2!} f''(h) + \dfrac{x^3}{3!} f'''(h) + \cdots$$

3. If $f(x)$ is a function possessing derivatives of all orders throughout the interval $a \leq x \leq b$, then there is a value X, with $a < X < b$, such that

$$f(b) = f(a) + (b - a)f'(a) + \dfrac{(b - a)^2}{2!} f''(a) + \cdots$$

$$+ \dfrac{(b - a)^{n-1}}{(n - 1)!} f^{(n-1)}(a) + \dfrac{(b - a)^n}{n!} f^{(n)}(X)$$

$$f(a + h) = f(a) + hf'(a) + \dfrac{h^2}{2!} f''(a) + \cdots + \dfrac{h^{n-1}}{(n - 1)!} f^{(n-1)}(a)$$

$$+ \dfrac{h^n}{n!} f^{(n)}(a + \theta h), \quad b = a + h, 0 < \theta < 1.$$

or

$$f(x) = f(a) + (x - a)f'(a) + \dfrac{(x - a)^2}{2!} f''(a) + \cdots + (x - a)^{n-1} \dfrac{f^{(n-1)}(a)}{(n - 1)!} + R_n,$$

where

$$R_n = \dfrac{f^{(n)}[a + \theta \cdot (x - a)]}{n!} (x - a)^n, \quad 0 < \theta < 1.$$

The above forms are known as Taylor's series with the remainder term.

4. *Taylor's series for a function of two variables*

If $\left(h \dfrac{\partial}{\partial x} + k \dfrac{\partial}{\partial y} \right) f(x, y) = h \dfrac{\partial f(x, y)}{\partial x} + k \dfrac{\partial f(x, y)}{\partial y}$;

$$\left(h \dfrac{\partial}{\partial x} + k \dfrac{\partial}{\partial y} \right)^2 f(x, y) = h^2 \dfrac{\partial^2 f(x, y)}{\partial x^2} + 2hk \dfrac{\partial^2 f(x, y)}{\partial x \, \partial y} + k^2 \dfrac{\partial^2 f(x, y)}{\partial y^2}$$

etc., and if $h \left(\dfrac{\partial}{\partial x} + k \dfrac{\partial}{\partial y} \right)^n f(x, y) \Big|_{\substack{x=a \\ y=b}}$ with the bar and subscripts means that after differentiation we are to replace x by a and y by b,

$$f(a + h, b + k) = f(a, b) + \left(h \dfrac{\partial}{\partial x} + k \dfrac{\partial}{\partial y} \right) f(x, y) \Big|_{\substack{x=a \\ y=b}} + \cdots$$

$$+ \dfrac{1}{n!} \left(h \dfrac{\partial}{\partial x} + k \dfrac{\partial}{\partial y} \right)^n f(x, y) \Big|_{\substack{x=a \\ y=b}} + \cdots$$

MACLAURIN

$$f(x) = f(0) + xf'(0) + \dfrac{x^2}{2!} f''(0) + \dfrac{x^3}{3!} f'''(0) + \cdots + x^{n-1} \dfrac{f^{(n-1)}(0)}{(n - 1)!} + R_n,$$

where

$$R_n = \dfrac{x^n f^{(n)}(\theta x)}{n!}, \quad 0 < \theta < 1.$$

EXPONENTIAL

$$e = 1 + \frac{1}{1!} + \frac{1}{2!} + \frac{1}{3!} + \frac{1}{4!} + \cdots$$

$$e^x = 1 + x + \frac{x^2}{2!} + \frac{x^3}{3!} + \frac{x^4}{4!} + \cdots \qquad \text{(all real values of } x\text{)}$$

$$a^x = 1 + x \log_e a + \frac{(x \log_e a)^2}{2!} + \frac{(x \log_e a)^3}{3!} + \cdots$$

$$e^x = e^a \left[1 + (x - a) + \frac{(x - a)^2}{2!} + \frac{(x - a)^3}{3!} + \cdots \right]$$

LOGARITHMIC

$$\log_e x = \frac{x - 1}{x} + \frac{1}{2} \left(\frac{x - 1}{x} \right)^2 + \frac{1}{3} \left(\frac{x - 1}{x} \right)^3 + \cdots \qquad (x > \tfrac{1}{2})$$

$$\log_e x = (x - 1) - \tfrac{1}{2}(x - 1)^2 + \tfrac{1}{3}(x - 1)^3 - \cdots \qquad (2 \geq x > 0)$$

$$\log_e x = 2 \left[\frac{x - 1}{x + 1} + \frac{1}{3} \left(\frac{x - 1}{x + 1} \right)^3 + \frac{1}{5} \left(\frac{x - 1}{x + 1} \right)^5 + \cdots \right] \qquad (x > 0)$$

$$\log_e (1 + x) = x - \tfrac{1}{2}x^2 + \tfrac{1}{3}x^3 - \tfrac{1}{4}x^4 + \cdots \qquad (-1 < x < 1)$$

$$\log_e (n + 1) - \log_e (n - 1) = 2 \left[\frac{1}{n} + \frac{1}{3n^3} + \frac{1}{5n^5} + \cdots \right]$$

$$\log_e (a + x) = \log_e a + 2 \left[\frac{x}{2a + x} + \frac{1}{3} \left(\frac{x}{2a + x} \right)^3 + \frac{1}{5} \left(\frac{x}{2a + x} \right)^5 + \cdots \right]$$
$$(a > 0, \, -a < x < +\infty)$$

$$\log_e \frac{1 + x}{1 - x} = 2 \left[x + \frac{x^3}{3} + \frac{x^5}{5} + \cdots + \frac{x^{2n-1}}{2n - 1} + \cdots \right], \qquad -1 < x < 1$$

$$\log_e x = \log_e a + \frac{(x - a)}{a} - \frac{(x - a)^2}{2a^2} + \frac{(x - a)^3}{3a^3} - + \cdots, \qquad 0 < x \leq 2a$$

TRIGONOMETRIC

$$\sin x = x - \frac{x^3}{3!} + \frac{x^5}{5!} - \frac{x^7}{7!} + \cdots \qquad \text{(all real values of } x\text{)}$$

$$\cos x = 1 - \frac{x^2}{2!} + \frac{x^4}{4!} - \frac{x^6}{6!} + \cdots \qquad \text{(all real values of } x\text{)}$$

$$\tan x = x + \frac{x^3}{3} + \frac{2x^5}{15} + \frac{17x^7}{315} + \frac{62x^9}{2835} + \cdots + \frac{2^{2n}(2^{2n} - 1) B_n}{(2n)!} x^{2n-1} + \cdots,$$
$$\left[x^2 < \frac{\pi^2}{4}, \text{ and } B_n \text{ represents the } n\text{'th Bernoulli number.} \right]$$

$$\cot x = \frac{1}{x} - \frac{x}{3} - \frac{x^3}{45} - \frac{2x^5}{945} - \frac{x^7}{4725} - \cdots - \frac{2^{2n} B_n}{(2n)!} x^{2n-1} - \cdots,$$
$$[x^2 < \pi^2, \text{ and } B_n \text{ represents the } n\text{'th Bernoulli number.}]$$

$$\sec x = 1 + \frac{x^2}{2} + \frac{5}{24} x^4 + \frac{61}{720} x^6 + \frac{277}{8064} x^8 + \cdots + \frac{E_n x^{2n}}{(2n)!} + \cdots,$$

$$\left[x^2 < \frac{\pi^2}{4}, \text{ and } E_n \text{ represents the } n\text{'th Euler number.} \right]$$

$$\csc x = \frac{1}{x} + \frac{x}{6} + \frac{7}{360} x^3 + \frac{31}{15,120} x^5 + \frac{127}{604,800} x^7 + \cdots$$

$$+ \frac{2(2^{2n-1} - 1)}{(2n)!} B_n x^{2n-1} + \cdots,$$

$$[x^2 < \pi^2, \text{ and } B_n \text{ represents } n\text{'th Bernoulli number.}]$$

$$\sin x = x \left(1 - \frac{x^2}{\pi^2} \right)\left(1 - \frac{x^2}{2^2 \pi^2} \right)\left(1 - \frac{x^2}{3^2 \pi^2} \right) \cdots \qquad (x^2 < \infty)$$

$$\cos x = \left(1 - \frac{4x^2}{\pi^2} \right)\left(1 - \frac{4x^2}{3^2 \pi^2} \right)\left(1 - \frac{4x^2}{5^2 \pi^2} \right) \cdots \qquad (x^2 < \infty)$$

$$\sin^{-1} x = x + \frac{x^3}{2 \cdot 3} + \frac{1 \cdot 3}{2 \cdot 4 \cdot 5} x^5 + \frac{1 \cdot 3 \cdot 5}{2 \cdot 4 \cdot 6 \cdot 7} x^7 + \cdots \qquad \left(x^2 < 1, -\frac{\pi}{2} < \sin^{-1} x < \frac{\pi}{2} \right)$$

$$\cos^{-1} x = \frac{\pi}{2} - \left(x + \frac{x^3}{2 \cdot 3} + \frac{1 \cdot 3}{2 \cdot 4 \cdot 5} x^5 + \frac{1 \cdot 3 \cdot 5 x^7}{2 \cdot 4 \cdot 6 \cdot 7} + \cdots \right) \qquad (x^2 < 1, 0 < \cos^{-1} x < \pi)$$

$$\tan^{-1} x = x - \frac{x^3}{3} + \frac{x^5}{5} - \frac{x^7}{7} + \cdots \qquad (x^2 < 1)$$

$$\tan^{-1} x = \frac{\pi}{2} - \frac{1}{x} + \frac{1}{3x^2} - \frac{1}{5x^5} + \frac{1}{7x^7} - \cdots \qquad (x > 1)$$

$$\tan^{-1} x = -\frac{\pi}{2} - \frac{1}{x} + \frac{1}{3x^2} - \frac{1}{5x^5} + \frac{1}{7x^7} - \cdots \qquad (x < -1)$$

$$\cot^{-1} x = \frac{\pi}{2} - x + \frac{x^3}{3} - \frac{x^5}{5} + \frac{x^7}{7} - \cdots \qquad (x^2 < 1)$$

$$\log_e \sin x = \log_e x - \frac{x^2}{6} - \frac{x^4}{180} - \frac{x^6}{2835} - \cdots \qquad (x^2 < \pi^2)$$

$$\log_e \cos x = -\frac{x^2}{2} - \frac{x^4}{12} - \frac{x^6}{45} - \frac{17x^8}{2520} - \cdots \qquad \left(x^2 < \frac{\pi^2}{4} \right)$$

$$\log_e \tan x = \log_e x + \frac{x^2}{3} + \frac{7x^4}{90} + \frac{62x^6}{2835} + \cdots \qquad \left(x^2 < \frac{\pi^2}{4} \right)$$

$$e^{\sin x} = 1 + x + \frac{x^2}{2!} - \frac{3x^4}{4!} - \frac{8x^5}{5!} - \frac{3x^6}{6!} + \frac{56x^7}{7!} + \cdots$$

$$e^{\cos x} = e \left(1 - \frac{x^2}{2!} + \frac{4x^4}{4!} - \frac{31x^6}{6!} + \cdots \right)$$

$$e^{\tan x} = 1 + x + \frac{x^2}{2!} + \frac{3x^3}{3!} + \frac{9x^4}{4!} + \frac{37x^5}{5!} + \cdots \qquad \left(x^2 < \frac{\pi^2}{4} \right)$$

$$\sin x = \sin a + (x - a) \cos a - \frac{(x - a)^2}{2!} \sin a$$

$$- \frac{(x - a)^3}{3!} \cos a + \frac{(x - a)^4}{4!} \sin a + \cdots$$

HYPERBOLIC AND INVERSE HYPERBOLIC

Table of expansion of certain functions into power series

$$\sinh x = x + \frac{x^3}{3!} + \frac{x^5}{5!} + \frac{x^7}{7!} + \cdots + \frac{x^{2n+1}}{(2n+1)!} + \cdots \qquad |x| < \infty$$

$$\cosh x = 1 + \frac{x^2}{2!} + \frac{x^4}{4!} + \frac{x^6}{6!} + \cdots + \frac{x^{2n}}{(2n)!} + \cdots \qquad |x| < \infty$$

$$\tanh x = x - \frac{1}{3}x^3 + \frac{2}{15}x^5 - \frac{17}{315}x^7 + \frac{62}{2835}x^9 - \cdots$$
$$+ \frac{(-1)^{n+1}2^{2n}(2^{2n}-1)}{(2n)!}B_n x^{2n-1} \pm \cdots ^{(1)} \qquad |x| < \frac{\pi}{2}$$

$$\coth x = \frac{1}{x} + \frac{x}{3} - \frac{x^3}{45} + \frac{2x^5}{945} - \frac{x^7}{4725} + \cdots + \frac{(-1)^{n+1}2^{2n}}{(2n)!}B_n x^{2n-1} \pm \cdots ^{(1)}$$
$$0 < |x| < \pi$$

$$\text{sech } x = 1 - \frac{1}{2!}x^2 + \frac{5}{4!}x^4 - \frac{61}{6!}x^6 + \frac{1385}{8!}x^8 - \cdots + \frac{(-1)^n}{(2n)!}E_n x^{2n} \pm \cdots ^{(2)}$$
$$|x| < \frac{\pi}{2}$$

$$\text{cosech } x = \frac{1}{x} - \frac{x}{6} + \frac{7x^3}{360} - \frac{31x^5}{15,120} + \cdots + \frac{2(-1)^n(2^{2n-1}-1)}{(2n)!}B_n x^{2n-1} + \cdots ^{(1)}$$
$$0 < |x| < \pi$$

$$\text{arg sinh } x = x - \frac{1}{2 \cdot 3}x^3 + \frac{1 \cdot 3}{2 \cdot 4 \cdot 5}x^5 - \frac{1 \cdot 3 \cdot 5}{2 \cdot 4 \cdot 6 \cdot 7}x^7 + \cdots$$
$$+ (-1)^n \cdot \frac{1 \cdot 3 \cdot 5 (2n-1)}{2 \cdot 4 \cdot 6 \ldots 2n(2n+1)}x^{2n+1} \pm \cdots \qquad |x| < 1$$

$$\text{arg cosh } x = \pm \left[\ln(2x) - \frac{1}{2 \cdot 2x^2} - \frac{1 \cdot 3}{2 \cdot 4 \cdot 4x^4} - \frac{1 \cdot 3 \cdot 5}{2 \cdot 4 \cdot 6 \cdot 6x^6} - \cdots \right] \qquad x > 1$$

$$\text{arg tanh } x = x + \frac{x^3}{3} + \frac{x^5}{5} + \frac{x^7}{7} + \cdots + \frac{x^{2n+1}}{2n+1} + \cdots \qquad |x| < 1$$

$$\text{arg coth } x = \frac{1}{x} + \frac{1}{3x^3} + \frac{1}{5x^5} + \frac{1}{7x^7} + \cdots + \frac{1}{(2n+1)x^{2n+1}} + \cdots \qquad |x| > 1$$

[1] B_n denotes Bernoulli's numbers (see p. 478).
[2] E_n denotes Euler's numbers (see p. 478).

FOURIER

(Also see Index for Cosine and Sine Transforms)

1. If $f(x)$ is a bounded periodic function of period $2L$ (i.e. $f(x + 2L) = f(x)$), and satisfies the *Dirichlet conditions*:

   a) In any period $f(x)$ is continuous, except possibly for a finite number of jump discontinuities.

b) In any period $f(x)$ has only a finite number of maxima and minima.
Then $f(x)$ may be represented by the *Fourier series*

$$\frac{a_0}{2} + \sum_{n=1}^{\infty} \left(a_n \cos \frac{n\pi x}{L} + b_n \sin \frac{n\pi x}{L} \right),$$

where a_n and b_n are as determined below. This series will converge to $f(x)$ at every point where $f(x)$ is continuous, and to

$$\frac{f(x^+) + f(x^-)}{2}$$

(i.e. the average of the left-hand and right-hand limits) at every point where $f(x)$ has a jump discontinuity.

$$a_n = \frac{1}{L} \int_{-L}^{L} f(x) \cos \frac{n\pi x}{L} \, dx, \quad n = 0, 1, 2, 3, \ldots;$$

$$b_n = \frac{1}{L} \int_{-L}^{L} f(x) \sin \frac{n\pi x}{L} \, dx, \quad n = 1, 2, 3, \ldots$$

We may also write

$$a_n = \frac{1}{L} \int_{\alpha}^{\alpha+2L} f(x) \cos \frac{n\pi x}{L} \, dx \text{ and } b_n = \frac{1}{L} \int_{\alpha}^{\alpha+2L} f(x) \sin \frac{n\pi x}{L} \, dx,$$

where α is any real number. Thus if $\alpha = 0$,

$$a_n = \frac{1}{L} \int_{0}^{2L} f(x) \cos \frac{n\pi x}{L} \, dx, \quad n = 0, 1, 2, 3, \ldots;$$

$$b_n = \frac{1}{L} \int_{0}^{2L} f(x) \sin \frac{n\pi x}{L} \, dx, \quad n = 1, 2, 3, \ldots$$

2. If in addition to the above restrictions, $f(x)$ is even (i.e. $f(-x) = f(x)$), the Fourier series reduces to

$$\frac{a_0}{2} + \sum_{n=1}^{\infty} a_n \cos \frac{n\pi x}{L}.$$

That is, $b_n = 0$. In this case, a simpler formula for a_n is

$$a_n = \frac{2}{L} \int_{0}^{L} f(x) \cos \frac{n\pi x}{L} \, dx, \quad n = 0, 1, 2, 3, \ldots$$

3. If in addition to the restrictions in (1), $f(x)$ is an odd function (i.e. $f(-x) = -f(x)$), then the Fourier series reduces to

$$\sum_{n=1}^{\infty} b_n \sin \frac{n\pi x}{L}.$$

That is, $a_n = 0$. In this case, a simpler formula for the b_n is

$$b_n = \frac{2}{L} \int_{0}^{L} f(x) \sin \frac{n\pi x}{L} \, dx, \quad n = 1, 2, 3, \ldots$$

4. If in addition to the restrictions in (2) above, $f(x) = -f(L - x)$, then a_n will be 0 for all even values of n, including $n = 0$. Thus in this case, the expansion reduces to

$$\sum_{m=1}^{\infty} a_{2m-1} \cos \frac{(2m - 1)\pi x}{L} .$$

5. If in addition to the restrictions in (3) above, $f(x) = f(L - x)$, then b_n will be 0 for all even values of n. Thus in this case, the expansion reduces to

$$\sum_{m=1}^{\infty} b_{2m-1} \sin \frac{(2m - 1)\pi x}{L} .$$

(The series in (4) and (5) are known as *odd-harmonic series*, since only the odd harmonics appear. Similar rules may be stated for even-harmonic series, but when a series appears in the even-harmonic form, it means that $2L$ has not been taken as the smallest period of $f(x)$. Since any integral multiple of a period is also a period, series obtained in this way will also work, but in general computation is simplified if $2L$ is taken to be the smallest period.)

6. If we write the Euler definitions for $\cos \theta$ and $\sin \theta$, we obtain the complex form of the Fourier Series known either as the "Complex Fourier Series" or the "Exponential Fourier Series" of $f(x)$. It is represented as

$$f(x) = \tfrac{1}{2} \sum_{n=-\infty}^{n=+\infty} c_n e^{i\omega_n x},$$

where

$$c_n = \frac{1}{L} \int_{-L}^{L} f(x) e^{-i\omega_n x} dx, \quad n = 0, \pm 1, \pm 2, \pm 3, \ldots$$

with $\omega_n = \dfrac{n\pi}{L}$, $n = 0, \pm 1, \pm 2, \ldots$

The set of coefficients $\{c_n\}$ is often referred to as the Fourier spectrum.

7. If both sine and cosine terms are present and if $f(x)$ is of period $2L$ and expandable by a Fourier series, it can be represented as

$$f(x) = \frac{a_0}{2} + \sum_{n=1}^{\infty} c_n \sin \left(\frac{n\pi x}{L} + \phi_n \right), \text{ where } a_n = c_n \sin \phi_n,$$

$$b_n = c_n \cos \phi_n, \quad c_n = \sqrt{a_n^2 + b_n^2}, \quad \phi_n = \arctan \left(\frac{a_n}{b_n} \right)$$

It can also be represented as

$$f(x) = \frac{a_0}{2} + \sum_{n=1}^{\infty} c_n \cos \left(\frac{n\pi x}{L} + \phi_n \right), \text{ where } a_n = c_n \cos \phi_n,$$

$$b_n = -c_n \sin \phi_n, \quad c_n = \sqrt{a_n^2 + b_n^2}, \quad \phi_n = \arctan \left(-\frac{b_n}{a_n} \right)$$

where ϕ_n is chosen so as to make a_n, b_n, and c_n hold.

8. The following table of trigonometric identities should be helpful for developing Fourier Series.

	n	n even	n odd	$n/2$ odd	$n/2$ even
$\sin n\pi$	0	0	0	0	0
$\cos n\pi$	$(-1)^n$	$+1$	-1	$+1$	$+1$
*$\sin \dfrac{n\pi}{2}$		0	$(-1)^{(n-1)/2}$	0	0
*$\cos \dfrac{n\pi}{2}$		$(-1)^{n/2}$	0	-1	$+1$
$\sin \dfrac{n\pi}{4}$			$\dfrac{\sqrt{2}}{2}(-1)^{(n^2+4n+11)/8}$	$(-1)^{(n-2)/4}$	0

*A useful formula for $\sin \dfrac{n\pi}{2}$ and $\cos \dfrac{n\pi}{2}$ is given by

$$\sin \frac{n\pi}{2} = \frac{(i)^{n+1}}{2}[(-1)^n - 1] \text{ and } \cos \frac{n\pi}{2} = \frac{(i)^n}{2}[(-1)^n + 1], \text{ where } i^2 = -1.$$

AUXILIARY FORMULAS FOR FOURIER SERIES

$$1 = \frac{4}{\pi}\left[\sin \frac{\pi x}{k} + \frac{1}{3}\sin \frac{3\pi x}{k} + \frac{1}{5}\sin \frac{5\pi x}{k} + \cdots\right] \qquad [0 < x < k]$$

$$x = \frac{2k}{\pi}\left[\sin \frac{\pi x}{k} - \frac{1}{2}\sin \frac{2\pi x}{k} + \frac{1}{3}\sin \frac{3\pi x}{k} - \cdots\right] \qquad [-k < x < k]$$

$$x = \frac{k}{2} - \frac{4k}{\pi^2}\left[\cos \frac{\pi x}{k} + \frac{1}{3^2}\cos \frac{3\pi x}{k} + \frac{1}{5^2}\cos \frac{5\pi x}{k} + \cdots\right] \qquad [0 < x < k]$$

$$x^2 = \frac{2k^2}{\pi^3}\left[\left(\frac{\pi^2}{1} - \frac{4}{1}\right)\sin \frac{\pi x}{k} - \frac{\pi^2}{2}\sin \frac{2\pi x}{k} + \left(\frac{\pi^2}{3} - \frac{4}{3^3}\right)\sin \frac{3\pi x}{k}\right.$$
$$\left. - \frac{\pi^2}{4}\sin \frac{4\pi x}{k} + \left(\frac{\pi^2}{5} - \frac{4}{5^3}\right)\sin \frac{5\pi x}{k} + \cdots\right] \;[0 < x < k]$$

$$x^2 = \frac{k^2}{3} - \frac{4k^2}{\pi^2}\left[\cos \frac{\pi x}{k} - \frac{1}{2^2}\cos \frac{2\pi x}{k} + \frac{1}{3^2}\cos \frac{3\pi x}{k} - \frac{1}{4^2}\cos \frac{4\pi x}{k} + \cdots\right]$$
$$[-k < x < k]$$

$$1 - \frac{1}{3} + \frac{1}{5} - \frac{1}{7} + \cdots = \frac{\pi}{4}$$

$$1 + \frac{1}{2^2} + \frac{1}{3^2} + \frac{1}{4^2} + \cdots = \frac{\pi^2}{6}$$

$$1 - \frac{1}{2^2} + \frac{1}{3^2} - \frac{1}{4^2} + \cdots = \frac{\pi^2}{12}$$

$$1 + \frac{1}{3^2} + \frac{1}{5^2} + \frac{1}{7^2} + \cdots = \frac{\pi^2}{8}$$

$$\frac{1}{2^2} + \frac{1}{4^2} + \frac{1}{6^2} + \frac{1}{8^2} + \cdots = \frac{\pi^2}{24}$$

*SUMS OF RECIPROCAL POWERS

n	$\sum\limits_{k=1}^{\infty} k^{-n}$				$\sum\limits_{k=1}^{\infty} (-1)^{k-1} k^{-n}$			
1	∞				0.69314	71805	59945	30942
2	1.64493	40668	48226	43637	0.82246	70334	24113	21824
3	1.20205	69031	59594	28540	0.90154	26773	69695	71405
4	1.08232	32337	11138	19152	0.94703	28294	97245	91758
5	1.03692	77551	43369	92633	0.97211	97704	46909	30594
6	1.01734	30619	84449	13971	0.98555	10912	97435	10410
7	1.00834	92773	81922	82684	0.99259	38199	22830	28267
8	1.00407	73561	97944	33938	0.99623	30018	52647	89923
9	1.00200	83928	26082	21442	0.99809	42975	41605	33077
10	1.00099	45751	27818	08534	0.99903	95075	98271	56564
11	1.00049	41886	04119	46456	0.99951	71434	98060	75414
12	1.00024	60865	53308	04830	0.99975	76851	43858	19085
13	1.00012	27133	47578	48915	0.99987	85427	63265	11549
14	1.00006	12481	35058	70483	0.99993	91703	45979	71817
15	1.00003	05882	36307	02049	0.99996	95512	13099	23808
16	1.00001	52822	59408	65187	0.99998	47642	14906	10644
17	1.00000	76371	97637	89976	0.99999	23782	92041	01198
18	1.00000	38172	93264	99984	0.99999	61878	69610	11348
19	1.00000	19082	12716	55394	0.99999	80935	08171	67511
20	1.00000	09539	62033	87280	0.99999	90466	11581	52212
21	1.00000	04769	32986	78781	0.99999	95232	58215	54282
22	1.00000	02384	50502	72773	0.99999	97616	13230	82255
23	1.00000	01192	19925	96531	0.99999	98808	01318	43950
24	1.00000	00596	08189	05126	0.99999	99403	98892	39463
25	1.00000	00298	03503	51465	0.99999	99701	98856	96283
26	1.00000	00149	01554	82837	0.99999	99850	99231	99657
27	1.00000	00074	50711	78984	0.99999	99925	49550	48496
28	1.00000	00037	25334	02479	0.99999	99962	74753	40011
29	1.00000	00018	62659	72351	0.99999	99981	37369	41811
30	1.00000	00009	31327	43242	0.99999	99990	68682	28145
31	1.00000	00004	65662	90650	0.99999	99995	34340	33145
32	1.00000	00002	32831	18337	0.99999	99997	67169	89595
33	1.00000	00001	16415	50173	0.99999	99998	83584	85805
34	1.00000	00000	58207	72088	0.99999	99999	41792	39905
35	1.00000	00000	29103	85044	0.99999	99999	70896	18953
36	1.00000	00000	14551	92189	0.99999	99999	85448	09143
37	1.00000	00000	07275	95984	0.99999	99999	92724	04461
38	1.00000	00000	03637	97955	0.99999	99999	96362	02193
39	1.00000	00000	01818	98965	0.99999	99999	98181	01084
40	1.00000	00000	00909	49478	0.99999	99999	99090	50538
41	1.00000	00000	00454	74738	0.99999	99999	99545	25268
42	1.00000	00000	00227	37368	0.99999	99999	99772	62633

For $n > 42$, $\sum\limits_{k=1}^{\infty} k^{-(n+1)} = \dfrac{1}{2}\left[1 + \sum\limits_{k=1}^{\infty} k^{-n}\right]$, $\sum\limits_{k=1}^{\infty} (-1)^{k-1} k^{-(n+1)} = \dfrac{1}{2}\left[1 + \sum\limits_{k=1}^{\infty} (-1)^{k-1} k^{-n}\right]$

*This table is related to Riemann's Zeta Function, where

$$1 + \frac{1}{2^p} + \frac{1}{3^p} + \frac{1}{4^p} + \cdots = \zeta(p) = \text{Zeta}(p)$$

*SUMS OF RECIPROCAL POWERS

n	$\sum_{k=0}^{\infty} (2k+1)^{-n}$				$\sum_{k=0}^{\infty} (-1)^k (2k+1)^{-n}$			
1		∞			0.78539	81633	97448	310
2	1.23370	05501	36169	82735	0.91596	55941	77219	015
3	1.05179	97902	64644	99972	0.96894	61462	59369	380
4	1.01467	80316	04192	05455	0.98894	45517	41105	336
5	1.00452	37627	95139	61613	0.99615	78280	77088	064
6	1.00144	70766	40942	12191	0.99868	52222	18438	135
7	1.00047	15486	52376	55476	0.99955	45078	90539	909
8	1.00015	51790	25296	11930	0.99984	99902	46829	657
9	1.00005	13451	83843	77259	0.99994	96841	87220	090
10	1.00001	70413	63044	82549	0.99998	31640	26196	877
11	1.00000	56660	51090	10935	0.99999	43749	73823	699
12	1.00000	18858	48583	11958	0.99999	81223	50587	882
13	1.00000	06280	55421	80232	0.99999	93735	83771	841
14	1.00000	02092	40519	21150	0.99999	97910	87248	735
15	1.00000	00697	24703	12929	0.99999	99303	40842	624
16	1.00000	00232	37157	37916	0.99999	99767	75950	903
17	1.00000	00077	44839	45587	0.99999	99922	57782	104
18	1.00000	00025	81437	55666	0.99999	99974	19086	745
19	1.00000	00008	60444	11452	0.99999	99991	39660	745
20	1.00000	00002	86807	69746	0.99999	99997	13213	274
21	1.00000	00000	95601	16531	0.99999	99999	04403	029
22	1.00000	00000	31866	77514	0.99999	99999	68134	064
23	1.00000	00000	10622	20241	0.99999	99999	89377	965
24	1.00000	00000	03540	72294	0.99999	99999	96459	311
25	1.00000	00000	01180	23874	0.99999	99999	98819	768
26	1.00000	00000	00393	41247	0.99999	99999	99606	589
27	1.00000	00000	00131	13740	0.99999	99999	99868	863
28	1.00000	00000	00043	71245	0.99999	99999	99956	288
29	1.00000	00000	00014	57081	0.99999	99999	99985	429
30	1.00000	00000	00004	85694	0.99999	99999	99995	143
31	1.00000	00000	00001	61898	0.99999	99999	99998	381
32	1.00000	00000	00000	53966	0.99999	99999	99999	460
33	1.00000	00000	00000	17989	0.99999	99999	99999	820
34	1.00000	00000	00000	05996	0.99999	99999	99999	940
35	1.00000	00000	00000	01999	0.99999	99999	99999	980
36	1.00000	00000	00000	00666	0.99999	99999	99999	993
37	1.00000	00000	00000	00222	0.99999	99999	99999	998
38	1.00000	00000	00000	00074	0.99999	99999	99999	999
39	1.00000	00000	00000	00025				
40	1.00000	00000	00000	00008				
41	1.00000	00000	00000	00003				
42	1.00000	00000	00000	00001				

*This table is related to Riemann's Zeta Function, where

$$1 + \frac{1}{2^p} + \frac{1}{3^p} + \frac{1}{4^p} + \cdots = \zeta(p) = \text{Zeta}(p)$$

FOURIER EXPANSIONS FOR BASIC PERIODIC FUNCTIONS

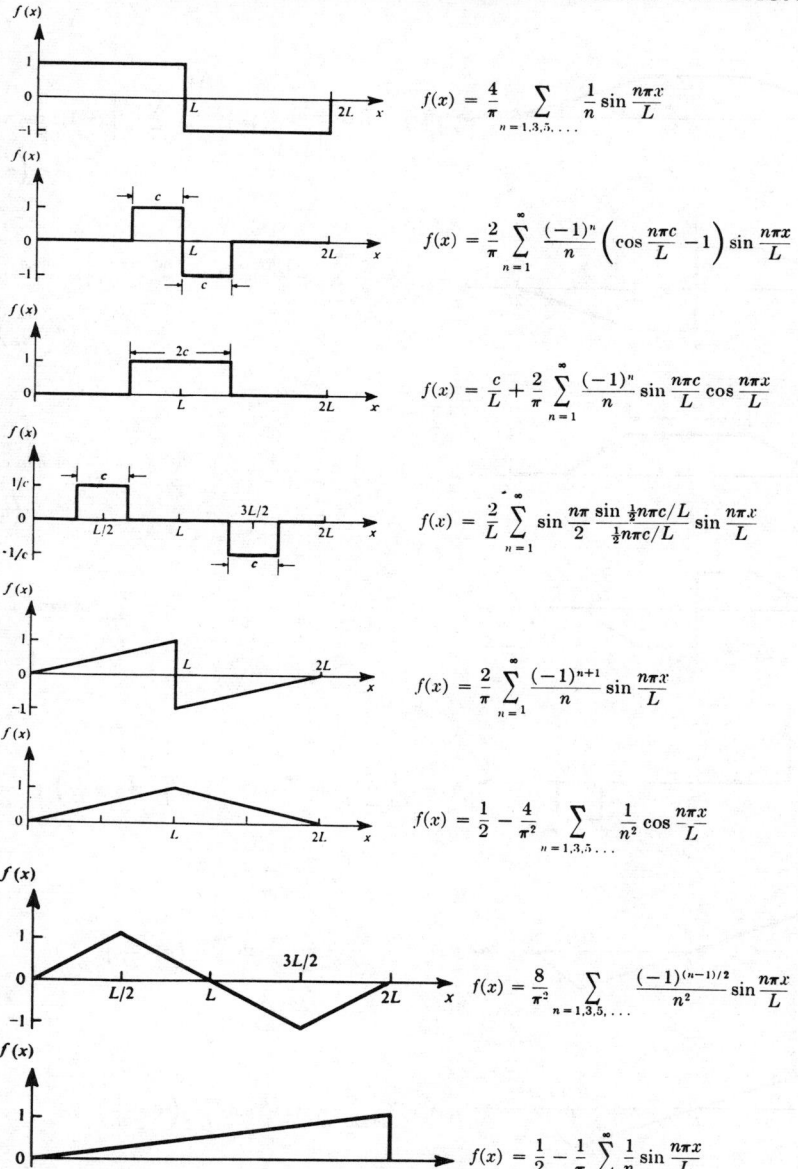

$$f(x) = \frac{4}{\pi} \sum_{n=1,3,5,\ldots} \frac{1}{n} \sin \frac{n\pi x}{L}$$

$$f(x) = \frac{2}{\pi} \sum_{n=1}^{\infty} \frac{(-1)^n}{n} \left(\cos \frac{n\pi c}{L} - 1 \right) \sin \frac{n\pi x}{L}$$

$$f(x) = \frac{c}{L} + \frac{2}{\pi} \sum_{n=1}^{\infty} \frac{(-1)^n}{n} \sin \frac{n\pi c}{L} \cos \frac{n\pi x}{L}$$

$$f(x) = \frac{2}{L} \sum_{n=1}^{\infty} \sin \frac{n\pi}{2} \frac{\sin \frac{1}{2} n\pi c/L}{\frac{1}{2} n\pi c/L} \sin \frac{n\pi x}{L}$$

$$f(x) = \frac{2}{\pi} \sum_{n=1}^{\infty} \frac{(-1)^{n+1}}{n} \sin \frac{n\pi x}{L}$$

$$f(x) = \frac{1}{2} - \frac{4}{\pi^2} \sum_{n=1,3,5,\ldots} \frac{1}{n^2} \cos \frac{n\pi x}{L}$$

$$f(x) = \frac{8}{\pi^2} \sum_{n=1,3,5,\ldots} \frac{(-1)^{(n-1)/2}}{n^2} \sin \frac{n\pi x}{L}$$

$$f(x) = \frac{1}{2} - \frac{1}{\pi} \sum_{n=}^{\infty} \frac{1}{n} \sin \frac{n\pi x}{L}$$

FOURIER EXPANSIONS FOR BASIC PERIODIC FUNCTIONS (Continued)

$f(x)$

$$f(x) = \frac{1}{2}(1+a) + \frac{2}{\pi^2(1-a)} \sum_{n=1}^{\infty} \frac{1}{n^2}\left[(-1)^n \cos n\pi a\right.$$
$$\left.\cos \frac{n\pi x}{L}\right; \left(a = \frac{c}{2}\right.$$

$f(x)$

$$f(x) = \frac{2}{\pi} \sum_{n=1}^{\infty} \frac{(-1)^{n-1}}{n}\left[1 + \frac{\sin n\pi a}{n\pi(1-a)}\right]\sin \frac{n\pi x}{L};$$
$$\left(a = \frac{c}{2L}\right)$$

$f(x)$

$$f(x) = f\frac{1}{2} - \frac{4}{\pi^2(1-2a)} \sum_{n=1,3,5,\ldots} \frac{1}{n_2}\cos n\pi a \cos \frac{n}{}$$
$$\left(a = \frac{c}{2}\right.$$

$f(x)$

$$f(x) = -\frac{2}{\pi} \sum_{n=1}^{\infty} \frac{(-1)^n}{n}\left[1 + \frac{1+(-1)^n}{n\pi(1-2a)}\sin n\pi a\right]\sin \frac{n\pi}{L}$$
$$\left(a = \frac{c}{2L}\right.$$

$f(x)$

$$f(x) = \frac{4}{\pi} \sum_{n=1}^{\infty} \frac{1}{n}\sin \frac{n\pi}{4}\sin n\pi a \sin \frac{n\pi x}{L}; \left(a = \frac{c}{2L}\right)$$

$f(x)$

$$f(x) = \frac{9}{\pi^2} \sum_{n=1}^{\infty} \frac{1}{n^2}\sin \frac{n\pi}{3}\sin \frac{n\pi x}{L}; \left(a = \frac{c}{2L}\right)$$

$f(x)$

$$f(x) = \frac{32}{3\pi^2} \sum_{n=1}^{\infty} \frac{1}{n^2}\sin \frac{n\pi}{4}\sin \frac{n\pi x}{L}; \left(a = \frac{c}{2L}\right)$$

$f(t)$

$$f(t) = \frac{1}{\pi} + \frac{1}{2}\sin \omega t - \frac{2}{\pi} \sum_{n=2,4,6,\ldots} \frac{1}{n^2-1}\cos n\omega t$$

BERNOULLI AND EULER NUMBERS—POLYNOMIALS

There are numerous sets of defined numbers and polynomials, among which the more important ones are those classified under the names of Bernoulli and Euler.

The *Bernoulli Polynomials* are generated by the defining condition

$$\frac{te^{tx}}{e^t - 1} = B_0(x) + B_1(x)t + B_2(x)\frac{t^2}{2!} + B_3(x)\frac{t^3}{3!} + \cdots$$

$$B_0(x) = 1, \quad B_1(x) = x - \tfrac{1}{2}, \quad B_2(x) = x^2 - x + \tfrac{1}{6}$$

$$B_3(x) = x^3 - \frac{3}{2}x^2 + \frac{x}{2}, \quad B_4(x) = x^4 - 2x^3 + x^2 - \tfrac{1}{30}, \ldots$$

The following useful relations should be noted

$$B_n'(x) = nB_{n-1}(x), \quad \int_a^x B_n(x)\,dx = \frac{1}{n+1}[B_{n+1}(x) - B_{n+1}(a)]$$

The Bernoulli numbers $B_0, B_1, B_2, \ldots$, can be obtained by putting $x = 0$ in the respective polynomials. A simpler method is to use the generating function

$$\frac{x}{e^x - 1} = \sum_{n=0}^{\infty} \frac{B_n x^n}{n!}$$

and read the coefficients from the expansion. Here,

$$B_0 = 1, \quad B_1 = -\tfrac{1}{2}, \quad B_2 = \tfrac{1}{6}, \quad B_4 = -\tfrac{1}{30},$$

$$B_6 = \tfrac{1}{42}, \quad B_8 = -\tfrac{1}{30}, \ldots B_{2n+1} = 0 \qquad (n \geq 1)$$

An important application for the Bernoulli coefficients is in its use involved for the Euler-McLaurin Sum Formula:

$$\sum_{x=1}^{n-1} f(x) = \int_1^n f(x)\,dx + \left[\sum_{i=1}^{\infty}\frac{B_i}{i!}f^{(i-1)}(x)\right]_{x=1}^{x=n}$$

$$\doteq \left[\int f(x)\,dx - \frac{1}{2}f(x) + \frac{1}{12}f'(x) - \frac{1}{720}f'''(x)\right.$$

$$\left. + \frac{1}{30,240}f^{(V)}(x) - \frac{1}{1,209,600}f^{(VII)}(x)\right]_{x=1}^{x=n}$$

$$\sum_{x=1}^{n-1}\sqrt{x} = \sqrt{n}\left\{\frac{2}{3}n - \frac{1}{2} + \frac{1}{24n} - \frac{1}{1,920n^3}\right.$$

$$\left. + \frac{1}{9,216n^5} - \frac{11}{163,840n^7}\right\} - 0.207,886,224,977,336$$

correct to 12 places for $n \geq 10$.

$$\log(x!) = \log \Gamma(x+1)$$

$$= \left(x + \frac{1}{2}\right)\log_e x - x + \frac{1}{12x} - \frac{1}{360x^3} + \frac{1}{1,260x^5} - \frac{1}{1,680x^7}$$

$$+ 0.918,938,533,205$$

accurate to 12 places for $x \geq 10$.

$$f(x) \text{(digamma function)} = \frac{d \log \Gamma(x)}{dx}$$

$$= 1 + \frac{1}{2} + \frac{1}{3} + \cdots + \frac{1}{x-1} - \gamma$$

(Euler Constant) for x integer

By Euler-McLaurin

$$f(x) = \log_e x - \frac{1}{2x} - \frac{1}{12x^2} + \frac{1}{120x^4} - \frac{1}{252x^6} + \frac{1}{240x^8} - \frac{5}{660x^{10}} + \frac{691}{32,760x^{12}}$$

correct to 12 places for $x \geq 10$.

The Euler numbers together with their respective polynomials can be generated from

$$\frac{2e^{tx}}{e^t + 1} = \sum_{i=0}^{\infty} E_i(x) t^i$$

and the relation

$$\frac{x^n}{n!} = \frac{1}{2} [E_n(x + 1) + E_n(x)]$$

The Euler polynomials are

$$E_0(x) = 1, \quad E_1(x) = x - \frac{1}{2}, \quad E_2(x) = \frac{x^2}{2} - \frac{x}{2}$$

$$E_3(x) = \frac{x^3}{6} - \frac{x^2}{4} + \frac{1}{24}, \quad E_4(x) = \frac{x^4}{24} - \frac{x^3}{12} + \frac{x}{24}$$

$$E_5(x) = \frac{x^5}{120} - \frac{x^4}{48} + \frac{x^2}{48} - \frac{1}{240}$$

Tables which follow record the first fifteen polynomials of $B_k(x)$ and $E_k(x)$. The first sixty Bernoulli and Euler numbers are given in a separate table. The value of $x^n/n!$ is also important and this is given in a succeeding table for values of x from 1 to 9 and n from 1 to 50.

COEFFICIENTS b_k OF THE BERNOULLI POLYNOMIALS $B_n(x) = \sum\limits_{k=0}^{n} b_k x^k$

$n\backslash k$	0	1	2	3	4	5	6	7	8	9	10	11	12	13	14	15
0	1															
1	$-\frac{1}{2}$	1														
2	$\frac{1}{6}$	-1	1													
3	0	$\frac{1}{2}$	$-\frac{3}{2}$	1												
4	$-\frac{1}{30}$	0	1	-2	1											
5	0	$-\frac{1}{6}$	0	$\frac{5}{3}$	$-\frac{5}{2}$	1										
6	$\frac{1}{42}$	0	$-\frac{1}{2}$	0	$\frac{5}{2}$	-3	1									
7	0	$\frac{1}{6}$	0	$-\frac{7}{6}$	0	$\frac{7}{2}$	$-\frac{7}{2}$	1								
8	$-\frac{1}{30}$	0	$\frac{2}{3}$	0	$-\frac{7}{3}$	0	$\frac{14}{3}$	-4	1							
9	0	$-\frac{3}{10}$	0	2	0	$-\frac{21}{5}$	0	6	$-\frac{9}{2}$	1						
10	$\frac{5}{66}$	0	$-\frac{3}{2}$	0	5	0	-7	0	$\frac{15}{2}$	-5	1					
11	0	$\frac{5}{6}$	0	$-\frac{11}{2}$	0	11	0	-11	0	$\frac{55}{6}$	$-\frac{11}{2}$	1				
12	$-\frac{691}{2730}$	0	5	0	$-\frac{33}{2}$	0	22	0	$-\frac{33}{2}$	0	11	-6	1			
13	0	$-\frac{691}{210}$	0	$\frac{65}{3}$	0	$-\frac{429}{10}$	0	$\frac{286}{7}$	0	$-\frac{143}{6}$	0	13	$-\frac{13}{2}$	1		
14	$\frac{7}{6}$	0	$-\frac{691}{30}$	0	$\frac{455}{6}$	0	$-\frac{1001}{10}$	0	$\frac{143}{6}$	0	$-\frac{1001}{30}$	0	$\frac{91}{6}$	-7	1	
15	0	$\frac{35}{2}$	0	$-\frac{691}{6}$	0	$\frac{455}{2}$	0	$-\frac{429}{2}$	0	$\frac{715}{6}$	0	$-\frac{91}{2}$	0	$\frac{35}{2}$	$-\frac{15}{2}$	1

COEFFICIENTS e_k OF THE EULER POLYNOMIALS $E_n(x) = \sum\limits_{k=0}^{n} e_k x^k$

$n\backslash k$	0	1	2	3	4	5	6	7	8	9	10	11	12	13	14	15
0	1															
1	$-\frac{1}{2}$	1														
2	0	-1	1													
3	$\frac{1}{4}$	0	$-\frac{3}{2}$	1												
4	0	1	0	-2	1											
5	$-\frac{1}{2}$	0	$\frac{5}{2}$	0	$-\frac{5}{2}$	1										
6	0	-3	0	5	0	-3	1									
7	$\frac{17}{8}$	0	$-\frac{21}{2}$	0	$\frac{35}{4}$	0	$-\frac{7}{2}$	1								
8	0	17	0	-28	0	14	0	-4	1							
9	$-\frac{31}{2}$	0	$\frac{153}{2}$	0	-63	0	21	0	$-\frac{9}{2}$	1						
10	0	-155	0	255	0	-126	0	30	0	-5	1					
11	$\frac{691}{4}$	0	$-\frac{1705}{2}$	0	$\frac{2805}{4}$	0	-231	0	$\frac{165}{4}$	0	$-\frac{11}{2}$	1				
12	0	2073	0	-3410	0	1683	0	-396	0	55	0	-6	1			
13	$-\frac{5461}{2}$	0	$\frac{26949}{2}$	0	$-\frac{22165}{2}$	0	$\frac{7293}{2}$	0	$-\frac{1287}{2}$	0	$\frac{143}{2}$	0	$-\frac{13}{2}$	1		
14	0	-38227	0	62881	0	-31031	0	7293	0	-1001	0	91	0	-7	1	
15	$\frac{929569}{16}$	0	$-\frac{573405}{2}$	0	$\frac{943215}{4}$	0	$-\frac{155155}{2}$	0	$\frac{109395}{8}$	0	$-\frac{3003}{2}$	0	$\frac{455}{4}$	0	$-\frac{15}{2}$	1

BERNOULLI AND EULER NUMBERS

$$B_n = N/D$$

n	N	D	B_n
0	1	1	(0) 1.0000 00000
1	−1	2	(−1) − 5.0000 00000*
2	1	6	(−1) 1.6666 66667
4	−1	30	(−2) − 3.3333 33333
6	1	42	(−2) 2.3809 52381
8	−1	30	(−2) − 3.3333 33333
10	5	66	(−2) 7.5757 57576
12	−691	2730	(−1) − 2.5311 35531
14	7	6	(0) 1.1666 66667
16	−3617	510	(0) − 7.0921 56863
18	43867	798	(1) 5.4971 17794
20	−1 74611	330	(2) − 5.2912 42424
22	8 54513	138	(3) 6.1921 23188
24	−2363 64091	2730	(4) − 8.6580 25311
26	85 53103	6	(6) 1.4255 17167
28	−2 37494 61029	870	(7) − 2.7298 23107
30	861 58412 76005	14322	(8) 6.0158 08739
32	−770 93210 41217	510	(10) − 1.5116 31577
34	257 76878 58367	6	(11) 4.2961 46431
36	−26315 27155 30534 77373	19 19190	(13) − 1.3711 65521
38	2 92999 39138 41559	6	(14) 4.8833 23190
40	−2 61082 71849 64491 22051	13530	(16) − 1.9296 57934
42	15 20097 64391 80708 02691	1806	(17) 8.4169 30476
44	−278 33269 57930 10242 35023	690	(19) − 4.0338 07185
46	5964 51111 59391 21632 77961	282	(21) 2.1150 74864
48	−560 94033 68997 81768 62491 27547	46410	(23) − 1.2086 62652
50	49 50572 05241 07964 82124 77525	66	(24) 7.5008 66746
52	−80116 57181 35489 95734 79249 91853	1590	(26) − 5.0387 78101
54	29 14996 36348 84862 42141 81238 12691	798	(28) 3.6528 77648
56	−2479 39292 93132 26753 68541 57396 63229	870	(30) − 2.8498 76930
58	84483 61334 88800 41862 04677 59940 36021	354	(32) 2.3865 42750
60	−121 52331 40483 75557 20403 04994 07982 02460 41491	567 86730	(34) − 2.1399 94926

*The floating decimal point notation is used here. For example for $n = 1$, $B_1 = -\frac{1}{2} = -.500000 = (−5.00000)(10^{-1}) = (−1) − 5.0000,0000$.

BERNOULLI AND EULER NUMBERS (Continued)

$$B_n = N/D$$

n	E_n
0	1
2	-1
4	5
6	-61
8	1385
10	-50521
12	27 02765
14	-1993 60981
16	1 93915 12145
18	-240 48796 75441
20	37037 11882 37525
22	-69 34887 43931 37901
24	15514 53416 35570 86905
26	-40 87072 50929 31238 92361
28	12522 59641 40362 98654 68285
30	-44 15438 93249 02310 45536 82821
32	17751 93915 79539 28943 66647 89665
34	-80 72329 92358 87898 06216 82474 53281
36	41222 06033 95177 02122 34707 96712 59045
38	-234 89580 52704 31082 52017 82857 61989 47741
40	1 48511 50718 11498 00178 77156 78140 58266 84425
42	-1036 46227 33519 61211 93979 57304 74518 59763 10201
44	7 94757 94225 97592 70360 80405 10088 07061 95192 73805
46	-6667 53751 66855 44977 43502 84747 73748 19752 41076 84661
48	60 96278 64556 85421 58691 68574 28768 43153 97653 90444 35185
50	-60532 85248 18862 18963 14383 78511 16490 88103 49822 51468 15121
52	650 61624 86684 60884 77158 70634 08082 29834 83644 23676 53855 76565
54	-7 54665 99390 08739 09806 14325 65889 73674 42122 40024 71169 98586 45581
56	9420 32189 64202 41204 90228 62376 90583 22720 93888 52599 64600 93949 05945
58	-126 22019 25180 62187 19903 40923 72874 89255 48234 10611 91825 59406 99649 20041
60	181089 11496 57923 04965 45807 74165 21586 88733 48734 92363 14106 00809 54542 31325

BERNOULLI AND EULER POLYNOMIALS, RIEMANN ZETA FUNCTION
$x^n/n!$

$n\backslash x$	2		3		4		5	
1	(0) 2.0000	00000	(0) 3.0000	00000	(0) 4.0000	00000	(0) 5.0000	00000
2	(0) 2.0000	00000	(0) 4.5000	00000	(0) 8.0000	00000	(1) 1.2500	00000
3	(0) 1.3333	33333	(0) 4.5000	00000	(1) 1.0666	66667	(1) 2.0833	33333
4	(− 1) 6.6666	66667	(0) 3.3750	00000	(1) 1.0666	66667	(1) 2.6041	66667
5	(− 1) 2.6666	66667	(0) 2.0250	00000	(0) 8.5333	33333	(1) 2.6041	66667
6	(− 2) 8.8888	88889	(0) 1.0125	00000	(0) 5.6888	88889	(1) 2.1701	38889
7	(− 2) 2.5396	82540	(− 1) 4.3392	85714	(0) 3.2507	93651	(1) 1.5500	99206
8	(− 3) 6.3492	06349	(− 1) 1.6272	32143	(0) 1.6253	96825	(0) 9.6881	20040
9	(− 3) 1.4109	34744	(− 2) 5.4241	07143	(− 1) 7.2239	85891	(0) 5.3822	88911
10	(− 4) 2.8218	69489	(− 2) 1.6272	32144	(− 1) 2.8895	94356	(0) 2.6911	44455
11	(− 5) 5.1306	71797	(− 3) 4.4379	05844	(− 1) 1.0507	61584	(0) 1.2232	47480
12	(− 6) 8.5511	19662	(− 3) 1.1094	76461	(− 2) 3.5025	38614	(− 1) 5.0968	64499
13	(− 6) 1.3155	56871	(− 4) 2.5603	30295	(− 2) 1.0777	04189	(− 1) 1.9603	32500
14	(− 7) 1.8793	66959	(− 5) 5.4864	22060	(− 3) 3.0791	54825	(− 2) 7.0011	87499
15	(− 8) 2.5058	22612	(− 5) 1.0972	84412	(− 4) 8.2110	79534	(− 2) 2.3337	29166
16	(− 9) 3.1322	78264	(− 6) 2.0574	08272	(− 4) 2.0527	69883	(− 3) 7.2929	03644
17	(−10) 3.6850	33252	(− 7) 3.6307	20481	(− 5) 4.8300	46785	(− 3) 2.1449	71660
18	(−11) 4.0944	81391	(− 8) 6.0512	00801	(− 5) 1.0733	43730	(− 4) 5.9582	54611
19	(−12) 4.3099	80412	(− 9) 9.5545	27582	(− 6) 2.2596	71011	(− 4) 1.5679	61740
20	(−13) 4.3099	80413	(− 9) 1.4331	79137	(− 7) 4.5193	42021	(− 5) 3.9199	04350
21	(−14) 4.1047	43250	(−10) 2.0473	98768	(− 8) 8.6082	70516	(− 6) 9.3331	05595
22	(−15) 3.7315	84772	(−11) 2.7919	07410	(− 8) 1.5651	40093	(− 6) 2.1211	60362
23	(−16) 3.2448	56324	(−12) 3.6416	18361	(− 9) 2.7219	82772	(− 7) 4.6112	18179
24	(−17) 2.7040	46937	(−13) 4.5520	22952	(−10) 4.5366	37953	(− 8) 9.6067	04540
25	(−18) 2.1632	37550	(−14) 5.4624	27543	(−11) 7.2586	20726	(− 8) 1.9213	40908
26	(−19) 1.6640	28884	(−15) 6.3028	01010	(−11) 1.1167	10881	(− 9) 3.6948	86362
27	(−20) 1.2326	13988	(−16) 7.0031	12233	(−12) 1.6543	86490	(−10) 6.8423	82151
28	(−22) 8.8043	85630	(−17) 7.5033	34535	(−13) 2.3634	09271	(−10) 1.2218	53956
29	(−23) 6.0719	90089	(−18) 7.7620	70209	(−14) 3.2598	74857	(−11) 2.1066	44751
30	(−24) 4.0479	93393	(−19) 7.7620	70209	(−15) 4.3464	99810	(−12) 3.5110	74585
31	(−25) 2.6116	08641	(−20) 7.5116	80847	(−16) 5.6083	86851	(−13) 5.6630	23524
32	(−26) 1.6322	55401	(−21) 7.0422	00795	(−17) 7.0104	83564	(−14) 8.8484	74257
33	(−28) 9.8924	56972	(−22) 6.4020	00722	(−18) 8.4975	55834	(−14) 1.3406	77918
34	(−29) 5.8190	92337	(−23) 5.6488	24167	(−19) 9.9971	24513	(−15) 1.9715	85173
35	(−30) 3.3251	95620	(−24) 4.8418	49284	(−19) 1.1425	28515	(−16) 2.8165	50246
36	(−31) 1.8473	30900	(−25) 4.0348	74405	(−20) 1.2694	76128	(−17) 3.9118	75343
37	(−33) 9.9855	72436	(−26) 3.2715	19788	(−21) 1.3724	06625	(−18) 5.2863	18032
38	(−34) 5.2555	64439	(−27) 2.5827	78779	(−22) 1.4446	38552	(−19) 6.9556	81619
39	(−35) 2.6951	61251	(−28) 1.9867	52908	(−23) 1.4816	80567	(−20) 8.9175	40539
40	(−36) 1.3475	80626	(−29) 1.4900	64681	(−24) 1.4816	80567	(−20) 1.1146	92567
41	(−38) 6.5735	64028	(−30) 1.0902	91230	(−25) 1.4455	42017	(−21) 1.3593	81180
42	(−39) 3.1302	68584	(−32) 7.7877	94496	(−26) 1.3767	06682	(−22) 1.6183	10928
43	(−40) 1.4559	38876	(−33) 5.4333	44999	(−27) 1.2806	57379	(−23) 1.8817	56893
44	(−42) 6.6179	03983	(−34) 3.7045	53408	(−28) 1.1642	33981	(−24) 2.1383	60106
45	(−43) 2.9412	90659	(−35) 2.4697	02271	(−29) 1.0348	74650	(−25) 2.3759	55673
46	(−44) 1.2788	22026	(−36) 1.6106	75395	(−31) 8.9989	09998	(−26) 2.5825	60514
47	(−46) 5.4417	95855	(−37) 1.0280	90677	(−32) 7.6586	46807	(−27) 2.7474	04803
48	(−47) 2.2674	14940	(−39) 6.4255	66736	(−33) 6.3822	05674	(−28) 2.8618	80003
49	(−49) 9.2547	54855	(−40) 3.9340	20450	(−34) 5.2099	63815	(−29) 2.9202	85717
50	(−50) 3.7019	10942	(−41) 2.3604	12270	(−35) 4.1679	71052	(−30) 2.9202	85717

BERNOULLI AND EULER POLYNOMIALS, RIEMANN ZETA FUNCTION

$$x^n/n!$$

$n \backslash x$	6		7		8		9	
1	(0) 6.0000	00000	(0) 7.0000	00000	(0) 8.0000	00000	(0) 9.0000	00000
*2	(1) 1.8000	00000	(1) 2.4500	00000	(1) 3.2000	00000	(1) 4.0500	00000
3	(1) 3.6000	00000	(1) 5.7166	66667	(1) 8.5333	33333	(2) 1.2150	00000
4	(1) 5.4000	00000	(2) 1.0004	16667	(2) 1.7066	66667	(2) 2.7337	50000
5	(1) 6.4800	00000	(2) 1.4005	83333	(2) 2.7306	66667	(2) 4.9207	50000
6	(1) 6.4800	00000	(2) 1.6340	13889	(2) 3.6408	88889	(2) 7.3811	25000
7	(1) 5.5542	85714	(2) 1.6340	13889	(2) 4.1610	15873	(2) 9.4900	17857
8	(1) 4.1657	14286	(2) 1.4297	62153	(2) 4.1610	15873	(3) 1.0676	27009
9	(1) 2.7771	42857	(2) 1.1120	37230	(2) 3.6986	80776	(3) 1.0676	27009
10	(1) 1.6662	85714	(1) 7.7842	60610	(2) 2.9589	44621	(2) 9.6086	43080
11	(0) 9.0888	31169	(1) 4.9536	20388	(2) 2.1519	59724	(2) 7.8616	17066
12	(0) 4.5444	15584	(1) 2.8896	11893	(2) 1.4346	39816	(2) 5.8962	12799
13	(0) 2.0974	22577	(1) 1.5559	44865	(1) 8.8285	52715	(2) 4.0819	93476
14	(− 1) 8.9889	53903	(0) 7.7797	24327	(1) 5.0448	87266	(2) 2.6241	38663
15	(− 1) 3.5955	81561	(0) 3.6305	38019	(1) 2.6906	06542	(2) 1.5744	83198
16	(− 1) 1.3483	43085	(0) 1.5883	60383	(1) 1.3453	03271	(1) 8.8564	67988
17	(− 2) 4.7588	57949	(− 1) 6.5403	07461	(0) 6.3308	38921	(1) 4.6887	18347
18	(− 2) 1.5862	85983	(− 1) 2.5434	52902	(0) 2.8137	06187	(1) 2.3443	59173
19	(− 3) 5.0093	24157	(− 2) 9.3706	15954	(0) 1.1847	18395	(1) 1.1104	85924
20	(− 3) 1.5027	97247	(− 2) 3.2797	15584	(− 1) 4.7388	73579	(0) 4.9971	86660
21	(− 4) 4.2937	06421	(− 2) 1.0932	38528	(− 1) 1.8052	85173	(0) 2.1416	51426
22	(− 4) 1.1710	10841	(− 3) 3.4784	86224	(− 2) 6.5646	73354	(− 1) 8.7613	01284
23	(− 5) 3.0548	10892	(− 3) 1.0586	69721	(− 2) 2.2833	64645	(− 1) 3.4283	35286
24	(− 6) 7.6370	27230	(− 4) 3.0877	86685	(− 3) 7.6112	15485	(− 1) 1.2856	25732
25	(− 6) 1.8328	86535	(− 5) 8.6458	02721	(− 3) 2.4355	88956	(− 2) 4.6282	52637
26	(− 7) 4.2297	38158	(− 5) 2.3277	16117	(− 4) 7.4941	19863	(− 2) 1.6020	87451
27	(− 8) 9.3994	18129	(− 6) 6.0348	19562	(− 4) 2.2204	79959	(− 3) 5.3402	91503
28	(− 8) 2.0141	61028	(− 6) 1.5087	04890	(− 5) 6.3442	28454	(− 3) 1.7165	22269
29	(− 9) 4.1672	29712	(− 7) 3.6417	01460	(− 5) 1.7501	31987	(− 4) 5.3271	38075
30	(−10) 8.3344	59424	(− 8) 8.4973	03406	(− 6) 4.6670	18634	(− 4) 1.5981	41423
31	(−10) 1.6131	21179	(− 8) 1.9187	45930	(− 6) 1.2043	91905	(− 5) 4.6397	65421
32	(−11) 3.0246	02211	(− 9) 4.1972	56723	(− 7) 3.0109	79764	(− 5) 1.3049	34025
33	(−12) 5.4992	76746	(−10) 8.9032	71836	(− 8) 7.2993	44881	(− 6) 3.5589	10976
34	(−13) 9.7046	06024	(−10) 1.8330	26555	(− 8) 1.7174	92913	(− 7) 9.4206	46703
35	(−13) 1.6636	46746	(−11) 3.6660	53108	(− 9) 3.9256	98086	(− 7) 2.4224	52008
36	(−14) 2.7727	44578	(−12) 7.1284	36600	(−10) 8.7237	73527	(− 8) 6.0561	30022
37	(−15) 4.4963	42559	(−12) 1.3486	23141	(−10) 1.8862	21303	(− 8) 1.4731	12708
38	(−16) 7.0994	88250	(−13) 2.4843	05785	(−11) 3.9709	92217	(− 9) 3.4889	51151
39	(−16) 1.0922	28962	(−14) 4.4590	10384	(−12) 8.1456	25061	(−10) 8.0514	25733
40	(−17) 1.6383	43443	(−15) 7.8032	68172	(−12) 1.6291	25012	(−10) 1.8115	70790
41	(−18) 2.3975	75770	(−15) 1.3322	65298	(−13) 3.1787	80512	(−11) 3.9766	18807
42	(−19) 3.4251	08241	(−16) 2.2204	42162	(−14) 6.0548	20021	(−12) 8.5213	26014
43	(−20) 4.7792	20803	(−17) 3.6146	73288	(−14) 1.1264	78144	(−12) 1.7835	33352
44	(−21) 6.5171	19276	(−18) 5.7506	16594	(−15) 2.0481	42079	(−13) 3.6481	36401
45	(−22) 8.6894	92366	(−19) 8.9454	03590	(−16) 3.6411	41473	(−14) 7.2962	72802
46	(−22) 1.1334	12048	(−19) 1.3612	57068	(−17) 6.3324	19955	(−14) 1.4275	31635
47	(−23) 1.4469	08998	(−20) 2.0274	04144	(−17) 1.0778	58716	(−15) 2.7335	71217
48	(−24) 1.8086	36247	(−21) 2.9566	31045	(−18) 1.7964	31193	(−16) 5.1254	46033
49	(−25) 2.2146	56629	(−22) 4.2237	58634	(−19) 2.9329	48887	(−17) 9.4140	84548
50	(−26) 2.6575	87955	(−23) 5.9132	62088	(−20) 4.6927	18219	(−17) 1.6945	35219

*The floating decimal point notation is used here. For example (1) 1.8000,000 = (1.8000,000) 10.

STIRLING NUMBERS

Stirling numbers

The Stirling numbers are used for reducing factorials such as $x^{(n)}$ to polynomials in x and vice versa.

Stirling numbers of the first kind

The factorial polynomial $x^{(n)}$ is defined and represented by

$$x^{(n)} = x(x - 1)(x - 2)\cdots(x - n + 1)$$

where $x^{(0)}$ is 1 by definition.

If n is a non-negative integer, then

$$x^{(n)} = s_{n1}x + s_{n2}x^2 + \cdots + s_{nn}x^n.$$

Here the numbers $s_{n1}, s_{n2}, s_{n3}, \ldots$, are Stirling numbers of the first kind. A table listing these numbers with an example using same follows.

STIRLING NUMBERS OF THE FIRST KIND

n	s_{n1}	s_{n2}	s_{n3}	s_{n4}	s_{n5}	s_{n6}	s_{n7}	s_{n8}
1	1	0	0	0	0	0	0	0
2	-1	1	0	0	0	0	0	0
3	2	-3	1	0	0	0	0	0
4	-6	11	-6	1	0	0	0	0
5	24	-50	35	-10	1	0	0	0
6	-120	274	-225	85	-15	1	0	0
7	720	$-1\ 764$	$1\ 624$	-735	175	-21	1	0
8	$-5\ 040$	$13\ 068$	$-13\ 132$	$6\ 769$	$-1\ 960$	322	-28	1

The table may be continued by using the recurrence formula

$$s_{ni} = s_{n-1,i-1} - (n - 1)s_{n-1,i}, \quad i = 1, 2, \ldots, n$$

where $s_{n0} = 0$ for all n.

Example

Express $3x^{(3)} + 2x^{(1)}$ using Stirling's numbers of the first kind

$$3x^{(3)} = 3(2x - 3x^2 + x^3)$$
$$= 6x - 9x^2 + 3x^3$$
$$2x^{(1)} = 2x$$
$$\therefore 3x^{(3)} + 2x^{(1)} = 8x - 9x^2 + 3x^3$$

This may be verified by carrying out the indicated operations as follows

$$3x^{(3)} + 2x^{(1)} = 3(x)(x - 1)(x - 2) + 2x$$
$$= 3x^3 - 9x^2 + 6x + 2x$$
$$= 8x - 9x^2 + 3x^3$$

Stirling numbers of the second kind

For every non-negative integer n the function defined by x^n can be expressed as a linear combination of factorial powers of x not higher than the n'th. In other words

$$x^n = t_{n1}x^{(1)} + t_{n2}x^{(2)} + \cdots + t_{nn}x^{(n)}.$$

The numbers $t_{n1}, t_{n2}, \ldots, t_{nn}$ are called Stirling's numbers of the second kind.

A table listing these numbers with an example using same follows.

STIRLING NUMBERS OF THE SECOND KIND

n	t_{n1}	t_{n2}	t_{n3}	t_{n4}	t_{n5}	t_{n6}	t_{n7}	t_{n8}
1	1	0	0	0	0	0	0	0
2	1	1	0	0	0	0	0	0
3	1	3	1	0	0	0	0	0
4	1	7	6	1	0	0	0	0
5	1	15	25	10	1	0	0	0
6	1	31	90	65	15	1	0	0
7	1	63	301	350	140	21	1	0
8	1	127	966	1 701	1 050	266	28	1

This table may be continued by using the recurrence formula

$$t_{ni} = it_{n-1,i} + t_{n-1,i-1}, \quad i = 1, 2, \ldots, n$$

where $t_{n0} = 0$ for all n.

Example

Express $2x^3 - 3x^2 + x + 2$ by use of factorial powers

$$2x^3 = 2[x^{(1)} + 3x^{(2)} + x^{(3)}] = 2x^{(1)} + 6x^{(2)} + 2x^{(3)}$$
$$-3x^2 = -3[x^{(1)} + x^{(2)}] \quad\quad = -3x^{(1)} - 3x^{(2)}$$
$$x = x^{(1)} \quad\quad\quad\quad\quad\quad = x^{(1)}$$
$$+2 = +2x^{(0)} \quad\quad\quad\quad\quad = 2x^{(0)}$$
$$\therefore 2x^3 - 3x^2 + x + 2 = 2 + 3x^{(2)} + 2x^{(3)}$$

DIFFERENTIAL EQUATIONS

SPECIAL FORMULAS

Certain types of differential equations occur sufficiently often to justify the use of formulas for the corresponding particular solutions. The following set of tables I to XIV covers all first, second and nth order ordinary linear differential equations with constant coefficients for which the right members are of the form $P(x)e^{rx} \sin sx$ or $P(x)e^{rx} \cos sx$, where r and s are constants and $P(x)$ is a polynomial of degree n.

When the right member of a reducible linear partial differential equation with constant coefficients is not zero, particular solutions for certain types of right members are contained in tables XV to XXI. In these tables both F and P are used to denote polynomials, and it is assumed that no denominator is zero. In any formula the roles of x and y may be reversed throughout, changing a formula in which x dominates to one in which y dominates. Tables XIX, XX, XXI are applicable whether the equations are reducible or not.

The symbol $\binom{m}{n}$ stands for $\dfrac{m!}{(m-n)!n!}$ and is the $n + 1$ st coefficient in the expansion of $(a + b)^m$. Also $0! = 1$ by definition.

The tables as herewith given are those contained in the text *Differential Equations* by Ginn and Company (1955) and are published with their kind permission and that of the author, Professor Frederick H. Steen.

Solution of Linear Differential Equations with Constant Coefficients

Any linear differential equation with constant coefficients may be written in the form

$$p(D)y = R(x),$$

where D is the differential operation

$$Dy = \frac{dy}{dx},$$

$p(D)$ is a polynomial in D,
y is the dependent variable,
x is the independent variable,
$R(x)$ is an arbitrary function of x.

A power of D represents repeated differentiation, that is

$$D^n y = \frac{d^n y}{dx^n}.$$

For such an equation, the general solution may be written in the form

$$y = y_c + y_p,$$

where y_p is any particular solution, and y_c is called the *complementary function*. This complementary function is defined as the general solution of the *homogeneous equation*, which is the original differential equation with the right side replaced by zero, i.e.

$$p(D)y = 0$$

The complementary function y_c may be determined as follows:

1. Factor the polynomial $p(D)$ into real and complex linear factors, just as if D were a variable instead of an operator.

2. For each non-repeated linear factor of the form $(D - a)$, where a is real, write down a term of the form

$$ce^{ax},$$

where c is an arbitrary constant.

3. For each repeated real linear factor of the form $(D - a)^n$, write down n terms of the form

$$c_1 e^{ax} + c_2 x e^{ax} + c_3 x^2 e^{ax} + \cdots + c_n x^{n-1} e^{ax},$$

where the c_i's are arbitrary constants.

4. For each non-repeated conjugate complex pair of factors of the form $(D - a + ib)(D - a - ib)$, write down 2 terms of the form

$$c_1 e^{ax} \cos bx + c_2 e^{ax} \sin bx$$

5. For each repeated conjugate complex pair of factors of the form $(D - a + ib)^n (D - a - ib)^n$, write down $2n$ terms of the form

$$c_1 e^{ax} \cos bx + c_2 e^{ax} \sin bx + c_3 x e^{ax} \cos bx + c_4 x e^{ax} \sin bx + \cdots$$
$$+ c_{2n-1} x^{n-1} e^{ax} \cos bx + c_{2n} x^{n-1} e^{ax} \sin bx$$

6. The sum of all the terms thus written down is the complementary function y_c.

To find the particular solution y_p, use the following tables, as shown in the examples. For cases not shown in the tables, there are various methods of finding y_p. The most general method is called *variation of parameters*. The following example illustrates the method:

Find y_p for $(D^2 - 4)y = e^x$.

This example can be solved most easily by use of equation 63 in the tables following. However it is given here as an example of the method of variation of parameters.

The complementary function is

$$y_c = c_1 e^{2x} + c_2 e^{-2x}$$

To find y_p, replace the constants in the complementary function with unknown functions,

$$y_p = u e^{2x} + v e^{-2x}.$$

We now prepare to substitute this assumed solution into the original equation. We begin by taking all the necessary derivatives:

$$y_p = u e^{2x} + v e^{-2x}$$
$$y_p' = 2u e^{2x} - 2v e^{-2x} + u' e^{2x} + v' e^{-2x}$$

For each derivative of y_p except the highest, we set the sum of all the terms containing u' and v' to 0. Thus the above equation becomes

$$u' e^{2x} + v' e^{-2x} = 0 \quad \text{and} \quad y_p' = 2u e^{2x} - 2v e^{-2x}$$

Continuing to differentiate, we have

$$y_p'' = 4u e^{2x} + 4v e^{-2x} + 2u' e^{2x} - 2v' e^{-2x}$$

When we substitute into the original equation, all the terms not containing u' or v' cancel out. This is a consequence of the method by which y_p was set up.

Thus all that is necessary is to write down the terms containing u' or v' in the highest order derivative of y_p, multiply by the constant coefficient of the highest power of D in $p(D)$, and set it equal to $R(x)$. Together with the previous terms in u' and v' which were set equal to 0, this gives us as many linear equations in the first derivatives of the unknown functions as there are unknown functions. The first derivatives may then be solved for by algebra, and the unknown functions found by integration. In the present example, this becomes

$$u'e^{2x} + v'e^{-2x} = 0$$
$$2u'e^{2x} - 2v'e^{-2x} = e^x.$$

We eliminate v' and u' separately, getting

$$4u'e^{2x} = e^x$$
$$4v'e^{-2x} = -e^x.$$

Thus

$$u' = \tfrac{1}{4}e^{-x}$$
$$v' = -\tfrac{1}{4}e^{3x}.$$

Therefore, by integrating

$$u = -\tfrac{1}{4}e^{-x}$$
$$v = -\tfrac{1}{12}e^{3x}.$$

A constant of integration is not needed, since we need only one particular solution. Thus

$$y_p = ue^{2x} + ve^{-2x} = -\tfrac{1}{4}e^{-x}e^{2x} - \tfrac{1}{12}e^{3x}e^{-2x}$$
$$= -\tfrac{1}{4}e^x - \tfrac{1}{12}e^x = -\tfrac{1}{3}e^x,$$

and the general solution is

$$y = y_c + y_p = c_1e^{2x} + c_2e^{-2x} - \tfrac{1}{3}e^x.$$

The following examples illustrate the use of the tables.
Example 1. Solve $(D^2 - 4)y = \sin 3x$.
Substitution of $q = -4, s = 3$ in formula 24 gives

$$y_p = \frac{\sin 3x}{-9 - 4},$$

wherefore the general solution is

$$y = c_1e^{2x} + c_2e^{-2x} - \frac{\sin 3x}{13}.$$

Example 2. Obtain a particular solution of $(D^2 - 4D + 5)y = x^2e^{3x} \sin x$.
Applying formula 40 with $a = 2, b = 1, r = 3, s = 1, P(x) = x^2, s + b = 2, s - b = 0,$
$a - r = -1, (a - r)^2 + (s + b)^2 = 5, (a - r)^2 + (s - b)^2 = 1,$ we have

$$y_p = \frac{e^{3x} \sin x}{2} \left[\left(\frac{2}{5} - \frac{0}{1} \right) x^2 + \left(\frac{2(-1)2}{25} - \frac{2(-1)0}{1} \right) 2x \right.$$

$$+ \left. \left(\frac{3 \cdot 1 \cdot 2 - 2^3}{125} - \frac{3 \cdot 1 \cdot 0 - 0}{1} \right) 2 \right]$$

$$- \frac{e^{3x} \cos x}{2} \left[\left(\frac{-1}{5} - \frac{-1}{1} \right) x^2 + \left(\frac{1 - 4}{25} - \frac{1 - 0}{1} \right) 2x \right.$$

$$+ \left. \left(\frac{-1 - 3(-1)4}{125} - \frac{-1 - 3(-1)0}{1} \right) 2 \right]$$

$$= (\tfrac{1}{5}x^2 - \tfrac{4}{25}x - \tfrac{2}{125})e^{3x} \sin x + (-\tfrac{2}{5}x^2 + \tfrac{28}{25}x - \tfrac{136}{125})e^{3x} \cos x.$$

The special formulas effect a very considerable saving of time in problems of this type.

Example 3. Obtain a particular solution of $(D^2 - 4D + 5)y = x^2 e^{2x} \cos x$. (Compare with Example 2.)

Formula 40 is not applicable here since for this equation $r = a$, $s = b$, wherefore the denominator $(a - r)^2 + (s - b)^2 = 0$. We turn instead to formula 44. Substituting $a = 2, b = 1, P(x) = x^2$ and replacing sin by cos, cos by $-\sin$, we obtain

$$y_p = \frac{e^{2x} \cos x}{4} (x^2 - \tfrac{2}{4}) + \frac{e^{2x} \sin x}{2} \int (x^2 - \tfrac{1}{2}) \, dx$$

$$= \left(\frac{x^2}{4} - \frac{1}{8}\right) e^{2x} \cos x + \left(\frac{x^3}{6} - \frac{x}{4}\right) e^{2x} \sin x,$$

which is the required solution.

Example 4. Find z_p for $(D_x - 3D_y)z = \ln(y + 3x)$.

Referring to Table XV we note that formula 69 (not 68) is applicable. This gives

$$z_p = x \ln(y + 3x).$$

It is easily seen that $-\dfrac{y}{3} \ln(y + 3x)$ would serve equally well.

Example 5. Solve $(D_x + 2D_y - 4)z = y \cos(y - 2x)$.

Since R in formula 76 contains a polynomial in x, not y, we rewrite the given equation in the form

$$(D_y + \tfrac{1}{2}D_x - 2)z = \tfrac{1}{2}y \cos(y - 2x).$$

Then

$$z_c = e^{2y} F(x - \tfrac{1}{2}y) = e^{2y} f(2x - y),$$

and by the formula

$$z_p = -\tfrac{1}{2} \cos(y - 2x) \cdot \left(\frac{y}{2} + \frac{\tfrac{1}{2}}{2}\right)$$

$$= -\tfrac{1}{8}(2y + 1) \cos(y - 2x).$$

Example 6. Find z_p for $(D_x + 4D_y)^3 z = (2x - y)^2$.

Using formula 79, we obtain

$$z_p = \frac{\int \int \int u^2 \, du^3}{[2 + 4(-1)]^3} = \frac{u^5}{5 \cdot 4 \cdot 3 \cdot (-8)} = -\frac{(2x - y)^5}{480}.$$

Example 7. Find z_p for $(D_x^3 + 5D_x^2 D_y - 7D_x + 4)z = e^{2x+3y}$.

By formula 87

$$z_p = \frac{e^{2x+3y}}{2^3 + 5 \cdot 2^2 \cdot 3 - 7 \cdot 2 + 4} = \frac{e^{2x+3y}}{58}.$$

Example 8. Find z_p for

$$(D_x^4 + 6D_x^3 D_y + D_x D_y + D_y^2 + 9)z = \sin(3x + 4y).$$

Since every term in the left member is of *even* degree in the two operators D_x and D_y, formula 90 is applicable.

It gives

$$z_p = \frac{\sin(3x + 4y)}{(-9)^2 + 6(-9)(-12) + (-12) + (-16) + 9}$$

$$= \frac{\sin(3x + 4y)}{710}.$$

DIFFERENTIAL EQUATIONS

TABLE I: $(D - a)y = R$

R	y_p
1. e^{rx}	$\dfrac{e^{rx}}{r-a}$
2. $\sin sx$*	$-\dfrac{a\sin sx + s\cos sx}{a^2 + s^2} = -\dfrac{1}{\sqrt{a^2+s^2}}\sin\left(sx + \tan^{-1}\dfrac{s}{a}\right)$
3. $P(x)$	$-\dfrac{1}{a}\left[P(x) + \dfrac{P'(x)}{a} + \dfrac{P''(x)}{a^2} + \cdots + \dfrac{P^{(n)}(x)}{a^n}\right]$
4. $e^{rx}\sin sx$*	Replace a by $a - r$ in formula 2 and multiply by e^{rx}.
5. $P(x)e^{rx}$	Replace a by $a - r$ in formula 3 and multiply by e^{rx}.
6. $P(x)\sin sx$*	$-\sin sx\left[\dfrac{a}{a^2+s^2}P(x) + \dfrac{a^2-s^2}{(a^2+s^2)^2}P'(x) + \dfrac{a^3-3as^2}{(a^2+s^2)^3}P''(x) + \cdots \right.$ $\left. + \dfrac{a^k - \binom{k}{2}a^{k-2}s^2 + \binom{k}{4}a^{k-4}s^4 - \cdots}{(a^2+s^2)^k}P^{(k-1)}(x) + \cdots\right]$ $-\cos sx\left[\dfrac{s}{a^2+s^2}P(x) + \dfrac{2as}{(a^2+s^2)^2}P'(x) + \dfrac{3a^2s - s^3}{(a^2+s^2)^3}P''(x) + \cdots \right.$ $\left. + \dfrac{\binom{k}{1}a^{k-1}s - \binom{k}{3}a^{k-3}s^3 + \cdots}{(a^2+s^2)^k}P^{(k-1)}(x) + \cdots\right]$
7. $P(x)e^{rx}\sin sx$*	Replace a by $a - r$ in formula 6 and multiply by e^{rx}.
8. e^{ax}	xe^{ax}
9. $e^{ax}\sin sx$*	$-\dfrac{e^{ax}\cos sx}{s}$
10. $P(x)e^{ax}$	$e^{ax}\displaystyle\int P(x)\,dx$
11. $P(x)e^{ax}\sin sx$*	$\dfrac{e^{ax}\sin sx}{s}\left[\dfrac{P'(x)}{s} - \dfrac{P'''(x)}{s^3} + \dfrac{P^v(x)}{s^5} - \cdots\right] - \dfrac{e^{ax}\cos sx}{s}\left[P(x) - \dfrac{P''(x)}{s^2} + \dfrac{P^{iv}(x)}{s^4} - \cdots\right]$

* For $\cos sx$ in R replace "sin" by "cos" and "cos" by "$-$ sin" in y_p.

$$D^n = \dfrac{d^n}{dx^n} \qquad \binom{m}{n} = \dfrac{m!}{(m-n)!\,n!} \qquad 0! = 1$$

DIFFERENTIAL EQUATIONS (Continued)

TABLE II: $(D - a)^2 y = R$

R	y_p
12. e^{rx}	$\dfrac{e^{rx}}{(r-a)^2}$
13. $\sin sx$*	$\dfrac{1}{(a^2+s^2)^2}\left[(a^2-s^2)\sin sx + 2as\cos sx\right] = \dfrac{1}{a^2+s^2}\sin\left(sx + \tan^{-1}\dfrac{2as}{a^2-s^2}\right)$
14. $P(x)$	$\dfrac{1}{a^2}\left[P(x) + \dfrac{2P'(x)}{a} + \dfrac{3P''(x)}{a^2} + \cdots + \dfrac{(n+1)P^{(n)}(x)}{a^n}\right]$
15. $e^{rx}\sin sx$*	Replace a by $a - r$ in formula 13 and multiply by e^{rx}.
16. $P(x)e^{rx}$	Replace a by $a - r$ in formula 14 and multiply by e^{rx}.
17. $P(x)\sin sx$*	$\sin sx\left[\dfrac{a^2-s^2}{(a^2+s^2)^2}P(x) + 2\dfrac{a^3-3as^2}{(a^2+s^2)^3}P'(x) + 3\dfrac{a^4-6a^2s^2+s^4}{(a^2+s^2)^4}P''(x) + \cdots \right.$
	$\left. + (k-1)\dfrac{a^k - \binom{k}{2}a^{k-2}s^2 + \binom{k}{4}a^{k-4}s^4 - \cdots}{(a^2+s^2)^k}P^{(k-2)}(x) + \cdots\right]$
	$+ \cos sx\left[\dfrac{2as}{(a^2+s^2)^2}P(x) + 2\dfrac{3a^2s-s^3}{(a^2+s^2)^3}P'(x) + 3\dfrac{4a^3s-4as^3}{(a^2+s^2)^4}P''(x) + \cdots \right.$
	$\left. + (k-1)\dfrac{\binom{k}{1}a^{k-1}s - \binom{k}{3}a^{k-3}s^3 + \cdots}{(a^2+s^2)^k}P^{(k-2)}(x) + \cdots\right]$
18. $P(x)e^{rx}\sin sx$*	Replace a by $a - r$ in formula 17 and multiply by e^{rx}.
19. e^{ax}	$\tfrac{1}{2}x^2 e^{ax}$
20. $e^{ax}\sin sx$*	$-\dfrac{e^{ax}\sin sx}{s^2}$
21. $P(x)e^{ax}$	$e^{ax}\displaystyle\iint P(x)\,dx\,dx$
22. $P(x)e^{ax}\sin sx$*	$-\dfrac{e^{ax}\sin sx}{s^2}\left[P(x) - \dfrac{3P''(x)}{s^2} + \dfrac{5P^{iv}(x)}{s^4} - \dfrac{7P^{vi}(x)}{s^6} + \cdots\right]$
	$-\dfrac{e^{ax}\cos sx}{s^2}\left[\dfrac{2P'(x)}{s} - \dfrac{4P'''(x)}{s^3} + \dfrac{6P^v(x)}{s^5} - \cdots\right]$

*For cos sx in R replace "sin" by "cos" and "cos" by "− sin" in y_p.

DIFFERENTIAL EQUATIONS (Continued)

TABLE III: $(D^2 + q)y = R$

R	y_p
23. e^{rx}	$\dfrac{e^{rx}}{r^2+q}$
24. $\sin sx*$	$\dfrac{\sin sx}{-s^2+q}$
25. $P(x)$	$\dfrac{1}{q}\left[P(x) - \dfrac{P''(x)}{q} + \dfrac{P^{iv}(x)}{q^2} - \cdots + (-1)^k \dfrac{P^{(2k)}(x)}{q^k} \cdots\right]$
26. $e^{rx}\sin sx*$	$\dfrac{(r^2 - s^2 + q)e^{rx}\sin sx - 2rse^{rx}\cos sx}{(r^2 - s^2 + q)^2 + (2rs)^2}$
	$= \dfrac{e^{rx}}{\sqrt{(r^2 - s^2 + q)^2 + (2rs)^2}}\sin\left[sx - \tan^{-1}\dfrac{2rs}{r^2 - s^2 + q}\right]$
27. $P(x)e^{rx}$	$\dfrac{e^{rx}}{r^2+q}\left[P(x) - \dfrac{2r}{r^2+q}P'(x) + \dfrac{3r^2 - q}{(r^2+q)^2}P''(x) - \dfrac{4r^3 - 4qr}{(r^2+q)^3}P'''(x)\right.$
	$+ \cdots + (-1)^{k-1}\left[\binom{k}{1}r^{k-1} - \binom{k}{3}r^{k-3}q + \binom{k}{5}r^{k-5}q^2 - \cdots\right]\dfrac{P^{(k-1)}(x)}{(r^2+q)^{k-1}} + \cdots$
28. $P(x)\sin sx*$	$\dfrac{\sin sx}{(-s^2+q)}\left[P(x) - \dfrac{3s^2+q}{(-s^2+q)^2}P''(x) + \dfrac{5s^4+10s^2q+q^2}{(-s^2+q)^4}P^{iv}(x) + \cdots\right.$
	$+ (-1)^k\dfrac{\binom{2k+1}{1}s^{2k} + \binom{2k+1}{3}s^{2k-2}q + \binom{2k+1}{5}s^{2k-4}q^2 + \cdots}{(-s^2+q)^{2k}}P^{(2k)}(x) + \cdots$
	$- \dfrac{s\cos sx}{(-s^2+q)}\left[\dfrac{2P'(x)}{(-s^2+q)} - \dfrac{4s^2+4q}{(-s^2+q)^3}P'''(x) + \cdots\right.$
	$+ (-1)^{k+1}\dfrac{\binom{2k}{1}s^{2k-2} + \binom{2k}{3}s^{2k-4}q + \cdots}{(-s^2+q)^{2k-1}}P^{(2k-1)}(x) + \cdots$

TABLE IV: $(D^2 + b^2)y = R$

R	y_p
29. $\sin bx*$	$-\dfrac{x\cos bx}{2b}$
30. $P(x)\sin bx*$	$\dfrac{\sin bx}{(2b)^2}\left[P(x) - \dfrac{P''(x)}{(2b)^2} + \dfrac{P^{iv}(x)}{(2b)^4} - \cdots\right] - \dfrac{\cos bx}{2b}\int\left[P(x) - \dfrac{P''(x)}{(2b)^2} + \cdots\right]dx$

* For cos sx in R replace "sin" by "cos" and "cos" by "$-$ sin" in y_p.

DIFFERENTIAL EQUATIONS (Continued)

TABLE V: $(D^2 + pD + q)y = R$

R	y_p
31. e^{rx}	$\dfrac{e^{rx}}{r^2 + pr + q}$
32. $\sin sx$*	$\dfrac{(q - s^2)\sin sx - ps\cos sx}{(q - s^2)^2 + (ps)^2} = \dfrac{1}{\sqrt{(q - s^2)^2 + (ps)^2}}\sin\left(sx - \tan^{-1}\dfrac{ps}{q - s^2}\right)$
33. $P(x)$	$\dfrac{1}{q}\left[P(x) - \dfrac{p}{q}P'(x) + \dfrac{p^2 - q}{q^2}P''(x) - \dfrac{p^3 - 2pq}{q^3}P'''(x) + \cdots \right.$ $\left. + (-1)^n\left[p^n - \binom{n-1}{1}p^{n-2}q + \binom{n-2}{2}p^{n-4}q^2 - \cdots \right]\dfrac{P^{(n)}(x)}{q^n}\right]$
34. $e^{rx}\sin sx$*	Replace p by $p + 2r$, q by $q + pr + r^2$ in formula 32 and multiply by e^{rx}.
35. $P(x)e^{rx}$	Replace p by $p + 2r$, q by $q + pr + r^2$ in formula 33 and multiply by e^{rx}.

TABLE VI: $(D - b)(D - a)y = R$

R	y_p
36. $P(x)\sin sx$*	$\dfrac{\sin sx}{b - a}\left[\left(\dfrac{a}{a^2 + s^2} - \dfrac{b}{b^2 + s^2}\right)P(x) + \left(\dfrac{a^2 - s^2}{(a^2 + s^2)^2} - \dfrac{b^2 - s^2}{(b^2 + s^2)^2}\right)P'(x) \right.$ $\left. + \left(\dfrac{a^3 - 3as^2}{(a^2 + s^2)^3} - \dfrac{b^3 - 3bs^2}{(b^2 + s^2)^3}\right)P''(x) + \cdots \right]$ $+ \dfrac{\cos sx}{b - a}\left[\left(\dfrac{s}{a^2 + s^2} - \dfrac{s}{b^2 + s^2}\right)P(x) + \left(\dfrac{2as}{(a^2 + s^2)^2} - \dfrac{2bs}{(b^2 + s^2)^2}\right)P'(x) \right.$ $\left. + \left(\dfrac{3a^2s - s^3}{(a^2 + s^2)^3} - \dfrac{3b^2s - s^3}{(b^2 + s^2)^3}\right)P''(x) + \cdots \right]^{\dagger}$
37. $P(x)e^{rx}\sin sx$*	Replace a by $a - r$, b by $b - r$ in formula 36 and multiply by e^{rx}.
38. $P(x)e^{ax}$	$\dfrac{e^{ax}}{a - b}\left[\int P(x)dx + \dfrac{P(x)}{(b - a)} + \dfrac{P'(x)}{(b - a)^2} + \dfrac{P''(x)}{(b - a)^3} + \cdots + \dfrac{P^{(n)}(x)}{(b - a)^{n+1}}\right]$

* For $\cos sx$ in R replace "sin" by "cos" and "cos" by "−sin" in y_p.
† For additional terms, compare with formula 6.

DIFFERENTIAL EQUATIONS (Continued)

TABLE VII: $(D^2 - 2aD + a^2 + b^2)y = R$

R	y_p

39. $P(x)e^{rx}\sin sx$*

$$y_p = \frac{\sin sx}{2b}\left[\left(\frac{s+b}{a^2+(s+b)^2} - \frac{s-b}{a^2+(s-b)^2}\right)P(x) + \left(\frac{2a(s+b)}{[a^2+(s+b)^2]^2} - \frac{2a(s-b)}{[a^2+(s-b)^2]^2}\right)P'(x)\right.$$

$$+\left(\frac{3a^2(s+b)-(s+b)^3}{[a^2+(s+b)^2]^3} - \frac{3a^2(s-b)-(s-b)^3}{[a^2+(s-b)^2]^3}\right)P''(x)+\cdots\right]$$

$$-\frac{\cos sx}{2b}\left[\left(\frac{a}{a^2+(s+b)^2} - \frac{a}{a^2+(s-b)^2}\right)P(x) + \left(\frac{a^2-(s+b)^2}{[a^2+(s+b)^2]^2} - \frac{a^2-(s-b)^2}{[a^2+(s-b)^2]^2}\right)P'(x)\right.$$

$$+\left(\frac{a^3-3a(s+b)^2}{[a^2+(s+b)^2]^3} - \frac{a^3-3a(s-b)^2}{[a^2+(s-b)^2]^3}\right)P''(x)+\cdots\right]†$$

40. $P(x)e^{rx}\sin sx$*   Replace a by $a-r$ in formula 39 and multiply by e^{rx}.

41. $P(x)e^{ax}$ $\dfrac{e^{ax}}{b^2}\left[P(x) - \dfrac{P''(x)}{b^2} + \dfrac{P^{iv}(x)}{b^4} - \cdots\right]$

42. $e^{ax}\sin sx$* $\dfrac{e^{ax}\sin sx}{-s^2+b^2}$

43. $e^{ax}\sin bx$* $-\dfrac{xe^{ax}\cos bx}{2b}$

44. $P(x)e^{ax}\sin bx$* $\dfrac{e^{ax}\sin bx}{(2b)^2}\left[P(x) - \dfrac{P''(x)}{(2b)^2} + \dfrac{P^{iv}(x)}{(2b)^4} - \cdots\right] - \dfrac{e^{ax}\cos bx}{2b}\displaystyle\int\left[P(x) - \dfrac{P''(x)}{(2b)^2} + \dfrac{P^{iv}(x)}{(2b)^4} - \cdots\right]dx$

* For cos sx in R replace "sin" by "cos" and "cos" by "−sin" in y_p.
† For additional terms, compare with formula 6.

DIFFERENTIAL EQUATIONS (Continued)

TABLE VIII: $f(D)y = [D^n + a_{n-1}D^{n-1} + \cdots + a_1 D + a_0]y = R$

R	y_p
45. e^{rx}	$\dfrac{e^{rx}}{f(r)}$
46. $\sin sx$*	$\dfrac{[a_0 - a_2s^2 + a_4s^4 - \cdots]\sin sx - [a_1s - a_3s^3 + a_5s^5 + \cdots]\cos sx}{[a_0 - a_2s^2 + a_4s^4 - \cdots]^2 + [a_1s - a_3s^3 + a_5s^5 - \cdots]^2}$

TABLE IX: $f(D^2)y = R$

R	y_p
47. $\sin sx$*	$\dfrac{\sin sx}{f(-s^2)} = \dfrac{\sin sx}{a_0 - a_2s^2 + \cdots \pm s^{2n}}$

TABLE X: $(D - a)^n y = R$

R	y_p
48. e^{rx}	$\dfrac{e^{rx}}{(r - a)^n}$
49. $\sin sx$*	$\dfrac{(-1)^n}{(a^2 + s^2)^n}\left\{[a^n - \binom{n}{2}a^{n-2}s^2 + \binom{n}{4}a^{n-4}s^4 - \cdots]\sin sx + [\binom{n}{1}a^{n-1}s - \binom{n}{3}a^{n-3}s^3 + \cdots]\cos sx\right\}$
50. $P(x)$	$\dfrac{(-1)^n}{a^n}\left[P(x) + \binom{n}{1}\dfrac{P'(x)}{a} + \binom{n+1}{2}\dfrac{P''(x)}{a^2} + \binom{n+2}{3}\dfrac{P'''(x)}{a^3} + \cdots\right]$
51. $e^{rx}\sin sx$*	Replace a by $a - r$ in formula 49 and multiply by e^{rx}.
52. $e^{rx}P(x)$	Replace a by $a - r$ in formula 50 and multiply by e^{rx}.

* For cos sx in R replace "sin" by "cos" and "cos" by "$-$ sin" in y_p.

DIFFERENTIAL EQUATIONS (Continued)

53. $P(x) \sin sx$*

$(-1)^n \sin sx[A_nP(x) + \binom{n}{1}A_{n+1}P'(x) + \binom{n}{2}A_{n+2}P''(x) + \binom{n+1}{3}A_{n+3}P'''(x) + \cdots]$
$+ (-1)^n \cos sx[B_nP(x) + \binom{n}{1}B_{n+1}P'(x) + \binom{n+1}{2}B_{n+2}P''(x) + \binom{n+1}{3}B_{n+3}P'''(x) + \cdots]$

$$A_1 = \frac{a}{a^2+s^2}, \quad A_2 = \frac{a^2-s^2}{(a^2+s^2)^2}, \quad \cdots, \quad A_k = \frac{a^k - \binom{k}{2}a^{k-2}s^2 + \binom{k}{4}a^{k-4}s^4 - \cdots}{(a^2+s^2)^k}$$

$$B_1 = \frac{s}{a^2+s^2}, \quad B_2 = \frac{2as}{(a^2+s^2)^2}, \quad \cdots, \quad B_k = \frac{\binom{k}{1}a^{k-1}s - \binom{k}{3}a^{k-3}s^3 + \cdots}{(a^2+s^2)^k}$$

54. $P(x)e^{rx} \sin sx$*   Replace a by $a - r$ in formula 53 and multiply by e^{rx}.

55. $e^{ax}P(x)$ $e^{ax} \iint \cdots \int P(x)dx^n$

56. $P(x)e^{ax} \sin sx$*

$(-1)^{\frac{n-1}{2}} \dfrac{e^{az}\sin sx}{s^n}\left[\binom{n}{n-1}\dfrac{P'(x)}{s} - \binom{n+2}{n-1}\dfrac{P'''(x)}{s^3} + \binom{n+4}{n-1}\dfrac{P^v(x)}{s^5} - \cdots\right]$
$+ (-1)^{\frac{n+1}{2}} \dfrac{e^{az}\cos sx}{s^n}\left[\binom{n}{n-1}P(x) - \binom{n+1}{n-1}\dfrac{P''(x)}{s^2} + \binom{n+3}{n-1}\dfrac{P^{iv}(x)}{s^4} - \cdots\right]$ (n odd)

$(-1)^{\frac{n}{2}} \dfrac{e^{az}\sin sx}{s^n}\left[\binom{n-1}{n-1}P(x) - \binom{n+1}{n-1}\dfrac{P''(x)}{s^2} + \binom{n+3}{n-1}\dfrac{P^{iv}(x)}{s^4} - \cdots\right]$
$+ (-1)^{\frac{n}{2}} \dfrac{e^{az}\cos sx}{s^n}\left[\binom{n}{n-1}\dfrac{P'(x)}{s} - \binom{n+2}{n-1}\dfrac{P'''(x)}{s^3} + \binom{n+4}{n-1}\dfrac{P^v(x)}{s^5} - \cdots\right]$ (n even)

TABLE XI: $(D - a)^n f(D)y = R$

57. e^{ax} $\dfrac{x^n}{n!} \cdot \dfrac{e^{ax}}{f(a)}$

* For cos sx in R replace "sin" by "cos" and "cos" by "− sin" in y_p.

DIFFERENTIAL EQUATIONS (Continued)

TABLE XII: $(D^2 + q)^n y = R$

R	y_p
58. e^{rx}	$e^{rx}/(r^2 + q)^n$
59. $\sin sx$*	$\sin sx/(q - s^2)^n$
60. $P(x)$	$\dfrac{1}{q^n}\left[P(x) - \binom{n}{1}\dfrac{P''(x)}{q} + \binom{n+1}{2}\dfrac{P^{iv}(x)}{q^2} - \binom{n+2}{3}\dfrac{P^{vi}(x)}{q^3} + \cdots\right]$
61. $e^{rx}\sin sx$*	$\dfrac{e^{rx}}{(A^2 + B^2)^n}\{[A^n - \binom{n}{2}A^{n-2}B^2 + \binom{n}{4}A^{n-4}B^4 - \cdots]\sin sx - [\binom{n}{1}A^{n-1}B - \binom{n}{3}A^{n-3}B^3 + \cdots]\cos sx\}$

$$A = r^2 - s^2 + q, \quad B = 2rs$$

TABLE XIII: $(D^2 + b^2)^n y = R$

62. $\sin bx$*	$(-1)^{\frac{n+1}{2}}\dfrac{x^n \cos bx}{n!(2b)^n}$ (n odd), $(-1)^{\frac{n}{2}}\dfrac{x^n \sin bx}{n!(2b)^n}$ (n even)

TABLE XIV: $(D^n - q)y = R$

63. e^{rx}	$e^{rx}/(r^n - q)$
64. $P(x)$	$-\dfrac{1}{q}\left[P(x) + \dfrac{P^{(n)}(x)}{q} + \dfrac{P^{(2n)}(x)}{q^2} + \cdots\right]$
65. $\sin sx$*	$-\dfrac{q\sin sx + (-1)^{\frac{n-1}{2}}\, s^n \cos sx}{q^2 + s^{2n}}$ (n odd), $\dfrac{\sin sx}{(-s^2)^{n/2} - q}$ (n even)
66. $e^{rx}\sin sx$*	$\dfrac{Ae^{rx}\sin sr - Be^{rx}\cos sx}{A^2 + B^2} = \dfrac{e^{rx}}{\sqrt{A^2 + B^2}}\sin\left(sx - \tan^{-1}\dfrac{B}{A}\right)$

$$A = [r^n - \binom{n}{2}r^{n-2}s^2 + \binom{n}{4}r^{n-4}s^4 - \cdots] - q, \quad B = [\binom{n}{1}r^{n-1}s - \binom{n}{3}r^{n-3}s^3 + \cdots]$$

* For $\cos sx$ in R replace "sin" by "cos" and "cos" by "$-\sin$" in y_p.

DIFFERENTIAL EQUATIONS (Continued)

TABLE XV: $(D_x + mD_y)z = R$

R	z_p
67. e^{ax+by}	$\dfrac{e^{ax+by}}{a+mb}$
68. $f(ax+by)$	$\dfrac{\int f(u)du}{a+mb}$, $u = ax + by$
69. $f(y-mx)$	$xf(y-mx)$
70. $\phi(x,y)f(y-mx)$	$f(y-mx)\int \phi(x, a+mx)dx$ $\quad(a = y-mx$ after integration)

TABLE XVI: $(D_x + mD_y - k)z = R$

71. e^{ax+by}	$\dfrac{e^{ax+by}}{a+mb-k}$
72. $\sin(ax+by)$*	$-\dfrac{(a+bm)\cos(ax+by)+k\sin(ax+by)}{(a+bm)^2+k^2}$
73. $e^{\alpha x+\beta y}\sin(ax+by)$*	Replace k in 72 by $k-\alpha-m\beta$ and multiply by $e^{\alpha x+\beta y}$
74. $e^{xk}f(ax+by)$	$\dfrac{e^{kx}\int f(u)du}{a+mb}$, $u = ax+by$
75. $f(y-mx)$	$-\dfrac{f(y-mx)}{k}$
76. $P(x)f(y-mx)$	$-\dfrac{1}{k}f(y-mx)\left[P(x)+\dfrac{P'(x)}{k}+\dfrac{P''(x)}{k^2}+\cdots+\dfrac{P^{(n)}(x)}{k^n}\right]$
77. $e^{kx}f(y-mx)$	$xe^{kx}f(y-mx)$

* For $\cos(ax+by)$ replace "sin" by "cos," and "cos" by "$-$sin" in z_p.

$$D_x = \frac{\partial}{\partial x}; \qquad D_y = \frac{\partial}{\partial y}; \qquad D_x^k D_y^r = \frac{\partial^{k+r}}{\partial_x{}^k \partial_y{}^r}$$

DIFFERENTIAL EQUATIONS (Continued)

TABLE XVII: $(D_x + mD_y)^n z = R$

R	z_p
78. e^{ax+by}	$\dfrac{e^{ax+by}}{(a+mb)^n}$
79. $f(ax+by)$	$\dfrac{\int\int\cdots\int f(u)du^n}{(a+mb)^n}$, $u = ax + by$
80. $f(y-mx)$	$\dfrac{x^n}{n!}f(y-mx)$
81. $\phi(x,y)f(y+mx)$	$f(y-mx)\int\int\cdots\int\phi(x,a+mx)dx^n$ $\quad(a = y - mx$ after integration$)$

TABLE XVIII: $(D_x + mD_y - k)^n z = R$

R	z_p
82. e^{ax+by}	$\dfrac{e^{ax+by}}{(a+mb-k)^n}$
83. $f(y-mx)$	$\dfrac{(-1)^n f(y-mx)}{k^n}$
84. $P(x)f(y-mx)$	$\dfrac{(-1)^n}{k^n}f(y-mx)\left[P(x)+\binom{n}{1}\dfrac{P'(x)}{k}+\binom{n+1}{2}\dfrac{P''(x)}{k^2}+\binom{n+2}{3}\dfrac{P'''(x)}{k^3}+\cdots\right]$
85. $e^{kx}f(ax+by)$	$\dfrac{e^{kx}\int\int\cdots\int f(u)du^n}{(a+mb)^n}$, $u = ax + by$
86. $e^{kx}f(y-mx)$	$\dfrac{x^n}{n!}e^{kx}f(y-mx)$

DIFFERENTIAL EQUATIONS (Continued)

TABLE XIX: $[D_x^n + a_1 D_x^{n-1} D_y + a_2 D_x^{n-2} D_y^2 + \cdots + a^n D_y^n]z = R$

87. e^{ax+by}
$$\frac{e^{ax+by}}{a + a_1 a^{n-1} b + a_2 a^{n-2} b^2 + \cdots + a_n b^n}$$

88. $f(ax + by)$
$$\frac{\int \int \cdots \int f(u) du^n}{a^n + a_1 a^{n-1} b + a_2 a^{n-2} b^2 + \cdots + a^n b^n}, \quad (u = ax + by)$$

TABLE XX: $F(D_x, D_y)z = R$

89. e^{ax+by}
$$\frac{e^{ax+by}}{F(a, b)}$$

TABLE XXI: $F(D_x^2, D_x D_y, D_y^2)z = R$

90. $\sin (ax + by)$*
$$\frac{\sin (ax + by)}{F(-a^2, -ab, -b^2)}$$

* For cos $(ax + by)$ replace "sin" by "cos", and "cos" by "$-$sin" in z_p.

THE LAPLACE TRANSFORM

Dr. R. E. Gaskell

If $F(t)$ is a piecewise continuous real-valued function of the real variable $t (0 \leq t < \infty)$, and if $F(t)$ is of exponential order, that is if $|F(t)| < Me^{at} (t > T; M, a, T$ positive constants) then the *Laplace transform* of $F(t)$,

$$L\{F(t)\} = f(s) = \int_0^\infty e^{-st} F(t) \, dt, \tag{1}$$

exists in the half-plane of the complex variable s for which the real part of s is greater than some fixed value s_0, i.e., $R(s) \geq s_0$. Furthermore

$$F(t) = \frac{1}{2\pi i} \int_{a-i\infty}^{a+i\infty} e^{st} f(s) \, ds, \tag{2}$$

where $a > s_0$. The important property

$$L\{F^{(r)}(t)\} = \int_0^\infty e^{-st} \left(\frac{d^r F}{dt^r} \right) dt$$

$$= s^r f(s) - \sum_{n=0}^{r-1} s^{r-1-n} F^{(n)}(+0) \tag{3}$$

makes the Laplace transform very useful for solving linear differential equations with constant coefficients, and many boundary value problems.

THE FINITE FOURIER TRANSFORM

Dr. R. E. Gaskell

For a piecewise continuous function $F(x)$ over a finite interval $0 \leq x \leq \pi$, the *finite Fourier cosine transform* of $F(x)$ is

$$f_c(n) = \int_0^\pi F(x) \cos nx \, dx \quad (n = 0, 1, 2, \ldots). \tag{4}$$

If x ranges over the interval $0 \leq x \leq L$, the substitution $x' = \pi x / L$ allows the use of this definition, also. The inverse transform is written

$$\overline{F}(x) = \frac{1}{\pi} f_c(0) - \frac{2}{\pi} \sum_{n=1}^\infty f_c(n) \cos nx \quad (0 < x < \pi) \tag{5}$$

where $\overline{F}(x) = \dfrac{[F(x + 0) + F(x - 0)]}{2}$. We observe that $\overline{F}(x) = F(x)$ at points of continuity. The formula

$$f_c^{(2)}(n) = \int_0^\pi F''(x) \cos nx \, dx$$
$$= -n^2 f_c(n) - F'(0) + (-1)^n F'(\pi) \tag{6}$$

makes the finite Fourier cosine transform useful in certain boundary value problems.

Analogously, the *finite Fourier sine transform* of $F(x)$ is

$$f_s(n) = \int_0^\pi F(x) \sin nx \, dx \quad (n = 1, 2, 3, \ldots) \tag{7}$$

and

$$\overline{F}(x) = \frac{2}{\pi} \sum_{n=1}^\infty f_s(n) \sin nx \quad (0 < x < \pi) \tag{8}$$

Corresponding to (6) we have

$$f_s^{(2)}(n) = \int_0^\pi F''(x) \sin nx \, dx$$
$$= -n^2 f_s(n) - nF(0) - n(-1)^n F(\pi). \tag{9}$$

FOURIER TRANSFORMS

If $F(x)$ is defined for $x \geq 0$ and is piecewise continuous over any finite interval, and if

$$\int_0^\infty F(x) \, dx$$

is absolutely convergent, then

$$f_c(\alpha) = \sqrt{\frac{2}{\pi}} \int_0^\infty F(x) \cos (\alpha x) \, dx \tag{10}$$

is the *Fourier cosine transform* of $F(x)$. Furthermore,

$$\overline{F}(x) = \sqrt{\frac{2}{\pi}} \int_0^\infty f_c(\alpha) \cos (\alpha x) \, d\alpha. \tag{11}$$

If $\lim\limits_{x \to \infty} \dfrac{d^n F}{dx^n} = 0$, an important property of the Fourier cosine transform

$$f_c^{(2r)}(\alpha) = \sqrt{\frac{2}{\pi}} \int_0^\infty \left(\frac{d^{2r}F}{dx^{2r}}\right) \cos(\alpha x)\, dx$$

$$= -\sum_{n=0}^{r-1} (-1)^n a_{2r-2n-1} \alpha^{2n} + (-1)^r \alpha^{2r} f_c(\alpha) \tag{12}$$

where $\lim\limits_{x \to 0} \dfrac{d^r F}{dx^r} = a_r$, makes it useful in the solution of many problems.

Under the same conditions,

$$f_s(\alpha) = \sqrt{\frac{2}{\pi}} \int_0^\infty F(x) \sin(\alpha x)\, dx \tag{13}$$

defines the *Fourier sine transform* of $F(x)$, and

$$\bar{F}(x) = \sqrt{\frac{2}{\pi}} \int_0^\infty f_s(\alpha) \sin(\alpha x)\, d\alpha. \tag{14}$$

Corresponding to (12) we have

$$f_s^{(2r)}(\alpha) = \sqrt{\frac{2}{\pi}} \int_0^\infty \frac{d^{2r}F}{dx^{2r}} \sin(\alpha x)\, dx$$

$$= -\sum_{n=1}^{r} (-1)^n \alpha^{2n-1} a_{2r-2n} + (-1)^{r-1} \alpha^{2r} f_s(\alpha). \tag{15}$$

Similarly, if $F(x)$ is defined for $-\infty < x < \infty$, and if $\displaystyle\int_{-\infty}^{\infty} F(x)\, dx$ is absolutely convergent, then

$$f(\alpha) = \frac{1}{\sqrt{2\pi}} \int_{-\infty}^{\infty} F(x) e^{i\alpha x}\, dx \tag{16}$$

is the *Fourier transform* of $F(x)$, and

$$\bar{F}(x) = \frac{1}{\sqrt{2\pi}} \int_{-\infty}^{\infty} f(\alpha) e^{-i\alpha x}\, d\alpha. \tag{17}$$

Also, if

$$\lim_{|x| \to \infty} \left| \frac{d^n F}{dx^n} \right| = 0 \quad (n = 1, 2, \ldots, r-1),$$

then

$$f^{(r)}(\alpha) = \frac{1}{\sqrt{2\pi}} \int_{-\infty}^{\infty} F^{(r)}(x) e^{i\alpha x}\, dx = (-i\alpha)^r f(\alpha). \tag{18}$$

	$F(t)$	$f(s)$
1	$F(t)$	$\displaystyle\int_0^\infty e^{-st}F(t)\,dt$
2	$AF(t) + BG(t)$	$Af(s) + Bg(s)$
3	$F'(t)$	$sf(s) - F(+0)$
4	$F^{(n)}(t)$	$s^n f(s) - s^{n-1}F(+0) - s^{n-2}F'(+0) - \cdots$ $\qquad\qquad\qquad - F^{(n-1)}(+0)$
5	$\displaystyle\int_0^t F(\tau)\,d\tau$	$\dfrac{1}{s}f(s)$
6	$\displaystyle\int_0^t \int_0^\tau F(\lambda)\,d\lambda\,d\tau$	$\dfrac{1}{s^2}f(s)$
7	$\displaystyle\int_0^t F_1(t-\tau)F_2(\tau)\,d\tau = F_1*F_2$	$f_1(s)f_2(s)$
8	$tF(t)$	$-f'(s)$
9	$t^n F(t)$	$(-1)^n f^{(n)}(s)$
10	$\dfrac{1}{t}F(t)$	$\displaystyle\int_s^\infty f(x)\,dx$
11	$e^{at}F(t)$	$f(s-a)$
12	$F(t-b)$, where $F(t) = 0$ when $t < 0$	$e^{-bs}f(s)$
13	$\dfrac{1}{c}F\left(\dfrac{t}{c}\right)$	$f(cs)$
14	$\dfrac{1}{c}e^{(bt)/c}F\left(\dfrac{t}{c}\right)$	$f(cs-b)$
15	$F(t+a) = F(t)$	$\dfrac{\displaystyle\int_0^a e^{-st}F(t)\,dt}{1-e^{-as}}$
16	$F(t+a) = -F(t)$	$\dfrac{\displaystyle\int_0^a e^{-st}F(t)\,dt}{1+e^{-as}}$
17	$F_1(t)$, the half-wave rectification of $F(t)$ in No. 16	$\dfrac{f(s)}{1-e^{-as}}$
18	$F_2(t)$, the full-wave rectification of $F(t)$ in No. 16	$f(s)\coth\dfrac{as}{2}$
19	$\displaystyle\sum_1^m \dfrac{p(a_n)}{q'(a_n)}e^{a_n t}$	$\dfrac{p(s)}{q(s)}$, $q(s) = (s-a_1)(s-a_2)\cdots(s-a_m)$
20	$e^{at}\displaystyle\sum_{n=1}^r \dfrac{\phi^{(r-n)}(a)}{(r-n)!}\dfrac{t^{n-1}}{(n-1)!} + \cdots$	$\dfrac{p(s)}{q(s)} = \dfrac{\phi(s)}{(s-a)^r}$

[1]These tables of Laplace Operations, Laplace Transforms, and Finite Fourier sine and cosine transforms were taken from "Modern Operational Mathematics in Engineering", by permission of the author, R. V. Churchill, and the publisher, McGraw-Hill Book Company, Inc.

LAPLACE TRANSFORMS

	$f(s)$	$F(t)$
1	$\dfrac{1}{s}$	1
2	$\dfrac{1}{s^2}$	t
3	$\dfrac{1}{s^n}$ $(n = 1, 2, \ldots)$	$\dfrac{t^{n-1}}{(n-1)!}$
4	$\dfrac{1}{\sqrt{s}}$	$\dfrac{1}{\sqrt{\pi t}}$
5	$s^{-3/2}$	$2\sqrt{\dfrac{t}{\pi}}$
6	$s^{-[n+(1/2)]}$ $(n = 1, 2, \ldots)$	$\dfrac{2^n t^{n-(1/2)}}{1\cdot3\cdot5\cdots(2n-1)\sqrt{\pi}}$
7	$\dfrac{\Gamma(k)}{s^k}$ $(k \geq 0)$	t^{k-1}
8	$\dfrac{1}{s-a}$	e^{at}
9	$\dfrac{1}{(s-a)^2}$	te^{at}
10	$\dfrac{1}{(s-a)^n}$ $(n = 1, 2, \ldots)$	$\dfrac{1}{(n-1)!} t^{n-1} e^{at}$
11	$\dfrac{\Gamma(k)}{(s-a)^k}$ $(k \geq 0)$	$t^{k-1} e^{at}$
12*	$\dfrac{1}{(s-a)(s-b)}$	$\dfrac{1}{a-b}(e^{at} - e^{bt})$
13*	$\dfrac{s}{(s-a)(s-b)}$	$\dfrac{1}{a-b}(ae^{at} - be^{bt})$
14*	$\dfrac{1}{(s-a)(s-b)(s-c)}$	$-\dfrac{(b-c)e^{at} + (c-a)e^{bt} + (a-b)e^{ct}}{(a-b)(b-c)(c-a)}$
15	$\dfrac{1}{s^2 + a^2}$	$\dfrac{1}{a}\sin at$
16	$\dfrac{s}{s^2 + a^2}$	$\cos at$
17	$\dfrac{1}{s^2 - a^2}$	$\dfrac{1}{a}\sinh at$
18	$\dfrac{s}{s^2 - a^2}$	$\cosh at$

*Here a, b, and (in 14) c represent distinct constants.

LAPLACE TRANSFORMS (Continued)

	$f(s)$	$F(t)$
19	$\dfrac{1}{s(s^2 + a^2)}$	$\dfrac{1}{a^2}(1 - \cos at)$
20	$\dfrac{1}{s^2(s^2 + a^2)}$	$\dfrac{1}{a^3}(at - \sin at)$
21	$\dfrac{1}{(s^2 + a^2)^2}$	$\dfrac{1}{2a^3}(\sin at - at \cos at)$
22	$\dfrac{s}{(s^2 + a^2)^2}$	$\dfrac{t}{2a}\sin at$
23	$\dfrac{s^2}{(s^2 + a^2)^2}$	$\dfrac{1}{2a}(\sin at + at \cos at)$
24	$\dfrac{s^2 - a^2}{(s^2 + a^2)^2}$	$t \cos at$
25	$\dfrac{s}{(s^2 + a^2)(s^2 + b^2)}\ (a^2 \neq b^2)$	$\dfrac{\cos at - \cos bt}{b^2 - a^2}$
26	$\dfrac{1}{(s - a)^2 + b^2}$	$\dfrac{1}{b}e^{at}\sin bt$
27	$\dfrac{s - a}{(s - a)^2 + b^2}$	$e^{at}\cos bt$
27.1	$\dfrac{1}{[(s + a)^2 + b^2]^n}$	$\dfrac{-e^{-at}}{4^{n-1}b^{2n}}\displaystyle\sum_{r=1}^{n}\binom{2n - r - 1}{n - 1}(-2t)^{r-1}\dfrac{d^r}{dt^r}[\cos(bt)]$
27.2	$\dfrac{s}{[(s + a)^2 + b^2]^n}$	$\dfrac{e^{-at}}{4^{n-1}b^{2n}}\left\{\displaystyle\sum_{r=1}^{n}\binom{2n - r - 1}{n - 1}\right.$ $(-2t)^{r-1}\dfrac{d^r}{dt^r}[a\cos(bt) + b\sin(bt)]$ $\left.-2b\displaystyle\sum_{r=1}^{n-1}r\binom{2n - r - 2}{n - 1}\right.$ $\left.(-2t)^{r-1}\dfrac{d^r}{dt^r}[\sin bt]\right\}$
28	$\dfrac{3a^2}{s^3 + a^3}$	$e^{-at} - e^{(at)/2}\left(\cos\dfrac{at\sqrt{3}}{2} - \sqrt{3}\sin\dfrac{at\sqrt{3}}{2}\right)$
29	$\dfrac{4a^3}{s^4 + 4a^4}$	$\sin at \cosh at - \cos at \sinh at$
30	$\dfrac{s}{s^4 + 4a^4}$	$\dfrac{1}{2a^2}\sin at \sinh at$

LAPLACE TRANSFORMS (Continued)

	$f(s)$	$F(t)$
31	$\dfrac{1}{s^4 - a^4}$	$\dfrac{1}{2a^3}(\sinh at - \sin at)$
32	$\dfrac{s}{s^4 - a^4}$	$\dfrac{1}{2a^2}(\cosh at - \cos at)$
33	$\dfrac{8a^3 s^2}{(s^2 + a^2)^3}$	$(1 + a^2 t^2)\sin at - \cos at$
34*	$\dfrac{1}{s}\left(\dfrac{s-1}{s}\right)^n$	$L_n(t) = \dfrac{e^t}{n!}\dfrac{d^n}{dt^n}(t^n e^{-t})$
35	$\dfrac{s}{(s-a)^{3/2}}$	$\dfrac{1}{\sqrt{\pi t}}e^{at}(1 + 2at)$
36	$\sqrt{s-a} - \sqrt{s-b}$	$\dfrac{1}{2\sqrt{\pi t^3}}(e^{bt} - e^{at})$
37	$\dfrac{1}{\sqrt{s}+a}$	$\dfrac{1}{\sqrt{\pi t}} - ae^{a^2 t}\,\mathrm{erfc}\,(a\sqrt{t})$
38	$\dfrac{\sqrt{s}}{s - a^2}$	$\dfrac{1}{\sqrt{\pi t}} + ae^{a^2 t}\,\mathrm{erf}\,(a\sqrt{t})$
39	$\dfrac{\sqrt{s}}{s + a^2}$	$\dfrac{1}{\sqrt{\pi t}} - \dfrac{2a}{\sqrt{\pi}}e^{-a^2 t}\displaystyle\int_0^{a\sqrt{t}}e^{\lambda^2}\,d\lambda$
40	$\dfrac{1}{\sqrt{s}(s - a^2)}$	$\dfrac{1}{a}e^{a^2 t}\,\mathrm{erf}\,(a\sqrt{t})$
41	$\dfrac{1}{\sqrt{s}(s + a^2)}$	$\dfrac{2}{a\sqrt{\pi}}e^{-a^2 t}\displaystyle\int_0^{a\sqrt{t}}e^{\lambda^2}\,d\lambda$
42	$\dfrac{b^2 - a^2}{(s - a^2)(b + \sqrt{s})}$	$e^{a^2 t}[b - a\,\mathrm{erf}\,(a\sqrt{t})] - be^{b^2 t}\,\mathrm{erfc}\,(b\sqrt{t})$
43	$\dfrac{1}{\sqrt{s}(\sqrt{s}+a)}$	$e^{a^2 t}\,\mathrm{erfc}\,(a\sqrt{t})$
44	$\dfrac{1}{(s+a)\sqrt{s+b}}$	$\dfrac{1}{\sqrt{b-a}}e^{-at}\,\mathrm{erf}\,(\sqrt{b-a}\,\sqrt{t})$
45	$\dfrac{b^2 - a^2}{\sqrt{s}(s - a^2)(\sqrt{s}+b)}$	$e^{a^2 t}\left[\dfrac{b}{a}\,\mathrm{erf}\,(a\sqrt{t}) - 1\right] + e^{b^2 t}\,\mathrm{erfc}\,(b\sqrt{t})$
46†	$\dfrac{(1-s)^n}{s^{n+(1/2)}}$	$\dfrac{n!}{(2n)!\sqrt{\pi t}}H_{2n}(\sqrt{t})$
47	$\dfrac{(1-s)^n}{s^{n+(3/2)}}$	$-\dfrac{n!}{\sqrt{\pi}(2n+1)!}H_{2n+1}(\sqrt{t})$

*$L_n(t)$ is the Laguerre polynomial of degree n.

†$H_n(x)$ is the Hermite polynomial, $H_n(x) = e^{x^2}\dfrac{d^n}{dx^n}(e^{-x^2})$.

LAPLACE TRANSFORMS (Continued)

	$f(s)$	$F(t)$
48†	$\dfrac{\sqrt{s + 2a}}{\sqrt{s}} - 1$	$ae^{-at}[I_1(at) + I_0(at)]$
49	$\dfrac{1}{\sqrt{s + a}\sqrt{s + b}}$	$e^{-(1/2)(a+b)t}I_0\left(\dfrac{a - b}{2} t\right)$
50	$\dfrac{\Gamma(k)}{(s + a)^k(s + b)^k} \ (k \geq 0)$	$\sqrt{\pi}\left(\dfrac{t}{a - b}\right)^{k-(1/2)} e^{-(1/2)(a+b)t}I_{k-(1/2)}\left(\dfrac{a - b}{2} t\right)$
51	$\dfrac{1}{(s + a)^{1/2}(s + b)^{3/2}}$	$te^{-(1/2)(a+b)t}\left[I_0\left(\dfrac{a - b}{2} t\right) + I_1\left(\dfrac{a - b}{2} t\right)\right]$
52	$\dfrac{\sqrt{s + 2a} - \sqrt{s}}{\sqrt{s + 2a} + \sqrt{s}}$	$\dfrac{1}{t} e^{-at}I_1(at)$
53	$\dfrac{(a - b)^k}{(\sqrt{s + a} + \sqrt{s + b})^{2k}} \ (k > 0)$	$\dfrac{k}{t} e^{-(1/2)(a+b)t}I_k\left(\dfrac{a - b}{2} t\right)$
54	$\dfrac{(\sqrt{s + a} + \sqrt{s})^{-2\nu}}{\sqrt{s}\sqrt{s + a}} \ (\nu > -1)$	$\dfrac{1}{a^\nu} e^{-(1/2)(at)}I_\nu\left(\dfrac{1}{2} at\right)$
55	$\dfrac{1}{\sqrt{s^2 + a^2}}$	$J_0(at)$
56	$\dfrac{(\sqrt{s^2 + a^2} - s)^\nu}{\sqrt{s^2 + a^2}} \ (\nu > -1)$	$a^\nu J_\nu(at)$
57	$\dfrac{1}{(s^2 + a^2)^k} \ (k > 0)$	$\dfrac{\sqrt{\pi}}{\Gamma(k)}\left(\dfrac{t}{2a}\right)^{k-(1/2)} J_{k-(1/2)}(at)$
58	$(\sqrt{s^2 + a^2} - s)^k(k > 0)$	$\dfrac{ka^k}{t} J_k(at)$
59	$\dfrac{(s - \sqrt{s^2 - a^2})^\nu}{\sqrt{s^2 - a^2}} \ (\nu > -1)$	$a^\nu I_\nu(at)$
60	$\dfrac{1}{(s^2 - a^2)^k} \ (k > 0)$	$\dfrac{\sqrt{\pi}}{\Gamma(k)}\left(\dfrac{t}{2a}\right)^{k-(1/2)} I_{k-(1/2)}(at)$
61	$\dfrac{e^{-ks}}{s}$	$S_k(t) = \begin{cases} 0 \text{ when } 0 < t < k \\ 1 \text{ when } t > k \end{cases}$
62	$\dfrac{e^{-ks}}{s^2}$	$\begin{cases} 0 \text{ when } 0 < t < k \\ t - k \text{ when } t > k \end{cases}$
63	$\dfrac{e^{-ks}}{s^\mu} \ (\mu > 0)$	$\begin{cases} 0 & \text{when } 0 < t < k \\ \dfrac{(t - k)^{\mu-1}}{\Gamma(\mu)} & \text{when } t > k \end{cases}$
64	$\dfrac{1 - e^{-ks}}{s}$	$\begin{cases} 1 \text{ when } 0 < t < k \\ 0 \text{ when } t > k \end{cases}$

†$I_n(x) = i^{-n}J_n(ix)$, where J_n is Bessel's function of the first kind.

LAPLACE TRANSFORMS (Continued)

	$f(s)$	$F(t)$
65	$\dfrac{1}{s(1 - e^{-ks})} = \dfrac{1 + \coth \frac{1}{2}ks}{2s}$	$S(k, t) = n$ when $\qquad (n - 1)k < t < nk(n = 1, 2, \ldots)$
66	$\dfrac{1}{s(e^{ks} - a)}$	$\begin{cases} 0 \text{ when } 0 < t < k \\ 1 + a + a^2 + \cdots + a^{n-1} \\ \qquad \text{when } nk < t < (n + 1)k(n = 1, 2, \ldots) \end{cases}$
67	$\dfrac{1}{s} \tanh ks$	$M(2k, t) = (-1)^{n-1}$ $\quad$ when $2k(n - 1) < t < 2kn$ $\qquad\qquad\qquad (n = 1, 2, \ldots)$
68	$\dfrac{1}{s(1 + e^{-ks})}$	$\dfrac{1}{2} M(k, t) + \dfrac{1}{2} = \dfrac{1 - (-1)^n}{2}$ $\qquad$ when $(n - 1)k < t < nk$
69*	$\dfrac{1}{s^2} \tanh ks$	$H(2k, t)$
70	$\dfrac{1}{s \sinh ks}$	$2S(2k, t + k) - 2 = 2(n - 1)$ $\quad$ when $(2n - 3)k < t < (2n - 1)k \quad (t > 0)$
71	$\dfrac{1}{s \cosh ks}$	$M(2k, t + 3k) + 1 = 1 + (-1)^n$ $\quad$ when $(2n - 3)k < t < (2n - 1)k \quad (t > 0)$
72	$\dfrac{1}{s} \coth ks$	$2S(2k, t) - 1 = 2n - 1$ $\qquad$ when $2k(n - 1) < t < 2kn$
73	$\dfrac{k}{s^2 + k^2} \coth \dfrac{\pi s}{2k}$	$\lvert \sin kt \rvert$
74	$\dfrac{1}{(s^2 + 1)(1 - e^{-\pi s})}$	$\begin{cases} \sin t \text{ when } (2n - 2)\pi < t < (2n - 1)\pi \\ 0 \quad \text{when } (2n - 1)\pi < t < 2n\pi \end{cases}$
75	$\dfrac{1}{s} e^{-k/s}$	$J_0(2\sqrt{kt})$
76	$\dfrac{1}{\sqrt{s}} e^{-k/s}$	$\dfrac{1}{\sqrt{\pi t}} \cos 2\sqrt{kt}$
77	$\dfrac{1}{\sqrt{s}} e^{k/s}$	$\dfrac{1}{\sqrt{\pi t}} \cosh 2\sqrt{kt}$
78	$\dfrac{1}{s^{3/2}} e^{-k/s}$	$\dfrac{1}{\sqrt{\pi k}} \sin 2\sqrt{kt}$
79	$\dfrac{1}{s^{3/2}} e^{k/s}$	$\dfrac{1}{\sqrt{\pi k}} \sinh 2\sqrt{kt}$
80	$\dfrac{1}{s^\mu} e^{-k/s}(\mu > 0)$	$\left(\dfrac{t}{k}\right)^{(\mu-1)/2} J_{\mu-1}(2\sqrt{kt})$

*$H(2k, t) = k + (r - k)(-1)^n$ where $t = 2kn + r; 0 \leq r < 2k; n = 0, 1, 2, \ldots$.

LAPLACE TRANSFORMS (Continued)

	$f(s)$	$F(t)$
81	$\dfrac{1}{s^{\mu}}\, e^{k/s}(\mu > 0)$	$\left(\dfrac{t}{k}\right)^{(\mu-1)/2} I_{\mu-1}(2\sqrt{kt})$
82	$e^{-k\sqrt{s}}(k > 0)$	$\dfrac{k}{2\sqrt{\pi t^3}}\exp\left(-\dfrac{k^2}{4t}\right)$
83	$\dfrac{1}{s}\, e^{-k\sqrt{s}}(k \geqq 0)$	$\mathrm{erfc}\left(\dfrac{k}{2\sqrt{t}}\right)$
84	$\dfrac{1}{\sqrt{s}}\, e^{-k\sqrt{s}}(k \geqq 0)$	$\dfrac{1}{\sqrt{\pi t}}\exp\left(-\dfrac{k^2}{4t}\right)$
85	$s^{-3/2}e^{-k\sqrt{s}}(k \geqq 0)$	$2\sqrt{\dfrac{t}{\pi}}\exp\left(-\dfrac{k^2}{4t}\right)- k\,\mathrm{erfc}\left(\dfrac{k}{2\sqrt{t}}\right)$
86	$\dfrac{ae^{-k\sqrt{s}}}{s(a + \sqrt{s})}\ (k \geqq 0)$	$-e^{ak}e^{a^2t}\,\mathrm{erfc}\left(a\sqrt{t} + \dfrac{k}{2\sqrt{t}}\right)+ \mathrm{erfc}\left(\dfrac{k}{2\sqrt{t}}\right)$
87	$\dfrac{e^{-k\sqrt{s}}}{\sqrt{s}(a + \sqrt{s})}\ (k \geqq 0)$	$e^{ak}e^{a^2t}\,\mathrm{erfc}\left(a\sqrt{t} + \dfrac{k}{2\sqrt{t}}\right)$
88	$\dfrac{e^{-k\sqrt{s(s+a)}}}{\sqrt{s(s + a)}}$	$\begin{cases} 0 & \text{when } 0 < t < k \\ e^{-(1/2)(at)}I_0(\tfrac{1}{2}a\sqrt{t^2 - k^2}) & \text{when } t > k \end{cases}$
89	$\dfrac{e^{-k\sqrt{s^2+a^2}}}{\sqrt{s^2 + a^2}}$	$\begin{cases} 0 & \text{when } 0 < t < k \\ J_0(a\sqrt{t^2 - k^2}) & \text{when } t > k \end{cases}$
90	$\dfrac{e^{-k\sqrt{s^2-a^2}}}{\sqrt{s^2 - a^2}}$	$\begin{cases} 0 & \text{when } 0 < t < k \\ I_0(a\sqrt{t^2 - k^2}) & \text{when } t > k \end{cases}$
91	$\dfrac{e^{-k(\sqrt{s^2+a^2}-s)}}{\sqrt{s^2 + a^2}}\ (k \geqq 0)$	$J_0(a\sqrt{t^2 + 2kt})$
92	$e^{-ks} - e^{-k\sqrt{s^2+a^2}}$	$\begin{cases} 0 & \text{when } 0 < t < k \\ \dfrac{ak}{\sqrt{t^2 - k^2}}\, J_1(a\sqrt{t^2 - k^2}) & \text{when } t > k \end{cases}$
93	$e^{-k\sqrt{s^2+a^2}} - e^{-ks}$	$\begin{cases} 0 & \text{when } 0 < t < k \\ \dfrac{ak}{\sqrt{t^2 - k^2}}\, I_1(a\sqrt{t^2 - k^2}) & \text{when } t > k \end{cases}$
94	$\dfrac{a^{\nu}e^{-k\sqrt{s^2-a^2}}}{\sqrt{s^2 + a^2}(\sqrt{s^2 + a^2} + s)^{\nu}}$ $(\nu > -1)$	$\begin{cases} 0 & \text{when } 0 < t < k \\ \left(\dfrac{t - k}{t + k}\right)^{(1/2)\nu} J_{\nu}(a\sqrt{t^2 - k^2}) & \text{when } t > k \end{cases}$
95	$\dfrac{1}{s}\log s$	$\Gamma'(1) - \log t\ [\Gamma'(1) = -0.5772]$
96	$\dfrac{1}{s^k}\log s\ (k > 0)$	$t^{k-1}\left\{\dfrac{\Gamma'(k)}{[\Gamma(k)]^2} \dfrac{\log t}{\Gamma(k)}\right\}$
97	$\dfrac{\log s}{s - a}\ (a > 0)$	$e^{at}[\log a - \mathrm{Ei}(-at)]$

LAPLACE TRANSFORMS (Continued)

	$f(s)$	$F(t)$
98	$\dfrac{\log s}{s^2 + 1}$	$\cos t\, \mathrm{Si}(t) - \sin t\, \mathrm{Ci}(t)$
99	$\dfrac{s \log s}{s^2 + 1}$	$-\sin t\, \mathrm{Si}(t) - \cos t\, \mathrm{Ci}(t)$
100	$\dfrac{1}{s} \log (1 + ks)\,(k > 0)$	$-\mathrm{Ei}\left(-\dfrac{t}{k}\right)$
101	$\log \dfrac{s - a}{s - b}$	$\dfrac{1}{t}\,(e^{bt} - e^{at})$
102	$\dfrac{1}{s} \log (1 + k^2 s^2)$	$-2\mathrm{Ci}\left(\dfrac{t}{k}\right)$
103	$\dfrac{1}{s} \log (s^2 + a^2)\ \ (a > 0)$	$2 \log a - 2\mathrm{Ci}(at)$
104	$\dfrac{1}{s^2} \log (s^2 + a^2)\ \ (a > 0)$	$\dfrac{2}{a}\,[at \log a + \sin at - at\, \mathrm{Ci}(at)]$
105	$\log \dfrac{s^2 + a^2}{s^2}$	$\dfrac{2}{t}\,(1 - \cos at)$
106	$\log \dfrac{s^2 - a^2}{s^2}$	$\dfrac{2}{t}\,(1 - \cosh at)$
107	$\arctan \dfrac{k}{s}$	$\dfrac{1}{t} \sin kt$
108	$\dfrac{1}{s} \arctan \dfrac{k}{s}$	$\mathrm{Si}(kt)$
109	$e^{k^2 s^2} \operatorname{erfc}(ks)\ \ (k > 0)$	$\dfrac{1}{k \sqrt{\pi}} \exp\left(-\dfrac{t^2}{4k^2}\right)$
110	$\dfrac{1}{s}\, e^{k^2 s^2} \operatorname{erfc}(ks)\ \ (k > 0)$	$\operatorname{erf}\left(\dfrac{t}{2k}\right)$
111	$e^{ks} \operatorname{erfc}(\sqrt{ks})\ \ (k > 0)$	$\dfrac{\sqrt{k}}{\pi \sqrt{t}(t + k)}$
112	$\dfrac{1}{\sqrt{s}} \operatorname{erfc}(\sqrt{ks})$	$\begin{cases} 0 & \text{when } 0 < t < k \\ (\pi t)^{-1/2} & \text{when } t > k \end{cases}$
113	$\dfrac{1}{\sqrt{s}}\, e^{ks} \operatorname{erfc}(\sqrt{ks})\,(k > 0)$	$\dfrac{1}{\sqrt{\pi(t + k)}}$
114	$\operatorname{erf}\left(\dfrac{k}{\sqrt{s}}\right)$	$\dfrac{1}{\pi t} \sin (2k \sqrt{t})$
115	$\dfrac{1}{\sqrt{s}}\, e^{k^2/s} \operatorname{erfc}\left(\dfrac{k}{\sqrt{s}}\right)$	$\dfrac{1}{\sqrt{\pi t}}\, e^{-2k\sqrt{t}}$

LAPLACE TRANSFORMS (Continued)

	$f(s)$	$F(t)$
115.1	$-e^{as} \text{Ei}(-as)$	$\dfrac{1}{t+a}; (a > 0)$
115.2	$\dfrac{1}{a} + se^{as} \text{Ei}(-as)$	$\dfrac{1}{(t+a)^2}; (a > 0)$
115.3	$\left[\dfrac{\pi}{2} - \text{Si}(s)\right]\cos s + \text{Ci}(s)\sin s$	$\dfrac{1}{t^2+1}$
116*	$K_0(ks)$	$\begin{cases} 0 & \text{when } 0 < t < k \\ (t^2 - k^2)^{-1/2} & \text{when } t > k \end{cases}$
117	$K_0(k\sqrt{s})$	$\dfrac{1}{2t}\exp\left(-\dfrac{k^2}{4t}\right)$
118	$\dfrac{1}{s} e^{ks} K_1(ks)$	$\dfrac{1}{k}\sqrt{t(t+2k)}$
119	$\dfrac{1}{\sqrt{s}} K_1(k\sqrt{s})$	$\dfrac{1}{k}\exp\left(-\dfrac{k^2}{4t}\right)$
120	$\dfrac{1}{\sqrt{s}} e^{k/s} K_0\left(\dfrac{k}{s}\right)$	$\dfrac{2}{\sqrt{\pi t}} K_0(2\sqrt{2kt})$
121	$\pi e^{-ks} I_0(ks)$	$\begin{cases} [t(2k-t)]^{-1/2} & \text{when } 0 < t < 2k \\ 0 & \text{when } t > 2k \end{cases}$
122†	$e^{-ks} I_1(ks)$	$\begin{cases} \dfrac{k-t}{\pi k \sqrt{t(2k-t)}} & \text{when } 0 < t < 2k \\ 0 & \text{when } t > 2k \end{cases}$

*$K_n(x)$ is Bessel's function of the second kind for the imaginary argument.

†Several additional transforms, especially those involving other Bessel functions, can be found in the tables by G. A. Campbell and R. M. Foster, "Fourier Integrals for Practical Applications", or "Vol. 1, Bateman Manuscript Project, Transform Tables, McGraw-Hill, 1955", or N. W. McLachlan and P. Humbert, "Formulaire pour le calcul symbolique". In the tables by Campbell and Foster, only those entries containing the condition $0 < g$ or $k < g$, where g is our t, are Laplace transforms.

FOURIER TRANSFORMS
FINITE SINE TRANSFORMS

$f_s(n)$	$F(x)$
1 $f_s(n) = \displaystyle\int_0^\pi F(x) \sin nx \, dx \; (n = 1, 2, \cdots)$	$F(x)$
2 $(-1)^{n+1} f_s(n)$	$F(\pi - x)$
3 $\dfrac{1}{n}$	$\dfrac{\pi - x}{\pi}$
4 $\dfrac{(-1)^{n+1}}{n}$	$\dfrac{x}{\pi}$
5 $\dfrac{1 - (-1)^n}{n}$	1
6 $\dfrac{2}{n^2} \sin \dfrac{n\pi}{2}$	$\begin{cases} x & \text{when } 0 < x < \pi/2 \\ \pi - x & \text{when } \pi/2 < x < \pi \end{cases}$
7 $\dfrac{(-1)^{n+1}}{n^3}$	$\dfrac{x(\pi^2 - x^2)}{6\pi}$
8 $\dfrac{1 - (-1)^n}{n^3}$	$\dfrac{x(\pi - x)}{2}$
9 $\dfrac{\pi^2(-1)^{n-1}}{n} - \dfrac{2[1 - (-1)^n]}{n^3}$	x^2
10 $\pi(-1)^n \left(\dfrac{6}{n^3} - \dfrac{\pi^2}{n} \right)$	x^3
11 $\dfrac{n}{n^2 + c^2} [1 - (-1)^n e^{c\pi}]$	e^{cx}
12 $\dfrac{n}{n^2 + c^2}$	$\dfrac{\sinh c(\pi - x)}{\sinh c\pi}$
13 $\dfrac{n}{n^2 - k^2} \; (k \neq 0, 1, 2, \cdots)$	$\dfrac{\sin k(\pi - x)}{\sin k\pi}$
14 $\begin{cases} \dfrac{\pi}{2} & \text{when } n = m \\ 0 & \text{when } n \neq m \end{cases} \; (m = 1, 2, \cdots)$	$\sin mx$
15 $\dfrac{n}{n^2 - k^2} [1 - (-1)^n \cos k\pi]$ $(k \neq 1, 2, \cdots)$	$\cos kx$
16 $\begin{cases} \dfrac{n}{n^2 - m^2} [1 - (-1)^{n+m}] \\ \qquad \text{when } n \neq m = 1, 2, \cdots \\ 0 \qquad \text{when } n = m \end{cases}$	$\cos mx$
17 $\dfrac{n}{(n^2 - k^2)^2} \; (k \neq 0, 1, 2, \cdots)$	$\dfrac{\pi \sin kx}{2k \sin^2 k\pi} - \dfrac{x \cos k(\pi - x)}{2k \sin k\pi}$
18 $\dfrac{b^n}{n} \; (|b| \leq 1)$	$\dfrac{2}{\pi} \arctan \dfrac{b \sin x}{1 - b \cos x}$
19 $\dfrac{1 - (-1)^n}{n} b^n \; (|b| \leq 1)$	$\dfrac{2}{\pi} \arctan \dfrac{2b \sin x}{1 - b^2}$

FINITE COSINE TRANSFORMS

	$f_c(n)$	$F(x)$
1	$f_c(n) = \displaystyle\int_0^\pi F(x) \cos nx \, dx \quad (n = 0, 1, 2, \cdots)$	$F(x)$
2	$(-1)^n f_c(n)$	$F(\pi - x)$
3	0 when $n = 1, 2, \cdots$; $f_c(0) = \pi$	1
4	$\dfrac{2}{n} \sin \dfrac{n\pi}{2}$; $f_c(0) = 0$	$\begin{cases} 1 \text{ when } 0 < x < \pi/2 \\ -1 \text{ when } \pi/2 < x < \pi \end{cases}$
5	$-\dfrac{1 - (-1)^n}{n^2}$; $f_c(0) = \dfrac{\pi^2}{2}$	x
6	$\dfrac{(-1)^n}{n^2}$; $f_c(0) = \dfrac{\pi^2}{6}$	$\dfrac{x^2}{2\pi}$
7	$\dfrac{1}{n^2}$; $f_c(0) = 0$	$\dfrac{(\pi - x)^2}{2\pi} - \dfrac{\pi}{6}$
8	$3\pi^2 \dfrac{(-1)^n}{n^2} - 6\dfrac{1 - (-1)^n}{n^4}$; $f_c(0) = \dfrac{\pi^4}{4}$	x^3
9	$\dfrac{(-1)^n e^c \pi - 1}{n^2 + c^2}$	$\dfrac{1}{c} e^{cx}$
10	$\dfrac{1}{n^2 + c^2}$	$\dfrac{\cosh c(\pi - x)}{c \sinh c\pi}$
11	$\dfrac{k}{n^2 - k^2}[(-1)^n \cos \pi k - 1]$ $(k \neq 0, 1, 2, \cdots)$	$\sin kx$
12	$\dfrac{(-1)^{n+m} - 1}{n^2 - m^2}$; $f_c(m) = 0 \quad (m = 1, 2, \cdots)$	$\dfrac{1}{m} \sin mx$
13	$\dfrac{1}{n^2 - k^2} \quad (k \neq 0, 1, 2, \cdots)$	$-\dfrac{\cos k(\pi - x)}{k \sin k\pi}$
14	0 when $n = 1, 2, \cdots$; $f_c(m) = \dfrac{\pi}{2} \quad (m = 1, 2, \cdots)$	$\cos mx$

FOURIER SINE TRANSFORMS[1]

	$F(x)$	$f_s(\alpha)$
1	$\begin{cases} 1 & (0 < x < a) \\ 0 & (x > a) \end{cases}$	$\sqrt{\dfrac{2}{\pi}}\left[\dfrac{1 - \cos \alpha}{\alpha}\right]$
2	$x^{p-1}\ (0 < p < 1)$	$\sqrt{\dfrac{2}{\pi}}\,\dfrac{\Gamma(p)}{\alpha^p}\sin\dfrac{p\pi}{2}$
3	$\begin{cases} \sin x & (0 < x < a) \\ 0 & (x > a) \end{cases}$	$\dfrac{1}{\sqrt{2\pi}}\left[\dfrac{\sin[a(1 - \alpha)]}{1 - \alpha} - \dfrac{\sin[a(1 + \alpha)]}{1 + \alpha}\right]$
4	e^{-x}	$\sqrt{\dfrac{2}{\pi}}\left[\dfrac{\alpha}{1 + \alpha^2}\right]$
5	$xe^{-x^2/2}$	$\alpha e^{-\alpha^2/2}$
6	$\cos\dfrac{x^2}{2}$	$\sqrt{2}\left[\sin\dfrac{\alpha^2}{2}\,C\!\left(\dfrac{\alpha^2}{2}\right) - \cos\dfrac{\alpha^2}{2}\,S\!\left(\dfrac{\alpha^2}{2}\right)\right]$ *
7	$\sin\dfrac{x^2}{2}$	$\sqrt{2}\left[\cos\dfrac{\alpha^2}{2}\,C\!\left(\dfrac{\alpha^2}{2}\right) + \sin\dfrac{\alpha^2}{2}\,S\!\left(\dfrac{\alpha^2}{2}\right)\right]$ *

*$C(y)$ and $S(y)$ are the Fresnel integrals

$$C(y) = \frac{1}{\sqrt{2\pi}}\int_0^y \frac{1}{\sqrt{t}}\cos t\, dt,$$

$$S(y) = \frac{1}{\sqrt{2\pi}}\int_0^y \frac{1}{\sqrt{t}}\sin t\, dt.$$

[1] More extensive tables of the Fourier sine and cosine transforms can be found in Fritz Oberhettinger, "Tabellen zur Fourier Transformation," Springer (1957).

FOURIER COSINE TRANSFORMS

	$F(x)$	$f_c(\alpha)$
1	$\begin{cases} 1 & (0 < x < a) \\ 0 & (x > a) \end{cases}$	$\sqrt{\dfrac{2}{\pi}}\,\dfrac{\sin a\alpha}{\alpha}$
2	$x^{p-1}\ \ (0 < p < 1)$	$\sqrt{\dfrac{2}{\pi}}\,\dfrac{\Gamma(p)}{\alpha^p}\cos\dfrac{p\pi}{2}$
3	$\begin{cases} \cos x & (0 < x < a) \\ 0 & (x > a) \end{cases}$	$\dfrac{1}{\sqrt{2\pi}}\left[\dfrac{\sin[a(1 - \alpha)]}{1 - \alpha} + \dfrac{\sin[a(1 + \alpha)]}{1 + \alpha}\right]$
4	e^{-x}	$\sqrt{\dfrac{2}{\pi}}\left(\dfrac{1}{1 + \alpha^2}\right)$
5	$e^{-x^2/2}$	$e^{-\alpha^2/2}$
6	$\cos\dfrac{x^2}{2}$	$\cos\left(\dfrac{\alpha^2}{2} - \dfrac{\pi}{4}\right)$
7	$\sin\dfrac{x^2}{2}$	$\cos\left(\dfrac{\alpha^2}{2} + \dfrac{\pi}{4}\right)$

FOURIER TRANSFORMS[1]

$F(x)$	$f(\alpha)$
1 $\dfrac{\sin ax}{x}$	$\begin{cases} \sqrt{\dfrac{\pi}{2}} & \|\alpha\| < a \\ 0 & \|\alpha\| > a \end{cases}$
2 $\begin{cases} e^{iwx} & (p < x < q) \\ 0 & (x < p,\ x > q) \end{cases}$	$\dfrac{i}{\sqrt{2\pi}} \dfrac{e^{ip(w+\alpha)} - e^{iq(w+\alpha)}}{(w+\alpha)}$
3 $\begin{cases} e^{-cx+iwx} & (x > 0) \\ 0 & (x < 0) \end{cases}$ $(c > 0)$	$\dfrac{i}{\sqrt{2\pi}(w+\alpha+ic)}$
4 e^{-px^2} $R(p) > 0$	$\dfrac{1}{\sqrt{2p}} e^{-\alpha^2/4p}$
5 $\cos px^2$	$\dfrac{1}{\sqrt{2p}} \cos\left[\dfrac{\alpha^2}{4p} - \dfrac{\pi}{4}\right]$
6 $\sin px^2$	$\dfrac{1}{\sqrt{2p}} \cos\left[\dfrac{\alpha^2}{4p} + \dfrac{\pi}{4}\right]$
7 $\|x\|^{-p}$ $(0 < p < 1)$	$\sqrt{\dfrac{2}{\pi}} \dfrac{\Gamma(1-p)\sin\dfrac{p\pi}{2}}{\|\alpha\|^{(1-p)}}$
8 $\dfrac{e^{-a\|x\|}}{\sqrt{\|x\|}}$	$\dfrac{\sqrt{\sqrt{(a^2+\alpha^2)}+a}}{\sqrt{a^2+\alpha^2}}$
9 $\dfrac{\cosh ax}{\cosh \pi x}$ $(-\pi < a < \pi)$	$\sqrt{\dfrac{2}{\pi}} \dfrac{\cos\dfrac{a}{2}\cosh\dfrac{\alpha}{2}}{\cosh\alpha + \cos a}$
10 $\dfrac{\sinh ax}{\sinh \pi x}$ $(-\pi < a < \pi)$	$\dfrac{1}{\sqrt{2\pi}} \dfrac{\sin a}{\cosh\alpha + \cos a}$
11 $\begin{cases} \dfrac{1}{\sqrt{a^2-x^2}} & (\|x\| < a) \\ 0 & (\|x\| > a) \end{cases}$	$\sqrt{\dfrac{\pi}{2}} J_0(a\alpha)$
12 $\dfrac{\sin[b\sqrt{a^2+x^2}]}{\sqrt{a^2+x^2}}$	$\begin{cases} 0 & (\|\alpha\| > b) \\ \sqrt{\dfrac{\pi}{2}} J_0(a\sqrt{b^2-\alpha^2}) & (\|\alpha\| < b) \end{cases}$
13 $\begin{cases} P_n(x) & (\|x\| < 1) \\ 0 & (\|x\| > 1) \end{cases}$	$\dfrac{i^n}{\sqrt{\alpha}} J_{n+\frac{1}{2}}(\alpha)$
14 $\begin{cases} \dfrac{\cos[b\sqrt{a^2-x^2}]}{\sqrt{a^2-x^2}} & (\|x\| < a) \\ 0 & (\|x\| > a) \end{cases}$	$\sqrt{\dfrac{\pi}{2}} J_0(a\sqrt{a^2+b^2})$
15 $\begin{cases} \dfrac{\cosh[b\sqrt{a^2-x^2}]}{\sqrt{a^2-x^2}} & (\|x\| < a) \\ 0 & (\|x\| > a) \end{cases}$	$\sqrt{\dfrac{\pi}{2}} J_0(a\sqrt{\alpha^2-b^2})$

[1]More extensive tables of Fourier transforms can be found in W. Magnus and F. Oberhettinger, "Formulas and Theorems of the Special Functions of Mathematical Physics," pp. 116–120. Chelsea (1949).

The following functions appear among the entries of the tables on transforms.

Function	Definition	Name
$Ei(x)$	$\displaystyle\int_{-\infty}^{x} \frac{e^{v}}{v}\, dv$; or sometimes defined as $$-Ei(-x) = \int_{x}^{\infty} \frac{e^{-v}}{v}\, dv$$	See index for Sine, Cosine, and Exponential Integral tables
$Si(x)$	$\displaystyle\int_{0}^{x} \frac{\sin v}{v}\, dv$	See index for Sine, Cosine, and Exponential Integral tables
$Ci(x)$	$\displaystyle\int_{\infty}^{x} \frac{\cos v}{v}\, dv$; or sometimes defined as negative of this integral	See index for Sine, Cosine, and Exponential Integral tables
$erf(x)$	$\displaystyle\frac{2}{\sqrt{\pi}} \int_{0}^{x} e^{-v^{2}}\, dv$	Error function
$erfc(x)$	$1 - erf(x) = \displaystyle\frac{2}{\sqrt{\pi}} \int_{x}^{\infty} e^{-v^{2}}\, dv$	Complementary function to error function
$L_{n}(x)$	$\displaystyle\frac{e^{x}}{n!} \frac{d^{n}}{dx^{n}} (x^{n}e^{-x}), \quad n = 0, 1, \cdots$	Laguerre polynomial of degree n

ORTHOGONAL POLYNOMIALS

I

Name: Legendre   *Symbol*: $P_n(x)$ *Interval*: $[-1, 1]$

Differential Equation: $(1 - x^2)y'' - 2xy' + n(n + 1)y = 0$

$$y = P_n(x)$$

Explicit Expression: $P_n(x) = \dfrac{1}{2^n} \sum\limits_{m=0}^{[n/2]} (-1)^m \binom{n}{m}\binom{2n - 2m}{n} x^{n-2m}$

Recurrence Relation: $(n + 1)P_{n+1}(x) = (2n + 1)xP_n(x) - nP_{n-1}(x)$

Weight: 1 *Standardization*: $P_n(1) = 1$

Norm: $\displaystyle\int_{-1}^{+1} [P_n(x)]^2 dx = \dfrac{2}{2n + 1}$

Rodrigues' Formula: $P_n(x) = \dfrac{(-1)^n}{2^n n!} \dfrac{d^n}{dx^n} \{(1 - x^2)^n\}$

Generating Function: $R^{-1} = \sum\limits_{n=0}^{\infty} P_n(x)z^n; \quad -1 < x < 1, \quad |z| < 1,$

$$R = \sqrt{1 - 2xz + z^2}.$$

Inequality: $|P_n(x)| \le 1, \quad -1 \le x \le 1.$

II

Name: Tschebysheff, First Kind   *Symbol*: $T_n(x)$ *Interval*: $[-1, 1]$

Differential Equation: $(1 - x^2)y'' - xy' + n^2 y = 0$

$$y = T_n(x)$$

Explicit Expression: $\dfrac{n}{2} \sum\limits_{m=0}^{[n/2]} (-1)^m \dfrac{(n - m - 1)!}{m!(n - 2m)!} (2x)^{n-2m} = \cos(n \arccos x) = T_n(x)$

Recurrence Relation: $T_{n+1}(x) = 2xT_n(x) - T_{n-1}(x)$

Weight: $(1 - x^2)^{-1/2}$ *Standardization*: $T_n(1) = 1$

Norm: $\displaystyle\int_{-1}^{+1} (1 - x^2)^{-1/2}[T_n(x)]^2 dx = \begin{cases} \pi/2, & n \neq 0 \\ \pi, & n = 0 \end{cases}$

Rodrigues' Formula: $\dfrac{(-1)^n (1 - x^2)^{1/2} \sqrt{\pi}}{2^{n+1} \Gamma(n + \frac{1}{2})} \dfrac{d^n}{dx^n} \{(1 - x^2)^{n-(1/2)}\} = T_n(x)$

Generating Function: $\dfrac{1 - xz}{1 - 2xz + z^2} = \sum\limits_{n=0}^{\infty} T_n(x)z^n, \quad -1 < x < 1, \quad |z| < 1.$

Inequality: $|T_n(x)| \le 1, \quad -1 \le x \le 1.$

III

Name: Tschebysheff, Second Kind   *Symbol*: $U_n(x)$ *Interval*: $[-1, 1]$

Differential Equation: $(1 - x^2)y'' - 3xy' + n(n + 2)y = 0$

$$y = U_n(x)$$

Explicit Expression: $U_n(x) = \sum_{m=0}^{[n/2]} (-1)^m \frac{(m - n)!}{m!(n - 2m)!} (2x)^{n-2m}$

$$U_n(\cos \theta) = \frac{\sin[(n + 1)\theta]}{\sin \theta}$$

Recurrence Relation: $U_{n+1}(x) = 2x U_n(x) - U_{n-1}(x)$

Weight: $(1 - x^2)^{1/2}$ *Standardization*: $U_n(1) = n + 1$

Norm: $\displaystyle\int_{-1}^{+1} (1 - x^2)^{1/2}[U_n(x)]^2\, dx = \frac{\pi}{2}$

Rodrigues' Formula: $U_n(x) = \dfrac{(-1)^n(n + 1)\sqrt{\pi}}{(1 - x^2)^{1/2} 2^{n+1}\Gamma(n + \frac{3}{2})} \dfrac{d^n}{dx^n} \{(1 - x^2)^{n+(1/2)}\}$

Generating Function: $\dfrac{1}{1 - 2xz + z^2} = \displaystyle\sum_{n=0}^{\infty} U_n(x)z^n, \; -1 < x < 1, \; |z| < 1.$

Inequality: $|U_n(x)| \le n + 1, \; -1 \le x \le 1.$

IV

Name: Jacobi   *Symbol*: $P_n^{(\alpha,\beta)}(x)$ *Interval*: $[-1, 1]$

Differential Equation:

$$(1 - x^2)y'' + [\beta - \alpha - (\alpha + \beta + 2)x]y' + n(n + \alpha + \beta + 1)y = 0$$

$$y = P_n^{(\alpha,\beta)}(x)$$

Explicit Expression: $P_n^{(\alpha,\beta)}(x) = \dfrac{1}{2^n} \displaystyle\sum_{m=0}^{n} \binom{n + \alpha}{m}\binom{n + \beta}{n - m}(x - 1)^{n-m}(x + 1)^m$

Recurrence Relation: $2(n + 1)(n + \alpha + \beta + 1)(2n + \alpha + \beta)P_{n+1}^{(\alpha,\beta)}(x)$

$$= (2n + \alpha + \beta + 1)[(\alpha^2 - \beta^2) + (2n + \alpha + \beta + 2)$$
$$\times (2n + \alpha + \beta)x]P_n^{(\alpha,\beta)}(x)$$
$$- 2(n + \alpha)(n + \beta)(2n + \alpha + \beta + 2)P_{n-1}^{(\alpha,\beta)}(x)$$

Weight: $(1 - x)^\alpha(1 + x)^\beta; \; \alpha, \beta > 1$ *Standardization*: $P_n^{(\alpha,\beta)}(x) = \binom{n + \alpha}{n}$

Norm: $\displaystyle\int_{-1}^{+1}(1 - x)^\alpha(1 + x)^\beta[P_n^{(\alpha,\beta)}(x)]^2\, dx = \dfrac{2^{\alpha+\beta+1}\Gamma(n + \alpha + 1)\Gamma(n + \beta + 1)}{(2n + \alpha + \beta + 1)n!\,\Gamma(n + \alpha + \beta + 1)}$

Rodrigues' Formula: $P_n^{(\alpha,\beta)}(x) = \dfrac{(-1)^n}{2^n n!(1 - x)^\alpha(1 + x)^\beta} \dfrac{d^n}{dx^n} \{(1 - x)^{n+\alpha}(1 + x)^{n+\beta}\}$

IV

Generating Function: $R^{-1}(1 - z + R)^{-\alpha}(1 + z + R)^{-\beta} = \sum_{n=0}^{\infty} 2^{-\alpha-\beta} P_n^{(\alpha,\beta)}(x) z^n,$

$$R = \sqrt{1 - 2xz + z^2}, \ |z| < 1$$

Inequality: $\displaystyle\max_{-1 \leq x \leq 1} |P_n^{(\alpha,\beta)}(x)| = \begin{cases} \dbinom{n+q}{n} \sim n^q \text{ if } q = \max(\alpha, \beta) \geq -\tfrac{1}{2} \\[2mm] |P_n^{(\alpha,\beta)}(x')| \sim n^{-1/2} \text{ if } q < -\tfrac{1}{2} \\ x' \text{ is one of the two maximum points nearest} \\[2mm] \dfrac{\beta - \alpha}{\alpha + \beta + 1} \end{cases}$

V

Name: Generalized Laguerre   *Symbol*: $L_n^{(\alpha)}(x)$ *Interval*: $[0, \infty]$

Differential Equation: $xy'' + (\alpha + 1 - x)y' + ny = 0$

$$y = L_n^{(\alpha)}(x)$$

Explicit Expression: $L_n^{(\alpha)}(x) = \displaystyle\sum_{m=0}^{n} (-1)^m \binom{n+\alpha}{n-m} \frac{1}{m!} x^m$

Recurrence Relation: $(n+1)L_{n+1}^{(\alpha)}(x) = [(2n + \alpha + 1) - x]L_n^{(\alpha)}(x) - (n + \alpha)L_{n-1}^{(\alpha)}(x)$

Weight: $x^\alpha e^{-x}, \ \alpha > -1$ *Standardization*: $L_n^{(\alpha)}(x) = \dfrac{(-1)^n}{n!} x^n + \cdots$

Norm: $\displaystyle\int_0^\infty x^\alpha e^{-x} [L_n^{(\alpha)}(x)]^2 \, dx = \dfrac{\Gamma(n + \alpha + 1)}{n!}$

Rodrigues' Formula: $L_n^{(\alpha)}(x) = \dfrac{1}{n! \, x^\alpha e^{-x}} \dfrac{d^n}{dx^n} \{x^{n+\alpha} e^{-x}\}$

Generating Function: $(1 - z)^{-\alpha-1} \exp\left(\dfrac{xz}{z-1}\right) = \displaystyle\sum_{n=0}^{\infty} L_n^{(\alpha)}(x) z^n$

Inequality: $|L_n^{(\alpha)}(x)| \leq \dfrac{\Gamma(n + \alpha + 1)}{n! \, \Gamma(\alpha + 1)} e^{x/2}; \quad \begin{array}{l} x \geq 0 \\ \alpha > 0 \end{array}$

$$|L_n^{(\alpha)}(x)| \leq \left[2 - \dfrac{\Gamma(\alpha + n + 1)}{n! \, \Gamma(\alpha + 1)}\right] e^{x/2}; \quad \begin{array}{l} x \geq 0 \\ -1 < \alpha < 0 \end{array}$$

SINE, COSINE, AND EXPONENTIAL INTEGRALS

$$Si(x) = \int_0^x \frac{\sin v}{v}\,dv; \qquad Ci(x) = \int_\infty^x \frac{\cos v}{v}\,dv;$$

$$Ei(x) = \int_{-\infty}^x \frac{e^v}{v}\,dv; \qquad -Ei(-x) = \int_x^\infty \frac{e^{-v}}{v}\,dv$$

x	$Si(x)$	$Ci(x)$	$Ei(x)$	$-Ei(-x)$
0.0	0.00000	$-\infty$	$-\infty$	$+\infty$
0.1	0.09994	-1.72787	-1.62281	1.82292
0.2	.19956	-1.04221	$-.82176$	1.22265
0.3	.29850	$-.64917$	$-.30267$	.90568
0.4	.39646	$-.37881$	.10477	.70238
0.5	.49311	$-.17778$	.45422	.55977
0.6	.58813	$-.02227$	.76988	.45438
0.7	.68122	.10051	1.06491	.37377
0.8	.77210	.19828	1.34740	.31060
0.9	.86047	.27607	1.62281	.26018
1.0	.94608	.33740	1.89512	.21938
1.1	1.02869	.38487	2.16738	.18599
1.2	1.10805	.42046	2.44209	.15841
1.3	1.18396	.44574	2.72140	.13545
1.4	1.25623	.46201	3.00721	.11622
1.5	1.32468	.47036	3.30128	.10002
1.6	1.38918	.47173	3.60532	.08631
1.7	1.44959	.46697	3.92096	.07465
1.8	1.50582	.45681	4.24987	.06471
1.9	1.55778	.44194	4.59371	.05620
2.0	1.60541	.42298	4.95423	.04890
2.1	1.64870	.40051	5.33324	.04261
2.2	1.68762	.37507	5.73261	.03719
2.3	1.72221	.34718	6.15438	.03250
2.4	1.75249	.31729	6.60067	.02844
2.5	1.77852	.28587	7.07377	.02491
2.6	1.80039	.25337	7.57611	.02185
2.7	1.81821	.22008	8.11035	.01918
2.8	1.83210	.18649	8.67930	.01686
2.9	1.84219	.15290	9.28602	.01482
3.0	1.84865	.11963	9.93383	.01305
3.1	1.85166	.08699	10.6263	.01149
3.2	1.85140	.05526	11.3673	.01013
3.3	1.84808	.02468	12.1610	.00894
3.4	1.84191	$-.00452$	13.0121	.00789
3.5	1.83313	$-.03213$	13.9254	.00697
3.6	1.82195	$-.05797$	14.9063	.00616
3.7	1.80862	$-.08190$	15.9606	.00545
3.8	1.79339	$-.10378$	17.0948	.00482
3.9	1.77650	$-.12350$	18.3157	.00427
4.0	1.75820	$-.14098$	19.6309	.00378
4.1	1.73874	$-.15617$	21.0485	.00335
4.2	1.71837	$-.16901$	22.5774	.00297
4.3	1.69732	$-.17951$	24.2274	.00263
4.4	1.67583	$-.18766$	26.0090	.00234

SINE, COSINE, AND EXPONENTIAL INTEGRALS (Continued)

x	$Si(x)$	$Ci(x)$	$Ei(x)$	$-Ei(-x)$
4.5	1.65414	− .19349	27.9337	.00207
4.6	1.63246	− .19705	30.0141	.00184
4.7	1.61100	− .19839	32.2639	.00164
4.8	1.58998	− .19760	34.6979	.00145
4.9	1.56956	− .19478	37.3325	.00129
5.0	1.54993	− .19002	40.1853	.00115
5.1	1.53125	− .18348	43.2757	.00102
5.2	1.51367	− .17525	46.6249	.00091
5.3	1.49731	− .16551	50.2557	.00081
5.4	1.48230	− .15439	54.1935	.00072
5.5	1.46872	− .14205	58.4655	.00064
5.6	1.45667	− .12867	63.1018	.00057
5.7	1.44620	− .11441	68.1350	.00051
5.8	1.43736	− .09944	73.6008	.00045
5.9	1.43018	− .08393	79.5382	.00040
6.0	1.42469	− .06806	85.9898	.00036
6.1	1.42087	− .05198	93.0020	.00032
6.2	1.41871	− .03587	100.626	.00029
6.3	1.41817	− .01988	108.916	.00026
6.4	1.41922	− .00418	117.935	.00023
6.5	1.42179	+ .01110	127.747	.00020
6.6	1.42582	+ .02582	138.426	.00018
6.7	1.43121	.03986	150.050	.00016
6.8	1.43787	.05308	162.707	.00014
6.9	1.44570	.06539	176.491	.00013
7.0	1.45460	.07670	191.505	.00012
7.1	1.46443	.08691	207.863	.00010
7.2	1.47509	.09596	225.688	.00009
7.3	1.48644	.10379	245.116	.00008
7.4	1.49834	.11036	266.296	.00007
7.5	1.51068	.11563	289.388	.00007
7.6	1.52331	.11960	314.572	.00006
7.7	1.53611	.12225	342.040	.00005
7.8	1.54894	.12359	372.006	.00005
7.9	1.56167	.12364	404.701	.00004
8.0	1.57419	.12243	440.380	.00004
8.1	1.58637	.12002	479.322	.00003
8.2	1.59810	.11644	521.831	.00003
8.3	1.60928	.11177	568.242	.00003
8.4	1.61981	.10607	618.919	.00002
8.5	1.62960	.09943	674.264	.00002
8.6	1.63857	.09194	734.714	.00002
8.7	1.64665	.08368	800.749	.00002
8.8	1.65379	.07476	872.895	.00002
8.9	1.65993	.06528	951.728	.00001
9.0	1.66504	.05535	1037.88	.00001
9.1	1.66908	.04507	1132.04	.00001
9.2	1.67205	.03455	1234.96	.00001
9.3	1.67393	.02391	1347.48	.00001
9.4	1.67473	.01325	1470.51	.00001

SINE, COSINE, AND EXPONENTIAL INTEGRALS (Continued)

x	$Si(x)$	$Ci(x)$	$Ei(x)$	$-Ei(-x)$
9.5	1.67446	.00268	1605.03	.00001
9.6	1.67316	$-$ .00771	1752.14	.00001
9.7	1.67084	$-$ .01780	1913.05	.00001
9.8	1.66757	$-$ .02752	2089.05	.00001
9.9	1.66338	$-$ .03676	2281.58	.00000
10.0	1.65834	$-$ .04546	2492.23	.00000
10.5	1.62294	$-$ .07828	3883.74	.00000
11.0	1.57831	$-$ .08956	6071.41	.00000
11.5	1.53572	$-$ .07857	9518.20	.00000
12.0	1.50497	$-$ .04978	14959.5	.00000
12.5	1.49234	$-$ .01141	23565.1	.00000
13.0	1.49936	$+$ .02676	37197.7	.00000
13.5	1.52291	$+$ .05576	58827.6	.00000
14.0	1.55621	.06940	93193.0	.00000
14.5	1.59072	.06554	147866.	.00000
15.0	1.61819	.04628	234955.	.00000

*GAMMA FUNCTION

Values of $\Gamma(n) = \int_0^\infty e^{-x}x^{n-1}dx$; $\Gamma(n+1) = n\Gamma(n)$

n	$\Gamma(n)$	n	$\Gamma(n)$	n	$\Gamma(n)$	n	$\Gamma(n)$
1.00	1.00000	1.25	.90640	1.50	.88623	1.75	.91906
1.01	.99433	1.26	.90440	1.51	.88659	1.76	.92137
1.02	.98884	1.27	.90250	1.52	.88704	1.77	.92376
1.03	.98355	1.28	.90072	1.53	.88757	1.78	.92623
1.04	.97844	1.29	.89904	1.54	.88818	1.79	.92877
1.05	.97350	1.30	.89747	1.55	.88887	1.80	.93138
1.06	.96874	1.31	.89600	1.56	.88964	1.81	.93408
1.07	.96415	1.32	.89464	1.57	.89049	1.82	.93685
1.08	.95973	1.33	.89338	1.58	.89142	1.83	.93969
1.09	.95546	1.34	.89222	1.59	.89243	1.84	.94261
1.10	.95135	1.35	.89115	1.60	.89352	1.85	.94561
1.11	.94739	1.36	.89018	1.61	.89468	1.86	.94869
1.12	.94359	1.37	.88931	1.62	.89592	1.87	.95184
1.13	.93993	1.38	.88854	1.63	.89724	1.88	.95507
1.14	.93642	1.39	.88785	1.64	.89864	1.89	.95838
1.15	.93304	1.40	.88726	1.65	.90012	1.90	.96177
1.16	.92980	1.41	.88676	1.66	.90167	1.91	.96523
1.17	.92670	1.42	.88636	1.67	.90330	1.92	.96878
1.18	.92373	1.43	.88604	1.68	.90500	1.93	.97240
1.19	.92088	1.44	.88580	1.69	.90678	1.94	.97610
1.20	.91817	1.45	.88565	1.70	.90864	1.95	.97988
1.21	.91558	1.46	.88560	1.71	.91057	1.96	.98374
1.22	.91311	1.47	.88563	1.72	.91258	1.97	.98768
1.23	.91075	1.48	.88575	1.73	.91466	1.98	.99171
1.24	.90852	1.49	.88595	1.74	.91683	1.99	.99581
						2.00	1.00000

* For large positive values of x, $\Gamma(x)$ approximates the asymptotic series

$$x^x e^{-x}\sqrt{\frac{2\pi}{x}}\left[1 + \frac{1}{12x} + \frac{1}{288x^2} - \frac{139}{51840x^2} - \frac{571}{2488320x^4} + \cdots\right].$$

BESSEL FUNCTIONS

1. Bessel's differential equations for a real variable x is

$$x^2 \frac{d^2 y}{dx^2} + x \frac{dy}{dx} + (x^2 - n^2) y = 0$$

2. When n is not an integer, two independent solutions of the equation are $J_n(x)$ and $J_{-n}(x)$, where

$$J_n(x) = \sum_{k=0}^{\infty} \frac{(-1)^k}{k! \, \Gamma(n + k + 1)} \left(\frac{x}{2}\right)^{n+2k}$$

3. If n is an integer $J_{-n}(x) = (-1)^n J_n(x)$, where

$$J_n(x) = \frac{x^n}{2^n n!} \left\{ 1 - \frac{x^2}{2^2 \cdot 1!(n + 1)} + \frac{x^4}{2^4 \cdot 2!(n + 1)(n + 2)} \right.$$
$$\left. - \frac{x^6}{2^6 \cdot 3!(n + 1)(n + 2)(n + 3)} + \cdots \right\}$$

4. For $n = 0$ and $n = 1$, this formula becomes

$$J_0(x) = 1 - \frac{x^2}{2^2(1!)^2} + \frac{x^4}{2^4(2!)^2} - \frac{x^6}{2^6(3!)^2} + \frac{x^8}{2^8(4!)^2} - \cdots$$

$$J_1(x) = \frac{x}{2} - \frac{x^3}{2^3 \cdot 1!2!} + \frac{x^5}{2^5 \cdot 2!3!} - \frac{x^7}{2^7 \cdot 3!4!} + \frac{x^9}{2^9 \cdot 4!5!} - \cdots$$

5. When x is large and positive, the following asymptotic series may be used

$$J_0(x) = \left(\frac{2}{\pi x}\right)^{\frac{1}{2}} \left\{ P_0(x) \cos\left(x - \frac{\pi}{4}\right) - Q_0(x) \sin\left(x - \frac{\pi}{4}\right) \right\}$$

$$J_1(x) = \left(\frac{2}{\pi x}\right)^{\frac{1}{2}} \left\{ P_1(x) \cos\left(x - \frac{3\pi}{4}\right) - Q_1(x) \sin\left(x - \frac{3\pi}{4}\right) \right\},$$

where

$$P_0(x) \sim 1 - \frac{1^2 \cdot 3^2}{2!(8x)^2} + \frac{1^2 \cdot 3^2 \cdot 5^2 \cdot 7^2}{4!(8x)^4} - \frac{1^2 \cdot 3^2 \cdot 5^2 \cdot 7^2 \cdot 9^2 \cdot 11^2}{6!(8x)^6} + \cdots$$

$$Q_0(x) \sim - \frac{1^2}{1!8x} + \frac{1^2 \cdot 3^2 \cdot 5^2}{3!(8x)^3} - \frac{1^2 \cdot 3^2 \cdot 5^2 \cdot 7^2 \cdot 9^2}{5!(8x)^5} + - \cdots$$

$$P_1(x) \sim 1 + \frac{1^2 \cdot 3 \cdot 5}{2!(8x)^2} - \frac{1^2 \cdot 3^2 \cdot 5^2 \cdot 7 \cdot 9}{4!(8x)^4} + \frac{1^2 \cdot 3^2 \cdot 5^2 \cdot 7^2 \cdot 9^2 \cdot 11 \cdot 13}{6!(8x)^6} - + \cdots$$

$$Q_1(x) \sim \frac{1 \cdot 3}{1!8x} - \frac{1^2 \cdot 3^2 \cdot 5 \cdot 7}{3!(8x)^3} + \frac{1^2 \cdot 3^2 \cdot 5^2 \cdot 7^2 \cdot 9 \cdot 11}{5!(8x)^6} - \cdots$$

[In $P_1(x)$ the signs alternate from + to − after the first term]

6. If $x > 25$, it is convenient to use the formulas

$$J_0(x) = A_0(x) \sin x + B_0(x) \cos x$$
$$J_1(x) = B_T(x) \sin x - A_1(x) \cos x,$$

where

$$A_0(x) = \frac{P_0(x) - Q_0(x)}{(\pi x)^{\frac{1}{2}}} \quad \text{and} \quad A_1(x) = \frac{P_1(x) - Q_1(x)}{(\pi x)^{\frac{1}{2}}}$$

$$B_0(x) = \frac{P_0(x) + Q_0(x)}{(\pi x)^{\frac{1}{2}}} \quad \text{and} \quad B_1(x) = \frac{P_1(x) + Q_1(x)}{(\pi x)^{\frac{1}{2}}}$$

7. The zeros of $J_0(x)$, and $J_1(x)$

If $j_{0,s}$ and $j_{1,s}$ are the s'th zeros of $J_0(x)$ and $J_1(x)$ respectively, and if $a = 4s - 1$, $b = 4s + 1$

$$j_{0,s} \sim \frac{1}{4}\pi a \left\{ 1 + \frac{2}{\pi^2 a^2} - \frac{62}{3\pi^4 a^4} + \frac{15,116}{15\pi^6 a^6} - \frac{12,554,474}{105\pi^8 a^8} + \frac{8,368,654,292}{315\pi^{10}a^{10}} - + \cdots \right\}$$

$$j_{1,s} \sim \frac{1}{4}\pi b \left\{ 1 - \frac{6}{\pi^2 b^2} + \frac{6}{\pi^4 b^4} - \frac{4716}{5\pi^6 b^6} + \frac{3,902,418}{35\pi^8 b^8} - \frac{8,952,167,324}{35\pi^{10}b^{10}} + \cdots \right\}$$

$$J_1(j_{0,s}) \sim \frac{(-1)^{s+1}2^{\frac{3}{2}}}{\pi a^{\frac{1}{2}}} \left\{ 1 - \frac{56}{3\pi^4 a^4} + \frac{9664}{5\pi^6 a^6} - \frac{7,381,280}{21\pi^8 a^8} + \cdots \right\}$$

$$J_0(j_{1,s}) \sim \frac{(-1)^s 2^{\frac{3}{2}}}{\pi b^{\frac{1}{2}}} \left\{ 1 + \frac{24}{\pi^4 b^4} - \frac{19,584}{10\pi^6 b^6} + \frac{2,466,720}{7\pi^8 b^8} - \cdots \right\}$$

8. Table of zeros for $J_0(x)$ and $J_1(x)$

$$J_0(\alpha_n) = 0 \qquad J_1(\beta_n) = 0$$

Roots α_n	$J_1(\alpha_n)$	Roots β_n	$J_0(\beta_n)$
2.4048	0.5191	0.0000	1.0000
5.5201	−0.3403	3.8317	−0.4028
8.6537	0.2715	7.0156	0.3001
11.7915	−0.2325	10.1735	−0.2497
14.9309	0.2065	13.3237	0.2184
18.0711	−0.1877	16.4706	−0.1965
21.2116	0.1733	19.6159	0.1801

9. Recurrence formulas

$$J_{n-1}(x) + J_{n+1}(x) = \frac{2n}{x} J_n(x) \qquad n J_n(x) + x J_n'(x) = x J_{n-1}(x)$$

$$J_{n-1}(x) - J_{n+1}(x) = 2 J_n'(x) \qquad n J_n(x) - x J_n'(x) = x J_{n+1}(x)$$

10. If J_n is written for $J_n(x)$ and $J_n^{(k)}$ is written for $\dfrac{d^k}{dx^k}\{J_n(x)\}$, then the following derivative relationships are important

$$J_0^{(r)} = -J_1^{(r-1)}$$

$$J_0^{(2)} = -J_0 + \frac{1}{x} J_1 = \frac{1}{2} (J_2 - J_0)$$

$$J_0^{(3)} = \frac{1}{x} J_0 + \left(1 - \frac{2}{x^2}\right) J_1 = \frac{1}{4} (-J_3 + 3J_1)$$

$$J_0^{(4)} = \left(1 - \frac{3}{x^2}\right) J_0 - \left(\frac{2}{x} - \frac{6}{x^3}\right) J_1 = \frac{1}{8} (J_4 - 4J_2 + 3J_0), \text{ etc.}$$

11. Half order Bessel functions

$$J_{\frac{1}{2}}(x) = \sqrt{\frac{2}{\pi x}} \sin x$$

$$J_{-\frac{1}{2}}(x) = \sqrt{\frac{2}{\pi x}} \cos x$$

$$J_{n+\frac{1}{2}}(x) = -x^{n+\frac{1}{2}} \frac{d}{dx} \{x^{-(n+\frac{1}{2})} J_{n+\frac{1}{2}}(x)\}$$

$$J_{n-\frac{1}{2}}(x) = x^{-(n+\frac{1}{2})} \frac{d}{dx} \{x^{n+\frac{1}{2}} J_{n+\frac{1}{2}}(x)\}$$

n	$\left(\frac{\pi x}{2}\right)^{\frac{1}{2}} J_{n+\frac{1}{2}}(x)$	$\left(\frac{\pi x}{2}\right)^{\frac{1}{2}} J_{-(n+\frac{1}{2})}(x)$
0	$\sin x$	$\cos x$
1	$\frac{\sin x}{x} - \cos x$	$-\frac{\cos x}{x} - \sin x$
2	$\left(\frac{3}{x^2} - 1\right) \sin x - \frac{3}{x} \cos x$	$\left(\frac{3}{x^2} - 1\right) \cos x + \frac{3}{x} \sin x$
3	$\left(\frac{15}{x^3} - \frac{6}{x}\right) \sin x - \left(\frac{15}{x^2} - 1\right) \cos x$	$-\left(\frac{15}{x^3} - \frac{6}{x}\right) \cos x - \left(\frac{15}{x^2} - 1\right) \sin x$
	etc.	

12. Additional solutions to Bessel's equation are

$Y_n(x)$ (also called Weber's function, and sometimes denoted by $N_n(x)$)
$H_n^{(1)}(x)$ and $H_n^{(2)}(x)$ (also called Hankel functions)

These solutions are defined as follows

$$Y_n(x) = \begin{cases} \dfrac{J_n(x) \cos (n\pi) - J_{-n}(x)}{\sin (n\pi)} & n \text{ not an integer} \\[2ex] \lim_{v \to n} \dfrac{J_v(x) \cos (v\pi) - J_{-v}(x)}{\sin (v\pi)} & n \text{ an integer} \end{cases}$$

$$H_n^{(1)}(x) = J_n(x) + iY_n(x)$$
$$H_n^{(2)}(x) = J_n(x) - iY_n(x)$$

The additional properties of these functions may all be derived from the above relations and the known properties of $J_n(x)$.

13. Complete solutions to Bessel's equation may be written as

$$c_1 J_n(x) + c_2 J_{-n}(x) \qquad \text{if } n \text{ is not an integer,}$$

or

$$c_1 J_n(x) + c_2 Y_n(x)$$

or

$$c_1 H_n^{(1)}(x) + c_2 H_n^{(2)}(x)$$

$$\left.\begin{array}{r}\end{array}\right\} \text{for any value of } n$$

14. The modified (or hyperbolic) Bessel's differential equation is

$$x^2 \frac{d^2 y}{dx^2} + x \frac{dy}{dx} - (x^2 + n^2)y = 0$$

15. When n is not an integer, two independent solutions of the equation are $I_n(x)$ and $I_{-n}(x)$, where

$$I_n(x) = \sum_{k=0}^{\infty} \frac{1}{k! \Gamma(n + k + 1)} \left(\frac{x}{2}\right)^{n+2k}$$

16. If n is an integer,

$$I_n(x) = I_{-n}(x) = \frac{x^n}{2^n n!} \left\{ 1 + \frac{x^2}{2^2 \cdot 1!(n+1)} + \frac{x^4}{2^4 \cdot 2!(n+1)(n+2)} \right.$$

$$\left. + \frac{x^6}{2^6 \cdot 3!(n+1)(n+2)(n+3)} + \cdots \right\}$$

17. For $n = 0$ and $n = 1$, this formula becomes

$$I_0(x) = 1 + \frac{x^2}{2^2(1!)^2} + \frac{x^4}{2^4(2!)^2} + \frac{x^6}{2^6(3!)^2} + \frac{x^8}{2^8(4!)^2} + \cdots$$

$$I_1(x) = \frac{x}{2} + \frac{x^3}{2^3 \cdot 1!2!} + \frac{x^5}{2^5 \cdot 2!3!} + \frac{x^7}{2^7 \cdot 3!4!} + \frac{x^9}{2^9 \cdot 4!5!} + \cdots$$

18. Another solution to the modified Bessel's equation is

$$K_n(x) = \begin{cases} \dfrac{1}{2} \pi \dfrac{I_{-n}(x) - I_n(x)}{\sin(n\pi)} & n \text{ not an integer} \\[3mm] \lim_{v \to n} \dfrac{1}{2} \pi \dfrac{I_{-v}(x) - I_v(x)}{\sin(v\pi)} & n \text{ an integer} \end{cases}$$

This function is linearly independent of $I_n(x)$ for all values of n. Thus the complete solution to the modified Bessel's equation may be written as

$$c_1 I_n(x) + c_2 I_{-n}(x) \qquad n \text{ not an integer}$$

or

$$c_1 I_n(x) + c_2 K_n(x) \qquad \text{any } n$$

19. The following relations hold among the various Bessel functions:

$$I_n(z) = i^{-m} J_m(iz)$$

$$Y_n(iz) = (i)^{n+1} I_n(z) - \frac{2}{\pi} i^{-n} K_n(z)$$

Most of the properties of the modified Bessel function may be deduced from the known properties of $J_n(x)$ by use of these relations and those previously given.

20. Recurrence formulas

$$I_{n-1}(x) - I_{n+1}(x) = \frac{2n}{x} I_n(x) \qquad I_{n-1}(x) + I_{n+1}(x) = 2I_n'(x)$$

$$I_{n-1}(x) - \frac{n}{x} I_n(x) = I_n'(x) \qquad I_n'(x) = I_{n+1}(x) + \frac{n}{x} I_n(z)$$

BESSEL FUNCTIONS $J_0(x)$ AND $J_1(x)$

x	$J_0(x)$	$J_1(x)$	x	$J_0(x)$	$J_1(x)$	x	$J_0(x)$	$J_1(x)$
0.0	1.0000	.0000	**5.0**	−.1776	−.3276	**10.0**	−.2459	.0435
0.1	.9975	.0499	5.1	−.1443	−.3371	10.1	−.2490	.0184
0.2	.9900	.0995	5.2	−.1103	−.3432	10.2	−.2496	−.0066
0.3	.9776	.1483	5.3	−.0758	−.3460	10.3	−.2477	−.0313
0.4	.9604	.1960	5.4	−.0412	−.3453	10.4	−.2434	−.0555
0.5	.9385	.2423	**5.5**	−.0068	−.3414	**10.5**	−.2366	−.0789
0.6	.9120	.2867	5.6	.0270	−.3343	10.6	−.2276	−.1012
0.7	.8812	.3290	5.7	.0599	−.3241	10.7	−.2164	−.1224
0.8	.8463	.3688	5.8	.0917	−.3110	10.8	−.2032	−.1422
0.9	.8075	.4059	5.9	.1220	−.2951	10.9	−.1881	−.1603
1.0	.7652	.4401	**6.0**	.1506	−.2767	**11.0**	−.1712	−.1768
1.1	.7196	.4709	6.1	.1773	−.2559	11.1	−.1528	−.1913
1.2	.6711	.4983	6.2	.2017	−.2329	11.2	−.1330	−.2039
1.3	.6201	.5220	6.3	.2238	−.2081	11.3	−.1121	−.2143
1.4	.5669	.5419	6.4	.2433	−.1816	11.4	−.0902	−.2225
1.5	.5118	.5579	**6.5**	.2601	−.1538	**11.5**	−.0677	−.2284
1.6	.4554	.5699	6.6	.2740	−.1250	11.6	−.0446	−.2320
1.7	.3980	.5778	6.7	.2851	−.0953	11.7	−.0213	−.2333
1.8	.3400	.5815	6.8	.2931	−.0652	11.8	.0020	−.2323
1.9	.2818	.5812	6.9	.2981	−.0349	11.9	.0250	−.2290
2.0	.2239	.5767	**7.0**	.3001	−.0047	**12.0**	.0477	−.2234
2.1	.1666	.5683	7.1	.2991	.0252	12.1	.0697	−.2157
2.2	.1104	.5560	7.2	.2951	.0543	12.2	.0908	−.2060
2.3	.0555	.5399	7.3	.2882	.0826	12.3	.1108	−.1943
2.4	.0025	.5202	7.4	.2786	.1096	12.4	.1296	−.1807
2.5	−.0484	.4971	**7.5**	.2663	.1352	**12.5**	.1469	−.1655
2.6	−.0968	.4708	7.6	.2516	.1592	12.6	.1626	−.1487
2.7	−.1424	.4416	7.7	.2346	.1813	12.7	.1766	−.1307
2.8	−.1850	.4097	7.8	.2154	.2014	12.8	.1887	−.1114
2.9	−.2243	.3754	7.9	.1944	.2192	12.9	.1988	−.0912
3.0	−.2601	.3391	**8.0**	.1717	.2346	**13.0**	.2069	−.0703
3.1	−.2921	.3009	8.1	.1475	.2476	13.1	.2129	−.0489
3.2	−.3202	.2613	8.2	.1222	.2580	13.2	.2167	−.0271
3.3	−.3443	.2207	8.3	.0960	.2657	13.3	.2183	−.0052
3.4	−.3643	.1792	8.4	.0692	.2708	13.4	.2177	.0166
3.5	−.3801	.1374	**8.5**	.0419	.2731	**13.5**	.2150	.0380
3.6	−.3918	.0955	8.6	.0146	.2728	13.6	.2101	.0590
3.7	−.3992	.0538	8.7	−.0125	.2697	13.7	.2032	.0791
3.8	−.4026	.0128	8.8	−.0392	.2641	13.8	.1943	.0984
3.9	−.4018	−.0272	8.9	−.0653	.2559	13.9	.1836	.1165
4.0	−.3971	−.0660	**9.0**	−.0903	.2453	**14.0**	.1711	.1334
4.1	−.3887	−.1033	9.1	−.1142	.2324	14.1	.1570	.1488
4.2	−.3766	−.1386	9.2	−.1367	.2174	14.2	.1414	.1626
4.3	−.3610	−.1719	9.3	−.1577	.2004	14.3	.1245	.1747
4.4	−.3423	−.2028	9.4	−.1768	.1816	14.4	.1065	.1850
4.5	−.3205	−.2311	**9.5**	−.1939	.1613	**14.5**	.0875	.1934
4.6	−.2961	−.2566	9.6	−.2090	.1395	14.6	.0679	.1999
4.7	−.2693	−.2791	9.7	−.2218	.1166	14.7	.0476	.2043
4.8	−.2404	−.2985	9.8	−.2323	.0928	14.8	.0271	.2066
4.9	−.2097	−.3147	9.9	−.2403	.0684	14.9	.0064	.2069

BESSEL FUNCTIONS FOR SPHERICAL COORDINATES

$$j_n(x) = \sqrt{\frac{\pi}{2x}}\, J_{(n+\frac{1}{2})}(x), \quad y_n(x) = \sqrt{\frac{\pi}{2x}}\, Y_{(n+\frac{1}{2})}(x) = (-1)^{n+1}\sqrt{\frac{\pi}{2x}}\, J_{-(n+\frac{1}{2})}(x)$$

x	$j_0(x)$	$y_0(x)$	$j_1(x)$	$y_1(x)$	$j_2(x)$	$y_2(x)$
0.0	1.0000	$-\infty$	0.0000	$-\infty$	0.0000	$-\infty$
0.1	0.9983	−9.9500	0.0333	−100.50	0.0007	−3005.0
0.2	0.9933	−4.9003	0.0664	−25.495	0.0027	−377.52
0.4	0.9735	−2.3027	0.1312	−6.7302	0.0105	−48.174
0.6	0.9411	−1.3756	0.1929	−3.2337	0.0234	−14.793
0.8	0.8967	−0.8709	0.2500	−1.9853	0.0408	−6.5740
1.0	0.8415	−0.5403	0.3012	−1.3818	0.0620	−3.6050
1.2	0.7767	−0.3020	0.3453	−1.0283	0.0865	−2.2689
1.4	0.7039	−0.1214	0.3814	−0.7906	0.1133	−1.5728
1.6	0.6247	+0.0183	0.4087	−0.6133	0.1416	−1.1682
1.8	0.5410	0.1262	0.4268	−0.4709	0.1703	−0.9111
2.0	0.4546	0.2081	0.4354	−0.3506	0.1985	−0.7340
2.2	0.3675	0.2675	0.4346	−0.2459	0.2251	−0.6028
2.4	0.2814	0.3072	0.4245	−0.1534	0.2492	−0.4990
2.6	0.1983	0.3296	0.4058	−0.0715	0.2700	−0.4121
2.8	0.1196	0.3365	0.3792	+0.0005	0.2867	−0.3359
3.0	+0.0470	0.3300	0.3457	0.0630	0.2986	−0.2670
3.2	−0.0182	0.3120	0.3063	0.1157	0.3054	−0.2035
3.4	−0.0752	0.2844	0.2623	0.1588	0.3066	−0.1442
3.6	−0.1229	0.2491	0.2150	0.1921	0.3021	−0.0890
3.8	−0.1610	0.2082	0.1658	0.2158	0.2919	−0.0378
4.0	−0.1892	0.1634	0.1161	0.2300	0.2763	+0.0091
4.2	−0.2075	0.1167	0.0673	0.2353	0.2556	0.0514
4.4	−0.2163	0.0699	+0.0207	0.2321	0.2304	0.0884
4.6	−0.2160	+0.0244	−0.0226	0.2213	0.2013	0.1200
4.8	−0.2075	−0.0182	−0.0615	0.2037	0.1691	0.1456
5.0	−0.1918	−0.0567	−0.0951	0.1804	0.1347	0.1650
5.2	−0.1699	−0.0901	−0.1228	0.1526	0.0991	0.1781
5.4	−0.1431	−0.1175	−0.1440	0.1213	0.0631	0.1850
5.6	−0.1127	−0.1385	−0.1586	0.0880	+0.0278	0.1856
5.8	−0.0801	−0.1527	−0.1665	0.0538	−0.0060	0.1805
6.0	−0.0466	−0.1600	−0.1678	+0.0199	−0.0373	0.1700
6.2	−0.0134	−0.1607	−0.1629	−0.0125	−0.0654	0.1547
6.4	+0.0182	−0.1552	−0.1523	−0.0425	−0.0896	0.1353
6.6	0.0472	−0.1440	−0.1368	−0.0690	−0.1094	0.1126
6.8	0.0727	−0.1278	−0.1172	−0.0915	−0.1243	0.0875
7.0	0.0939	−0.1077	−0.0943	−0.1092	−0.1343	0.0609
7.2	0.1102	−0.0845	−0.0692	−0.1220	−0.1391	0.0337
7.4	0.1215	−0.0593	−0.0429	−0.1294	−0.1388	+0.0068
7.6	0.1274	−0.0331	−0.0163	−0.1317	−0.1338	−0.0189
7.8	0.1280	−0.0069	+0.0095	−0.1289	−0.1244	−0.0427
8.0	0.1237	+0.0182	0.0336	−0.1214	−0.1111	−0.0637

Taken from Vibration and Sound with the permission of Philip Morse, author, and McGraw-Hill Book Company, Inc., publisher.

Special Function Tables

HYPERBOLIC BESSEL FUNCTIONS

$$I_m(x) = i^{-m} J_m(ix)$$

x	$I_0(x)$	$I_1(x)$	$I_2(x)$
0.0	1.0000	0.0000	0.0000
0.1	1.0025	0.0501	0.0012
0.2	1.0100	0.1005	0.0050
0.4	1.0404	0.2040	0.0203
0.6	1.0921	0.3137	0.0464
0.8	1.1665	0.4329	0.0843
1.0	1.2661	0.5652	0.1358
1.2	1.3937	0.7147	0.2026
1.4	1.5534	0.8861	0.2876
1.6	1.7500	1.0848	0.3940
1.8	1.9895	1.3172	0.5260
2.0	2.2796	1.5906	0.6890
2.2	2.6292	1.9141	0.8891
2.4	3.0492	2.2981	1.1342
2.6	3.5532	2.7554	1.4338
2.8	4.1574	3.3011	1.7994
3.0	4.8808	3.9534	2.2452
3.2	5.7472	4.7343	2.7884
3.4	6.7848	5.6701	3.4495
3.6	8.0278	6.7926	4.2538
3.8	9.5169	8.1405	5.2323
4.0	11.302	9.7594	6.4224
4.2	13.443	11.705	7.8683
4.4	16.010	14.046	9.6259
4.6	19.093	16.863	11.761
4.8	22.794	20.253	14.355
5.0	27.240	24.335	17.505
5.2	32.584	29.254	21.332
5.4	39.010	35.181	25.980
5.6	46.738	42.327	31.621
5.8	56.039	50.945	38.472
6.0	67.235	61.341	46.788
6.2	80.717	73.886	56.882
6.4	96.963	89.025	69.143
6.6	116.54	107.31	84.021
6.8	140.14	129.38	102.08
7.0	168.59	156.04	124.01
7.2	202.92	188.25	150.63
7.4	244.34	227.17	182.94
7.6	294.33	274.22	222.17
7.8	354.68	331.10	269.79
8.0	427.57	399.87	327.60

Taken from *Vibration and Sound* with the permission of Philip Morse, author, and McGraw-Hill Book Company, Inc., publisher.

ELLIPTIC INTEGRALS OF THE FIRST, SECOND AND THIRD KIND

An elliptic integral has the form $\int R(x, \sqrt{f(x)})\, dx$, where R represents a rational function and $f(x) = a + bx + cx^2 + dx^3 + ex^4$, an algebraic function of the third or fourth degree.

1. Elliptic integrals of the *first kind* are represented by

$$F(k, \phi) = \int_0^\phi \frac{d\Phi}{\sqrt{1 - k^2 \sin^2 \Phi}}$$

$$= \int_0^x \frac{d\xi}{\sqrt{(1 - \xi^2)(1 - k^2\xi^2)}}, \quad x = \sin \phi,\ k^2 < 1.$$

2. Elliptic integrals of the second kind are represented by

$$E(k, \phi) = \int_0^\phi \sqrt{1 - k^2 \sin^2 \Phi}\, d\Phi$$

$$= \int_0^x \frac{\sqrt{1 - k^2\xi^2}}{\sqrt{1 - \xi^2}}\, d\xi, \quad x = \sin \phi,\ k^2 < 1.$$

3. Elliptic integrals of the third kind are represented as

$$\pi(k, n, \phi) = \int_0^\phi \frac{d\Phi}{(1 + n \sin^2 \Phi)\sqrt{1 - k^2 \sin^2 \Phi}},$$

$$k^2 < 1,\ n \text{ an integer.}$$

Elliptic integrals of the third kind are also presented as

$$\pi_1(k, n, x) = \int_0^x \frac{d\xi}{(1 + n\xi^2)\sqrt{(1 - \xi^2)(1 - k^2\xi^2)}},$$

$$x = \sin \phi,\ k^2 < 1,\ n \text{ an integer.}$$

4. The complete integrals are

$$K = F\left(k, \frac{\pi}{2}\right) = \frac{\pi}{2}\left[1 + \left(\frac{1}{2}\right)^2 k^2 + \left(\frac{3}{2 \cdot 4}\right)^2 k^4 \right.$$

$$\left. + \left(\frac{3 \cdot 5}{2 \cdot 4 \cdot 6}\right)^2 k^6 + \cdots\right]$$

$$E = E\left(k, \frac{\pi}{2}\right) = \frac{\pi}{2}\left[1 - \left(\frac{1}{2^2}\right) k^2 - \left(\frac{3^2}{2^2 \cdot 4^2}\right)\frac{k^4}{3}\right.$$

$$\left. - \left(\frac{3^2 \cdot 5^2}{2^2 \cdot 4^2 \cdot 6^2}\right)\frac{k^6}{5} - \left(\frac{3^2 \cdot 5^2 \cdot 7^2}{2^2 \cdot 4^2 \cdot 6^2 \cdot 8^2}\right)\frac{k^8}{7} - \cdots\right].$$

$$K' = F\left(\sqrt{1 - k^2}, \frac{\pi}{2}\right),\ E' = E\left(\sqrt{1 - k^2}, \frac{\pi}{2}\right)$$

5. The following relation holds between K, K', E, E', namely

$$KE' + EK' - KK' = \frac{\pi}{2}$$

ELLIPTIC INTEGRALS OF THE FIRST, SECOND AND THIRD KIND (Continued)

   6. To evaluate elliptic integrals for values outside the range contained in the following tables, these relations are useful

$$F(k, \pi) = 2K; \, E(k, \pi) = 2E$$

$$F(k, \phi + m\pi) = mF(k, \pi) + F(k, \phi) = 2mK + F(k, \phi)$$
$$m = 0, 1, 2, 3, \ldots$$

$$E(k, \phi + m\pi) = mE(k, \pi) + E(k, \phi) = 2mE + E(k, \phi)$$
$$m = 0, 1, 2, 3, \ldots$$

   7. If $u = F(k, \phi) = \displaystyle\int_0^\phi \frac{d\Phi}{\sqrt{1 - k^2 \sin^2 \Phi}}$ $(k^2 < 1)$,

$$= \text{elliptic integral of the first kind.}$$

$$u = \int_0^x \frac{dx}{\sqrt{(1 - \xi^2)(1 - k^2\xi^2)}}, \text{ where } x = \sin \phi.$$

ϕ is called the amplitude of u or am u.

k is called the modulus.

$$k' = \sqrt{1 - k^2} = \text{the complementary modulus.}$$

$\sin \phi = \text{sn } u = x$ $\tan \phi = \text{tn } u = \dfrac{x}{\sqrt{1 - x^2}}$.

$\cos \phi = \text{cn } u = \sqrt{1 - x^2}$. $\Delta\phi = \text{dn } u = \sqrt{1 - k^2x^2}$.

am $0 = 0$.   sn $0 = 0$.

cn $0 = 1$.   dn $0 = 1$.

am $(-u) = -$am u.   sn $(-u) = -$sn u.

cn $(-u) = $ cn u.   dn $(-u) = $ dn u.

tn $(-u) = -$tn u.

$\text{sn}^2 u + \text{cn}^2 u = 1$.

$\text{dn}^2 u + k^2 \text{sn}^2 u = 1$.

$\text{dn}^2 u - k^2 \text{cn}^2 u = 1 - k^2 = k'^2$.

*ELLIPTIC INTEGRALS OF THE FIRST KIND: $F(k, \phi)$

$$F(k, \phi) = \int_0^\phi \frac{d\Phi}{\sqrt{1 - k^2 \sin^2 \Phi}}, \qquad \theta = \sin^{-1} k$$

θ ϕ	5°	10°	15°	20°	25°	30°	35°	40°	45°
1°	0.0175	0.0175	0.0175	0.0175	0.0175	0.0175	0.0175	0.0175	0.0175
2°	0.0349	0.0349	0.0349	0.0349	0.0349	0.0349	0.0349	0.0349	0.0349
3°	0.0524	0.0524	0.0524	0.0524	0.0524	0.0524	0.0524	0.0524	0.0524
4°	0.0698	0.0698	0.0698	0.0698	0.0698	0.0698	0.0698	0.0698	0.0698
5°	0.0873	0.0873	0.0873	0.0873	0.0873	0.0873	0.0873	0.0873	0.0873
6°	0.1047	0.1047	0.1047	0.1047	0.1048	0.1048	0.1048	0.1048	0.1048
7°	0.1222	0.1222	0.1222	0.1222	0.1222	0.1222	0.1223	0.1223	0.1223
8°	0.1396	0.1396	0.1397	0.1397	0.1397	0.1397	0.1398	0.1398	0.1399
9°	0.1571	0.1571	0.1571	0.1572	0.1572	0.1572	0.1573	0.1573	0.1574
10°	0.1745	0.1746	0.1746	0.1746	0.1747	0.1748	0.1748	0.1749	0.1750
11°	0.1920	0.1920	0.1921	0.1921	0.1922	0.1923	0.1924	0.1925	0.1926
12°	0.2095	0.2095	0.2095	0.2096	0.2097	0.2098	0.2099	0.2101	0.2102
13°	0.2269	0.2270	0.2270	0.2271	0.2272	0.2274	0.2275	0.2277	0.2279
14°	0.2444	0.2444	0.2445	0.2446	0.2448	0.2450	0.2451	0.2453	0.2456
15°	0.2618	0.2619	0.2620	0.2621	0.2623	0.2625	0.2628	0.2630	0.2633
16°	0.2793	0.2794	0.2795	0.2797	0.2799	0.2802	0.2804	0.2808	0.2811
17°	0.2967	0.2968	0.2970	0.2972	0.2975	0.2978	0.2981	0.2985	0.2989
18°	0.3142	0.3143	0.3145	0.3148	0.3151	0.3154	0.3159	0.3163	0.3167
19°	0.3317	0.3318	0.3320	0.3323	0.3327	0.3331	0.3336	0.3341	0.3347
20°	0.3491	0.3493	0.3495	0.3499	0.3503	0.3508	0.3514	0.3520	0.3526
21°	0.3666	0.3668	0.3671	0.3675	0.3680	0.3685	0.3692	0.3699	0.3706
22°	0.3840	0.3842	0.3846	0.3851	0.3856	0.3863	0.3871	0.3879	0.3887
23°	0.4015	0.4017	0.4021	0.4027	0.4033	0.4041	0.4049	0.4059	0.4068
24°	0.4190	0.4192	0.4197	0.4203	0.4210	0.4219	0.4229	0.4239	0.4250
25°	0.4364	0.4367	0.4372	0.4379	0.4387	0.4397	0.4408	0.4420	0.4433
26°	0.4539	0.4542	0.4548	0.4556	0.4565	0.4576	0.4588	0.4602	0.4616
27°	0.4714	0.4717	0.4724	0.4732	0.4743	0.4755	0.4769	0.4784	0.4800
28°	0.4888	0.4893	0.4899	0.4909	0.4921	0.4934	0.4950	0.4967	0.4985
29°	0.5063	0.5068	0.5075	0.5086	0.5099	0.5114	0.5132	0.5150	0.5170
30°	0.5238	0.5243	0.5251	0.5263	0.5277	0.5294	0.5313	0.5334	0.5356
31°	0.5412	0.5418	0.5427	0.5440	0.5456	0.5475	0.5496	0.5519	0.5543
32°	0.5587	0.5593	0.5603	0.5617	0.5635	0.5656	0.5679	0.5704	0.5731
33°	0.5762	0.5769	0.5780	0.5795	0.5814	0.5837	0.5862	0.5890	0.5920
34°	0.5937	0.5944	0.5956	0.5973	0.5994	0.6018	0.6046	0.6077	0.6109
35°	0.6111	0.6119	0.6133	0.6151	0.6173	0.6200	0.6231	0.6264	0.6300
36°	0.6286	0.6295	0.6309	0.6329	0.6353	0.6383	0.6416	0.6452	0.6491
37°	0.6461	0.6470	0.6486	0.6507	0.6534	0.6565	0.6602	0.6641	0.6684
38°	0.6636	0.6646	0.6662	0.6685	0.6714	0.6749	0.6788	0.6831	0.6877
39°	0.6810	0.6821	0.6839	0.6864	0.6895	0.6932	0.6975	0.7021	0.7071
40°	0.6985	0.6997	0.7016	0.7043	0.7076	0.7116	0.7162	0.7213	0.7267
41°	0.7160	0.7173	0.7193	0.7222	0.7258	0.7301	0.7350	0.7405	0.7463
42°	0.7335	0.7348	0.7370	0.7401	0.7440	0.7486	0.7539	0.7598	0.7661
43°	0.7510	0.7524	0.7548	0.7580	0.7622	0.7671	0.7728	0.7791	0.7859
44°	0.7685	0.7700	0.7725	0.7760	0.7804	0.7857	0.7918	0.7986	0.8059
45°	0.7859	0.7876	0.7903	0.7940	0.7987	0.8044	0.8109	0.8181	0.8260

* For useful information about these tables see preceding page.

*ELLIPTIC INTEGRALS OF THE FIRST KIND: $F(k, \phi)$ (Continued)

$$F(k, \phi) = \int_0^\phi \frac{d\Phi}{\sqrt{1 - k^2 \sin^2 \Phi}}, \qquad \theta = \sin^{-1} k$$

θ / ϕ	50°	55°	60°	65°	70°	75°	80°	85°	90°
1°	0.0175	0.0175	0.0175	0.0175	0.0175	0.0175	0.0175	0.0175	0.0175
2°	0.0349	0.0349	0.0349	0.0349	0.0349	0.0349	0.0349	0.0349	0.0349
3°	0.0524	0.0524	0.0524	0.0524	0.0524	0.0524	0.0524	0.0524	0.0524
4°	0.0698	0.0699	0.0699	0.0699	0.0699	0.0699	0.0699	0.0699	0.0699
5°	0.0873	0.0873	0.0873	0.0874	0.0874	0.0874	0.0874	0.0874	0.0874
6°	0.1048	0.1048	0.1049	0.1049	0.1049	0.1049	0.1049	0.1049	0.1049
7°	0.1224	0.1224	0.1224	0.1224	0.1224	0.1225	0.1225	0.1225	0.1225
8°	0.1399	0.1399	0.1400	0.1400	0.1400	0.1401	0.1401	0.1401	0.1401
9°	0.1575	0.1575	0.1576	0.1576	0.1577	0.1577	0.1577	0.1577	0.1577
10°	0.1751	0.1751	0.1752	0.1753	0.1753	0.1754	0.1754	0.1754	0.1754
11°	0.1927	0.1928	0.1929	0.1930	0.1930	0.1931	0.1931	0.1932	0.1932
12°	0.2103	0.2105	0.2106	0.2107	0.2108	0.2109	0.2109	0.2110	0.2110
13°	0.2280	0.2282	0.2284	0.2285	0.2286	0.2287	0.2288	0.2288	0.2289
14°	0.2458	0.2460	0.2462	0.2464	0.2465	0.2466	0.2467	0.2468	0.2468
15°	0.2636	0.2638	0.2641	0.2643	0.2645	0.2646	0.2647	0.2648	0.2648
16°	0.2814	0.2817	0.2820	0.2823	0.2825	0.2827	0.2828	0.2829	0.2830
17°	0.2993	0.2997	0.3000	0.3003	0.3006	0.3008	0.3010	0.3011	0.3012
18°	0.3172	0.3177	0.3181	0.3185	0.3188	0.3191	0.3193	0.3194	0.3195
19°	0.3352	0.3357	0.3362	0.3367	0.3371	0.3374	0.3377	0.3378	0.3379
20°	0.3533	0.3539	0.3545	0.3550	0.3555	0.3559	0.3561	0.3563	0.3564
21°	0.3714	0.3721	0.3728	0.3734	0.3740	0.3744	0.3747	0.3749	0.3750
22°	0.3896	0.3904	0.3912	0.3919	0.3926	0.3931	0.3935	0.3937	0.3938
23°	0.4078	0.4088	0.4097	0.4105	0.4113	0.4119	0.4123	0.4126	0.4127
24°	0.4261	0.4272	0.4283	0.4292	0.4301	0.4308	0.4313	0.4316	0.4317
25°	0.4446	0.4458	0.4470	0.4481	0.4490	0.4498	0.4504	0.4508	0.4509
26°	0.4630	0.4645	0.4658	0.4670	0.4681	0.4690	0.4697	0.4701	0.4702
27°	0.4816	0.4832	0.4847	0.4861	0.4873	0.4884	0.4891	0.4896	0.4897
28°	0.5003	0.5021	0.5038	0.5053	0.5067	0.5079	0.5087	0.5092	0.5094
29°	0.5190	0.5210	0.5229	0.5247	0.5262	0.5275	0.5285	0.5291	0.5293
30°	0.5379	0.5401	0.5422	0.5442	0.5459	0.5474	0.5484	0.5491	0.5493
31°	0.5568	0.5593	0.5617	0.5639	0.5658	0.5674	0.5686	0.5693	0.5696
32°	0.5759	0.5786	0.5812	0.5837	0.5858	0.5876	0.5889	0.5898	0.5900
33°	0.5950	0.5980	0.6010	0.6037	0.6060	0.6080	0.6095	0.6104	0.6107
34°	0.6143	0.6176	0.6208	0.6238	0.6265	0.6287	0.6303	0.6313	0.6317
35°	0.6336	0.6373	0.6408	0.6441	0.6471	0.6495	0.6513	0.6525	0.6528
36°	0.6531	0.6571	0.6610	0.6647	0.6679	0.6706	0.6726	0.6739	0.6743
37°	0.6727	0.6771	0.6814	0.6854	0.6890	0.6919	0.6941	0.6955	0.6960
38°	0.6925	0.6973	0.7019	0.7063	0.7102	0.7135	0.7159	0.7175	0.7180
39°	0.7123	0.7176	0.7227	0.7275	0.7318	0.7353	0.7380	0.7397	0.7403
40°	0.7323	0.7380	0.7436	0.7488	0.7535	0.7575	0.7604	0.7623	0.7629
41°	0.7524	0.7586	0.7647	0.7704	0.7756	0.7799	0.7831	0.7852	0.7859
42°	0.7727	0.7794	0.7860	0.7922	0.7979	0.8026	0.8062	0.8084	0.8092
43°	0.7931	0.8004	0.8075	0.8143	0.8204	0.8256	0.8295	0.8320	0.8328
44°	0.8136	0.8215	0.8293	0.8367	0.8433	0.8490	0.8533	0.8560	0.8569
45°	0.8343	0.8428	0.8512	0.8592	0.8665	0.8727	0.8774	0.8804	0.8814

*ELLIPTIC INTEGRALS OF THE FIRST KIND: $F(k, \phi)$ (Continued)

$$F(k, \phi) = \int_0^\phi \frac{d\Phi}{\sqrt{1 - k^2 \sin^2 \Phi}}, \qquad \theta = \sin^{-1} k$$

θ / ϕ	5°	10°	15°	20°	25°	30°	35°	40°	45°
46°	0.8034	0.8052	0.8080	0.8120	0.8170	0.8230	0.8300	0.8378	0.8462
47°	0.8209	0.8227	0.8258	0.8300	0.8353	0.8418	0.8492	0.8575	0.8666
48°	0.8384	0.8403	0.8436	0.8480	0.8537	0.8606	0.8685	0.8773	0.8870
49°	0.8559	0.8579	0.8614	0.8661	0.8721	0.8794	0.8878	0.8972	0.9076
50°	0.8734	0.8756	0.8792	0.8842	0.8905	0.8982	0.9072	0.9173	0.9283
51°	0.8909	0.8932	0.8970	0.9023	0.9090	0.9172	0.9267	0.9374	0.9491
52°	0.9084	0.9108	0.9148	0.9204	0.9275	0.9361	0.9462	0.9575	0.9701
53°	0.9259	0.9284	0.9326	0.9385	0.9460	0.9551	0.9658	0.9778	0.9912
54°	0.9434	0.9460	0.9505	0.9567	0.9646	0.9742	0.9855	0.9982	1.0124
55°	0.9609	0.9637	0.9683	0.9748	0.9832	0.9933	1.0052	1.0187	1.0337
56°	0.9784	0.9813	0.9862	0.9930	1.0018	1.0125	1.0250	1.0393	1.0552
57°	0.9959	0.9989	1.0041	1.0112	1.0204	1.0317	1.0449	1.0600	1.0768
58°	1.0134	1.0166	1.0219	1.0295	1.0391	1.0509	1.0648	1.0807	1.0985
59°	1.0309	1.0342	1.0398	1.0477	1.0578	1.0702	1.0848	1.1016	1.1204
60°	1.0484	1.0519	1.0577	1.0660	1.0766	1.0896	1.1049	1.1226	1.1424
61°	1.0659	1.0695	1.0757	1.0843	1.0953	1.1089	1.1250	1.1436	1.1646
62°	1.0834	1.0872	1.0936	1.1026	1.1141	1.1284	1.1452	1.1648	1.1868
63°	1.1009	1.1049	1.1115	1.1209	1.1330	1.1478	1.1655	1.1860	1.2093
64°	1.1184	1.1225	1.1295	1.1392	1.1518	1.1674	1.1859	1.2073	1.2318
65°	1.1359	1.1402	1.1474	1.1575	1.1707	1.1869	1.2063	1.2288	1.2545
66°	1.1534	1.1579	1.1654	1.1759	1.1896	1.2065	1.2267	1.2503	1.2773
67°	1.1709	1.1756	1.1833	1.1943	1.2085	1.2262	1.2472	1.2719	1.3002
68°	1.1884	1.1932	1.2013	1.2127	1.2275	1.2458	1.2678	1.2936	1.3232
69°	1.2059	1.2109	1.2193	1.2311	1.2465	1.2655	1.2885	1.3154	1.3464
70°	1.2234	1.2286	1.2373	1.2495	1.2655	1.2853	1.3092	1.3372	1.3697
71°	1.2410	1.2463	1.2553	1.2680	1.2845	1.3051	1.3299	1.3592	1.3931
72°	1.2585	1.2640	1.2733	1.2864	1.3036	1.3249	1.3507	1.3812	1.4167
73°	1.2760	1.2817	1.2913	1.3049	1.3226	1.3448	1.3715	1.4033	1.4403
74°	1.2935	1.2994	1.3093	1.3234	1.3417	1.3647	1.3924	1.4254	1.4640
75°	1.3110	1.3171	1.3273	1.3418	1.3608	1.3846	1.4134	1.4477	1.4879
76°	1.3285	1.3348	1.3454	1.3603	1.3800	1.4045	1.4344	1.4700	1.5118
77°	1.3460	1.3525	1.3634	1.3788	1.3991	1.4245	1.4554	1.4923	1.5359
78°	1.3636	1.3702	1.3814	1.3974	1.4183	1.4445	1.4765	1.5147	1.5600
79°	1.3811	1.3879	1.3995	1.4159	1.4374	1.4645	1.4976	1.5372	1.5842
80°	1.3986	1.4056	1.4175	1.4344	1.4566	1.4846	1.5187	1.5597	1.6085
81°	1.4161	1.4234	1.4356	1.4530	1.4758	1.5046	1.5399	1.5823	1.6328
82°	1.4336	1.4411	1.4536	1.4715	1.4950	1.5247	1.5611	1.6049	1.6572
83°	1.4512	1.4588	1.4717	1.4901	1.5143	1.5448	1.5823	1.6276	1.6817
84°	1.4687	1.4765	1.4897	1.5086	1.5335	1.5649	1.6035	1.6502	1.7062
85°	1.4862	1.4942	1.5078	1.5272	1.5527	1.5850	1.6248	1.6730	1.7308
86°	1.5037	1.5120	1.5259	1.5457	1.5720	1.6052	1.6461	1.6957	1.7554
87°	1.5212	1.5297	1.5439	1.5643	1.5912	1.6253	1.6673	1.7184	1.7801
88°	1.5388	1.5474	1.5620	1.5829	1.6105	1.6454	1.6886	1.7412	1.8047
89°	1.5563	1.5651	1.5801	1.6015	1.6297	1.6656	1.7099	1.7640	1.8294
90°	1.5738	1.5828	1.5981	1.6200	1.6490	1.6858	1.7312	1.7863	1.8541

*ELLIPTIC INTEGRALS OF THE FIRST KIND: $F(k, \phi)$ (Continued)

$$F(k,\ \phi) = \int_0^\phi \frac{d\Phi}{\sqrt{1 - k^2 \sin^2 \Phi}}, \qquad \theta = \sin^{-1} k$$

θ / ϕ	50°	55°	60°	65°	70°	75°	80°	85°	90°
46°	0.8552	0.8643	0.8734	0.8821	0.8900	0.8968	0.9019	0.9052	0.9063
47°	0.8761	0.8860	0.8958	0.9053	0.9139	0.9212	0.9269	0.9304	0.9316
48°	0.8973	0.9079	0.9185	0.9287	0.9381	0.9461	0.9523	0.9561	0.9575
49°	0.9186	0.9300	0.9415	0.9525	0.9627	0.9714	0.9781	0.9824	0.9838
50°	0.9401	0.9523	0.9647	0.9766	0.9876	0.9971	1.0044	1.0091	1.0107
51°	0.9617	0.9748	0.9881	1.0010	1.0130	1.0233	1.0313	1.0364	1.0381
52°	0.9835	0.9976	1.0118	1.0258	1.0387	1.0499	1.0587	1.0642	1.0662
53°	1.0055	1.0205	1.0359	1.0509	1.0649	1.0771	1.0866	1.0927	1.0948
54°	1.0277	1.0437	1.0602	1.0764	1.0915	1.1048	1.1152	1.1219	1.1242
55°	1.0500	1.0672	1.0848	1.1022	1.1186	1.1331	1.1444	1.1517	1.1542
56°	1.0725	1.0908	1.1097	1.1285	1.1462	1.1619	1.1743	1.1823	1.1851
57°	1.0952	1.1147	1.1349	1.1551	1.1743	1.1914	1.2049	1.2136	1.2167
58°	1.1180	1.1389	1.1605	1.1822	1.2030	1.2215	1.2362	1.2458	1.2492
59°	1.1411	1.1632	1.1864	1.2097	1.2321	1.2522	1.2684	1.2789	1.2826
60°	1.1643	1.1879	1.2125	1.2376	1.2619	1.2837	1.3014	1.3129	1.3170
61°	1.1877	1.2128	1.2392	1.2660	1.2922	1.3159	1.3352	1.3480	1.3524
62°	1.2113	1.2379	1.2661	1.2949	1.3231	1.3490	1.3701	1.3841	1.3890
63°	1.2351	1.2633	1.2933	1.3242	1.3547	1.3828	1.4059	1.4214	1.4268
64°	1.2591	1.2890	1.3209	1.3541	1.3870	1.4175	1.4429	1.4599	1.4659
65°	1.2833	1.3149	1.3489	1.3844	1.4199	1.4532	1.4810	1.4998	1.5065
66°	1.3076	1.3411	1.3773	1.4153	1.4536	1.4898	1.5203	1.5411	1.5485
67°	1.3321	1.3675	1.4060	1.4467	1.4880	1.5274	1.5610	1.5840	1.5923
68°	1.3568	1.3942	1.4351	1.4786	1.5232	1.5661	1.6030	1.6287	1.6379
69°	1.3817	1.4212	1.4646	1.5111	1.5591	1.6059	1.6466	1.6752	1.6856
70°	1.4068	1.4484	1.4944	1.5441	1.5959	1.6468	1.6918	1.7237	1.7354
71°	1.4320	1.4759	1.5246	1.5777	1.6335	1.6891	1.7388	1.7745	1.7877
72°	1.4574	1.5036	1.5552	1.6118	1.6720	1.7326	1.7876	1.8277	1.8427
73°	1.4830	1.5315	1.5862	1.6465	1.7113	1.7774	1.8384	1.8837	1.9008
74°	1.5087	1.5597	1.6175	1.6818	1.7516	1.8237	1.8915	1.9427	1.9623
75°	1.5345	1.5882	1.6492	1.7176	1.7927	1.8715	1.9468	2.0050	2.0276
76°	1.5606	1.6168	1.6812	1.7540	1.8347	1.9207	2.0047	2.0711	2.0973
77°	1.5867	1.6457	1.7136	1.7909	1.8777	1.9716	2.0653	2.1414	2.1721
78°	1.6130	1.6748	1.7462	1.8284	1.9215	2.0240	2.1288	2.2164	2.2528
79°	1.6394	1.7040	1.7792	1.8664	1.9663	2.0781	2.1954	2.2969	2.3404
80°	1.6660	1.7335	1.8125	1.9048	2.0119	2.1339	2.2653	2.3836	2.4362
81°	1.6926	1.7631	1.8461	1.9438	2.0584	2.1913	2.3387	2.4775	2.5421
82°	1.7193	1.7929	1.8799	1.9831	2.1057	2.2504	2.4157	2.5795	2.6603
83°	1.7462	1.8228	1.9140	2.0229	2.1537	2.3110	2.4965	2.6911	2.7942
84°	1.7731	1.8528	1.9482	2.0630	2.2024	2.3731	2.5811	2.8136	2.9487
85°	1.8001	1.8830	1.9826	2.1035	2.2518	2.4366	2.6694	2.9487	3.1313
86°	1.8271	1.9132	2.0172	2.1442	2.3017	2.5013	2.7612	3.0978	3.3547
87°	1.8542	1.9435	2.0519	2.1852	2.3520	2.5670	2.8561	3.2620	3.6425
88°	1.8813	1.9739	2.0867	2.2263	2.4026	2.6336	2.9537	3.4412	4.0481
89°	1.9084	2.0043	2.1216	2.2675	2.4535	2.7007	3.0530	3.6328	4.7413
90°	1.9356	2.0347	2.1565	2.3088	2.5046	2.7681	3.1534	3.8317	———

ELLIPTIC INTEGRALS OF THE SECOND KIND: $E(k, \phi)$

$$E(k, \phi) = \int_0^\phi \sqrt{(1 - k^2 \sin^2 \Phi)}\, d\Phi, \quad \theta = \sin^{-1} k$$

ϕ \ θ	5°	10°	15°	20°	25°	30°	35°	40°	45°
1°	0.0175	0.0175	0.0175	0.0175	0.0175	0.0175	0.0175	0.0175	0.0175
2°	0.0349	0.0349	0.0349	0.0349	0.0349	0.0349	0.0349	0.0349	0.0349
3°	0.0524	0.0524	0.0524	0.0524	0.0524	0.0524	0.0524	0.0523	0.0523
4°	0.0698	0.0698	0.0698	0.0698	0.0698	0.0698	0.0698	0.0698	0.0698
5°	0.0873	0.0873	0.0873	0.0873	0.0872	0.0872	0.0872	0.0872	0.0872
6°	0.1047	0.1047	0.1047	0.1047	0.1047	0.1047	0.1047	0.1046	0.1046
7°	0.1222	0.1222	0.1222	0.1221	0.1221	0.1221	0.1221	0.1220	0.1220
8°	0.1396	0.1396	0.1396	0.1396	0.1395	0.1395	0.1395	0.1394	0.1394
9°	0.1571	0.1571	0.1570	0.1570	0.1570	0.1569	0.1569	0.1568	0.1568
10°	0.1745	0.1745	0.1745	0.1744	0.1744	0.1743	0.1742	0.1742	0.1741
11°	0.1920	0.1920	0.1919	0.1918	0.1918	0.1917	0.1916	0.1915	0.1914
12°	0.2094	0.2094	0.2093	0.2093	0.2092	0.2091	0.2089	0.2088	0.2087
13°	0.2269	0.2268	0.2268	0.2267	0.2265	0.2264	0.2263	0.2261	0.2259
14°	0.2443	0.2443	0.2442	0.2441	0.2439	0.2437	0.2436	0.2433	0.2431
15°	0.2618	0.2617	0.2616	0.2615	0.2613	0.2611	0.2608	0.2606	0.2603
16°	0.2792	0.2791	0.2790	0.2788	0.2786	0.2784	0.2781	0.2778	0.2775
17°	0.2967	0.2966	0.2964	0.2962	0.2959	0.2956	0.2953	0.2949	0.2946
18°	0.3141	0.3140	0.3138	0.3136	0.3133	0.3129	0.3125	0.3121	0.3116
19°	0.3316	0.3314	0.3312	0.3309	0.3305	0.3301	0.3296	0.3291	0.3286
20°	0.3490	0.3489	0.3486	0.3483	0.3478	0.3473	0.3468	0.3462	0.3456
21°	0.3665	0.3663	0.3660	0.3656	0.3651	0.3645	0.3639	0.3632	0.3625
22°	0.3839	0.3837	0.3834	0.3829	0.3823	0.3817	0.3809	0.3802	0.3793
23°	0.4013	0.4011	0.4007	0.4002	0.3996	0.3988	0.3980	0.3971	0.3961
24°	0.4188	0.4185	0.4181	0.4175	0.4168	0.4159	0.4150	0.4139	0.4129
25°	0.4362	0.4359	0.4354	0.4348	0.4339	0.4330	0.4319	0.4308	0.4296
26°	0.4537	0.4533	0.4528	0.4520	0.4511	0.4500	0.4488	0.4475	0.4462
27°	0.4711	0.4707	0.4701	0.4693	0.4682	0.4670	0.4657	0.4643	0.4628
28°	0.4886	0.4881	0.4874	0.4865	0.4854	0.4840	0.4825	0.4809	0.4793
29°	0.5060	0.5055	0.5048	0.5037	0.5025	0.5010	0.4993	0.4975	0.4957
30°	0.5234	0.5229	0.5221	0.5209	0.5195	0.5179	0.5161	0.5141	0.5120
31°	0.5409	0.5403	0.5394	0.5381	0.5366	0.5348	0.5327	0.5306	0.5283
32°	0.5583	0.5577	0.5567	0.5553	0.5536	0.5516	0.5494	0.5470	0.5446
33°	0.5757	0.5751	0.5740	0.5725	0.5706	0.5684	0.5660	0.5634	0.5607
34°	0.5932	0.5924	0.5912	0.5896	0.5876	0.5852	0.5826	0.5797	0.5768
35°	0.6106	0.6098	0.6085	0.6067	0.6045	0.6019	0.5991	0.5960	0.5928
36°	0.6280	0.6272	0.6258	0.6238	0.6214	0.6186	0.6155	0.6122	0.6087
37°	0.6455	0.6445	0.6430	0.6409	0.6383	0.6353	0.6319	0.6283	0.6245
38°	0.6629	0.6619	0.6602	0.6580	0.6552	0.6519	0.6483	0.6444	0.6403
39°	0.6803	0.6792	0.6775	0.6750	0.6720	0.6685	0.6646	0.6604	0.6559
40°	0.6977	0.6966	0.6947	0.6921	0.6888	0.6851	0.6808	0.6763	0.6715
41°	0.7152	0.7139	0.7119	0.7091	0.7056	0.7016	0.6970	0.6921	0.6870
42°	0.7326	0.7313	0.7291	0.7261	0.7224	0.7180	0.7132	0.7079	0.7024
43°	0.7500	0.7486	0.7463	0.7431	0.7391	0.7345	0.7293	0.7237	0.7178
44°	0.7674	0.7659	0.7634	0.7600	0.7558	0.7508	0.7453	0.7393	0.7330
45°	0.7849	0.7832	0.7806	0.7770	0.7725	0.7672	0.7613	0.7549	0.7482

ELLIPTIC INTEGRALS OF THE SECOND KIND: $E(k, \phi)$ (Continued)

$$E(k, \phi) = \int_0^\phi \sqrt{(1 - k^2 \sin^2 \Phi)}\,d\Phi, \quad \theta = \sin^{-1} k$$

θ / ϕ	50°	55°	60°	65°	70°	75°	80°	85°	90°
1°	0.0175	0.0175	0.0175	0.0175	0.0175	0.0175	0.0175	0.0175	0.0175
2°	0.0349	0.0349	0.0349	0.0349	0.0349	0.0349	0.0349	0.0349	0.0349
3°	0.0523	0.0523	0.0523	0.0523	0.0523	0.0523	0.0523	0.0523	0.0523
4°	0.0698	0.0698	0.0698	0.0698	0.0698	0.0698	0.0698	0.0698	0.0698
5°	0.0872	0.0872	0.0872	0.0872	0.0872	0.0872	0.0872	0.0872	0.0872
6°	0.1046	0.1046	0.1046	0.1046	0.1046	0.1045	0.1045	0.1045	0.1045
7°	0.1220	0.1220	0.1219	0.1219	0.1219	0.1219	0.1219	0.1219	0.1219
8°	0.1394	0.1393	0.1393	0.1393	0.1392	0.1392	0.1392	0.1392	0.1392
9°	0.1567	0.1566	0.1566	0.1566	0.1565	0.1565	0.1565	0.1564	0.1564
10°	0.1740	0.1739	0.1739	0.1738	0.1738	0.1737	0.1737	0.1737	0.1736
11°	0.1913	0.1912	0.1911	0.1910	0.1909	0.1909	0.1908	0.1908	0.1908
12°	0.2085	0.2084	0.2083	0.2082	0.2081	0.2080	0.2080	0.2079	0.2079
13°	0.2258	0.2256	0.2254	0.2253	0.2252	0.2251	0.2250	0.2250	0.2250
14°	0.2429	0.2427	0.2425	0.2424	0.2422	0.2421	0.2420	0.2419	0.2419
15°	0.2601	0.2598	0.2596	0.2594	0.2592	0.2590	0.2589	0.2588	0.2588
16°	0.2771	0.2768	0.2765	0.2763	0.2761	0.2759	0.2757	0.2757	0.2756
17°	0.2942	0.2938	0.2935	0.2932	0.2929	0.2927	0.2925	0.2924	0.2924
18°	0.3112	0.3107	0.3103	0.3099	0.3096	0.3094	0.3092	0.3091	0.3090
19°	0.3281	0.3276	0.3271	0.3267	0.3263	0.3260	0.3258	0.3256	0.3256
20°	0.3450	0.3444	0.3438	0.3433	0.3429	0.3425	0.3422	0.3421	0.3420
21°	0.3618	0.3611	0.3604	0.3598	0.3593	0.3589	0.3586	0.3584	0.3584
22°	0.3785	0.3777	0.3770	0.3763	0.3757	0.3752	0.3749	0.3747	0.3746
23°	0.3952	0.3943	0.3935	0.3927	0.3920	0.3915	0.3911	0.3908	0.3907
24°	0.4118	0.4108	0.4098	0.4090	0.4082	0.4076	0.4071	0.4068	0.4067
25°	0.4284	0.4272	0.4261	0.4251	0.4243	0.4236	0.4230	0.4227	0.4226
26°	0.4449	0.4436	0.4423	0.4412	0.4402	0.4394	0.4389	0.4385	0.4384
27°	0.4613	0.4598	0.4584	0.4572	0.4561	0.4552	0.4545	0.4541	0.4540
28°	0.4776	0.4760	0.4744	0.4730	0.4718	0.4708	0.4701	0.4696	0.4695
29°	0.4938	0.4920	0.4903	0.4887	0.4874	0.4863	0.4855	0.4850	0.4848
30°	0.5100	0.5080	0.5061	0.5044	0.5029	0.5016	0.5007	0.5002	0.5000
31°	0.5261	0.5239	0.5218	0.5199	0.5182	0.5169	0.5159	0.5152	0.5150
32°	0.5421	0.5396	0.5373	0.5352	0.5334	0.5319	0.5308	0.5301	0.5299
33°	0.5580	0.5553	0.5528	0.5505	0.5485	0.5468	0.5456	0.5449	0.5446
34°	0.5738	0.5709	0.5681	0.5656	0.5634	0.5616	0.5603	0.5595	0.5592
35°	0.5895	0.5863	0.5833	0.5806	0.5782	0.5762	0.5748	0.5739	0.5736
36°	0.6051	0.6017	0.5984	0.5954	0.5928	0.5907	0.5891	0.5881	0.5878
37°	0.6207	0.6169	0.6134	0.6101	0.6073	0.6050	0.6032	0.6022	0.6018
38°	0.6361	0.6321	0.6282	0.6247	0.6216	0.6191	0.6172	0.6160	0.6157
39°	0.6515	0.6471	0.6429	0.6391	0.6357	0.6330	0.6310	0.6297	0.6293
40°	0.6667	0.6620	0.6575	0.6533	0.6497	0.6468	0.6446	0.6432	0.6428
41°	0.6818	0.6767	0.6719	0.6674	0.6636	0.6604	0.6580	0.6566	0.6561
42°	0.6969	0.6914	0.6862	0.6814	0.6772	0.6738	0.6712	0.6697	0.6691
43°	0.7118	0.7059	0.7003	0.6952	0.6907	0.6870	0.6843	0.6826	0.6820
44°	0.7266	0.7204	0.7144	0.7088	0.7040	0.7000	0.6971	0.6953	0.6947
45°	0.7414	0.7346	0.7282	0.7223	0.7171	0.7129	0.7097	0.7078	0.7071

ELLIPTIC INTEGRALS OF THE SECOND KIND: $E(k, \phi)$ (Continued)

$$E(k, \phi) = \int_0^\phi \sqrt{(1 - k^2 \sin^2 \Phi)}\,d\Phi, \quad \theta = \sin^{-1} k$$

θ ϕ	5°	10°	15°	20°	25°	30°	35°	40°	45°
46°	0.8023	0.8006	0.7977	0.7939	0.7891	0.7835	0.7772	0.7704	0.7633
47°	0.8197	0.8179	0.8149	0.8108	0.8057	0.7998	0.7931	0.7858	0.7782
48°	0.8371	0.8352	0.8320	0.8277	0.8223	0.8160	0.8089	0.8012	0.7931
49°	0.8545	0.8525	0.8491	0.8446	0.8389	0.8322	0.8247	0.8165	0.8079
50°	0.8719	0.8698	0.8663	0.8614	0.8554	0.8483	0.8404	0.8317	0.8227
51°	0.8894	0.8871	0.8834	0.8783	0.8719	0.8644	0.8560	0.8469	0.8373
52°	0.9068	0.9044	0.9004	0.8951	0.8884	0.8805	0.8716	0.8620	0.8518
53°	0.9242	0.9217	0.9175	0.9119	0.9048	0.8965	0.8872	0.8770	0.8663
54°	0.9416	0.9389	0.9345	0.9287	0.9212	0.9125	0.9026	0.8919	0.8806
55°	0.9590	0.9562	0.9517	0.9454	0.9376	0.9284	0.9181	0.9068	0.8949
56°	0.9764	0.9735	0.9687	0.9622	0.9540	0.9443	0.9335	0.9216	0.9091
57°	0.9938	0.9908	0.9858	0.9789	0.9703	0.9602	0.9488	0.9363	0.9232
58°	1.0112	1.0080	1.0028	0.9956	0.9866	0.9760	0.9641	0.9510	0.9372
59°	1.0286	1.0253	1.0198	1.0123	1.0029	1.9918	0.9793	0.9656	0.9511
60°	1.0460	1.0426	1.0368	1.0290	1.0191	1.0076	0.9945	0.9801	0.9650
61°	1.0634	1.0598	1.0538	1.0456	1.0354	1.0233	1.0096	0.9946	0.9787
62°	1.0808	1.0771	1.0708	1.0623	1.0516	1.0389	1.0246	1 0090	0.9924
63°	1.0982	1.0943	1.0878	1.0789	1.0678	1.0546	1.0397	1.0233	1.0060
64°	1.1156	1.1115	1.1048	1.0955	1.0839	1.0702	1.0547	1.0376	1.0195
65°	1.1330	1.1288	1.1218	1.1121	1.1001	1.0858	1.0696	1.0518	1.0329
66°	1.1504	1.1460	1.1387	1.1287	1.1162	1.1013	1.0845	1.0660	1.0463
67°	1.1678	1.1632	1.1557	1.1453	1.1323	1.1168	1.0993	1.0801	1.0596
68°	1.1852	1.1805	1.1726	1.1618	1.1483	1.1323	1.1141	1.0941	1.0728
69°	1.2026	1.1977	1.1896	1.1784	1.1644	1.1478	1.1289	1.1081	1.0859
70°	1.2200	1.2149	1.2065	1.1949	1.1804	1.1632	1.1436	1.1221	1.0990
71°	1.2374	1.2321	1.2234	1.2114	1.1964	1.1786	1.1583	1.1359	1.1120
72°	1.2548	1.2493	1.2403	1.2280	1.2124	1.1939	1.1729	1.1498	1.1250
73°	1.2722	1.2666	1.2573	1.2445	1.2284	1.2093	1.1875	1.1636	1.1379
74°	1.2896	1.2838	1.2742	1.2609	1.2443	1.2246	1.2021	1.1773	1.1507
75°	1.3070	1.3010	1.2911	1.2774	1.2603	1.2399	1.2167	1.1910	1.1635
76°	1.3244	1.3182	1.3080	1.2939	1.2762	1.2552	1.2312	1.2047	1.1762
77°	1.3418	1.3354	1.3249	1.3104	1.2921	1.2704	1.2457	1.2183	1.1889
78°	1.3592	1.3526	1.3417	1.3268	1.3080	1.2856	1.2601	1.2319	1.2015
79°	1.3765	1.3698	1.3586	1.3432	1.3239	1.3009	1.2746	1.2454	1.2141
80°	1.3939	1.3870	1.3755	1.3597	1.3398	1.3161	1.2890	1.2590	1.2266
81°	1.4113	1.4042	1.3924	1.3761	1.3556	1.3312	1.3034	1.2725	1.2391
82°	1.4287	1.4214	1.4093	1.3925	1.3715	1.3464	1.3177	1.2859	1.2516
83°	1.4461	1.4386	1.4261	1.4090	1.3873	1.3616	1.3321	1.2994	1.2640
84°	1.4635	1.4558	1.4430	1.4254	1.4032	1.3767	1.3464	1.3128	1.2765
85°	1.4809	1.4729	1.4598	1.4418	1.4190	1.3919	1.3608	1.3262	1.2889
86°	1.4983	1.4901	1.4767	1.4582	1.4348	1.4070	1.3751	1.3396	1.3012
87°	1.5156	1.5073	1.4936	1.4746	1.4507	1.4221	1.3894	1.3530	1.3136
88°	1.5330	1.5245	1.5104	1.4910	1.4665	1.4372	1.4037	1.3664	1.3260
89°	1.5504	1.5417	1.5273	1.5074	1.4823	1.4523	1.4180	1.3798	1.3383
90°	1.5678	1.5589	1.5442	1.5238	1.4981	1.4675	1.4323	1.3931	1.3506

ELLIPTIC INTEGRALS OF THE SECOND KIND: $E(k, \phi)$ (Continued)

$$E(k, \phi) = \int_0^\phi \sqrt{(1 - k^2 \sin^2 \Phi)}d\Phi, \quad \theta = \sin^{-1} k$$

ϕ \ θ	50°	55°	60°	65°	70°	75°	80°	85°	90°
46°	0.7560	0.7488	0.7419	0.7356	0.7301	0.7255	0.7221	0.7200	0.7193
47°	0.7705	0.7628	0.7555	0.7488	0.7429	0.7380	0.7344	0.7321	0.7314
48°	0.7849	0.7768	0.7690	0.7618	0.7555	0.7502	0.7464	0.7440	0.7431
49°	0.7992	0.7905	0.7822	0.7746	0.7679	0.7623	0.7581	0.7556	0.7547
50°	0.8134	0.8042	0.7954	0.7872	0.7801	0.7741	0.7697	0.7670	0.7660
51°	0.8275	0.8177	0.8084	0.7997	0.7921	0.7858	0.7811	0.7781	0.7771
52°	0.8414	0.8311	0.8212	0.8120	0.8039	0.7972	0.7922	0.7891	0.7880
53°	0.8553	0.8444	0.8339	0.8241	0.8155	0.8084	0.8031	0.7998	0.7986
54°	0.8690	0.8575	0.8464	0.8361	0.8270	0.8194	0.8137	0.8102	0.8090
55°	0.8827	0.8705	0.8588	0.8479	0.8382	0.8302	0.8242	0.8204	0.8192
56°	0.8962	0.8834	0.8710	0.8595	0.8493	0.8408	0.8344	0.8304	0.8290
57°	0.9096	0.8961	0.8831	0.8709	0.8601	0.8511	0.8443	0.8401	0.8387
58°	0.9230	0.9088	0.8950	0.8822	0.8707	0.8612	0.8540	0.8496	0.8480
59°	0.9362	0.9213	0.9068	0.8932	0.8812	0.8711	0.8635	0.8588	0.8572
60°	0.9493	0.9336	0.9184	0.9042	0.8914	0.8808	0.8728	0.8677	0.8660
61°	0.9623	0.9459	0.9299	0.9149	0.9015	0.8903	0.8817	0.8764	0.8746
62°	0.9752	0.9580	0.9412	0.9254	0.9113	0.8995	0.8905	0.8849	0.8829
63°	0.9880	0.9700	0.9524	0.9358	0.9210	0.9085	0.8990	0.8930	0.8910
64°	1.0007	0.9818	0.9634	0.9460	0.9304	0.9173	0.9072	0.9009	0.8988
65°	1.0133	0.9936	0.9743	0.9561	0.9397	0.9258	0.9152	0.9086	0.9063
66°	1.0258	1.0052	0.9850	0.9659	0.9487	0.9341	0.9230	0.9159	0.9135
67°	1.0383	1.0167	0.9956	0.9756	0.9576	0.9422	0.9305	0.9230	0.9205
68°	1.0506	1.0281	1.0061	0.9852	0.9662	0.9501	0.9377	0.9299	0.9272
69°	1.0628	1.0394	1.0164	0.9946	0.9747	0.9578	0.9447	0.9364	0.9336
70°	1.0750	1.0506	1.0266	1.0038	0.9830	0.9652	0.9514	0.9427	0.9397
71°	1.0871	1.0617	1.0367	1.0129	0.9911	0.9724	0.9579	0.9487	0.9455
72°	1.0991	1.0727	1.0467	1.0218	0.9990	0.9794	0.9642	0.9544	0.9511
73°	1.1110	1.0836	1.0565	1.0306	1.0067	0.9862	0.9702	0.9599	0.9563
74°	1.1228	1.0944	1.0662	1.0392	1.0143	0.9928	0.9759	0.9650	0.9613
75°	1.1346	1.1051	1.0759	1.0477	1.0217	0.9992	0.9814	0.9699	0.9659
76°	1.1463	1.1158	1.0854	1.0561	1.0290	1.0053	0.9867	0.9745	0.9703
77°	1.1580	1.1263	1.0948	1.0643	1.0361	1.0113	0.9917	0.9789	0.9744
78°	1.1695	1.1368	1.1041	1.0724	1.0430	1.0171	0.9965	0.9829	0.9781
79°	1.1811	1.1472	1.1133	1.0805	1.0498	1.0228	1.0011	0.9867	0.9816
80°	1.1926	1.1576	1.1225	1.0884	1.0565	1.0282	1.0054	0.9902	0.9848
81°	1.2040	1.1678	1.1316	1.0962	1.0630	1.0335	1.0096	0.9935	0.9877
82°	1.2154	1.1781	1.1406	1.1040	1.0695	1.0387	1.0135	0.9965	0.9903
83°	1.2267	1.1883	1.1495	1.1116	1.0758	1.0437	1.0173	0.9992	0.9925
84°	1.2381	1.1984	1.1584	1.1192	1.0821	1.0486	1.0209	1.0017	0.9945
85°	1.2493	1.2085	1.1673	1.1267	1.0882	1.0534	1.0244	1.0039	0.9962
86°	1.2606	1.2186	1.1761	1.1342	1.0944	1.0581	1.0277	1.0060	0.9976
87°	1.2719	1.2286	1.1848	1.1417	1.1004	1.0628	1.0309	1.0078	0.9986
88°	1.2831	1.2386	1.1936	1.1491	1.1064	1.0673	1.0340	1.0095	0.9994
89°	1.2943	1.2487	1.2023	1.1565	1.1124	1.0719	1.0371	1.0111	0.9998
90°	1.3055	1.2587	1.2111	1.1638	1.1184	1.0764	1.0401	1.0127	1.0000

COMPLETE ELLIPTIC INTEGRALS

$$K = \int_0^{\pi/2} \frac{d\Phi}{\sqrt{1 - k^2 \sin^2 \Phi}} = F\left(k, \frac{\pi}{2}\right) \quad E = \int_0^{\pi/2} \sqrt{1 - k^2 \sin^2 \Phi} \cdot d\Phi = E\left(k, \frac{\pi}{2}\right)$$

$\sin^{-1} k$	K	$\log K$	$\sin^{-1} k$	K	$\log K$
0°	1.5708	0.196120	**40°**	1.7868	0.252068
1	1.5709	0.196153	41	1.7992	0.255085
2	1.5713	0.196252	42	1.8122	0.258197
3	1.5719	0.196418	43	1.8256	0.261406
4	1.5727	0.196649	44	1.8396	0.264716
5	1.5738	0.196947	**45**	1.8541	0.268127
6	1.5751	0.197312	46	1.8691	0.271644
7	1.5767	0.197743	47	1.8848	0.275267
8	1.5785	0.198241	48	1.9011	0.279001
9	1.5805	0.198806	49	1.9180	0.282848
10	1.5828	0.199438	**50**	1.9356	0.286811
11	1.5854	0.200137	51	1.9539	0.290895
12	1.5882	0.200904	52	1.9729	0.295101
13	1.5913	0.201740	53	1.9927	0.299435
14	1.5946	0.202643	54	2.0133	0.303901
15	1.5981	0.203615	**55**	2.0347	0.308504
16	1.6020	0.204657	56	2.0571	0.313247
17	1.6061	0.205768	57	2.0804	0.318138
18	1.6105	0.206948	58	2.1047	0.323182
19	1.6151	0.208200	59	2.1300	0.328384
20	1.6200	0.209522	**60**	2.1565	0.333753
21	1.6252	0.210916	61	2.1842	0.339295
22	1.6307	0.212382	62	2.2132	0.345020
23	1.6365	0.213921	63	2.2435	0.350936
24	1.6426	0.215533	64	2.2754	0.357053
25	1.6490	0.217219	**65**	2.3088	0.363384
26	1.6557	0.218981	66	2.3439	0.369940
27	1.6627	0.220818	67	2.3809	0.376736
28	1.6701	0.222732	68	2.4198	0.383787
29	1.6777	0.224723	69	2.4610	0.391112
30	1.6858	0.226793	**70**	2.5046	0.398730
31	1.6941	0.228943	71	2.5507	0.406665
32	1.7028	0.231173	72	2.5998	0.414943
33	1.7119	0.233485	73	2.6521	0.423596
34	1.7214	0.235880	74	2.7081	0.432660
35	1.7312	0.238359	**75**	2.7681	0.442176
36	1.7415	0.240923	76	2.8327	0.452196
37	1.7522	0.243575	77	2.9026	0.462782
38	1.7633	0.246315	78	2.9786	0.474008
39	1.7748	0.249146	79	3.0617	0.485967
40	1.7868	0.252068	**80**	3.1534	0.498777

COMPLETE ELLIPTIC INTEGRALS (Continued)

$\sin^{-1} k$	K	$\log K$	$\sin^{-1} k$	K	$\log K$
80°	3.1534	0.498777	**85°**	3.8317	0.583396
81	3.2553	0.512591	86	4.0528	0.607751
82	3.3699	0.527613	87	4.3387	0.637355
83	3.5004	0.544120	88	4.7427	0.676027
84	3.6519	0.562514	89	5.4349	0.735192
85	3.8317	0.583396	**90**	∞	∞

Values of K for $\sin^{-1} k$ = 85° to 89° by 0.1° and 89° to 90° by minutes

$\sin^{-1} k$	K	$\log K$	$\sin^{-1} k$		K	$\log K$
85.0°	3.832	0.58343	**89°**	**0′**	5.435	0.73520
85.1	3.852	0.58569	89	2	5.469	0.73791
85.2	3.872	0.58794	89	4	5.504	0.74068
85.3	3.893	0.59028	89	6	5.540	0.74351
85.4	3.914	0.59262	89	8	5.578	0.74648
85.5	3.936	0.59506	**89**	**10**	5.617	0.74950
85.6	3.958	0.59748	89	12	5.658	0.75266
85.7	3.981	0.59999	89	14	5.700	0.75587
85.8	4.004	0.60249	89	16	5.745	0.75929
85.9	4.028	0.60509	89	18	5.791	0.76275
86.0	4.053	0.60778	**89**	**20**	5.840	0.76641
86.1	4.078	0.61045	89	22	5.891	0.77019
86.2	4.104	0.61321	89	24	5.946	0.77422
86.3	4.130	0.61595	89	26	6.003	0.77837
86.4	4.157	0.61878	89	28	6.063	0.78269
86.5	4.185	0.62170	**89**	**30**	6.128	0.78732
86.6	4.214	0.62469	89	32	6.197	0.79218
86.7	4.244	0.62778	89	34	6.271	0.79734
86.8	4.274	0.63083	89	36	6.351	0.80284
86.9	4.306	0.63407	89	38	6.438	0.80875
87.0	4.339	0.63739	**89**	**40**	6.533	0.81511
87.1	4.372	0.64068	89	41	6.584	0.81849
87.2	4.407	0.64414	89	42	6.639	0.82210
87.3	4.444	0.64777	89	43	6.696	0.82582
87.4	4.481	0.65137	89	44	6.756	0.82969
87.5	4.520	0.65514	**89**	**45**	6.821	0.83385
87.6	4.562	0.65916	89	46	6.890	0.83822
87.7	4.603	0.66304	89	47	6.964	0.84286
87.8	4.648	0.66727	89	48	7.044	0.84782
87.9	4.694	0.67154	89	49	7.131	0.85315
88.0	4.743	0.67605	**89**	**50**	7.226	0.85890
88.1	4.794	0.68070	89	51	7.332	0.86522
88.2	4.848	0.68556	89	52	7.449	0.87210
88.3	4.905	0.69064	89	53	7.583	0.87984
88.4	4.965	0.69592	89	54	7.737	0.88857
88.5	5.030	0.70157	**89**	**55**	7.919	0.89867
88.6	5.099	0.70749	89	56	8.143	0.91078
88.7	5.173	0.71374	89	57	8.430	0.92583
88.8	5.253	0.72041	89	58	8.836	0.94626
88.9	5.340	0.72754	89	59	9.529	0.97905
89.0	5.435	0.73520	**90**	**0**	∞	∞

COMPLETE ELLIPTIC INTEGRALS (Continued)

$\sin^{-1} k$	E	$\log E$	$\sin^{-1} k$	E	$\log E$
0°	1.5708	0.196120	**45°**	1.3506	0.130541
1	1.5707	0.196087	46	1.3418	0.127690
2	1.5703	0.195988	47	1.3329	0.124788
3	1.5697	0.195822	48	1.3238	0.121836
4	1.5689	0.195591	49	1.3147	0.118836
5	1.5678	0.195293	**50**	1.3055	0.115790
6	1.5665	0.194930	51	1.2963	0.112698
7	1.5649	0.194500	52	1.2870	0.109563
8	1.5632	0.194004	53	1.2776	0.106386
9	1.5611	0.193442	54	1.2681	0.103169
10	1.5589	0.192815	**55**	1.2587	0.099915
11	1.5564	0.192121	56	1.2492	0.096626
12	1.5537	0.191362	57	1.2397	0.093303
13	1.5507	0.190537	58	1.2301	0.089950
14	1.5476	0.189646	59	1.2206	0.086569
15	1.5442	0.188690	**60**	1.2111	0.083164
16	1.5405	0.187668	61	1.2015	0.079738
17	1.5367	0.186581	62	1.1920	0.076293
18	1.5326	0.185428	63	1.1826	0.072834
19	1.5283	0.184210	64	1.1732	0.069364
20	1.5238	0.182928	**65**	1.1638	0.065889
21	1.5191	0.181580	66	1.1545	0.062412
22	1.5141	0.180168	67	1.1453	0.058937
23	1.5090	0.178691	68	1.1362	0.055472
24	1.5037	0.177150	69	1.1272	0.052020
25	1.4981	0.175545	**70**	1.1184	0.048589
26	1.4924	0.173876	71	1.1096	0.045183
27	1.4864	0.172144	72	1.1011	0.041812
28	1.4803	0.170348	73	1.0927	0.038481
29	1.4740	0.168489	74	1.0844	0.035200
30	1.4675	0.166567	**75**	1.0764	0.031976
31	1.4608	0.164583	76	1.0686	0.028819
32	1.4539	0.162537	77	1.0611	0.025740
33	1.4469	0.160429	78	1.0538	0.022749
34	1.4397	0.158261	79	1.0468	0.019858
35	1.4323	0.156031	**80**	1.0401	0.017081
36	1.4248	0.153742	81	1.0338	0.014432
37	1.4171	0.151393	82	1.0278	0.011927
38	1.4092	0.148985	83	1.0223	0.009584
39	1.4013	0.146519	84	1.0172	0.007422
40	1.3931	0.143995	**85**	1.0127	0.005465
41	1.3849	0.141414	86	1.0086	0.003740
42	1.3765	0.138778	87	1.0053	0.002278
43	1.3680	0.136086	88	1.0026	0.001121
44	1.3594	0.133340	89	1.0008	0.000326
45	1.3506	0.130541	**90**	1.0000	0.000000

VECTOR ANALYSIS

Definitions

Any quantity which is completely determined by its magnitude is called a *scalar*. Examples of such are mass, density, temperature, etc. Any quantity which is completely determined by its magnitude and direction is called a *vector*. Examples of such are velocity, acceleration, force, etc. A vector quantity is represented by a directed line segment, the length of which represents the magnitude of the vector. A vector quantity is usually represented by a boldfaced letter such as $\mathbf{V}$. Two vectors $\mathbf{V}_1$ and $\mathbf{V}_2$ are equal to one another if they have equal magnitudes and are acting in the same directions. A negative vector, written as $-\mathbf{V}$, is one which acts in the opposite direction to $\mathbf{V}$, but is of equal magnitude to it. If we represent the magnitude of $\mathbf{V}$ by v, we write $|\mathbf{V}| = v$. A vector parallel to $\mathbf{V}$, but equal to the reciprocal of its magnitude is written as $\mathbf{V}^{-1}$ or as $\dfrac{1}{\mathbf{V}}$.

The *unit vector* $\dfrac{\mathbf{V}}{v}$ $(v \neq 0)$ is that vector which has the same direction as $\mathbf{V}$, but has a magnitude of unity (sometimes represented as $\mathbf{V}_0$ or $\hat{\mathbf{v}}$).

Vector Algebra

The vector sum of $\mathbf{V}_1$ and $\mathbf{V}_2$ is represented by $\mathbf{V}_1 + \mathbf{V}_2$. The vector sum of $\mathbf{V}_1$ and $-\mathbf{V}_2$, or the difference of the vector $\mathbf{V}_2$ from $\mathbf{V}_1$ is represented by $\mathbf{V}_1 - \mathbf{V}_2$.

If r is a scalar, then $r\mathbf{V} = \mathbf{V}r$, and represents a vector r times the magnitude of $\mathbf{V}$, in the same direction as $\mathbf{V}$ if r is positive, and in the opposite direction if r is negative. If r and s are scalars, $\mathbf{V}_1$, $\mathbf{V}_2$, $\mathbf{V}_3$, vectors, then the following rules of scalars and vectors hold:

$$\mathbf{V}_1 + \mathbf{V}_2 = \mathbf{V}_2 + \mathbf{V}_1$$
$$(r + s)\mathbf{V}_1 = r\mathbf{V}_1 + s\mathbf{V}_1; \qquad r(\mathbf{V}_1 + \mathbf{V}_2) = r\mathbf{V}_1 + r\mathbf{V}_2$$
$$\mathbf{V}_1 + (\mathbf{V}_2 + \mathbf{V}_3) = (\mathbf{V}_1 + \mathbf{V}_2) + \mathbf{V}_3 = \mathbf{V}_1 + \mathbf{V}_2 + \mathbf{V}_3$$

Vectors in Space

A plane is described by two distinct vectors $\mathbf{V}_1$ and $\mathbf{V}_2$. Should these vectors not intersect each other, then one is displaced parallel to itself until they do (fig. 1.) Any other vector $\mathbf{V}$ lying in this plane is given by

$$\mathbf{V} = r\mathbf{V}_1 + s\mathbf{V}_2$$

VECTOR ANALYSIS (Continued)

A *position vector* specifies the position in space of a point relative to a fixed origin. If therefore $\mathbf{V}_1$ and $\mathbf{V}_2$ are the position vectors of the points A and B, relative to the origin O, then any point P on the line AB has a position vector $\mathbf{V}$ given by

$$\mathbf{V} = r\mathbf{V}_1 + (1 - r)\mathbf{V}_2$$

The scalar "r" can be taken as the parametric representation of P since $r = 0$ implies $P = B$ and $r = 1$ implies $P = A$. (fig. 2). If P divides the line AB in the ratio $r:s$ then

$$\mathbf{V} = \left(\frac{r}{r + s}\right)\mathbf{V}_1 + \left(\frac{s}{r + s}\right)\mathbf{V}_2$$

Fig. 1.

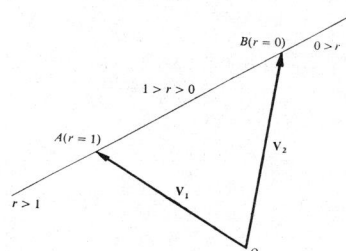

Fig. 2.

The vectors $\mathbf{V}_1$, $\mathbf{V}_2$, $\mathbf{V}_3$, . . . , $\mathbf{V}_n$ are said to be *linearly dependent* if there exist scalars $r_1, r_2, r_3, \ldots, r_n$, not all zero, such that

$$r_1\mathbf{V}_1 + r_2\mathbf{V}_2 + \cdots + r_n\mathbf{V}_n = 0$$

A vector $\mathbf{V}$ is linearly dependent upon the set of vectors $\mathbf{V}_1$, $\mathbf{V}_2$, $\mathbf{V}_3$, . . . , $\mathbf{V}_n$ if

$$\mathbf{V} = r_1\mathbf{V}_1 + r_2\mathbf{V}_2 + r_3\mathbf{V}_3 + \cdots + r_n\mathbf{V}_n$$

Three vectors are linearly dependent if and only if they are co-planar.

All points in space can be uniquely determined by linear dependence upon three *base vectors* i.e. three vectors any one of which is linearly independent of the other two. The simplest set of base vectors are the unit vectors along the coordinate Ox, Oy and Oz axes. These are usually designated by $\mathbf{i}$, $\mathbf{j}$ and $\mathbf{k}$ respectively.

If $\mathbf{V}$ is a vector in space, and a, b and c are the respective magnitudes of the projections of the vector along the axes then

$$\mathbf{V} = a\mathbf{i} + b\mathbf{j} + c\mathbf{k}$$

and

$$v = \sqrt{a^2 + b^2 + c^2}$$

and the direction cosines of $\mathbf{V}$ are

$$\cos \alpha = a/v, \quad \cos \beta = b/v, \quad \cos \gamma = c/v.$$

The law of addition yields

$$\mathbf{V}_1 + \mathbf{V}_2 = (a_1 + a_2)\mathbf{i} + (b_1 + b_2)\mathbf{j} + (c_1 + c_2)\mathbf{k}$$

The Scalar, Dot, or Inner Product of Two Vectors V_1 and V_2

This product is represented as $V_1 \cdot V_2$ and is defined to be equal to $v_1 v_2 \cos \theta$, where θ is the angle from V_1 to V_2, i.e.,

$$V_1 \cdot V_2 = v_1 v_2 \cos \theta$$

The following rules apply for this product:

$$V_1 \cdot V_2 = a_1 a_2 + b_1 b_2 + c_1 c_2 = V_2 \cdot V_1$$

It should be noted that this verifies that scalar multiplication is commutative.

$$(V_1 + V_2) \cdot V_3 = V_1 \cdot V_3 + V_2 \cdot V_3$$
$$V_1 \cdot (V_2 + V_3) = V_1 \cdot V_2 + V_1 \cdot V_3$$

If V_1 is perpendicular to V_2 then $V_1 \cdot V_2 = 0$, and if V_1 is parallel to V_2 then $V_1 \cdot V_2 = v_1 v_2 = r w_1{}^2$

In particular

and
$$i \cdot i = j \cdot j = k \cdot k = 1,$$
$$i \cdot j = j \cdot k = k \cdot i = 0$$

The Vector or Cross Product of Vectors V_1 and V_2

This product is represented as $V_1 \times V_2$ and is defined to be equal to $v_1 v_2 (\sin \theta) 1$, where θ is the angle from V_1 to V_2 and 1 is a unit vector perpendicular to the plane of V_1 and V_2 and so directed that a right-handed screw driven in the direction of 1 would carry V_1 into V_2, i.e.,

$$V_1 \times V_2 = v_1 v_2 (\sin \theta) 1$$

and
$$\tan \theta = \frac{|V_1 \times V_2|}{V_1 \cdot V_2}$$

The following rules apply for vector products:

$$V_1 \times V_2 = -V_2 \times V_1$$
$$V_1 \times (V_2 + V_3) = V_1 \times V_2 + V_1 \times V_3$$
$$(V_1 + V_2) \times V_3 = V_1 \times V_3 + V_2 \times V_3$$
$$V_1 \times (V_2 \times V_3) = V_2(V_3 \cdot V_1 - V_3(V_1 \cdot V_2)$$
$$i \times i = j \times j = k \times k = 0.1 \text{ (zero vector)}$$
$$= 0$$

$$i \times j = k, \qquad j \times k = i, \qquad k \times i = j$$

If $V_1 = a_1 i + b_1 j + c_1 k,$ $\qquad V_2 = a_2 i + b_2 j + c_2 k,$ $\qquad V_3 = a_3 i + b_3 j + c_3 k,$

then

$$V_1 \times V_2 = \begin{vmatrix} i & j & k \\ a_1 & b_1 & c_1 \\ a_2 & b_2 & c_2 \end{vmatrix} = (b_1 c_2 - b_2 c_1)i + (c_1 a_2 - c_2 a_1)j + (a_1 b_2 - a_2 b_1)k$$

It should be noted that, since $V_1 \times V_2 = -V_2 \times V_1$, the vector product is not commutative.

Scalar Triple Product

There is only one possible interpretation of the expression $\mathbf{V}_1 \cdot \mathbf{V}_2 \times \mathbf{V}_3$ and that is $\mathbf{V}_1 \cdot (\mathbf{V}_2 \times \mathbf{V}_3)$ which is obviously a scalar.

Further $\mathbf{V}_1 \cdot (\mathbf{V}_2 \times \mathbf{V}_3) = (\mathbf{V}_1 \times \mathbf{V}_2) \cdot \mathbf{V}_3 = \mathbf{V}_2 \cdot (\mathbf{V}_3 \times \mathbf{V}_1)$

$$= \begin{vmatrix} a_1 & b_1 & c_1 \\ a_2 & b_2 & c_2 \\ a_3 & b_3 & c_3 \end{vmatrix}$$

$$= v_1 v_2 v_3 \cos \phi \sin \theta,$$

Where θ is the angle between $\mathbf{V}_2$ and $\mathbf{V}_3$ and ϕ is the angle between $\mathbf{V}_1$ and the normal to the plane of $\mathbf{V}_2$ and $\mathbf{V}_3$.

This product is called the *scalar triple product* and is written as $[\mathbf{V}_1\mathbf{V}_2\mathbf{V}_3]$.

The determinant indicates that it can be considered as the volume of the parallelepiped whose three determining edges are $\mathbf{V}_1$, $\mathbf{V}_2$ and $\mathbf{V}_3$.

It also follows that cyclic permutation of the subscripts does not change the value of the scalar triple product so that

$$[\mathbf{V}_1\mathbf{V}_2\mathbf{V}_3] = [\mathbf{V}_2\mathbf{V}_3\mathbf{V}_1] = [\mathbf{V}_3\mathbf{V}_1\mathbf{V}_2]$$

but $\quad [\mathbf{V}_1\mathbf{V}_2\mathbf{V}_3] = -[\mathbf{V}_2\mathbf{V}_1\mathbf{V}_3] \quad$ etc. $\quad$ and $\quad [\mathbf{V}_1\mathbf{V}_1\mathbf{V}_2] \equiv 0$ etc.

Given three non-coplanar reference vectors $\mathbf{V}_1$, $\mathbf{V}_2$ and $\mathbf{V}_3$, the *reciprocal system is* given by $\mathbf{V}_1^*$, $\mathbf{V}_2^*$ and $\mathbf{V}_3^*$, where

$$1 = v_1 v_1^* = v_2 v_2^* = v_3 v_3^*$$

$$0 = v_1 v_2^* = v_1 v_3^* = v_2 v_1^* \quad \text{etc.}$$

$$\mathbf{V}_1^* = \frac{\mathbf{V}_2 \times \mathbf{V}_3}{[\mathbf{V}_1\mathbf{V}_2\mathbf{V}_3]}, \qquad \mathbf{V}_2^* = \frac{\mathbf{V}_3 \times \mathbf{V}_1}{[\mathbf{V}_1\mathbf{V}_2\mathbf{V}_3]}, \qquad \mathbf{V}_3^* = \frac{\mathbf{V}_1 \times \mathbf{V}_2}{[\mathbf{V}_1\mathbf{V}_2\mathbf{V}_3]}$$

The system $\mathbf{i}$, $\mathbf{j}$, $\mathbf{k}$ is its own reciprocal.

Vector Triple Product

The product $\mathbf{V}_1 \times (\mathbf{V}_2 \times \mathbf{V}_3)$ defines the *vector triple product*. Obviously, in this case, the brackets are vital to the definition.

$$\mathbf{V}_1 \times (\mathbf{V}_2 \times \mathbf{V}_3) = (\mathbf{V}_1 \cdot \mathbf{V}_3)\mathbf{V}_2 - (\mathbf{V}_1 \cdot \mathbf{V}_2)\mathbf{V}_3$$

$$= \begin{vmatrix} \mathbf{i} & \mathbf{j} & \mathbf{k} \\ a_1 & b_1 & c_1 \\ \begin{vmatrix} b_2 & c_2 \\ b_3 & c_3 \end{vmatrix} & \begin{vmatrix} c_2 & a_2 \\ c_3 & a_3 \end{vmatrix} & \begin{vmatrix} a_2 & b_2 \\ a_3 & b_3 \end{vmatrix} \end{vmatrix}$$

i.e. it is a vector, perpendicular to $\mathbf{V}_1$, lying in the plane of $\mathbf{V}_2$, $\mathbf{V}_3$.

Similarly $\quad (\mathbf{V}_1 \times \mathbf{V}_2) \times \mathbf{V}_3 = \begin{vmatrix} \mathbf{i} & \mathbf{j} & \mathbf{k} \\ \begin{vmatrix} b_1 & c_1 \\ b_2 & c_2 \end{vmatrix} & \begin{vmatrix} c_1 & a_1 \\ c_2 & a_2 \end{vmatrix} & \begin{vmatrix} a_1 & b_1 \\ a_2 & b_2 \end{vmatrix} \\ a_3 & b_3 & c_3 \end{vmatrix}$

$$\mathbf{V}_1 \times (\mathbf{V}_2 \times \mathbf{V}_3) + \mathbf{V}_2 \times (\mathbf{V}_3 \times \mathbf{V}_1) + \mathbf{V}_3 \times (\mathbf{V}_1 + \mathbf{V}_2) \equiv 0$$

If $\mathbf{V}_1 \times (\mathbf{V}_2 \times \mathbf{V}_3) = (\mathbf{V}_1 \times \mathbf{V}_2) \times \mathbf{V}_3$ then $\mathbf{V}_1$, $\mathbf{V}_2$, $\mathbf{V}_3$ form an *orthogonal set*. Thus $\mathbf{i}$, $\mathbf{j}$, $\mathbf{k}$ form an orthogonal set.

Geometry of the Plane, Straight Line and Sphere

The position vectors of the fixed points A, B, C, D relative to O are $\mathbf{V}_1$, $\mathbf{V}_2$, $\mathbf{V}_3$, $\mathbf{V}_4$ and the position vector of the variable point P is $\mathbf{V}$.

The vector form of the equation of the straight line through A parallel to $\mathbf{V}_2$ is

$$\mathbf{V} = \mathbf{V}_1 + r\mathbf{V}_2$$

or $\qquad (\mathbf{V} - \mathbf{V}_1) = r\mathbf{V}_2$

or $\qquad (\mathbf{V} - \mathbf{V}_1) \times \mathbf{V}_2 = 0$

while that of the plane through A perpendicular to $\mathbf{V}_2$ is

$$(\mathbf{V} - \mathbf{V}_1) \cdot \mathbf{V}_2 = 0$$

The equation of the line AB is

$$\mathbf{V} = r\mathbf{V}_1 + (1 - r)\mathbf{V}_2$$

and those of the bisectors of the angles between $\mathbf{V}_1$ and $\mathbf{V}_2$ are

$$\mathbf{V} = r\left(\frac{\mathbf{V}_1}{v} \pm \frac{\mathbf{V}_2}{v_2}\right)$$

or $\qquad \mathbf{V} = r(\hat{\mathbf{v}}_1 \pm \hat{\mathbf{v}}_2)$

The perpendicular from C to the line through A parallel to $\mathbf{V}_2$ has as its equation

$$\mathbf{V} = \mathbf{V}_1 - \mathbf{V}_3 - \hat{\mathbf{v}}_2 \cdot (\mathbf{V}_1 - \mathbf{V}_3)\hat{\mathbf{v}}_2.$$

The condition for the intersection of the two lines,

$$\mathbf{V} = \mathbf{V}_1 + r\mathbf{V}_3$$

and $\qquad \mathbf{V} = \mathbf{V}_2 + s\mathbf{V}_4$

is $\qquad [(\mathbf{V}_1 - \mathbf{V}_2)\mathbf{V}_3\mathbf{V}_4] = 0.$

The common perpendicular to the above two lines is the line of intersection of the two planes

$$[(\mathbf{V} - \mathbf{V}_1)\mathbf{V}_3(\mathbf{V}_3 \times \mathbf{V}_4)] = 0$$

and $\qquad [(\mathbf{V} - \mathbf{V}_2)\mathbf{V}_4(\mathbf{V}_3 \times \mathbf{V}_4)] = 0$

and the length of this perpendicular is

$$\frac{[(\mathbf{V}_1 - \mathbf{V}_2)\mathbf{V}_3\mathbf{V}_4]}{|\mathbf{V}_3 \times \mathbf{V}_4|}.$$

The equation of the line perpendicular to the plane ABC is

$$\mathbf{V} = \mathbf{V}_1 \times \mathbf{V}_2 + \mathbf{V}_2 \times \mathbf{V}_3 + \mathbf{V}_3 \times \mathbf{V}_1$$

and the distance of the plane from the origin is

$$\frac{[\mathbf{V}_1\mathbf{V}_2\mathbf{V}_3]}{|(\mathbf{V}_2 - \mathbf{V}_1) \times (\mathbf{V}_3 - \mathbf{V}_1)|}.$$

In general the vector equation

$$\mathbf{V} \cdot \mathbf{V}_2 = r$$

defines the plane which is perpendicular to $\mathbf{V}_2$, and the perpendicular distance from A to this plane is

$$\frac{r - \mathbf{V}_1 \cdot \mathbf{V}_2}{v_2}.$$

The distance from A, measured along a line parallel to $\mathbf{V}_3$, is

$$\frac{r - \mathbf{V}_1 \cdot \mathbf{V}_2}{\mathbf{V}_2 \cdot \hat{\mathbf{v}}_3} \quad \text{or} \quad \frac{r - \mathbf{V}_1 \cdot \mathbf{V}_2}{v_2 \cos \theta}$$

where θ is the angle beween $\mathbf{V}_2$ and $\mathbf{V}_3$.
(If this plane contains the point C then $r = \mathbf{V}_3 \cdot \mathbf{V}_2$ and if it passes through the origin then $r = 0$.)

Given two planes

$$\mathbf{V} \cdot \mathbf{V}_1 = r$$
$$\mathbf{V} \cdot \mathbf{V}_2 = s$$

then any plane through the line of intersection of these two planes is given by

$$\mathbf{V} \cdot (\mathbf{V}_1 + \lambda \mathbf{V}_2) = r + \lambda s$$

where λ is a scalar parameter. In particular $\lambda = \pm v_1/v_2$ yields the equation of the two planes bisecting the angle between the given planes.

The plane through A parallel to the plane of $\mathbf{V}_2$, $\mathbf{V}_3$ is

$$\mathbf{V} = \mathbf{V}_1 + r\mathbf{V}_2 + s\mathbf{V}_3$$

$$\text{or} \quad (\mathbf{V} - \mathbf{V}_1) \cdot \mathbf{V}_2 \times \mathbf{V}_3 = 0$$

$$\text{or} \quad [\mathbf{V}\mathbf{V}_2\mathbf{V}_3] - [\mathbf{V}_1\mathbf{V}_2\mathbf{V}_3] = 0$$

so that the expansion in rectangular Cartesian coordinates yields

$$\begin{vmatrix} (x - a_1) & (y - b_1) & (z - c_1) \\ a_2 & b_2 & c_2 \\ a_3 & b_3 & c_3 \end{vmatrix} = 0 \qquad (\mathbf{V} \equiv x\mathbf{i} + y\mathbf{j} + z\mathbf{k})$$

which is obviously the usual linear equation in x, y and z.

The plane through AB parallel to $\mathbf{V}_3$ is given by

$$[(\mathbf{V} - \mathbf{V}_1)(\mathbf{V}_1 - \mathbf{V}_2)\mathbf{V}_3] = 0$$

$$\text{or} \quad [\mathbf{V}\mathbf{V}_2\mathbf{V}_3] - [\mathbf{V}\mathbf{V}_1\mathbf{V}_3] - [\mathbf{V}_1\mathbf{V}_2\mathbf{V}_3] = 0$$

The plane through the three points A, B and C is

$$\mathbf{V} = \mathbf{V}_1 + s(\mathbf{V}_2 - \mathbf{V}_1) + t(\mathbf{V}_3 - \mathbf{V}_1)$$

$$\text{or} \quad \mathbf{V} = r\mathbf{V}_1 + s\mathbf{V}_2 + t\mathbf{V}_3 \qquad (r + s + t \equiv 1)$$

$$\text{or} \quad [(\mathbf{V} - \mathbf{V}_1)(\mathbf{V}_1 - \mathbf{V}_2)(\mathbf{V}_2 - \mathbf{V}_3)] = 0$$

$$\text{or} \quad [\mathbf{V}\mathbf{V}_1\mathbf{V}_2] + [\mathbf{V}\mathbf{V}_2\mathbf{V}_3] + [\mathbf{V}\mathbf{V}_3\mathbf{V}_1] - [\mathbf{V}_1\mathbf{V}_2\mathbf{V}_3] = 0$$

For four points A, B, C, D to be coplanar, then

$$r\mathbf{V}_1 + s\mathbf{V}_2 + t\mathbf{V}_3 + u\mathbf{V}_4 \equiv 0 \equiv r + s + t + u$$

The following formulae relate to a sphere when the vectors are taken to lie in three dimensional space and to a circle when the space is two dimensional. For a circle in three dimensions take the intersection of the sphere with a plane.

The equation of a sphere with center O and radius OA is

$$\mathbf{V} \cdot \mathbf{V} = v_1^2 \qquad \text{(not } \mathbf{V} = \mathbf{V}_1)$$

or $\qquad (\mathbf{V} - \mathbf{V}_1) \cdot (\mathbf{V} + \mathbf{V}_1) = 0$

while that of a sphere with center B radius r_1 is

$$(\mathbf{V} - \mathbf{V}_2) \cdot (\mathbf{V} - \mathbf{V}_2) = v_1^2$$

or $\qquad \mathbf{V} \cdot (\mathbf{V} - 2\mathbf{V}_2) = v_1^2 - v_2^2$

If the above sphere passes through the origin then

$$\mathbf{V} \cdot (\mathbf{V} - 2\mathbf{V}_2) = 0$$

(note that in two dimensional polar coordinates this is simply)

$$r = 2a \cdot \cos \theta$$

while in three dimensional Cartesian coordinates it is

$$x^2 + y^2 + z^2 - 2(a_2 x + b_2 y + c_2 x) = 0.$$

The equation of a sphere having the points A and B as the extremities of a diameter is

$$(\mathbf{V} - \mathbf{V}_1) \cdot (\mathbf{V} - \mathbf{V}_2) = 0.$$

The square of the length of the tangent from C to the sphere with center B and radius v_1 is given by

$$(\mathbf{V}_3 - \mathbf{V}_2) \cdot (\mathbf{V}_3 - \mathbf{V}_2) = v_1^2$$

The condition that the plane $\mathbf{V} \cdot \mathbf{V}_3 = s$ is tangential to the sphere $(\mathbf{V} - \mathbf{V}_2) \cdot (\mathbf{V} - \mathbf{V}_2) = v_1^2$ is

$$(s - \mathbf{V}_3 \cdot \mathbf{V}_2) \cdot (s - \mathbf{V}_3 \cdot \mathbf{V}_2) = v_1^2 v_3^2.$$

The equation of the tangent plane at D, on the surface of sphere $(\mathbf{V} - \mathbf{V}_2) \cdot (\mathbf{V} - \mathbf{V}_2) = v_1^2$, is

$$(\mathbf{V} - \mathbf{V}_4) \cdot (\mathbf{V}_4 - \mathbf{V}_2) = 0$$

or $\qquad \mathbf{V} \cdot \mathbf{V}_4 - \mathbf{V}_2 \cdot (\mathbf{V} + \mathbf{V}_4) = v_1^2 - v_2^2$

The condition that the two circles $(\mathbf{V} - \mathbf{V}_2) \cdot (\mathbf{V} - \mathbf{V}_2) = v_1^2$ and $(\mathbf{V} - \mathbf{V}_4) \cdot (\mathbf{V} - \mathbf{V}_4) = v_3^2$ intersect orthogonally is clearly

$$(\mathbf{V}_2 - \mathbf{V}_4) \cdot (\mathbf{V}_2 - \mathbf{V}_4) = v_1^2 + v_3^2$$

The polar plane of D with respect to the circle

$$(\mathbf{V} - \mathbf{V}_2) \cdot (\mathbf{V} - \mathbf{V}_2) = v_1^2 \quad \text{is}$$

$$\mathbf{V} \cdot \mathbf{V}_4 - \mathbf{V}_2 \cdot (\mathbf{V} + \mathbf{V}_4) = v_1^2 - v_2^2$$

Any sphere through the intersection of the two spheres $(\mathbf{V} - \mathbf{V}_2) \cdot (\mathbf{V} - \mathbf{V}_2) = v_1^2$ and $(\mathbf{V} - \mathbf{V}_4) \cdot (\mathbf{V} - \mathbf{V}_4) = v_3^2$ is given by

$$(\mathbf{V} - \mathbf{V}_2) \cdot (\mathbf{V} - \mathbf{V}_2) + \lambda(\mathbf{V} - \mathbf{V}_4) \cdot (\mathbf{V} - \mathbf{V}_4) = v_1^2 + \lambda v_3^2$$

while the radical plane of two such spheres is

$$\mathbf{V} \cdot (\mathbf{V}_2 - \mathbf{V}_4) = -\tfrac{1}{2}(v_1^2 - v_2^2 - v_3^2 + v_4^2)$$

Differentiation of Vectors

If $\mathbf{V}_1 = a_1\mathbf{i} + b_1\mathbf{j} + c_1\mathbf{k}$, and $\mathbf{V}_2 = a_2\mathbf{i} + b_2\mathbf{j} + c_2\mathbf{k}$, and if $\mathbf{V}_1$ and $\mathbf{V}_2$ are functions of the scalar t, then

$$\frac{d}{dt}(\mathbf{V}_1 + \mathbf{V}_2 + \cdots) = \frac{d\mathbf{V}_1}{dt} + \frac{d\mathbf{V}_2}{dt} + \cdots,$$

where $\dfrac{d\mathbf{V}_1}{dt} = \dfrac{da_1}{dt}\mathbf{i} + \dfrac{db_1}{dt}\mathbf{j} + \dfrac{dc_1}{dt}\mathbf{k}$, etc.

$$\frac{d}{dt}(\mathbf{V}_1 \cdot \mathbf{V}_2) = \frac{d\mathbf{V}_1}{dt} \cdot \mathbf{V}_2 + \mathbf{V}_1 \cdot \frac{d\mathbf{V}_2}{dt}$$

$$\frac{d}{dt}(\mathbf{V}_1 \times \mathbf{V}_2) = \frac{d\mathbf{V}_1}{dt} \times \mathbf{V}_2 + \mathbf{V}_1 \times \frac{d\mathbf{V}_2}{dt}$$

$$\mathbf{V} \cdot \frac{d\mathbf{V}}{dt} = v \cdot \frac{dv}{dt}$$

In particular, if $\mathbf{V}$ is a vector of constant length then the right hand side of the last equation is identically zero showing that $\mathbf{V}$ is perpendicular to its derivative.

The derivatives of the triple products are

$$\frac{d}{dt}[\mathbf{V}_1\mathbf{V}_2\mathbf{V}_3] = \left[\left(\frac{d\mathbf{V}_1}{dt}\right)\mathbf{V}_2\mathbf{V}_3\right] + \left[\mathbf{V}_1\left(\frac{d\mathbf{V}_2}{dt}\right)\mathbf{V}_3\right] + \left[\mathbf{V}_1\mathbf{V}_2\left(\frac{d\mathbf{V}_3}{dt}\right)\right]$$

and $\dfrac{d}{dt}\left\{\mathbf{V}_1 \times (\mathbf{V}_2 \times \mathbf{V}_3)\right\} = \left(\dfrac{d\mathbf{V}_1}{dt}\right) \times (\mathbf{V}_2 \times \mathbf{V}_3) + \mathbf{V}_1$

$$\times\left(\left(\frac{d\mathbf{V}_2}{dt}\right) \times \mathbf{V}_3\right) + \mathbf{V}_1 \times \left(\mathbf{V}_2 \times \left(\frac{d\mathbf{V}_3}{dt}\right)\right).$$

Geometry of Curves in Space

s = the *length of arc*, measured from some fixed point on the curve (fig. 3).

$\mathbf{V}_1$ = the position vector of the point A on the curve

$\mathbf{V}_1 + \delta\mathbf{V}_1$ = the position vector of the point P in the neighborhood of A

$\hat{\mathbf{t}}$ = the *unit tangent* to the curve at the point A, measured in the direction of s increasing.

The *normal plane* is that plane which is perpendicular to the unit tangent. The principal normal is defined as the intersection of the normal plane with the plane defined by $\mathbf{V}_1$ and $\mathbf{V}_1 + \delta\mathbf{V}_1$ in the limit as $\delta\mathbf{V}_1 - 0$.

$\hat{\mathbf{n}}$ = the *unit normal* (principal) at the point A. The plane defined by $\hat{\mathbf{t}}$ and $\hat{\mathbf{n}}$ is called the *osculating plane* (alternatively plane of curvature or local plane).

ρ = the radius of curvature at A

$\delta\theta$ = the angle subtended at the origin by $\delta\mathbf{V}_1$.

$\kappa = \dfrac{d\theta}{ds} = \dfrac{1}{\rho}$

$\hat{\mathbf{b}}$ = the *unit binormal* i.e. the unit vector which is parallel to $\hat{\mathbf{t}} \times \hat{\mathbf{n}}$ at the point A:
λ = the *torsion* of the curve at A

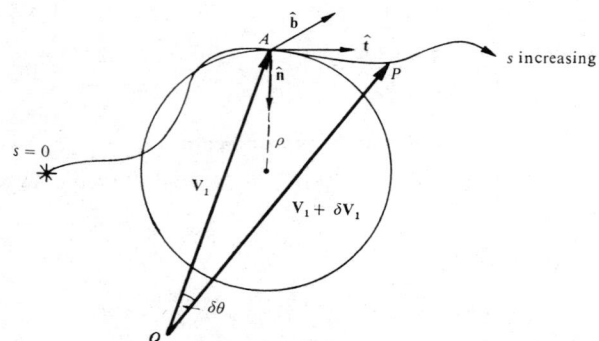

Figure 3.

Frenet's Formulae:

$$\frac{d\hat{\mathbf{t}}}{ds} = \kappa\hat{\mathbf{n}}$$

$$\frac{d\hat{\mathbf{n}}}{ds} = -\kappa\hat{\mathbf{t}} \quad\quad + \lambda\hat{\mathbf{b}}$$

$$\frac{d\hat{\mathbf{b}}}{ds} = \quad\quad -\lambda\hat{\mathbf{n}}$$

The following formulae are also applicable:

Unit tangent $\quad\quad\quad\quad\quad\quad\quad\quad\quad \hat{\mathbf{t}} = \dfrac{d\mathbf{V}_1}{ds}$

Equation of the tangent $\quad\quad\quad\quad (\mathbf{V} - \mathbf{V}_1) \times \hat{\mathbf{t}} = 0$

$\quad\quad\quad\quad\quad$ or $\quad\quad \mathbf{V} = \mathbf{V}_1 + q\hat{\mathbf{t}}$

Unit normal $\quad\quad\quad\quad\quad\quad\quad\quad \hat{\mathbf{n}} = \dfrac{1}{\kappa}\dfrac{d^2\mathbf{V}_1}{ds^2}$

Equation of the normal plane $\quad\quad (\mathbf{V} - \mathbf{V}_1) \cdot \hat{\mathbf{t}} = 0$

Equation of the normal $\quad\quad\quad\quad (\mathbf{V} - \mathbf{V}_1) \times \hat{\mathbf{n}} = 0$

$\quad\quad\quad\quad\quad$ or $\quad\quad \mathbf{V} = \mathbf{V}_1 + r\hat{\mathbf{n}}$

Unit binormal $\quad\quad\quad \hat{\mathbf{b}} = \hat{\mathbf{t}} \times \hat{\mathbf{n}}$

Equation of the binormal $\quad\quad\quad\quad (\mathbf{V} - \mathbf{V}_1) \times \hat{\mathbf{b}} = 0$

$\quad\quad\quad$ or $\quad\quad\quad\quad \mathbf{V} = \mathbf{V}_1 + u\hat{\mathbf{b}}$

$\quad\quad\quad$ or $\quad\quad\quad\quad \mathbf{V} = \mathbf{V}_1 + w\dfrac{d\mathbf{V}_1}{ds} \times \dfrac{d^2\mathbf{V}_1}{ds^2}$

Equation of the osculating plane:

$$[(\mathbf{V} - \mathbf{V}_1)\hat{\mathbf{t}}\hat{\mathbf{n}}] = 0$$

$\quad\quad$ or $\quad\quad \left[(\mathbf{V} - \mathbf{V}_1)\left(\dfrac{d\mathbf{V}_1}{ds}\right)\left(\dfrac{d^2\mathbf{V}_1}{ds^2}\right) \right] = 0$

A *geodetic line* on a surface is a curve, the osculating plane of which is everywhere normal to the surface.

The differential equation of the geodetic is

$$[\hat{\mathbf{n}} d\mathbf{V}_1 \, d^2\mathbf{V}_1] = 0$$

Differential Operators—Rectangular Coordinates

$$dS = \frac{\partial S}{\partial x} \cdot dx + \frac{\partial S}{\partial y} \cdot dy + \frac{\partial S}{\partial z} \cdot dz$$

By definition

$$\nabla \equiv \text{del} \equiv \mathbf{i}\,\frac{\partial}{\partial x} + \mathbf{j}\,\frac{\partial}{\partial y} + \mathbf{k}\,\frac{\partial}{\partial z}$$

$$\nabla^2 \equiv \text{Laplacian} \equiv \frac{\partial^2}{\partial x^2} + \frac{\partial^2}{\partial y^2} + \frac{\partial^2}{\partial z^2}$$

If S is a scalar function, then

$$\nabla S \equiv \text{grad } S \equiv \frac{\partial S}{\partial x}\,\mathbf{i} + \frac{\partial S}{\partial y}\,\mathbf{j} + \frac{\partial S}{\partial z}\,\mathbf{k}$$

Grad S defines both the direction and magnitude of the maximum rate of increase of S at any point. Hence the name *gradient* and also its vectorial nature. ∇S is independent of the choice of rectangular coordinates.

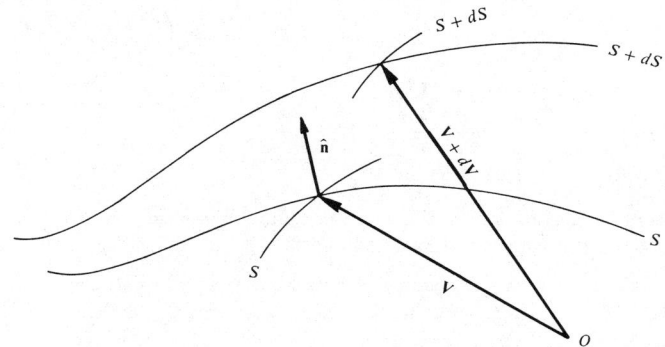

Figure 4

$$\nabla S = \frac{\partial S}{\partial n}\,\hat{\mathbf{n}}$$

where $\hat{\mathbf{n}}$ is the unit normal to the surface S = constant, in the direction of S increasing. The total derivative of S at a point having the position vector $\mathbf{V}$ is given by (fig. 4)

$$dS = \frac{\partial S}{\partial n}\,\hat{\mathbf{n}} \cdot d\mathbf{V}$$

$$= d\mathbf{V} \cdot \nabla S$$

and the directional derivative of S in the direction of $\mathbf{U}$ is

$$\mathbf{U} \cdot \nabla S = \mathbf{U} \cdot (\nabla S) = (\mathbf{U} \cdot \nabla)S$$

Similarly the directional derivative of the vector $\mathbf{V}$ in the direction of $\mathbf{U}$ is

$$(\mathbf{U} \cdot \nabla)\mathbf{V}$$

The *distributive* law holds for finding a gradient. Thus if S and T are scalar functions

$$\nabla(S + T) = \nabla S + \nabla T$$

The *associative* law becomes the rule for differentiating a product:

$$\nabla(ST) = S\nabla T + T\nabla S$$

If **V** is a vector function with the magnitudes of the components parallel to the three coordinate axes V_x, V_y, V_z, then

$$\nabla \cdot \mathbf{V} \equiv \text{div } \mathbf{V} \equiv \frac{\partial V_x}{\partial x} + \frac{\partial V_y}{\partial y} + \frac{\partial V_z}{\partial z}$$

The divergence obeys the distributive law. Thus, if **V** and **U** are vectors functions, then

$$\nabla \cdot (\mathbf{V} + \mathbf{U}) = \nabla \cdot \mathbf{V} + \nabla \cdot \mathbf{U}$$
$$\nabla \cdot (S\mathbf{V}) = (\nabla S) \cdot \mathbf{V} + S(\nabla \cdot \mathbf{V})$$
$$\nabla \cdot (\mathbf{U} \times \mathbf{V}) = \mathbf{V} \cdot (\nabla \times \mathbf{U}) - \mathbf{U} \cdot (\nabla \times \mathbf{V})$$

As with the gradient of a scalar, the divergence of a vector is invariant under a transformation from one set of rectangular coordinates to another.

$$\nabla \times \mathbf{V} \equiv \text{curl } \mathbf{V} \quad (\text{sometimes } \nabla \wedge \mathbf{V} \text{ or rot } \mathbf{V})$$

$$\equiv \left(\frac{\partial \mathbf{V}_z}{\partial y} - \frac{\partial \mathbf{V}_y}{\partial z}\right)\mathbf{i} + \left(\frac{\partial \mathbf{V}_x}{\partial z} - \frac{\partial \mathbf{V}_z}{\partial x}\right)\mathbf{j} + \left(\frac{\partial \mathbf{V}_y}{\partial x} - \frac{\partial \mathbf{V}_x}{\partial y}\right)\mathbf{k}$$

$$= \begin{vmatrix} \mathbf{i} & \mathbf{j} & \mathbf{k} \\ \dfrac{\partial}{\partial x} & \dfrac{\partial}{\partial y} & \dfrac{\partial}{\partial z} \\ V_x & V_y & V_z \end{vmatrix}$$

The *curl* (or *rotation*) of a vector is a vector which is invariant under a transformation from one set of rectangular coordinates to another.

$$\nabla \times (\mathbf{U} + \mathbf{V}) = \nabla \times \mathbf{U} + \nabla \times \mathbf{V}$$
$$\nabla \times (S\mathbf{V}) = (\nabla S) \times \mathbf{V} + S(\nabla \times \mathbf{V})$$
$$\nabla \times (\mathbf{U} \times \mathbf{V}) = (\mathbf{V} \cdot \nabla)\mathbf{U} - (\mathbf{U} \cdot \nabla)\mathbf{V} + \mathbf{U}(\nabla \cdot \mathbf{V}) - \mathbf{V}(\nabla \cdot \mathbf{U})$$

$$\text{grad } (\mathbf{U} \cdot \mathbf{V}) = \nabla(\mathbf{U} \cdot \mathbf{V})$$
$$= (\mathbf{V} \cdot \nabla)\mathbf{U} + (\mathbf{U} \cdot \nabla)\mathbf{V} + \mathbf{V} \times (\nabla \times \mathbf{U}) + \mathbf{U} \times (\nabla \times \mathbf{V})$$

If
$$\mathbf{V} = V_x\mathbf{i} + V_y\mathbf{j} + V_z\mathbf{k}$$
$$\nabla \cdot \mathbf{V} = \nabla V_x \cdot \mathbf{i} + \nabla V_y \cdot \mathbf{j} + \nabla V_z \cdot \mathbf{k}$$
and
$$\nabla \times \mathbf{V} = \nabla V_x \times \mathbf{i} + \nabla V_y \times \mathbf{j} + \nabla V_z \times \mathbf{k}$$

The operator ∇ can be used more than once. The number of possibilities where ∇ is used twice are

$$\nabla \cdot (\nabla\theta) \equiv \text{div grad } \theta$$
$$\nabla \times (\nabla\theta) \equiv \text{curl grad } \theta$$
$$\nabla(\nabla \cdot \mathbf{V}) \equiv \text{grad div } \mathbf{V}$$
$$\nabla \cdot (\nabla \times \mathbf{V}) \equiv \text{div curl } \mathbf{V}$$
$$\nabla \times (\nabla \times \mathbf{V}) \equiv \text{curl curl } \mathbf{V}$$

Thus: div grad $S \equiv \nabla \cdot (\nabla S) \equiv$ Laplacian $S \equiv \nabla^2 S$

$$\equiv \frac{\partial^2 S}{\partial x^2} + \frac{\partial^2 S}{\partial y^2} + \frac{\partial^2 S}{\partial z^2}$$

curl grad $S \equiv 0$; curl curl $\mathbf{V} \equiv$ grad div $\mathbf{V} - \nabla^2 \mathbf{V}$;

div curl $\mathbf{V} \equiv \qquad 0$

Taylor's expansion in three dimensions can be written

$$f(\mathbf{V} + \boldsymbol{\varepsilon}) = e^{\boldsymbol{\varepsilon} \cdot \nabla} f(\mathbf{V})$$

where $\qquad \mathbf{V} = x\mathbf{i} + y\mathbf{j} + z\mathbf{k}$

and $\qquad \boldsymbol{\varepsilon} = h\mathbf{i} + l\mathbf{j} + m\mathbf{k}$

(note the analogy with $f_p = e^{phD} f_0$ in finite difference methods).

Orthogonal Curvilinear Coordinates

If at a point P there exist three uniform point functions u, v and w so that the surfaces $u = $ const., $v = $ const., and $w = $ const., intersect in three distinct curves through P then the surfaces are called the *coordinate surfaces* through P. The three lines of intersection are referred to as the *coordinate lines* and their tangents a, b, and c as the *coordinate axes*. When the coordinate axes form an orthogonal set the system is said to define *orthogonal curvilinear coordinates* at P.

Consider an infinitesimal volume enclosed by the surfaces u, v, w, $u + du$, $v + dv$, and $w + dw$ (fig. 5).

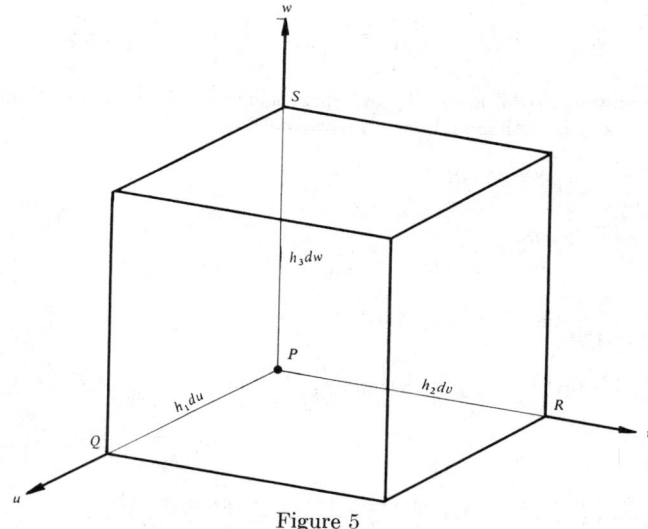

Figure 5

The surface $PRS \equiv u =$ const., and the face of the curvilinear figure immediately opposite this is $u + du =$ const. etc.

In terms of these surface constants

$$
\begin{aligned}
P &= P(u,v,w) \\
Q &= Q(u + du,v,w) \\
R &= R(u,v + dv,w) \\
S &= S(u,v,w + dw)
\end{aligned}
\qquad \text{and} \qquad
\begin{aligned}
PQ &= h_1 du \\
PR &= h_2 dv \\
PS &= h_3 dw
\end{aligned}
$$

where h_1, h_2, and h_3 are functions of u, v, and w.

In rectangular Cartesians $\mathbf{i}$, $\mathbf{j}$, $\mathbf{k}$

$$h_1 = 1, \qquad h_2 = 1, \qquad h_3 = 1.$$

$$\frac{\hat{\mathbf{a}}}{h_1} \frac{\partial}{\partial u} = \mathbf{i} \frac{\partial}{\partial x}, \qquad \frac{\hat{\mathbf{b}}}{h_2} \frac{\partial}{\partial v} = \mathbf{j} \frac{\partial}{\partial y}, \qquad \frac{\hat{\mathbf{c}}}{h_3} \frac{\partial}{\partial w} = \mathbf{k} \frac{\partial}{\partial z}.$$

In cylindrical coordinates $\hat{\mathbf{r}}$, $\hat{\boldsymbol{\phi}}$, $\hat{\mathbf{k}}$

$$h_1 = 1, \qquad h_2 = r \qquad h_3 = 1.$$

$$\frac{\hat{\mathbf{a}}}{h_1} \frac{\partial}{\partial u} = \hat{\mathbf{r}} \frac{\partial}{\partial r}, \qquad \frac{\hat{\mathbf{b}}}{h_2} \frac{\partial}{\partial v} = \frac{\hat{\boldsymbol{\phi}}}{r} \frac{\partial}{\partial \phi} \qquad \frac{\hat{\mathbf{c}}}{h_3} \frac{\partial}{\partial w} = \hat{\mathbf{k}} \frac{\partial}{\partial z}$$

In spherical coordinates $\hat{\mathbf{r}}$, $\hat{\boldsymbol{\theta}}$, $\hat{\boldsymbol{\phi}}$

$$h_1 = 1, \qquad h_2 = r, \qquad h_3 = r \sin \theta$$

$$\frac{\hat{\mathbf{a}}}{h_1} \frac{\partial}{\partial u} = \hat{\mathbf{r}} \frac{\partial}{\partial r}, \qquad \frac{\mathbf{b}}{h_2} \frac{\partial}{\partial v} = \frac{\hat{\boldsymbol{\phi}}}{r} \frac{\partial}{\partial \theta}, \qquad \frac{\hat{\mathbf{c}}}{h_3} \frac{\partial}{\partial w} = \frac{\hat{\boldsymbol{\phi}}}{r \sin \theta} \frac{\partial}{\partial \phi}$$

The general expressions for grad, div and curl together with those for ∇^2 and the directional derivative are, in orthogonal curvilinear coordinates, given by

$$\nabla S = \frac{\hat{\mathbf{a}}}{h_1} \frac{\partial S}{\partial u} + \frac{\hat{\mathbf{b}}}{h_2} \frac{\partial S}{\partial v} + \frac{\hat{\mathbf{c}}}{h_3} \frac{\partial S}{\partial w}$$

$$(\mathbf{V} \cdot \nabla)S = \frac{V_1}{h_1} \frac{\partial S}{\partial u} + \frac{V_2}{h_2} \frac{\partial S}{\partial v} + \frac{V_3}{h_3} \frac{\partial S}{\partial w}$$

$$\nabla \cdot \mathbf{V} = \frac{1}{h_1 h_2 h_3} \left\{ \frac{\partial}{\partial u} (h_2 h_3 V_1) + \frac{\partial}{\partial v} (h_3 h_1 V_2) + \frac{\partial}{\partial w} (h_1 h_2 V_3) \right.$$

$$\nabla \times \mathbf{V} = \frac{\hat{\mathbf{a}}}{h_2 h_3} \left\{ \frac{\partial}{\partial v} (h_3 V_3) - \frac{\partial}{\partial w} (h_2 V_2) \right\} + \frac{\hat{\mathbf{b}}}{h_3 h_1} \left\{ \frac{\partial}{\partial w} (h_1 V_1) - \frac{\partial}{\partial u} (h_3 V_3) \right\}$$

$$+ \frac{\hat{\mathbf{c}}}{h_1 h_2} \left\{ \frac{\partial}{\partial u} (h_2 V_2) - \frac{\partial}{\partial v} (h_1 V_1) \right\}$$

$$\nabla^2 S = \frac{1}{h_1 h_2 h_3} \left\{ \frac{\partial}{\partial u} \left(\frac{h_2 h_3}{h_1} \frac{\partial S}{\partial u} \right) + \frac{\partial}{\partial v} \left(\frac{h_3 h_1}{h_2} \frac{\partial S}{\partial v} \right) + \frac{\partial}{\partial w} \left(\frac{h_1 h_2}{h_3} \frac{\partial S}{\partial w} \right) \right\}$$

FORMULAS OF VECTOR ANALYSIS

	Rectangular coordinates	Cylindrical coordinates	Spherical coordinates
Conversion to rectangular coordinates		$x = r\cos\varphi \quad y = r\sin\varphi \quad z = z$	$x = r\cos\varphi\sin\theta \quad y = r\sin\varphi\sin\theta$ $z = r\cos\theta$
Gradient	$\nabla\phi = \dfrac{\partial\phi}{\partial x}\mathbf{i} + \dfrac{\partial\phi}{\partial y}\mathbf{j} + \dfrac{\partial\phi}{\partial z}\mathbf{k}$	$\nabla\phi = \dfrac{\partial\phi}{\partial r}\mathbf{r} + \dfrac{1}{r}\dfrac{\partial\phi}{\partial\varphi}\boldsymbol{\phi} + \dfrac{\partial\phi}{\partial z}\mathbf{k}$	$\nabla\phi = \dfrac{\partial\phi}{\partial r}\mathbf{r} + \dfrac{1}{r}\dfrac{\partial\phi}{\partial\theta}\boldsymbol{\theta} + \dfrac{1}{r\sin\theta}\dfrac{\partial\phi}{\partial\varphi}\boldsymbol{\phi}$
Divergence	$\nabla\cdot\mathbf{A} = \dfrac{\partial A_x}{\partial x} + \dfrac{\partial A_y}{\partial y} + \dfrac{\partial A_z}{\partial z}$	$\nabla\cdot\mathbf{A} = \dfrac{1}{r}\dfrac{\partial(rA_r)}{\partial r} + \dfrac{1}{r}\dfrac{\partial A_\varphi}{\partial\varphi} + \dfrac{\partial A_z}{\partial z}$	$\nabla\cdot\mathbf{A} = \dfrac{1}{r^2}\dfrac{\partial(r^2A_r)}{\partial r} + \dfrac{1}{r\sin\theta}\dfrac{\partial(A_\theta\sin\theta)}{\partial\theta} + \dfrac{1}{r\sin\theta}\dfrac{\partial A_\varphi}{\partial\varphi}$
Curl	$\nabla\times\mathbf{A} = \begin{vmatrix} \mathbf{i} & \mathbf{j} & \mathbf{k} \\ \dfrac{\partial}{\partial x} & \dfrac{\partial}{\partial y} & \dfrac{\partial}{\partial z} \\ A_x & A_y & A_z \end{vmatrix}$	$\nabla\times\mathbf{A} = \begin{vmatrix} \dfrac{1}{r}\mathbf{r} & \boldsymbol{\phi} & \dfrac{1}{r}\mathbf{k} \\ \dfrac{\partial}{\partial r} & \dfrac{\partial}{\partial\varphi} & \dfrac{\partial}{\partial z} \\ A_r & rA_\varphi & A_z \end{vmatrix}$	$\nabla\times\mathbf{A} = \begin{vmatrix} \dfrac{\mathbf{r}}{r^2\sin\theta} & \dfrac{\boldsymbol{\theta}}{r\sin\theta} & \dfrac{\boldsymbol{\phi}}{r} \\ \dfrac{\partial}{\partial r} & \dfrac{\partial}{\partial\theta} & \dfrac{\partial}{\partial\varphi} \\ A_r & rA_\theta & rA_\varphi\sin\theta \end{vmatrix}$
Laplacian	$\nabla^2\phi = \dfrac{\partial^2\phi}{\partial x^2} + \dfrac{\partial^2\phi}{\partial y^2} + \dfrac{\partial^2\phi}{\partial z^2}$	$\nabla^2\phi = \dfrac{1}{r}\dfrac{\partial}{\partial r}\left(r\dfrac{\partial\phi}{\partial r}\right) + \dfrac{1}{r^2}\dfrac{\partial^2\phi}{\partial\varphi^2} + \dfrac{\partial^2\phi}{\partial z^2}$	$\nabla^2\phi = \dfrac{1}{r^2}\dfrac{\partial}{\partial r}\left(r^2\dfrac{\partial\phi}{\partial r}\right) + \dfrac{1}{r^2\sin\theta}\dfrac{\partial}{\partial\theta}\left(\sin\theta\dfrac{\partial\phi}{\partial\theta}\right) + \dfrac{1}{r^2\sin^2\theta}\dfrac{\partial^2\phi}{\partial\varphi^2}$

Transformation of Integrals

s = the distance along some curve "C" in space and is measured from some fixed point.
S = a surface area
V = a volume contained by a specified surface
$\hat{\mathbf{t}}$ = the unit tangent to C at the point P
$\hat{\mathbf{n}}$ = the unit outward pointing normal
F = some vector function
ds = the vector element of curve ($= \hat{\mathbf{t}}\, ds$)
dS = the vector element of surface ($= \hat{\mathbf{n}}\, dS$)

Then
$$\int_{(c)} \mathbf{F} \cdot \hat{\mathbf{t}}\, ds = \int_{(c)} \mathbf{F} \cdot \mathbf{ds}$$

and when
$$\mathbf{F} = \nabla\phi$$

$$\int_{(c)} (\nabla\phi) \cdot \hat{\mathbf{t}}\, ds = \int_{(c)} d\phi$$

Gauss' Theorem (Green's Theorem)

When S defines a closed region having a volume V

$$\iiint_{(v)} (\nabla \cdot \mathbf{F})\, dV = \iint_{(s)} (\mathbf{F} \cdot \hat{\mathbf{n}})\, dS = \iint_{(s)} \mathbf{F} \cdot d\mathbf{S}$$

also
$$\iiint_{(v)} (\nabla\phi)\, dV = \iint_{(s)} \phi\hat{\mathbf{n}}\, dS$$

and
$$\iiint_{(v)} (\nabla \times \mathbf{F})\, dV = \iint_{(s)} (\hat{\mathbf{n}} \times \mathbf{F})\, dS$$

Stokes' Theorem

When C is closed and bounds the open surface S.

$$\iint_{(s)} \hat{\mathbf{n}} \cdot (\nabla \times \mathbf{F})\, dS = \int_{(c)} \mathbf{F} \cdot \mathbf{ds}$$

also
$$\iint_{(s)} (\hat{\mathbf{n}} \times \nabla\phi)\, dS = \int_{(c)} \phi\, \mathbf{ds}$$

Green's Theorem

$$\iint_{(s)} (\nabla\phi \cdot \nabla\theta)\, dS = \iint_{(s)} \phi\hat{\mathbf{n}} \cdot (\nabla\theta)\, dS = \iiint_{(v)} \phi(\nabla^2\theta)\, dV$$

$$= \iint_{(s)} \theta \cdot \hat{\mathbf{n}}(\nabla\phi)\, dS = \iiint_{(v)} \theta(\nabla^2\phi)\, dV$$

FINITE DIFFERENCES

For equi-spaced arguments x_i, and associated y_i, the successive **advancing y-differences** are $\Delta^0 y_i = y_i$, $\Delta y_i = y_{i+1} - y_i$, $\Delta^2 y_i = \Delta y_{i+1} - \Delta y_i = y_{i+2} - 2y_{i+1} + y_i$, . . . , $\Delta^m y_i = \Delta^{m-1} y_{i+1} - \Delta^{m-1} y_i = \sum_r (-1)^r \binom{m}{r} y_{i+m-r}$. With arbitrary origin A and class-interval length, $x_{i+1} - x_i = h$, using $u_i = (x_i - A)/h$, write $y(u_i)$ for y_i. Then if for some fixed m, for the portion of the table considered, the values of $\Delta^{m+1} y_i$ be zero (or approximately, if these be regarded as negligible) **Newton's formula** gives

$$y(u) = \sum \frac{u^{(r)}}{r!} \Delta^r y(0) = y(0) + u\Delta y(0) + \frac{u(u-1)}{1 \cdot 2} \Delta^2 y(0) + \cdots$$

$$+ \frac{u(u-1) \cdots (u - m + 1)}{m!} \Delta^m y(0).$$

This formula reduces to an identity for $u = u_0, u_1, \ldots, u_n$, $(u_i = i)$, and may be used to interpolate for intermediate values.

Example. Given

x	-4,	-2,	0,	2,	4,	6,	8,	$\ldots$
y	10,	14,	30,	64,	122,	210,	334,	$\ldots$

to find a value for y when $x = 10$, and when $x = 1$. Suppose for some reason A has been taken at $x = 2$. The work may be arranged as follows:

u	x	y	Δ	Δ^2	Δ^3	Δ^4
-3	-4	10				
			4			
-2	-2	14		12		
			16		6	
-1	0	30		18		0
			34		6	
0	2	64		24		0
			58		6	
1	4	122		30		0
			88		6	
2	6	210		36		—
			124		—	
3	8	334		—		—
			—			
—	—	—	—	—	—	—

$$y(u) = 64 + 58u + 30\,\frac{u(u-1)}{1 \cdot 2} + 6\,\frac{u(u-1)(u-2)}{1 \cdot 2 \cdot 3},$$

$$= 64 + 58u + 15u(u-1) + u(u-1)(u-2).$$

At $x = 10$, $u = 4$. Substituting $u = 4$, one has $y\big|_{x=10} = 500.$

At $x = 1$, $u = -\frac{1}{2}$. Substituting $u = -\frac{1}{2}$, one has $y\big|_{x=1} = 44\frac{3}{8}.$

Probability and Statistics

DESCRIPTIVE STATISTICS

a) Ungrouped Data

The formulas of this section designated as a) apply to a random sample of size n, denoted by x_i, $i = 1, 2, \ldots, n$.

b) Grouped Data

The formulas of this section designated as b) apply to data grouped into a frequency distribution having class marks x_i, $i = 1, 2, \ldots, k$, and corresponding class frequencies f_i, $i = 1, 2, \ldots, k$. The total number of observations given by

$$n = \sum_{i=1}^{k} f_i$$

In the formulas that follow, c denotes the width of the class interval, x_o denotes one of the class marks taken to be the computing origin, and $u_i = \dfrac{x_i - x_o}{c}$. Then coded class marks are obtained by replacing the original class marks with the integers $\ldots, -3, -2, -1, 0, 1, 2, 3, \ldots$ where 0 corresponds to class mark x_o in the original scale.

Mean (Arithmetic Mean)

a) $\bar{x} = \dfrac{1}{n} \sum_{i=1}^{n} x_i = x_1 + x_2 + \cdots + x_n$

b.1) $\bar{x} = \dfrac{1}{n} \sum_{i=1}^{k} f_i x_i = \dfrac{f_1 x_1 + f_2 x_2 + \cdots + f_k x_k}{n}$

If data is coded

b.2) $\bar{x} = x_o + c \dfrac{\displaystyle\sum_{i=1}^{k} f_i u_i}{n}$

Weighted Mean (Weighted Arithmetic Mean)

If with each value x_i is associated a weighting factor $w_i \geq 0$, then $\displaystyle\sum_{i=1}^{n} w_i$ is the total weight, and

a) $\bar{x} = \dfrac{\displaystyle\sum_{i=1}^{n} w_i x_i}{\displaystyle\sum_{i=1}^{n} w_i} = \dfrac{w_1 x_1 + w_2 x_2 + \cdots + w_n x_n}{w_1 + w_2 + \cdots + w_n}$

Geometric Mean

a) G.M. $= \sqrt[n]{x_1 \cdot x_2 \cdots x_n}$

In logarithmic form

$$\log (\text{G.M.}) = \frac{1}{n} \sum_{i=1}^{n} \log x_i = \frac{\log x_1 + \log x_2 + \cdots + \log x_n}{n}$$

b) $\text{G.M.} = \sqrt[n]{x_1^{f_1} \cdot x_2^{f_2} \cdots x_k^{f_k}}$

In logarithmic form

$$\log (\text{G.M.}) = \frac{1}{n} \sum_{i=1}^{k} f_i \log x_i = \frac{f_1 \log x_1 + f_2 \log x_2 + \cdots + f_k \log x_k}{n}$$

Harmonic Mean

a) $\text{H.M.} = \dfrac{n}{\displaystyle\sum_{i=1}^{n} \dfrac{1}{x_i}} = \dfrac{n}{\dfrac{1}{x_1} + \dfrac{1}{x_2} + \cdots + \dfrac{1}{x_n}}$

b) $\text{H.M.} = \dfrac{n}{\displaystyle\sum_{i=1}^{k} \dfrac{f_i}{x_i}} = \dfrac{n}{\dfrac{f_1}{x_1} + \dfrac{f_2}{x_2} + \cdots + \dfrac{f_k}{x_k}}$

Relation Between Arithmetic, Geometric, and Harmonic Mean

H.M. $\leq$ G.M. $\leq \bar{x}$, (Equality sign holds only if all sample values are identical.)

Mode

a) A mode M_o of a sample of size n is a value which occurs with greatest frequency, i.e., it is the most common value. A mode may not exist, and even if it does exist it may not be unique.

b) $M_o = L + C \dfrac{\Delta_1}{\Delta_1 + \Delta_2}$,

where L is the lower class boundary of the modal class (class containing the mode),
 Δ_1 is the excess of modal frequency over frequency of next lower class,
 Δ_2 is the excess of modal frequency over frequency of next higher class.

Median

a) If the sample is arranged in ascending order of magnitude, then the median M_d is given by the $\dfrac{n+1}{2}$ *nd* value. When n is odd, the median is the middle value of the set of ordered data; when n is even, the median is usually taken as the mean of the two middle values of the set of ordered data.

b) $M_d = L + c \dfrac{\dfrac{n}{2} - F_c}{f_m}$,

where L is lower class boundary of median class (class containing the median),
 F_c is the sum of the frequencies of all classes lower than the median class,
 f_m is the frequency of the median class.

Empirical Relation Between Mean, Median, and Mode

$$\text{Mean-Mode} = 3 \, (\text{Mean-Median})$$

Quartiles

a) If the data is arranged in ascending order of magnitude, the jth quartile Q_j, $j = 1$, 2, or 3, is given by the $\dfrac{j(n+1)}{4}$ th value. It may be necessary to interpolate between successive values.

b) The jth quartile Q_j, $j = 1$, 2, or 3, is obtained from formula $b)$ for the median by counting $\dfrac{jn}{4}$ cases starting at the bottom of the distribution.

Deciles

a) If the sample is arranged in ascending order of magnitude, the jth decile D_j, $j = 1, 2, \ldots$, or 9, is given by the $\dfrac{j(n+1)}{10}$ th value. It may be necessary to interpolate between successive values.

b) The jth decile D_j, $j = 1, 2, \ldots$, or 9, is obtained from formula $b)$ for the median by counting $\dfrac{jn}{10}$ cases starting at the bottom of the distribution.

Percentiles

a) If the sample is arranged in ascending order of magnitude, the jth percentile P_j, $j = 1, 2, \ldots$, or 99 is given by the $\dfrac{j(n+1)}{100}$ th value. It may be necessary to interpolate between successive values.

b) The jth percentile P_j, $j = 1, 2, \ldots$, or 99, is obtained from formulas $b)$ for the median by counting $\dfrac{jn}{100}$ cases starting at the bottom of the distribution.

Mean Deviation

a) $\text{M.D.} = \dfrac{1}{n} \sum\limits_{i=1}^{n} |x_i - \bar{x}|$

or

$$\text{M.D.} = \frac{1}{n} \sum_{i=1}^{n} |x_i - M_d|$$

where $\bar{x}$ is the mean and M_d is the median of the sample.

b) $\text{M.D.} = \dfrac{1}{n} \sum\limits_{i=1}^{k} f_i |x_i - \bar{x}|$

or

$$\text{M.D.} = \frac{1}{n} \sum_{i=1}^{k} f_i |x_i - M_d|$$

where $\bar{x}$ is the mean and M_d the median of the sample.

Standard Deviation

a) $s = \sqrt{\dfrac{\sum\limits_{i=1}^{n}(x_i - \bar{x})^2}{n - 1}}$, where $\bar{x}$ is the mean of the sample.

For computational purposes,

$$s = \sqrt{\frac{\sum\limits_{i=1}^{n} x_i^2 - n\bar{x}^2}{n - 1}}$$

$$s = \sqrt{\frac{n\sum\limits_{i=1}^{n} x_i^2 - \left(\sum\limits_{i=1}^{n} x_i\right)^2}{n(n - 1)}}$$

b) $s = \sqrt{\dfrac{\sum\limits_{i=1}^{k} f_i(x_i - \bar{x})^2}{n - 1}}$, where $\bar{x}$ is the mean of the sample.

For computational purposes

$$s = \sqrt{\frac{\sum\limits_{i=1}^{k} f_i x_i^2 - n\bar{x}^2}{n - 1}}$$

$$s = \sqrt{\frac{n\sum\limits_{i=1}^{k} f_i x_i^2 - \left(\sum\limits_{i=1}^{k} f_i x_i\right)^2}{n(n - 1)}}$$

If data is coded,

$$s = c\sqrt{\frac{n\sum\limits_{i=1}^{k} f_i u_i^2 - \left(\sum\limits_{i=1}^{k} f_i u_i\right)^2}{n(n - 1)}}$$

Variance

The variance is the square of the standard deviation.

Range

The range of a set of values is the difference between the largest and smallest values in the set.

Root Mean Square

a) R.M.S. $= \dfrac{1}{n}\sum\limits_{i=1}^{n} x_i^2$

b) R.M.S. $= \dfrac{1}{n}\sum\limits_{i=1}^{k} f_i x_i^2$

Interquartile Range

$$Q_3 - Q_1,$$

where Q_1 and Q_3 are the first and third quartiles.

Quartile Deviation (Semi-Interquartile Range)

$$\frac{Q_3 - Q_1}{2},$$

where Q_1 and Q_3 are the first and third quartiles.

Coefficient of Variation

$$V = \frac{100s}{\bar{x}},$$

where $\bar{x}$ is the mean and s the standard deviation of the sample.

Coefficient of Quartile Variation

$$V = 100 \frac{Q_3 - Q_1}{Q_3 + Q_1},$$

where Q_1 and Q_3 are the first and third quartiles.

Standardized Variable (Standard Scores)

$$z = \frac{x_i - \bar{x}}{s},$$

where $\bar{x}$ is the mean and s the standard deviation of the sample.

Moments

    a) The rth moment about the origin is given by

$$m_r' = \frac{1}{n} \sum_{i=1}^{n} x_i^r$$

The rth moment about the mean $\bar{x}$ is given by

$$m_r = \frac{1}{n} \sum_{i=1}^{n} (x_i - \bar{x})^r$$

If $\sum_{i=1}^{n} (x_i - \bar{x})^r$ is expanded by use of the binomial theorem, moments about the mean may be expressed in terms of moments about the origin.

    b) The rth moment about the origin is given by

$$m_r' = \frac{1}{n} \sum_{i=1}^{k} f_i x_i^r$$

The rth moment about the mean $\bar{x}$ is given by

$$m_r = \frac{1}{n} \sum_{i=1}^{k} f_i (x_i - \bar{x})^r$$

If $\sum_{i=1}^{k} f_i(x_i - \bar{x})^r$ is expanded by use of the binomial theorem, moments about the mean may be expressed in terms of moments about the origin.

If data is coded

$$m_r' = c^r \frac{\sum_{i=1}^{k} f_i u_i^r}{n}$$

Coefficient of Skewness

$$\alpha_3 = \frac{m_3}{(m_2)^{3/2}},$$

where m_2 and m_3 are the second and third moments about the mean of the sample.

Coefficient of Momental Skewness

$$\frac{\alpha_3}{2} = \frac{m_3}{2(m_2)^{3/2}},$$

where m_2 and m_3 are the second and third moments about the mean of the sample.

Pearson's First Coefficient of Skewness

$$S_{k_1} = \frac{3(\bar{x} - M_o)}{s},$$

where $\bar{x}$ is the mean, M_o the mode, and s the standard deviation of the sample.

Pearson's Second Coefficient of Skewness

$$S_{k_2} = \frac{3(\bar{x} - M_d)}{s},$$

where $\bar{x}$ is the mean, M_d the median, and s the standard deviation of the sample.

Quartile Coefficient of Skewness

$$S_{kq} = \frac{Q_3 - 2Q_2 + Q_1}{Q_3 - Q_1},$$

where Q_1, Q_2, and Q_3 are the first, second, and third quartiles.

Coefficient of Kurtosis

$$\alpha_4 = \frac{m_4}{(m_2)^2},$$

where m_2 and m_4 are the second and fourth moments about the mean of the sample.

Coefficient of Excess (Kurtosis)

$$\alpha_4 - 3 = \frac{m_4}{(m_2)^2} - 3,$$

where m_2 and m_4 are the second and fourth moments about the mean of the sample.

Sheppards Corrections for Grouping

Let all class intervals be of equal length c. If the distribution of x has a high order of contact with the x-axis at both tails, (i.e., if the distribution of x has tails which are very nearly tangent to the x-axis), one may improve the grouped data approximation to the variance by adding Sheppard's correction $-\dfrac{c^2}{12}$. Thus

$$\text{corrected variance} = \text{grouped data variance} - \frac{c^2}{12}$$

Analogous corrections for grouped data sample moments

$$m_r' = \frac{1}{n} \sum_{i=1}^{k} f_i x_i^r \qquad \text{and} \qquad m_r = \frac{1}{n} \sum_{i=1}^{k} f_i (x_i - \bar{x})^r$$

yield improved estimates m_{r_e}' and m_{r_e} given by

$$m_{1_e}' = m_1' \qquad\qquad\qquad m_{1_e} = m_1$$

$$m_{2_e}' = m_2' - \frac{c^2}{12} \qquad\qquad m_{2_e} = m_2 - \frac{c^2}{12}$$

$$m_{3_e}' = m_3' - \frac{c^2}{4} m_1' \qquad\qquad m_{3_e} = m_3$$

$$m_{4_e}' = m_4' - \frac{c^2}{2} m_1' + \frac{7c^4}{240} \qquad m_{4_e} = m_4 - \frac{c^2}{2} m_2 + \frac{7c^4}{240}$$

Curve Fitting, Regression, and Correlation

The following formulas apply to a set of n ordered pairs $\{(x_i, y_i)\}$, $i = 1, 2, \ldots, n$. The assumptions of normal regression analysis are that the x's are fixed variables, and the y's are independent random variables having normal distributions with common variance σ^2. The assumptions of normal correlation analysis are that $\{(x_i, y_i)\}$ constitute a random sample from a bivariate normal population.

Curve Fitting

   1. Polynomial Function

$$y = b_0 + b_1 x + b_2 x^2 + \cdots + b_m x^m$$

For a polynomial function fit by the method of least squares, the values of $b_0, b_1, \ldots, b_m$ are obtained by solving the system of $m + 1$ normal equations

$$nb_0 + b_1 \Sigma x_i + b_2 \Sigma x_i^2 + \cdots + b_m \Sigma x_i^m = \Sigma y_i$$
$$b_0 \Sigma x_i + b_1 \Sigma x_i^2 + b_2 \Sigma x_i^3 + \cdots + b_m \Sigma x_i^{m+1} = \Sigma x_i y_i$$
$$\cdots\cdots\cdots\cdots\cdots\cdots\cdots\cdots\cdots\cdots\cdots\cdots\cdots\cdots$$
$$b_0 \Sigma x_i^m + b_1 \Sigma x_i^{m+1} + b_2 \Sigma x_i^{m+2} + \cdots + b_m \Sigma x_i^{2m} = \Sigma x_i^m y_i$$

   2. Straight Line

$$y = b_0 + b_1 x$$

For a straight line fit by the method of least squares, the values b_0 and b_1 are obtained by solving the normal equations

$$nb_0 + b_1 \Sigma x_i = \Sigma y_i$$
$$b_0 \Sigma x_i + b_1 \Sigma x_i^2 = \Sigma x_i y_i$$

The solutions of these normal equations are

$$b_1 = \frac{n\Sigma x_i y_i - (\Sigma x_i)(\Sigma y_i)}{n\Sigma x_i^2 - (\Sigma x_i)^2}$$

$$b_0 = \frac{\Sigma y_i}{n} - b_1 \frac{\Sigma x_i}{n} = \bar{y} - b_1 \bar{x}$$

3. Exponential Curve

$$y = ab^x$$

or

$$\log y = \log a + (\log b)x$$

For an exponential curve fit by the method of least squares, the values $\log a$ and $\log b$ are obtained by fitting a straight line to the set of ordered pairs $\{(x_i, \log y_i)\}$.

4. Power Function

$$y = ax^b$$

or

$$\log y = \log a + b \log x$$

For a power function fit by the method of least squares, the values $\log a$ and b are obtained by fitting a straight line to the set or ordered pairs $\{(\log x_i, \log y_i)\}$.

Regression and Correlation

1. Simple Linear Regression.

For a regression of y on x

$$E(y/x) = \beta_0 + \beta_1 x,$$

where $E(y/x)$ is the mean of the distribution of y for a given x.

Standard Error of Estimate

$$s_e = \sqrt{\frac{\Sigma[y_i - (b_0 + b_1 x_i)]^2}{n - 2}},$$

where b_0 and b_1 are given by

$$b_1 = \frac{n\Sigma x_i y_i - (\Sigma x_i)(\Sigma y_i)}{n\Sigma x_i^2 - (\Sigma x_i)^2}$$

$$b_0 = \frac{\Sigma y_i}{n} - b_1 \frac{\Sigma x_i}{n} = \bar{y} - b_1\bar{x}$$

2. Correlation.

An estimate of the population correlation coefficient ρ is given by

$$r = \frac{\Sigma(x_i - \bar{x})(y_i - \bar{y})}{\sqrt{[\Sigma(x_i - \bar{x})^2][\Sigma(y_i - \bar{y})^2]}}$$

or by the computing formula

$$r = \frac{n\Sigma x_i y_i - (\Sigma x_i)(\Sigma y_i)}{\sqrt{[n\Sigma x_i^2 - (\Sigma x_i)^2][n\Sigma y_i^2 - (\Sigma y_i)]^2}}$$

For grouped data

$$r = \frac{n\Sigma f x_i y_i - (\Sigma f_x x_i)(\Sigma f_y y_i)}{\sqrt{[n\Sigma f_x x_i^2 - (\Sigma f_x x_i)^2][n\Sigma f_y y_i^2 - (\Sigma f_y y_i)^2]}}$$

where f_x and f_y denote the frequencies corresponding to the class marks x and y, and f denotes the frequency of the corresponding cell of the correlation table.

If the data is coded

$$r = \frac{n\Sigma f uv - (\Sigma f_u u)(\Sigma f_v v)}{\sqrt{[n\Sigma f_u u^2 - (\Sigma f_u u)^2][n\Sigma f_v v^2 - (\Sigma f_v v)^2]}}$$

where the u's and v's are coded class marks. The frequencies f_u and f_v are defined analogous to f_x and f_y.

Probability and Statistics
PROBABILITY

Definitions

A sample space S associated with an experiment is a set S of elements such that any outcome of the experiment corresponds to one and only one element of the set. An event E is a subset of a sample space S. An element in a sample space is called a sample point or a simple event (Unit subset of S).

Definition of Probability

If an experiment can occur in n mutually exclusive and equally likely ways, and if exactly m of these ways correspond to an event E, then the probability of E is given by

$$P(E) = \frac{m}{n}.$$

If E is a subset of S, and if to each unit subset of S, a non-negative number, called its probability, is assigned, and if E is the union of two or more different simple events, then the probability of E, denoted by $P(E)$, is the sum of the probabilities of those simple events whose union is E.

Marginal and Conditional Probability

Suppose a sample space S is partioned into rs disjoint subsets where the general subset is denoted by $E_i \cap F_j$. Then the marginal probability of E_i is defined as

$$P(E_i) = \sum_{j=1}^{s} P(E_i \cap F_j)$$

and the marginal probability of F_j is defined as

$$P(F_j) = \sum_{i=1}^{r} P(E_i \cap F_j) .$$

The conditional probability of E_i, given that F_j has occurred, is defined as

$$P(E_i/F_j) = \frac{P(E_i \cap F_j)}{P(F_j)} , \qquad P(F_j) \neq 0$$

and that of F_j, given that E_i has occurred, is defined as

$$P(F_j/E_i) = \frac{P(E_i \cap F_j)}{P(E_i)} , \qquad P(E_i) \neq 0 .$$

Probability Theorems

1. If ϕ is the null set, $P(\phi) = 0$.
2. If S is the sample space, $P(S) = 1$.
3. If E and F are two events

$$P(E \cup F) = P(E) + P(F) - P(E \cap F).$$

4. If E and F are mutually exclusive events,

$$P(E \cup F) = P(E) + P(F).$$

5. If E and E' are complementary events,

$$P(E) = 1 - P(E').$$

6. The conditional probability of an event E, given an event F, is denoted by $P(E/F)$ and is defined as

$$P(E/F) = \frac{P(E \cap F)}{P(F)},$$

where $P(F) \neq 0$.

7. Two events E and F are said to be independent if and only if

$$P(E \cap F) = P(E) \cdot P(F).$$

E is said to be statistically independent of F if $P(E/F) = P(E)$ and $P(F/E) = P(F)$.

8. The events $E_1, E_2, \ldots, E_n$ are called mutually independent for all combinations if and only if every combination of these events taken any number at a time is independent.

9. *Bayes Theorem.*

If $E_1, E_2, \ldots, E_n$ are n mutually exclusive events whose union is the sample space S, and E is any arbitrary event of S such that $P(E) \neq 0$, then

$$P(E_k/E) = \frac{P(E_k) \cdot P(E/E_k)}{\displaystyle\sum_{j=1}^{n} [P(E_j) \cdot P(E/E_j)]}$$

EXAMPLE: Two unbiased six sided dice, one red and one green, are tossed and the number of dots appearing on their upper faces is observed.

The sample space S consists of 36 elements, i.e.

$$S = \{(1, 1), (1, 2), \ldots, (6, 5), (6, 6)\} \ .$$

1. What is the probability of throwing a seven, denoted by the event A?

$$A = \{(1, 6)\} \cup \{(2, 5)\} \cup \{(3, 4)\} \cup \{(4, 3)\} \cup \{(5, 2)\} \cup \{(6, 1)\}$$
$$P(A) = \tfrac{1}{36} + \tfrac{1}{36} + \tfrac{1}{36} + \tfrac{1}{36} + \tfrac{1}{36} + \tfrac{1}{36} = \tfrac{1}{6}$$

2. What is the probability of throwing a seven or a ten? Denote by A the event "throwing a 7" and by B the event "throwing a ten" .

$$P(A) = \tfrac{1}{6} \qquad P(A \cup B) = P(A) + P(B)$$
$$P(B) = \tfrac{1}{12} \qquad \qquad = \tfrac{1}{6} + \tfrac{1}{12}$$
$$\qquad \qquad \qquad = \tfrac{1}{4}$$

3. What is the probability that the red die shows a number less than or equal to three and the green die shows a number greater than or equal to five? Denote by C the event "red die shows number ≤ 3" and by D the event "green die shows number ≥ 5" .

$$C \cap D = \{(1, 5), (2, 5), (3, 5), (1, 6), (2, 6), (3, 6)\}$$
$$P(C \cap D) = \tfrac{6}{36} = \tfrac{1}{6}$$

Note:
$$P(C) = \tfrac{18}{36} = \tfrac{1}{2}$$
$$P(D) = \tfrac{12}{36} = \tfrac{1}{3}$$
$$P(C) \cdot P(D) = \tfrac{1}{2} \cdot \tfrac{1}{3} = \tfrac{1}{6}$$

Thus $P(C \cap D) = P(C) \cdot P(D)$ and events C and D are independent.

4. What is the probability that the green die shows a one, given that the sum of the numbers on the two dice is less than four? Denote by E the event "green die shows 1" and by F the event "sum of numbers on dice <4" .

$$E = \{(1, 1), (1, 2), (1, 3), (1, 4), (1, 5), (1, 6)\}$$
$$F = \{(1, 1), (1, 2), (2, 1)\}$$
$$E \cap F = \{(1, 1), (1, 2)\}$$
$$P(E/F) = \frac{P(E \cap F)}{P(F)} = \frac{\frac{2}{36}}{\frac{3}{36}} = \frac{2}{3}$$

5. What is the probability that the sum of the numbers on the two dice is not seven?

$$P(A) = \tfrac{1}{6}$$
$$P(A') = 1 - \tfrac{1}{6} = \tfrac{5}{6}$$

Random Variable

A function whose domain is a sample space S and whose range is some set of real numbers is called a random variable, denoted by **X**. The function **X** transforms sample points of S into points on the x-axis. **X** will be called a discrete random variable if it is a random variable that assumes only a finite or denumerable number of values on the x-axis. **X** will be called a continuous random variable if it assumes a continuum of values on the x-axis.

Probability Function (Discrete Case)

The random variable **X** will be called a discrete random variable if there exists a function f such that $f(x_i) \geq 0$ and $\sum_i f(x_i) = 1$ for $i = 1, 2, 3, \ldots$ and such that for any event E,

$$P(E) = P[\mathbf{X} \text{ is in } E] = \sum_E f(x)$$

where $\sum_E$ means sum $f(x)$ over those values x_i that are in E and where $f(x) = P[\mathbf{X} = x]$. The probability that the value of **X** is some real number x, is given by $f(x) = P[\mathbf{X} = x]$, where f is called the probability function of the random variable **X**.

Cumulative Distribution Function (Discrete Case)

The probability that the value of a random variable **X** is less than or equal to some real number x is defined as

$$F(x) = P(\mathbf{X} \leq x)$$
$$= \Sigma f(x_i), \qquad -\infty < x < \infty,$$

where the summation extends over those values of i such that $x_i \leq x$.

Probability Density (Continuous Case)

The random variable **X** will be called a continuous random variable if there exists a function f such that $f(x) \geq 0$ and $\int_{-\infty}^{\infty} f(x)\, dx = 1$ for all x in interval $-\infty < x < \infty$ and such that for any event E

$$P(E) = P(\mathbf{X} \text{ is in } E) = \int_E f(x)\, dx.$$

$f(x)$ is called the probability density of the random variable **X**. The probability that **X** assumes any given value of x is equal to zero and the probability that it assumes a value on the interval from a to b, including or excluding either end point, is equal to

$$\int_a^b f(x)\,dx.$$

Cumulative Distribution Function (Continuous Case)

The probability that the value of a random variable **X** is less than or equal to some real number x is defined as

$$F(x) = P(\mathbf{X} \le x), \quad -\infty < x < \infty$$
$$= \int_{-\infty}^x f(x)\,dx.$$

From the cumulative distribution, the density, if it exists, can be found from

$$f(x) = \frac{dF(x)}{dx}.$$

From the cumulative distribution

$$P(a \le \mathbf{X} \le b) = P(\mathbf{X} \le b) - P(\mathbf{X} \le a)$$
$$= F(b) - F(a)$$

Mathematical Expectation

A. Expected Value

Let **X** be a random variable with density $f(x)$. Then the expected value of **X**, $E(\mathbf{X})$, is defined to be

$$E(\mathbf{X}) = \sum_x x f(x)$$

if **X** is discrete and

$$E(\mathbf{X}) = \int_{-\infty}^\infty x f(x)\,dx$$

if **X** is continuous. The expected value of a function g of a random variable **X** is defined as

$$E[g(\mathbf{X})] = \sum_x g(x) \cdot f(x)$$

if **X** is discrete and

$$E[g(\mathbf{X})] = \int_{-\infty}^\infty g(x) \cdot f(x)\,dx$$

if **X** is continuous.

Theorems

1. $E[a\mathbf{X} + b\mathbf{Y}] = aE(\mathbf{X}) + bE(\mathbf{Y})$
2. $E[\mathbf{X} \cdot \mathbf{Y}] = E(\mathbf{X}) \cdot E(\mathbf{Y})$ if **X** and **Y** are statistically independent.

B. Moments

a. *Moments About the Origin.* The moments about the origin of a probability distribution are the expected values of the random variable which has the given distribution. The rth moment of **X**, usually denoted by μ'_r, is defined as

$$\mu'_r = E[\mathbf{X}^r] = \sum_x x^r f(x)$$

if **X** is discrete and

$$\mu'_r = E[X^r] = \int_{-\infty}^{\infty} x^r f(x)\, dx$$

if **X** is continuous.

The first moment, μ'_1, is called the mean of the random variable **X** and is usually denoted by μ.

b. Moments About the Mean. The rth moment about the mean, usually denoted by μ_r, is defined as

$$\mu_r = E[(X - \mu)^r] = \sum_x (x - \mu)^r f(x)$$

if **X** is discrete and

$$\mu_r = E[(X - \mu)^r] = \int_{-\infty}^{\infty} (x - \mu)^r f(x)\, dx$$

if **X** is continuous.

The second moment about the mean, μ_2, is given by

$$\mu_2 = E[(X - \mu)^2] = \mu'_2 - \mu^2$$

and is called the variance of the random variable **X**, and is denoted by σ^2. The square root of the variance, σ, is called the standard deviation.

Theorems

1. $\sigma^2_{cX} = c^2 \sigma^2_X$
2. $\sigma^2_{c+X} = \sigma^2_X$
3. $\sigma^2_{aX+b} = a^2 \sigma^2_X$

c. Factorial Moments. The rth factorial moment of a probability distribution is defined as

$$\mu'_{(r)} = E[X^{[r]}] = \sum_x x^{[r]} f(x)$$

if **X** is discrete and

$$\mu'_{(r)} = E[X^{[r]}] = \int_{-\infty}^{\infty} x^{[r]} f(x)\, dx$$

if **X** is continuous, where the symbol $x^{[r]}$ denotes the factorial expression

$$x^{[r]} = x(x - 1)(x - 2) \cdots (x - r + 1), \quad r = 1, 2, 3, \ldots$$

C. Generating Functions

a. Moment Generating Functions. The moment generating function (m.g.f.) of the random variable **X** is defined as

$$m_x(t) = E(e^{tX}) = \sum_x e^{tx} f(x)$$

if **X** is discrete and

$$m_x(t) = E(e^{tX}) = \int_{-\infty}^{\infty} e^{tx} f(x)\, dx$$

if **X** is continuous.

$E(e^{tX})$ is the expected value of e^{tX}. If $m_x(t)$ and its derivatives exist, $|t| < h^2$, the rth moment about the origin is

$$\mu'_r = m_x^{(r)}(0), \quad r = 0, 1, 2, \ldots$$

where $m_x^{(r)}(0)$ is the rth derivative of $m_x(t)$ with respect to t, evaluated at $t = 0$. For

$$m_x(t) = E(e^{tX})$$
$$= E\left[1 + Xt + \frac{(Xt)^2}{2!} + \cdots \right]$$
$$= 1 + \mu'_1 t + \mu'_2 \frac{t^2}{2} + \cdots$$

Thus, the moments μ'_r appear as coefficients of $\frac{t^r}{r!}$, and $m_x(t)$ may be regarded as generating the moments ν_r. The moments μ_r may be generated by the generating function

$$M_x(t) = E[e^{t(X-\mu)}] = e^{-\mu t}E(e^{tX}) = e^{-\mu t}m_x(t) \ .$$

   b. Factorial Moment Generating Function. The factorial moment generating function is defined as

$$E(t^X) = \sum_x t^x f(x) \qquad \text{(probability generation function)}$$

if X is discrete and

$$E(t^X) = \int_{-\infty}^{\infty} t^x f(x) \, dx$$

if X is continuous.

   The rth factorial moment is obtained from the factorial moment generating function by differentiating it r times with respect to t and then evaluating the result when $t = 1$.

Theorems

1. If c is a constant, the m.g.f. of $c + X$ is $e^{ct}m_x(t)$.
2. If c is a constant, the m.g.f. of cX is $m_x(ct)$.
3. If $Y = \sum_{i=1}^{n} X_i$, and $m_x(t)$ is the m.g.f. of X_i, where $X_1, \ldots, X_n$ is a random sample from $f(x)$, then the m.g.f. of Y is $[m_x(t)]^n$.

D. CUMULANT GENERATING FUNCTION

   Let $m_x(t)$ be a m.g.f. If $\ln m_x(t)$ can be expanded in the form

$$c(t) = \ln m_x(t) = \kappa_1 t + \kappa_2 \frac{t^2}{2!} + \kappa_3 \frac{t^3}{3!} + \cdots + \kappa_r \frac{t^r}{r!} + \cdots ,$$

then $c(t)$ is called the cumulant generating function (semi-invariant generating function) and κ_r are called the cumulants (semi-invariants) of a distribution.

$$\kappa_r = c^{(r)}(0)$$

where $c^{(r)}(0)$ is the rth derivative of $c(t)$ with respect to t evaluated at $t = 0$.

E. CHARACTERISTIC FUNCTIONS

   The characteristic function of a distribution is defined as

$$\phi(t) = E(e^{itX}) = \sum_x e^{itx} \cdot f(x)$$

if X is discrete and

$$\phi(t) = E(e^{itX}) = \int_{-\infty}^{\infty} e^{itx} \cdot f(x) \, dx$$

if X is continuous.

Here t is a real number, $i^2 = -1$, and $e^{itX} = \cos(tX) + i\sin(tX)$. The characteristic function also generates moments, if they exist for

$$i^r \mu'_r = \phi^{(r)}(0)$$

where $\phi^{(r)}(0)$ is the rth derivative of $\phi(t)$ with respect to t evaluated at $t = 0$.

Multivariate Distributions

A. DISCRETE CASE

The k-dimensional random variable $(X_1, X_2, \ldots, X_k)$ is a k-dimensional discrete random variable if it assumes values only at a finite or denumerable number of points $(x_1, x_2, \ldots, x_k)$. Define

$$P[X_1 = x_1, X_2 = x_2, \ldots, X_k = x_k] = f(x_1, x_2, \ldots, x_k)$$

for every value that the random variable can assume. $f(x_1, x_2, \ldots, x_k)$ is called the joint density of the k-dimensional random variable. If E is any subset of the set of values that the random variable can assume, then

$$P(E) = P[(X_1, X_2, \ldots, X_k) \text{ is in } E] = \sum_E f(x_1, x_2, \ldots, x_k)$$

where the sum is over all those points in E. The cumulative distribution is defined as

$$F(x_1, x_2, \ldots, x_k) = \sum_{x_1} \sum_{x_2} \cdots \sum_{x_k} f(x_1, x_2, \ldots, x_k).$$

B. CONTINUOUS CASE

The k random variables $X_1, X_2, \ldots, X_k$ are said to be jointly distributed if there exists a function f such that $f(x_1, x_2, \ldots, x_k) \geq 0$ for all $-\infty < x_i < \infty$, $i = 1, 2, \ldots, k$ and such that for any event E

$$P(E) = P[(X_1, X_2, \ldots, X_k) \text{ is in } E]$$
$$= \int_E f(x_1, x_2, \ldots, x_k) \, dx_1 \, dx_2 \cdots dx_k.$$

$f(x_1, x_2, \ldots, x_k)$ is called the joint density of the random variables $X_1, X_2, \ldots, X_k$. The cumulative distribution is defined as

$$F(x_1, x_2, \ldots, x_k) = \int_{-\infty}^{x_1} \int_{-\infty}^{x_2} \cdots \int_{-\infty}^{x_k} f(x_1, x_2, \ldots, x_k) \, dx_k \cdots dx_2 \, dx_1 \, .$$

Given the cumulative distribution, the density may be found by

$$f(x_1, x_2, \ldots, x_k) = \frac{\partial}{\partial x_1} \cdot \frac{\partial}{\partial x_2} \cdots \frac{\partial}{\partial x_k} F(x_1, x_2, \ldots, x_k) \, .$$

Moments

The rth moment of X_i, say, is defined as

$$E(X_i^r) = \sum_{x_1} \sum_{x_2} \cdots \sum_{x_k} x_i^r f(x_1, x_2, \ldots, x_k)$$

if the X_i are discrete and

$$E(X_i^r) = \int_{-\infty}^{\infty} \int_{-\infty}^{\infty} \cdots \int_{-\infty}^{\infty} x_i^r f(x_1, x_2, \ldots, x_k) \, dx_k \cdots dx_2 \, dx_1$$

if the X_i are continuous.

Joint moments about the origin are defined as

$$E(X_1^{r_1}X_2^{r_2} \cdots X_k^{r_k})$$

where $r_1 + r_2 + \cdots + r_k$ is the order of the moment.

Joint moments about the mean are defined as

$$E[(X_1 - \mu_1)^{r_1}(X_2 - \mu_2)^{r_2} \cdots (X_k - \mu_k)^{r_k}].$$

Marginal and Conditional Distributions

If the random variables X_1, X_2, . . . , X_k have the joint density function $f(x_1, x_2, \ldots, x_k)$, then the marginal distribution of the subset of the random variables, say, X_1. X_2, . . . , X_p $(p < k)$, is given by

$$g(x_1, x_2, \ldots, x_p) = \sum_{x_{p+1}} \sum_{x_{p+2}} \cdots \sum_{x_k} f(x_1, x_2, \ldots, x_k)$$

if the X's are discrete, and

$$g(x_1, x_2, \ldots, x_p) = \int_{-\infty}^{\infty} \int_{-\infty}^{\infty} \cdots \int_{-\infty}^{\infty} f(x_1, x_2, \ldots, x_k) \, dx_{p+1} \cdots dx_{k-1} \, dx_k$$

if the X's are continuous.

The conditional distribution of a certain subset of the random variables is the joint distribution of this subset under the condition that the remaining variables are given certain values. The conditional distribution of X_1, X_2, . . . , X_p given X_{p+1}, X_{p+2}, . . . , X_k is

$$h(x_1, x_2, \ldots, x_p | x_{p+1}, x_{p+2}, \ldots, x_k) = \frac{f(x_1, x_2, \ldots, x_k)}{g(x_{p+1}, x_{p+2}, \ldots, x_k)}$$

if $g(x_{p+1}, x_{p+2}, \ldots, x_k) \neq 0$.

The variance σ_{ii} of X_i and the covariance σ_{ij} of X_i and X_j are given by

$$\sigma_{ii} = \sigma_i^2 = E[(X_i - \mu_i)^2]$$

and

$$\sigma_{ij} = \rho_{ij}\sigma_i\sigma_j = E[(X_i - \mu_i)(X_j - \mu_j)]$$

where ρ_{ij} is the correlation coefficient and σ_i and σ_j are the standard deviations of X_i and X_j.

A joint m.g.f. is defined as

$$m(t_1, t_2, \ldots, t_k) = E[e^{t_1 X_1 + t_2 X_2 + \cdots + t_k X_k}]$$

if it exists for all values of t_i such that $|t_i| < h^2$.

The rth moment of X_i may be obtained by differentiating the m.g.f. r times with respect to t_i and then evaluating the result when all t's are set equal to zero. Similarly, a joint moment would be found by differentiatins the m.g.f. r_1 times with respect to t_1, . . . , r_k times with respect to t_k, and then evaluating the result when all t's are set equal to zero.

Probability Distributions

A. DISCRETE CASE

1. *Discrete Uniform Distribution.* If the random variable X has a probability function given by

$$P(X = x) = f(x) = \frac{1}{n}, \qquad x = x_1, x_2, \ldots, x_n,$$

then the variable **X** is said to possess a discrete uniform distribution.

Properties

When $x_i = i$ for $i = 1, 2, \ldots$, and n

$$\text{Mean} = \mu = \frac{n + 1}{2}$$

$$\text{Variance} = \sigma^2 = \frac{n^2 - 1}{12}$$

$$\text{Standard Deviation} = \sigma = \sqrt{\frac{n^2 - 1}{12}}$$

$$\text{Moment Generating Function} = m_x(t) = \frac{e^t(1 - e^{nt})}{n(1 - e^t)}$$

2. *Binomial Distribution.* If the random variable **X** has a probability function given by

$$P(\mathbf{X} = x) = f(x) = \binom{n}{x} \theta^x (1 - \theta)^{n-x}, \qquad x = 0, 1, 2, \ldots, n$$

where

$$\binom{n}{x} = \frac{n!}{x!(n - x)!},$$

then the variable **X** is said to possess a binomial distribution. $f(x)$ is the general term of the expansion of $[\theta + (1 - \theta)]^n$.

Properties

$$\text{Mean} = \mu = n\theta$$
$$\text{Variance} = \sigma^2 = n\theta(1 - \theta)$$
$$\text{Standard Deviation} = \sigma = \sqrt{n\theta(1 - \theta)}$$
$$\text{Moment Generating Function} = m_{\mathbf{x}}(t) = [\theta e^t + (1 - \theta)]^n$$

3. *Geometric Distribution.* If the random variable **X** has a probability function given by

$$P(\mathbf{X} = x) = f(x) = \theta(1 - \theta)^{x-1}, \qquad x = 1, 2, 3, \ldots,$$

then the variable **X** is said to possess a geometric distribution.

Properties

$$\text{Mean} = \mu = \frac{1}{\theta}$$

$$\text{Variance} = \sigma^2 = \frac{1 - \theta}{\theta^2}$$

$$\text{Standard Deviation} = \sigma = \sqrt{\frac{1 - \theta}{\theta^2}}$$

$$\text{Moment Generating Function} = m_x(t) = \frac{\theta e^t}{1 - e^t(1 - \theta)}$$

4. *Multinomial Distribution.* If a set of random variables $\mathbf{X}_1, \mathbf{X}_2, \ldots, \mathbf{X}_n$ has a probability function given by

$$P(\mathbf{X}_1 = x_1, \mathbf{X}_2 = x_2, \ldots, \mathbf{X}_n = x_n) = f(x_1, x_2, \ldots, x_n) = \frac{N!}{\prod\limits_{i=1}^{n} x_i!} \prod\limits_{i=1}^{n} \theta_i^{x_i}$$

where x_i are positive integers and each $\theta_i > 0$ for $i = 1, 2, \ldots, n$ and

$$\sum_{i=1}^{n} \theta_i = 1, \qquad \sum_{i=1}^{n} x_i = N,$$

then the joint distribution of $\mathbf{X}_1, \mathbf{X}_2, \ldots, \mathbf{X}_n$ is called the multinomial distribution. $f(x_1, x_2, \ldots, x_n)$ is the general term of the expansion of $(\theta_1 + \theta_2 + \cdots + \theta_n)^N$.

Properties

$$\text{Mean of } \mathbf{X}_i = \mu_i = N\theta_i$$
$$\text{Variance of } \mathbf{X}_i = \sigma_i{}^2 = N\theta_i(1 - \theta_i)$$
$$\text{Covariance of } \mathbf{X}_i \text{ and } \mathbf{X}_j = \sigma_{ij}{}^2 = -N\theta_i\theta_j$$
$$\text{Joint Moment Generating Function} = (\theta_1 e^{t_1} + \cdots + \theta_n e^{t_n})^N$$

5. *Poisson Distribution.* If the random variable $\mathbf{X}$ has a probability function given by

$$P(\mathbf{X} = x) = f(x) = \frac{e^{-\lambda}\lambda^x}{x!}, \qquad \lambda > 0, \, x = 0, 1, \ldots,$$

then the variable $\mathbf{X}$ is said to possess a Poisson distribution.

Properties

$$\text{Mean} = \mu = \lambda$$
$$\text{Variance} = \sigma^2 = \lambda$$
$$\text{Standard Deviation} = \sigma = \sqrt{\lambda}$$
$$\text{Moment Generating Function} = m_x(t) = e^{\lambda(e^t - 1)}$$

6. *Hypergeometric Distribution.* If the random variable $\mathbf{X}$ has a probability function given by

$$P(\mathbf{X} = x) = f(x) = \frac{\binom{k}{x}\binom{N-k}{n-x}}{\binom{N}{n}}, \qquad x = 0, 1, 2, \ldots, [n, k],$$

where $[n, k]$ means the smaller of the two numbers n, k, then the variable $\mathbf{X}$ is said to possess a hypergeometric distribution.

Properties

$$\text{Mean} = \mu = \frac{kn}{N}$$

$$\text{Variance} = \sigma^2 = \frac{k(N-k)n(N-n)}{N^2(N-1)}$$

$$\text{Standard Deviation} = \sigma = \sqrt{\frac{k(N-k)n(N-n)}{N^2(N-1)}}$$

7. *Negative Binomial Distribution.* If the random variable $\mathbf{X}$ has a probability function given by

$$P(\mathbf{X} = x) = f(x) = \binom{x+r-1}{r-1}\theta^r(1-\theta)^x, \qquad x = 0, 1, 2, \ldots;$$

then the variable $\mathbf{X}$ is said to possess a negative binomial distribution, known also as the Pascal or Pólya distribution.

Properties

$$\text{Mean} = \mu = \frac{r}{\theta}$$

$$\text{Variance} = \sigma^2 = \frac{r}{\theta}\left(\frac{1}{\theta} - 1\right) = \frac{r(1-\theta)}{\theta^2}$$

$$\text{Standard Deviation} = \sigma = \sqrt{\frac{r}{\theta}\left(\frac{1}{\theta} - 1\right)} = \sqrt{\frac{r(1 - \theta)}{\theta^2}}$$

$$\text{Moment Generating Function} = m_x(t) = e^{tr}\theta^r[1 - (1 - \theta)e^t]^{-r}$$

B. Continuous Case

1. *Uniform Distribution.* A random variable **X** is said to be distributed as the uniform distribution if the density function is given by

$$f(x) = \frac{1}{\beta - \alpha}, \qquad \alpha < x < \beta,$$

where α and β are parameters with $\alpha < \beta$.

Properties

$$\text{Mean} = \mu = \frac{\alpha + \beta}{2}$$

$$\text{Variance} = \sigma^2 = \frac{(\beta - \alpha)^2}{12}$$

$$\text{Standard Deviation} = \sigma = \sqrt{\frac{(\beta - \alpha)^2}{12}}$$

$$\text{Moment Generating Function} = m_x(t) = \frac{2}{(\beta - \alpha)t}\sin\left[\frac{(\beta - \alpha)t}{2}\right]e^{\frac{\alpha+\beta}{2}t}$$

2. *Normal Distribution.* A random variable **X** is said to be normally distributed if its density function is given by

$$f(x) = \frac{1}{\sqrt{2\pi}\,\sigma}e^{-(x-\mu)^2/2\sigma^2}, \qquad -\infty < x < \infty$$

where μ and σ are parameters, called the mean and the standard deviation or the random variable **X**, respectively.

Properties

$$\text{Mean} = \mu$$
$$\text{Variance} = \sigma^2$$
$$\text{Standard Deviation} = \sigma$$
$$\text{Moment Generating Function} = m_x(t) = e^{t\mu + \frac{\sigma^2 t^2}{2}}$$

Cumulative Distribution

$$F(x) = \int_{-\infty}^{x}\frac{1}{\sqrt{2\pi}\,\sigma}e^{-(x-\mu)^2/2\sigma^2}\,dx$$

Set $y = \dfrac{x - \mu}{\sigma}$ to obtain the cumulative standard normal.

3. *Gamma Distribution.* A random variable **X** is said to be distributed as the gamma distribution if the density function is given by

$$f(x) = \frac{1}{\Gamma(\alpha + 1)\beta^{\alpha+1}}x^\alpha e^{-x/\beta}, \qquad 0 < x < \infty$$

where α and β are parameters with $\alpha > -1$ and $\beta > 0$.

Properties

$$\text{Mean} = \mu = \beta(\alpha + 1)$$
$$\text{Variance} = \sigma^2 = \beta^2(\alpha + 1)$$
$$\text{Standard Deviation} = \sigma = \beta\sqrt{\alpha + 1}$$
$$\text{Moment Generating Function} = m_x(t) = (1 - \beta t)^{-(\alpha+1)}, \qquad t < \frac{1}{\beta}.$$

4. *Exponential Distribution.* A random variable **X** is said to be distributed as the exponential distribution if the density function is given by

$$f(x) = \frac{1}{\theta} e^{-x/\theta}, \qquad x > 0$$

where θ is a parameter and $\theta > 0$.

Properties

$$\text{Mean} = \mu = \theta$$
$$\text{Variance} = \sigma^2 = \theta^2$$
$$\text{Standard Deviation} = \sigma = \sqrt{\theta^2}$$
$$\text{Moment Generating Function} = m_x(t) = (1 - \theta t)^{-1}$$

5. *Beta Distribution.* A random variable **X** is said to be distributed as the beta distribution if the density function is given by

$$f(x) = \frac{\Gamma(\alpha + \beta + 2)}{\Gamma(\alpha + 1)\Gamma(\beta + 1)} x^\alpha (1 - x)^\beta, \qquad 0 < x < 1$$

where α and β are parameters with $\alpha > -1$ and $\beta > -1$.

Properties

$$\text{Mean} = \mu = \frac{\alpha + 1}{\alpha + \beta + 2}$$
$$\text{Variance} = \sigma^2 = \frac{(\alpha + 1)(\beta + 1)}{(\alpha + \beta + 2)^2(\alpha + \beta + 3)}$$
$$r\text{th moment about the origin} = \nu_r = \frac{\Gamma(\alpha + \beta + 2)\Gamma(\alpha + r + 1)}{\Gamma(\alpha + \beta + r + 2)\Gamma(\alpha + 1)}.$$

Sampling Distributions

Population—A finite or infinite set of elements of a random variable **X**.

Random Sample—If the random variables $\mathbf{X}_1, \mathbf{X}_2, \ldots, \mathbf{X}_n$ have a joint density,

$$g(x_1, x_2, \ldots, x_n) = f(x_1)f(x_2) \cdots f(x_n)$$

where the density of each $\mathbf{X}_i$ is $f(x)$, then $\mathbf{X}_1, \mathbf{X}_2, \ldots, \mathbf{X}_n$ is said to be a random sample of size n from the population with density $f(x)$.

Sampling Distributions

A random sample is selected from a population in which the form of the probability function is known, and from the joint density of the random variables a distribution, called the sampling distribution, of a function of the random variables is derived.

1. *Chi-Square Distribution.* If $\mathbf{Y}_1, \mathbf{Y}_2, \ldots, \mathbf{Y}_n$ are normally and independently distributed with mean 0 and variance 1, then

$$\chi^2 = \sum_{i=1}^{n} \mathbf{Y}_i^2$$

is distributed as Chi-Square (χ^2) with n degrees of freedom. The density function is given by

$$f(\chi^2) = \frac{(\chi^2)^{\frac{1}{2}(n-2)}}{2^{\frac{n}{2}}\Gamma\left(\frac{n}{2}\right)} e^{-\chi^2/2}, \qquad 0 < \chi^2 < \infty .$$

Properties

$$\text{Mean} = \mu = n$$
$$\text{Variance} = \sigma^2 = 2n$$

Reproductive Property of χ^2 - Distribution

If $\chi_1^2, \chi_2^2, \ldots, \chi_k^2$ are independently distributed according to χ^2 - distributions with $n_1, n_2, \ldots, n_k$ degrees of freedom, respectively, then $\sum_{j=1}^{k} \chi_j^2$ is distributed according to a χ^2 - distribution with $n = \sum_{j=1}^{k} n_j$ degrees of freedom.

2. *Snedecor's F-Distribution.* If a random variable X is distributed as χ^2 with m degrees of freedom (χ_m^2) and a random variable Y is distributed as χ^2 with n degrees of freedom (χ_n^2) and if X and Y are independent, then $F = \dfrac{X/m}{Y/n}$ is distributed as Snedecor's F with m and n degrees of freedom, denoted by $F(m, n)$. The density function of the F-distribution is given by

$$f(F) = \frac{\Gamma\left(\dfrac{m+n}{2}\right)\left(\dfrac{m}{n}\right)^{m/2} F^{(m-2)/2}}{\Gamma\left(\dfrac{m}{2}\right)\Gamma\left(\dfrac{n}{2}\right)\left(1 + \dfrac{m}{n}F\right)^{(m+n)/2}}, \qquad 0 < F < \infty.$$

Properties

$$\text{Mean} = \mu = \frac{n}{n-2}, \qquad n > 2$$
$$\text{Variance} = \sigma^2 = \frac{2n^2(m+n-2)}{m(n-2)^2(n-4)}, \qquad n > 4 .$$

The transformation $w = \dfrac{mF/n}{1 + \dfrac{mF}{n}}$ transforms the F-density into a Beta density.

3. *Student's t-Distribution.* If a random variable X is normally distributed with mean 0 and variance σ^2, and if Y^2/σ^2 is distributed as χ^2 with n degrees of freedom and if X and Y are independent, then

$$t = \frac{X\sqrt{n}}{Y}$$

is distributed as Student's t with n degrees of freedom. The density function is given by

$$f(t) = \frac{\Gamma\left(\dfrac{n+1}{2}\right)}{\sqrt{n\pi}\,\Gamma\left(\dfrac{n}{2}\right)\left(1 + \dfrac{t^2}{n}\right)^{\frac{1}{2}(n+1)}}, \qquad -\infty < t < \infty .$$

Properties

$$\text{Mean} = \mu = 0$$
$$\text{Variance} = \sigma^2 = \frac{n}{n-2}, \qquad n > 2 .$$

THE NORMAL PROBABILITY FUNCTION
AND RELATED FUNCTIONS

This table gives values of:

a) $f(x)$ = the probability density of a standardized random variable

$$= \frac{1}{\sqrt{2\pi}} e^{-\frac{1}{2}x^2}$$

For negative values of x, one uses the fact that $f(-x) = f(x)$.

b) $F(x)$ = the cumulative distribution function of a standardized normal random variable

$$= \int_{-\infty}^{x} \frac{1}{\sqrt{2\pi}} e^{-\frac{1}{2}t^2} \, dt$$

For negative values of x, one uses the relationship $F(-x) = 1 - F(x)$. Values of x corresponding to a few special values of $F(x)$ are given in a separate table following the main table.

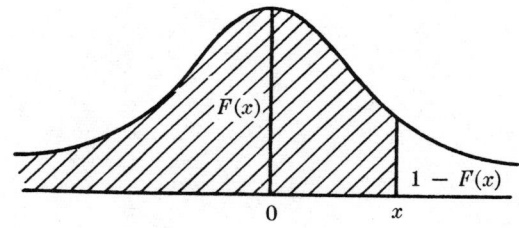

c) $f'(x)$ = the first derivative of $f(x)$ with respect to x

$$= -\frac{x}{\sqrt{2\pi}} e^{-\frac{1}{2}x^2} = -xf(x)$$

d) $f''(x)$ = the second derivative of $f(x)$ with respect to x

$$= \frac{(x^2 - 1)}{\sqrt{2\pi}} e^{-\frac{1}{2}x^2} = (x^2 - 1)f(x)$$

e) $f'''(x)$ = the third derivative of $f(x)$ with respect to x

$$= \frac{3x - x^3}{\sqrt{2\pi}} e^{-\frac{1}{2}x^2} = (3x - x^3)f(x)$$

f) $f^{iv}(x)$ = the fourth derivative of $f(x)$ with respect to x

$$= \frac{x^4 - 6x^2 + 3}{\sqrt{2\pi}} e^{-\frac{1}{2}x^2} = (x^4 - 6x^2 + 3)f(x)$$

579

THE NORMAL PROBABILITY FUNCTION AND
RELATED FUNCTIONS (Continued)

It should be noted that other probability integrals can be evaluated by the use of these tables. For example,

$$\int_0^x f(t)dt = \tfrac{1}{2} \, \text{erf}\left(\frac{x}{\sqrt{2}}\right),$$

where $\text{erf}\left(\dfrac{x}{\sqrt{2}}\right)$ represents the error function associated with the normal curve.

To evaluate erf (2.3) one proceeds as follows: Since $\dfrac{x}{\sqrt{2}} = 2.3$, one finds $x = (2.3)(\sqrt{2}) = 3.25$. In the entry opposite $x = 3.25$, the value 0.9994 is given. Subtracting 0.5000 from the tabular value, one finds the value 0.4994. Thus erf (2.3) = 2(0.4994) = 0.9988.

NORMAL PROBABILITY FUNCTION AND RELATED FUNCTIONS (Continued)

x	$F(x)$	$1 - F(x)$	$f(x)$	$f'(x)$	$f''(x)$	$f'''(x)$	$f^{iv}(x)$
.00	.5000	.5000	.3989	− .0000	− .3989	.0000	1.1968
.01	.5040	.4960	.3989	− .0040	− .3989	.0120	1.1965
.02	.5080	.4920	.3989	− .0080	− .3987	.0239	1.1956
.03	.5120	.4880	.3988	− .0120	− .3984	.0359	1.1941
.04	.5160	.4840	.3986	· − .0159	− .3980	.0478	1.1920
.05	.5199	.4801	.3984	− .0199	− .3975	.0597	1.1894
.06	.5239	.4761	.3982	− .0239	− .3968	.0716	1.1861
.07	.5279	.4721	.3980	− .0279	− .3960	.0834	1.1822
.08	.5319	.4681	.3977	− .0318	− .3951	.0952	1.1778
.09	.5359	.4641	.3973	− .0358	− .3941	.1070	1.1727
.10	.5398	.4602	.3970	− .0397	− .3930	.1187	1.1671
.11	.5438	.4562	.3965	− .0436	− .3917	.1303	1.1609
.12	.5478	.4522	.3961	− .0475	− .3904	.1419	1.1541
.13	.5517	.4483	.3956	− .0514	− .3889	.1534	1.1468
.14	.5557	.4443	.3951	− .0553	− .3873	.1648	1.1389
.15	.5596	.4404	.3945	− .0592	− .3856	.1762	1.1304
.16	.5636	.4364	.3939	− .0630	− .3838	.1874	1.1214
.17	.5675	.4325	.3932	− .0668	− .3819	.1986	1.1118
.18	.5714	.4286	.3925	− .0707	− .3798	.2097	1.1017
.19	.5753	.4247	.3918	− .0744	− .3777	.2206	1.0911
.20	.5793	.4207	.3910	− .0782	− .3754	.2315	1.0799
.21	.5832	.4168	.3902	− .0820	− .3730	.2422	1.0682
.22	.5871	.4129	.3894	− .0857	− .3706	.2529	1.0560
.23	.5910	.4090	.3885	− .0894	− .3680	.2634	1.0434
.24	.5948	.4052	.3876	− .0930	− .3653	.2737	1.0302
.25	.5987	.4013	.3867	− .0967	− .3625	.2840	1.0165
.26	.6026	.3974	.3857	− .1003	− .3596	.2941	1.0024
.27	.6064	.3936	.3847	− .1039	− .3566	.3040	0.9878
.28	.6103	.3897	.3836	− .1074	− .3535	.3138	0.9727
.29	.6141	.3859	.3825	− .1109	− .3504	.3235	0.9572
.30	.6179	.3821	.3814	− .1144	− .3471	.3330	0.9413
.31	.6217	.3783	.3802	− .1179	− .3437	.3423	0.9250
.32	.6255	.3745	.3790	− .1213	− .3402	.3515	0.9082
.33	.6293	.3707	.3778	− .1247	− .3367	.3605	0.8910
.34	.6331	.3669	.3765	− .1280	− .3330	.3693	0.8735
.35	.6368	.3632	.3752	− .1313	− .3293	.3779	0.8556
.36	.6406	.3594	.3739	− .1346	− .3255	.3864	0.8373
.37	.6443	.3557	.3726	− .1378	− .3216	.3947	0.8186
.38	.6480	.3520	.3712	− .1410	− .3176	.4028	0.7996
.39	.6517	.3483	.3697	− .1442	− .3135	.4107	0.7803
.40	.6554	.3446	.3683	− .1473	− .3094	.4184	0.7607
.41	.6591	.3409	.3668	− .1504	− .3051	.4259	0.7408
.42	.6628	.3372	.3653	− .1534	− .3008	.4332	0.7206
.43	.6664	.3336	.3637	− .1564	− .2965	.4403	0.7001
.44	.6700	.3300	.3621	− .1593	− .2920	.4472	0.6793
.45	.6736	.3264	.3605	− .1622	− .2875	.4539	0.6583
.46	.6772	.3228	.3589	− .1651	− .2830	.4603	0.6371
.47	.6808	.3192	.3572	− .1679	− .2783	.4666	0.6156
.48	.6844	.3156	.3555	− .1707	− .2736	.4727	0.5940
.49	.6879	.3121	.3538	− .1734	− .2689	.4785	0.5721
.50	.6915	.3085	.3521	− .1760	− .2641	.4841	0.5501

NORMAL PROBABILITY FUNCTION AND RELATED FUNCTIONS (Continued)

x	$F(x)$	$1 - F(x)$	$f(x)$	$f'(x)$	$f''(x)$	$f'''(x)$	$f^{iv}(x)$
.50	.6915	.3085	.3521	$-.1760$	$-.2641$	.4841	.5501
.51	.6950	.3050	.3503	$-.1787$	$-.2592$	.4895	.5279
.52	.6985	.3015	.3485	$-.1812$	$-.2543$	.4947	.5056
.53	.7019	.2981	.3467	$-.1837$	$-.2493$	.4996	.4831
.54	.7054	.2946	.3448	$-.1862$	$-.2443$	.5043	.4605
.55	.7088	.2912	.3429	$-.1886$	$-.2392$	.5088	.4378
.56	.7123	.2877	.3410	$-.1920$	$-.2341$	.5131	.4150
.57	.7157	.2843	.3391	$-.1933$	$-.2289$	.5171	.3921
.58	.7190	.2810	.3372	$-.1956$	$-.2238$	.5209	.3691
.59	.7224	.2776	.3352	$-.1978$	$-.2185$	.5245	.3461
.60	.7257	.2743	.3332	$-.1999$	$-.2133$	.5278	.3231
.61	.7291	.2709	.3312	$-.2020$	$-.2080$	.5309	.3000
.62	.7324	.2676	.3292	$-.2041$	$-.2027$	.5338	.2770
.63	.7357	.2643	.3271	$-.2061$	$-.1973$	.5365	.2539
.64	.7389	.2611	.3251	$-.2080$	$-.1919$	.5389	.2309
.65	.7422	.2578	.3230	$-.2099$	$-.1865$	.5411	.2078
.66	.7454	.2546	.3209	$-.2118$	$-.1811$	.5431	.1849
.67	.7486	.2514	.3187	$-.2136$	$-.1757$	.5448	.1620
.68	.7517	.2483	.3166	$-.2153$	$-.1702$	.5463	.1391
.69	.7549	.2451	.3144	$-.2170$	$-.1647$	.5476	.1164
.70	.7580	.2420	.3123	$-.2186$	$-.1593$	.5486	.0937
.71	.7611	.2389	.3101	$-.2201$	$-.1538$	.5495	.0712
.72	.7642	.2358	.3079	$-.2217$	$-.1483$	.5501	.0487
.73	.7673	.2327	.3056	$-.2231$	$-.1428$	.5504	.0265
.74	.7704	.2296	.3034	$-.2245$	$-.1373$	.5506	.0043
.75	.7734	.2266	.3011	$-.2259$	$-.1318$	.5505	$-.0176$
.76	.7764	.2236	.2989	$-.2271$	$-.1262$	.5502	$-.0394$
.77	.7794	.2206	.2966	$-.2284$	$-.1207$	.5497	$-.0611$
.78	.7823	.2177	.2943	$-.2296$	$-.1153$	.5490	$-.0825$
.79	.7852	.2148	.2920	$-.2307$	$-.1098$	.5481	$-.1037$
.80	.7881	.2119	.2897	$-.2318$	$-.1043$	.5469	$-.1247$
.81	.7910	.2090	.2874	$-.2328$	$-.0988$	.5456	$-.1455$
.82	.7939	.2061	.2850	$-.2337$	$-.0934$	.5440	$-.1660$
.83	.7967	.2033	.2827	$-.2346$	$-.0880$	.5423	$-.1862$
.84	.7995	.2005	.2803	$-.2355$	$-.0825$	.5403	$-.2063$
.85	.8023	.1977	.2780	$-.2363$	$-.0771$	.5381	$-.2260$
.86	.8051	.1949	.2756	$-.2370$	$-.0718$	.5358	$-.2455$
.87	.8079	.1921	.2732	$-.2377$	$-.0664$	.5332	$-.2646$
.88	.8106	.1894	.2709	$-.2384$	$-.0611$	.5305	$-.2835$
.89	.8133	.1867	.2685	$-.2389$	$-.0558$	.5276	$-.3021$
.90	.8159	.1841	.2661	$-.2395$	$-.0506$	.5245	$-.3203$
.91	.8186	.1814	.2637	$-.2400$	$-.0453$	.5212	$-.3383$
.92	.8212	.1788	.2613	$-.2404$	$-.0401$	.5177	$-.3559$
.93	.8238	.1762	.2589	$-.2408$	$-.0350$	.5140	$-.3731$
.94	.8264	.1736	.2565	$-.2411$	$-.0299$	.5102	$-.3901$
.95	.8289	.1711	.2541	$-.2414$	$-.0248$	.5062	$-.4066$
.96	.8315	.1685	.2516	$-.2416$	$-.0197$	.5021	$-.4228$
.97	.8340	.1660	.2492	$-.2417$	$-.0147$	.4978	$-.4387$
.98	.8365	.1635	.2468	$-.2419$	$-.0098$	.4933	$-.4541$
.99	.8389	.1611	.2444	$-.2420$	$-.0049$	.4887	$-.4692$
1.00	.8413	.1587	.2420	$-.2420$	.0000	.4839	$-.4839$

NORMAL PROBABILITY FUNCTION AND RELATED FUNCTIONS (Continued)

x	$F(x)$	$1 - F(x)$	$f(x)$	$f'(x)$	$f''(x)$	$f'''(x)$	$f^{\mathrm{IV}}(x)$
1.00	.8413	.1587	.2420	− .2420	.0000	.4839	− .4839
1.01	.8438	.1562	.2396	− .2420	.0048	.4790	− .4983
1.02	.8461	.1539	.2371	− .2419	.0096	.4740	− .5122
1.03	.8485	.1515	.2347	− .2418	.0143	.4688	− .5257
1.04	.8508	.1492	.2323	− .2416	.0190	.4635	− .5389
1.05	.8531	.1469	.2299	− .2414	.0236	.4580	− .5516
1.06	.8554	.1446	.2275	− .2411	.0281	.4524	− .5639
1.07	.8577	.1423	.2251	− .2408	.0326	.4467	− .5758
1.08	.8599	.1401	.2227	− .2405	.0371	.4409	− .5873
1.09	.8621	.1379	.2203	− .2401	.0414	.4350	− .5984
1.10	.8643	.1357	.2179	− .2396	.0458	.4290	− .6091
1.11	.8665	.1335	.2155	− .2392	.0500	.4228	− .6193
1.12	.8686	.1314	.2131	− .2386	.0542	.4166	− .6292
1.13	.8708	.1292	.2107	− .2381	.0583	.4102	− .6386
1.14	.8729	.1271	.2083	− .2375	.0624	.4038	− .6476
1.15	.8749	.1251	.2059	− .2368	.0664	.3973	− .6561
1.16	.8770	.1230	.2036	− .2361	.0704	.3907	− .6643
1.17	.8790	.1210	.2012	− .2354	.0742	.3840	− .6720
1.18	.8810	.1190	.1989	− .2347	.0780	.3772	− .6792
1.19	.8830	.1170	.1965	− .2339	.0818	.3704	− .6861
1.20	.8849	.1151	.1942	− .2330	.0854	.3635	− .6926
1.21	.8869	.1131	.1919	− .2322	.0890	.3566	− .6986
1.22	.8888	.1112	.1895	− .2312	.0926	.3496	− .7042
1.23	.8907	.1093	.1872	− .2303	.0960	.3425	− .7094
1.24	.8925	.1075	.1849	− .2293	.0994	.3354	− .7141
1.25	.8944	.1056	.1826	− .2283	.1027	.3282	− .7185
1.26	.8962	.1038	.1804	− .2273	.1060	.3210	− .7224
1.27	.8980	.1020	.1781	− .2262	.1092	.3138	− .7259
1.28	.8997	.1003	.1758	− .2251	.1123	.3065	− .7291
1.29	.9015	.0985	.1736	− .2240	.1153	.2992	− .7318
1.30	.9032	.0968	.1714	− .2228	.1182	.2918	− .7341
1.31	.9049	.0951	.1691	− .2216	.1211	.2845	− .7361
1.32	.9066	.0934	.1669	− .2204	.1239	.2771	− .7376
1.33	.9082	.0918	.1647	− .2191	.1267	.2697	− .7388
1.34	.9099	.0901	.1626	− .2178	.1293	.2624	− .7395
1.35	.9115	.0885	.1604	− .2165	.1319	.2550	− .7399
1.36	.9131	.0869	.1582	− .2152	.1344	.2476	− .7400
1.37	.9147	.0853	.1561	− .2138	.1369	.2402	− .7396
1.38	.9162	.0838	.1539	− .2125	.1392	.2328	− .7389
1.39	.9177	.0823	.1518	− .2110	.1415	.2254	− .7378
1.40	.9192	.0808	.1497	− .2096	.1437	.2180	− .7364
1.41	.9207	.0793	.1476	− .2082	.1459	.2107	− .7347
1.42	.9222	.0778	.1456	− .2067	.1480	.2033	− .7326
1.43	.9236	.0764	.1435	− .2052	.1500	.1960	− .7301
1.44	.9251	.0749	.1415	− .2037	.1519	.1887	− .7274
1.45	.9265	.0735	.1394	− .2022	.1537	.1815	− .7243
1.46	.9279	.0721	.1374	− .2006	.1555	.1742	− .7209
1.47	.9292	.0708	.1354	− .1991	.1572	.1670	− .7172
1.48	.9306	.0694	.1334	− .1975	.1588	.1599	− .7132
1.49	.9319	.0681	.1315	− .1959	.1604	.1528	− .7089
1.50	.9332	.0668	.1295	− .1943	.1619	.1457	− .7043

NORMAL PROBABILITY FUNCTION AND RELATED FUNCTIONS (Continued)

x	$F(x)$	$1 - F(x)$	$f(x)$	$f'(x)$	$f''(x)$	$f'''(x)$	$f^{iv}(x)$
1.50	.9332	.0668	.1295	−.1943	.1619	.1457	−.7043
1.51	.9345	.0655	.1276	−.1927	.1633	.1387	−.6994
1.52	.9357	.0643	.1257	−.1910	.1647	.1317	−.6942
1.53	.9370	.0630	.1238	−.1894	.1660	.1248	−.6888
1.54	.9382	.0618	.1219	−.1877	.1672	.1180	−.6831
1.55	.9394	.0606	.1200	−.1860	.1683	.1111	−.6772
1.56	.9406	.0594	.1182	−.1843	.1694	.1044	−.6710
1.57	.9418	.0582	.1163	−.1826	.1704	.0977	−.6646
1.58	.9429	.0571	.1145	−.1809	.1714	.0911	−.6580
1.59	.9441	.0559	.1127	−.1792	.1722	.0846	−.6511
1.60	.9452	.0548	.1109	−.1775	.1730	.0781	−.6441
1.61	.9463	.0537	.1092	−.1757	.1738	.0717	−.6368
1.62	.9474	.0526	.1074	−.1740	.1745	.0654	−.6293
1.63	.9484	.0516	.1057	−.1723	.1751	.0591	−.6216
1.64	.9495	.0505	.1040	−.1705	.1757	.0529	−.6138
1.65	.9505	.0495	.1023	−.1687	.1762	.0468	−.6057
1.66	.9515	.0485	.1006	−.1670	.1766	.0408	−.5975
1.67	.9525	.0475	.0989	−.1652	.1770	.0349	−.5891
1.68	.9535	.0465	.0973	−.1634	.1773	.0290	−.5806
1.69	.9545	.0455	.0957	−.1617	.1776	.0233	−.5720
1.70	.9554	.0446	.0940	−.1599	.1778	.0176	−.5632
1.71	.9564	.0436	.0925	−.1581	.1779	.0120	−.5542
1.72	.9573	.0427	.0909	−.1563	.1780	.0065	−.5452
1.73	.9582	.0418	.0893	−.1546	.1780	.0011	−.5360
1.74	.9591	.0409	.0878	−.1528	.1780	−.0042	−.5267
1.75	.9599	.0401	.0863	−.1510	.1780	−.0094	−.5173
1.76	.9608	.0392	.0848	−.1492	.1778	−.0146	−.5079
1.77	.9616	.0384	.0833	−.1474	.1777	−.0196	−.4983
1.78	.9625	.0375	.0818	−.1457	.1774	−.0245	−.4887
1.79	.9633	.0367	.0804	−.1439	.1772	−.0294	−.4789
1.80	.9641	.0359	.0790	−.1421	.1769	−.0341	−.4692
1.81	.9649	.0351	.0775	−.1403	.1765	−.0388	−.4593
1.82	.9656	.0344	.0761	−.1386	.1761	−.0433	−.4494
1.83	.9664	.0336	.0748	−.1368	.1756	−.0477	−.4395
1.84	.9671	.0329	.0734	−.1351	.1751	−.0521	−.4295
1.85	.9678	.0322	.0721	−.1333	.1746	−.0563	−.4195
1.86	.9686	.0314	.0707	−.1316	.1740	−.0605	−.4095
1.87	.9693	.0307	.0694	−.1298	.1734	−.0645	−.3995
1.88	.9699	.0301	.0681	−.1281	.1727	−.0685	−.3894
1.89	.9706	.0294	.0669	−.1264	.1720	−.0723	−.3793
1.90	.9713	.0287	.0656	−.1247	.1713	−.0761	−.3693
1.91	.9719	.0281	.0644	−.1230	.1705	−.0797	−.3592
1.92	.9726	.0274	.0632	−.1213	.1697	−.0832	−.3492
1.93	.9732	.0268	.0620	−.1196	.1688	−.0867	−.3392
1.94	.9738	.0262	.0608	−.1179	.1679	−.0900	−.3292
1.95	.9744	.0256	.0596	−.1162	.1670	−.0933	−.3192
1.96	.9750	.0250	.0584	−.1145	.1661	−.0964	−.3093
1.97	.9756	.0244	.0573	−.1129	.1651	−.0994	−.2994
1.98	.9761	.0239	.0562	−.1112	.1641	−.1024	−.2895
1.99	.9767	.0233	.0551	−.1096	.1630	−.1052	−.2797
2.00	.9773	.0227	.0540	−.1080	.1620	−.1080	−.2700

NORMAL PROBABILITY FUNCTION AND RELATED FUNCTIONS (Continued)

x	$F(x)$	$1 - F(x)$	$f(x)$	$f'(x)$	$f''(x)$	$f'''(x)$	$f^{iv}(x)$
2.00	.9773	.0227	.0540	− .1080	.1620	− .1080	− .2700
2.01	.9778	.0222	.0529	− .1064	.1609	− .1106	− .2603
2.02	.9783	.0217	.0519	− .1048	.1598	− .1132	− .2506
2.03	.9788	.0212	.0508	− .1032	.1586	− .1157	− .2411
2.04	.9793	.0207	.0498	− .1016	.1575	− .1180	− .2316
2.05	.9798	.0202	.0488	− .1000	.1563	− .1203	− .2222
2.06	.9803	.0197	.0478	− .0985	.1550	− .1225	− .2129
2.07	.9808	.0192	.0468	− .0969	.1538	− .1245	− .2036
2.08	.9812	.0188	.0459	− .0954	.1526	− .1265	− .1945
2.09	.9817	.0183	.0449	− .0939	.1513	− .1284	− .1854
2.10	.9821	.0179	.0440	− .0924	.1500	− .1302	− .1765
2.11	.9826	.0174	.0431	− .0909	.1487	− .1320	− .1676
2.12	.9830	.0170	.0422	− .0894	.1474	− .1336	− .1588
2.13	.9834	.0166	.0413	− .0879	.1460	− .1351	− .1502
2.14	.9838	.0162	.0404	− .0865	.1446	− .1366	− .1416
2.15	.9842	.0158	.0396	− .0850	.1433	− .1380	− .1332
2.16	.9846	.0154	.0387	− .0836	.1419	− .1393	− .1249
2.17	.9850	.0150	.0379	− .0822	.1405	− .1405	− .1167
2.18	.9854	.0146	.0371	− .0808	.1391	− .1416	− .1086
2.19	.9857	.0143	.0363	− .0794	.1377	− .1426	− .1006
2.20	.9861	.0139	.0355	− .0780	.1362	− .1436	− .0927
2.21	.9864	.0136	.0347	− .0767	.1348	− .1445	− .0850
2.22	.9868	.0132	.0339	− .0754	.1333	− .1453	− .0774
2.23	.9871	.0129	.0332	− .0740	.1319	− .1460	− .0700
2.24	.9875	.0125	.0325	− .0727	.1304	− .1467	− .0626
2.25	.9878	.0122	.0317	− .0714	.1289	− .1473	− .0554
2.26	.9881	.0119	.0310	− .0701	.1275	− .1478	− .0484
2.27	.9884	.0116	.0303	− .0689	.1260	− .1483	− .0414
2.28	.9887	.0113	.0297	− .0676	.1245	− .1486	− .0346
2.29	.9890	.0110	.0290	− .0664	.1230	− .1490	− .0279
2.30	.9893	.0107	.0283	− .0652	.1215	− .1492	− .0214
2.31	.9896	.0104	.0277	− .0639	.1200	− .1494	− .0150
2.32	.9898	.0102	.0270	− .0628	.1185	− .1495	− .0088
2.33	.9901	.0099	.0264	− .0616	.1170	− .1496	− .0027
2.34	.9904	.0096	.0258	− .0604	.1155	− .1496	.0033
2.35	.9906	.0094	.0252	− .0593	.1141	− .1495	.0092
2.36	.9909	.0091	.0246	− .0581	.1126	− .1494	.0149
2.37	.9911	.0089	.0241	− .0570	.1111	− .1492	.0204
2.38	.9913	.0087	.0235	− .0559	.1096	− .1490	.0258
2.39	.9916	.0084	.0229	− .0548	.1081	− .1487	.0311
2.40	.9918	.0082	.0224	− .0538	.1066	− .1483	.0362
2.41	.9920	.0080	.0219	− .0527	.1051	− .1480	.0412
2.42	.9922	.0078	.0213	− .0516	.1036	− .1475	.0461
2.43	.9925	.0075	.0208	− .0506	.1022	− .1470	.0508
2.44	.9927	.0073	.0203	− .0496	.1007	− .1465	.0554
2.45	.9929	.0071	.0198	− .0486	.0992	− .1459	.0598
2.46	.9931	.0069	.0194	− .0476	.0978	− .1453	.0641
2.47	.9932	.0068	.0189	− .0467	.0963	− .1446	.0683
2.48	.9934	.0066	.0184	− .0457	.0949	− .1439	.0723
2.49	.9936	.0064	.0180	− .0448	.0935	− .1432	.0762
2.50	.9938	.0062	.0175	− .0438	.0920	− .1424	.0800

NORMAL PROBABILITY FUNCTION AND RELATED FUNCTIONS (Continued)

x	$F(x)$	$1 - F(x)$	$f(x)$	$f'(x)$	$f''(x)$	$f'''(x)$	$f^{iv}(x)$
2.50	.9938	.0062	.0175	− .0438	.0920	− .1424	.0800
2.51	.9940	.0060	.0171	− .0429	.0906	− .1416	.0836
2.52	.9941	.0059	.0167	− .0420	.0892	− .1408	.0871
2.53	.9943	.0057	.0163	− .0411	.0878	− .1399	.0905
2.54	.9945	.0055	.0158	− .0403	.0864	− .1389	.0937
2.55	.9946	.0054	.0155	− .0394	.0850	− .1380	.0968
2.56	.9948	.0052	.0151	− .0386	.0836	− .1370	.0998
2.57	.9949	.0051	.0147	− .0377	.0823	− .1360	.1027
2.58	.9951	.0049	.0143	− .0369	.0809	− .1350	.1054
2.59	.9952	.0048	.0139	− .0361	.0796	− .1339	.1080
2.60	.9953	.0047	.0136	− .0353	.0782	− .1328	.1105
2.61	.9955	.0045	.0132	− .0345	.0769	− .1317	.1129
2.62	.9956	.0044	.0129	− .0338	.0756	− .1305	.1152
2.63	.9957	.0043	.0126	− .0330	.0743	− .1294	.1173
2.64	.9959	.0041	.0122	− .0323	.0730	− .1282	.1194
2.65	.9960	.0040	.0119	− .0316	.0717	− .1270	.1213
2.66	.9961	.0039	.0116	− .0309	.0705	− .1258	.1231
2.67	.9962	.0038	.0113	− .0302	.0692	− .1245	.1248
2.68	.9963	.0037	.0110	− .0295	.0680	− .1233	.1264
2.69	.9964	.0036	.0107	− .0288	.0668	− .1220	.1279
2.70	.9965	.0035	.0104	− .0281	.0656	− .1207	.1293
2.71	.9966	.0034	.0101	− .0275	.0644	− .1194	.1306
2.72	.9967	.0033	.0099	− .0269	.0632	− .1181	.1317
2.73	.9968	.0032	.0096	− .0262	.0620	− .1168	.1328
2.74	.9969	.0031	.0093	− .0256	.0608	− .1154	.1338
2.75	.9970	.0030	.0091	− .0250	.0597	− .1141	.1347
2.76	.9971	.0029	.0088	− .0244	.0585	− .1127	.1356
2.77	.9972	.0028	.0086	− .0238	.0574	− .1114	.1363
2.78	.9973	.0027	.0084	− .0233	.0563	− .1100	.1369
2.79	.9974	.0026	.0081	− .0227	.0552	− .1087	.1375
2.80	.9974	.0026	.0079	− .0222	.0541	− .1073	.1379
2.81	.9975	.0025	.0077	− .0216	.0531	− .1059	.1383
2.82	.9976	.0024	.0075	− .0211	.0520	− .1045	.1386
2.83	.9977	.0023	.0073	− .0206	.0510	− .1031	.1389
2.84	.9977	.0023	.0071	− .0201	.0500	− .1017	.1390
2.85	.9978	.0022	.0069	− .0196	.0490	− .1003	.1391
2.86	.9979	.0021	.0067	− .0191	.0480	− .0990	.1391
2.87	.9979	.0021	.0065	− .0186	.0470	− .0976	.1391
2.88	.9980	.0020	.0063	− .0182	.0460	− .0962	.1389
2.89	.9981	.0019	.0061	− .0177	.0451	− .0948	.1388
2.90	.9981	.0019	.0060	− .0173	.0441	− .0934	.1385
2.91	.9982	.0018	.0058	− .0168	.0432	− .0920	.1382
2.92	.9983	.0017	.0056	− .0164	.0423	− .0906	.1378
2.93	.9983	.0017	.0055	− .0160	.0414	− .0893	.1374
2.94	.9984	.0016	.0053	− .0156	.0405	− .0879	.1369
2.95	.9984	.0016	.0051	− .0152	.0396	− .0865	.1364
2.96	.9985	.0015	.0050	− .0148	.0388	− .0852	.1358
2.97	.9985	.0015	.0048	− .0144	.0379	− .0838	.1352
2.98	.9986	.0014	.0047	− .0140	.0371	− .0825	.1345
2.99	.9986	.0014	.0046	− .0137	.0363	− .0811	.1337
3.00	.9987	.0013	.0044	− .0133	.0355	− .0798	.1330

NORMAL PROBABILITY FUNCTION AND RELATED FUNCTIONS (Continued)

x	$F(x)$	$1 - F(x)$	$f(x)$	$f'(x)$	$f''(x)$	$f'''(x)$	$f^{iv}(x)$
3.00	.9987	.0013	.0044	− .0133	.0355	− .0798	.1330
3.01	.9987	.0013	.0043	− .0130	.0347	− .0785	.1321
3.02	.9987	.0013	.0042	− .0126	.0339	− .0771	.1313
3.03	.9988	.0012	.0040	− .0123	.0331	− .0758	.1304
3.04	.9988	.0012	.0039	− .0119	.0324	− .0745	.1294
3.05	.9989	.0011	.0038	− .0116	.0316	− .0732	.1285
3.06	.9989	.0011	.0037	− .0113	.0309	− .0720	.1275
3.07	.9989	.0011	.0036	− .0110	.0302	− .0707	.1264
3.08	.9990	.0010	.0035	− .0107	.0295	− .0694	.1254
3.09	.9990	.0010	.0034	− .0104	.0288	− .0682	.1243
3.10	.9990	.0010	.0033	− .0101	.0281	− .0669	.1231
3.11	.9991	.0009	.0032	− .0099	.0275	− .0657	.1220
3.12	.9991	.0009	.0031	− .0096	.0268	− .0645	.1208
3.13	.9991	.0009	.0030	− .0093	.0262	− .0633	.1196
3.14	.9992	.0008	.0029	− .0091	.0256	− .0621	.1184
3.15	.9992	.0008	.0028	− .0088	.0249	− .0609	.1171
3.16	.9992	.0008	.0027	− .0086	.0243	− .0598	.1159
3.17	.9992	.0008	.0026	− .0083	.0237	− .0586	.1146
3.18	.9993	.0007	.0025	− .0081	.0232	− .0575	.1133
3.19	.9993	.0007	.0025	− .0079	.0226	− .0564	.1120
3.20	.9993	.0007	.0024	− .0076	.0220	− .0552	.1107
3.21	.9993	.0007	.0023	− .0074	.0215	− .0541	.1093
3.22	.9994	.0006	.0022	− .0072	.0210	− .0531	.1080
3.23	.9994	.0006	.0022	− .0070	.0204	− .0520	.1066
3.24	.9994	.0006	.0021	− .0068	.0199	− .0509	.1053
3.25	.9994	.0006	.0020	− .0066	.0194	− .0499	.1039
3.26	.9994	.0006	.0020	− .0064	.0189	− .0488	.1025
3.27	.9995	.0005	.0019	− .0062	.0184	− .0478	.1011
3.28	.9995	.0005	.0018	− .0060	.0180	− .0468	.0997
3.29	.9995	.0005	.0018	− .0059	.0175	− .0458	.0983
3.30	.9995	.0005	.0017	− .0057	.0170	− .0449	.0969
3.31	.9995	.0005	.0017	− .0055	.0166	− .0439	.0955
3.32	.9996	.0004	.0016	− .0054	.0162	− .0429	.0941
3.33	.9996	.0004	.0016	− .0052	.0157	− .0420	.0927
3.34	.9996	.0004	.0015	− .0050	.0153	− .0411	.0913
3.35	.9996	.0004	.0015	− .0049	.0149	− .0402	.0899
3.36	.9996	.0004	.0014	− .0047	.0145	− .0393	.0885
3.37	.9996	.0004	.0014	− .0046	.0141	− .0384	.0871
3.38	.9996	.0004	.0013	− .0045	.0138	− .0376	.0857
3.39	.9997	.0003	.0013	− .0043	.0134	− .0367	.0843
3.40	.9997	.0003	.0012	− .0042	.0130	− .0359	.0829
3.41	.9997	.0003	.0012	− .0041	.0127	− .0350	.0815
3.42	.9997	.0003	.0012	− .0039	.0123	− .0342	.0801
3.43	.9997	.0003	.0011	− .0038	.0120	− .0334	.0788
3.44	.9997	.0003	.0011	− .0037	.0116	− .0327	.0774
3.45	.9997	.0003	.0010	− .0036	.0113	− .0319	.0761
3.46	.9997	.0003	.0010	− .0035	.0110	− .0311	.0747
3.47	.9997	.0003	.0010	− .0034	.0107	-- .0304	.0734
3.48	.9997	.0003	.0009	− .0033	.0104	− .0297	.0721
3.49	.9998	.0002	.0009	− .0032	.0101	− .0290	.0707
3.50	.9998	.0002	.0009	− .0031	.0098	− .0283	.0694

NORMAL PROBABILITY FUNCTION AND RELATED FUNCTIONS (Continued)

x	$F(x)$	$1 - F(x)$	$f(x)$	$f'(x)$	$f''(x)$	$f'''(x)$	$f^{\mathrm{iv}}(x)$
3.50	.9998	.0002	.0009	− .0031	.0098	− .0283	.0694
3.51	.9998	.0002	.0008	− .0030	.0095	− .0276	.0681
3.52	.9998	.0002	.0008	− .0029	.0093	− .0269	.0669
3.53	.9998	.0002	.0008	− .0028	.0090	− .0262	.0656
3.54	.9998	.0002	.0008	− .0027	.0087	− .0256	.0643
3.55	.9998	.0002	.0007	− .0026	.0085	− .0249	.0631
3.56	.9998	.0002	.0007	− .0025	.0082	− .0243	.0618
3.57	.9998	.0002	.0007	− .0024	.0080	− .0237	.0606
3.58	.9998	.0002	.0007	− .0024	.0078	− .0231	.0594
3.59	.9998	.0002	.0006	− .0023	.0075	− .0225	.0582
3.60	.9998	.0002	.0006	− .0022	.0073	− .0219	.0570
3.61	.9998	.0002	.0006	− .0021	.0071	− .0214	.0559
3.62	.9999	.0001	.0006	− .0021	.0069	− .0208	.0547
3.63	.9999	.0001	.0005	− .0020	.0067	− .0203	.0536
3.64	.9999	.0001	.0005	− .0019	.0065	− .0198	.0524
3.65	.9999	.0001	.0005	− .0019	.0063	− .0192	.0513
3.66	.9999	.0001	.0005	− .0018	.0061	− .0187	.0502
3.67	.9999	.0001	.0005	− .0017	.0059	− .0182	.0492
3.68	.9999	.0001	.0005	− .0017	.0057	− .0177	.0481
3.69	.9999	.0001	.0004	− .0016	.0056	− .0173	.0470
3.70	.9999	.0001	.0004	− .0016	.0054	− .0168	.0460
3.71	.9999	.0001	.0004	− .0015	.0052	− .0164	.0450
3.72	.9999	.0001	.0004	− .0015	.0051	− .0159	.0440
3.73	.9999	.0001	.0004	− .0014	.0049	− .0155	.0430
3.74	.9999	.0001	.0004	− .0014	.0048	− .0150	.0420
3.75	.9999	.0001	.0004	− .0013	.0046	− .0146	.0410
3.76	.9999	.0001	.0003	− .0013	.0045	− .0142	.0401
3.77	.9999	.0001	.0003	− .0012	.0043	− .0138	.0392
3.78	.9999	.0001	.0003	− .0012	.0042	− .0134	.0382
3.79	.9999	.0001	.0003	− .0012	.0041	− .0131	.0373
3.80	.9999	.0001	.0003	− .0011	.0039	− .0127	.0365
3.81	.9999	.0001	.0003	− .0011	.0038	− .0123	.0356
3.82	.9999	.0001	.0003	− .0010	.0037	− .0120	.0347
3.83	.9999	.0001	.0003	− .0010	.0036	− .0116	.0339
3.84	.9999	.0001	.0003	− .0010	.0034	− .0113	.0331
3.85	.9999	.0001	.0002	− .0009	.0033	− .0110	.0323
3.86	.9999	.0001	.0002	− .0009	.0032	− .0107	.0315
3.87	.9999	.0001	.0002	− .0009	.0031	− .0104	.0307
3.88	.9999	.0001	.0002	− .0008	.0030	− .0100	.0299
3.89	1.0000	.0000	.0002	− .0008	.0029	− .0098	.0292
3.90	1.0000	.0000	.0002	− .0008	.0028	− .0095	.0284
3.91	1.0000	.0000	.0002	− .0008	.0027	− .0092	.0277
3.92	1.0000	.0000	.0002	− .0007	.0026	− .0089	.0270
3.93	1.0000	.0000	.0002	− .0007	.0026	− .0086	.0263
3.94	1.0000	.0000	.0002	− .0007	.0025	− .0084	.0256
3.95	1.0000	.0000	.0002	− .0006	.0024	− .0081	.0250
3.96	1.0000	.0000	.0002	− .0006	.0023	− .0079	.0243
3.97	1.0000	.0000	.0002	− .0006	.0022	− .0076	.0237
3.98	1.0000	.0000	.0001	− .0006	.0022	− .0074	.0230
3.99	1.0000	.0000	.0001	− .0006	.0021	− .0072	.0224
4.00	1.0000	.0000	.0001	− .0005	.0020	− .0070	.0218

x	1.282	1.645	1.960	2.326	2.576	3.090
$F(x)$	.90	.95	.975	.99	.995	.999
$2[1 - F(x)]$	.20	.10	.05	.02	.01	.002

INDIVIDUAL TERMS, BINOMIAL DISTRIBUTION

The $(x + 1)^{st}$ term in the expansion of the binomial $[\theta + (1 - \theta)]^n$ is given by

$$f(x;n,\theta) = \binom{n}{x} \theta^x (1 - \theta)^{n-x}, \qquad x = 0, 1, 2, \ldots , n.$$

This is the probability of exactly x successes in n independent binomial trials with probability of success on a single trial equal to θ. This table contains the individual terms of $f(x;n,\theta)$ for specified choices of x, n, and θ.

For $\theta > 0.5$, the value of $\binom{n}{x} \theta^x (1 - \theta)^{n-x}$ is found by using the table entry for

$$\binom{n}{n - x} (1 - \theta)^{n-x} \theta^x.$$

INDIVIDUAL TERMS, BINOMIAL DISTRIBUTION (Continued)

n	x	.05	.10	.15	.20	θ .25	.30	.35	.40	.45	.50
1	0	.9500	.9000	.8500	.8000	.7500	.7000	.6500	.6000	.5500	.5000
	1	.0500	.1000	.1500	.2000	.2500	.3000	.3500	.4000	.4500	.5000
2	0	.9025	.8100	.7225	.6400	.5625	.4900	.4225	.3600	.3025	.2500
	1	.0950	.1800	.2550	.3200	.3750	.4200	.4550	.4800	.4950	.5000
	2	.0025	.0100	.0225	.0400	.0625	.0900	.1225	.1600	.2025	.2500
3	0	.8574	.7290	.6141	.5120	.4219	.3430	.2746	.2160	.1664	.1250
	1	.1354	.2430	.3251	.3840	.4219	.4410	.4436	.4320	.4084	.3750
	2	.0071	.0270	.0574	.0960	.1406	.1890	.2389	.2880	.3341	.3750
	3	.0001	.0010	.0034	.0080	.0156	.0270	.0429	.0640	.0911	.1250
4	0	.8145	.6561	.5220	.4096	.3164	.2401	.1785	.1296	.0915	.0625
	1	.1715	.2916	.3685	.4096	.4219	.4116	.3845	.3456	.2995	.2500
	2	.0135	.0486	.0975	.1536	.2109	.2646	.3105	.3456	.3675	.3750
	3	.0005	.0036	.0115	.0256	.0469	.0756	.1115	.1536	.2005	.2500
	4	.0000	.0001	.0005	.0016	.0039	.0081	.0150	.0256	.0410	.0625
5	0	.7738	.5905	.4437	.3277	.2373	.1681	.1160	.0778	.0503	.0312
	1	.2036	.3280	.3915	.4096	.3955	.3602	.3124	.2592	.2059	.1562
	2	.0214	.0729	.1382	.2048	.2637	.3087	.3364	.3456	.3369	.3125
	3	.0011	.0081	.0244	.0512	.0879	.1323	.1811	.2304	.2757	.3125
	4	.0000	.0004	.0022	.0064	.0146	.0284	.0488	.0768	.1128	.1562
	5	.0000	.0000	.0001	.0003	.0010	.0024	.0053	.0102	.0185	.0312
6	0	.7351	.5314	.3771	.2621	.1780	.1176	.0754	.0467	.0277	.0156
	1	.2321	.3543	.3993	.3932	.3560	.3025	.2437	.1866	.1359	.0938
	2	.0305	.0984	.1762	.2458	.2966	.3241	.3280	.3110	.2780	.2344
	3	.0021	.0146	.0415	.0819	.1318	.1852	.2355	.2765	.3032	.3125
	4	.0001	.0012	.0055	.0154	.0330	.0595	.0951	.1382	.1861	.2344
	5	.0000	.0001	.0004	.0015	.0044	.0102	.0205	.0369	.0609	.0938
	6	.0000	.0000	.0000	.0001	.0002	.0007	.0018	.0041	.0083	.0156
7	0	.6983	.4783	.3206	.2097	.1335	.0824	.0490	.0280	.0152	.0078
	1	.2573	.3720	.3960	.3670	.3115	.2471	.1848	.1306	.0872	.0547
	2	.0406	.1240	.2097	.2753	.3115	.3177	.2985	.2613	.2140	.1641
	3	.0036	.0230	.0617	.1147	.1730	.2269	.2679	.2903	.2918	.2734
	4	.0002	.0026	.0109	.0287	.0577	.0972	.1442	.1935	.2388	.2734
	5	.0000	.0002	.0012	.0043	.0115	.0250	.0466	.0774	.1172	.1641
	6	.0000	.0000	.0001	.0004	.0013	.0036	.0084	.0172	.0320	.0547
	7	.0000	.0000	.0000	.0000	.0001	.0002	.0006	.0016	.0037	.0078
8	0	.6634	.4305	.2725	.1678	.1001	.0576	.0319	.0168	.0084	.0039
	1	.2793	.3826	.3847	.3355	.2670	.1977	.1373	.0896	.0548	.0312
	2	.0515	.1488	.2376	.2936	.3115	.2965	.2587	.2090	.1569	.1094
	3	.0054	.0331	.0839	.1468	.2076	.2541	.2786	.2787	.2568	.2188
	4	.0004	.0046	.0185	.0459	.0865	.1361	.1875	.2322	.2627	.2734
	5	.0000	.0004	.0026	.0092	.0231	.0467	.0808	.1239	.1719	.2188
	6	.0000	.0000	.0002	.0011	.0038	.0100	.0217	.0413	.0703	.1094
	7	.0000	.0000	.0000	.0001	.0004	.0012	.0033	.0079	.0164	.0312
	8	.0000	.0000	.0000	.0000	.0000	.0001	.0002	.0007	.0017	.0039

Linear interpolations with respect to p will in general be accurate at most to two decimal places.

INDIVIDUAL TERMS, BINOMIAL DISTRIBUTION (Continued)

n	x	.05	.10	.15	.20	θ .25	.30	.35	.40	.45	.50
9	0	.6302	.3874	.2316	.1342	.0751	.0404	.0207	.0101	.0046	.0020
	1	.2985	.3874	.3679	.3020	.2253	.1556	.1004	.0605	.0339	.0176
	2	.0629	.1722	.2597	.3020	.3003	.2668	.2162	.1612	.1110	.0703
	3	.0077	.0446	.1069	.1762	.2336	.2668	.2716	.2508	.2119	.1641
	4	.0006	.0074	.0283	.0661	.1168	.1715	.2194	.2508	.2600	.2461
	5	.0000	.0008	.0050	.0165	.0389	.0735	.1181	.1672	.2128	.2461
	6	.0000	.0001	.0006	.0028	.0087	.0210	.0424	.0743	.1160	.1641
	7	.0000	.0000	.0000	.0003	.0012	.0039	.0098	.0212	.0407	.0703
	8	.0000	.0000	.0000	.0000	.0001	.0004	.0013	.0035	.0083	.0176
	9	.0000	.0000	.0000	.0000	.0000	.0000	.0001	.0003	.0008	.0020
10	0	.5987	.3487	.1969	.1074	.0563	.0282	.0135	.0060	.0025	.0010
	1	.3151	.3874	.3474	.2684	.1877	.1211	.0725	.0403	.0207	.0098
	2	.0746	.1937	.2759	.3020	.2816	.2335	.1757	.1209	.0763	.0439
	3	.0105	.0574	.1298	.2013	.2503	.2668	.2522	.2150	.1665	.1172
	4	.0010	.0112	.0401	.0881	.1460	.2001	.2377	.2508	.2384	.2051
	5	.0001	.0015	.0085	.0264	.0584	.1029	.1536	.2007	.2340	.2461
	6	.0000	.0001	.0012	.0055	.0162	.0368	.0689	.1115	.1596	.2051
	7	.0000	.0000	.0001	.0008	.0031	.0090	.0212	.0425	.0746	.1172
	8	.0000	.0000	.0000	.0001	.0004	.0014	.0043	.0106	.0229	.0439
	9	.0000	.0000	.0000	.0000	.0000	.0001	.0005	.0016	.0042	.0098
	10	.0000	.0000	.0000	.0000	.0000	.0000	.0000	.0001	.0003	.0010
11	0	.5688	.3138	.1673	.0859	.0422	.0198	.0088	.0036	.0014	.0004
	1	.3293	.3835	.3248	.2362	.1549	.0932	.0518	.0266	.0125	.0055
	2	.0867	.2131	.2866	.2953	.2581	.1998	.1395	.0887	.0513	.0269
	3	.0137	.0710	.1517	.2215	.2581	.2568	.2254	.1774	.1259	.0806
	4	.0014	.0158	.0536	.1107	.1721	.2201	.2428	.2365	.2060	.1611
	5	.0001	.0025	.0132	.0388	.0803	.1321	.1830	.2207	.2360	.2256
	6	.0000	.0003	.0023	.0097	.0268	.0566	.0985	.1471	.1931	.2256
	7	.0000	.0000	.0003	.0017	.0064	.0173	.0379	.0701	.1128	.1611
	8	.0000	.0000	.0000	.0002	.0011	.0037	.0102	.0234	.0462	.0806
	9	.0000	.0000	.0000	.0000	.0001	.0005	.0018	.0052	.0126	.0269
	10	.0000	.0000	.0000	.0000	.0000	.0000	.0002	.0007	.0021	.0054
	11	.0000	.0000	.0000	.0000	.0000	.0000	.0000	.0000	.0002	.0005
12	0	.5404	.2824	.1422	.0687	.0317	.0138	.0057	.0022	.0008	.0002
	1	.3413	.3766	.3012	.2062	.1267	.0712	.0368	.0174	.0075	.0029
	2	.0988	.2301	.2924	.2835	.2323	.1678	.1088	.0639	.0339	.0161
	3	.0173	.0852	.1720	.2362	.2581	.2397	.1954	.1419	.0923	.0537
	4	.0021	.0213	.0683	.1329	.1936	.2311	.2367	.2128	.1700	.1208
	5	.0002	.0038	.0193	.0532	.1032	.1585	.2039	.2270	.2225	.1934
	6	.0000	.0005	.0040	.0155	.0401	.0792	.1281	.1766	.2124	.2256
	7	.0000	.0000	.0006	.0033	.0115	.0291	.0591	.1009	.1489	.1934
	8	.0000	.0000	.0001	.0005	.0024	.0078	.0199	.0420	.0762	.1208
	9	.0000	.0000	.0000	.0001	.0004	.0015	.0048	.0125	.0277	.0537
	10	.0000	.0000	.0000	.0000	.0000	.0002	.0008	.0025	.0068	.0161
	11	.0000	.0000	.0000	.0000	.0000	.0000	.0001	.0003	.0010	.0029
	12	.0000	.0000	.0000	.0000	.0000	.0000	.0000	.0000	.0001	.0002

INDIVIDUAL TERMS, BINOMIAL DISTRIBUTION (Continued)

n	x	.05	.10	.15	.20	.25 θ	.30	.35	.40	.45	.50
13	0	.5133	.2542	.1209	.0550	.0238	.0097	.0037	.0013	.0004	.0001
	1	.3512	.3672	.2774	.1787	.1029	.0540	.0259	.0113	.0045	.0016
	2	.1109	.2448	.2937	.2680	.2059	.1388	.0836	.0453	.0220	.0095
	3	.0214	.0997	.1900	.2457	.2517	.2181	.1651	.1107	.0660	.0349
	4	.0028	.0277	.0838	.1535	.2097	.2337	.2222	.1845	.1350	.0873
	5	.0003	.0055	.0266	.0691	.1258	.1803	.2154	.2214	.1989	.1571
	6	.0000	.0008	.0063	.0230	.0559	.1030	.1546	.1968	.2169	.2095
	7	.0000	.0001	.0011	.0058	.0186	.0442	.0833	.1312	.1775	.2095
	8	.0000	.0000	.0001	.0011	.0047	.0142	.0336	.0656	.1089	.1571
	9	.0000	.0000	.0000	.0001	.0009	.0034	.0101	.0243	.0495	.0873
	10	.0000	.0000	.0000	.0000	.0001	.0006	.0022	.0065	.0162	.0349
	11	.0000	.0000	.0000	.0000	.0000	.0001	.0003	.0012	.0036	.0095
	12	.0000	.0000	.0000	.0000	.0000	.0000	.0000	.0001	.0005	.0016
	13	.0000	.0000	.0000	.0000	.0000	.0000	.0000	.0000	.0000	.0001
14	0	.4877	.2288	.1028	.0440	.0178	.0068	.0024	.0008	.0002	.0001
	1	.3593	.3559	.2539	.1539	.0832	.0407	.0181	.0073	.0027	.0009
	2	.1229	.2570	.2912	.2501	.1802	.1134	.0634	.0317	.0141	.0056
	3	.0259	.1142	.2056	.2501	.2402	.1943	.1366	.0845	.0462	.0222
	4	.0037	.0349	.0998	.1720	.2202	.2290	.2022	.1549	.1040	.0611
	5	.0004	.0078	.0352	.0860	.1468	.1963	.2178	.2066	.1701	.1222
	6	.0000	.0013	.0093	.0322	.0734	.1262	.1759	.2066	.2088	.1833
	7	.0000	.0002	.0019	.0092	.0280	.0618	.1082	.1574	.1952	.2095
	8	.0000	.0000	.0003	.0020	.0082	.0232	.0510	.0918	.1398	.1833
	9	.0000	.0000	.0000	.0003	.0018	.0066	.0183	.0408	.0762	.1222
	10	.0000	.0000	.0000	.0000	.0003	.0014	.0049	.0136	.0312	.0611
	11	.0000	.0000	.0000	.0000	.0000	.0002	.0010	.0033	.0093	.0222
	12	.0000	.0000	.0000	.0000	.0000	.0000	.0001	.0005	.0019	.0056
	13	.0000	.0000	.0000	.0000	.0000	.0000	.0000	.0001	.0002	.0009
	14	.0000	.0000	.0000	.0000	.0000	.0000	.0000	.0000	.0000	.0001
15	0	.4633	.2059	.0874	.0352	.0134	.0047	.0016	.0005	.0001	.0000
	1	.3658	.3432	.2312	.1319	.0668	.0305	.0126	.0047	.0016	.0005
	2	.1348	.2669	.2856	.2309	.1559	.0916	.0476	.0219	.0090	.0032
	3	.0307	.1285	.2184	.2501	.2252	.1700	.1110	.0634	.0318	.0139
	4	.0049	.0428	.1156	.1876	.2252	.2186	.1792	.1268	.0780	.0417
	5	.0006	.0105	.0449	.1032	.1651	.2061	.2123	.1859	.1404	.0916
	6	.0000	.0019	.0132	.0430	.0917	.1472	.1906	.2066	.1914	.1527
	7	.0000	.0003	.0030	.0138	.0393	.0811	.1319	.1771	.2013	.1964
	8	.0000	.0000	.0005	.0035	.0131	.0348	.0710	.1181	.1647	.1964
	9	.0000	.0000	.0001	.0007	.0034	.0116	.0298	.0612	.1048	.1527
	10	.0000	.0000	.0000	.0001	.0007	.0030	.0096	.0245	.0515	.0916
	11	.0000	.0000	.0000	.0000	.0001	.0006	.0024	.0074	.0191	.0417
	12	.0000	.0000	.0000	.0000	.0000	.0001	.0004	.0016	.0052	.0139
	13	.0000	.0000	.0000	.0000	.0000	.0000	.0001	.0003	.0010	.0032
	14	.0000	.0000	.0000	.0000	.0000	.0000	.0000	.0000	.0001	.0005
	15	.0000	.0000	.0000	.0000	.0000	.0000	.0000	.0000	.0000	.0000

INDIVIDUAL TERMS, BINOMIAL DISTRIBUTION (Continued)

n	x	.05	.10	.15	.20	θ .25	.30	.35	.40	.45	.50
16	0	.4401	.1853	.0743	.0281	.0100	.0033	.0010	.0003	.0001	.0000
	1	.3706	.3294	.2097	.1126	.0535	.0228	.0087	.0030	.0009	.0002
	2	.1463	.2745	.2775	.2111	.1336	.0732	.0353	.0150	.0056	.0018
	3	.0359	.1423	.2285	.2463	.2079	.1465	.0888	.0468	.0215	.0085
	4	.0061	.0514	.1311	.2001	.2252	.2040	.1553	.1014	.0572	.0278
	5	.0008	.0137	.0555	.1201	.1802	.2099	.2008	.1623	.1123	.0667
	6	.0001	.0028	.0180	.0550	.1101	.1649	.1982	.1983	.1684	.1222
	7	.0000	.0004	.0045	.0197	.0524	.1010	.1524	.1889	.1969	.1746
	8	.0000	.0001	.0009	.0055	.0197	.0487	.0923	.1417	.1812	.1964
	9	.0000	.0000	.0001	.0012	.0058	.0185	.0442	.0840	.1318	.1746
	10	.0000	.0000	.0000	.0002	.0014	.0056	.0167	.0392	.0755	.1222
	11	.0000	.0000	.0000	.0000	.0002	.0013	.0049	.0142	.0337	.0667
	12	.0000	.0000	.0000	.0000	.0000	.0002	.0011	.0040	.0115	.0278
	13	.0000	.0000	.0000	.0000	.0000	.0000	.0002	.0008	.0029	.0085
	14	.0000	.0000	.0000	.0000	.0000	.0000	.0000	.0001	.0005	.0018
	15	.0000	.0000	.0000	.0000	.0000	.0000	.0000	.0000	.0001	.0002
	16	.0000	.0000	.0000	.0000	.0000	.0000	.0000	.0000	.0000	.0000
17	0	.4181	.1668	.0631	.0225	.0075	.0023	.0007	.0002	.0000	.0000
	1	.3741	.3150	.1893	.0957	.0426	.0169	.0060	.0019	.0005	.0001
	2	.1575	.2800	.2673	.1914	.1136	.0581	.0260	.0102	.0035	.0010
	3	.0415	.1556	.2359	.2393	.1893	.1245	.0701	.0341	.0144	.0052
	4	.9076	.0605	.1457	.2093	.2209	.1868	.1320	.0796	.0411	.0182
	5	.0010	.0175	.0668	.1361	.1914	.2081	.1849	.1379	.0875	.0472
	6	.0001	.0039	.0236	.0680	.1276	.1784	.1991	.1839	.1432	.0944
	7	.0000	.0007	.0065	.0267	.0668	.1201	.1685	.1927	.1841	.1484
	8	.0000	.0001	.0014	.0084	.0279	.0644	.1134	.1606	.1883	.1855
	9	.0000	.0000	.0003	.0021	.0093	.0276	.0611	.1070	.1540	.1855
	10	.0000	.0000	.0000	.0004	.0025	.0095	.0263	.0571	.1008	.1484
	11	.0000	.0000	.0000	.0001	.0005	.0026	.0090	.0242	.0525	.0944
	12	.0000	.0000	.0000	.0000	.0001	.0006	.0024	.0081	.0215	.0472
	13	.0000	.0000	.0000	.0000	.0000	.0001	.0005	.0021	.0068	.0182
	14	.0000	.0000	.0000	.0000	.0000	.0000	.0001	.0004	.0016	.0052
	15	.0000	.0000	.0000	.0000	.0000	.0000	.0000	.0001	.0003	.0010
	16	.0000	.0000	.0000	.0000	.0000	.0000	.0000	.0000	.0000	.0001
	17	.0000	.0000	.0000	.0000	.0000	.0000	.0000	.0000	.0000	.0000
18	0	.3972	.1501	.0536	.0180	.0056	.0016	.0004	.0001	.0000	.0000
	1	.3763	.3002	.1704	.0811	.0338	.0126	.0042	.0012	.0003	.0001
	2	.1683	.2835	.2556	.1723	.0958	.0458	.0190	.0069	.0022	.0006
	3	.0473	.1680	.2406	.2297	.1704	.1046	.0547	.0246	.0095	.0031
	4	.0093	.0700	.1592	.2153	.2130	.1681	.1104	.0614	.0291	.0117
	5	.0014	.0218	.0787	.1507	.1988	.2017	.1664	.1146	.0666	.0327
	6	.0002	.0052	.0301	.0816	.1436	.1873	.1941	.1655	.1181	.0708
	7	.0000	.0010	.0091	.0350	.0820	.1376	.1792	.1892	.1657	.1214
	8	.0000	.0002	.0022	.0120	.0376	.0811	.1327	.1734	.1864	.1669
	9	.0000	.0000	.0004	.0033	.0139	.0386	.0794	.1284	.1694	.1855
	10	.0000	.0000	.0001	.0008	.0042	.0149	.0385	.0771	.1248	.1669
	11	.0000	.0000	.0000	.0001	.0010	.0046	.0151	.0374	.0742	.1214

INDIVIDUAL TERMS, BINOMIAL DISTRIBUTION (Continued)

n	x	.05	.10	.15	.20	θ .25	.30	.35	.40	.45	.50
18	12	.0000	.0000	.0000	.0000	.0002	.0012	.0047	.0145	.0354	.0708
	13	.0000	.0000	.0000	.0000	.0000	.0002	.0012	.0045	.0134	.0327
	14	.0000	.0000	.0000	.0000	.0000	.0000	.0002	.0011	.0039	.0117
	15	.0000	.0000	.0000	.0000	.0000	.0000	.0000	.0002	.0009	.0031
	16	.0000	.0000	.0000	.0000	.0000	.0000	.0000	.0000	.0001	.0006
	17	.0000	.0000	.0000	.0000	.0000	.0000	.0000	.0000	.0000	.0001
	18	.0000	.0000	.0000	.0000	.0000	.0000	.0000	.0000	.0000	.0000
19	0	.3774	.1351	.0456	.0144	.0042	.0011	.0003	.0001	.0000	.0000
	1	.3774	.2852	.1529	.0685	.0268	.0093	.0029	.0008	.0002	.0000
	2	.1787	.2852	.2428	.1540	.0803	.0358	.0138	.0046	.0013	.0003
	3	.0533	.1796	.2428	.2182	.1517	.0869	.0422	.0175	.0062	.0018
	4	.0112	.0798	.1714	.2182	.2023	.1491	.0909	.0467	.0203	.0074
	5	.0018	.0266	.0907	.1636	.2023	.1916	.1468	.0933	.0497	.0222
	6	.0002	.0069	.0374	.0955	.1574	.1916	.1844	.1451	.0949	.0518
	7	.0000	.0014	.0122	.0443	.0974	.1525	.1844	.1797	.1443	.0961
	8	.0000	.0002	.0032	.0166	.0487	.0981	.1489	.1797	.1771	.1442
	9	.0000	.0000	.0007	.0051	.0198	.0514	.0980	.1464	.1771	.1762
	10	.0000	.0000	.0001	.0013	.0066	.0220	.0528	.0976	.1449	.1762
	11	.0000	.0000	.0000	.0003	.0018	.0077	.0233	.0532	.0970	.1442
	12	.0000	.0000	.0000	.0000	.0004	.0022	.0083	.0237	.0529	.0961
	13	.0000	.0000	.0000	.0000	.0001	.0005	.0024	.0085	.0233	.0518
	14	.0000	.0000	.0000	.0000	.0000	.0001	.0006	.0024	.0082	.0222
	15	.0000	.0000	.0000	.0000	.0000	.0000	.0001	.0005	.0022	.0074
	16	.0000	.0000	.0000	.0000	.0000	.0000	.0000	.0001	.0005	.0018
	17	.0000	.0000	.0000	.0000	.0000	.0000	.0000	.0000	.0001	.0003
	18	.0000	.0000	.0000	.0000	.0000	.0000	.0000	.0000	.0000	.0000
	19	.0000	.0000	.0000	.0000	.0000	.0000	.0000	.0000	.0000	.0000
20	0	.3585	.1216	.0388	.0115	.0032	.0008	.0002	.0000	.0000	.0000
	1	.3774	.2702	.1368	.0576	.0211	.0068	.0020	.0005	.0001	.0000
	2	.1887	.2852	.2293	.1369	.0669	.0278	.0100	.0031	.0008	.0002
	3	.0596	.1901	.2428	.2054	.1339	.0716	.0323	.0123	.0040	.0011
	4	.0133	.0898	.1821	.2182	.1897	.1304	.0738	.0350	.0139	.0046
	5	.0022	.0319	.1028	.1746	.2023	.1789	.1272	.0746	.0365	.0148
	6	.0003	.0089	.0454	.1091	.1686	.1916	.1712	.1244	.0746	.0370
	7	.0000	.0020	.0160	.0545	.1124	.1643	.1844	.1659	.1221	.0739
	8	.0000	.0004	.0046	.0222	.0609	.1144	.1614	.1797	.1623	.1201
	9	.0000	.0001	.0011	.0074	.0271	.0654	.1158	.1597	.1771	.1602
	10	.0000	.0000	.0002	.0020	.0099	.0308	.0686	.1171	.1593	.1762
	11	.0000	.0000	.0000	.0005	.0030	.0120	.0336	.0710	.1185	.1602
	12	.0000	.0000	.0000	.0001	.0008	.0039	.0136	.0355	.0727	.1201
	13	.0000	.0000	.0000	.0000	.0002	.0010	.0045	.0146	.0366	.0739
	14	.0000	.0000	.0000	.0000	.0000	.0002	.0012	.0049	.0150	.0370
	15	.0000	.0000	.0000	.0000	.0000	.0000	.0003	.0013	.0049	.0148
	16	.0000	.0000	.0000	.0000	.0000	.0000	.0000	.0003	.0013	.0046
	17	.0000	.0000	.0000	.0000	.0000	.0000	.0000	.0000	.0002	.0011
	18	.0000	.0000	.0000	.0000	.0000	.0000	.0000	.0000	.0000	.0002
	19	.0000	.0000	.0000	.0000	.0000	.0000	.0000	.0000	.0000	.0000
	20	.0000	.0000	.0000	.0000	.0000	.0000	.0000	.0000	.0000	.0000

CUMULATIVE TERMS, BINOMIAL DISTRIBUTION

For the binomial probability function $f(x;n,\theta)$ the probability of observing x' or more successes is given by

$$\sum_{x=x'}^{n} \binom{n}{x} \theta^x (1-\theta)^{n-x},$$

This table contains the values of $\sum_{x=x'}^{n} \binom{n}{x} \theta^x (1-\theta)^{n-x}$ for specified values of n, x', and

θ. If $\theta > 0.5$, the values for $\sum_{x=x'}^{n} \binom{n}{x} \theta^x (1-\theta)^{n-x}$ are obtained using the corresponding

results obtained from

$$1 - \sum_{x=n-x'+1}^{n} \binom{n}{x} (1-\theta)^x \theta^{n-x}$$

The cumulative binomial distribution is related to the incomplete beta function as follows:

$$\sum_{x=x'}^{n} \binom{n}{x} \theta^x (1-\theta)^{n-x} = I_\theta(x', n-x'+1) \,,$$

$$\sum_{x=0}^{x'-1} \binom{n}{x} \theta^x (1-\theta)^{n-x} = 1 - I_\theta(x', n-x'+1)$$

$$= 1 - \int_0^\theta u^{x'-1}(1-u)^{n-x'} \, du \Big/ \int_0^1 u^{x'-1}(1-u)^{n-x'} \, du \,.$$

The cumulative binomial distribution is related to the cumulative negative binomial distribution as follows:

$$1 - \sum_{x'=0}^{r-1} \binom{x+r}{x'} \theta^{x'}(1-\theta)^{x+r-x'} = \sum_{x'=0}^{x} \binom{x'+r-1}{r-1} \theta^r (1-\theta)^{x'}$$

or

$$\sum_{x'=r}^{x+r} \binom{x+r}{x'} \theta^{x'}(1-\theta)^{x+r-x'} = \sum_{x'=0}^{x} \binom{x'+r-1}{r-1} \theta^r (1-\theta)^{x'} \,.$$

CUMULATIVE TERMS, BINOMIAL DISTRIBUTION (Continued)

n	x'	.05	.10	.15	.20	θ .25	.30	.35	.40	.45	.50
2	1	.0975	.1900	.2775	.3600	.4375	.5100	.5775	.6400	.6975	.7500
	2	.0025	.0100	.0225	.0400	.0625	.0900	.1225	.1600	.2025	.2500
3	1	.1426	.2710	.3859	.4880	.5781	.6570	.7254	.7840	.8336	.8750
	2	.0072	.0280	.0608	.1040	.1562	.2160	.2818	.3520	.4252	.5000
	3	.0001	.0010	.0034	.0080	.0156	.0270	.0429	.0640	.0911	.1250
4	1	.1855	.3439	.4780	.5904	.6836	.7599	.8215	.8704	.9085	.9375
	2	.0140	.0523	.1095	.1808	.2617	.3483	.4370	.5248	.6090	.6875
	3	.0005	.0037	.0120	.0272	.0508	.0837	.1265	.1792	.2415	.3125
	4	.0000	.0001	.0005	.0016	.0039	.0081	.0150	.0256	.0410	.0625
5	1	.2262	.4095	.5563	.6723	.7627	.8319	.8840	.9222	.9497	.9688
	2	.0226	.0815	.1648	.2627	.3672	.4718	.5716	.6630	.7438	.8125
	3	.0012	.0086	.0266	.0579	.1035	.1631	.2352	.3174	.4069	.5000
	4	.0000	.0005	.0022	.0067	.0156	.0308	.0540	.0870	.1312	.1875
	5	.0000	.0000	.0001	.0003	.0010	.0024	.0053	.0102	.0185	.0312
6	1	.2649	.4686	.6229	.7379	.8220	.8824	.9246	.9533	.9723	.9844
	2	.0328	.1143	.2235	.3447	.4661	.5798	.6809	.7667	.8364	.8906
	3	.0022	.0158	.0473	.0989	.1694	.2557	.3529	.4557	.5585	.6562
	4	.0001	.0013	.0059	.0170	.0376	.0705	.1174	.1792	.2553	.3438
	5	.0000	.0001	.0004	.0016	.0046	.0109	.0223	.0410	.0692	.1094
	6	.0000	.0000	.0000	.0001	.0002	.0007	.0018	.0041	.0083	.0156
7	1	.3017	.5217	.6794	.7903	.8665	.9176	.9510	.9720	.9848	.9922
	2	.0444	.1497	.2834	.4233	.5551	.6706	.7662	.8414	.8976	.9375
	3	.0038	.0257	.0738	.1480	.2436	.3529	.4677	.5801	.6836	.7734
	4	.0002	.0027	.0121	.0333	.0706	.1260	.1998	.2898	.3917	.5000
	5	.0000	.0002	.0012	.0047	.0129	.0288	.0556	.0963	.1529	.2266
	6	.0000	.0000	.0001	.0004	.0013	.0038	.0090	.0188	.0357	.0625
	7	.0000	.0000	.0000	.0000	.0001	.0002	.0006	.0016	.0037	.0078
8	1	.3366	.5695	.7275	.8322	.8999	.9424	.9681	.9832	.9916	.9961
	2	.0572	.1869	.3428	.4967	.6329	.7447	.8309	.8936	.9368	.9648
	3	.0058	.0381	.1052	.2031	.3215	.4482	.5722	.6846	.7799	.8555
	4	.0004	.0050	.0214	.0563	.1138	.1941	.2936	.4059	.5230	.6367
	5	.0000	.0004	.0029	.0104	.0273	.0580	.1061	.1737	.2604	.3633
	6	.0000	.0000	.0002	.0012	.0042	.0113	.0253	.0498	.0885	.1445
	7	.0000	.0000	.0000	.0001	.0004	.0013	.0036	.0085	.0181	.0352
	8	.0000	.0000	.0000	.0000	.0000	.0001	.0002	.0007	.0017	.0039
9	1	.3698	.6126	.7684	.8658	.9249	.9596	.9793	.9899	.9954	.9980
	2	.0712	.2252	.4005	.5638	.6997	.8040	.8789	.9295	.9615	.9805
	3	.0084	.0530	.1409	.2618	.3993	.5372	.6627	.7682	.8505	.9102
	4	.0006	.0083	.0339	.0856	.1657	.2703	.3911	.5174	.6386	.7461
	5	.0000	.0009	.0056	.0196	.0489	.0988	.1717	.2666	.3786	.5000
	6	.0000	.0001	.0006	.0031	.0100	.0253	.0536	.0994	.1658	.2539
	7	.0000	.0000	.0000	.0003	.0013	.0043	.0112	.0250	.0498	.0898
	8	.0000	.0000	.0000	.0000	.0001	.0004	.0014	.0038	.0091	.0195
	9	.0000	.0000	.0000	.0000	.0000	.0000	.0001	.0003	.0008	.0020

Linear interpolation will be accurate at most to two decimal places.

CUMULATIVE TERMS, BINOMIAL DISTRIBUTION (Continued)

n	x'	.05	.10	.15	.20	θ .25	.30	.35	.40	.45	.50
10	1	.4013	.6513	.8031	.8926	.9437	.9718	.9865	.9940	.9975	.9990
	2	.0861	.2639	.4557	.6242	.7560	.8507	.9140	.9536	.9767	.9893
	3	.0115	.0702	.1798	.3222	.4744	.6172	.7384	.8327	.9004	.9453
	4	.0010	.0128	.0500	.1209	.2241	.3504	.4862	.6177	.7340	.8281
	5	.0001	.0016	.0099	.0328	.0781	.1503	.2485	.3669	.4956	.6230
	6	.0000	.0001	.0014	.0064	.0197	.0473	.0949	.1662	.2616	.3770
	7	.0000	.0000	.0001	.0009	.0035	.0106	.0260	.0548	.1020	.1719
	8	.0000	.0000	.0000	.0001	.0004	.0016	.0048	.0123	.0274	.0547
	9	.0000	.0000	.0000	.0000	.0000	.0001	.0005	.0017	.0045	.0107
	10	.0000	.0000	.0000	.0000	.0000	.0000	.0000	.0001	.0003	.0010
11	1	.4312	.6862	.8327	.9141	.9578	.9802	.9912	.9964	.9986	.9995
	2	.1019	.3026	.5078	.6779	.8029	.8870	.9394	.9698	.9861	.9941
	3	.0152	.0896	.2212	.3826	.5448	.6873	.7999	.8811	.9348	.9673
	4	.0016	.0185	.0694	.1611	.2867	.4304	.5744	.7037	.8089	.8867
	5	.0001	.0028	.0159	.0504	.1146	.2103	.3317	.4672	.6029	.7256
	6	.0000	.0003	.0027	.0117	.0343	.0782	.1487	.2465	.3669	.5000
	7	.0000	.0000	.0003	.0020	.0076	.0216	.0501	.0994	.1738	.2744
	8	.0000	.0000	.0000	.0002	.0012	.0043	.0122	.0293	.0610	.1133
	9	.0000	.0000	.0000	.0000	.0001	.0006	.0020	.0059	.0148	.0327
	10	.0000	.0000	.0000	.0000	.0000	.0000	.0002	.0007	.0022	.0059
	11	.0000	.0000	.0000	.0000	.0000	.0000	.0000	.0000	.0002	.0005
12	1	.4596	.7176	.8578	.9313	.9683	.9862	.9943	.9978	.9992	.9998
	2	.1184	.3410	.5565	.7251	.8416	.9150	.9576	.9804	.9917	.9968
	3	.0196	.1109	.2642	.4417	.6093	.7472	.8487	.9166	.9579	.9807
	4	.0022	.0256	.0922	.2054	.3512	.5075	.6533	.7747	.8655	.9270
	5	.0002	.0043	.0239	.0726	.1576	.2763	.4167	.5618	.6956	.8062
	6	.0000	.0005	.0046	.0194	.0544	.1178	.2127	.3348	.4731	.6128
	7	.0000	.0001	.0007	.0039	.0143	.0386	.0846	.1582	.2607	.3872
	8	.0000	.0000	.0001	.0006	.0028	.0095	.0255	.0573	.1117	.1938
	9	.0000	.0000	.0000	.0001	.0004	.0017	.0056	.0153	.0356	.0730
	10	.0000	.0000	.0000	.0000	.0000	.0002	.0008	.0028	.0079	.0193
	11	.0000	.0000	.0000	.0000	.0000	.0000	.0001	.0003	.0011	.0032
	12	.0000	.0000	.0000	.0000	.0000	.0000	.0000	.0000	.0001	.0002
13	1	.4867	.7458	.8791	.9450	.9762	.9903	.9963	.9987	.9996	.9999
	2	.1354	.3787	.6017	.7664	.8733	.9363	.9704	.9874	.9951	.9983
	3	.0245	.1339	.2704	.4983	.6674	.7975	.8868	.9421	.9731	.9888
	4	.0031	.0342	.0967	.2527	.4157	.5794	.7217	.8314	.9071	.9539
	5	.0003	.0065	.0260	.0991	.2060	.3457	.4995	.6470	.7721	.8666
	6	.0000	.0009	.0053	.0300	.0802	.1654	.2841	.4256	.5732	.7095
	7	.0000	.0001	.0013	.0070	.0243	.0624	.1295	.2288	.3563	.5000
	8	.0000	.0000	.0002	.0012	.0056	.0182	.0462	.0977	.1788	.2905
	9	.0000	.0000	.0000	.0002	.0010	.0040	.0126	.0321	.0698	.1334
	10	.0000	.0000	.0000	.0000	.0001	.0007	.0025	.0078	.0203	.0461
	11	.0000	.0000	.0000	.0000	.0000	.0001	.0003	.0013	.0041	.0112
	12	.0000	.0000	.0000	.0000	.0000	.0000	.0000	.0001	.0005	.0017
	13	.0000	.0000	.0000	.0000	.0000	.0000	.0000	.0000	.0000	.0001

CUMULATIVE TERMS, BINOMIAL DISTRIBUTION (Continued)

n	x′	.05	.10	.15	.20	θ .25	.30	.35	.40	.45	.50
14	1	.5123	.7712	.8972	.9560	.9822	.9932	.9976	.9992	.9998	.9999
	2	.1530	.4154	.6433	.8021	.8990	.9525	.9795	.9919	.9971	.9991
	3	.0301	.1584	.3521	.5519	.7189	.8392	.9161	.9602	.9830	.9935
	4	.0042	.0441	.1465	.3018	.4787	.6448	.7795	.8757	.9368	.9713
	5	.0004	.0092	.0467	.1298	.2585	.4158	.5773	.7207	.8328	.9102
	6	.0000	.0015	.0115	.0439	.1117	.2195	.3595	.5141	.6627	.7880
	7	.0000	.0002	.0022	.0116	.0383	.0933	.1836	.3075	.4539	.6047
	8	.0000	.0000	.0003	.0024	.0103	.0315	.0753	.1501	.2586	.3953
	9	.0000	.0000	.0000	.0004	.0022	.0083	.0243	.0583	.1189	.2120
	10	.0000	.0000	.0000	.0000	.0003	.0017	.0060	.0175	.0426	.0898
	11	.0000	.0000	.0000	.0000	.0000	.0002	.0011	.0039	.0114	.0287
	12	.0000	.0000	.0000	.0000	.0000	.0000	.0001	.0006	.0022	.0065
	13	.0000	.0000	.0000	.0000	.0000	.0000	.0000	.0001	.0003	.0009
	14	.0000	.0000	.0000	.0000	.0000	.0000	.0000	.0000	.0000	.0001
15	1	.5367	.7941	.9126	.9648	.9866	.9953	.9984	.9995	.9999	1.0000
	2	.1710	.4510	.6814	.8329	.9198	.9647	.9858	.9948	.9983	.9995
	3	.0362	.1841	.3958	.6020	.7639	.8732	.9383	.9729	.9893	.9963
	4	.0055	.0556	.1773	.3518	.5387	.7031	.8273	.9095	.9576	.9824
	5	.0006	.0127	.0617	.1642	.3135	.4845	.6481	.7827	.8796	.9408
	6	.0001	.0022	.0168	.0611	.1484	.2784	.4357	.5968	.7392	.8491
	7	.0000	.0003	.0036	.0181	.0566	.1311	.2452	.3902	.5478	.6964
	8	.0000	.0000	.0006	.0042	.0173	.0500	.1132	.2131	.3465	.5000
	9	.0000	.0000	.0001	.0008	.0042	.0152	.0422	.0950	.1818	.3036
	10	.0000	.0000	.0000	.0001	.0008	.0037	.0124	.0338	.0769	.1509
	11	.0000	.0000	.0000	.0000	.0001	.0007	.0028	.0093	.0255	.0592
	12	.0000	.0000	.0000	.0000	.0000	.0001	.0005	.0019	.0063	.0176
	13	.0000	.0000	.0000	.0000	.0000	.0000	.0001	.0003	.0011	.0037
	14	.0000	.0000	.0000	.0000	.0000	.0000	.0000	.0000	.0001	.0005
	15	.0000	.0000	.0000	.0000	.0000	.0000	.0000	.0000	.0000	.0000
16	1	.5599	.8147	.9257	.9719	.9900	.9967	.9990	.9997	.9999	1.0000
	2	.1892	.4853	.7161	.8593	.9365	.9739	.9902	.9967	.9990	.9997
	3	.0429	.2108	.4386	.6482	.8029	.9006	.9549	.9817	.9934	.9979
	4	.0070	.0684	.2101	.4019	.5950	.7541	.8661	.9349	.9719	.9894
	5	.0009	.0170	.0791	.2018	.3698	.5501	.7108	.8334	.9147	.9616
	6	.0001	.0033	.0235	.0817	.1897	.3402	.5100	.6712	.8024	.8949
	7	.0000	.0005	.0056	.0267	.0796	.1753	.3119	.4728	.6340	.7228
	8	.0000	.0001	.0011	.0070	.0271	.0744	.1594	.2839	.4371	.5982
	9	.0000	.0000	.0002	.0015	.0075	.0257	.0671	.1423	.2559	.4018
	10	.0000	.0000	.0000	.0002	.0016	.0071	.0229	.0583	.1241	.2272
	11	.0000	.0000	.0000	.0000	.0003	.0016	.0062	.0191	.0486	.1051
	12	.0000	.0000	.0000	.0000	.0000	.0003	.0013	.0049	.0149	.0384
	13	.0000	.0000	.0000	.0000	.0000	.0000	.0002	.0009	.0035	.0106
	14	.0000	.0000	.0000	.0000	.0000	.0000	.0000	.0001	.0006	.0021
	15	.0000	.0000	.0000	.0000	.0000	.0000	.0000	.0000	.0001	.0003
	16	.0000	.0000	.0000	.0000	.0000	.0000	.0000	.0000	.0000	.0000

CUMULATIVE TERMS, BINOMIAL DISTRIBUTION (Continued)

n	x′	.05	.10	.15	.20	.25	.30	.35	.40	.45	.50
17	1	.5819	.8332	.9369	.9775	.9925	.9977	.9993	.9998	1.0000	1.0000
	2	.2078	.5182	.7475	.8818	.9499	.9807	.9933	.9979	.9994	.9999
	3	.0503	.2382	.4802	.6904	.8363	.9226	.9673	.9877	.9959	.9988
	4	.0088	.0826	.2444	.4511	.6470	.7981	.8972	.9536	.9816	.9936
	5	.0012	.0221	.0987	.2418	.4261	.6113	.7652	.8740	.9404	.9755
	6	.0001	.0047	.0319	.1057	.2347	.4032	.5803	.7361	.8529	.9283
	7	.0000	.0008	.0083	.0377	.1071	.2248	.3812	.5522	.7098	.8338
	8	.0000	.0001	.0017	.0109	.0402	.1046	.2128	.3595	.5257	.6855
	9	.0000	.0000	.0003	.0026	.0124	.0403	.0994	.1989	.3374	.5000
	10	.0000	.0000	.0000	.0005	.0031	.0127	.0383	.0919	.1834	.3145
	11	.0000	.0000	.0000	.0001	.0006	.0032	.0120	.0348	.0826	.1662
	12	.0000	.0000	.0000	.0000	.0001	.0007	.0030	.0106	.0301	.0717
	13	.0000	.0000	.0000	.0000	.0000	.0001	.0006	.0025	.0086	.0245
	14	.0000	.0000	.0000	.0000	.0000	.0000	.0000	.0005	.0019	.0064
	15	.0000	.0000	.0000	.0000	.0000	.0000	.0000	.0000	.0003	.0012
	16	.0000	.0000	.0000	.0000	.0000	.0000	.0000	.0000	.0000	.0001
	17	.0000	.0000	.0000	.0000	.0000	.0000	.0000	.0000	.0000	.0000
18	1	.6028	.8499	.9464	.9820	.9944	.9984	.9996	.9999	1.0000	1.0000
	2	.2265	.5497	.7759	.9009	.9605	.9858	.9954	.9987	.9997	.9999
	3	.0581	.2662	.5203	.7287	.8647	.9400	.9764	.9918	.9975	.9993
	4	.0109	.0982	.2798	.4990	.6943	.8354	.9217	.9672	.9880	.9962
	5	.0015	.0282	.1206	.2836	.4813	.6673	.8114	.9058	.9589	.9846
	6	.0002	.0064	.0419	.1329	.2825	.4656	.6450	.7912	.8923	.9519
	7	.0000	.0012	.0118	.0513	.1390	.2783	.4509	.6257	.7742	.8811
	8	.0000	.0002	.0027	.0163	.0569	.1407	.2717	.4366	.6085	.7597
	9	.0000	.0000	.0005	.0043	.0193	.0596	.1391	.2632	.4222	.5927
	10	.0000	.0000	.0001	.0009	.0054	.0210	.0597	.1347	.2527	.4073
	11	.0000	.0000	.0000	.0002	.0012	.0061	.0212	.0576	.1280	.2403
	12	.0000	.0000	.0000	.0000	.0002	.0014	.0062	.0203	.0537	.1189
	13	.0000	.0000	.0000	.0000	.0000	.0003	.0014	.0058	.0183	.0481
	14	.0000	.0000	.0000	.0000	.0000	.0000	.0003	.0013	.0049	.0154
	15	.0000	.0000	.0000	.0000	.0000	.0000	.0000	.0002	.0010	.0038
	16	.0000	.0000	.0000	.0000	.0000	.0000	.0000	.0000	.0001	.0007
	17	.0000	.0000	.0000	.0000	.0000	.0000	.0000	.0000	.0000	.0001
	18	.0000	.0000	.0000	.0000	.0000	.0000	.0000	.0000	.0000	.0000
19	1	.6226	.8649	.9544	.9856	.9958	.9989	.9997	.9999	1.0000	1.0000
	2	.2453	.5797	.8015	.9171	.9690	.9896	.9969	.9992	.9998	1.0000
	3	.0665	.2946	.5587	.7631	.8887	.9538	.9830	.9945	.9985	.9996
	4	.0132	.1150	.3159	.5449	.7369	.8668	.9409	.9770	.9923	.9978
	5	.0020	.0352	.1444	.3267	.5346	.7178	.8500	.9304	.9720	.9904
	6	.0002	.0086	.0537	.1631	.3322	.5261	.7032	.8371	.9223	.9682
	7	.0000	.0017	.0163	.0676	.1749	.3345	.5188	.6919	.8273	.9165
	8	.0000	.0003	.0041	.0233	.0775	.1820	.3344	.5122	.6831	.8204
	9	.0000	.0000	.0008	.0067	.0287	.0839	.1855	.3325	.5060	.6762
	10	.0000	.0000	.0001	.0016	.0089	.0326	.0875	.1861	.3290	.5000

CUMULATIVE TERMS, BINOMIAL DISTRIBUTION (Continued)

n	x'	.05	.10	.15	.20	.25	.30	.35	.40	.45	.50
19	11	.0000	.0000	.0000	.0003	.0023	.0105	.0347	.0885	.1841	.3238
	12	.0000	.0000	.0000	.0000	.0005	.0028	.0114	.0352	.0871	.1796
	13	.0000	.0000	.0000	.0000	.0001	.0006	.0031	.0116	.0342	.0835
	14	.0000	.0000	.0000	.0000	.0000	.0001	.0007	.0031	.0109	.0318
	15	.0000	.0000	.0000	.0000	.0000	.0000	.0001	.0006	.0028	.0096
	16	.0000	.0000	.0000	.0000	.0000	.0000	.0000	.0001	.0005	.0022
	17	.0000	.0000	.0000	.0000	.0000	.0000	.0000	.0000	.0001	.0004
	18	.0000	.0000	.0000	.0000	.0000	.0000	.0000	.0000	.0000	.0000
	19	.0000	.0000	.0000	.0000	.0000	.0000	.0000	.0000	.0000	.0000
20	1	.6415	.8784	.9612	.9885	.9968	.9992	.9998	1.0000	1.0000	1.0000
	2	.2642	.6083	.8244	.9308	.9757	.9924	.9979	.9995	.9999	1.0000
	3	.0755	.3231	.5951	.7939	.9087	.9645	.9879	.9964	.9991	.9998
	4	.0159	.1330	.3523	.5886	.7748	.8929	.9556	.9840	.9951	.9987
	5	.0026	.0432	.1702	.3704	.5852	.7625	.8818	.9490	.9811	.9941
	6	.0003	.0113	.0673	.1958	.3828	.5836	.7546	.8744	.9447	.9793
	7	.0000	.0024	.0219	.0867	.2142	.3920	.5834	.7500	.8701	.9423
	8	.0000	.0004	.0059	.0321	.1018	.2277	.3990	.5841	.7480	.8684
	9	.0000	.0001	.0013	.0100	.0409	.1133	.2376	.4044	.5857	.7483
	10	.0000	.0000	.0002	.0026	.0139	.0480	.1218	.2447	.4086	.5881
	11	.0000	.0000	.0000	.0006	.0039	.0171	.0532	.1275	.2493	.4119
	12	.0000	.0000	.0000	.0001	.0009	.0051	.0196	.0565	.1308	.2517
	13	.0000	.0000	.0000	.0000	.0002	.0013	.0060	.0210	.0580	.1316
	14	.0000	.0000	.0000	.0000	.0000	.0003	.0015	.0065	.0214	.0577
	15	.0000	.0000	.0000	.0000	.0000	.0000	.0003	.0016	.0064	.0207
	16	.0000	.0000	.0000	.0000	.0000	.0000	.0000	.0003	.0015	.0059
	17	.0000	.0000	.0000	.0000	.0000	.0000	.0000	.0000	.0003	.0013
	18	.0000	.0000	.0000	.0000	.0000	.0000	.0000	.0000	.0000	.0002
	19	.0000	.0000	.0000	.0000	.0000	.0000	.0000	.0000	.0000	.0000
	20	.0000	.0000	.0000	.0000	.0000	.0000	.0000	.0000	.0000	.0000

INDIVIDUAL TERMS, POISSON DISTRIBUTION

The Poisson probability function is given by

$$f(x;\lambda) = \frac{\lambda^x e^{-\lambda}}{x!}, \qquad \lambda > 0, \; x = 0, 1, 2, \ldots .$$

This table contains the individual terms of $f(x;\lambda)$ for specified values of x and λ.

INDIVIDUAL TERMS, POISSON DISTRIBUTION (Continued)

λ

x	0.1	0.2	0.3	0.4	0.5	0.6	0.7	0.8	0.9	1.0
0	.9048	.8187	.7408	.6703	.6065	.5488	.4966	.4493	.4066	.3679
1	.0905	.1637	.2222	.2681	.3033	.3293	.3476	.3595	.3659	.3679
2	.0045	.0164	.0333	.0536	.0758	.0988	.1217	.1438	.1647	.1839
3	.0002	.0011	.0033	.0072	.0126	.0198	.0284	.0383	.0494	.0613
4	.0000	.0001	.0002	.0007	.0016	.0030	.0050	.0077	.0111	.0153
5	.0000	.0000	.0000	.0001	.0002	.0004	.0007	.0012	.0020	.0031
6	.0000	.0000	.0000	.0000	.0000	.0000	.0001	.0002	.0003	.0005
7	.0000	.0000	.0000	.0000	.0000	.0000	.0000	.0000	.0000	.0001

λ

x	1.1	1.2	1.3	1.4	1.5	1.6	1.7	1.8	1.9	2.0
0	.3329	.3012	.2725	.2466	.2231	.2019	.1827	.1653	.1496	.1353
1	.3662	.3614	.3543	.3452	.3347	.3230	.3106	.2975	.2842	.2707
2	.2014	.2169	.2303	.2417	.2510	.2584	.2640	.2678	.2700	.2707
3	.0738	.0867	.0998	.1128	.1255	.1378	.1496	.1607	.1710	.1804
4	.0203	.0260	.0324	.0395	.0471	.0551	.0636	.0723	.0812	.0902
5	.0045	.0062	.0084	.0111	.0141	.0176	.0216	.0260	.0309	.0361
6	.0008	.0012	.0018	.0026	.0035	.0047	.0061	.0078	.0098	.0120
7	.0001	.0002	.0003	.0005	.0008	.0011	.0015	.0020	.0027	.0034
8	.0000	.0000	.0001	.0001	.0001	.0002	.0003	.0005	.0006	.0009
9	.0000	.0000	.0000	.0000	.0000	.0000	.0001	.0001	.0001	.0002

λ

x	2.1	2.2	2.3	2.4	2.5	2.6	2.7	2.8	2.9	3.0
0	.1225	.1108	.1003	.0907	.0821	.0743	.0672	.0608	.0550	.0498
1	.2572	.2438	.2306	.2177	.2052	.1931	.1815	.1703	.1596	.1494
2	.2700	.2681	.2652	.2613	.2565	.2510	.2450	.2384	.2314	.2240
3	.1890	.1966	.2033	.2090	.2138	.2176	.2205	.2225	.2237	.2240
4	.0992	.1082	.1169	.1254	.1336	.1414	.1488	.1557	.1622	.1680
5	.0417	.0476	.0538	.0602	.0668	.0735	.0804	.0872	.0940	.1008
6	.0146	.0174	.0206	.0241	.0278	.0319	.0362	.0407	.0455	.0504
7	.0044	.0055	.0068	.0083	.0099	.0118	.0139	.0163	.0188	.0216
8	.0011	.0015	.0019	.0025	.0031	.0038	.0047	.0057	.0068	.0081
9	.0003	.0004	.0005	.0007	.0009	.0011	.0014	.0018	.0022	.0027
10	.0001	.0001	.0001	.0002	.0002	.0003	.0004	.0005	.0006	.0008
11	.0000	.0000	.0000	.0000	.0000	.0001	.0001	.0001	.0002	.0002
12	.0000	.0000	.0000	.0000	.0000	.0000	.0000	.0000	.0000	.0001

λ

x	3.1	3.2	3.3	3.4	3.5	3.6	3.7	3.8	3.9	4.0
0	.0450	.0408	.0369	.0334	.0302	.0273	.0247	.0224	.0202	.0183
1	.1397	.1304	.1217	.1135	.1057	.0984	.0915	.0850	.0789	.0733
2	.2165	.2087	.2008	.1929	.1850	.1771	.1692	.1615	.1539	.1465
3	.2237	.2226	.2209	.2186	.2158	.2125	.2087	.2046	.2001	.1954
4	.1734	.1781	.1823	.1858	.1888	.1912	.1931	.1944	.1951	.1954
5	.1075	.1140	.1203	.1264	.1322	.1377	.1429	.1477	.1522	.1563
6	.0555	.0608	.0662	.0716	.0771	.0826	.0881	.0936	.0989	.1042
7	.0246	.0278	.0312	.0348	.0385	.0425	.0466	.0508	.0551	.0595
8	.0095	.0111	.0129	.0148	.0169	.0191	.0215	.0241	.0269	.0298
9	.0033	.0040	.0047	.0056	.0066	.0076	.0089	.0102	.0116	.0132

INDIVIDUAL TERMS, POISSON DISTRIBUTION (Continued)

λ

x	3.1	3.2	3.3	3.4	3.5	3.6	3.7	3.8	3.9	4.0
10	.0010	.0013	.0016	.0019	.0023	.0028	.0033	.0039	.0045	.0053
11	.0003	.0004	.0005	.0006	.0007	.0009	.0011	.0013	.0016	.0019
12	.0001	.0001	.0001	.0002	.0002	.0003	.0003	.0004	.0005	.0006
13	.0000	.0000	.0000	.0000	.0001	.0001	.0001	.0001	.0002	.0002
14	.0000	.0000	.0000	.0000	.0000	.0000	.0000	.0000	.0000	.0001

λ

x	4.1	4.2	4.3	4.4	4.5	4.6	4.7	4.8	4.9	5.0
0	.0166	.0150	.0136	.0123	.0111	.0101	.0091	.0082	.0074	.0067
1	.0679	.0630	.0583	.0540	.0500	.0462	.0427	.0395	.0365	.0337
2	.1393	.1323	.1254	.1188	.1125	.1063	.1005	.0948	.0894	.0842
3	.1904	.1852	.1798	.1743	.1687	.1631	.1574	.1517	.1460	.1404
4	.1951	.1944	.1933	.1917	.1898	.1875	.1849	.1820	.1789	.1755
5	.1600	.1633	.1662	.1687	.1708	.1725	.1738	.1747	.1753	.1755
6	.1093	.1143	.1191	.1237	.1281	.1323	.1362	.1398	.1432	.1462
7	.0640	.0686	.0732	.0778	.0824	.0869	.0914	.0959	.1002	.1044
8	.0328	.0360	.0393	.0428	.0463	.0500	.0537	.0575	.0614	.0653
9	.0150	.0168	.0188	.0209	.0232	.0255	.0280	.0307	.0334	.0363
10	.0061	.0071	.0081	.0092	.0104	.0118	.0132	.0147	.0164	.0181
11	.0023	.0027	.0032	.0037	.0043	.0049	.0056	.0064	.0073	.0082
12	.0008	.0009	.0011	.0014	.0016	.0019	.0022	.0026	.0030	.0034
13	.0002	.0003	.0004	.0005	.0006	.0007	.0008	.0009	.0011	.0013
14	.0001	.0001	.0001	.0001	.0002	.0002	.0003	.0003	.0004	.0005
15	.0000	.0000	.0000	.0000	.0001	.0001	.0001	.0001	.0001	.0002

λ

x	5.1	5.2	5.3	5.4	5.5	5.6	5.7	5.8	5.9	6.0
0	.0061	.0055	.0050	.0045	.0041	.0037	.0033	.0030	.0027	.0025
1	.0311	.0287	.0265	.0244	.0225	.0207	.0191	.0176	.0162	.0149
2	.0793	.0746	.0701	.0659	.0618	.0580	.0544	.0509	.0477	.0446
3	.1348	.1293	.1239	.1185	.1133	.1082	.1033	.0985	.0938	.0892
4	.1719	.1681	.1641	.1600	.1558	.1515	.1472	.1428	.1383	.1339
5	.1753	.1748	.1740	.1728	.1714	.1697	.1678	.1656	.1632	.1606
6	.1490	.1515	.1537	.1555	.1571	.1584	.1594	.1601	.1605	.1606
7	.1086	.1125	.1163	.1200	.1234	.1267	.1298	.1326	.1353	.1377
8	.0692	.0731	.0771	.0810	.0849	.0887	.0925	.0962	.0998	.1033
9	.0392	.0423	.0454	.0486	.0519	.0552	.0586	.0620	.0654	.0688
10	.0200	.0220	.0241	.0262	.0285	.0309	.0334	.0359	.0386	.0413
11	.0093	.0104	.0116	.0129	.0143	.0157	.0173	.0190	.0207	.0225
12	.0039	.0045	.0051	.0058	.0065	.0073	.0082	.0092	.0102	.0113
13	.0015	.0018	.0021	.0024	.0028	.0032	.0036	.0041	.0046	.0052
14	.0006	.0007	.0008	.0009	.0011	.0013	.0015	.0017	.0019	.0022
15	.0002	.0002	.0003	.0003	.0004	.0005	.0006	.0007	.0008	.0009
16	.0001	.0001	.0001	.0001	.0001	.0002	.0002	.0002	.0003	.0003
17	.0000	.0000	.0000	.0000	.0000	.0000	.0001	.0001	.0001	.0001

INDIVIDUAL TERMS, POISSON DISTRIBUTION (Continued)

λ

x	6.1	6.2	6.3	6.4	6.5	6.6	6.7	6.8	6.9	7.0
0	.0022	.0020	.0018	.0017	.0015	.0014	.0012	.0011	.0010	.0009
1	.0137	.0126	.0116	.0106	.0098	.0090	.0082	.0076	.0070	.0064
2	.0417	.0390	.0364	.0340	.0318	.0296	.0276	.0258	.0240	.0223
3	.0848	.0806	.0765	.0726	.0688	.0652	.0617	.0584	.0552	.0521
4	.1294	.1249	.1205	.1162	.1118	.1076	.1034	.0992	.0952	.0912
5	.1579	.1549	.1519	.1487	.1454	.1420	.1385	.1349	.1314	.1277
6	.1605	.1601	.1595	.1586	.1575	.1562	.1546	.1529	.1511	.1490
7	.1399	.1418	.1435	.1450	.1462	.1472	.1480	.1486	.1489	.1490
8	.1066	.1099	.1130	.1160	.1188	.1215	.1240	.1263	.1284	.1304
9	.0723	.0757	.0791	.0825	.0858	.0891	.0923	.0954	.0985	.1014
10	.0441	.0469	.0498	.0528	.0558	.0588	.0618	.0649	.0679	.0710
11	.0245	.0265	.0285	.0307	.0330	.0353	.0377	.0401	.0426	.0452
12	.0124	.0137	.0150	.0164	.0179	.0194	.0210	.0227	.0245	.0264
13	.0058	.0065	.0073	.0081	.0089	.0098	.0108	.0119	.0130	.0142
14	.0025	.0029	.0033	.0037	.0041	.0046	.0052	.0058	.0064	.0071
15	.0010	.0012	.0014	.0016	.0018	.0020	.0023	.0026	.0029	.0033
16	.0004	.0005	.0005	.0006	.0007	.0008	.0010	.0011	.0013	.0014
17	.0001	.0002	.0002	.0002	.0003	.0003	.0004	.0004	.0005	.0006
18	.0000	.0001	.0001	.0001	.0001	.0001	.0001	.0002	.0002	.0002
19	.0000	.0000	.0000	.0000	.0000	.0000	.0000	.0001	.0001	.0001

λ

x	7.1	7.2	7.3	7.4	7.5	7.6	7.7	7.8	7.9	8.0
0	.0008	.0007	.0007	.0006	.0006	.0005	.0005	.0004	.0004	.0003
1	.0059	.0054	.0049	.0045	.0041	.0038	.0035	.0032	.0029	.0027
2	.0208	.0194	.0180	.0167	.0156	.0145	.0134	.0125	.0116	.0107
3	.0492	.0464	.0438	.0413	.0389	.0366	.0345	.0324	.0305	.0286
4	.0874	.0836	.0799	.0764	.0729	.0696	.0663	.0632	.0602	.0573
5	.1241	.1204	.1167	.1130	.1094	.1057	.1021	.0986	.0951	.0916
6	.1468	.1445	.1420	.1394	.1367	.1339	.1311	.1282	.1252	.1221
7	.1489	.1486	.1481	.1474	.1465	.1454	.1442	.1428	.1413	.1396
8	.1321	.1337	.1351	.1363	.1373	.1382	.1388	.1392	.1395	.1396
9	.1042	.1070	.1096	.1121	.1144	.1167	.1187	.1207	.1224	.1241
10	.0740	.0770	.0800	.0829	.0858	.0887	.0914	.0941	.0967	.0993
11	.0478	.0504	.0531	.0558	.0585	.0613	.0640	.0667	.0695	.0722
12	.0283	.0303	.0323	.0344	.0366	.0388	.0411	.0434	.0457	.0481
13	.0154	.0168	.0181	.0196	.0211	.0227	.0243	.0260	.0278	.0296
14	.0078	.0086	.0095	.0104	.0113	.0123	.0134	.0145	.0157	.0169
15	.0037	.0041	.0046	.0051	.0057	.0062	.0069	.0075	.0083	.0090
16	.0016	.0019	.0021	.0024	.0026	.0030	.0033	.0037	.0041	.0045
17	.0007	.0008	.0009	.0010	.0012	.0013	.0015	.0017	.0019	.0021
18	.0003	.0003	.0004	.0004	.0005	.0006	.0006	.0007	.0008	.0009
19	.0001	.0001	.0001	.0002	.0002	.0002	.0003	.0003	.0003	.0004
20	.0000	.0000	.0001	.0001	.0001	.0001	.0001	.0001	.0001	.0002
21	.0000	.0000	.0000	.0000	.0000	.0000	.0000	.0000	.0001	.0001

INDIVIDUAL TERMS, POISSON DISTRIBUTION (Continued)

x	8.1	8.2	8.3	8.4	8.5	8.6	8.7	8.8	8.9	9.0
0	.0003	.0003	.0002	.0002	.0002	.0002	.0002	.0002	.0001	.0001
1	.0025	.0023	.0021	.0019	.0017	.0016	.0014	.0013	.0012	.0011
2	.0100	.0092	.0086	.0079	.0074	.0068	.0063	.0058	.0054	.0050
3	.0269	.0252	.0237	.0222	.0208	.0195	.0183	.0171	.0160	.0150
4	.0544	.0517	.0491	.0466	.0443	.0420	.0398	.0377	.0357	.0337
5	.0882	.0849	.0816	.0784	.0752	.0722	.0692	.0663	.0635	.0607
6	.1191	.1160	.1128	.1097	.1066	.1034	.1003	.0972	.0941	.0911
7	.1378	.1358	.1338	.1317	.1294	.1271	.1247	.1222	.1197	.1171
8	.1395	.1392	.1388	.1382	.1375	.1366	.1356	.1344	.1332	.1318
9	.1256	.1269	.1280	.1290	.1299	.1306	.1311	.1315	.1317	.1318
10	.1017	.1040	.1063	.1084	.1104	.1123	.1140	.1157	.1172	.1186
11	.0749	.0776	.0802	.0828	.0853	.0878	.0902	.0925	.0948	.0970
12	.0505	.0530	.0555	.0579	.0604	.0629	.0654	.0679	.0703	.0728
13	.0315	.0334	.0354	.0374	.0395	.0416	.0438	.0459	.0481	.0504
14	.0182	.0196	.0210	.0225	.0240	.0256	.0272	.0289	.0306	.0324
15	.0098	.0107	.0116	.0126	.0136	.0147	.0158	.0169	.0182	.0194
16	.0050	.0055	.0060	.0066	.0072	.0079	.0086	.0093	.0101	.0109
17	.0024	.0026	.0029	.0033	.0036	.0040	.0044	.0048	.0053	.0058
18	.0011	.0012	.0014	.0015	.0017	.0019	.0021	.0024	.0026	.0029
19	.0005	.0005	.0006	.0007	.0008	.0009	.0010	.0011	.0012	.0014
20	.0002	.0002	.0002	.0003	.0003	.0004	.0004	.0005	.0005	.0006
21	.0001	.0001	.0001	.0001	.0001	.0002	.0002	.0002	.0002	.0003
22	.0000	.0000	.0000	.0000	.0001	.0001	.0001	.0001	.0001	.0001

x	9.1	9.2	9.3	9.4	9.5	9.6	9.7	9.8	9.9	10
0	.0001	.0001	.0001	.0001	.0001	.0001	.0001	.0001	.0001	.0000
1	.0010	.0009	.0009	.0008	.0007	.0007	.0006	.0005	.0005	.0005
2	.0046	.0043	.0040	.0037	.0034	.0031	.0029	.0027	.0025	.0023
3	.0140	.0131	.0123	.0115	.0107	.0100	.0093	.0087	.0081	.0076
4	.0319	.0302	.0285	.0269	.0254	.0240	.0226	.0213	.0201	.0189
5	.0581	.0555	.0530	.0506	.0483	.0460	.0439	.0418	.0398	.0378
6	.0881	.0851	.0822	.0793	.0764	.0736	.0709	.0682	.0656	.0631
7	.1145	.1118	.1091	.1064	.1037	.1010	.0982	.0955	.0928	.0901
8	.1302	.1286	.1269	.1251	.1232	.1212	.1191	.1170	.1148	.1126
9	.1317	.1315	.1311	.1306	.1300	.1293	.1284	.1274	.1263	.1251
10	.1198	.1210	.1219	.1228	.1235	.1241	.1245	.1249	.1250	.1251
11	.0991	.1012	.1031	.1049	.1067	.1083	.1098	.1112	.1125	.1137
12	.0752	.0776	.0799	.0822	.0844	.0866	.0888	.0908	.0928	.0948
13	.0526	.0549	.0572	.0594	.0617	.0640	.0662	.0685	.0707	.0729
14	.0342	.0361	.0380	.0399	.0419	.0439	.0459	.0479	.0500	.0521
15	.0208	.0221	.0235	.0250	.0265	.0281	.0297	.0313	.0330	.0347
16	.0118	.0127	.0137	.0147	.0157	.0168	.0180	.0192	.0204	.0217
17	.0063	.0069	.0075	.0081	.0088	.0095	.0103	.0111	.0119	.0128
18	.0032	.0035	.0039	.0042	.0046	.0051	.0055	.0060	.0065	.0071
19	.0015	.0017	.0019	.0021	.0023	.0026	.0028	.0031	.0034	.0037

INDIVIDUAL TERMS, POISSON DISTRIBUTION (Continued)

x	9.1	9.2	9.3	9.4	9.5	9.6	9.7	9.8	9.9	10
20	.0007	.0008	.0009	.0010	.0011	.0012	.0014	.0015	.0017	.0019
21	.0003	.0003	.0004	.0004	.0005	.0006	.0006	.0007	.0008	.0009
22	.0001	.0001	.0002	.0002	.0002	.0002	.0003	.0003	.0004	.0004
23	.0000	.0001	.0001	.0001	.0001	.0001	.0001	.0001	.0002	.0002
24	.0000	.0000	.0000	.0000	.0000	.0000	.0000	.0001	.0001	.0001

λ

x	11	12	13	14	15	16	17	18	19	20
0	.0000	.0000	.0000	.0000	.0000	.0000	.0000	.0000	.0000	.0000
1	.0002	.0001	.0000	.0000	.0000	.0000	.0000	.0000	.0000	.0000
2	.0010	.0004	.0002	.0001	.0000	.0000	.0000	.0000	.0000	.0000
3	.0037	.0018	.0008	.0004	.0002	.0001	.0000	.0000	.0000	.0000
4	.0102	.0053	.0027	.0013	.0006	.0003	.0001	.0001	.0000	.0000
5	.0224	.0127	.0070	.0037	.0019	.0010	.0005	.0002	.0001	.0001
6	.0411	.0255	.0152	.0087	.0048	.0026	.0014	.0007	.0004	.0002
7	.0646	.0437	.0281	.0174	.0104	.0060	.0034	.0018	.0010	.0005
8	.0888	.0655	.0457	.0304	.0194	.0120	.0072	.0042	.0024	.0013
9	.1085	.0874	.0661	.0473	.0324	.0213	.0135	.0083	.0050	.0029
10	.1194	.1048	.0859	.0663	.0486	.0341	.0230	.0150	.0095	.0058
11	.1194	.1144	.1015	.0844	.0663	.0496	.0355	.0245	.0164	.0106
12	.1094	.1144	.1099	.0984	.0829	.0661	.0504	.0368	.0259	.0176
13	.0926	.1056	.1099	.1060	.0956	.0814	.0658	.0509	.0378	.0271
14	.0728	.0905	.1021	.1060	.1024	.0930	.0800	.0655	.0514	.0387
15	.0534	.0724	.0885	.0989	.1024	.0992	.0906	.0786	.0650	.0516
16	.0367	.0543	.0719	.0866	.0960	.0992	.0963	.0884	.0772	.0646
17	.0237	.0383	.0550	.0713	.0847	.0934	.0963	.0936	.0863	.0760
18	.0145	.0256	.0397	.0554	.0706	.0830	.0909	.0936	.0911	.0844
19	.0084	.0161	.0272	.0409	.0557	.0699	.0814	.0887	.0911	.0888
20	.0046	.0097	.0177	.0286	.0418	.0559	.0692	.0798	.0866	.0888
21	.0024	.0055	.0109	.0191	.0299	.0426	.0560	.0684	.0783	.0846
22	.0012	.0030	.0065	.0121	.0204	.0310	.0433	.0560	.0676	.0769
23	.0006	.0016	.0037	.0074	.0133	.0216	.0320	.0438	.0559	.0669
24	.0003	.0008	.0020	.0043	.0083	.0144	.0226	.0328	.0442	.0557
25	.0001	.0004	.0010	.0024	.0050	.0092	.0154	.0237	.0336	.0446
26	.0000	.0002	.0005	.0013	.0029	.0057	.0101	.0164	.0246	.0343
27	.0000	.0001	.0002	.0007	.0016	.0034	.0063	.0109	.0173	.0254
28	.0000	.0000	.0001	.0003	.0009	.0019	.0038	.0070	.0117	.0181
29	.0000	.0000	.0001	.0002	.0004	.0011	.0023	.0044	.0077	.0125
30	.0000	.0000	.0000	.0001	.0002	.0006	.0013	.0026	.0049	.0083
31	.0000	.0000	.0000	.0000	.0001	.0003	.0007	.0015	.0030	.0054
32	.0000	.0000	.0000	.0000	.0001	.0001	.0004	.0009	.0018	.0034
33	.0000	.0000	.0000	.0000	.0000	.0001	.0002	.0005	.0010	.0020
34	.0000	.0000	.0000	.0000	.0000	.0000	.0001	.0002	.0006	.0012
35	.0000	.0000	.0000	.0000	.0000	.0000	.0000	.0001	.0003	.0007
36	.0000	.0000	.0000	.0000	.0000	.0000	.0000	.0001	.0002	.0004
37	.0000	.0000	.0000	.0000	.0000	.0000	.0000	.0000	.0001	.0002
38	.0000	.0000	.0000	.0000	.0000	.0000	.0000	.0000	.0000	.0001
39	.0000	.0000	.0000	.0000	.0000	.0000	.0000	.0000	.0000	.0001

CUMULATIVE TERMS, POISSON DISTRIBUTION

This table contains the values of

$$\sum_{x=x'}^{\infty} \frac{e^{-\lambda}\lambda^x}{x!}$$

for specified values of x' and λ. The cumulative Poisson distribution and the cumulative chi-square (χ^2) distribution are related as follows:

$$\sum_{x=0}^{x'-1} \frac{e^{-\lambda}\lambda^x}{x!} = 1 - F(\chi^2)$$

$$= \frac{1}{2^{\frac{n}{2}}\Gamma\left(\frac{n}{2}\right)} \int_{\chi^2}^{\infty} x^{\frac{n}{2}-1} e^{-\frac{x}{2}} dx$$

where $\lambda = \frac{1}{2}\chi^2$ and $x' = \frac{1}{2}n$.

Binomial and Poisson Distribution

CUMULATIVE TERMS, POISSON DISTRIBUTION (Continued)

x'	0.1	0.2	0.3	0.4	0.5	0.6	0.7	0.8	0.9	1.0
0	1.0000	1.0000	1.0000	1.0000	1.0000	1.0000	1.0000	1.0000	1.0000	1.0000
1	.0952	.1813	.2592	.3297	.3935	.4512	.5034	.5507	.5934	.6321
2	.0047	.0175	.0369	.0616	.0902	.1219	.1558	.1912	.2275	.2642
3	.0002	.0011	.0036	.0079	.0144	.0231	.0341	.0474	.0629	.0803
4	.0000	.0001	.0003	.0008	.0018	.0034	.0058	.0091	.0135	.0190
5	.0000	.0000	.0000	.0001	.0002	.0004	.0008	.0014	.0023	.0037
6	.0000	.0000	.0000	.0000	.0000	.0000	.0001	.0002	.0003	.0006
7	.0000	.0000	.0000	.0000	.0000	.0000	.0000	.0000	.0000	.0001

x'	1.1	1.2	1.3	1.4	1.5	1.6	1.7	1.8	1.9	2.0
0	1.0000	1.0000	1.0000	1.0000	1.0000	1.0000	1.0000	1.0000	1.0000	1.0000
1	.6671	.6988	.7275	.7534	.7769	.7981	.8173	.8347	.8504	.8647
2	.3010	.3374	.3732	.4082	.4422	.4751	.5068	.5372	.5663	.5940
3	.0996	.1205	.1429	.1665	.1912	.2166	.2428	.2694	.2963	.3233
4	.0257	.0338	.0431	.0537	.0656	.0788	.0932	.1087	.1253	.1429
5	.0054	.0077	.0107	.0143	.0186	.0237	.0296	.0364	.0441	.0527
6	.0010	.0015	.0022	.0032	.0045	.0060	.0080	.0104	.0132	.0166
7	.0001	.0003	.0004	.0006	.0009	.0013	.0019	.0026	.0034	.0045
8	.0000	.0000	.0001	.0001	.0002	.0003	.0004	.0006	.0008	.0011
9	.0000	.0000	.0000	.0000	.0000	.0000	.0001	.0001	.0002	.0002

x'	2.1	2.2	2.3	2.4	2.5	2.6	2.7	2.8	2.9	3.0
0	1.0000	1.0000	1.0000	1.0000	1.0000	1.0000	1.0000	1.0000	1.0000	1.0000
1	.8775	.8892	.8997	.9093	.9179	.9257	.9328	.9392	.9450	.9502
2	.6204	.6454	.6691	.6916	.7127	.7326	.7513	.7689	.7854	.8009
3	.3504	.3773	.4040	.4303	.4562	.4816	.5064	.5305	.5540	.5768
4	.1614	.1806	.2007	.2213	.2424	.2640	.2859	.3081	.3304	.3528
5	.0621	.0725	.0838	.0959	.1088	.1226	.1371	.1523	.1682	.1847
6	.0204	.0249	.0300	.0357	.0420	.0490	.0567	.0651	.0742	.0839
7	.0059	.0075	.0094	.0116	.0142	.0172	.0206	.0244	.0287	.0335
8	.0015	.0020	.0026	.0033	.0042	.0053	.0066	.0081	.0099	.0119
9	.0003	.0005	.0006	.0009	.0011	.0015	.0019	.0024	.0031	.0038
10	.0001	.0001	.0001	.0002	.0003	.0004	.0005	.0007	.0009	.0011
11	.0000	.0000	.0000	.0000	.0001	.0001	.0001	.0002	.0002	.0003
12	.0000	.0000	.0000	.0000	.0000	.0000	.0000	.0000	.0001	.0001

x'	3.1	3.2	3.3	3.4	3.5	3.6	3.7	3.8	3.9	4.0
0	1.0000	1.0000	1.0000	1.0000	1.0000	1.0000	1.0000	1.0000	1.0000	1.0000
1	.9550	.9592	.9631	.9666	.9698	.9727	.9753	.9776	.9798	.9817
2	.8153	.8288	.8414	.8532	.8641	.8743	.8838	.8926	.9008	.9084
3	.5988	.6201	.6406	.6603	.6792	.6973	.7146	.7311	.7469	.7619
4	.3752	.3975	.4197	.4416	.4634	.4848	.5058	.5265	.5468	.5665

CUMULATIVE TERMS, POISSON DISTRIBUTION (Continued)

x'	3.1	3.2	3.3	3.4	λ 3.5	3.6	3.7	3.8	3.9	5.0
5	.2018	.2194	.2374	.2558	.2746	.2936	.3128	.3322	.3516	.3712
6	.0943	.1054	.1171	.1295	.1424	.1559	.1699	.1844	.1994	.2149
7	.0388	.0446	.0510	.0579	.0653	.0733	.0818	.0909	.1005	.1107
8	.0142	.0168	.0198	.0231	.0267	.0308	.0352	.0401	.0454	.0511
9	.0047	.0057	.0069	.0083	.0099	.0117	.0137	.0160	.0185	.0214
10	.0014	.0018	.0022	.0027	.0033	.0040	.0048	.0058	.0069	.0081
11	.0004	.0005	.0006	.0008	.0010	.0013	.0016	.0019	.0023	.0028
12	.0001	.0001	.0002	.0002	.0003	.0004	.0005	.0006	.0007	.0009
13	.0000	.0000	.0000	.0001	.0001	.0001	.0001	.0002	.0002	.0003
14	.0000	.0000	.0000	.0000	.0000	.0000	.0000	.0000	.0001	.0001

x'	4.1	4.2	4.3	4.4	λ 4.5	4.6	4.7	4.8	4.9	5.0
0	1.0000	1.0000	1.0000	1.0000	1.0000	1.0000	1.0000	1.0000	1.0000	1.0000
1	.9834	.9850	.9864	.9877	.9889	.9899	.9909	.9918	.9926	.9933
2	.9155	.9220	.9281	.9337	.9389	.9437	.9482	.9523	.9561	.9596
3	.7762	.7898	.8026	.8149	.8264	.8374	.8477	.8575	.8667	.8753
4	.5858	.6046	.6228	.6406	.6577	.6743	.6903	.7058	.7207	.7350
5	.3907	.4102	.4296	.4488	.4679	.4868	.5054	.5237	.5418	.5595
6	.2307	.2469	.2633	.2801	.2971	.3142	.3316	.3490	.3665	.3840
7	.1214	.1325	.1442	.1564	.1689	.1820	.1954	.2092	.2233	.2378
8	.0573	.0639	.0710	.0786	.0866	.0951	.1040	.1133	.1231	.1334
9	.0245	.0279	.0317	.0358	.0403	.0451	.0503	.0558	.0618	.0681
10	.0095	.0111	.0129	.0149	.0171	.0195	.0222	.0251	.0283	.0318
11	.0034	.0041	.0048	.0057	.0067	.0078	.0090	.0104	.0120	.0137
12	.0011	.0014	.0017	.0020	.0024	.0029	.0034	.0040	.0047	.0055
13	.0003	.0004	.0005	.0007	.0008	.0010	.0012	.0014	.0017	.0020
14	.0001	.0001	.0002	.0002	.0003	.0003	.0004	.0005	.0006	.0007
15	.0000	.0000	.0000	.0001	.0001	.0001	.0001	.0001	.0002	.0002
16	.0000	.0000	.0000	.0000	.0000	.0000	.0000	.0000	.0001	.0001

x'	5.1	5.2	5.3	5.4	λ 5.5	5.6	5.7	5.8	5.9	6.0
0	1.0000	1.0000	1.0000	1.0000	1.0000	1.0000	1.0000	1.0000	1.0000	1.0000
1	.9939	.9945	.9950	.9955	.9959	.9963	.9967	.9970	.9973	.9975
2	.9628	.9658	.9686	.9711	.9734	.9756	.9776	.9794	.9811	.9826
3	.8835	.8912	.8984	.9052	.9116	.9176	.9232	.9285	.9334	.9380
4	.7487	.7619	.7746	.7867	.7983	.8094	.8200	.8300	.8396	.8488
5	.5769	.5939	.6105	.6267	.6425	.6579	.6728	.6873	.7013	.7149
6	.4016	.4191	.4365	.4539	.4711	.4881	.5050	.5217	.5381	.5543
7	.2526	.2676	.2829	.2983	.3140	.3297	.3456	.3616	.3776	.3937
8	.1440	.1551	.1665	.1783	.1905	.2030	.2159	.2290	.2424	.2560
9	.0748	.0819	.0894	.0974	.1056	.1143	.1234	.1328	.1426	.1528

CUMULATIVE TERMS, POISSON DISTRIBUTION (Continued)

x	5.1	5.2	5.3	5.4	5.5	5.6	5.7	5.8	5.9	6.0
10	.0356	.0397	.0441	.0488	.0538	.0591	.0648	.0708	.0772	.0839
11	.0156	.0177	.0200	.0225	.0253	.0282	.0314	.0349	.0386	.0426
12	.0063	.0073	.0084	.0096	.0110	.0125	.0141	.0160	.0179	.0201
13	.0024	.0028	.0033	.0038	.0045	.0051	.0059	.0068	.0078	.0088
14	.0008	.0010	.0012	.0014	.0017	.0020	.0023	.0027	.0031	.0036
15	.0003	.0003	.0004	.0005	.0006	.0007	.0009	.0010	.0012	.0014
16	.0001	.0001	.0001	.0002	.0002	.0002	.0003	.0004	.0004	.0005
17	.0000	.0000	.0000	.0001	.0001	.0001	.0001	.0001	.0001	.0002
18	.0000	.0000	.0000	.0000	.0000	.0000	.0000	.0000	.0000	.0001

λ

x'	6.1	6.2	6.3	6.4	6.5	6.6	6.7	6.8	6.9	7.0
0	1.0000	1.0000	1.0000	1.0000	1.0000	1.0000	1.0000	1.0000	1.0000	1.0000
1	.9978	.9980	.9982	.9983	.9985	.9986	.9988	.9989	.9990	.9991
2	.9841	.9854	.9836	.9877	.9887	.9897	.9905	.9913	.9920	.9927
3	.9423	.9464	.9502	.9537	.9570	.9600	.9629	.9656	.9680	.9704
4	.8575	.8658	.8736	.8811	.8882	.8948	.9012	.9072	.9129	.9182
5	.7281	.7408	.7531	.7649	.7763	.7873	.7978	.8080	.8177	.8270
6	.5702	.5859	.6012	.6163	.6310	.6453	.6594	.6730	.6863	.6993
7	.4098	.4258	.4418	.4577	.4735	.4892	.5047	.5201	.5353	.5503
8	.2699	.2840	.2983	.3127	.3272	.3419	.3567	.3715	.3864	.4013
9	.1633	.1741	.1852	.1967	.2084	.2204	.2327	.2452	.2580	.2709
10	.0910	.0984	.1061	.1142	.1226	.1314	.1404	.1498	.1505	.1695
11	.0469	.0514	.0563	.0614	.0668	.0726	.0786	.0849	.0916	.0985
12	.0224	.0250	.0277	.0307	.0339	.0373	.0409	.0448	.0490	.0534
13	.0100	.0113	.0127	.0143	.0160	.0179	.0199	.0221	.0245	.0270
14	.0042	.0048	.0055	.0063	.0071	.0080	.0091	.0102	.0115	.0128
15	.0016	.0019	.0022	.0026	.0030	.0034	.0039	.0044	.0050	.0057
16	.0006	.0007	.0008	.0010	.0012	.0014	.0016	.0018	.0021	.0024
17	.0002	.0003	.0003	.0004	.0004	.0005	.0006	.0007	.0008	.0010
18	.0001	.0001	.0001	.0001	.0002	.0002	.0002	.0003	.0003	.0004
19	.0000	.0000	.0000	.0000	.0001	.0001	.0001	.0001	.0001	.0001

λ

x'	7.1	7.2	7.3	7.4	7.5	7.6	7.7	7.8	7.9	8.0
0	1.0000	1.0000	1.0000	1.0000	1.0000	1.0000	1.0000	1.0000	1.0000	1.0000
1	.9992	.9993	.9993	.9994	.9994	.9995	.9995	.9996	.9996	.9997
2	.9933	.9939	.9944	.9949	.9953	.9957	.9961	.9964	.9967	.9970
3	.9725	.9745	.9764	.0781	.9797	.9812	.9826	.9839	.9851	.9862
4	.9233	.9281	.9326	.9368	.9409	.9446	.9482	.9515	.9547	.9576
5	.8359	.8445	.8527	.8605	.8679	.8751	.8819	.8883	.8945	.9004
6	.7119	.7241	.7360	.7474	.7586	.7693	.7797	.7897	.7994	.8088
7	.5651	.5796	.5940	.6080	.6218	.6354	.6486	.6616	.6743	.6866
8	.4162	.4311	.4459	.4607	.4754	.4900	.5044	.5188	.5330	.5470
9	.2840	.2973	.3108	.3243	.3380	.3518	.3657	.3796	.3935	.4075
10	.1798	.1904	.2012	.2123	.2236	.2351	.2469	.2589	.2710	.2834
11	.1058	.1133	.1212	.1293	.1378	.1465	.1555	.1648	.1743	.1841
12	.0580	.0629	.0681	.0735	.0792	.0852	.0915	.0980	.1048	.1119
13	.0297	.0327	.0358	.0391	.0427	.0464	.0504	.0546	.0591	.0638
14	.0143	.0159	.0176	.0195	.0216	.0238	.0261	.0286	.0313	.0342

CUMULATIVE TERMS, POISSON DISTRIBUTION (Continued)

λ

x'	7.1	7.2	7.3	7.4	7.5	7.6	7.7	7.8	7.9	8.0
15	.0065	.0073	.0082	.0092	.0103	.0114	.0127	.0141	.0156	.0173
16	.0028	.0031	.0036	.0041	.0046	.0052	.0059	.0066	.0074	.0082
17	.0011	.0013	.0015	.0017	.0020	.0022	.0026	.0029	.0033	.0037
18	.0004	.0005	.0006	.0007	.0008	.0009	.0011	.0012	.0014	.0016
19	.0002	.0002	.0002	.0003	.0003	.0004	.0004	.0005	.0006	.0006
20	.0001	.0001	.0001	.0001	.0001	.0001	.0002	.0002	.0002	.0003
21	.0000	.0000	.0000	.0000	.0000	.0000	.0001	.0001	.0001	.0001

λ

x'	8.1	8.2	8.3	8.4	8.5	8.6	8.7	8.8	8.9	9.0
0	1.0000	1.0000	1.0000	1.0000	1.0000	1.0000	1.0000	1.0000	1.0000	1.0000
1	.9997	.9997	.9998	.9998	.9998	.9998	.9998	.9998	.9999	.9999
2	.9972	.9975	.9977	.9979	.9981	.9982	.9984	.9985	.9987	.9988
3	.9873	.9882	.9891	.9900	.9907	.9914	.9921	.9927	.9932	.9938
4	.9604	.9630	.9654	.9677	.9699	.9719	.9738	.9756	.9772	.9788
5	.9060	.9113	.9163	.9211	.9256	.9299	.9340	.9379	.9416	.9450
6	.8178	.8264	.8347	.8427	.8504	.8578	.8648	.8716	.8781	.8843
7	.6987	.7104	.7219	.7330	.7438	.7543	.7645	.7744	.7840	.7932
8	.5609	.5746	.5881	.6013	.6144	.6272	.6398	.6522	.6643	.6761
9	.4214	.4353	.4493	.4631	.4769	.4906	.5042	.5177	.5311	.5443
10	.2959	.3085	.3212	.3341	.3470	.3600	.3731	.3863	.3994	.4126
11	.1942	.2045	.2150	.2257	.2366	.2478	.2591	.2706	.2822	.2940
12	.1193	.1269	.1348	.1429	.1513	.1600	.1689	.1780	.1874	.1970
13	.0687	.0739	.0793	.0850	.0909	.0971	.1035	.1102	.1171	.1242
14	.0372	.0405	.0439	.0476	.0514	.0555	.0597	.0642	.0689	.0739
15	.0190	.0209	.0229	.0251	.0274	.0299	.0325	.0353	.0383	.0415
16	.0092	.0102	.0113	.0125	.0138	.0152	.0168	.0184	.0202	.0220
17	.0042	.0047	.0053	.0059	.0066	.0074	.0082	.0091	.0101	.0111
18	.0018	.0021	.0023	.0027	.0030	.0034	.0038	.0043	.0048	.0053
19	.0008	.0009	.0010	.0011	.0013	.0015	.0017	.0019	.0022	.0024
20	.0003	.0003	.0004	.0005	.0005	.0006	.0007	.0008	.0009	.0011
21	.0001	.0001	.0002	.0002	.0002	.0002	.0003	.0003	.0004	.0004
22	.0000	.0000	.0001	.0001	.0001	.0001	.0001	.0001	.0002	.0002
23	.0000	.0000	.0000	.0000	.0000	.0000	0000	.0000	.0001	.0001

λ

x'	9.1	9.2	9.3	9.4	9.5	9.6	9.7	9.8	9.9	10
0	1.0000	1.0000	1.0000	1.0000	1.0000	1.0000	1.0000	1.0000	1.0000	1.0000
1	.9999	.9999	.9999	.9999	.9999	.9999	.9999	.9999	1.0000	1.0000
2	.9989	.9990	.9991	.9991	.9992	.9993	.9993	.9994	.9995	.9995
3	.9942	.9947	.9951	.9955	.9958	.9962	.9965	.9967	.9970	.9972
4	.9802	.9816	.9828	.9840	.9851	.9862	.9871	.9880	.9889	.9897
5	.9483	.9514	.9544	.9571	.9597	.9622	.9645	.9667	.9688	.9707
6	.8902	.8959	.9014	.9065	.9115	.9162	.9207	.9250	.9290	.9329
7	.8022	.8108	.8192	.8273	.8351	.8426	.8498	.8567	.8634	.8699
8	.6877	.6990	.7101	.7208	.7313	.7416	.7515	.7612	.7706	.7798
9	.5574	.5704	.5832	.5958	.6082	.6204	.6324	.6442	.6558	.6672

CUMULATIVE TERMS, POISSON DISTRIBUTION (Continued)

x'	9.1	9.2	9.3	9.4	9.5 λ	9.6	9.7	9.8	9.9	10
10	.4258	.4389	.4521	.4651	.4782	.4911	.5040	.5168	.5295	.5421
11	.3059	.3180	.3301	.3424	.3547	.3671	.3795	.3920	.4045	.4170
12	.2068	.2168	.2270	.2374	.2480	.2588	.2697	.2807	.2919	.3032
13	.1316	.1393	.1471	.1552	.1636	.1721	.1809	.1899	.1991	.2084
14	.0790	.0844	.0900	.0958	.1019	.1081	.1147	.1214	.1284	.1355
15	.0448	.0483	.0520	.0559	.0600	.0643	.0688	.0735	.0784	.0835
16	.0240	.0262	.0285	.0309	.0335	.0362	.0391	.0421	.0454	.0487
17	.0122	.0135	.0148	.0162	.0177	.0194	.0211	.0230	.0249	.0270
18	.0059	.0066	.0073	.0081	.0089	.0098	.0108	.0119	.0130	.0143
19	.0027	.0031	.0034	.0038	.0043	.0048	.0053	.0059	.0065	.0072
20	.0012	.0014	.0015	.0017	.0020	.0022	.0025	.0028	.0031	.0035
21	.0005	.0006	.0007	.0008	.0009	.0010	.0011	.0013	.0014	.0016
22	.0002	.0002	.0003	.0003	.0004	.0004	.0005	.0005	.0006	.0007
23	.0001	.0001	.0001	.0001	.0001	.0002	.0002	.0002	.0003	.0003
24	.0000	.0000	.0000	.0000	.0001	.0001	.0001	.0001	.0001	.0001

x'	11	12	13	14	15 λ	16	17	18	19	20
0	1.0000	1.0000	1.0000	1.0000	1.0000	1.0000	1.0000	1.0000	1.0000	1.0000
1	1.0000	1.0000	1.0000	1.0000	1.0000	1.0000	1.0000	1.0000	1.0000	1.0000
2	.9998	.9999	1.0000	1.0000	1.0000	1.0000	1.0000	1.0000	1.0000	1.0000
3	.9988	.9995	.9998	.9999	1.0000	1.0000	1.0000	1.0000	1.0000	1.0000
4	.9951	.9977	.9990	.9995	.9998	.9999	1.0000	1.0000	1.0000	1.0000
5	.9849	.9924	.9963	.9982	9991	.9996	.9998	.9999	1.0000	1.0000
6	.9625	.9797	.9893	.9945	.9972	.9986	.9993	.9997	.9998	.9999
7	.9214	.9542	.9741	.9858	.9924	.9960	.9979	.9990	.9995	.9997
8	.8568	.9105	.9460	.9684	.9820	.9900	.9946	.9971	.9985	.9992
9	.7680	.8450	.9002	.9379	.9626	.9780	.9874	.9929	.9961	.9979
10	.6595	.7576	.8342	.8906	.9301	.9567	.9739	.9846	.9911	.9950
11	.5401	.6528	.7483	.8243	.8815	.9226	.9509	.9696	.9817	.9892
12	.4207	.5384	.6468	.7400	.8152	.8730	.9153	.9451	.9653	.9786
13	.3113	.4240	.5369	.6415	.7324	.8069	.8650	.9083	.9394	.9610
14	.2187	.3185	.4270	.5356	.6368	.7255	.7991	.8574	.9016	.9339
15	.1460	.2280	.3249	.4296	.5343	.6325	.7192	.7919	.8503	.8951
16	.0926	.1556	.2364	.3306	.4319	.5333	.6285	.7133	.7852	.8435
17	.0559	.1013	.1645	.2441	.3359	.4340	.5323	.6250	.7080	.7789
18	.0322	.0630	.1095	.1728	.2511	.3407	.4360	.5314	.6216	.7030
19	.0177	.0374	.0698	.1174	.1805	.2577	.3450	.4378	.5305	.6186
20	.0093	.0213	.0427	.0765	.1248	.1878	.2637	.3491	.4394	.5297
21	.0047	.0116	.0250	.0479	.0830	.1318	.1945	.2693	.3528	.4409
22	.0023	.0061	.0141	.0288	.0531	.0892	.1385	.2009	.2745	.3563
23	.0010	.0030	.0076	.0167	.0327	.0582	.0953	.1449	.2069	.2794
24	.0005	.0015	.0040	.0093	.0195	.0367	.0633	.1011	.1510	.2125
25	.0002	.0007	.0020	.0050	.0112	.0223	.0406	.0683	.1067	.1568
26	.0001	.0003	.0010	.0026	.0062	.0131	.0252	.0446	.0731	.1122
27	.0000	.0001	.0005	.0013	.0033	.0075	.0152	.0282	.0486	.0779
28	.0000	.0001	.0002	.0006	.0017	.0041	.0088	.0173	.0313	.0525
29	.0000	.0000	.0001	.0003	.0009	.0022	.0050	.0103	.0195	.0343

CUMULATIVE TERMS, POISSON DISTRIBUTION (Continued)

x'	11	12	13	14	15	16	17	18	19	20
30	.0000	.0000	.0000	.0001	.0004	.0011	.0027	.0059	.0118	.0218
31	.0000	.0000	.0000	.0001	.0002	.0006	.0014	.0033	.0070	.0135
32	.0000	.0000	.0000	.0000	.0001	.0003	.0007	.0018	.0040	.0081
33	.0000	.0000	.0000	.0000	.0000	.0001	.0004	.0010	.0022	.0047
34	.0000	.0000	.0000	.0000	.0000	.0001	.0002	.0005	.0012	.0027
35	.0000	.0000	.0000	.0000	.0000	.0000	.0001	.0002	.0006	.0015
36	.0000	.0000	.0000	.0000	.0000	.0000	.0000	.0001	.0003	.0008
37	.0000	.0000	.0000	.0000	.0000	.0000	.0000	.0001	.0002	.0004
38	.0000	.0000	.0000	.0000	.0000	.0000	.0000	.0000	.0001	.0002
39	.0000	.0000	.0000	.0000	.0000	.0000	.0000	.0000	.0000	.0001
40	.0000	.0000	.0000	.0000	.0000	.0000	.0000	.0000	.0000	.0001

The column headers span under the symbol λ.

PERCENTAGE POINTS, STUDENT'S t-DISTRIBUTION

This table gives values of t such that

$$F(t) = \int_{-\infty}^{t} \frac{\Gamma\left(\dfrac{n+1}{2}\right)}{\sqrt{n\pi}\ \Gamma\left(\dfrac{n}{2}\right)} \left(1 + \frac{x^2}{n}\right)^{-\frac{n+1}{2}} dx$$

for n, the number of degrees of freedom, equal to 1, 2, . . . , 30, 40, 60, 120, ∞; and for $F(t) = 0.60, 0.75, 0.90, 0.95, 0.975, 0.99, 0.995,$ and 0.9995. The t-distribution is symmetrical, so that $F(-t) = 1 - F(t)$.

n \ F	.60	.75	.90	.95	.975	.99	.995	.9995
1	.325	1.000	3.078	6.314	12.706	31.821	63.657	636.619
2	.289	.816	1.886	2.920	4.303	6.965	9.925	31.598
3	.277	.765	1.638	2.353	3.182	4.541	5.841	12.924
4	.271	.741	1.533	2.132	2.776	3.747	4.604	8.610
5	.267	.727	1.476	2.015	2.571	3.365	4.032	6.869
6	.265	.718	1.440	1.943	2.447	3.143	3.707	5.959
7	.263	.711	1.415	1.895	2.365	2.998	3.499	5.408
8	.262	.706	2.397	1.860	2.306	2.896	3.355	5.041
9	.261	.703	1.383	1.833	2.262	2.821	3.250	4.781
10	.260	.700	1.372	1.812	2.228	2.764	3.169	4.587
11	.260	.697	1.363	1.796	2.201	2.718	3.106	4.437
12	.259	.695	1.356	1.782	2.179	2.681	3.055	4.318
13	.259	.694	1.350	1.771	2.160	2.650	3.012	4.221
14	.258	.692	1.345	1.761	2.145	2.624	2.977	4.140
15	.258	.691	1.341	1.753	2.131	2.602	2.947	4.073
16	.258	.690	1.337	1.746	2.120	2.583	2.921	4.015
17	.257	.689	1.333	1.740	2.110	2.567	2.898	3.965
18	.257	.688	1.330	1.734	2.101	2.552	2.878	3.922
19	.257	.688	1.328	1.729	2.093	2.539	2.861	3.883
20	.257	.687	1.325	1.725	2.086	2.528	2.845	3.850
21	.257	.686	1.323	1.721	2.080	2.518	2.831	3.819
22	.256	.686	1.321	1.717	2.074	2.508	2.819	3.792
23	.256	.685	1.319	1.714	2.069	2.500	2.807	3.767
24	.256	.685	1.318	1.711	2.064	2.492	2.797	3.745
25	.256	.684	1.316	1.708	2.060	2.485	2.787	3.725
26	.256	.684	1.315	1.706	2.056	2.479	2.779	3.707
27	.256	.684	1.314	1.703	2.052	2.473	2.771	3.690
28	.256	.683	1.313	1.701	2.048	2.467	2.763	3.674
29	.256	.683	1.311	1.699	2.045	2.462	2.756	3.659
30	.256	.683	1.310	1.697	2.042	2.457	2.750	3.646
40	.255	.681	1.303	1.684	2.021	2.423	2.704	3.551
60	.254	.679	1.296	1.671	2.000	2.390	2.660	3.460
120	.254	.677	1.289	1.658	1.980	2.358	2.617	3.373
∞	.253	.674	1.282	1.645	1.960	2.326	2.576	3.291

* This table is abridged from the "Statistical Tables" of R. A. Fisher and Frank Yates published by Oliver & Boyd, Ltd., Edinburgh and London, 1938. It is here published with the kind permission of the authors and their publishers.

PERCENTAGE POINTS, CHI-SQUARE DISTRIBUTION

This table gives values of χ^2 such that

$$F(\chi^2) = \int_0^{\chi^2} \frac{1}{2^{\frac{n}{2}} \, \Gamma\left(\frac{n}{2}\right)} \, x^{\frac{n-2}{2}} \, e^{-\frac{x}{2}} \, dx$$

for n, the number of degrees of freedom, equal to 1, 2, . . . , 30. For $n > 30$, a normal approximation is quite accurate. The expression $\sqrt{2\chi^2} - \sqrt{2n-1}$ is approximately normally distributed as the standard normal distribution. Thus χ_α^2, the α-point of the distribution, may be computed by the formula

$$\chi_\alpha^2 = \tfrac{1}{2}[x_\sigma + \sqrt{2n-1}]^2,$$

where x_α is the α-point of the cumulative normal distribution. For even values of n, $F(\chi^2)$ can be written as

$$1 - F(\chi^2) = \sum_{x=0}^{x'-1} \frac{e^{-\lambda}\lambda^x}{x!}$$

with $\lambda = \tfrac{1}{2}\chi^2$ and $x' = \tfrac{1}{2}n$. Thus the cumulative Chi-Square distribution is related to the cumulative Poisson distribution.

PERCENTAGE POINTS, CHI-SQUARE DISTRIBUTION (Continued)

$$F(x^2) = \int_0^{x^2} \frac{1}{2^{\frac{n}{2}} \Gamma\left(\frac{n}{2}\right)} x^{\frac{n-2}{2}} e^{-\frac{x}{2}} dx$$

F / n	.995	.990	.975	.950	.900	.750	.500	.250	.100	.050	.025	.010	.005
1	7.88	6.63	5.02	3.84	2.71	1.32	.455	.102	.0158	.00393	.000982	.000157	.0000393
2	10.6	9.21	7.38	5.99	4.61	2.77	1.39	.575	.211	.103	.0506	.0201	.0100
3	12.8	11.3	9.35	7.81	6.25	4.11	2.37	1.21	.584	.352	.216	.115	.0717
4	14.9	13.3	11.1	9.49	7.78	5.39	3.36	1.92	1.06	.711	.484	.297	.207
5	16.7	15.1	12.8	11.1	9.24	6.63	4.35	2.67	1.61	1.15	.831	.554	.412
6	18.5	16.8	14.4	12.6	10.6	7.84	5.35	3.45	2.20	1.64	1.24	.872	.676
7	20.3	18.5	16.0	14.1	12.0	9.04	6.35	4.25	2.83	2.17	1.69	1.24	.989
8	22.0	20.1	17.5	15.5	13.4	10.2	7.34	5.07	3.49	2.73	2.18	1.65	1.34
9	23.6	21.7	19.0	16.9	14.7	11.4	8.34	5.90	4.17	3.33	2.70	2.09	1.73
10	25.2	23.2	20.5	18.3	16.0	12.5	9.34	6.74	4.87	3.94	3.25	2.56	2.16
11	26.8	24.7	21.9	19.7	17.3	13.7	10.3	7.58	5.58	4.57	3.82	3.05	2.60
12	28.3	26.2	23.3	21.0	18.5	14.8	11.3	8.44	6.30	5.23	4.40	3.57	3.07
13	29.8	27.7	24.7	22.4	19.8	16.0	12.3	9.30	7.04	5.89	5.01	4.11	3.57
14	31.3	29.1	26.1	23.7	21.1	17.1	13.3	10.2	7.79	6.57	5.63	4.66	4.07
15	32.8	30.6	27.5	25.0	22.3	18.2	.4.3	11.0	8.55	7.26	6.26	5.23	4.60
16	34.3	32.0	28.8	26.3	23.5	19.4	15.3	11.9	9.31	7.96	6.91	5.81	5.14
17	35.7	33.4	30.2	27.6	24.8	20.5	16.3	12.8	10.1	8.67	7.56	6.41	5.70
18	37.2	34.8	31.5	28.9	26.0	21.6	17.3	13.7	10.9	9.39	8.23	7.01	6.26
19	38.6	36.2	32.9	30.1	27.2	22.7	18.3	14.6	11.7	10.1	8.91	7.63	6.84
20	40.0	37.6	34.2	31.4	28.4	23.8	19.3	15.5	12.4	10.9	9.59	8.26	7.43
21	41.4	38.9	35.5	32.7	29.6	24.9	20.3	16.3	13.2	11.6	10.3	8.90	8.03
22	42.8	40.3	36.8	33.9	30.8	26.0	21.3	17.2	14.0	12.3	11.0	9.54	8.64
23	44.2	41.6	38.1	35.2	32.0	27.1	22.3	18.1	14.8	13.1	11.7	10.2	9.26
24	45.6	43.0	39.4	36.4	33.2	28.2	23.3	19.0	15.7	13.8	12.4	10.9	9.89
25	46.9	44.3	40.6	37.7	34.4	29.3	24.3	19.9	16.5	14.6	13.1	11.5	10.5
26	48.3	45.6	41.9	38.9	35.6	30.4	25.3	20.8	17.3	15.4	13.8	12.2	11.2
27	49.6	47.0	43.2	40.1	36.7	31.5	26.3	21.7	18.1	16.2	14.6	12.9	11.8
28	51.0	48.3	44.5	41.3	37.9	32.6	27.3	22.7	18.9	16.9	15.3	13.6	12.5
29	52.3	49.6	45.7	42.6	39.1	33.7	28.3	23.6	19.8	17.7	16.0	14.3	13.1
30	53.7	50.9	47.0	43.8	40.3	34.8	29.3	24.5	20.6	18.5	16.8	15.0	13.8

PERCENTAGE POINTS, *F*-DISTRIBUTION

This table gives values of F such that

$$F(F) = \int_0^F \frac{\Gamma\left(\dfrac{m+n}{2}\right)}{\Gamma\left(\dfrac{m}{2}\right)\Gamma\left(\dfrac{n}{2}\right)} m^{\frac{m}{2}} n^{\frac{n}{2}} x^{\frac{m-2}{2}} (n+mx)^{-\frac{m+n}{2}} dx$$

for selected values of m, the number of degrees of freedom of the numerator of F; and for selected values of n, the number of degrees of freedom of the denominator of F. The table also provides values corresponding to $F(F) = .10, .05, .025, .01, .005, .001$ since $F_{1-\alpha}$ for m and n degrees of freedom is the reciprocal of F_α for n and m degrees of freedom. Thus

$$F_{.05}(4, 7) = \frac{1}{F_{.95}(7, 4)} = \frac{1}{6.09} = .164 .$$

PERCENTAGE POINTS, F-DISTRIBUTION (Continued)

$$F(F) = \int_0^F \frac{\Gamma\left(\frac{m+n}{2}\right)}{\Gamma\left(\frac{m}{2}\right)\Gamma\left(\frac{n}{2}\right)} m^{\frac{m}{2}} n^{\frac{n}{2}} x^{\frac{m}{2}-1} (n+mx)^{-\frac{m+n}{2}}\, dx = .90$$

n \ m	1	2	3	4	5	6	7	8	9	10	12	15	20	24	30	40	60	120	∞
1	39.86	49.50	53.59	55.83	57.24	58.20	58.91	59.44	59.86	60.19	60.71	61.22	61.74	62.00	62.26	62.53	62.79	63.06	63.33
2	8.53	9.00	9.16	9.24	9.29	9.33	9.35	9.37	9.38	9.39	9.41	9.42	9.44	9.45	9.46	9.47	9.47	9.48	9.49
3	5.54	5.46	5.39	5.34	5.31	5.28	5.27	5.25	5.24	5.23	5.22	5.20	5.18	5.18	5.17	5.16	5.15	5.14	5.13
4	4.54	4.32	4.19	4.11	4.05	4.01	3.98	3.95	3.94	3.92	3.90	3.87	3.84	3.83	3.82	3.80	3.79	3.78	3.76
5	4.06	3.78	3.62	3.52	3.45	3.40	3.37	3.34	3.32	3.30	3.27	3.24	3.21	3.19	3.17	3.16	3.14	3.12	3.10
6	3.78	3.46	3.29	3.18	3.11	3.05	3.01	2.98	2.96	2.94	2.90	2.87	2.84	2.82	2.80	2.78	2.76	2.74	2.72
7	3.59	3.26	3.07	2.96	2.88	2.83	2.78	2.75	2.72	2.70	2.67	2.63	2.59	2.58	2.56	2.54	2.51	2.49	2.47
8	3.46	3.11	2.92	2.81	2.73	2.67	2.62	2.59	2.56	2.54	2.50	2.46	2.42	2.40	2.38	2.36	2.34	2.32	2.29
9	3.36	3.01	2.81	2.69	2.61	2.55	2.51	2.47	2.44	2.42	2.38	2.34	2.30	2.28	2.25	2.23	2.21	2.18	2.16
10	3.29	2.92	2.73	2.61	2.52	2.46	2.41	2.38	2.35	2.32	2.28	2.24	2.20	2.18	2.16	2.13	2.11	2.08	2.06
11	3.23	2.86	2.66	2.54	2.45	2.39	2.34	2.30	2.27	2.25	2.21	2.17	2.12	2.10	2.08	2.05	2.03	2.00	1.97
12	3.18	2.81	2.61	2.48	2.39	2.33	2.28	2.24	2.21	2.19	2.15	2.10	2.06	2.04	2.01	1.99	1.96	1.93	1.90
13	3.14	2.76	2.56	2.43	2.35	2.28	2.23	2.20	2.16	2.14	2.10	2.05	2.01	1.98	1.96	1.93	1.90	1.88	1.85
14	3.10	2.73	2.52	2.39	2.31	2.24	2.19	2.15	2.12	2.10	2.05	2.01	1.96	1.94	1.91	1.89	1.86	1.83	1.80
15	3.07	2.70	2.49	2.36	2.27	2.21	2.16	2.12	2.09	2.06	2.02	1.97	1.92	1.90	1.87	1.85	1.82	1.79	1.76
16	3.05	2.67	2.46	2.33	2.24	2.18	2.13	2.09	2.06	2.03	1.99	1.94	1.89	1.87	1.84	1.81	1.78	1.75	1.72
17	3.03	2.64	2.44	2.31	2.22	2.15	2.10	2.06	2.03	2.00	1.96	1.91	1.86	1.84	1.81	1.78	1.75	1.72	1.69
18	3.01	2.62	2.42	2.29	2.20	2.13	2.08	2.04	2.00	1.98	1.93	1.89	1.84	1.81	1.78	1.75	1.72	1.69	1.66
19	2.99	2.61	2.40	2.27	2.18	2.11	2.06	2.02	1.98	1.96	1.91	1.86	1.81	1.79	1.76	1.73	1.70	1.67	1.63
20	2.97	2.59	2.38	2.25	2.16	2.09	2.04	2.00	1.96	1.94	1.89	1.84	1.79	1.77	1.74	1.71	1.68	1.64	1.61
21	2.96	2.57	2.36	2.23	2.14	2.08	2.02	1.98	1.95	1.92	1.87	1.83	1.78	1.75	1.72	1.69	1.66	1.62	1.59
22	2.95	2.56	2.35	2.22	2.13	2.06	2.01	1.97	1.93	1.90	1.86	1.81	1.76	1.73	1.70	1.67	1.64	1.60	1.57
23	2.94	2.55	2.34	2.21	2.11	2.05	1.99	1.95	1.92	1.89	1.84	1.80	1.74	1.72	1.69	1.66	1.62	1.59	1.55
24	2.93	2.54	2.33	2.19	2.10	2.04	1.98	1.94	1.91	1.88	1.83	1.78	1.73	1.70	1.67	1.64	1.61	1.57	1.53
25	2.92	2.53	2.32	2.18	2.09	2.02	1.97	1.93	1.89	1.87	1.82	1.77	1.72	1.69	1.66	1.63	1.59	1.56	1.52
26	2.91	2.52	2.31	2.17	2.08	2.01	1.96	1.92	1.88	1.86	1.81	1.76	1.71	1.68	1.65	1.61	1.58	1.54	1.50
27	2.90	2.51	2.30	2.17	2.07	2.00	1.95	1.91	1.87	1.85	1.80	1.75	1.70	1.67	1.64	1.60	1.57	1.53	1.49
28	2.89	2.50	2.29	2.16	2.06	2.00	1.94	1.90	1.87	1.84	1.79	1.74	1.69	1.66	1.63	1.59	1.56	1.52	1.48
29	2.89	2.50	2.28	2.15	2.06	1.99	1.93	1.89	1.86	1.83	1.78	1.73	1.68	1.65	1.62	1.58	1.55	1.51	1.47
30	2.88	2.49	2.28	2.14	2.05	1.98	1.93	1.88	1.85	1.82	1.77	1.72	1.67	1.64	1.61	1.57	1.54	1.50	1.46
40	2.84	2.44	2.23	2.09	2.00	1.93	1.87	1.83	1.79	1.76	1.71	1.66	1.61	1.57	1.54	1.51	1.47	1.42	1.38
60	2.79	2.39	2.18	2.04	1.95	1.87	1.82	1.77	1.74	1.71	1.66	1.60	1.54	1.51	1.48	1.44	1.40	1.35	1.29
120	2.75	2.35	2.13	1.99	1.90	1.82	1.77	1.72	1.68	1.65	1.60	1.55	1.48	1.45	1.41	1.37	1.32	1.26	1.19
∞	2.71	2.30	2.08	1.94	1.85	1.77	1.72	1.67	1.63	1.60	1.55	1.49	1.42	1.38	1.34	1.30	1.24	1.17	1.00

$F = \dfrac{s_1^2}{s_2^2} = \dfrac{S_1}{m}\Big/\dfrac{S_2}{n}$, where $s_1^2 = S_1/m$ and $s_2^2 = S_2/n$ are independent mean squares estimating a common variance σ^2 and based on m and n degrees of freedom, respectively.

PERCENTAGE POINTS, F-DISTRIBUTION (Continued)

$$F(F) = \int_0^F \frac{\Gamma\left(\frac{m+n}{2}\right)}{\Gamma\left(\frac{m}{2}\right)\Gamma\left(\frac{n}{2}\right)} m^{\frac{m}{2}} n^{\frac{n}{2}} x^{\frac{m}{2}-1} (n+mx)^{-\frac{m+n}{2}}\, dx = .95$$

m \ n	1	2	3	4	5	6	7	8	9	10	12	15	20	24	30	40	60	120	∞
1	161.4	199.5	215.7	224.6	230.2	234.0	236.8	238.9	240.5	241.9	243.9	245.9	248.0	249.1	250.1	251.1	252.2	253.3	254.3
2	18.51	19.00	19.16	19.25	19.30	19.33	19.35	19.37	19.38	19.40	19.41	19.43	19.45	19.45	19.46	19.47	19.48	19.49	19.50
3	10.13	9.55	9.28	9.12	9.01	8.94	8.89	8.85	8.81	8.79	8.74	8.70	8.66	8.64	8.62	8.59	8.57	8.55	8.53
4	7.71	6.94	6.59	6.39	6.26	6.16	6.09	6.04	6.00	5.96	5.91	5.86	5.80	5.77	5.75	5.72	5.69	5.66	5.63
5	6.61	5.79	5.41	5.19	5.05	4.95	4.88	4.82	4.77	4.74	4.68	4.62	4.56	4.53	4.50	4.46	4.43	4.40	4.36
6	5.99	5.14	4.76	4.53	4.39	4.28	4.21	4.15	4.10	4.06	4.00	3.94	3.87	3.84	3.81	3.77	3.74	3.70	3.67
7	5.59	4.74	4.35	4.12	3.97	3.87	3.79	3.73	3.68	3.64	3.57	3.51	3.44	3.41	3.38	3.34	3.30	3.27	3.23
8	5.32	4.46	4.07	3.84	3.69	3.58	3.50	3.44	3.39	3.35	3.28	3.22	3.15	3.12	3.08	3.04	3.01	2.97	2.93
9	5.12	4.26	3.86	3.63	3.48	3.37	3.29	3.23	3.18	3.14	3.07	3.01	2.94	2.90	2.86	2.83	2.79	2.75	2.71
10	4.96	4.10	3.71	3.48	3.33	3.22	3.14	3.07	3.02	2.98	2.91	2.85	2.77	2.74	2.70	2.66	2.62	2.58	2.54
11	4.84	3.98	3.59	3.36	3.20	3.09	3.01	2.95	2.90	2.85	2.79	2.72	2.65	2.61	2.57	2.53	2.49	2.45	2.40
12	4.75	3.89	3.49	3.26	3.11	3.00	2.91	2.85	2.80	2.75	2.69	2.62	2.54	2.51	2.47	2.43	2.38	2.34	2.30
13	4.67	3.81	3.41	3.18	3.03	2.92	2.83	2.77	2.71	2.67	2.60	2.53	2.46	2.42	2.38	2.34	2.30	2.25	2.21
14	4.60	3.74	3.34	3.11	2.96	2.85	2.76	2.70	2.65	2.60	2.53	2.46	2.39	2.35	2.31	2.27	2.22	2.18	2.13
15	4.54	3.68	3.29	3.06	2.90	2.79	2.71	2.64	2.59	2.54	2.48	2.40	2.33	2.29	2.25	2.20	2.16	2.11	2.07
16	4.49	3.63	3.24	3.01	2.85	2.74	2.66	2.59	2.54	2.49	2.42	2.35	2.28	2.24	2.19	2.15	2.11	2.06	2.01
17	4.45	3.59	3.20	2.96	2.81	2.70	2.61	2.55	2.49	2.45	2.38	2.31	2.23	2.19	2.15	2.10	2.06	2.01	1.96
18	4.41	3.55	3.16	2.93	2.77	2.66	2.58	2.51	2.46	2.41	2.34	2.27	2.19	2.15	2.11	2.06	2.02	1.97	1.92
19	4.38	3.52	3.13	2.90	2.74	2.63	2.54	2.48	2.42	2.38	2.31	2.23	2.16	2.11	2.07	2.03	1.98	1.93	1.88
20	4.35	3.49	3.10	2.87	2.71	2.60	2.51	2.45	2.39	2.35	2.28	2.20	2.12	2.08	2.04	1.99	1.95	1.90	1.84
21	4.32	3.47	3.07	2.84	2.68	2.57	2.49	2.42	2.37	2.32	2.25	2.18	2.10	2.05	2.01	1.96	1.92	1.87	1.81
22	4.30	3.44	3.05	2.82	2.66	2.55	2.46	2.40	2.34	2.30	2.23	2.15	2.07	2.03	1.98	1.94	1.89	1.84	1.78
23	4.28	3.42	3.03	2.80	2.64	2.53	2.44	2.37	2.32	2.27	2.20	2.13	2.05	2.01	1.96	1.91	1.86	1.81	1.76
24	4.26	3.40	3.01	2.78	2.62	2.51	2.42	2.36	2.30	2.25	2.18	2.11	2.03	1.98	1.94	1.89	1.84	1.79	1.73
25	4.24	3.39	2.99	2.76	2.60	2.49	2.40	2.34	2.28	2.24	2.16	2.09	2.01	1.96	1.92	1.87	1.82	1.77	1.71
26	4.23	3.37	2.98	2.74	2.59	2.47	2.39	2.32	2.27	2.22	2.15	2.07	1.99	1.95	1.90	1.85	1.80	1.75	1.69
27	4.21	3.35	2.96	2.73	2.57	2.46	2.37	2.31	2.25	2.20	2.13	2.06	1.97	1.93	1.88	1.84	1.79	1.73	1.67
28	4.20	3.34	2.95	2.71	2.56	2.45	2.36	2.29	2.24	2.19	2.12	2.04	1.96	1.91	1.87	1.82	1.77	1.71	1.65
29	4.18	3.33	2.93	2.70	2.55	2.43	2.35	2.28	2.22	2.18	2.10	2.03	1.94	1.90	1.85	1.81	1.75	1.70	1.64
30	4.17	3.32	2.92	2.69	2.53	2.42	2.33	2.27	2.21	2.16	2.09	2.01	1.93	1.89	1.84	1.79	1.74	1.68	1.62
40	4.08	3.23	2.84	2.61	2.45	2.34	2.25	2.18	2.12	2.08	2.00	1.92	1.84	1.79	1.74	1.69	1.64	1.58	1.51
60	4.00	3.15	2.76	2.53	2.37	2.25	2.17	2.10	2.04	1.99	1.92	1.84	1.75	1.70	1.65	1.59	1.53	1.47	1.39
120	3.92	3.07	2.68	2.45	2.29	2.17	2.09	2.02	1.96	1.91	1.83	1.75	1.66	1.61	1.55	1.50	1.43	1.35	1.25
∞	3.84	3.00	2.60	2.37	2.21	2.10	2.01	1.94	1.88	1.83	1.75	1.67	1.57	1.52	1.46	1.39	1.32	1.22	1.00

$F = \frac{s_1^2}{s_2^2} = \frac{S_1/m}{S_2/n}$, where $s_1^2 = S_1/m$ and $s_2^2 = S_2/n$ are independent mean squares estimating a common variance σ^2 and based on m and n degrees of freedom, respectively.

PERCENTAGE POINTS, F-DISTRIBUTION (Continued)

$$F(F) = \int_0^F \frac{\Gamma\left(\dfrac{m+n}{2}\right)}{\Gamma\left(\dfrac{m}{2}\right)\Gamma\left(\dfrac{n}{2}\right)} \, m^{\frac{m}{2}} n^{\frac{n}{2}} x^{\frac{m}{2}-1} \, (n+mx)^{-\frac{m+n}{2}} \, dx = .975$$

n \ m	1	2	3	4	5	6	7	8	9	10	12	15	20	24	30	40	60	120	∞
1	647.8	799.5	864.2	899.6	921.8	937.1	948.2	956.7	963.3	968.6	976.7	984.9	993.1	997.2	1001	1006	1010	1014	1018
2	38.51	39.00	39.17	39.25	39.30	39.33	39.36	39.37	39.39	39.40	39.41	39.43	39.45	39.46	39.46	39.47	39.48	39.49	39.50
3	17.44	16.04	15.44	15.10	14.88	14.73	14.62	14.54	14.47	14.42	14.34	14.25	14.17	14.12	14.08	14.04	13.99	13.95	13.90
4	12.22	10.65	9.98	9.60	9.36	9.20	9.07	8.98	8.90	8.84	8.75	8.66	8.56	8.51	8.46	8.41	8.36	8.31	8.26
5	10.01	8.43	7.76	7.39	7.15	6.98	6.85	6.76	6.68	6.62	6.52	6.43	6.33	6.28	6.23	6.18	6.12	6.07	6.02
6	8.81	7.26	6.60	6.23	5.99	5.82	5.70	5.60	5.52	5.46	5.37	5.27	5.17	5.12	5.07	5.01	4.96	4.90	4.85
7	8.07	6.54	5.89	5.52	5.29	5.12	4.99	4.90	4.82	4.76	4.67	4.57	4.47	4.42	4.36	4.31	4.25	4.20	4.14
8	7.57	6.06	5.42	5.05	4.82	4.65	4.53	4.43	4.36	4.30	4.20	4.10	4.00	3.95	3.89	3.84	3.78	3.73	3.67
9	7.21	5.71	5.08	4.72	4.48	4.32	4.20	4.10	4.03	3.96	3.87	3.77	3.67	3.61	3.56	3.51	3.45	3.39	3.33
10	6.94	5.46	4.83	4.47	4.24	4.07	3.95	3.85	3.78	3.72	3.62	3.52	3.42	3.37	3.31	3.26	3.20	3.14	3.08
11	6.72	5.26	4.63	4.28	4.04	3.88	3.76	3.66	3.59	3.53	3.43	3.33	3.23	3.17	3.12	3.06	3.00	2.94	2.88
12	6.55	5.10	4.47	4.12	3.89	3.73	3.61	3.51	3.44	3.37	3.28	3.18	3.07	3.02	2.96	2.91	2.85	2.79	2.72
13	6.41	4.97	4.35	4.00	3.77	3.60	3.48	3.39	3.31	3.25	3.15	3.05	2.95	2.89	2.84	2.78	2.72	2.66	2.60
14	6.30	4.86	4.24	3.89	3.66	3.50	3.38	3.29	3.21	3.15	3.05	2.95	2.84	2.79	2.73	2.67	2.61	2.55	2.49
15	6.20	4.77	4.15	3.80	3.58	3.41	3.29	3.20	3.12	3.06	2.96	2.86	2.76	2.70	2.64	2.59	2.52	2.46	2.40
16	6.12	4.69	4.08	3.73	3.50	3.34	3.22	3.12	3.05	2.99	2.89	2.79	2.68	2.63	2.57	2.51	2.45	2.38	2.32
17	6.04	4.62	4.01	3.66	3.44	3.28	3.16	3.06	2.98	2.92	2.82	2.72	2.62	2.56	2.50	2.44	2.38	2.32	2.25
18	5.98	4.56	3.95	3.61	3.38	3.22	3.10	3.01	2.93	2.87	2.77	2.67	2.56	2.50	2.44	2.38	2.32	2.26	2.19
19	5.92	4.51	3.90	3.56	3.33	3.17	3.05	2.96	2.88	2.82	2.72	2.62	2.51	2.45	2.39	2.33	2.27	2.20	2.13
20	5.87	4.46	3.86	3.51	3.29	3.13	3.01	2.91	2.84	2.77	2.68	2.57	2.46	2.41	2.35	2.29	2.22	2.16	2.09
21	5.83	4.42	3.82	3.48	3.25	3.09	2.97	2.87	2.80	2.73	2.64	2.53	2.42	2.37	2.31	2.25	2.18	2.11	2.04
22	5.79	4.38	3.78	3.44	3.22	3.05	2.93	2.84	2.76	2.70	2.60	2.50	2.39	2.33	2.27	2.21	2.14	2.08	2.00
23	5.75	4.35	3.75	3.41	3.18	3.02	2.90	2.81	2.73	2.67	2.57	2.47	2.36	2.30	2.24	2.18	2.11	2.04	1.97
24	5.72	4.32	3.72	3.38	3.15	2.99	2.87	2.78	2.70	2.64	2.54	2.44	2.33	2.27	2.21	2.15	2.08	2.01	1.94
25	5.69	4.29	3.69	3.35	3.13	2.97	2.85	2.75	2.68	2.61	2.51	2.41	2.30	2.24	2.18	2.12	2.05	1.98	1.91
26	5.66	4.27	3.67	3.33	3.10	2.94	2.82	2.73	2.65	2.59	2.49	2.39	2.28	2.22	2.16	2.09	2.03	1.95	1.88
27	5.63	4.24	3.65	3.31	3.08	2.92	2.80	2.71	2.63	2.57	2.47	2.36	2.25	2.19	2.13	2.07	2.00	1.93	1.85
28	5.61	4.22	3.63	3.29	3.06	2.90	2.78	2.69	2.61	2.55	2.45	2.34	2.23	2.17	2.11	2.05	1.98	1.91	1.83
29	5.59	4.20	3.61	3.27	3.04	2.88	2.76	2.67	2.59	2.53	2.43	2.32	2.21	2.15	2.09	2.03	1.96	1.89	1.81
30	5.57	4.18	3.59	3.25	3.03	2.87	2.75	2.65	2.57	2.51	2.41	2.31	2.20	2.14	2.07	2.01	1.94	1.87	1.79
40	5.42	4.05	3.46	3.13	2.90	2.74	2.62	2.53	2.45	2.39	2.29	2.18	2.07	2.01	1.94	1.88	1.80	1.72	1.64
60	5.29	3.93	3.34	3.01	2.79	2.63	2.51	2.41	2.33	2.27	2.17	2.06	1.94	1.88	1.82	1.74	1.67	1.58	1.48
120	5.15	3.80	3.23	2.89	2.67	2.52	2.39	2.30	2.22	2.16	2.05	1.94	1.82	1.76	1.69	1.61	1.53	1.43	1.31
∞	5.02	3.69	3.12	2.79	2.57	2.41	2.29	2.19	2.11	2.05	1.94	1.83	1.71	1.64	1.57	1.48	1.39	1.27	1.00

$F = \dfrac{s_1^2}{s_2^2} = \dfrac{S_1/m}{S_2/n}$, where $s_1^2 = S_1/m$ and $s_2^2 = S_2/n$ are independent mean squares estimating a common variance σ^2 and based on m and n degrees of freedom, respectively.

PERCENTAGE POINTS, F-DISTRIBUTION (Continued)

$$F(F) = \int_0^F \frac{\Gamma\left(\frac{m+n}{2}\right)}{\Gamma\left(\frac{m}{2}\right)\Gamma\left(\frac{n}{2}\right)}\, m^{\frac{m}{2}} n^{\frac{n}{2}} x^{\frac{m}{2}-1}\,(n+mx)^{-\frac{m+n}{2}}\,dx = .99$$

n \ m	1	2	3	4	5	6	7	8	9	10	12	15	20	24	30	40	60	120	∞
1	4052	4999.5	5403	5625	5764	5859	5928	5982	6022	6056	6106	6157	6209	6235	6261	6287	6313	6339	6366
2	98.50	99.00	99.17	99.25	99.30	99.33	99.36	99.37	99.39	99.40	99.42	99.43	99.45	99.46	99.47	99.47	99.48	99.49	99.50
3	34.12	30.82	29.46	28.71	28.24	27.91	27.67	27.49	27.35	27.23	27.05	26.87	26.69	26.60	26.50	26.41	26.32	26.22	26.13
4	21.20	18.00	16.69	15.98	15.52	15.21	14.98	14.80	14.66	14.55	14.37	14.20	14.02	13.93	13.84	13.75	13.65	13.56	13.46
5	16.26	13.27	12.06	11.39	10.97	10.67	10.46	10.29	10.16	10.05	9.89	9.72	9.55	9.47	9.38	9.29	9.20	9.11	9.02
6	13.75	10.92	9.78	9.15	8.75	8.47	8.26	8.10	7.98	7.87	7.72	7.56	7.40	7.31	7.23	7.14	7.06	6.97	6.88
7	12.25	9.55	8.45	7.85	7.46	7.19	6.99	6.84	6.72	6.62	6.47	6.31	6.16	6.07	5.99	5.91	5.82	5.74	5.65
8	11.26	8.65	7.59	7.01	6.63	6.37	6.18	6.03	5.91	5.81	5.67	5.52	5.36	5.28	5.20	5.12	5.03	4.95	4.86
9	10.56	8.02	6.99	6.42	6.06	5.80	5.61	5.47	5.35	5.26	5.11	4.96	4.81	4.73	4.65	4.57	4.48	4.40	4.31
10	10.04	7.56	6.55	5.99	5.64	5.39	5.20	5.06	4.94	4.85	4.71	4.56	4.41	4.33	4.25	4.17	4.08	4.00	3.91
11	9.65	7.21	6.22	5.67	5.32	5.07	4.89	4.74	4.63	4.54	4.40	4.25	4.10	4.02	3.94	3.86	3.78	3.69	3.60
12	9.33	6.93	5.95	5.41	5.06	4.82	4.64	4.50	4.39	4.30	4.16	4.01	3.86	3.78	3.70	3.62	3.54	3.45	3.36
13	9.07	6.70	5.74	5.21	4.86	4.62	4.44	4.30	4.19	4.10	3.96	3.82	3.66	3.59	3.51	3.43	3.34	3.25	3.17
14	8.86	6.51	5.56	5.04	4.69	4.46	4.28	4.14	4.03	3.94	3.80	3.66	3.51	3.43	3.35	3.27	3.18	3.09	3.00
15	8.68	6.36	5.42	4.89	4.56	4.32	4.14	4.00	3.89	3.80	3.67	3.52	3.37	3.29	3.21	3.13	3.05	2.96	2.87
16	8.53	6.23	5.29	4.77	4.44	4.20	4.03	3.89	3.78	3.69	3.55	3.41	3.26	3.18	3.10	3.02	2.93	2.84	2.75
17	8.40	6.11	5.18	4.67	4.34	4.10	3.93	3.79	3.68	3.59	3.46	3.31	3.16	3.08	3.00	2.92	2.83	2.75	2.65
18	8.29	6.01	5.09	4.58	4.25	4.01	3.84	3.71	3.60	3.51	3.37	3.23	3.08	3.00	2.92	2.84	2.75	2.66	2.57
19	8.18	5.93	5.01	4.50	4.17	3.94	3.77	3.63	3.52	3.43	3.30	3.15	3.00	2.92	2.84	2.76	2.67	2.58	2.49
20	8.10	5.85	4.94	4.43	4.10	3.87	3.70	3.56	3.46	3.37	3.23	3.09	2.94	2.86	2.78	2.69	2.61	2.52	2.42
21	8.02	5.78	4.87	4.37	4.04	3.81	3.64	3.51	3.40	3.31	3.17	3.03	2.88	2.80	2.72	2.64	2.55	2.46	2.36
22	7.95	5.72	4.82	4.31	3.99	3.76	3.59	3.45	3.35	3.26	3.12	2.98	2.83	2.75	2.67	2.58	2.50	2.40	2.31
23	7.88	5.66	4.76	4.26	3.94	3.71	3.54	3.41	3.30	3.21	3.07	2.93	2.78	2.70	2.62	2.54	2.45	2.35	2.26
24	7.82	5.61	4.72	4.22	3.90	3.67	3.50	3.36	3.26	3.17	3.03	2.89	2.74	2.66	2.58	2.49	2.40	2.31	2.21
25	7.77	5.57	4.68	4.18	3.85	3.63	3.46	3.32	3.22	3.13	2.99	2.85	2.70	2.62	2.54	2.45	2.36	2.27	2.17
26	7.72	5.53	4.64	4.14	3.82	3.59	3.42	3.29	3.18	3.09	2.96	2.81	2.66	2.58	2.50	2.42	2.33	2.23	2.13
27	7.68	5.49	4.60	4.11	3.78	3.56	3.39	3.26	3.15	3.06	2.93	2.78	2.63	2.55	2.47	2.38	2.29	2.20	2.10
28	7.64	5.45	4.57	4.07	3.75	3.53	3.36	3.23	3.12	3.03	2.90	2.75	2.60	2.52	2.44	2.35	2.26	2.17	2.06
29	7.60	5.42	4.54	4.04	3.73	3.50	3.33	3.20	3.09	3.00	2.87	2.73	2.57	2.49	2.41	2.33	2.23	2.14	2.03
30	7.56	5.39	4.51	4.02	3.70	3.47	3.30	3.17	3.07	2.98	2.84	2.70	2.55	2.47	2.39	2.30	2.21	2.11	2.01
40	7.31	5.18	4.31	3.83	3.51	3.29	3.12	2.99	2.89	2.80	2.66	2.52	2.37	2.29	2.20	2.11	2.02	1.92	1.80
60	7.08	4.98	4.13	3.65	3.34	3.12	2.95	2.82	2.72	2.63	2.50	2.35	2.20	2.12	2.03	1.94	1.84	1.73	1.60
120	6.85	4.79	3.95	3.48	3.17	2.96	2.79	2.66	2.56	2.47	2.34	2.19	2.03	1.95	1.86	1.76	1.66	1.53	1.38
∞	6.63	4.61	3.78	3.32	3.02	2.80	2.64	2.51	2.41	2.32	2.18	2.04	1.88	1.79	1.70	1.59	1.47	1.32	1.00

$F = \dfrac{s_1^2}{s_2^2} = \dfrac{S_1/m}{S_2/n}$, where $s_1^2 = S_1/m$ and $s_2^2 = S_2/n$ are independent mean squares estimating a common variance σ^2 and based on m and n degrees of freedom, respectively.

F-Distribution

PERCENTAGE POINTS, *F*-DISTRIBUTION (Continued)

$$F(F) = \int_0^F \frac{\Gamma\left(\frac{m+n}{2}\right)}{\Gamma\left(\frac{m}{2}\right)\Gamma\left(\frac{n}{2}\right)} m^{\frac{m}{2}} n^{\frac{n}{2}} x^{\frac{m}{2}-1} (n+mx)^{-\frac{m+n}{2}}\, dx = .995$$

m \\ n	1	2	3	4	5	6	7	8	9	10	12	15	20	24	30	40	60	120	∞
1	16211	20000	21615	22500	23056	23437	23715	23925	24091	24224	24426	24630	24836	24940	25044	25148	25253	25359	25465
2	198.5	199.0	199.2	199.2	199.3	199.3	199.4	199.4	199.4	199.4	199.4	199.4	199.4	199.5	199.5	199.5	199.5	199.5	199.5
3	55.55	49.80	47.47	46.19	45.39	44.84	44.43	44.13	43.88	43.69	43.39	43.08	42.78	42.62	42.47	42.31	42.15	41.99	41.83
4	31.33	26.28	24.26	23.15	22.46	21.97	21.62	21.35	21.14	20.97	20.70	20.44	20.17	20.03	19.89	19.75	19.61	19.47	19.32
5	22.78	18.31	16.53	15.56	14.94	14.51	14.20	13.96	13.77	13.62	13.38	13.15	12.90	12.78	12.66	12.53	12.40	12.27	12.14
6	18.63	14.54	12.92	12.03	11.46	11.07	10.79	10.57	10.39	10.25	10.03	9.81	9.59	9.47	9.36	9.24	9.12	9.00	8.88
7	16.24	12.40	10.88	10.05	9.52	9.16	8.89	8.68	8.51	8.38	8.18	7.97	7.75	7.65	7.53	7.42	7.31	7.19	7.08
8	14.69	11.04	9.60	8.81	8.30	7.95	7.69	7.50	7.34	7.21	7.01	6.81	6.61	6.50	6.40	6.29	6.18	6.06	5.95
9	13.61	10.11	8.72	7.96	7.47	7.13	6.88	6.69	6.54	6.42	6.23	6.03	5.83	5.73	5.62	5.52	5.41	5.30	5.19
10	12.83	9.43	8.08	7.34	6.87	6.54	6.30	6.12	5.97	5.85	5.66	5.47	5.27	5.17	5.07	4.97	4.86	4.75	4.64
11	12.23	8.91	7.60	6.88	6.42	6.10	5.86	5.68	5.54	5.42	5.24	5.05	4.86	4.76	4.65	4.55	4.44	4.34	4.23
12	11.75	8.51	7.23	6.52	6.07	5.76	5.52	5.35	5.20	5.09	4.91	4.72	4.53	4.43	4.33	4.23	4.12	4.01	3.90
13	11.37	8.19	6.93	6.23	5.79	5.48	5.25	5.08	4.94	4.82	4.64	4.46	4.27	4.17	4.07	3.97	3.87	3.76	3.65
14	11.06	7.92	6.68	6.00	5.56	5.26	5.03	4.86	4.72	4.60	4.43	4.25	4.06	3.96	3.86	3.76	3.66	3.55	3.44
15	10.80	7.70	6.48	5.80	5.37	5.07	4.85	4.67	4.54	4.42	4.25	4.07	3.88	3.79	3.69	3.58	3.48	3.37	3.26
16	10.58	7.51	6.30	5.64	5.21	4.91	4.69	4.52	4.38	4.27	4.10	3.92	3.73	3.64	3.54	3.44	3.33	3.22	3.11
17	10.38	7.35	6.16	5.50	5.07	4.78	4.56	4.39	4.25	4.14	3.97	3.79	3.61	3.51	3.41	3.31	3.21	3.10	2.98
18	10.22	7.21	6.03	5.37	4.96	4.66	4.44	4.28	4.14	4.03	3.86	3.68	3.50	3.40	3.30	3.20	3.10	2.99	2.87
19	10.07	7.09	5.92	5.27	4.85	4.56	4.34	4.18	4.04	3.93	3.76	3.59	3.40	3.31	3.21	3.11	3.00	2.89	2.78
20	9.94	6.99	5.82	5.17	4.76	4.47	4.26	4.09	3.96	3.85	3.68	3.50	3.32	3.22	3.12	3.02	2.92	2.81	2.69
21	9.83	6.89	5.73	5.09	4.68	4.39	4.18	4.01	3.88	3.77	3.60	3.43	3.24	3.15	3.05	2.95	2.84	2.73	2.61
22	9.73	6.81	5.65	5.02	4.61	4.32	4.11	3.94	3.81	3.70	3.54	3.36	3.18	3.08	2.98	2.88	2.77	2.66	2.55
23	9.63	6.73	5.58	4.95	4.54	4.26	4.05	3.88	3.75	3.64	3.47	3.30	3.12	3.02	2.92	2.82	2.71	2.60	2.48
24	9.55	6.66	5.52	4.89	4.49	4.20	3.99	3.83	3.69	3.59	3.42	3.25	3.06	2.97	2.87	2.77	2.66	2.55	2.43
25	9.48	6.60	5.46	4.84	4.43	4.15	3.94	3.78	3.64	3.54	3.37	3.20	3.01	2.92	2.82	2.72	2.61	2.50	2.38
26	9.41	6.54	5.41	4.79	4.38	4.10	3.89	3.73	3.60	3.49	3.33	3.15	2.97	2.87	2.77	2.67	2.56	2.45	2.33
27	9.34	6.49	5.36	4.74	4.34	4.06	3.85	3.69	3.56	3.45	3.28	3.11	2.93	2.83	2.73	2.63	2.52	2.41	2.29
28	9.28	6.44	5.32	4.70	4.30	4.02	3.81	3.65	3.52	3.41	3.25	3.07	2.89	2.79	2.69	2.59	2.48	2.37	2.25
29	9.23	6.40	5.28	4.66	4.26	3.98	3.77	3.61	3.48	3.38	3.21	3.04	2.86	2.76	2.66	2.56	2.45	2.33	2.24
30	9.18	6.35	5.24	4.62	4.23	3.95	3.74	3.58	3.45	3.34	3.18	3.01	2.82	2.73	2.63	2.52	2.42	2.30	2.18
40	8.83	6.07	4.98	4.37	3.99	3.71	3.51	3.35	3.22	3.12	2.95	2.78	2.60	2.50	2.40	2.30	2.18	2.06	1.93
60	8.49	5.79	4.73	4.14	3.76	3.49	3.29	3.13	3.01	2.90	2.74	2.57	2.39	2.29	2.19	2.08	1.96	1.83	1.69
120	8.18	5.54	4.50	3.92	3.55	3.28	3.09	2.93	2.81	2.71	2.54	2.37	2.19	2.09	1.98	1.87	1.75	1.61	1.43
∞	7.88	5.30	4.28	3.72	3.35	3.09	2.90	2.74	2.62	2.52	2.36	2.19	2.00	1.90	1.79	1.67	1.53	1.36	1.00

$F = \dfrac{s_1^2}{s_2^2} = \dfrac{S_1/S_2}{m/n}$, where $s_1^2 = S_1/m$ and $s_2^2 = S_2/n$ are independent mean squares estimating a common variance σ^2 and based on m and n degrees of freedom, respectively.

PERCENTAGE POINTS, F-DISTRIBUTION (Continued)

$$F(F) = \int_0^F \frac{\Gamma\left(\frac{m+n}{2}\right)}{\Gamma\left(\frac{m}{2}\right)\Gamma\left(\frac{n}{2}\right)} m^{\frac{m}{2}} n^{\frac{n}{2}} x^{\frac{m}{2}-1} (n+mx)^{-\frac{m+n}{2}}\, dx = .999$$

n \ m	1	2	3	4	5	6	7	8	9	10	12	15	20	24	30	40	60	120	∞
1	4053*	5000*	5404*	5625*	5764*	5859*	5929*	5981*	6023*	6056*	6107*	6158*	6209*	6235*	6261*	6287*	6313*	6340*	6366*
2	998.5	999.0	999.2	999.2	999.3	999.3	999.4	999.4	999.4	999.4	999.4	999.4	999.4	999.5	999.5	999.5	999.5	999.5	999.5
3	167.0	148.5	141.1	137.1	134.6	132.8	131.6	130.6	129.9	129.2	128.3	127.4	126.4	125.9	125.4	125.0	124.5	124.0	123.5
4	74.14	61.25	56.18	53.44	51.71	50.53	49.66	49.00	48.47	48.05	47.41	46.76	46.10	45.77	45.43	45.09	44.75	44.40	44.05
5	47.18	37.12	33.20	31.09	29.75	28.84	28.16	27.64	27.24	26.92	26.42	25.91	25.39	25.14	24.87	24.60	24.33	24.06	23.79
6	35.51	27.00	23.70	21.92	20.81	20.03	19.46	19.03	18.69	18.41	17.99	17.56	17.12	16.89	16.67	16.44	16.21	15.99	15.75
7	29.25	21.69	18.77	17.19	16.21	15.52	15.02	14.63	14.33	14.08	13.71	13.32	12.93	12.73	12.53	12.33	12.12	11.91	11.70
8	25.42	18.49	15.83	14.39	13.49	12.86	12.40	12.04	11.77	11.54	11.19	10.84	10.48	10.30	10.11	9.92	9.73	9.53	9.33
9	22.86	16.39	13.90	12.56	11.71	11.13	10.70	10.37	10.11	9.89	9.57	9.24	8.90	8.72	8.55	8.37	8.19	8.00	7.81
10	21.04	14.91	12.55	11.28	10.48	9.92	9.52	9.20	8.96	8.75	8.45	8.13	7.80	7.64	7.47	7.30	7.12	6.94	6.76
11	19.69	13.81	11.56	10.35	9.58	9.05	8.66	8.35	8.12	7.92	7.63	7.32	7.01	6.85	6.68	6.52	6.35	6.17	6.00
12	18.64	12.97	10.80	9.63	8.89	8.38	8.00	7.71	7.48	7.29	7.00	6.71	6.40	6.25	6.09	5.93	5.76	5.59	5.42
13	17.81	12.31	10.21	9.07	8.35	7.86	7.49	7.21	6.98	6.80	6.52	6.23	5.93	5.78	5.63	5.47	5.30	5.14	4.97
14	17.14	11.78	9.73	8.62	7.92	7.43	7.08	6.80	6.58	6.40	6.13	5.85	5.56	5.41	5.25	5.10	4.94	4.77	4.60
15	16.59	11.34	9.34	8.25	7.57	7.09	6.74	6.47	6.26	6.08	5.81	5.54	5.25	5.10	4.95	4.80	4.64	4.47	4.31
16	16.12	10.97	9.00	7.94	7.27	6.81	6.46	6.19	5.98	5.81	5.55	5.27	4.99	4.85	4.70	4.54	4.39	4.23	4.06
17	15.72	10.66	8.73	7.68	7.02	6.56	6.22	5.96	5.75	5.58	5.32	5.05	4.78	4.63	4.48	4.33	4.18	4.02	3.85
18	15.38	10.39	8.49	7.46	6.81	6.35	6.02	5.76	5.56	5.39	5.13	4.87	4.59	4.45	4.30	4.15	4.00	3.84	3.67
19	15.08	10.16	8.28	7.26	6.62	6.18	5.85	5.59	5.39	5.22	4.97	4.70	4.43	4.29	4.14	3.99	3.84	3.68	3.51
20	14.82	9.95	8.10	7.10	6.46	6.02	5.69	5.44	5.24	5.08	4.82	4.56	4.29	4.15	4.00	3.86	3.70	3.54	3.38
21	14.59	9.77	7.94	6.95	6.32	5.88	5.56	5.31	5.11	4.95	4.70	4.44	4.17	4.03	3.88	3.74	3.58	3.42	3.26
22	14.38	9.61	7.80	6.81	6.19	5.76	5.44	5.19	4.99	4.83	4.58	4.33	4.06	3.92	3.78	3.63	3.48	3.32	3.15
23	14.19	9.47	7.67	6.69	6.08	5.65	5.33	5.09	4.89	4.73	4.48	4.23	3.96	3.82	3.68	3.53	3.38	3.22	3.05
24	14.03	9.34	7.55	6.59	5.98	5.55	5.23	4.99	4.80	4.64	4.39	4.14	3.87	3.74	3.59	3.45	3.29	3.14	2.97
25	13.88	9.22	7.45	6.49	5.88	5.46	5.15	4.91	4.71	4.56	4.31	4.06	3.79	3.66	3.52	3.37	3.22	3.06	2.89
26	13.74	9.12	7.36	6.41	5.80	5.38	5.07	4.83	4.64	4.48	4.24	3.99	3.72	3.59	3.44	3.30	3.15	2.99	2.82
27	13.61	9.02	7.27	6.33	5.73	5.31	5.00	4.76	4.57	4.41	4.17	3.92	3.66	3.52	3.38	3.23	3.08	2.92	2.75
28	13.50	8.93	7.19	6.25	5.66	5.24	4.93	4.69	4.50	4.35	4.11	3.86	3.60	3.46	3.32	3.18	3.02	2.86	2.69
29	13.39	8.85	7.12	6.19	5.59	5.18	4.87	4.64	4.45	4.29	4.05	3.80	3.54	3.41	3.27	3.12	2.97	2.81	2.64
30	13.29	8.77	7.05	6.12	5.53	5.12	4.82	4.58	4.39	4.24	4.00	3.75	3.49	3.36	3.22	3.07	2.92	2.76	2.59
40	12.61	8.25	6.60	5.70	5.13	4.73	4.44	4.21	4.02	3.87	3.64	3.40	3.15	3.01	2.87	2.73	2.57	2.41	2.23
60	11.97	7.76	6.17	5.31	4.76	4.37	4.09	3.87	3.69	3.54	3.31	3.08	2.83	2.69	2.55	2.41	2.25	2.08	1.89
120	11.38	7.32	5.79	4.95	4.42	4.04	3.77	3.55	3.38	3.24	3.02	2.78	2.53	2.40	2.26	2.11	1.95	1.76	1.54
∞	10.83	6.91	5.42	4.62	4.10	3.74	3.47	3.27	3.10	2.96	2.74	2.51	2.27	2.13	1.99	1.84	1.66	1.45	1.00

* Multiply these entries by 100.

TABLE OF BINOMIAL COEFFICIENTS

n	$\binom{n}{0}$	$\binom{n}{1}$	$\binom{n}{2}$	$\binom{n}{3}$	$\binom{n}{4}$	$\binom{n}{5}$	$\binom{n}{6}$	$\binom{n}{7}$	$\binom{n}{8}$	$\binom{n}{9}$	$\binom{n}{10}$
0	1										
1	1	1									
2	1	2	1								
3	1	3	3	1							
4	1	4	6	4	1						
5	1	5	10	10	5	1					
6	1	6	15	20	15	6	1				
7	1	7	21	35	35	21	7	1			
8	1	8	28	56	70	56	28	8	1		
9	1	9	36	84	126	126	84	36	9	1	
10	1	10	45	120	210	252	210	120	45	10	1
11	1	11	55	165	330	462	462	330	165	55	11
12	1	12	66	220	495	792	924	792	495	220	66
13	1	13	78	286	715	1287	1716	1716	1287	715	286
14	1	14	91	364	1001	2002	3003	3432	3003	2002	1001
15	1	15	105	455	1365	3003	5005	6435	6435	5005	3003
16	1	16	120	560	1820	4368	8008	11440	12870	11440	8008
17	1	17	136	680	2380	6188	12376	19448	24310	24310	19448
18	1	18	153	816	3060	8568	18564	31824	43758	48620	43758
19	1	19	171	969	3876	11628	27132	50388	75582	92378	92378
20	1	20	190	1140	4845	15504	38760	77520	125970	167960	184756

NOTE: $\binom{n}{m} = \dfrac{n(n-1)(n-2) \cdots (n-m+1)}{m(m-1)(m-2) \cdots 3.2.1}$; $\binom{n}{0} = 1$; $\binom{n}{1} = n$.

For coefficients missing from the above table, use the relation

$$\binom{n}{m} = \binom{n}{n-m}, \text{ e.g. } \binom{20}{11} = \binom{20}{9} = 167960.$$

RANDOM UNITS

Use of Table. If one wishes to select a random sample of N items from a universe of M items, the following procedure may be applied. $(M > N.)$

1. Decide upon some arbitrary scheme of selecting entries from the table. For example, one may decide to use the entries in the first line, second column; second line, third column; third line, fourth column; etc.

2. Assign numbers to each of the items in the universe from 1 to M. Thus, if $M = 500$, the items would be numbered from 001 to 500, and therefore, each designated item is associated with a three digit number.

3. Decide upon some arbitrary scheme of selecting positional digits from each entry chosen according to Step 1. Thus, if $M = 500$, one may decide to use the first, third, and fourth digit of each entry selected, and as a consequence a three digit number is created for each entry choice.

4. If the number formed is $\leq M$, the correspondingly designated item in the universe is chosen for the random sample of N items. If a number formed is $> M$ or is a repeated number of one already chosen, it is passed over and the next desirable number is taken. This process is continued until the random sample of N items is selected.

A TABLE OF 14,000 RANDOM UNITS

Line/Col.	(1)	(2)	(3)	(4)	(5)	(6)	(7)	(8)	(9)	(10)	(11)	(12)	(13)	(1
1	10480	15011	01536	02011	81647	91646	69179	14194	62590	36207	20969	99570	91291	907
2	22368	46573	25595	85393	30995	89198	27982	53402	93965	34095	52666	19174	39615	995
3	24130	48360	22527	97265	76393	64809	15179	24830	49340	32081	30680	19655	63348	586
4	42167	93093	06243	61680	07856	16376	39440	53537	71341	57004	00849	74917	97758	163
5	37570	39975	81837	16656	06121	91782	60468	81305	49684	60672	14110	06927	01263	546
6	77921	06907	11008	42751	27756	53498	18602	70659	90655	15053	21916	81825	44394	428
7	99562	72905	56420	69994	98872	31016	71194	18738	44013	48840	63213	21069	10634	129
8	96301	91977	05463	07972	18876	20922	94595	56869	69014	60045	18425	84903	42508	323
9	89579	14342	63661	10281	17453	18103	57740	84378	25331	12566	58678	44947	05585	569
10	85475	36857	43342	53988	53060	59533	38867	62300	08158	17983	16439	11458	18593	649
11	28918	69578	88231	33276	70997	79936	56865	05859	90106	31595	01547	85590	91610	781
12	63553	40961	48235	03427	49626	69445	18663	72695	52180	20847	12234	90511	33703	903
13	09429	93969	52636	92737	88974	33488	36320	17617	30015	08272	84115	27156	30613	749
14	10365	61129	87529	85689	48237	52267	67689	93394	01511	26358	85104	20285	29975	898
15	07119	97336	71048	08178	77233	13916	47564	81056	97735	85977	29372	74461	28551	907
16	51085	12765	51821	51259	77452	16308	60756	92144	49442	53900	70960	63990	75601	407
17	02368	21382	52404	60268	89368	19885	55322	44819	01188	65255	64835	44919	05944	551
18	01011	54092	33362	94904	31273	04146	18594	29852	71585	85030	51132	01915	92747	649
19	52162	53916	46369	58586	23216	14513	83149	98736	23495	64350	94738	17752	35156	357
20	07056	97628	33787	09998	42698	06691	76988	13602	51851	46104	88916	19509	25625	581
21	48663	91245	85828	14346	09172	30168	90229	04734	59193	22178	30421	61666	99904	328
22	54164	58492	22421	74103	47070	25306	76468	26384	58151	06646	21524	15227	96909	445
23	32639	32363	05597	24200	13363	38005	94342	28728	35806	06912	17012	64161	18296	228
24	29334	27001	87637	87308	58731	00256	45834	15398	46557	41135	10367	07684	36188	185
25	02488	33062	28834	07351	19731	92420	60952	61280	50001	67658	32586	86679	50720	949
26	81525	72295	04839	96423	24878	82651	66566	14778	76797	14780	13300	87074	79666	957
27	29676	20591	68086	26432	46901	20849	89768	81536	86645	12659	92259	57102	80428	252
28	00742	57392	39064	66432	84673	40027	32832	61362	98947	96067	64760	64584	96096	982
29	05366	04213	25669	26422	44407	44048	37937	63904	45766	66134	75470	66520	34693	904
30	91921	26418	64117	94305	26766	25940	39972	22209	71500	64568	91402	42416	07844	696
31	00582	04711	87917	77341	42206	35126	74087	99547	81817	42607	43808	76655	62028	766
32	00725	69884	62797	56170	86324	88072	76222	36086	84637	93161	76038	65855	77919	880
33	69011	65797	95876	55293	18988	27354	26575	08625	40801	59920	29841	80150	12777	485
34	25976	57948	29888	88604	67917	48708	18912	82271	65424	69774	33611	54262	85963	035
35	09763	83473	73577	12908	30883	18317	28290	35797	05998	41688	34952	37888	38917	880
36	91567	42595	27958	30134	04024	86385	29880	99730	55536	84855	29080	09250	79656	732
37	17955	56349	90999	49127	20044	59931	06115	20542	18059	02008	73708	83517	36103	427
38	46503	18584	18845	49618	02304	51038	20655	58727	28168	15475	56942	53389	20562	873
39	92157	89634	94824	78171	84610	82834	09922	25417	44137	48413	25555	21246	35509	2046
40	14577	62765	35605	81263	39667	47358	56873	56307	61607	49518	89656	20103	77490	1806
41	98427	07523	33362	64270	01638	92477	66969	98420	04880	45585	46565	04102	46880	4570
42	34914	63976	88720	82765	34476	17032	87589	40836	32427	70002	70663	88863	77775	6934
43	70060	28277	39475	46473	23219	53416	94970	25832	69975	94884	19661	72828	00102	6679
44	53976	54914	06990	67245	68350	82948	11398	42878	80287	88267	47363	46634	06541	9780
45	76072	29515	40980	07391	58745	25774	22987	80059	39911	96189	41151	14222	60697	5958
46	90725	52210	83974	29992	65831	38857	50490	83765	55657	14361	31720	57375	56228	4154
47	64364	67412	33339	31926	14883	24413	59744	92351	97473	89286	35931	04110	23726	5190
48	08962	00358	31662	25388	61642	34072	81249	35648	56891	69352	48373	45578	78547	8178
49	95012	68379	93526	70765	10593	04542	76463	54328	02349	17247	28865	14777	62730	9227
50	15664	10493	20492	38391	91132	21999	59516	81652	27195	48223	46751	22923	32261	8565

A TABLE OF 14,000 RANDOM UNITS (Continued)

Line/Col.	(1)	(2)	(3)	(4)	(5)	(6)	(7)	(8)	(9)	(10)	(11)	(12)	(13)	(14)
51	16408	81899	04153	53381	79401	21438	83035	92350	36693	31238	59649	91754	72772	02338
52	18629	81953	05520	91962	04739	13092	97662	24822	94730	06496	35090	04822	86772	98289
53	73115	35101	47498	87637	99016	71060	88824	71013	18735	20286	23153	72924	35165	43040
54	57491	16703	23167	49323	45021	33132	12544	41035	80780	45393	44812	12515	98931	91202
55	30405	83946	23792	14422	15059	45799	22716	19792	09983	74353	68668	30429	70735	25499
56	16631	35006	85900	98275	32388	52390	16815	69298	82732	38480	73817	32523	41961	44437
57	96773	20206	42559	78985	05300	22164	24369	54224	35083	19687	11052	91491	60383	19746
58	38935	64202	14349	82674	66523	44133	00697	35552	35970	19124	63318	29686	03387	59846
59	31624	76384	17403	53363	44167	64486	64758	75366	76554	31601	12614	33072	60332	92325
60	78919	19474	23632	27889	47914	02584	37680	20801	72152	39339	34806	08930	85001	87820
61	03931	33309	57047	74211	63445	17361	62825	39908	05607	91284	68833	25570	38818	46920
62	74426	33278	43972	10119	89917	15665	52872	73823	73144	88662	88970	74492	51805	99378
63	09066	00903	20795	95452	92648	45454	09552	88815	16553	51125	79375	97596	16296	66092
64	42238	12426	87025	14267	20979	04508	64535	31355	86064	29472	47689	05974	52468	16834
65	16153	08002	26504	41744	81959	65642	74240	56302	00033	67107	77510	70625	28725	34191
66	21457	40742	29820	96783	29400	21840	15035	34537	33310	06116	95240	15957	16572	06004
67	21581	57802	02050	89728	17937	37621	47075	42080	97403	48626	68995	43805	33386	21597
68	55612	78095	83197	33732	05810	24813	86902	60397	16489	03264	88525	42786	05269	92532
69	44657	66999	99324	51281	84463	60563	79312	93454	68876	25471	93911	25650	12682	73572
70	91340	84979	46949	81973	37949	61023	43997	15263	80644	43942	89203	71795	99533	50501
71	91227	21199	31935	27022	84067	05462	35216	14486	29891	68607	41867	14951	91696	85065
72	50001	38140	66321	19924	72163	09538	12151	06878	91903	18749	34405	56087	82790	70925
73	65390	05224	72958	28609	81406	39147	25549	48542	42627	45233	57202	94617	23772	07896
74	27504	96131	83944	41575	10573	08619	64482	73923	36152	05184	94142	25299	84387	34925
75	37169	94851	39117	89632	00959	16487	65536	49071	39782	17095	02330	74301	00275	48280
76	11508	70225	51111	38351	19444	66499	71945	05422	13442	78675	84081	66938	93654	59894
77	37449	30362	06694	54690	04052	53115	62757	95348	78662	11163	81651	50245	34971	52924
78	46515	70331	85922	38329	57015	15765	97161	17869	45349	61796	66345	81073	49106	79860
79	30986	81223	42416	58353	21532	30502	32305	86482	05174	07901	54339	58861	74818	46942
80	63798	64995	46583	09765	44160	78128	83991	42865	92520	83531	80377	35909	81250	54238
81	82486	84846	99254	67632	43218	50076	21361	64816	51202	88124	41870	52689	51275	83556
82	21885	32906	92431	09060	64297	51674	64126	62570	26123	05155	59194	52799	28225	85762
83	60336	98782	07408	53458	13564	59089	26445	29789	85205	41001	12535	12133	14645	23541
84	43937	46891	24010	25560	86355	33941	25786	54990	71899	15475	95434	98227	21824	19585
85	97656	63175	89303	16275	07100	92063	21942	18611	47348	20203	18534	03862	78095	50136
86	03299	01221	05418	38982	55758	92237	26759	86367	21216	98442	08303	56613	91511	75928
87	79626	06486	03574	17668	07785	76020	79924	25651	83325	88428	85076	72811	22717	50585
88	85636	68335	47539	03129	65651	11977	02510	26113	99447	68645	34327	15152	55230	93448
89	18039	14367	61337	06177	12143	46609	32989	74014	64708	00533	35398	58408	13261	47908
90	08362	15656	60627	36478	65648	16764	53412	09013	07832	41574	17639	82163	60859	75567
91	79556	29068	04142	16268	15387	12856	66227	38358	22478	73373	88732	09443	82558	05250
92	92608	82674	27072	32534	17075	27698	98204	63863	11951	34648	88022	56148	34925	57031
93	23982	25835	40055	67006	12293	02753	14827	22235	35071	99704	37543	11601	35503	85171
94	09915	96306	05908	97901	28395	14186	00821	80703	70426	75647	76310	88717	37890	40129
95	50937	33300	26695	62247	69927	76123	50842	43834	86654	70959	79725	93872	28117	19233
96	42488	78077	69882	61657	34136	79180	97526	43092	04098	73571	80799	76536	71255	64239
97	46764	86273	63003	93017	31204	36692	40202	35275	57306	55543	53203	18098	47625	88684
98	03237	45430	55417	63282	90816	17349	88298	90183	36600	78406	06216	95787	42579	90730
99	86591	81482	52667	61583	14972	90053	89534	76036	49199	43716	97548	04379	46370	28672
100	38534	01715	94964	87288	65680	43772	39560	12918	86537	62738	19636	51132	25739	56947

A TABLE OF 14,000 RANDOM UNITS (Continued)

Line/Col.	(1)	(2)	(3)	(4)	(5)	(6)	(7)	(8)	(9)	(10)	(11)	(12)	(13)	(14)
101	13284	16834	74151	92027	24670	36665	00770	22878	02179	51602	07270	76517	97275	45960
102	21224	00370	30420	03883	96648	89428	41583	17564	27395	63904	41548	49197	82277	24120
103	99052	47887	81085	64933	66279	80432	65793	83287	34142	13241	30590	97760	35848	91983
104	00199	50993	98603	38452	87890	94624	69721	57484	67501	77638	44331	11257	71131	11059
105	60578	06483	28733	37867	07936	98710	98539	27186	31237	80612	44488	97819	70401	95419
106	91240	18312	17441	01929	18163	69201	31211	54288	39296	37318	65724	90401	79017	62077
107	97458	14229	12063	59611	32249	90466	33216	19358	02591	54263	88449	01912	07436	50813
108	35249	38646	34475	72417	60514	69257	12489	51924	86871	92446	36607	11458	30440	52639
109	38980	46600	11759	11900	46743	27860	77940	39298	97838	95145	32378	68038	89351	37005
110	10750	52745	38749	87365	58959	53731	89295	59062	39404	13198	59960	70408	29812	83126
111	36247	27850	73958	20673	37800	63835	71051	84724	52492	22342	78071	17456	96104	18327
112	70994	66986	99744	72438	01174	42159	11392	20724	54322	36923	70009	23233	65438	59685
113	99638	94702	11463	18148	81386	80431	90628	52506	02016	85151	88598	47821	00265	82525
114	72055	15774	43857	99805	10419	76939	25993	03544	21560	83471	43989	90770	22965	44247
115	24038	65541	85788	55835	38835	59399	13790	35112	01324	39520	76210	22467	83275	32286
116	74976	14631	35908	28221	39470	91548	12854	30166	09073	75887	36782	00268	97121	57676
117	35553	71628	70189	26436	63407	91178	90348	55359	80392	41012	36270	77786	89578	21059
118	35676	12797	51434	82976	42010	26344	92920	92155	58807	54644	58581	95331	78629	73344
119	74815	67523	72985	23183	02446	63594	98924	20633	58842	85961	07648	70164	34994	67662
120	45246	88048	65173	50989	91060	89894	36063	32819	68559	99221	49475	50558	34698	71800
121	76509	47069	86378	41797	11910	49672	88575	97966	32466	10083	54728	81972	58975	30761
122	19689	90332	04315	21358	97248	11188	39062	63312	52496	07349	79178	33692	57352	72862
123	42751	35318	97513	61537	54955	08159	00337	80778	27507	95478	21252	12746	37554	97775
124	11946	22681	45045	13964	57517	59419	58045	44067	58716	58840	45557	96345	33271	53464
125	96518	48688	20996	11090	48396	57177	83867	86464	14342	21545	46717	72364	86954	55580
126	35726	58643	76869	84622	39098	36083	72505	92265	23107	60278	05822	46760	44294	07672
127	39737	42750	48968	70536	84864	64952	38404	94317	65402	13589	01055	79044	19308	83623
128	97025	66492	56177	04049	80312	48028	26408	43591	75528	65341	49044	95495	81256	53214
129	62814	08075	09788	56350	76787	51591	54509	49295	85830	59860	30883	89660	96142	18354
130	25578	22950	15227	83291	41737	79599	96191	71845	86899	70694	24290	01551	80092	82118
131	68763	69576	88991	49662	46704	63362	56625	00481	73323	91427	15264	06969	57048	54149
132	17900	00813	64361	60725	88974	61005	99709	30666	26451	11528	44323	34778	60342	60388
133	71944	60227	63551	71109	05624	43836	58254	26160	32116	63403	35404	57146	10909	07346
134	54684	93691	85132	64399	29182	44324	14491	55226	78793	34107	30374	48429	51376	09559
135	25946	27623	11258	65204	52832	50880	22273	05554	99521	73791	85744	29276	70326	60251
136	01353	39318	44961	44972	91766	90262	56073	06606	51826	18893	83448	31915	97764	75091
137	99083	88191	27662	99113	57174	35571	99884	13951	71057	53961	61448	74909	07322	80960
138	52021	45406	37945	75234	24327	86978	22644	87779	23753	99926	63898	54886	18051	96314
139	78755	47744	43776	83098	03225	14281	83637	55984	13300	52212	58781	14905	46502	04472
140	25282	69106	59180	16257	22810	43609	12224	25643	89884	31149	85423	32581	34374	70873
141	11959	94202	02743	86847	79725	51811	12998	76844	05320	54236	53891	70226	38632	84776
142	11644	13792	98190	01424	30078	28197	55583	05197	47714	68440	22016	79204	06862	94451
143	06307	97912	68110	59812	95448	43244	31262	88880	13040	16458	43813	89416	42482	33939
144	76285	75714	89585	99296	52640	46518	55486	90754	88932	19937	57119	23251	55619	23679
145	55322	07589	39600	60866	63007	20007	66819	84164	61131	81429	60676	42807	78286	29015
146	78017	90928	90220	92503	83375	26986	74399	30885	88567	29169	72816	53357	15428	86932
147	44768	43342	20696	26331	43140	69744	82928	24988	94237	46138	77426	39039	55596	12655
148	25100	19336	14605	86603	51680	97678	24261	02464	86563	74812	60069	71674	15478	47642
149	83612	46623	62876	85197	07824	91392	58317	37726	84628	42221	10268	20692	15699	29167
150	41347	81666	82961	60413	71020	83658	02415	33322	66036	98712	46795	16308	28413	05417

A TABLE OF 14,000 RANDOM UNITS (Continued)

Line/Col.	(1)	(2)	(3)	(4)	(5)	(6)	(7)	(8)	(9)	(10)	(11)	(12)	(13)	(14)
151	38128	51178	75096	13609	16110	73533	42564	59870	29399	67834	91055	89917	51096	89011
152	60950	00455	73254	96067	50717	13878	03216	78274	65863	37011	91283	33914	91303	49326
153	90524	17320	29832	96118	75792	25326	22940	24904	80523	38928	91374	55597	97567	38914
154	49897	18278	67160	39408	97056	43517	84426	59650	20247	19293	02019	14790	02852	05819
155	18494	99209	81060	19488	65596	59787	47939	91225	98768	43688	00438	05548	09443	82897
156	65373	72984	30171	37741	70203	94094	87261	30056	58124	70133	18936	02138	59372	09075
157	40653	12843	04213	70925	95360	55774	76439	61768	52817	81151	52188	31940	54273	49032
158	51638	22238	56344	44587	83231	50317	74541	07719	25472	41602	77318	15145	57515	07633
159	69742	99303	62578	83575	30337	07488	51941	84316	42067	49692	28616	29101	03013	73449
160	58012	74072	67488	74580	47992	69482	58624	17106	47538	13452	22620	24260	40155	74716
161	18348	19855	42887	08279	43206	47077	42637	45606	00011	20662	14642	49984	94509	56380
162	59614	09193	58064	29086	44385	45740	70752	05663	49081	26960	57454	99264	24142	74648
163	75688	28630	39210	52897	62748	72658	98059	67202	72789	01869	13496	14663	87645	89713
164	13941	77802	69101	70061	35460	34576	15412	81304	58757	35498	94830	75521	00603	97701
165	96656	86420	96475	86458	54463	96419	55417	41375	76886	19008	66877	35934	59801	00497
166	03363	82042	15942	14549	38324	87094	19069	67590	11087	68570	22591	65232	85915	91499
167	70366	08390	69155	25496	13240	57407	91407	49160	07379	34444	94567	66035	38918	65708
168	47870	36605	12927	16043	53257	93796	52721	73120	48025	76074	95605	67422	41646	14557
169	79504	77606	22761	30518	28373	73898	30550	76684	77366	32276	04690	61667	64798	66276
170	46967	74841	50923	15339	37755	98995	40162	89561	69199	42257	11647	47603	48779	97907
171	14558	50769	35444	59030	87516	48193	02945	00922	48189	04724	21263	20892	92955	90251
172	12440	25057	01132	38611	28135	68089	10954	10097	54243	06460	50856	65435	79377	53890
173	32293	29938	68653	10497	98919	46587	77701	99119	93165	67788	17638	23097	21468	36992
174	10640	21875	72462	77981	56550	55999	87310	69643	45124	00349	25748	00844	96831	30651
175	47615	23169	39571	56972	20628	21788	51736	33133	72696	32605	41569	76148	91544	21121
176	16948	11128	71624	72754	49084	96303	27830	45817	67867	18062	87453	17226	72904	71474
177	21258	61092	66634	70335	92448	17354	83432	49608	66520	06442	59664	20420	39201	69549
178	15072	48853	15178	30730	47481	48490	41436	25015	49932	20474	53821	51015	79841	32405
179	99154	57412	09858	65671	70655	71479	63520	31357	56968	06729	34465	70685	04184	25250
180	08759	61089	23706	32994	35426	36666	63988	98844	37533	08269	27021	45886	22835	78451
181	67323	57839	61114	62192	47547	58023	64630	34886	98777	75442	95592	06141	45096	73117
182	09255	13986	84834	20764	72206	89393	34548	93438	88730	61805	78955	18952	46436	58740
183	36304	74712	00374	10107	85061	69228	81969	92216	03568	39630	81869	52824	50937	27954
184	15884	67429	86612	47367	10242	44880	12060	44309	46629	55105	66793	93173	00480	13311
185	18745	32031	35303	08134	33925	03044	59929	95418	04917	57596	24878	61733	92834	64454
186	72934	40086	88292	65728	38300	42323	64068	98373	48971	09049	59943	36538	05976	82118
187	17626	02944	20910	57662	80181	38579	24580	90529	52303	50436	29401	57824	86039	81062
188	27117	61399	50967	41399	81636	16663	15634	79717	94696	59240	25543	97989	63306	90946
189	93995	18678	90012	63645	85701	85269	62263	68331	00389	72571	15210	20769	44686	96176
190	67392	89421	09623	80725	62620	84162	87368	29560	00519	84545	08004	24526	41252	14521
191	04910	12261	37566	80016	21245	69377	50420	85658	55263	68667	78770	04533	14513	18099
192	81453	20283	79929	59839	23875	13245	46808	74124	74703	35769	95588	21014	37078	39170
193	19480	75790	48539	23703	15537	48885	02861	86587	74539	65227	90799	58789	96257	02708
194	21456	13162	74608	81011	55512	07481	93551	72189	76261	91206	89941	15132	37738	59284
195	89406	20912	46189	76376	25538	87212	20748	12831	57166	35026	16817	79121	18929	40628
196	09866	07414	55977	16419	01101	69343	13305	94302	80703	57910	36933	57771	42546	03003
197	86541	24681	23421	13521	28000	94917	07423	57523	97234	63951	42876	46829	09781	58160
198	10414	96941	06205	72222	57167	83902	07460	69507	10600	08858	07685	44472	64220	27040
199	49942	06683	41479	58982	56288	42853	92196	20632	62045	78812	35895	51851	83534	10689
200	23995	68882	42291	23374	24299	27024	67460	94783	40937	16961	26053	78749	46704	21983

THE NUMBER OF EACH DAY OF THE YEAR

Day of Mo.	Jan.	Feb.	Mar.	Apr.	May	Jun.	Jul.	Aug.	Sep.	Oct.	Nov.	Dec.	Day of Mo.
1	1	32	60	91	121	152	182	213	244	274	305	335	1
2	2	33	61	92	122	153	183	214	245	275	306	336	2
3	3	34	62	93	123	154	184	215	246	276	307	337	3
4	4	35	63	94	124	155	185	216	247	277	308	338	4
5	5	36	64	95	125	156	186	217	248	278	309	339	5
6	6	37	65	96	126	157	187	218	249	279	310	340	6
7	7	38	66	97	127	158	188	219	250	280	311	341	7
8	8	39	67	98	128	159	189	220	251	281	312	342	8
9	9	40	68	99	129	160	190	221	252	282	313	343	9
10	10	41	69	100	130	161	191	222	253	283	314	344	10
11	11	42	70	101	131	162	192	223	254	284	315	345	11
12	12	43	71	102	132	163	193	224	255	285	316	346	12
13	13	44	72	103	133	164	194	225	256	286	317	347	13
14	14	45	73	104	134	165	195	226	257	287	318	348	14
15	15	46	74	105	135	166	196	227	258	288	319	349	15
16	16	47	75	106	136	167	197	228	259	289	320	350	16
17	17	48	76	107	137	168	198	229	260	290	321	351	17
18	18	49	77	108	138	169	199	230	261	291	322	352	18
19	19	50	78	109	139	170	200	231	262	292	323	353	19
20	20	51	79	110	140	171	201	232	263	293	324	354	20
21	21	52	80	111	141	172	202	233	264	294	325	355	21
22	22	53	81	112	142	173	203	234	265	295	326	356	22
23	23	54	82	113	143	174	204	235	266	296	327	357	23
24	24	55	83	114	144	175	205	236	267	297	328	358	24
25	25	56	84	115	145	176	206	237	268	298	329	359	25
26	26	57	85	116	146	177	207	238	269	299	330	360	26
27	27	58	86	117	147	178	208	239	270	300	331	361	27
28	28	59	87	118	148	179	209	240	271	301	332	362	28
29	29	*	88	119	149	180	210	241	272	302	333	363	29
30	30		89	120	150	181	211	242	273	303	334	364	30
31	31		90		151		212	243		304		365	31

* In leap years, after February 28, add 1 to the tabulated number.

INTEREST TABLES

SIMPLE INTEREST

If P is the principal placed at interest at a rate i (expressed as a decimal), for a period of n years

The amount,

$$A = P(1 + ni)$$

Present value,

$$P = \frac{A}{1 + ni}$$

COMPOUND INTEREST

At interest compounded annually the **amount,—**

$$A = P(1 + i)^n$$

At interest compounded q times per year,—

$$A = P\left(1 + \frac{i}{q}\right)^{nq}$$

At interest compounded annually the **present value,—**

$$P = \frac{A}{(1 + i)^n} = A(1 + i)^{-n} = Av^n. \quad v = \frac{1}{1 + i}$$

At interest compounded q times per year,—

$$P = A\left(1 + \frac{i}{q}\right)^{-nq}$$

The **amount of an annuity of 1 per annum,—**

$$s_{\overline{n}|i} = \frac{(1 + i)^n - 1}{i}$$

The **present value of an annuity,—**

$$a_{\overline{n}|i} = \frac{1 - (1 + i)^{-n}}{i}$$

The **annuity whose present value is 1,—**

$$\frac{1}{a_{\overline{n}|i}} = \frac{1}{s_{\overline{n}|i}} + i = \frac{i}{(1 - v^n)}$$

Compound amount of 1 for fractional periods,—$(1+i)^{1/p}$

Nominal rate convertible p times per year equivalent to effective rate i,—

$$j_p = p[(1+i)^{1/p} - 1]$$

Amount for year of p deposits of $1/p$, p times per year,—i/j_p

AMOUNT AT COMPOUND INTEREST $(1 + i)^n$

The following table gives the amount after a term of n periods on unit original principal at rate of interest i.

Periods	Rate i				
n	.0025 ($\frac{1}{4}$%)	.004167 ($\frac{5}{12}$%)	.005 ($\frac{1}{2}$%)	.005833 ($\frac{7}{12}$%)	.0075 ($\frac{3}{4}$%)
1	1.0025 0000	1.0041 6667	1.0050 0000	1.0058 3333	1.0075 0000
2	1.0050 0625	1.0083 5069	1.0100 2500	1.0117 0069	1.0150 5625
3	1.0075 1877	1.0125 5216	1.0150 7513	1.0176 0228	1.0226 6917
4	1.0100 3756	1.0167 7112	1.0201 5050	1.0235 3830	1.0303 3919
5	1.0125 6266	1.0210 0767	1.0252 5125	1.0295 0894	1.0380 6673
6	1.0150 9406	1.0252 6187	1.0303 7751	1.0355 1440	1.0458 5224
7	1.0176 3180	1.0295 3379	1.0355 2940	1.0415 5490	1.0536 9613
8	1.0201 7588	1.0338 2352	1.0407 0704	1.0476 3064	1.0615 9885
9	1.0227 2632	1.0381 3111	1.0459 1058	1.0537 4182	1.0695 6084
10	1.0252 8313	1.0424 5666	1.0511 4013	1.0598 8865	1.0775 8255
11	1.0278 4634	1.0468 0023	1.0563 9583	1.0660 7133	1.0856 6441
12	1.0304 1596	1.0511 6190	1.0616 7781	1.0722 9008	1.0938 0690
13	1.0329 9200	1.0555 4174	1.0669 8620	1.0785 4511	1.1020 1045
14	1.0355 7448	1.0599 3983	1.0723 2113	1.0848 3662	1.1102 7553
15	1.0381 6341	1.0643 5625	1.0776 8274	1.0911 6483	1.1186 0259
16	1.0407 5882	1.0687 9106	1.0830 7115	1.0975 2996	1.1269 9211
17	1.0433 6072	1.0732 4436	1.0884 8651	1.1039 3222	1.1354 4455
18	1.0459 6912	1.0777 1621	1.0939 2894	1.1103 7182	1.1439 6039
19	1.0485 8404	1.0822 0670	1.0993 9858	1.1168 4899	1.1525 4009
20	1.0512 0550	1.0867 1589	1.1048 9558	1.1233 6395	1.1611 8414
21	1.0538 3352	1.0912 4387	1.1104 2006	1.1299 1690	1.1698 9302
22	1.0564 6810	1.0957 9072	1.1159 7216	1.1365 0808	1.1786 6722
23	1.0591 0927	1.1003 5652	1.1215 5202	1.1431 3771	1.1875 0723
24	1.0617 5704	1.1049 4134	1.1271 5978	1.1498 0602	1.1964 1353
25	1.0644 1144	1.1095 4526	1.1327 9558	1.1565 1322	1.2053 8663
26	1.0670 7247	1.1141 6836	1.1384 5955	1.1632 5955	1.2144 2703
27	1.0697 4015	1.1188 1073	1.1441 5185	1.1700 4523	1.2235 3523
28	1.0724 1450	1.1234 7244	1.1498 7261	1.1768 7049	1.2327 1175
29	1.0750 9553	1.1281 5358	1.1556 2197	1.1837 3557	1.2419 5709
30	1.0777 8327	1.1328 5422	1.1614 0008	1.1906 4069	1.2512 7176
31	1.0804 7773	1.1375 7444	1.1672 0708	1.1975 8610	1.2606 5630
32	1.0831 7892	1.1423 1434	1.1730 4312	1.2045 7202	1.2701 1122
33	1.0858 8687	1.1470 7398	1.1789 0833	1.2115 9869	1.2796 3706
34	1.0886 0159	1.1518 5346	1.1848 0288	1.2186 6634	1.2892 3434
35	1.0913 2309	1.1566 5284	1.1907 2689	1.2257 7523	1.2989 0359
36	1.0940 5140	1.1614 7223	1.1966 8052	1.2329 2559	1.3086 4537
37	1.0967 8653	1.1663 1170	1.2026 6393	1.2401 1765	1.3184 6021
38	1.0995 2850	1.1711 7133	1.2086 7725	1.2473 5167	1.3283 4866
39	1.1022 7732	1.1760 5121	1.2147 2063	1.2546 2789	1.3383 1128
40	1.1050 3301	1.1809 5142	1.2207 9424	1.2619 4655	1.3483 4861
41	1.1077 9559	1.1858 7206	1.2268 9821	1.2693 0791	1.3584 6123
42	1.1105 6508	1.1908 1319	1.2330 3270	1.2767 1220	1.3686 4969
43	1.1133 4149	1.1957 7491	1.2391 9786	1.2841 5969	1.3789 1456
44	1.1161 2485	1.2007 5731	1.2453 9385	1.2916 5062	1.3892 5642
45	1.1189 1516	1.2057 6046	1.2516 2082	1.2991 8525	1.3996 7584
46	1.1217 1245	1.2107 8446	1.2578 7892	1.3067 6383	1.4101 7341
47	1.1245 1673	1.2158 2940	1.2641 6832	1.3143 8662	1.4207 4971
48	1.1273 2802	1.2208 9536	1.2704 8916	1.3220 5388	1.4314 0533
49	1.1301 4634	1.2259 8242	1.2768 4161	1.3297 6586	1.4421 4087
50	1.1329 7171	1.2310 9068	1.2832 2581	1.3375 2283	1.4529 5693

AMOUNT AT COMPOUND INTEREST $(1 + i)^n$ (Continued)

Periods	Rate i				
n	.0025 ($\frac{1}{4}$%)	.004167($\frac{1}{12}$%)	.005 ($\frac{1}{2}$%)	.005833($\frac{7}{12}$%)	.0075 ($\frac{3}{4}$%)
50	1.1329 7171	1.2310 9068	1.2832 2581	1.3375 2283	1.4529 5693
51	1.1358 0414	1.2362 2022	1.2896 4194	1.3453 2504	1.4638 5411
52	1.1386 4365	1.2413 7114	1.2960 9015	1.3531 7277	1.4748 3301
53	1.1414 9026	1.2465 4352	1.3025 7060	1.3610 6628	1.4858 9426
54	1.1443 4398	1.2517 3745	1.3090 8346	1.3690 0583	1.4970 3847
55	1.1472 0484	1.2569 5302	1.3156 2887	1.3769 9170	1.5082 6626
56	1.1500 7285	1.2621 9033	1.3222 0702	1.3850 2415	1.5195 7825
57	1.1529 4804	1.2674 4946	1.3288 1805	1.3931 0346	1.5309 7509
58	1.1558 3041	1.2727 3050	1.3354 6214	1.4012 2990	1.5424 5740
59	1.1587 1998	1.2780 3354	1.3421 3946	1.4094 0374	1.5540 2583
60	1.1616 1678	1.2833 5868	1.3488 5015	1.4176 2526	1.5656 8103
61	1.1645 2082	1.2887 0601	1.3555 9440	1.4258 9474	1.5774 2363
62	1.1674 3213	1.2940 7561	1.3623 7238	1.4342 1246	1.5892 5431
63	1.1703 5071	1.2994 6760	1.3691 8424	1.4425 7870	1.6011 7372
64	1.1732 7658	1.3048 8204	1.3760 3016	1.4509 9374	1.6131 8252
65	1.1762 0977	1.3103 1905	1.3829 1031	1.4594 5787	1.6252 8139
66	1.1791 5030	1.3157 7872	1.3898 2486	1.4679 7138	1.6374 7100
67	1.1820 9817	1.3212 6113	1.3967 7399	1.4765 3454	1.6497 5203
68	1.1850 5342	1.3267 6638	1.4037 5785	1.4851 4766	1.6621 2517
69	1.1880 1605	1.3322 9458	1.4107 7664	1.4938 1102	1.6745 9111
70	1.1909 8609	1.3378 4580	1.4178 3053	1.5025 2492	1.6871 5055
71	1.1939 6356	1.3434 2016	1.4249 1968	1.5112 8965	1.6998 0418
72	1.1969 4847	1.3490 1774	1.4320 4428	1.5201 0550	1.7125 5271
73	1.1999 4084	1.3546 3865	1.4392 0450	1.5289 7279	1.7253 9685
74	1.2029 4069	1.3602 8298	1.4464 0052	1.5378 9179	1.7383 3733
75	1.2059 4804	1.3659 5082	1.4536 3252	1.5468 6283	1.7513 7486
76	1.2089 6291	1.3716 4229	1.4609 0069	1.5558 8620	1.7645 1017
77	1.2119 8532	1.3773 5746	1.4682 0519	1.5649 6220	1.7777 4400
78	1.2150 1528	1.3830 9645	1.4755 4622	1.5740 9115	1.7910 7708
79	1.2180 5282	1.3888 5935	1.4829 2395	1.5832 7334	1.8045 1015
80	1.2210 9795	1.3946 4627	1.4903 3857	1.5925 0910	1.8180 4398
81	1.2241 5070	1.4004 5729	1.4977 9026	1.6017 9874	1.8316 7931
82	1.2272 1108	1.4062 9253	1.5052 7921	1.6111 4257	1.8454 1691
83	1.2302 7910	1.4121 5209	1.5128 0561	1.6205 4090	1.8592 5753
84	1.2333 5480	1.4180 3605	1.5203 6964	1.6299 9405	1.8732 0196
85	1.2364 3819	1.4239 4454	1.5279 7148	1.6395 0235	1.8872 5098
86	1.2395 2928	1.4298 7764	1.5356 1134	1.6490 6612	1.9014 0536
87	1.2426 2811	1.4358 3546	1.5432 8940	1.6586 8567	1.9156 6590
88	1.2457 3468	1.4418 1811	1.5510 0585	1.6683 6134	1.9300 3339
89	1.2488 4901	1.4478 2568	1.5587 6087	1.6780 9344	1.9445 0865
90	1.2519 7114	1.4538 5829	1.5665 5468	1.6878 8232	1.9590 9246
91	1.2551 0106	1.4599 1603	1.5743 8745	1.6977 2830	1.9737 8565
92	1.2582 3882	1.4659 9902	1.5822 5939	1.7076 3172	1.9885 8905
93	1.2613 8441	1.4721 0735	1.5901 7069	1.7175 9290	2.0035 0346
94	1.2645 3787	1.4782 4113	1.5981 2154	1.7276 1219	2.0185 2974
95	1.2676 9922	1.4844 0047	1.6061 1215	1.7376 8993	2.0336 6871
96	1.2708 6847	1.4905 8547	1.6141 4271	1.7478 2646	2.0489 2123
97	1.2740 4564	1.4967 9624	1.6222 1342	1.7580 2211	2.0642 8814
98	1.2772 3075	1.5030 3289	1.6303 2449	1.7682 7724	2.0797 7030
99	1.2804 2383	1.5092 9553	1.6384 7611	1.7785 9219	2.0953 6858
100	1.2836 2489	1.5155 8426	1.6466 6849	1.7889 6731	2.1110 8384

AMOUNT AT COMPOUND INTEREST $(1 + i)^n$ (Continued)

Periods	Rate i				
n	.01 (1%)	.01125 (1⅛%)	.0125 (1¼%)	.015 (1½%)	.0175 (1¾%)
1	1.0100 0000	1.0112 5000	1.0125 0000	1.0150 0000	1.0175 0000
2	1.0201 0000	1.0226 2656	1.0251 5625	1.0302 2500	1.0353 0625
3	1.0303 0100	1.0341 3111	1.0379 7070	1.0456 7838	1.0534 2411
4	1.0406 0401	1.0457 6509	1.0509 4534	1.0613 6355	1.0718 5903
5	1.0510 1005	1.0575 2994	1.0640 8215	1.0772 8400	1.0906 1656
6	1.0615 2015	1.0694 2716	1.0773 8318	1.0934 4326	1.1097 0235
7	1.0721 3535	1.0814 5821	1.0908 5047	1.1098 4491	1.1291 2215
8	1.0828 5671	1.0936 2462	1.1044 8610	1.1264 9259	1.1488 8178
9	1.0936 8527	1.1059 2789	1.1182 9218	1.1433 8998	1.1689 8721
10	1.1046 2213	1.1183 6958	1.1322 7083	1.1605 4083	1.1894 4449
11	1.1156 6835	1.1309 5124	1.1464 2422	1.1779 4894	1.2102 5977
12	1.1268 2503	1.1436 7444	1.1607 5452	1.1956 1817	1.2314 3931
13	1.1380 9328	1.1565 4078	1.1752 6395	1.2135 5244	1.2529 8950
14	1.1494 7421	1.1695 5186	1.1899 5475	1.2317 5573	1.2749 1682
15	1.1609 6896	1.1827 0932	1.2048 2918	1.2502 3207	1.2972 2786
16	1.1725 7864	1.1960 1480	1.2198 8955	1.2689 8555	1.3199 2935
17	1.1843 0443	1.2094 6997	1.2351 3817	1.2880 2033	1.3430 2811
18	1.1961 4748	1.2230 7650	1.2505 7739	1.3073 4064	1.3665 3111
19	1.2081 0895	1.2368 3611	1.2662 0961	1.3269 5075	1.3904 4540
20	1.2201 9004	1.2507 5052	1.2820 3723	1.3468 5501	1.4147 7820
21	1.2323 9194	1.2648 2146	1.2980 6270	1.3670 5783	1.4395 3681
22	1.2447 1586	1.2790 5071	1.3142 8848	1.3875 6370	1.4647 2871
23	1.2571 6302	1.2934 4003	1.3307 1709	1.4083 7715	1.4903 6146
24	1.2697 3465	1.3079 9123	1.3473 5105	1.4295 0281	1.5164 4279
25	1.2824 3200	1.3227 0613	1.3641 9294	1.4509 4535	1.5429 8054
26	1.2952 5631	1.3375 8657	1.3812 4535	1.4727 0953	1.5699 8269
27	1.3082 0888	1.3526 3442	1.3985 1092	1.4948 0018	1.5974 5739
28	1.3212 9097	1.3678 5156	1.4159 9230	1.5172 2218	1.6254 1290
29	1.3345 0388	1.3832 3989	1.4336 9221	1.5399 8051	1.6538 5762
30	1.3478 4892	1.3988 0134	1.4516 1336	1.5630 8042	1.6828 0013
31	1.3613 2740	1.4145 3785	1.4697 5853	1.5865 2642	1.7122 4913
32	1.3749 4068	1.4304 5140	1.4881 3051	1.6103 2432	1.7422 1349
33	1.3886 9009	1.4465 4398	1.5067 3214	1.6344 7918	1.7727 0223
34	1.4025 7699	1.4628 1760	1.5255 6629	1.6589 9637	1.8037 2452
35	1.4166 0276	1.4792 7430	1.5446 3587	1.6838 8132	1.8352 8970
36	1.4307 6878	1.4959 1613	1.5639 4382	1.7091 3954	1.8674 0727
37	1.4450 7647	1.5127 4519	1.5834 9312	1.7347 7663	1.9000 8689
38	1.4595 2724	1.5297 6357	1.6032 8678	1.7607 9828	1.9333 3841
39	1.4741 2251	1.5469 7341	1.6233 2787	1.7872 1025	1.9671 7184
40	1.4888 6373	1.5643 7687	1.6436 1946	1.8140 1841	2.0015 9734
41	1.5037 5237	1.5819 7611	1.6641 6471	1.8412 2868	2.0366 2530
42	1.5187 8989	1.5997 7334	1.6849 6677	1.8688 4712	2.0722 6624
43	1.5339 7779	1.6177 7079	1.7060 2885	1.8968 7982	2.1085 3090
44	1.5493 1757	1.6359 7071	1.7273 5421	1.9253 3302	2.1454 3019
45	1.5648 1075	1.6543 7538	1.7489 4614	1.9542 1301	2.1829 7522
46	1.5804 5885	1.6729 8710	1.7708 0797	1.9835 2621	2.2211 7728
47	1.5962 6344	1.6918 0821	1.7929 4306	2.0132 7910	2.2600 4789
48	1.6122 2608	1.7108 4105	1.8153 5485	2.0434 7829	2.2995 9872
49	1.6283 4834	1.7300 8801	1.8380 4679	2.0741 3046	2.3398 4170
50	1.6446 3182	1.7495 5150	1.8610 2237	2.1052 4242	2.3807 8893

AMOUNT AT COMPOUND INTEREST $(1 + i)^n$ (Continued)

Periods	Rate i				
n	.01 (1%)	.01125 (1⅛%)	.0125 (1¼%)	.015 (1½%)	.0175 (1¾%)
50	1.6446 3182	1.7495 5150	1.8610 2237	2.1052 4242	2.3807 8893
51	1.6610 7814	1.7692 3395	1.8842 8515	2.1368 2106	2.4224 5274
52	1.6776 8892	1.7891 3784	1.9078 3872	2.1688 7337	2.4648 4566
53	1.6944 6581	1.8092 6564	1.9316 8670	2.2014 0647	2.5079 8046
54	1.7114 1047	1.8296 1988	1.9558 3279	2.2344 2757	2.5518 7012
55	1.7285 2457	1.8502 0310	1.9802 8070	2.2679 4398	2.5965 2785
56	1.7458 0982	1.8710 1788	2.0050 3420	2.3019 6314	2.6419 6708
57	1.7632 6792	1.8920 6684	2.0300 9713	2.3364 9259	2.6882 0151
58	1.7809 0060	1.9133 5259	2.0554 7335	2.3715 3998	2.7352 4503
59	1.7987 0960	1.9348 7780	2.0811 6676	2.4071 1308	2.7831 1182
60	1.8166 9670	1.9566 4518	2.1071 8135	2.4432 1978	2.8318 1628
61	1.8348 6367	1.9786 5744	2.1335 2111	2.4798 6807	2.8813 7306
62	1.8532 1230	2.0009 1733	2.1601 9013	2.5170 6609	2.9317 9709
63	1.8717 4443	2.0234 2765	2.1871 9250	2.5548 2208	2.9831 0354
64	1.8904 6187	2.0461 9121	2.2145 3241	2.5931 4442	3.0353 0785
65	1.9093 6649	2.0692 1087	2.2422 1407	2.6320 4158	3.0884 2574
66	1.9284 6015	2.0924 8949	2.2702 4174	2.6715 2221	3.1424 7319
67	1.9477 4475	2.1160 2999	2.2986 1976	2.7115 9504	3.1974 6647
68	1.9672 2220	2.1398 3533	2.3273 5251	2.7522 6896	3.2534 2213
69	1.9868 9442	2.1639 0848	2.3564 4442	2.7935 5300	3.3103 5702
70	2.0067 6337	2.1882 5245	2.3858 9997	2.8354 5629	3.3682 8827
71	2.0268 3100	2.2128 7029	2.4157 2372	2.8779 8814	3.4272 3331
72	2.0470 9931	2.2377 6508	2.4459 2027	2.9211 5796	3.4872 0990
73	2.0675 7031	2.2629 3994	2.4764 9427	2.9649 7533	3.5482 3607
74	2.0882 4601	2.2883 9801	2.5074 5045	3.0094 4996	3.6103 3020
75	2.1091 2847	2.3141 4249	2.5387 9358	3.0545 9171	3.6735 1098
76	2.1302 1975	2.3401 7659	2.5705 2850	3.1004 1059	3.7377 9742
77	2.1515 2195	2.3665 0358	2.6026 6011	3.1469 1674	3.8032 0888
78	2.1730 3717	2.3931 2675	2.6351 9336	3.1941 2050	3.8697 6503
79	2.1947 6754	2.4200 4942	2.6681 3327	3.2420 3230	3.9374 8592
80	2.2167 1522	2.4472 7498	2.7014 8494	3.2906 6279	4.0063 9192
81	2.2388 8237	2.4748 0682	2.7352 5350	3.3400 2273	4.0765 0378
82	2.2612 7119	2.5026 4840	2.7694 4417	3.3901 2307	4.1478 4260
83	2.2838 8390	2.5308 0319	2.8040 6222	3.4409 7492	4.2204 2984
84	2.3067 2274	2.5592 7473	2.8391 1300	3.4925 8954	4.2942 8737
85	2.3297 8997	2.5880 6657	2.8746 0191	3.5449 7838	4.3694 3740
86	2.3530 8787	2.6171 8232	2.9105 3444	3.5981 5306	4.4459 0255
87	2.3766 1875	2.6466 2562	2.9469 1612	3.6521 2535	4.5237 0584
88	2.4003 8494	2.6764 0016	2.9837 5257	3.7069 0723	4.6028 7070
89	2.4243 8879	2.7065 0966	3.0210 4948	3.7625 1084	4.6834 2093
90	2.4486 3267	2.7369 5789	3.0588 1260	3.8189 4851	4.7653 8080
91	2.4731 1900	2.7677 4867	3.0970 4775	3.8762 3273	4.8487 7496
92	2.4978 5019	2.7988 8584	3.1357 6085	3.9343 7622	4.9336 2853
93	2.5228 2869	2.8303 7331	3.1749 5786	3.9933 9187	5.0199 6703
94	2.5480 5698	2.8622 1501	3.2146 4483	4.0532 9275	5.1078 1645
95	2.5735 3755	2.8944 1492	3.2548 2789	4.1140 9214	5.1972 0324
96	2.5992 7293	2.9269 7709	3.2955 1324	4.1758 0352	5.2881 5429
97	2.6252 6565	2.9599 0559	3.3367 0716	4.2384 4057	5.3806 9699
98	2.6515 1831	2.9932 0452	3.3784 1600	4.3020 1718	5.4748 5919
99	2.6780 3349	3.0268 7807	3.4206 4620	4.3665 4744	5.5706 6923
100	2.7048 1383	3.0609 3045	3.4634 0427	4.4320 4565	5.6681 5594

AMOUNT AT COMPOUND INTEREST $(1 + i)^n$ (Continued)

Periods	Rate i				
n	.02 (2%)	.0225 (2¼%)	.025 (2½%)	.0275 (2¾%)	.03 (3%)
1	1.0200 0000	1.0225 0000	1.0250 0000	1.0275 0000	1.0300 0000
2	1.0404 0000	1.0455 0625	1.0506 2500	1.0557 5625	1.0609 0000
3	1.0612 0800	1.0690 3014	1.0768 9063	1.0847 8955	1.0927 2700
4	1.0824 3216	1.0930 8332	1.1038 1289	1.1146 2126	1.1255 0881
5	1.1040 8080	1.1176 7769	1.1314 0821	1.1452 7334	1.1592 7407
6	1.1261 6242	1.1428 2544	1.1596 9342	1.1767 6836	1.1940 5230
7	1.1486 8567	1.1685 3901	1.1886 8575	1.2091 2949	1.2298 7387
8	1.1716 5938	1.1948 3114	1.2184 0290	1.2423 8055	1.2667 7008
9	1.1950 9257	1.2217 1484	1.2488 6297	1.2765 4602	1.3047 7318
10	1.2189 9442	1.2492 0343	1.2800 8454	1.3116 5103	1.3439 1638
11	1.2433 7431	1.2773 1050	1.3120 8666	1.3477 2144	1.3842 3387
12	1.2682 4179	1.3060 4999	1.3448 8882	1.3847 8378	1.4257 6089
13	1.2936 0663	1.3354 3611	1.3785 1104	1.4228 6533	1.4685 3371
14	1.3194 7876	1.3654 8343	1.4129 7382	1.4619 9413	1.5125 8972
15	1.3458 6834	1.3962 0680	1.4482 9817	1.5021 9896	1.5579 6742
16	1.3727 8571	1.4276 2146	1.4845 0562	1.5435 0944	1.6047 0644
17	1.4002 4142	1.4597 4294	1.5216 1826	1.5859 5595	1.6528 4763
18	1.4282 4625	1.4925 8716	1.5596 5872	1.6295 6973	1.7024 3306
19	1.4568 1117	1.5261 7037	1.5986 5019	1.6743 8290	1.7535 0605
20	1.4859 4740	1.5605 0920	1.6386 1644	1.7204 2843	1.8061 1123
21	1.5156 6634	1.5956 2066	1.6795 8185	1.7677 4021	1.8602 9457
22	1.5459 7967	1.6315 2212	1.7215 7140	1.8163 5307	1.9161 0341
23	1.5768 9926	1.6682 3137	1.7646 1068	1.8663 0278	1.9735 8651
24	1.6084 3725	1.7057 6658	1.8087 2595	1.9176 2610	2.0327 9411
25	1.6406 0599	1.7441 4632	1.8539 4410	1.9703 6082	2.0937 7793
26	1.6734 1811	1.7833 8962	1.9002 9270	2.0245 4575	2.1565 9127
27	1.7068 8648	1.8235 1588	1.9478 0002	2.0802 2075	2.2212 8901
28	1.7410 2421	1.8645 4499	1.9964 9502	2.1374 2682	2.2879 2768
29	1.7758 4469	1.9064 9725	2.0464 0739	2.1962 0606	2.3565 6551
30	1.8113 6158	1.9493 9344	2.0975 6758	2.2566 0173	2.4272 6247
31	1.8475 8882	1.9932 5479	2.1500 0677	2.3186 5828	2.5000 8035
32	1.8845 4059	2.0381 0303	2.2037 5694	2.3824 2138	2.5750 8276
33	1.9222 3140	2.0839 6034	2.2588 5086	2.4479 3797	2.6523 3524
34	1.9606 7603	2.1308 4945	2.3153 2213	2.5152 5626	2.7319 0530
35	1.9998 8955	2.1787 9356	2.3732 0519	2.5844 2581	2.8138 6245
36	2.0398 8734	2.2278 1642	2.4325 3532	2.6554 9752	2.8982 7833
37	2.0806 8509	2.2779 4229	2.4933 4870	2.7285 2370	2.9852 2668
38	2.1222 9879	2.3291 9599	2.5556 8242	2.8035 5810	3.0747 8348
39	2.1647 4477	2.3816 0290	2.6195 7448	2.8806 5595	3.1670 2698
40	2.2080 3966	2.4351 8897	2.6850 6384	2.9598 7399	3.2620 3779
41	2.2522 0046	2.4899 8072	2.7521 9043	3.0412 7052	3.3598 9893
42	2.2972 4447	2.5460 0528	2.8209 9520	3.1249 0546	3.4606 9589
43	2.3431 8936	2.6032 9040	2.8915 2008	3.2108 4036	3.5645 1677
44	2.3900 5314	2.6618 6444	2.9638 0808	3.2991 3847	3.6714 5227
45	2.4378 5421	2.7217 5639	3.0379 0328	3.3898 6478	3.7815 9584
46	2.4866 1129	2.7829 9590	3.1138 5086	3.4830 8606	3.8950 4372
47	2.5363 4352	2.8456 1331	3.1916 9713	3.5788 7093	4.0118 9503
48	2.5870 7039	2.9096 3961	3.2714 8956	3.6772 8988	4.1322 5188
49	2.6388 1179	2.9751 0650	3.3532 7680	3.7784 1535	4.2562 1944
50	2.6915 8803	3.0420 4640	3.4371 0872	3.8823 2177	4.3839 0602

AMOUNT AT COMPOUND INTEREST $(1 + i)^n$ (Continued)

Periods	Rate i				
n	.02 (2%)	.0225 (2¼%)	.025 (2½%)	.0275 (2¾%)	.03 (3%)
50	2.6915 8803	3.0420 4640	3.4371 0872	3.8823 2177	4.3839 0602
51	2.7454 1979	3.1104 9244	3.5230 3644	3.9890 8562	4.5154 2320
52	2.8003 2819	3.1804 7852	3.6111 1235	4.0987 8547	4.6508 8590
53	2.8563 3475	3.2520 3929	3.7013 9016	4.2115 0208	4.7904 1247
54	2.9134 6144	3.3252 1017	3.7939 2491	4.3273 1838	4.9341 2485
55	2.9717 3067	3.4000 2740	3.8887 7303	4.4463 1964	5.0821 4859
56	3.0311 6529	3.4765 2802	3.9859 9236	4.5685 9343	5.2346 1305
57	3.0917 8859	3.5547 4990	4.0856 4217	4.6942 2975	5.3916 5144
58	3.1536 2436	3.6347 3177	4.1877 8322	4.8233 2107	5.5534 0098
59	3.2166 9685	3.7165 1324	4.2924 7780	4.9559 6239	5.7200 0301
60	3.2810 3079	3.8001 3479	4.3997 8975	5.0922 5136	5.8916 0310
61	3.3466 5140	3.8856 3782	4.5097 8449	5.2322 8827	6.0683 5120
62	3.4135 8443	3.9730 6467	4.6225 2910	5.3761 7620	6.2504 0173
63	3.4818 5612	4.0624 5862	4.7380 9233	5.5240 2105	6.4379 1379
64	3.5514 9324	4.1538 6394	4.8565 4464	5.6759 3162	6.6310 5120
65	3.6225 2311	4.2473 2588	4.9779 5826	5.8320 1974	6.8299 8273
66	3.6949 7357	4.3428 9071	5.1024 0721	5.9924 0029	7.0348 8222
67	3.7688 7304	4.4406 0576	5.2299 6739	6.1571 9130	7.2459 2868
68	3.8442 5050	4.5405 1939	5.3607 1658	6.3265 1406	7.4633 0654
69	3.9211 3551	4.6426 8107	5.4947 3449	6.5004 9319	7.6872 0574
70	3.9995 5822	4.7471 4140	5.6321 0286	6.6792 5676	7.9178 2191
71	4.0795 4939	4.8539 5208	5.7729 0543	6.8629 3632	8.1553 5657
72	4.1611 4038	4.9631 6600	5.9172 2806	7.0516 6706	8.4000 1727
73	4.2443 6318	5.0748 3723	6.0651 5876	7.2455 8791	8.6520 1778
74	4.3292 5045	5.1890 2107	6.2167 8773	7.4448 4158	8.9115 7832
75	4.4158 3546	5.3057 7405	6.3722 0743	7.6495 7472	9.1789 2567
76	4.5041 5216	5.4251 5396	6.5315 1261	7.8599 3802	9.4542 9344
77	4.5942 3521	5.5472 1993	6.6948 0043	8.0760 8632	9.7379 2224
78	4.6861 1991	5.6720 3237	6.8621 7044	8.2981 7869	10.0300 5991
79	4.7798 4231	5.7996 5310	7.0337 2470	8.5263 7861	10.3309 6171
80	4.8754 3916	5.9301 4530	7.2095 6782	8.7608 5402	10.6408 9056
81	4.9729 4794	6.0635 7357	7.3898 0701	9.0017 7751	10.9601 1727
82	5.0724 0690	6.2000 0397	7.5745 5219	9.2493 2639	11.2889 2079
83	5.1738 5504	6.3395 0406	7.7639 1599	9.5036 8286	11.6275 8842
84	5.2773 3214	6.4821 4290	7.9580 1389	9.7650 3414	11.9764 1607
85	5.3828 7878	6.6279 9112	8.1569 6424	10.0335 7258	12.3357 0855
86	5.4905 3636	6.7771 2092	8.3608 8834	10.3094 9583	12.7057 7981
87	5.6003 4708	6.9296 0614	8.5699 1055	10.5930 0696	13.0869 5320
88	5.7123 5402	7.0855 2228	8.7841 5832	10.8843 1465	13.4795 6180
89	5.8266 0110	7.2449 4653	9.0037 6228	11.1836 3331	13.8839 4865
90	5.9431 3313	7.4079 5782	9.2288 5633	11.4911 8322	14.3004 6711
91	6.0619 9579	7.5746 3688	9.4595 7774	11.8071 9076	14.7294 8112
92	6.1832 3570	7.7450 6621	9.6960 6718	12.1318 8851	15.1713 6556
93	6.3069 0042	7.9193 3020	9.9384 6886	12.4655 1544	15.6265 0652
94	6.4330 3843	8.0975 1512	10.1869 3058	12.8083 1711	16.0953 0172
95	6.5616 9920	8.2797 0921	10.4416 0385	13.1605 4584	16.5781 6077
96	6.6929 3318	8.4660 0267	10.7026 4395	13.5224 6085	17.0755 0559
97	6.8267 9184	8.6564 8773	10.9702 1004	13.8943 2852	17.5877 7076
98	6.9633 2768	8.8512 5871	11.2444 6530	14.2764 2255	18.1154 0388
99	7.1025 9423	9.0504 1203	11.5255 7693	14.6690 2417	18.6588 6600
100	7.2446 4612	9.2540 4630	11.8137 1635	15.0724 2234	19.2186 3198

AMOUNT AT COMPOUND INTEREST $(1 + i)^n$ (Continued)

Periods			Rate i		
n	.035 (3½%)	.04 (4%)	.045 (4½%)	.05 (5%)	.055 (5½%)
1	1.0350 0000	1.0400 0000	1.0450 0000	1.0500 0000	1.0550 0000
2	1.0712 2500	1.0816 0000	1.0920 2500	1.1025 0000	1.1130 2500
3	1.1087 1788	1.1248 6400	1.1411 6613	1.1576 2500	1.1742 4138
4	1.1475 2300	1.1698 5856	1.1925 1860	1.2155 0625	1 2388 2465
5	1.1876 8631	1.2166 5290	1.2461 8194	1.2762 8156	1.3069 6001
6	1.2292 5533	1.2653 1902	1.3022 6012	1.3400 9564	1.3788 4281
7	1.2722 7926	1.3159 3178	1.3608 6183	1.4071 0042	1.4546 7916
8	1.3168 0904	1.3685 6905	1.4221 0061	1.4774 5544	1.5346 8651
9	1.3628 9735	1.4233 1181	1.4860 9514	1.5513 2822	1.6190 9427
10	1.4105 9876	1.4802 4428	1.5529 6942	1.6288 9463	1.7081 4446
11	1.4599 6972	1.5394 5406	1.6228 5305	1.7103 3936	1.8020 9240
12	1.5110 6866	1.6010 3222	1.6958 8143	1.7958 5633	1.9012 0749
13	1.5639 5606	1 6650 7351	1.7721 9610	1.8856 4914	2.0057 7390
14	1.6186 9452	1.7316 7645	1.8519 4492	1.9799 3160	2.1160 9146
15	1.6753 4883	1.8009 4351	1.9352 8244	2.0789 2818	2.2324 7649
16	1.7339 8604	1.8729 8125	2.0223 7015	2.1828 7459	2.3552 6270
17	1.7946 7555	1.9479 0050	2.1133 7681	2.2920 1832	2.4848 0215
18	1.8574 8920	2.0258 1652	2.2084 7877	2.4066 1923	2.6214 6627
19	1.9225 0132	2.1068 4918	2.3078 6031	2.5269 5020	2.7656 4691
20	1.9897 8886	2.1911 2314	2.4117 1402	2.6532 9771	2.9177 5749
21	2.0594 3147	2.2787 6807	2.5202 4116	2.7859 6259	3.0782 3415
22	2.1315 1158	2.3699 1879	2.6336 5201	2.9252 6072	3.2475 3703
23	2.2061 1448	2.4647 1554	2.7521 6635	3.0715 2376	3.4261 5157
24	2.2833 2849	2.5633 0416	2.8760 1383	3.2250 9994	3.6145 8990
25	2.3632 4498	2.6658 3633	3.0054 3446	3.3863 5494	3.8133 9235
26	2.4459 5856	2.7724 6978	3.1406 7901	3.5556 7269	4.0231 2893
27	2.5315 6711	2.8833 6858	3.2820 0956	3.7334 5632	4.2444 0102
28	2.6201 7196	2.9987 0332	3.4296 9999	3.9201 2914	4.4778 4307
29	2.7118 7798	3.1186 5145	3.5840 3649	4.1161 3560	4.7241 2444
30	2.8067 9370	3.2433 9751	3.7453 1813	4.3219 4238	4.9839 5129
31	2.9050 3148	3.3731 3341	3.9138 5745	4.5380 3949	5.2580 6861
32	3.0067 0759	3.5080 5875	4.0899 8104	4.7649 4147	5.5472 6238
33	3.1119 4235	3.6483 8110	4.2740 3018	5.0031 8854	5.8523 6181
34	3.2208 6033	3.7943 1634	4.4663 6154	5.2533 4797	6.1742 4171
35	3.3335 9045	3.9460 8899	4.6673 4781	5.5160 1537	6.5138 2501
36	3.4502 6611	4.1039 3255	4.8773 7846	5.7918 1614	6.8720 8538
37	3.5710 2543	4.2680 8986	5.0968 6049	6.0814 0694	7.2500 5008
38	3.6960 1132	4.4388 1345	5.3262 1921	6.3854 7729	7.6488 0283
39	3.8253 7171	4.6163 6599	5.5658 9908	6.7047 5115	8.0694 8699
40	3.9592 5972	4.8010 2063	5.8163 6454	7.0399 8871	8.5133 0877
41	4.0978 3381	4.9930 6145	6.0781 0094	7.3919 8815	8.9815 4076
42	4.2412 5799	5.1927 8391	6.3516 1548	7.7615 8756	9.4755 2550
43	4.3897 0202	5.4004 9527	6 6374 3818	8.1496 6693	9.9966 7940
44	4.5433 4160	5.6165 1508	6.9361 2290	8.5571 5028	10.5464 9677
45	4.7023 5855	5.8411 7568	7.2482 4843	8.9850 0779	11.1265 5409
46	4.8669 4110	6.0748 2271	7.5744 1961	9 4342 5818	11.7385 1456
47	5.0372 8404	6.3178 1562	7.9152 6849	9.9059 7109	12.3841 3287
48	5.2135 8898	6.5705 2824	8.2714 5557	10.4012 6965	13.0652 6017
49	5.3960 6459	6.8333 4937	8.6436 7107	10.9213 3313	13.7838 4948
50	5.5849 2686	7.1066 8335	9.0326 3627	11.4673 9979	14.5419 6120

AMOUNT AT COMPOUND INTEREST $(1 + i)^n$ (Continued)

Periods	Rate i				
n	.06 (6%)	.065 (6½%)	.07 (7%)	.075 (7½%)	.08 (8%)
1	1.0600 0000	1.0650 0000	1.0700 0000	1.0750 0000	1.0800 0000
2	1.1236 0000	1.1342 2500	1.1449 0000	1.1556 2500	1.1664 0000
3	1.1910 1600	1.2079 4963	1.2250 4300	1.2422 9688	1.2597 1200
4	1.2624 7696	1.2864 6635	1.3107 9601	1.3354 6914	1 3604 8896
5	1.3382 2558	1.3700 8666	1.4025 5173	1.4356 2933	1.4693 2808
6	1.4185 1911	1.4591 4230	1.5007 3035	1.5433 0153	1.5868 7432
7	1.5036 3026	1.5539 8655	1.6057 8148	1.6590 4914	1.7138 2427
8	1.5938 4807	1.6549 9567	1.7181 8618	1.7834 7783	1.8509 3021
9	1.6894 7896	1.7625 7039	1.8384 5921	1.9172 3866	1.9990 0463
10	1.7908 4770	1.8771 3747	1.9671 5136	2.0610 3156	2.1589 2500
11	1.8982 9856	1.9991 5140	2.1048 5195	2.2156 0893	2.3316 3900
12	2.0121 9647	2.1290 9624	2.2521 9159	2.3817 7960	2.5181 7012
13	2.1329 2826	2.2674 8750	2.4098 4500	2.5604 1307	2.7196 2373
14	2.2609 0396	2.4148 7418	2.5785 3415	2.7524 4405	2.9371 9362
15	2.3965 5819	2.5718 4101	2.7590 3154	2.9588 7735	3.1721 6911
16	2.5403 5168	2.7390 1067	2.9521 6375	3.1807 9315	3.4259 4264
17	2.6927 7279	2.9170 4637	3.1588 1521	3.4193 5264	3.7000 1805
18	2.8543 3915	3.1066 5438	3.3799 3228	3.6758 0409	3.9960 1950
19	3.0255 9950	3.3085 8691	3.6165 2754	3.9514 8940	4.3157 0106
20	3.2071 3547	3.5236 4506	3.8696 8446	4.2478 5110	4.6609 5714
21	3.3995 6360	3.7526 8199	4.1405 6237	4.5664 3993	5.0338 3372
22	3.6035 3742	3.9966 0632	4.4304 0174	4.9089 2293	5.4365 4041
23	3.8197 4966	4.2563 8573	4.7405 2986	5.2770 9215	5.8714 6365
24	4.0489 3464	4.5330 5081	5.0723 6695	5.6728 7406	6.3411 8074
25	4.2918 7072	4.8276 9911	5.4274 3264	6.0983 3961	6.8484 7520
26	4.5493 8296	5.1414 9955	5.8073 5292	6.5557 1508	7.3963 5321
27	4.8223 4594	5.4756 9702	6.2138 6763	7.0473 9371	7.9880 6147
28	5.1116 8670	5.8316 1733	6.6488 3836	7.5759 4824	8.6271 0639
29	5.4183 8790	6.2106 7245	7.1142 5705	8.1441 4436	9.3172 7490
30	5.7434 9117	6.6143 6616	7.6122 5504	8.7549 5519	10.0626 5689
31	6.0881 0064	7.0442 9996	8.1451 1290	9.4115 7683	10.8676 6944
32	6.4533 8668	7.5021 7946	8.7152 7080	10.1174 4509	11.7370 8300
33	6.8405 8988	7.9898 2113	9.3253 3975	10.8762 5347	12.6760 4964
34	7.2510 2528	8.5091 5950	9.9781 1354	11.6919 7248	13.6901 3361
35	7.6860 8679	9.0622 5487	10.6765 8148	12.5688 7042	14.7853 4429
36	8.1472 5200	9.6513 0143	11.4239 4219	13.5115 3570	15.9681 7184
37	8.6360 8712	10.2786 3603	12.2236 1814	14.5249 0088	17.2456 2558
38	9.1542 5235	10.9467 4737	13.0792 7141	15.6142 6844	18.6252 7563
39	9.7035 0749	11.6582 8595	13.9948 2041	16.7853 3858	20.1152 9768
40	10.2857 1794	12.4160 7453	14.9744 5784	18.0442 3897	21.7245 2150
41	10.9028 6101	13.2231 1938	16.0226 6989	19.3975 5689	23.4624 8322
42	11.5570 3267	14.0826 2214	17.1442 5678	20.8523 7366	25.3394 8187
43	12.2504 5463	14.9979 9258	18.3443 5475	22.4163 0168	27.3666 4042
44	12.9854 8191	15.9728 6209	19.6284 5959	24.0975 2431	29.5559 7166
45	13.7646 1083	17.0110 9813	21.0024 5176	25.9048 3863	31.9204 4939
46	14.5904 8748	18.1168 1951	22.4726 2338	27.8477 0153	34.4740 8534
47	15.4659 1673	19.2944 1278	24.0457 0702	29.9362 7915	37.2320 1217
48	16.3938 7173	20.5485 4961	25.7289 0651	32.1815 0008	40.2105 7314
49	17.3775 0403	21.8842 0533	27.5299 2997	34.5951 1259	43.4274 1899
50	18.4201 5427	23.3066 7868	29.4570 2506	37.1897 4603	46.9016 1251

PRESENT VALUE $1/(1 + i)^n$

The following table gives the value of unit amount due in n years at rate of interest i, compounded annually, $1/(1 + i)^n = v^n$.

Periods	Rate i				
n	.0025 $(\frac{1}{4}\%)$	.004167 $(\frac{5}{12}\%)$	.005 $(\frac{1}{2}\%)$	.005833 $(\frac{7}{12}\%)$	.0075 $(\frac{3}{4}\%)$
1	.9975 0623	.9958 5062	.9950 2488	.9942 0050	.9925 5583
2	.9950 1869	.9917 1846	.9900 7450	.9884 3463	.9851 6708
3	.9925 3734	.9876 0345	.9851 4876	.9827 0220	.9778 3333
4	.9900 6219	.9835 0551	.9802 4752	.9770 0301	.9705 5417
5	.9875 9321	.9794 2457	.9753 7067	.9713 3688	.9633 2920
6	.9851 3038	.9753 6057	.9705 1808	.9657 0361	.9561 5802
7	.9826 7370	.9713 1343	.9656 8963	.9601 0301	.9490 4022
8	.9802 2314	.9672 8308	.9608 8520	.9545 3489	.9419 7540
9	.9777 7869	.9632 6946	.9561 0468	.9489 9906	.9349 6318
10	.9753 4034	.9592 7249	.9513 4794	.9434 9534	.9280 0315
11	.9729 0807	.9552 9211	.9466 1487	.9380 2354	.9210 9494
12	.9704 8187	.9513 2824	.9419 0534	.9325 8347	.9142 3815
13	.9680 6171	.9473 8082	.9372 1924	.9271 7495	.9074 3241
14	.9656 4759	.9434 4978	.9325 5646	.9217 9779	.9006 7733
15	.9632 3949	.9395 3505	.9279 1688	.9164 5182	.8939 7254
16	.9608 3740	.9356 3657	.9233 0037	.9111 3686	.8873 1766
17	.9584 4130	.9317 5426	.9187 0684	.9058 5272	.8807 1231
18	.9560 5117	.9278 8806	.9141 3616	.9005 9922	.8741 5614
19	.9536 6700	.9240 3790	.9095 8822	.8953 7619	.8676 4878
20	.9512 8878	.9202 0372	.9050 6290	.8901 8346	.8611 8985
21	.9489 1649	.9163 8544	.9005 6010	.8850 2084	.8547 7901
22	.9465 5011	.9125 8301	.8960 7971	.8798 8815	.8484 1589
23	.9441 8964	.9087 9636	.8916 2160	.8747 8524	.8421 0014
24	.9418 3505	.9050 2542	.8871 8567	.8697 1192	.8358 3140
25	.9394 8634	.9012 7013	.8827 7181	.8646 6802	.8296 0933
26	.9371 4348	.8975 3042	.8783 7991	.8596 5338	.8234 3358
27	.9348 0646	.8938 0623	.8740 0986	.8546 6782	.8173 0380
28	.9324 7527	.8900 9749	.8696 6155	.8497 1117	.8112 1966
29	.9301 4990	.8864 0414	.8653 3488	.8447 8327	.8051 8080
30	.9278 3032	.8827 2611	.8610 2973	.8398 8394	.7991 8690
31	.9255 1653	.8790 6335	.8567 4600	.8350 1303	.7932 3762
32	.9232 0851	.8754 1578	.8524 8358	.8301 7037	.7873 3262
33	.9209 0624	.8717 8335	.8482 4237	.8253 5580	.7814 7158
34	.9186 0972	.8681 6599	.8440 2226	.8205 6914	.7756 5418
35	.9163 1892	.8645 6365	.8398 2314	.8158 1025	.7698 8008
36	.9140 3384	.8609 7624	.8356 4492	.8110 7896	.7641 4896
37	.9117 5445	.8574 0373	.8314 8748	.8063 7510	.7584 6051
38	.9094 8075	.8538 4604	.8273 5073	.8016 9853	.7528 1440
39	.9072 1272	.8503 0311	.8232 3455	.7970 4907	.7472 1032
40	.9049 5034	.8467 7488	.8191 3886	.7924 2659	.7416 4796
41	.9026 9361	.8432 6129	.8150 6354	.7878 3091	.7361 2701
42	.9004 4250	.8397 6228	.8110 0850	.7832 6188	.7306 4716
43	.8981 9701	.8362 7779	.8069 7363	.7787 1935	.7252 0809
44	.8959 5712	.8328 0776	.8029 5884	.7742 0316	.7198 0952
45	.8937 2281	.8293 5212	.7989 6402	.7697 1317	.7144 5114
46	.8914 9407	.8259 1083	.7949 8907	.7652 4922	.7091 3264
47	.8892 7090	.8224 8381	.7910 3390	.7608 1115	.7038 5374
48	.8870 5326	.8190 7102	.7870 9841	.7563 9883	.6986 1414
49	.8848 4116	.8156 7238	.7831 8250	.7520 1209	.6934 1353
50	.8826 3457	.8122 8785	.7792 8607	.7476 5079	.6882 5165

PRESENT VALUE $1/(1 + i)^n$ (Continued)

Periods			Rate i		
n	.0025 ($\frac{1}{4}\%$)	.004167 ($\frac{5}{12}\%$)	.005 ($\frac{1}{2}\%$)	.005833 ($\frac{7}{12}\%$)	.0075 ($\frac{3}{4}\%$)
50	.8826 3457	.8122 8785	.7792 8607	.7476 5079	.6882 5165
51	.8804 3349	.8089 1736	.7754 0902	.7433 1479	.6831 2819
52	.8782 3790	.8055 6086	.7715 5127	.7390 0393	.6780 4286
53	.8760 4778	.8022 1828	.7677 1270	.7347 1808	.6729 9540
54	.8738 6312	.7988 8957	.7638 9324	.7304 5708	.6679 8551
55	.8716 8391	.7955 7468	.7600 9277	.7262 2079	.6630 1291
56	.8695 1013	.7922 7354	.7563 1122	.7220 0907	.6580 7733
57	.8673 4178	.7889 8610	.7525 4847	.7178 2178	.6531 7849
58	.8651 7883	.7857 1230	.7488 0445	.7136 5877	.6483 1612
59	.8630 2128	.7824 5208	.7450 7906	.7095 1990	.6434 8995
60	.8608 6911	.7792 0539	.7413 7220	.7054 0504	.6386 9970
61	.8587 2230	.7759 7217	.7376 8378	.7013 1404	.6339 4511
62	.8565 8085	.7727 5237	.7340 1371	.6972 4677	.6292 2592
63	.8544 4474	.7695 4593	.7303 6190	.6932 0308	.6245 4185
64	.8523 1395	.7663 5279	.7267 2826	.6891 8285	.6198 9266
65	.8501 8848	.7631 7291	.7231 1269	.6851 8593	.6152 7807
66	.8480 6831	.7600 0621	.7195 1512	.6812 1219	.6106 9784
67	.8459 5343	.7568 5266	.7159 3544	.6772 6150	.6061 5170
68	.8438 4382	.7537 1219	.7123 7357	.6733 3372	.6016 3940
69	.8417 3947	.7505 8476	.7088 2943	.6694 2872	.5971 6070
70	.8396 4037	.7474 7030	.7053 0291	.6655 4637	.5927 1533
71	.8375 4650	.7443 6876	.7017 9394	.6616 8653	.5883 0306
72	.8354 5786	.7412 8009	.6983 0243	.6578 4908	.5839 2363
73	.8333 7442	.7382 0424	.6948 2829	.6540 3338	.5795 7681
74	.8312 9618	.7351 4115	.6913 7143	.6502 4081	.5752 6234
75	.8292 2312	.7320 9078	.6879 3177	.6464 6973	.5709 7999
76	.8271 5523	.7290 5306	.6845 0923	.6427 2053	.5667 2952
77	.8250 9250	.7260 2794	.6811 0371	.6389 9306	.5625 1069
78	.8230 3491	.7230 1537	.6777 1513	.6352 8723	.5583 2326
79	.8209 8246	.7200 1531	.6743 4342	.6316 0288	.5541 6701
80	.8189 3512	.7170 2770	.6709 8847	.6279 3989	.5500 4170
81	.8168 9289	.7140 5248	.6676 5022	.6242 9816	.5459 4710
82	.8148 5575	.7110 8960	.6643 2858	.6206 7754	.5418 8297
83	.8128 2369	.7081 3902	.6610 2346	.6170 7792	.5378 4911
84	.8107 9670	.7052 0069	.6577 3479	.6134 9917	.5338 4527
85	.8087 7476	.7022 7454	.6544 6248	.6099 4118	.5298 7123
86	.8067 5787	.6993 6054	.6512 0644	.6064 0382	.5259 2678
87	.8047 4600	.6964 5863	.6479 6661	.6028 8698	.5220 1169
88	.8027 3915	.6935 6876	.6447 4290	.5993 9054	.5181 2575
89	.8007 3731	.6906 9088	.6415 3522	.5959 1437	.5142 6873
90	.7987 4046	.6878 2495	.6383 4350	.5924 5836	.5104 4043
91	.7967 4859	.6849 7090	.6351 6766	.5890 2240	.5066 4063
92	.7947 6168	.6821 2870	.6320 0763	.5856 0636	.5028 6911
93	.7927 7973	.6792 9829	.6288 6331	.5822 1014	.4991 2567
94	.7908 0273	.6764 7962	.6257 3464	.5788 3361	.4954 1009
95	.7888 3065	.6736 7265	.6226 2153	.5754 7666	.4917 2217
96	.7868 6349	.6708 7733	.6195 2391	.5721 3918	.4880 6171
97	.7849 0124	.6680 9361	.6164 4170	.5688 2106	.4844 2850
98	.7829 4388	.6653 2143	.6133 7483	.5655 2218	.4808 2233
99	.7809 9140	.6625 6076	.6103 2321	.5622 4243	.4772 4301
100	.7790 4379	.6598 1155	.6072 8678	.5589 8171	.4736 9033

Financial Tables

PRESENT VALUE $1/(1 + i)^n$ (Continued)

Periods	Rate i				
n	.01 (1%)	.01125 (1⅛%)	.0125 (1¼%)	.015 (1½%)	.0175 (1¾%)
1	.9900 9901	.9888 7515	.9876 5432	.9852 2167	.9828 0098
2	.9802 9605	.9778 7407	.9754 6106	.9706 6175	.9658 9777
3	.9705 9015	.9669 9537	.9634 1833	.9563 1699	.9492 8528
4	.9609 8034	.9562 3770	.9515 2428	.9421 8423	.9329 5851
5	.9514 6569	.9455 9970	.9397 7706	.9282 6033	.9169 1254
6	.9420 4524	.9350 8005	.9281 7488	.9145 4219	.9011 4254
7	.9327 1805	.9246 7743	.9167 1593	.9010 2679	.8856 4378
8	.9234 8322	.9143 9054	.9053 9845	.8877 1112	.8704 1157
9	.9143 3982	.9042 1808	.8942 2069	.8745 9224	.8554 4135
10	.9052 8695	.8941 5880	.8831 8093	.8616 6723	.8407 2860
11	.8963 2372	.8842 1142	.8722 7746	.8489 3323	.8262 6889
12	.8874 4923	.8743 7470	.8615 0860	.8363 8742	.8120 5788
13	.8786 6260	.8646 4742	.8508 7269	.8240 2702	.7980 9128
14	.8699 6297	.8550 2835	.8403 6809	.8118 4928	.7843 6490
15	.8613 4947	.8455 1629	.8299 9318	.7998 5150	.7708 7459
16	.8528 2126	.8361 1005	.8197 4635	.7880 3104	.7576 1631
17	.8443 7749	.8268 0846	.8096 2602	.7763 8526	.7445 8605
18	.8360 1731	.8176 1034	.7996 3064	.7649 1159	.7317 7990
19	.8277 3992	.8085 1455	.7897 5866	.7536 0747	.7191 9401
20	.8195 4447	.7995 1995	.7800 0855	.7424 7042	.7068 2458
21	.8114 3017	.7906 2542	.7703 7881	.7314 9795	.6946 6789
22	.8033 9621	.7818 2983	.7608 6796	.7206 8763	.6827 2028
23	.7954 4179	.7731 3210	.7514 7453	.7100 3708	.6709 7817
24	.7875 6613	.7645 3112	.7421 9707	.6995 4392	.6594 3800
25	.7797 6844	.7560 2583	.7330 3414	.6892 0583	.6480 9632
26	.7720 4796	.7476 1516	.7239 8434	.6790 2052	.6369 4970
27	.7644 0392	.7392 9806	.7150 4626	.6689 8574	.6259 9479
28	.7568 3557	.7310 7348	.7062 1853	.6590 9925	.6152 2829
29	.7493 4215	.7229 4040	.6974 9978	.6493 5887	.6046 4697
30	.7419 2292	.7148 9780	.6888 8867	.6397 6243	.5942 4764
31	.7345 7715	.7069 4467	.6803 8387	.6303 0781	.5840 2716
32	.7273 0411	.6990 8002	.6719 8407	.6209 9292	.5739 8247
33	.7201 0307	.6913 0287	.6636 8797	.6118 1568	.5641 1053
34	.7129 7334	.6836 1223	.6554 9429	.6027 7407	.5544 0839
35	.7059 1420	.6760 0715	.6474 0177	.5938 6608	.5448 7311
36	.6989 2495	.6684 8667	.6394 0916	.5850 8974	.5355 0183
37	.6920 0490	.6610 4986	.6315 1522	.5764 4309	.5262 9172
38	.6851 5337	.6536 9578	.6237 1873	.5679 2423	.5172 4002
39	.6783 6967	.6464 2352	.6160 1850	.5595 3126	.5083 4400
40	.6716 5314	.6392 3216	.6084 1334	.5512 6232	.4996 0098
41	.6650 0311	.6321 2080	.6009 0206	.5431 1559	.4910 0834
42	.6584 1892	.6250 8855	.5934 8352	.5350 8925	.4825 6348
43	.6518 9992	.6181 3454	.5861 5656	.5271 8153	.4742 6386
44	.6454 4546	.6112 5789	.5789 2006	.5193 9067	.4661 0699
45	.6390 5492	.6044 5774	.5717 7290	.5117 1494	.4580 9040
46	.6327 2764	.5977 3324	.5647 1397	.5041 5265	.4502 1170
47	.6264 6301	.5910 8355	.5577 4219	.4967 0212	.4424 6850
48	.6202 6041	.5845 0784	.5508 5649	.4893 6170	.4348 5848
49	.6141 1921	.5780 0528	.5440 5579	.4821 2975	.4273 7934
50	.6080 3882	.5715 7506	.5373 3905	.4750 0468	.4200 2883

PRESENT VALUE $1/(1 + i)^n$ (Continued)

Periods	Rate i				
n	.01 (1%)	.01125 ($1\frac{1}{8}$%)	.0125 ($1\frac{1}{4}$%)	.015 ($1\frac{1}{2}$%)	.0175 ($1\frac{3}{4}$%)
50	.6080 3882	.5715 7506	.5373 3905	.4750 0468	.4200 2883
51	.6020 1864	.5652 1637	.5307 0524	.4679 8491	.4128 0475
52	.5960 5806	.5589 2843	.5241 5332	.4610 6887	.4057 0492
53	.5901 5649	.5527 1044	.5176 8229	.4542 5505	.3987 2719
54	.5843 1336	.5465 6162	.5112 9115	.4475 4192	.3918 6947
55	.5785 2808	.5404 8120	.5049 7892	.4409 2800	.3851 2970
56	.5728 0008	.5344 6843	.4987 4461	.4344 1182	.3785 0585
57	.5671 2879	.5285 2256	.4925 8727	.4279 9194	.3719 9592
58	.5615 1365	.5226 4282	.4865 0594	.4216 6694	.3655 9796
59	.5559 5411	.5168 2850	.4804 9970	.4154 3541	.3593 1003
60	.5504 4962	.5110 7887	.4745 6760	.4092 9597	.3531 3025
61	.5449 9962	.5053 9319	.4687 0874	.4032 4726	.3470 5676
62	.5396 0358	.4997 7077	.4629 2222	.3972 8794	.3410 8772
63	.5342 6097	.4942 1090	.4572 0713	.3914 1669	.3352 2135
64	.5289 7126	.4887 1288	.4515 6259	.3856 3221	.3294 5587
65	.5237 3392	.4832 7602	.4459 8775	.3799 3321	.3237 8956
66	.5185 4844	.4778 9965	.4404 8173	.3743 1843	.3182 2069
67	.5134 1429	.4725 8309	.4350 4368	.3687 8663	.3127 4761
68	.5083 3099	.4673 2568	.4296 7277	.3633 3658	.3073 6866
69	.5032 9801	.4621 2675	.4243 6817	.3579 6708	.3020 8222
70	.4983 1486	.4569 8566	.4191 2905	.3526 7692	.2968 8670
71	.4933 8105	.4519 0177	.4139 5462	.3474 6495	.2917 8054
72	.4884 9609	.4468 7443	.4088 4407	.3423 3000	.2867 6221
73	.4836 5949	.4419 0302	.4037 9661	.3372 7093	.2818 3018
74	.4788 7078	.4369 8692	.3988 1147	.3322 8663	.2769 8298
75	.4741 2949	.4321 2551	.3938 8787	.3273 7599	.2722 1914
76	.4694 3514	.4273 1818	.3890 2506	.3225 3793	.2675 3724
77	.4647 8726	.4225 6433	.3842 2228	.3177 7136	.2629 3586
78	.4601 8541	.4178 6337	.3794 7879	.3130 7523	.2584 1362
79	.4556 2912	.4132 1470	.3747 9387	.3084 4850	.2539 6916
80	.4511 1794	.4086 1775	.3701 6679	.3038 9015	.2496 0114
81	.4466 5142	.4040 7194	.3655 9683	.2993 9916	.2453 0825
82	.4422 2913	.3995 7670	.3610 8329	.2949 7454	.2410 8919
83	.4378 5063	.3951 3148	.3566 2547	.2906 1531	.2369 4269
84	.4335 1547	.3907 3570	.3522 2268	.2863 2050	.2328 6751
85	.4292 2324	.3863 8882	.3478 7426	.2820 8917	.2288 6242
86	.4249 7350	.3820 9031	.3435 7941	.2779 2036	.2249 2621
87	.4207 6585	.3778 3961	.3393 3779	.2738 1316	.2210 5770
88	.4165 9985	.3736 3621	.3351 4843	.2697 6666	.2172 5572
89	.4124 7510	.3694 7956	.3310 1080	.2657 7996	.2135 1914
90	.4083 9119	.3653 6916	.3269 2425	.2618 5218	.2098 4682
91	.4043 4771	.3613 0448	.3228 8814	.2579 8245	.2062 3766
92	.4003 4427	.3572 8503	.3189 0187	.2541 6990	.2026 9057
93	.3963 8046	.3533 1029	.3149 6481	.2504 1369	.1992 0450
94	.3924 5590	.3493 7976	.3110 7636	.2467 1300	.1957 7837
95	.3885 7020	.3454 9297	.3072 3591	.2430 6699	.1924 1118
96	.3847 2297	.3416 4941	.3034 4287	.2394 7487	.1891 0190
97	.3809 1383	.3378 4861	.2996 9666	.2359 3583	.1858 4953
98	.3771 4241	.3340 9010	.2959 9670	.2324 4909	.1826 5310
99	.3734 0832	.3303 7340	.2923 4242	.2290 1389	.1795 1165
100	.3697 1121	.3266 9805	.2887 3326	.2256 2944	.1764 2422

PRESENT VALUE $1/(1 + i)^n$ (Continued)

Periods			Rate i		
n	.02 (2%)	.0225 (2¼%)	.025 (2½%)	.0275 (2¾%)	.03 (3%)
1	.9803 9216	.9779 9511	.9756 0976	.9732 3601	.9708 7379
2	.9611 6878	.9564 7444	.9518 1440	.9471 8833	.9425 9591
3	.9423 2233	.9354 2732	.9285 9941	.9218 3779	.9151 4166
4	.9238 4543	.9148 4335	.9059 5064	.8971 6573	.8884 8705
5	.9057 3081	.8947 1232	.8838 5429	.8731 5400	.8626 0878
6	.8879 7138	.8750 2427	.8622 9687	.8497 8491	.8374 8426
7	.8705 6018	.8557 6946	.8412 6524	.8270 4128	.8130 9151
8	.8534 9037	.8369 3835	.8207 4657	.8049 0635	.7894 0923
9	.8367 5527	.8185 2161	.8007 2836	.7833 6385	.7664 1673
10	.8203 4830	.8005 1013	.7811 9840	.7623 9791	.7440 9391
11	.8042 6304	.7828 9499	.7621 4478	.7419 9310	.7224 2128
12	.7884 9318	.7656 6748	.7435 5589	.7221 3440	.7013 7988
13	.7730 3253	.7488 1905	.7254 2038	.7028 0720	.6809 5134
14	.7578 7502	.7323 4137	.7077 2720	.6839 9728	.6611 1781
15	.7430 1473	.7162 2628	.6904 6556	.6656 9078	.6418 6195
16	.7284 4581	.7004 6580	.6736 2493	.6478 7424	.6231 6694
17	.7141 6256	.6850 5212	.6571 9506	.6305 3454	.6050 1645
18	.7001 5937	.6699 7763	.6411 6591	.6136 5892	.5873 9461
19	.6864 3076	.6552 3484	.6255 2772	.5972 3496	.5702 8603
20	.6729 7133	.6408 1647	.6102 7094	.5812 5057	.5536 7575
21	.6597 7582	.6267 1538	.5953 8629	.5656 9398	.5375 4928
22	.6468 3904	.6129 2457	.5808 6467	.5505 5375	.5218 9250
23	.6341 5592	.5994 3724	.5666 9724	.5358 1874	.5066 9175
24	.6217 2149	.5862 4668	.5528 7535	.5214 7809	.4919 3374
25	.6095 3087	.5733 4639	.5393 9059	.5075 2126	.4776 0557
26	.5975 7928	.5607 2997	.5262 3472	.4939 3796	.4636 9473
27	.5858 6204	.5483 9117	.5133 9973	.4807 1821	.4501 8906
28	.5743 7455	.5363 2388	.5008 7778	.4678 5227	.4370 7675
29	.5631 1231	.5245 2213	.4886 6125	.4553 3068	.4243 4636
30	.5520 7089	.5129 8008	.4767 4269	.4431 4421	.4119 8676
31	.5412 4597	.5016 9201	.4651 1481	.4312 8391	.3999 8715
32	.5306 3330	.4906 5233	.4537 7055	.4197 4103	.3883 3703
33	.5202 2873	.4798 5558	.4427 0298	.4085 0708	.3770 2625
34	.5100 2817	.4692 9641	.4319 0534	.3975 7380	.3660 4490
35	.5000 2761	.4589 6960	.4213 7107	.3869 3314	.3553 8340
36	.4902 2315	.4488 7002	.4110 9372	.3765 7727	.3450 3243
37	.4806 1093	.4389 9268	.4010 6705	.3664 9856	.3349 8294
38	.4711 8719	.4293 3270	.3912 8492	.3566 8959	.3252 2615
39	.4619 4822	.4198 8528	.3817 4139	.3471 4316	.3157 5355
40	.4528 9042	.4106 4575	.3724 3062	.3378 5222	.3065 5684
41	.4440 1021	.4016 0954	.3633 4695	.3288 0995	.2976 2800
42	.4353 0413	.3927 7216	.3544 8483	.3200 0958	.2889 5922
43	.4267 6875	.3841 2925	.3458 3886	.3114 4495	.2805 4294
44	.4184 0074	.3756 7653	.3374 0376	.3031 0944	.2723 7178
45	.4101 9680	.3674 0981	.3291 7440	.2949 9702	.2644 3862
46	.4021 5373	.3593 2500	.3211 4576	.2871 0172	.2567 3653
47	.3942 6836	.3514 1809	.3133 1294	.2794 1773	.2492 5876
48	.3865 3761	.3436 8518	.3056 7116	.2719 3940	.2419 9880
49	.3789 5844	.3361 2242	.2982 1576	.2646 6122	.2349 5029
50	.3715 2788	.3287 2608	.2909 4221	.2575 7783	.2281 0708

PRESENT VALUE $1/(1 + i)^n$ (Continued)

Periods	Rate i				
n	.02 (2%)	.0225 (2¼%)	.025 (2½%)	.0275 (2¾%)	.03 (3%)
50	.3715 2788	.3287 2608	.2909 4221	.2575 7783	.2281 0708
51	.3642 4302	.3214 9250	.2838 4606	.2506 8402	.2214 6318
52	.3571 0100	.3144 1810	.2769 2298	.2439 7471	.2150 1280
53	.3500 9902	.3074 9936	.2701 6876	.2374 4497	.2087 5029
54	.3432 3433	.3007 3287	.2635 7928	.2310 9000	.2026 7019
55	.3365 0425	.2941 1528	.2571 5952	.2249 0511	.1967 6717
56	.3299 0613	.2876 4330	.2508 7855	.2188 8575	.1910 3609
57	.3234 3738	.2813 1374	.2447 5956	.2130 2749	.1854 7193
58	.3170 9547	.2751 2347	.2387 8982	.2073 2603	.1800 6984
59	.3108 7791	.2690 6940	.2329 6568	.2017 7716	.1748 2508
60	.3047 8227	.2631 4856	.2272 8359	.1963 7679	.1697 3309
61	.2988 0614	.2573 5801	.2217 4009	.1911 2097	.1647 8941
62	.2929 4720	.2516 9487	.2163 3179	.1860 0581	.1599 8972
63	.2872 0314	.2461 5635	.2110 5541	.1810 2755	.1553 2982
64	.2815 7170	.2407 3971	.2059 0771	.1761 8253	.1508 0565
65	.2760 5069	.2354 4226	.2008 8557	.1714 6718	.1464 1325
66	.2706 3793	.2302 6138	.1959 8593	.1668 7804	.1421 4879
67	.2653 3130	.2251 9450	.1912 0578	.1624 1172	.1380 0853
68	.2601 2873	.2202 3912	.1865 4223	.1580 6493	.1339 8887
69	.2550 2817	.2153 9278	.1819 9241	.1538 3448	.1300 8628
70	.2500 2761	.2106 5309	.1775 5358	.1497 1726	.1262 9736
71	.2451 2511	.2060 1769	.1732 2300	.1457 1023	.1226 1880
72	.2403 1874	.2014 8429	.1689 9805	.1418 1044	.1190 4737
73	.2356 0661	.1970 5065	.1648 7615	.1380 1503	.1155 7998
74	.2309 8687	.1927 1458	.1608 5478	.1343 2119	.1122 1357
75	.2264 5771	.1884 7391	.1569 3149	.1307 2622	.1089 4521
76	.2220 1737	.1843 2657	.1531 0389	.1272 2747	.1057 7205
77	.2176 6408	.1802 7048	.1493 6965	.1238 2235	.1026 9131
78	.2133 9616	.1763 0365	.1457 2649	.1205 0837	.0997 0030
79	.2092 1192	.1724 2411	.1421 7218	.1172 8309	.0967 9641
80	.2051 0973	.1686 2993	.1387 0457	.1141 4412	.0939 7710
81	.2010 8797	.1649 1925	.1353 2153	.1110 8917	.0912 3990
82	.1971 4507	.1612 9022	.1320 2101	.1081 1598	.0885 8243
83	.1932 7948	.1577 4105	.1288 0098	.1052 2237	.0860 0236
84	.1894 8968	.1542 6997	.1256 5949	.1024 0620	.0834 9743
85	.1857 7420	.1508 7528	.1225 9463	.0996 6540	.0810 6547
86	.1821 3157	.1475 5528	.1196 0452	.0969 9795	.0787 0434
87	.1785 6036	.1443 0835	.1166 8733	.0944 0190	.0764 1198
88	.1750 5918	.1411 3286	.1138 4130	.0918 7533	.0741 8639
89	.1716 2665	.1380 2724	.1110 6468	.0894 1638	.0720 2562
90	.1682 6142	.1349 8997	.1083 5579	.0870 2324	.0699 2779
91	.1649 6217	.1320 1953	.1057 1296	.0846 9415	.0678 9105
92	.1617 2762	.1291 1445	.1031 3460	.0824 2740	.0659 1364
93	.1585 5649	.1262 7331	.1006 1912	.0802 2131	.0639 9383
94	.1554 4754	.1234 9468	.0981 6500	.0780 7427	.0621 2993
95	.1523 9955	.1207 7719	.0957 7073	.0759 8469	.0603 2032
96	.1494 1132	.1181 1950	.0934 3486	.0739 5104	.0585 6342
97	.1464 8169	.1155 2029	.0911 5596	.0719 7181	.0568 5769
98	.1436 0950	.1129 7828	.0889 3264	.0700 4556	.0552 0164
99	.1407 9363	.1104 9221	.0867 6355	.0681 7086	.0535 9383
100	.1380 3297	.1080 6084	.0846 4737	.0663 4634	.0520 3284

Financial Tables

PRESENT VALUE $1/(1 + i)^n$ (Continued)

Periods	Rate i				
n	.035 (3½%)	.04 (4%)	.045 (4½%)	.05 (5%)	.055 (5½%)
1	.9661 8357	.9615 3846	.9569 3780	.9523 8095	.9478 6730
2	.9335 1070	.9245 5621	.9157 2995	.9070 2948	.8984 5242
3	.9019 4271	.8889 9636	.8762 9660	.8638 3760	.8516 1366
4	.8714 4223	.8548 0419	.8385 6134	.8227 0247	.8072 1674
5	.8419 7317	.8219 2711	.8024 5105	.7835 2617	.7651 3435
6	.8135 0064	.7903 1453	.7678 9574	.7462 1540	.7252 4583
7	.7859 9096	.7599 1781	.7348 2846	.7106 8133	.6874 3681
8	.7594 1156	.7306 9021	.7031 8513	.6768 3936	.6515 9887
9	.7337 3097	.7025 8674	.6729 0443	.6446 0892	.6176 2926
10	.7089 1881	.6755 6417	.6439 2768	.6139 1325	.5854 3058
11	.6849 4571	.6495 8093	.6161 9874	.5846 7929	.5549 1050
12	.6617 8330	.6245 9705	.5896 6386	.5568 3742	.5259 8152
13	.6394 0415	.6005 7409	.5642 7164	.5303 2135	.4985 6068
14	.6177 8179	.5774 7508	.5399 7286	.5050 6795	.4725 6937
15	.5968 9062	.5552 6450	.5167 2044	.4810 1710	.4479 3305
16	.5767 0591	.5339 0818	.4944 6932	.4581 1152	.4245 8109
17	.5572 0378	.5133 7325	.4731 7639	.4362 9669	.4024 4653
18	.5383 6114	.4936 2812	.4528 0037	.4155 2065	.3814 6590
19	.5201 5569	.4746 4242	.4333 0179	.3957 3396	.3615 7906
20	.5025 6588	.4563 8695	.4146 4286	.3768 8948	.3427 2896
21	.4855 7090	.4388 3360	.3967 8743	.3589 4236	.3248 6158
22	.4691 5063	.4219 5539	.3797 0089	.3418 4987	.3079 2567
23	.4532 8563	.4057 2633	.3633 5013	.3255 7131	.2918 7267
24	.4379 5713	.3901 2147	.3477 0347	.3100 6791	.2766 5656
25	.4231 4699	.3751 1680	.3327 3060	.2953 0277	.2622 3370
26	.4088 3767	.3606 8923	.3184 0248	.2812 4073	.2485 6275
27	.3950 1224	.3468 1657	.3046 9137	.2678 4832	.2356 0450
28	.3816 5434	.3334 7747	.2915 7069	.2550 9364	.2233 2181
29	.3687 4815	.3206 5141	.2790 1502	.2429 4632	.2116 7944
30	.3562 7841	.3083 1867	.2670 0002	.2313 7745	.2006 4402
31	.3442 3035	.2964 6026	.2555 0241	.2203 5947	.1901 8390
32	.3325 8971	.2850 5794	.2444 9991	.2098 6617	.1802 6910
33	.3213 4271	.2740 9417	.2339 7121	.1998 7254	.1708 7119
34	.3104 7605	.2635 5209	.2238 9589	.1903 5480	.1619 6321
35	.2999 7686	.2534 1547	.2142 5444	.1812 9029	.1535 1963
36	.2898 3272	.2436 6872	.2050 2817	.1726 5741	.1455 1624
37	.2800 3161	.2342 9685	.1961 9921	.1644 3563	.1379 3008
38	.2705 6194	.2252 8543	.1877 5044	.1566 0536	.1307 3941
39	.2614 1250	.2166 2061	.1796 6549	.1491 4797	.1239 2362
40	.2525 7247	.2082 8904	.1719 2870	.1420 4568	.1174 6314
41	.2440 3137	.2002 7793	.1645 2507	.1352 8160	.1113 3947
42	.2357 7910	.1925 7493	.1574 4026	.1288 3962	.1055 3504
43	.2278 0590	.1851 6820	.1506 6054	.1227 0440	.1000 3322
44	.2201 0231	.1780 4635	.1441 7276	.1168 6133	.0948 1822
45	.2126 5924	.1711 9841	.1379 6437	.1112 9651	.0898 7509
46	.2054 6787	.1646 1386	.1320 2332	.1059 9668	.0851 8965
47	.1985 1968	.1582 8256	.1263 3810	.1009 4921	.0807 4849
48	.1918 0645	.1521 9476	.1208 9771	.0961 4211	.0765 3885
49	.1853 2024	.1463 4112	.1156 9158	.0915 6391	.0725 4867
50	.1790 5337	.1407 1262	.1107 0965	.0872 0373	.0687 6652

PRESENT VALUE $1/(1 + i)^n$ (Continued)

Periods	Rate i				
n	.06 (6%)	.065 (6½%)	.07 (7%)	.075 (7½%)	.08 (8%)
1	.9433 9623	.9389 6714	.9345 7944	.9302 3256	.9259 2593
2	.8899 9644	.8816 5928	.8734 3873	.8653 3261	.8573 3882
3	.8396 1928	.8278 4909	.8162 9788	.8049 6057	.7938 3224
4	.7920 9366	.7773 2309	.7628 9521	.7488 0053	.7350 2985
5	.7472 5817	.7298 8084	.7129 8618	.6965 5863	.6805 8320
6	.7049 6054	.6853 3412	.6663 4222	.6479 6152	.6301 6963
7	.6650 5711	.6435 0621	.6227 4974	.6027 5490	.5834 9040
8	.6274 1237	.6042 3119	.5820 0910	.5607 0223	.5402 6888
9	.5918 9846	.5673 5323	.5439 3374	.5215 8347	.5002 4897
10	.5583 9478	.5327 2604	.5083 4929	.4851 9393	.4631 9349
11	.5267 8753	.5002 1224	.4750 9280	.4513 4319	.4288 8286
12	.4969 6936	.4696 8285	.4440 1196	.4198 5413	.3971 1376
13	.4688 3902	.4410 1676	.4149 6445	.3905 6198	.3676 9792
14	.4423 0096	.4141 0025	.3878 1724	.3633 1347	.3404 6104
15	.4172 6506	.3888 2652	.3624 4602	.3379 6602	.3152 4170
16	.3936 4628	.3650 9533	.3387 3460	.3143 8699	.2918 9047
17	.3713 6442	.3428 1251	.3165 7439	.2924 5302	.2702 6895
18	.3503 4379	.3218 8969	.2958 6392	.2720 4932	.2502 4903
19	.3305 1301	.3022 4384	.2765 0833	.2530 6913	.2317 1206
20	.3118 0473	.2837 9703	.2584 1900	.2354 1315	.2145 4821
21	.2941 5540	.2664 7608	.2415 1309	.2189 8897	.1986 5575
22	.2775 0510	.2502 1228	.2257 1317	.2037 1067	.1839 4051
23	.2617 9726	.2349 4111	.2109 4688	.1894 9830	.1703 1528
24	.2469 7855	.2206 0198	.1971 4662	.1762 7749	.1576 9934
25	.2329 9863	.2071 3801	.1842 4918	.1639 7906	.1460 1790
26	.2198 1003	.1944 9579	.1721 9549	.1525 3866	.1352 0176
27	.2073 6795	.1826 2515	.1609 3037	.1418 9643	.1251 8682
28	.1956 3014	.1714 7902	.1504 0221	.1319 9668	.1159 1372
29	.1845 5674	.1610 1316	.1405 6282	.1227 8761	.1073 2752
30	.1741 1013	.1511 8607	.1313 6712	.1142 2103	.0993 7733
31	.1642 5484	.1419 5875	.1227 7301	.1062 5212	.0920 1605
32	.1549 5740	.1332 9460	.1147 4113	.0988 3918	.0852 0005
33	.1461 8622	.1251 5925	.1072 3470	.0919 4343	.0788 8893
34	.1379 1153	.1175 2042	.1002 1934	.0855 2877	.0730 4531
35	.1301 0522	.1103 4781	.0936 6294	.0795 6164	.0676 3454
36	.1227 4077	.1036 1297	.0875 3546	.0740 1083	.0626 2458
37	.1157 9318	.0972 8917	.0818 0884	.0688 4729	.0579 8572
38	.1092 3885	.0913 5134	.0764 5686	.0640 4399	.0536 9048
39	.1030 5552	.0857 7590	.0714 5501	.0595 7580	.0497 1341
40	.0972 2219	.0805 4075	.0667 8038	.0554 1935	.0460 3093
41	.0917 1905	.0756 2512	.0624 1157	.0515 5288	.0426 2123
42	.0865 2740	.0710 0950	.0583 2857	.0479 5617	.0394 6411
43	.0816 2962	.0666 7559	.0545 1268	.0446 1039	.0365 4084
44	.0770 0908	.0626 0619	.0509 4643	.0414 9804	.0338 3411
45	.0726 5007	.0587 8515	.0476 1349	.0386 0283	.0313 2788
46	.0685 3781	.0551 9733	.0444 9859	.0359 0961	.0290 0730
47	.0646 5831	.0518 2848	.0415 8747	.0334 0428	.0268 5861
48	.0609 9840	.0486 6524	.0388 6679	.0310 7375	.0248 6908
49	.0575 4566	.0456 9506	.0363 2410	.0289 0582	.0230 2693
50	.0542 8836	.0429 0616	.0339 4776	.0268 8913	.0213 2123

AMOUNT OF ANNUITY $[(1 + i)^n - 1]/i$

The following table gives the amount of an annuity of unit value per period after a term of n periods at rate of interest of i per period; usually indicated as $s_{\overline{n}|i}$.

Periods	Rate i				
n	.0025 ($\frac{1}{4}$%)	.004167 ($\frac{5}{12}$%)	.005 ($\frac{1}{2}$%)	.005833 ($\frac{7}{12}$%)	.0075 ($\frac{3}{4}$%)
1	1.0000 0000	1.0000 0000	1.0000 0000	1.0000 0000	1.0000 0000
2	2.0025 0000	2.0041 6667	2.0050 0000	2.0058 3333	2.0075 0000
3	3.0075 0625	3.0125 1736	3.0150 2500	3.0175 3403	3.0225 5625
4	4.0150 2502	4.0250 6952	4.0301 0013	4.0351 3631	4.0452 2542
5	5.0250 6258	5.0418 4064	5.0502 5063	5.0586 7460	5.0755 6461
6	6.0376 2523	6.0628 4831	6.0755 0188	6.0881 8354	6.1136 3135
7	7.0527 1930	7.0881 1018	7.1058 7939	7.1236 9794	7.1594 8358
8	8.0703 5110	8.1176 4397	8.1414 0879	8.1652 5285	8.2131 7971
9	9.0905 2697	9.1514 6749	9.1821 1583	9.2128 8349	9.2747 7856
10	10.1132 5329	10.1895 9860	10.2280 2641	10.2666 2531	10.3443 3940
11	11.1385 3642	11.2320 5526	11.2791 6654	11.3265 1396	11.4219 2194
12	12.1663 8277	12.2788 5549	12.3355 6237	12.3925 8529	12.5075 8636
13	13.1967 9872	13.3300 1739	13.3972 4018	13.4648 7523	13.6013 9325
14	14.2297 9072	14.3855 5913	14.4642 2639	14.5434 2048	14.7034 0370
15	15.2653 6520	15.4454 9896	15.5365 4752	15.6282 5710	15.8136 7923
16	16.3035 2861	16.5098 5520	16.6142 3026	16.7194 2193	16.9322 8183
17	17.3442 8743	17.5786 4627	17.6973 0141	17.8169 5189	18.0592 7394
18	18.3876 4815	18.6518 9063	18.7857 8791	18.9208 8411	19.1947 1849
19	19.4336 1727	19.7296 0684	19.8797 1685	20.0312 5593	20.3386 7888
20	20.4822 0131	20.8118 1353	20.9791 1544	21.1481 0493	21.4912 1897
21	21.5334 0682	21.8985 2942	22.0840 1101	22.2714 6887	22.6524 0312
22	22.5872 4033	22.9897 7330	23.1944 3107	23.4013 8577	23.8222 9614
23	23.6437 0843	24.0855 6402	24.3104 0323	24.5378 9386	25.0009 6336
24	24.7028 1770	25.1859 2053	25.4319 5524	25.6810 3157	26.1884 7059
25	25.7645 7475	26.2908 6187	26.5591 1502	26.8308 3759	27.3848 8411
26	26.8289 8619	27.4004 0713	27.6919 1059	27.9873 5081	28.5902 7075
27	27.8960 5865	28.5145 7549	28.8303 7015	29.1506 1036	29.8046 9778
28	28.9657 9880	29.6333 8622	29.9745 2200	30.3206 5558	31.0282 3301
29	30.0382 1330	30.7568 5866	31.1243 9461	31.4975 2607	32.2609 4476
30	31.1133 0883	31.8850 1224	32.2800 1658	32.6812 6164	33.5029 0184
31	32.1910 9210	33.0178 6646	33.4414 1666	33.8719 0233	34.7541 7361
32	33.2715 6983	34.1554 4090	34.6086 2375	35.0694 8843	36.0148 2991
33	34.3547 4876	35.2977 5524	35.7816 6686	36.2740 6045	37.2849 4113
34	35.4406 3563	36.4448 2922	36.9605 7520	37.4856 5913	38.5645 7819
35	36.5292 3722	37.5966 8268	38.1453 7807	38.7043 2548	39.8538 1253
36	37.6205 6031	38.7533 3552	39.3361 0497	39.9301 0071	41.1527 1612
37	38.7146 1171	39.9148 0775	40.5327 8549	41.1630 2630	42.4613 6149
38	39.8113 9824	41.0811 1945	41.7354 4942	42.4031 4395	43.7798 2170
39	40.9109 2674	42.2522 9078	42.9441 2666	43.6504 9562	45.1081 7037
40	42.0132 0405	43.4283 4199	44.1588 4730	44.9051 2352	46.4464 8164
41	43.1182 3706	44.6092 9342	45.3796 4153	46.1670 7007	47.7948 3026
42	44.2260 3265	45.7951 6547	46.6065 3974	47.4363 7798	49.1532 9148
43	45.3365 9774	46.9859 7866	47.8395 7244	48.7130 9018	50.5219 4117
44	46.4499 3923	48.1817 5357	49.0787 7030	49.9972 4988	51.9008 5573
45	47.5660 6408	49.3825 1088	50.3241 6415	51.2889 0050	53.2901 1215
46	48.6849 7924	50.5882 7134	51.5757 8498	52.5880 8575	54.6897 8799
47	49.8066 9169	51.7990 5581	52.8336 6390	53.8948 4959	56.0999 6140
48	50.9312 0842	53.0148 8521	54.0978 3222	55.2092 3621	57.5207 1111
49	52.0585 3644	54.2357 8056	55.3683 2138	56.5312 9009	58.9521 1644
50	53.1886 8278	55.4617 6298	56.6451 6299	57.8610 5595	60.3942 5732

AMOUNT OF ANNUITY $[(1 + i)^n - 1]/i$ (Continued)

Periods	Rate i				
n	.0025 ($\frac{1}{4}$%)	.004167 ($\frac{5}{12}$%)	.005 ($\frac{1}{2}$%)	.005833 ($\frac{7}{12}$%)	.0075 ($\frac{3}{4}$%)
50	53.1886 828	55.4617 630	56.6451 630	57.8610 559	60.3942 573
51	54.3216 545	56.6928 537	57.9283 888	59.1985 788	61.8472 142
52	55.4574 586	57.9290 739	59.2180 307	60.5439 038	63.3110 684
53	56.5961 023	59.1704 450	60.5141 209	61.8970 766	64.7859 014
54	57.7375 925	60.4169 885	61.8166 915	63.2581 429	66.2717 956
55	58.8819 365	61.6687 260	63.1257 750	64.6271 487	67.7688 341
56	60.0291 413	62.9256 790	64.4414 038	66.0041 404	69.2771 003
57	61.1792 142	64.1878 694	65.7636 109	67.3891 646	70.7966 786
58	62.3321 622	65.4553 188	67.0924 289	68.7822 680	72.3276 537
59	63.4879 926	66.7280 493	68.4278 911	70.1834 979	73.8701 111
60	64.6467 126	68.0060 828	69.7700 305	71.5929 016	75.4241 369
61	65.8083 294	69.2894 415	71.1188 807	73.0105 269	76.9898 180
62	66.9728 502	70.5781 475	72.4744 751	74.4364 216	78.5672 416
63	68.1402 824	71.8722 231	73.8368 474	75.8706 341	80.1564 959
64	69.3106 331	73.1716 907	75.2060 317	77.3132 128	81.7576 696
65	70.4839 096	74.4765 728	76.5820 618	78.7642 065	83.3708 521
66	71.6601 194	75.7868 918	77.9649 721	80.2236 644	84.9961 335
67	72.8392 697	77.1026 706	79.3547 970	81.6916 358	86.6336 045
68	74.0213 679	78.4239 317	80.7515 710	83.1681 703	88.2833 566
69	75.2064 213	79.7506 981	82.1553 288	84.6533 180	89.9454 817
70	76.3944 374	81.0829 926	83.5661 055	86.1471 290	91.6200 729
71	77.5854 235	82.4208 384	84.9839 360	87.6496 539	93.3072 234
72	78.7793 870	83.7642 586	86.4088 557	89.1609 436	95.0070 276
73	79.9763 355	85.1132 753	87.8409 000	90.6810 491	96.7195 803
74	81.1762 763	86.4679 150	89.2801 045	92.2100 219	98.4449 771
75	82.3792 170	87.8281 980	90.7265 050	93.7479 137	100.1833 145
76	83.5851 651	89.1941 488	92.1801 375	95.2947 765	101.9346 893
77	84.7941 280	90.5657 911	93.6410 382	96.8506 627	103.6991 995
78	86.0061 133	91.9431 485	95.1092 434	98.4156 249	105.4769 435
79	87.2211 286	93.3262 450	96.5847 896	99.9897 160	107.2680 206
80	88.4391 814	94.7151 044	98.0677 136	101.5729 894	109.0725 307
81	89.6602 793	96.1097 506	99.5580 521	103.1654 985	110.8905 747
82	90.8844 300	97.5102 079	101.0558 424	104.7672 972	112.7222 540
83	92.1116 411	98.9165 004	102.5611 216	106.3784 398	114.5676 709
84	93.3419 202	100.3286 525	104.0739 272	107.9989 807	116.4269 284
85	94.5752 750	101.7466 886	105.5942 969	109.6289 748	118.3001 304
86	95.8117 132	103.1706 331	107.1222 683	111.2684 771	120.1873 814
87	97.0512 425	104.6005 108	108.6578 797	112.9175 432	122.0887 867
88	98.2938 706	106.0363 462	110.2011 691	114.5762 289	124.0044 526
89	99.5396 053	107.4781 643	111.7521 749	116.2445 902	125.9344 860
90	100.7884 543	108.9259 900	113.3109 358	117.9226 837	127.8789 947
91	102.0404 254	110.3798 483	114.8774 905	119.6105 660	129.8380 871
92	103.2955 265	111.8397 643	116.4518 779	121.3082 943	131.8118 728
93	104.5537 653	113.3057 634	118.0341 373	123.0159 260	133.8004 618
94	105.8151 497	114.7778 707	119.6243 080	124.7335 189	135.8039 653
95	107.0796 876	116.2561 118	121.2224 295	126.4611 311	137.8224 951
96	108.3473 868	117.7405 123	122.8285 417	128.1988 210	139.8561 638
97	109.6182 553	119.2310 978	124.4426 844	129.9466 475	141.9050 850
98	110.8923 009	120.7278 940	126.0648 978	131.7046 696	143.9693 731
99	112.1695 317	122.2309 269	127.6952 223	133.4729 468	146.0491 434
100	113.4499 555	123.7402 224	129.3336 984	135.2515 390	148.1445 120

AMOUNT OF ANNUITY $[(1 + i)^n - 1]/i$ (Continued)

Periods	Rate i				
n	.01 (1%)	.01125 (1⅛%)	.0125 (1¼%)	.015 (1½%)	.0175 (1¾%)
1	1.0000 0000	1.0000 0000	1.0000 0000	1.0000 0000	1.0000 0000
2	2.0100 0000	2.0112 5000	2.0125 0000	2.0150 0000	2.0175 0000
3	3.0301 0000	3.0338 7656	3.0376 5625	3.0452 2500	3.0528 0625
4	4.0604 0100	4.0680 0767	4.0756 2695	4.0909 0338	4.1062 3036
5	5.1010 0501	5.1137 7276	5.1265 7229	5.1522 6693	5.1780 8939
6	6.1520 1506	6.1713 0270	6.1906 5444	6.2295 5093	6.2687 0596
7	7.2135 3521	7.2407 2986	7.2680 3762	7.3229 9419	7.3784 0831
8	8.2856 7056	8.3221 8807	8.3588 8809	8.4328 3911	8.5075 3045
9	9.3685 2727	9.4158 1269	9.4633 7420	9.5593 3169	9.6564 1224
10	10.4622 1254	10.5217 4058	10.5816 6637	10.7027 2167	10.8253 9945
11	11.5668 3467	11.6401 1016	11.7139 3720	11.8632 6249	12.0148 4394
12	12.6825 0301	12.7710 6140	12.8603 6142	13.0412 1143	13.2251 0371
13	13.8093 2804	13.9147 3584	14.0211 1594	14.2368 2960	14.4565 4303
14	14.9474 2132	15.0712 7662	15.1963 7988	15.4503 8205	15.7095 3253
15	16.0968 9554	16.2408 2848	16.3863 3463	16.6821 3778	16.9844 4935
16	17.2578 6449	17.4235 3780	17.5911 6382	17.9323 6984	18.2816 7721
17	18.4304 4314	18.6195 5260	18.8110 5336	19.2013 5539	19.6016 0656
18	19.6147 4757	19.8290 2257	20.0461 9153	20.4893 7572	20.9446 3468
19	20.8108 9504	21.0520 9907	21.2967 6893	21.7967 1636	22.3111 6578
20	22.0190 0399	22.2889 3519	22.5629 7854	23.1236 6710	23.7016 1119
21	23.2391 9403	23.5396 8571	23.8450 1577	24.4705 2211	25.1163 8938
22	24.4715 8598	24.8045 0717	25.1430 7847	25.8375 7994	26.5559 2620
23	25.7163 0183	26.0835 5788	26.4573 6695	27.2251 4364	28.0206 5490
24	26.9734 6485	27.3769 9790	27.7880 8403	28.6335 2080	29.5110 1637
25	28.2431 9950	28.6849 8913	29.1354 3508	30.0630 2361	31.0274 5915
26	29.5256 3150	30.0076 9526	30.4996 2802	31.5139 6896	32.5704 3969
27	30.8208 8781	31.3452 8183	31.8808 7337	32.9866 7850	34.1404 2238
28	32.1290 9669	32.6979 1625	33.2793 8429	34.4814 7867	35.7378 7977
29	33.4503 8766	34.0657 6781	34.6953 7659	35.9987 0085	37.3632 9267
30	34.7848 9153	35.4490 0769	36.1290 6880	37.5386 8137	39.0171 5029
31	36.1327 4045	36.8478 0903	37.5806 8216	39.1017 6159	40.6999 5042
32	37.4940 6785	38.2623 4688	39.0504 4069	40.6882 8801	42.4121 9955
33	38.8690 0853	39.6927 9829	40.5385 7120	42.2986 1233	44.1544 1305
34	40.2576 9862	41.1393 4227	42.0453 0334	43.9330 9152	45.9271 1527
35	41.6602 7560	42.6021 5987	43.5708 6963	45.5920 8789	47.7308 3979
36	43.0768 7836	44.0814 3417	45.1155 0550	47.2759 6921	49.5661 2949
37	44.5076 4714	45.5773 5030	46.6794 4932	48.9851 0874	51.4335 3675
38	45.9527 2361	47.0900 9549	48.2629 4243	50.7198 8538	53.3336 2365
39	47.4122 5085	48.6198 5906	49.8662 2921	52.4806 8366	55.2669 6206
40	48.8863 7336	50.1668 3248	51.4895 5708	54.2678 9391	57.2341 3390
41	50.3752 3709	51.7312 0934	53.1331 7654	56.0819 1232	59.2357 3124
42	51.8789 8946	53.3131 8545	54.7973 4125	57.9231 4100	61.2723 5654
43	53.3977 7936	54.9129 5879	56.4823 0801	59.7919 8812	63.3446 2278
44	54.9317 5715	56.5307 2957	58.1883 3686	61.6888 6794	65.4531 5367
45	56.4810 7472	58.1667 0028	59.9156 9108	63.6142 0096	67.5985 8386
46	58.0458 8547	59.8210 7566	61.6646 3721	65.5684 1398	69.7815 5908
47	59.6263 4432	61.4940 6276	63.4354 4518	67.5519 4018	72.0027 3637
48	61.2226 0777	63.1858 7097	65.2283 8824	69.5652 1929	74.2627 8425
49	62.8348 3385	64.8967 1201	67.0437 4310	71.6086 9758	76.5623 8298
50	64.4631 8218	66.6268 0002	68.8817 8989	73.6828 2804	78.9022 2468

AMOUNT OF ANNUITY $[(1 + i)^n - 1]/i$ (Continued)

Periods	Rate i				
n	.01 (1 %)	.01125 (1⅛ %)	.0125 (1¼ %)	.015 (1½ %)	.0175 (1¾ %)
50	64.4631 822	66.6268 000	68.8817 899	73.6828 280	78.9022 247
51	66.1078 140	68.3763 515	70.7428 123	75.7880 705	81.2830 136
52	67.7688 921	70.1455 855	72.6270 974	77.9248 915	83.7054 663
53	69.4465 811	71.9347 233	74.5349 361	80.0937 649	86.1703 120
54	71.1410 469	73.7439 890	76.4666 228	82.2951 714	88.6782 925
55	72.8524 573	75.5736 088	78.4224 556	84.5295 989	91.2301 626
56	74.5809 819	77.4238 119	80.4027 363	86.7975 429	93.8266 904
57	76.3267 917	79.2948 298	82.4077 705	89.0995 061	96.4686 575
58	78.0900 597	81.1868 966	84.4378 676	91.4359 987	99.1568 590
59	79.8709 603	83.1002 492	86.4933 410	93.8075 386	101.8921 041
60	81.6696 699	85.0351 270	88.5745 078	96.2146 517	104.6752 159
61	83.4863 666	86.9917 722	90.6816 891	98.6578 715	107.5070 322
62	85.3212 302	88.9704 297	92.8152 102	101.1377 396	110.3884 052
63	87.1744 425	90.9713 470	94.9754 003	103.6548 057	113.3202 023
64	89.0461 869	92.9947 746	97.1625 928	106.2096 277	116.3033 058
65	90.9366 488	95.0409 659	99.3771 253	108.8027 722	119.3386 137
66	92.8460 153	97.1101 767	101.6193 393	111.4348 137	122.4270 394
67	94.7744 755	99.2026 662	103.8895 811	114.1063 359	125.5695 126
68	96.7222 202	101.3186 962	106.1882 008	116.8179 310	128.7669 791
69	98.6894 424	103.4585 315	108.5155 533	119.5701 999	132.0204 012
70	100.6763 368	105.6224 400	110.8719 978	122.3637 529	135.3307 583
71	102.6831 002	107.8106 925	113.2578 977	125.1992 092	138.6990 465
72	104.7099 312	110.0235 628	115.6736 215	128.0771 974	142.1262 798
73	106.7570 305	112.2613 278	118.1195 417	130.9983 553	145.6134 897
74	108.8246 008	114.5242 678	120.5960 360	133.9633 307	149.1617 258
75	110.9128 468	116.8126 658	123.1034 864	136.9727 806	152.7720 560
76	113.0219 753	119.1268 083	125.6422 800	140.0273 723	156.4455 670
77	115.1521 951	121.4669 849	128.2128 085	143.1277 829	160.1833 644
78	117.3037 170	123.8334 885	130.8154 686	146.2746 997	163.9865 733
79	119.4767 542	126.2266 152	133.4506 620	149.4688 202	167.8563 383
80	121.6715 217	128.6466 646	136.1187 953	152.7108 525	171.7938 242
81	123.8882 369	131.0939 396	138.8202 802	156.0015 153	175.8002 162
82	126.1271 193	133.5687 464	141.5555 337	159.3415 380	179.8767 200
83	128.3883 905	136.0713 948	144.3249 779	162.7316 611	184.0245 625
84	130.6722 744	138.6021 980	147.1290 401	166.1726 360	188.2449 924
85	132.9789 971	141.1614 727	149.9681 531	169.6652 255	192.5392 798
86	135.3087 871	143.7495 393	152.8427 550	173.2102 039	196.9087 172
87	137.6618 750	146.3667 216	155.7532 895	176.8083 569	201.3546 197
88	140.0384 937	149.0133 472	158.7002 056	180.4604 823	205.8783 256
89	142.4388 787	151.6897 474	161.6839 581	184.1673 895	210.4811 962
90	144.8632 675	154.3962 571	164.7050 076	187.9299 004	215.1646 172
91	147.3119 001	157.1332 149	167.7638 202	191.7488 489	219.9299 980
92	149.7850 191	159.9009 636	170.8608 680	195.6250 816	224.7787 729
93	152.2828 693	162.6998 495	173.9966 288	199.5594 578	229.7124 015
94	154.8056 980	165.5302 228	177.1715 867	203.5528 497	234.7323 685
95	157.3537 550	168.3924 378	180.3862 315	207.6061 425	239.8401 850
96	159.9272 926	171.2868 527	183.6410 594	211.7202 346	245.0373 882
97	162.5265 655	174.2138 298	186.9365 726	215.8960 381	250.3255 425
98	165.1518 311	177.1737 354	190.2732 798	220.1344 787	255.7062 395
99	167.8033 494	180.1669 399	193.6516 958	224.4364 959	261.1810 987
100	170.4813 829	183.1938 180	197.0723 420	228.8030 433	266.7517 679

Financial Tables

AMOUNT OF ANNUITY $[(1 + i)^n - 1]/i$ (Continued)

Periods	Rate i				
n	.02 (2%)	.0225 (2¼%)	.025 (2½%)	.0275 (2¾%)	.03 (3%)
1	1.0000 0000	1.0000 0000	1.0000 0000	1.0000 0000	1.0000 0000
2	2.0200 0000	2.0225 0000	2.0250 0000	2.0275 0000	2.0300 0000
3	3.0604 0000	3.0680 0625	3.0756 2500	3.0832 5625	3.0909 0000
4	4.1216 0800	4.1370 3639	4.1525 1563	4.1680 4580	4.1836 2700
5	5.2040 4016	5.2301 1971	5.2563 2852	5.2826 6706	5.3091 3581
6	6.3081 2096	6.3477 9740	6.3877 3673	6.4279 4040	6.4684 0988
7	7.4342 8338	7.4906 2284	7.5474 3015	7.6047 0876	7.6624 6218
8	8.5829 6905	8.6591 6186	8.7361 1590	8.8138 3825	8.8923 3605
9	9.7546 2843	9.8539 9300	9.9545 1880	10.0562 1880	10.1591 0613
10	10.9497 2100	11.0757 0784	11.2033 8177	11.3327 6482	11.4638 7931
11	12.1687 1542	12.3249 1127	12.4834 6631	12.6444 1585	12.8077 9569
12	13.4120 8973	13.6022 2177	13.7955 5297	13.9921 3729	14.1920 2956
13	14.6803 3152	14.9082 7176	15.1404 4179	15.3769 2107	15.6177 9045
14	15.9739 3815	16.2437 0788	16.5189 5284	16.7997 8639	17.0863 2416
15	17.2934 1692	17.6091 9130	17.9319 2666	18.2617 8052	18.5989 1389
16	18.6392 8525	19.0053 9811	19.3802 2483	19.7639 7948	20.1568 8130
17	20.0120 7096	20.4330 1957	20.8647 3045	21.3074 8892	21.7615 8774
18	21.4123 1238	21.8927 6251	22.3863 4871	22.8934 4487	23.4144 3537
19	22.8405 5863	23.3853 4966	23.9460 0743	24.5230 1460	25.1168 6844
20	24.2973 6980	24.9115 2003	25.5446 5761	26.1973 9750	26.8703 7449
21	25.7833 1719	26.4720 2923	27.1832 7405	27.9178 2593	28.6764 8572
22	27.2989 8354	28.0676 4989	28.8628 5590	29.6855 6615	30.5367 8030
23	28.8449 6321	29.6991 7201	30.5844 2730	31.5019 1921	32.4528 8370
24	30.4218 6247	31.3674 0338	32.3490 3798	33.3682 2199	34.4264 7022
25	32.0302 9972	33.0731 6996	34.1577 6393	35.2858 4810	36.4592 6432
26	33.6709 0572	34.8173 1628	36.0117 0803	37.2562 0892	38.5530 4225
27	35.3443 2383	36.6007 0590	37.9120 0073	39.2807 5467	40.7096 3352
28	37.0512 1031	38.4242 2178	39.8598 0075	41.3609 7542	42.9309 2252
29	38.7922 3451	40.2887 6677	41.8562 9577	43.4984 0224	45.2188 5020
30	40.5680 7921	42.1952 6402	43.9027 0316	45.6946 0831	47.5754 1571
31	42.3794 4079	44.1446 5746	46.0002 7074	47.9512 1003	50.0026 7818
32	44.2270 2961	46.1379 1226	48.1502 7751	50.2698 6831	52.5027 5852
33	46.1115 7020	48.1760 1528	50.3540 3445	52.6522 8969	55.0778 4128
34	48.0338 0160	50.2599 7563	52.6128 8531	55.1002 2765	57.7301 7652
35	49.9944 7763	52.3908 2508	54.9282 0744	57.6154 8391	60.4620 8181
36	51.9943 6719	54.5696 1864	57.3014 1263	60.1999 0972	63.2759 4427
37	54.0342 5453	56.7974 3506	59.7339 4794	62.8554 0724	66.1742 2259
38	56.1149 3962	59.0753 7735	62.2272 9664	65.5839 3094	69.1594 4927
39	58.2372 3841	61.4045 7334	64.7829 7906	68.3874 8904	72.2342 3275
40	60.4019 8318	63.7861 7624	67.4025 5354	71.2681 4499	75.4012 5973
41	62.6100 2284	66.2213 6521	70.0876 1737	74.2280 1898	78.6632 9753
42	64.8622 2330	68.7113 4592	72.8398 0781	77.2692 8950	82.0231 9645
43	67.1594 6777	71.2573 5121	75.6608 0300	80.3941 9496	85.4838 9234
44	69.5026 5712	73.8606 4161	78.5523 2308	83.6050 3532	89.0484 0911
45	71.8927 1027	76.5225 0605	81.5161 3116	86.9041 7379	92.7198 6139
46	74.3305 6447	79.2442 6243	84.5540 3443	90.2940 3857	96.5014 5723
47	76.8171 7576	82.0272 5834	87.6678 8530	93.7771 2463	100.3965 0095
48	79.3535 1928	84.8728 7165	90.8595 8243	97.3559 9556	104.4083 9598
49	81.9405 8966	87.7825 1126	94.1310 7199	101.0332 8544	108.5406 4785
50	84.5794 0145	90.7576 1776	97.4843 4879	104.8117 0079	112.7968 6729

AMOUNT OF ANNUITY $[(1 + i)^n - 1]/i$ (Continued)

Periods		Rate i			
n	.02 (2 %)	.0225 (2¼ %)	.025 (2½ %)	.0275 (2¾ %)	.03 (3 %)
50	84.5794 015	90.7576 178	97.4843 488	104.8117 008	112.7968 673
51	87.2709 895	93.7996 642	100.9214 575	108.6940 226	117.1807 733
52	90.0164 093	96.9101 566	104.4444 939	112.6831 082	121.6961 965
53	92.8167 375	100.0906 351	108.0556 063	116.7818 937	126.3470 824
54	95.6730 722	103.3426 744	111.7569 965	120.9933 957	131.1374 949
55	98.5865 337	106.6678 846	115.5509 214	125.3207 141	136.0716 197
56	101.5582 643	110.0679 120	119.4396 944	129.7670 337	141.1537 683
57	104.5894 296	113.5444 400	123.4256 868	134.3356 272	146.3883 814
58	107.6812 182	117.0991 899	127.5113 289	139.0298 569	151.7800 328
59	110.8348 426	120.7339 217	131.6991 121	143.8531 780	157.3334 338
60	114.0515 394	124.4504 349	135.9915 900	148.8091 404	163.0534 368
61	117.3325 702	128.2505 697	140.3913 797	153.9013 917	168.9450 399
62	120.6792 216	132.1362 075	144.9011 642	159.1336 800	175.0133 911
63	124.0928 060	136.1092 722	149.5236 933	164.5098 562	181.2637 928
64	127.5746 622	140.1717 308	154.2617 856	170.0338 773	187.7017 066
65	131.1261 554	144.3255 948	159.1183 303	175.7098 089	194.3327 578
66	134.7486 785	148.5729 207	164.0962 885	181.5418 286	201.1627 406
67	138.4436 521	152.9158 114	169.1986 957	187.5342 289	208.1976 228
68	142.2125 251	157.3564 171	174.4286 631	193.6914 202	215.4435 515
69	146.0567 756	161.8969 365	179.7893 797	200.0179 343	222.9068 580
70	149.9779 111	166.5396 176	185.2841 142	206.5184 275	230.5940 637
71	153.9774 694	171.2867 590	190.9162 171	213.1976 842	238.5118 856
72	158.0570 188	176.1407 111	196.6891 225	220.0606 205	246.6672 422
73	162.2181 591	181.1038 771	202.6063 506	227.1122 876	255.0672 595
74	166.4625 223	186.1787 143	208.6715 093	234.3578 755	263.7192 773
75	170.7917 728	191.3677 354	214.8882 970	241.8027 171	272.6308 556
76	175.2076 082	196.6735 094	221.2605 045	249.4522 918	281.8097 813
77	179.7117 604	202.0986 634	227.7920 171	257.3122 298	291.2640 747
78	184.3059 956	207.6458 833	234.4868 175	265.3883 162	301.0019 969
79	188.9921 155	213.3179 157	241.3489 880	273.6864 948	311.0320 568
80	193.7719 578	219.1175 688	248.3827 126	282.2128 735	321.3630 185
81	198.6473 970	225.0477 141	255.5922 805	290.9737 275	332.0039 091
82	203.6203 449	231.1112 876	262.9820 875	299.9755 050	342.9640 264
83	208.6927 518	237.3112 916	270.5566 397	309.2248 314	354.2529 472
84	213.8666 068	243.6507 957	278.3205 557	318.7285 142	365.8805 356
85	219.1439 390	250.1329 386	286.2785 695	328.4935 484	377.8569 517
86	224.5268 178	256.7609 297	294.4355 338	338.5271 209	390.1926 602
87	230.0173 541	263.5380 506	302.7964 221	348.8366 168	402.8984 400
88	235.6177 012	270.4676 567	311.3663 327	359.4296 237	415.9853 932
89	241.3300 552	277.5531 790	320.1504 910	370.3139 384	429.4649 550
90	247.1566 563	284.7981 255	329.1542 533	381.4975 717	443.3489 037
91	253.0997 894	292.2060 834	338.3831 096	392.9887 549	457.6493 708
92	259.1617 852	299.7807 202	347.8426 873	404.7959 457	472.3788 519
93	265.3450 209	307.5257 865	357.5387 545	416.9278 342	487.5502 174
94	271.6519 214	315.4451 166	367.4772 234	429.3933 496	503.1767 240
95	278.0849 598	323.5426 318	377.6641 540	442.2016 667	519.2720 257
96	284.6466 590	331.8223 410	388.1057 578	455.3622 126	535.8501 865
97	291.3395 922	340.2883 437	398.8084 018	468.8846 734	552.9256 920
98	298.1663 840	348.9448 314	409.7786 118	482.7790 019	570.5134 628
99	305.1297 117	357.7960 901	421.0230 771	497.0554 245	588.6288 667
100	312.2323 059	366.8465 021	432.5486 540	511.7244 487	607.2877 327

AMOUNT OF ANNUITY $[(1 + i)^n - 1]/i$ (Continued)

Periods	Rate i				
n	.035 ($3\frac{1}{2}$ %)	.04 (4 %)	.045 ($4\frac{1}{2}$ %)	.05 (5 %)	.055 ($5\frac{1}{2}$ %)
1	1.0000 000	1.0000 000	1.0000 000	1.0000 000	1.0000 000
2	2.0350 000	2.0400 000	2.0450 000	2.0500 000	2.0550 000
3	3.1062 250	3.1216 000	3.1370 250	3.1525 000	3.1680 250
4	4.2149 429	4.2464 640	4.2781 911	4.3101 250	4.3422 664
5	5.3624 659	5.4163 226	5.4707 097	5.5256 313	5.5810 910
6	6.5501 522	6.6329 755	6.7168 917	6.8019 128	6.8880 510
7	7.7794 075	7.8982 945	8.0191 518	8.1420 085	8.2668 938
8	9.0516 868	9.2142 263	9.3800 136	9.5491 089	9.7215 730
9	10.3684 958	10.5827 953	10.8021 142	11.0265 643	11.2562 595
10	11.7313 932	12.0061 071	12.2882 094	12.5778 925	12.8753 538
11	13.1419 919	13.4863 514	13.8411 788	14.2067 872	14.5834 982
12	14.6019 616	15.0258 055	15.4640 318	15.9171 265	16.3855 907
13	16.1130 303	16.6268 377	17.1599 133	17.7129 828	18.2867 981
14	17.6769 864	18.2919 112	18.9321 094	19.5986 320	20.2925 720
15	19.2956 809	20.0235 876	20.7840 543	21.5785 636	22.4086 635
16	20.9710 297	21.8245 311	22.7193 367	23.6574 918	24.6411 400
17	22.7050 157	23.6975 124	24.7417 069	25.8403 664	26.9964 027
18	24.4996 913	25.6454 129	26.8550 837	28.1323 847	29.4812 048
19	26.3571 805	27.6712 294	29.0635 625	30.5390 039	32.1026 711
20	28.2796 818	29.7780 786	31.3714 228	33.0659 541	34.8683 180
21	30.2694 707	31.9692 017	33.7831 368	35.7192 518	37.7860 755
22	32.3289 022	34.2479 698	36.3033 780	38.5052 144	40.8643 097
23	34.4604 137	36.6178 886	38.9370 300	41.4304 751	44.1118 467
24	36.6665 282	39.0826 041	41.6891 963	44.5019 989	47.5379 983
25	38.9498 567	41.6459 083	44.5652 101	47.7270 988	51.1525 882
26	41.3131 017	44.3117 446	47.5706 446	51.1134 538	54.9659 805
27	43.7590 602	47.0842 144	50.7113 236	54.6691 264	58.9891 094
28	46.2906 273	49.9675 830	53.9933 332	58.4025 828	63.2335 105
29	48.9107 993	52.9662 863	57.4230 332	62.3227 119	67.7113 535
30	51.6226 773	56.0849 378	61.0070 697	66.4388 475	72.4354 780
31	54.4294 710	59.3283 353	64.7523 878	70.7607 899	77.4194 293
32	57.3345 025	62.7014 687	68.6662 452	75.2988 294	82.6774 979
33	60.3412 101	66.2095 274	72.7562 263	80.0637 708	88.2247 603
34	63.4531 524	69.8579 085	77.0302 565	85.0669 594	94.0771 221
35	66.6740 127	73.6522 249	81.4966 180	90.3203 074	100.2513 638
36	70.0076 032	77.5983 138	86.1639 658	95.8363 227	106.7651 888
37	73.4578 693	81.7022 464	91.0413 443	101.6281 389	113.6372 742
38	77.0288 947	85.9703 363	96.1382 048	107.7095 458	120.8873 242
39	80.7249 060	90.4091 497	101.4644 240	114.0950 231	128.5361 271
40	84.5502 777	95.0255 157	107.0303 231	120.7997 742	136.6056 141
41	88.5095 375	99.8265 363	112.8466 876	127.8397 630	145.1189 228
42	92.6073 713	104.8195 978	118.9247 885	135.2317 511	154.1004 636
43	96.8486 293	110.0123 817	125.2764 040	142.9933 387	163.5759 891
44	101.2383 313	115.4128 770	131.9138 422	151.1430 056	173.5726 685
45	105.7816 729	121.0293 920	138.8499 651	159.7001 559	184.1191 653
46	110.4840 314	126.8705 677	146.0982 135	168.6851 637	195.2457 194
47	115.3509 725	132.9453 904	153.6726 331	178.1194 218	206.9842 339
48	120.3882 566	139.2632 060	161.5879 016	188.0253 929	219.3683 668
49	125.6018 456	145.8337 343	169.8593 572	198.4266 626	232.4336 270
50	130.9979 102	152.6670 837	178.5030 283	209.3479 957	246.2174 764

AMOUNT OF ANNUITY $[(1 + i)^n - 1]/i$ (Continued)

Periods	Rate i				
n	.06 (6 %)	.065 (6½ %)	.07 (7 %)	.075 (7½ %)	.08 (8 %)
1	1.0000 000	1.0000 000	1.0000 000	1.0000 000	1.0000 000
2	2.0600 000	2.0650 000	2.0700 000	2.0750 000	2.0800 000
3	3.1836 000	3.1992 250	3.2149 000	3.2306 250	3.2464 000
4	4.3746 160	4.4071 746	4.4399 430	4.4729 219	4.5061 120
5	5.6370 930	5.6936 410	5.7507 390	5.8083 910	5.8666 010
6	6.9753 185	7.0637 276	7.1532 907	7.2440 203	7.3359 290
7	8.3938 376	8.5228 699	8.6540 211	8.7873 219	8.9228 034
8	9.8974 679	10.0768 565	10.2598 026	10.4463 710	10.6366 276
9	11.4913 160	11.7318 522	11.9779 887	12.2298 488	12.4875 578
10	13.1807 949	13.4944 225	13.8164 480	14.1470 875	14.4865 625
11	14.9716 426	15.3715 600	15.7835 993	16.2081 191	16.6454 875
12	16.8699 412	17.3707 114	17.8884 513	18.4237 280	18.9771 265
13	18.8821 377	19.4998 076	20.1406 429	20.8055 076	21.4952 966
14	21.0150 659	21.7672 951	22.5504 879	23.3659 207	24.2149 203
15	23.2759 699	24.1821 693	25.1290 220	26.1183 647	27.1521 139
16	25.6725 281	26.7540 103	27.8880 536	29.0772 421	30.3242 830
17	28.2128 798	29.4930 210	30.8402 173	32.2580 352	33.7502 257
18	30.9056 525	32.4100 674	33.9990 325	35.6773 879	37.4502 437
19	33.7599 917	35.5167 218	37.3789 648	39.3531 919	41.4462 632
20	36.7855 912	38.8253 087	40.9954 923	43.3046 813	45.7619 643
21	39.9927 267	42.3489 537	44.8651 768	47.5525 324	50.4229 214
22	43.3922 903	46.1016 357	49.0057 392	52.1189 724	55.4567 552
23	46.9958 277	50.0982 420	53.4361 409	57.0278 953	60.8932 956
24	50.8155 774	54.3546 278	58.1766 708	62.3049 874	66.7647 592
25	54.8645 120	58.8876 786	63.2490 377	67.9778 615	73.1059 400
26	59.1563 827	63.7153 777	68.6764 704	74.0762 011	79.9544 151
27	63.7057 657	68.8568 772	74.4838 233	80.6319 162	87.3507 684
28	68.5281 116	74.3325 743	80.6976 909	87.6793 099	95.3388 298
29	73.6397 983	80.1641 916	87.3465 293	95.2552 582	103.9659 362
30	79.0581 862	86.3748 640	94.4607 863	103.3994 025	113.2832 111
31	84.8016 774	92.9892 302	102.0730 414	112.1543 577	123.3458 680
32	90.8897 780	100.0335 302	110.2181 543	121.5659 345	134.2135 374
33	97.3431 647	107.5357 096	118.9334 251	131.6833 796	145.9506 204
34	104.1837 546	115.5255 308	128.2587 648	142.5596 331	158.6266 701
35	111.4347 799	124.0346 903	138.2368 784	154.2516 056	172.3168 037
36	119.1208 667	133.1069 451	148.9134 598	166.8204 760	187.1021 480
37	127.2681 187	142.7482 466	160.3374 020	180.3320 117	203.0703 198
38	135.9042 058	153.0268 826	172.5610 202	194.8569 126	220.3159 454
39	145.0584 581	163.9736 300	185.6402 916	210.4711 810	238.9412 210
40	154.7619 656	175.6319 159	199.6351 120	227.2565 196	259.0565 187
41	165.0476 836	188.0479 904	214.6095 698	245.3007 586	280.7810 402
42	175.9505 446	201.2711 098	230.6322 397	264.6983 155	304.2435 234
43	187.5075 772	215.3537 320	247.7764 965	285.5506 891	329.5830 053
44	199.7580 319	230.3517 245	266.1208 513	307.9669 908	356.9496 457
45	212.7435 138	246.3245 866	285.7493 108	332.0645 151	386.5056 174
46	226.5081 246	263.3356 848	306.7517 626	357.9693 537	418.4260 668
47	241.0986 121	281.4525 043	329.2243 860	385.8170 553	452.9001 521
48	256.5645 288	300.7469 170	353.2700 930	415.7533 344	490.1321 643
49	272.9584 006	321.2954 666	378.9989 995	447.9348 345	530.3427 374
50	290.3359 046	343.1796 720	406.5289 295	482.5299 471	573.7701 564

PRESENT VALUE OF ANNUITY $[1 - (1 + i)^{-n}]/i$

The following table gives the present value of an annuity of unit value per period for a term of *n* periods at rate of interest *i* per period; usually indicated as $a_{\overline{n}|i}$.

Periods	Rate *i*				
n	.0025 ($\frac{1}{4}$ %)	.004167 ($\frac{1}{12}$ %)	.005 ($\frac{1}{2}$ %)	.005833 ($\frac{7}{12}$ %)	.0075 ($\frac{3}{4}$ %)
1	0.9975 0623	0.9958 5062	0.9950 2488	0.9942 0050	0.9925 5583
2	1.9925 2492	1.9875 6908	1.9850 9938	1.9826 3513	1.9777 2291
3	2.9850 6227	2.9751 7253	2.9702 4814	2.9653 3732	2.9555 5624
4	3.9751 2446	3.9586 7804	3.9504 9566	3.9423 4034	3.9261 1041
5	4.9627 1766	4.9381 0261	4.9258 6633	4.9136 7722	4.8894 3961
6	5.9478 4804	5.9134 6318	5.8963 8441	5.8793 8083	5.8455 9763
7	6.9305 2174	6.8847 7661	6.8620 7404	6.8394 8384	6.7946 3785
8	7.9107 4487	7.8520 5970	7.8229 5924	7.7940 1874	7.7366 1325
9	8.8885 2357	8.8153 2916	8.7790 6392	8.7430 1780	8.6715 7642
10	9.8638 6391	9.7746 0165	9.7304 1186	9.6865 1314	9.5995 7958
11	10.8367 7198	10.7298 9376	10.6770 2673	10.6245 3667	10.5206 7452
12	11.8072 5384	11.6812 2200	11.6189 3207	11.5571 2014	11.4349 1267
13	12.7753 1555	12.6286 0283	12.5561 5131	12.4842 9509	12.3423 4508
14	13.7409 6314	13.5720 5261	13.4887 0777	13.4060 9288	13.2430 2242
15	14.7042 0264	14.5115 8766	14.4166 2465	14.3225 4470	14.1369 9495
16	15.6650 4004	15.4472 2422	15.3399 2502	15.2336 8156	15.0243 1261
17	16.6234 8133	16.3789 7848	16.2586 3186	16.1395 3427	15.9050 2492
18	17.5795 3250	17.3068 6654	17.1727 6802	17.0401 3350	16.7791 8107
19	18.5331 9950	18.2309 0443	18.0823 5624	17.9355 0969	17.6468 2984
20	19.4844 8828	19.1511 0815	18.9874 1915	18.8256 9315	18.5080 1969
21	20.4334 0477	20.0674 9359	19.8879 7925	19.7107 1398	19.3627 9870
22	21.3799 5488	20.9800 7661	20.7840 5896	20.5906 0213	20.2112 1459
23	22.3241 4452	21.8888 7297	21.6756 8055	21.4653 8738	21.0533 1473
24	23.2659 7957	22.7938 9839	22.5628 6622	22.3350 9930	21.8891 4614
25	24.2054 6591	23.6951 6853	23.4456 3803	23.1997 6732	22.7187 5547
26	25.1426 0939	24.5926 9895	24.3240 1794	24.0594 2070	23.5421 8905
27	26.0774 1585	25.4865 0517	25.1980 2780	24.9140 8852	24.3594 9286
28	27.0098 9112	26.3766 0266	26.0676 8936	25.7637 9968	25.1707 1251
29	27.9400 4102	27.2630 0680	26.9330 2424	26.6085 8295	25.9758 9331
30	28.8678 7134	28.1457 3291	27.7940 5397	27.4484 6689	26.7750 8021
31	29.7933 8787	29.0247 9626	28.6507 9997	28.2834 7993	27.5683 1783
32	30.7165 9638	29.9002 1205	29.5032 8355	29.1136 5030	28.3556 5045
33	31.6375 0262	30.7719 9540	30.3515 2592	29.9390 0610	29.1371 2203
34	32.5561 1234	31.6401 6139	31.1955 4818	30.7595 7524	29.9127 7621
35	33.4724 3126	32.5047 2504	32.0353 7132	31.5753 8549	30.6826 5629
36	34.3864 6510	33.3657 0128	32.8710 1624	32.3864 6445	31.4468 0525
37	35.2982 1955	34.2231 0501	33.7025 0372	33.1928 3955	32.2052 6576
38	36.2077 0030	35.0769 5105	34.5298 5445	33.9945 3808	32.9580 8016
39	37.1149 1302	35.9272 5416	35.3530 8900	34.7915 8716	33.7052 9048
40	38.0198 6336	36.7740 2904	36.1722 2786	35.5840 1374	34.4469 3844
41	38.9225 5697	37.6172 9033	36.9872 9141	36.3718 4465	35.1830 6545
42	39.8229 9947	38.4570 5261	37.7982 9991	37.1551 0653	35.9137 1260
43	40.7211 9648	39.2933 3040	38.6052 7354	37.9338 2588	36.6389 2070
44	41.6171 5359	40.1261 3816	39.4082 3238	38.7080 2904	37.3587 3022
45	42.5108 7640	40.9554 9028	40.2071 9640	39.4777 4221	38.0731 8136
46	43.4023 7048	41.7814 0111	41.0021 8547	40.2429 9143	38.7823 1401
47	44.2916 4137	42.6038 8492	41.7932 1937	41.0038 0258	39.4861 6775
48	45.1786 9464	43.4229 5594	42.5803 1778	41.7602 0141	40.1847 8189
49	46.0635 3580	44.2386 2832	43.3635 0028	42.5122 1349	40.8781 9542
50	46.9461 7037	45.0509 1617	44.1427 8635	43.2598 6428	41.5664 4707

PRESENT VALUE OF ANNUITY $[1 - (1 + i)^{-n}]/i$ (Continued)

Periods	Rate i				
n	.0025 ($\frac{1}{4}$%)	.004167 ($\frac{1}{12}$%)	.005 ($\frac{1}{2}$%)	.005833 ($\frac{7}{12}$%)	.0075 ($\frac{3}{4}$%)
50	46.9461 7037	45.0509 1617	44.1427 8635	43.2598 6428	41.5664 4707
51	47.8266 0386	45.8598 3353	44.9181 9537	44.0031 7907	42.2495 7525
52	48.7048 4176	46.6653 9439	45.6897 4664	44.7421 8301	42.9276 1812
53	49.5808 8953	47.4676 1267	46.4574 5934	45.4769 0108	43.6006 1351
54	50.4547 5265	48.2665 0224	47.2213 5258	46.2073 5816	44.2685 9902
55	51.3264 3656	49.0620 7692	47.9814 4535	46.9335 7895	44.9316 1193
56	52.1959 4669	49.8543 5046	48.7377 5657	47.6555 8802	45.5896 8926
57	53.0632 8847	50.6433 3656	49.4903 0505	48.3734 0980	46.2428 6776
58	53.9284 6730	51.4290 4885	50.2391 0950	49.0870 6856	46.8911 8388
59	54.7914 8858	52.2115 0093	50.9841 8856	49.7965 8846	47.5346 7382
60	55.6523 5769	52.9907 0632	51.7255 6075	50.5019 9350	48.1733 7352
61	56.5110 7999	53.7666 7850	52.4632 4453	51.2033 0754	48.8073 1863
62	57.3676 6083	54.5394 3087	53.1972 5824	51.9005 5431	49.4365 4455
63	58.2221 0557	55.3089 7680	53.9276 2014	52.5937 5739	50.0610 8640
64	59.0744 1952	56.0753 2959	54.6543 4840	53.2829 4024	50.6809 7906
65	59.9246 0800	56.8385 0250	55.3774 6109	53.9681 2617	51.2962 5713
66	60.7726 7631	57.5985 0871	56.0969 7621	54.6493 3836	51.9069 5497
67	61.6186 2974	58.3553 6137	56.8129 1165	55.3265 9986	52.5131 0667
68	62.4624 7355	59.1090 7357	57.5252 8522	55.9999 3358	53.1147 4607
69	63.3042 1302	59.8596 5832	58.2341 1465	56.6693 6230	53.7119 0677
70	64.1438 5339	60.6071 2862	58.9394 1756	57.3349 0867	54.3046 2210
71	64.9813 9989	61.3514 9738	59.6412 1151	57.9965 9520	54.8929 2516
72	65.8168 5774	62.0927 7748	60.3395 1394	58.6544 4427	55.4768 4880
73	66.6502 3216	62.8309 8172	61.0343 4222	59.3084 7815	56.0564 2561
74	67.4815 2834	63.5661 2287	61.7257 1366	59.9587 1896	56.6316 8795
75	68.3107 5146	64.2982 1365	62.4136 4543	60.6051 8869	57.2026 6794
76	69.1379 0670	65.0272 6670	63.0981 5466	61.2479 0922	57.7693 9746
77	69.9629 9920	65.7532 9464	63.7792 5836	61.8869 0229	58.3319 0815
78	70.7860 3411	66.4763 1002	64.4569 7350	62.5221 8952	58.8902 3141
79	71.6070 1657	67.1963 2533	65.1313 1691	63.1537 9239	59.4443 9842
80	72.4259 5169	67.9133 5303	65.8023 0539	63.7817 3229	59.9944 4012
81	73.2428 4458	68.6274 0550	66.4699 5561	64.4060 3044	60.5403 8722
82	74.0577 0033	69.3384 9511	67.1342 8419	65.0267 0798	61.0822 7019
83	74.8705 2402	70.0466 3413	67.7953 0765	65.6437 8590	61.6201 1930
84	75.6813 2072	70.7518 3482	68.4530 4244	66.2572 8507	62.1539 6456
85	76.4900 9548	71.4541 0936	69.1075 0491	66.8672 2625	62.6838 3579
86	77.2968 5335	72.1534 6991	69.7587 1135	67.4736 3007	63.2097 6257
87	78.1015 9935	72.8499 2854	70.4066 7796	68.0765 1706	63.7317 7427
88	78.9043 3850	73.5434 9730	71.0514 2086	68.6759 0759	64.2499 0002
89	79.7050 7581	74.2341 8818	71.6929 5608	69.2718 2197	64.7641 6875
90	80.5038 1627	74.9220 1313	72.3312 9958	69.8642 8033	65.2746 0918
91	81.3005 6486	75.6069 8403	72.9664 6725	70.4533 0273	65.7812 4981
92	82.0953 2654	76.2891 1272	73.5984 7487	71.0389 0910	66.2841 1892
93	82.8881 0628	76.9684 1101	74.2273 3818	71.6211 1923	66.7832 4458
94	83.6789 0901	77.6448 9063	74.8530 7282	72.1999 5284	67.2786 5467
95	84.4677 3966	78.3185 6329	75.4756 9434	72.7754 2950	67.7703 7685
96	85.2546 0315	78.9894 4062	76.0952 1825	73.3475 6869	68.2584 3856
97	86.0395 0439	79.6575 3422	76.7116 5995	73.9163 8975	68.7428 6705
98	86.8224 4827	80.3228 5566	77.3250 3478	74.4819 1193	69.2236 8938
99	87.6034 3967	80.9854 1642	77.9353 5799	75.0441 5436	69.7009 3239
100	88.3824 8346	81.6452 2797	78.5426 4477	75.6031 3607	70.1746 2272

PRESENT VALUE OF ANNUITY $[1 - (1 + i)^{-n}]/i$ (Continued)

Periods	Rate i				
n	.01 (1%)	.01125 ($1\frac{1}{8}$%)	.0125 ($1\frac{1}{4}$%)	.015 ($1\frac{1}{2}$%)	.0175 ($1\frac{3}{4}$%)
1	0.9900 9901	0.9888 7515	0.9876 5432	0.9852 2167	0.9828 0098
2	1.9703 9506	1.9667 4923	1.9631 1538	1.9558 8342	1.9486 9875
3	2.9409 8521	2.9337 4460	2.9265 3371	2.9122 0042	2.8979 8403
4	3.9019 6555	3.8899 8230	3.8780 5798	3.8543 8465	3.8309 4254
5	4.8534 3124	4.8355 8200	4.8178 3504	4.7826 4497	4.7478 5508
6	5.7954 7647	5.7706 6205	5.7460 0992	5.6971 8717	5.6489 9762
7	6.7281 9453	6.6953 3948	6.6627 2585	6.5982 1396	6.5346 4139
8	7.6516 7775	7.6097 3002	7.5681 2429	7.4859 2508	7.4050 5297
9	8.5660 1758	8.5139 4810	8.4623 4498	8.3605 1732	8.2604 9432
10	9.4713 0453	9.4081 0690	9.3455 2591	9.2221 8455	9.1012 2291
11	10.3676 2825	10.2923 1832	10.2178 0337	10.0711 1779	9.9274 9181
12	11.2550 7747	11.1666 9302	11.0793 1197	10.9075 0521	10.7395 4969
13	12.1337 4007	12.0313 4044	11.9301 8466	11.7315 3222	11.5376 4097
14	13.0037 0304	12.8863 6880	12.7705 5275	12.5433 8150	12.3220 0587
15	13.8650 5252	13.7318 8509	13.6005 4592	13.3432 3301	13.0928 8046
16	14.7178 7378	14.5679 9514	14.4202 9227	14.1312 6405	13.8504 9677
17	15.5622 5127	15.3948 0360	15.2299 1829	14.9076 4931	14.5950 8282
18	16.3982 6858	16.2124 1395	16.0295 4893	15.6725 6089	15.3268 6272
19	17.2260 0850	17.0209 2850	16.8193 0759	16.4261 6837	16.0460 5673
20	18.0455 5297	17.8204 4845	17.5993 1613	17.1686 3879	16.7528 8130
21	18.8569 8313	18.6110 7387	18.3696 9495	17.9001 3673	17.4475 4919
22	19.6603 7934	19.3929 0371	19.1305 6291	18.6208 2437	18.1302 6948
23	20.4558 2113	20.1660 3580	19.8820 3744	19.3308 6145	18.8012 4764
24	21.2433 8726	20.9305 6693	20.6242 3451	20.0304 0537	19.4606 8565
25	22.0231 5570	21.6865 9276	21.3572 6865	20.7196 1120	20.1087 8196
26	22.7952 0366	22.4342 0792	22.0812 5299	21.3986 3172	20.7547 3166
27	23.5596 0759	23.1735 0598	22.7962 9925	22.0676 1746	21.3717 2644
28	24.3164 4316	23.9045 7946	23.5025 1778	22.7267 1671	21.9869 5474
29	25.0657 8530	24.6275 1986	24.2000 1756	23.3760 7558	22.5916 0171
30	25.8077 0822	25.3424 1766	24.8889 0623	24.0158 3801	23.1858 4934
31	26.5422 8537	26.0493 6233	25.5692 9010	24.6461 4582	23.7698 7650
32	27.2695 8947	26.7484 4236	26.2412 7418	25.2671 3874	24.3438 5897
33	27.9896 9255	27.4397 4522	26.9049 6215	25.8789 5442	24.9079 6951
34	28.7026 6589	28.1233 5745	27.5604 5644	26.4817 2849	25.4623 7789
35	29.4085 8009	28.7993 6460	28.2078 5822	27.0755 9458	26.0072 5100
36	30.1075 0504	29.4678 5127	28.8472 6737	27.6606 8431	26.5427 5283
37	30.7995 0994	30.1289 0114	29.4787 8259	28.2371 2740	27.0690 4455
38	31.4846 6330	30.7825 9692	30.1025 0133	28.8050 5163	27.5862 8457
39	32.1630 3298	31.4290 2044	30.7185 1983	29.3645 8288	28.0946 2857
40	32.8346 8611	32.0682 5260	31.3269 3316	29.9158 4520	28.5942 2955
41	33.4996 8922	32.7003 7340	31.9278 3522	30.4589 6079	29.0852 3789
42	34.1581 0814	33.3254 6195	32.5213 1874	30.9940 5004	29.5678 0136
43	34.8100 0806	33.9435 9649	33.1074 7530	31.5212 3157	30.0420 6522
44	35.4554 5352	34.5548 5438	33.6863 9536	32.0406 2223	30.5081 7221
45	36.0945 0844	35.1593 1212	34.2581 6825	32.5523 3718	30.9662 6261
46	36.7272 3608	35.7570 4536	34.8228 8222	33.0564 8983	31.4164 7431
47	37.3536 9909	36.3481 2891	35.3806 2442	33.5531 9195	31.8589 4281
48	37.9739 5949	36.9326 3674	35.9314 8091	34.0425 5365	32.2938 0129
49	38.5880 7871	37.5106 4202	36.4755 3670	34.5246 8339	32.7211 8063
50	39.1961 1753	38.0822 1708	37.0128 7575	34.9996 8807	33.1412 0946

PRESENT VALUE OF ANNUITY $[1 - (1 + i)^{-n}]/i$ (Continued)

Periods	Rate i				
n	.01 (1%)	.01125 ($1\frac{1}{8}$%)	.0125 ($1\frac{1}{4}$%)	.015 ($1\frac{1}{2}$%)	.0175 ($1\frac{3}{4}$%)
50	39.1961 1753	38.0822 1708	37.0128 7575	34.9996 8807	33.1412 0946
51	39.7981 3617	38.6474 3345	37.5435 8099	35.4676 7298	33.5540 1421
52	40.3941 9423	39.2063 6188	38.0677 3431	35.9287 4185	33.9597 1913
53	40.9843 5072	39.7590 7232	38.5854 1660	36.3829 9690	34.3584 4632
54	41.5686 6408	40.3056 3394	39.0967 0776	36.8305 3882	34.7503 1579
55	42.1471 9216	40.8461 1514	39.6016 8667	37.2714 6681	35.1354 4550
56	42.7199 9224	41.3805 8358	40.1004 3128	37.7058 7863	35.5139 5135
57	43.2871 2102	41.9091 0613	40.5930 1855	38.1338 7058	35.8859 4727
58	43.8486 3468	42.4317 4896	41.0795 2449	38.5555 3751	36.2515 4523
59	44.4045 8879	42.9485 7746	41.5600 2419	38.9709 7292	36.6108 5526
60	44.9550 3841	43.4596 5633	42.0345 9179	39.3802 6889	36.9639 8552
61	45.5000 3803	43.9650 4952	42.5033 0054	39.7835 1614	37.3110 4228
62	46.0396 4161	44.4648 2029	42.9662 2275	40.1808 0408	37.6521 3000
63	46.5739 0258	44.9590 3119	43.4234 2988	40.5722 2077	37.9873 5135
64	47.1028 7385	45.4477 4407	43.8749 9247	40.9578 5298	38.3168 0723
65	47.6266 0777	45.9310 2009	44.3209 8022	41.3377 8618	38.6405 9678
66	48.1451 5621	46.4089 1975	44.7614 6195	41.7121 0461	38.9588 1748
67	48.6585 7050	46.8815 0284	45.1965 0563	42.0808 9125	39.2715 6509
68	49.1669 0149	47.3488 2852	45.6261 7840	42.4442 2783	39.5789 3375
69	49.6701 9949	47.8109 5527	46.0505 4656	42.8021 9490	39.8810 1597
70	50.1685 1435	48.2679 4094	46.4696 7562	43.1548 7183	40.1779 0267
71	50.6618 9539	48.7198 4270	46.8836 3024	43.5023 3678	40.4696 8321
72	51.1503 9148	49.1667 1714	47.2924 7431	43.8446 6677	40.7564 4542
73	51.6340 5097	49.6086 2016	47.6962 7093	44.1819 3771	41.0382 7560
74	52.1129 2175	50.0456 0708	48.0950 8240	44.5142 2434	41.3152 5857
75	52.5870 5124	50.4777 3259	48.4889 7027	44.8416 0034	41.5874 7771
76	53.0564 8638	50.9050 5077	48.8779 9533	45.1641 3826	41.8550 1495
77	53.5212 7364	51.3276 1510	49.2622 1761	45.4819 0962	42.1179 5081
78	53.9814 5905	51.7454 7847	49.6416 9640	45.7949 8485	42.3763 6443
79	54.4370 8817	52.1586 9317	50.0164 9027	46.1034 3335	42.6303 3359
80	54.8882 0611	52.5673 1092	50.3866 5706	46.4073 2349	42.8799 3474
81	55.3348 5753	52.9713 8286	50.7522 5389	46.7067 2265	43.1252 4298
82	55.7770 8666	53.3709 5957	51.1133 3717	47.0016 9720	43.3663 3217
83	56.2149 3729	53.7660 9104	51.4699 6264	47.2923 1251	43.6032 7486
84	56.6484 5276	54.1568 2674	51.8221 8532	47.5786 3301	43.8361 4237
85	57.0776 7600	54.5432 1557	52.1700 5958	47.8607 2218	44.0650 0479
86	57.5026 4951	54.9253 0588	52.5136 3909	48.1386 4254	44.2899 3099
87	57.9234 1535	55.3031 4549	52.8529 7688	48.4124 5571	44.5109 8869
88	58.3400 1520	55.6767 8169	53.1881 2531	48.6822 2237	44.7282 4441
89	58.7524 9030	56.0462 6126	53.5191 3611	48.9480 0234	44.9417 6355
90	59.1608 8148	56.4116 3041	53.8460 6035	49.2098 5452	45.1516 1037
91	59.5652 2919	56.7729 3490	54.1689 4850	49.4678 3696	45.3578 4803
92	59.9655 7346	57.1302 1992	54.4878 5037	49.7220 0686	45.5605 3860
93	60.3619 5392	57.4835 3021	54.8028 1518	49.9724 2055	45.7597 4310
94	60.7544 0982	57.8329 0997	55.1138 9154	50.2191 3355	45.9555 2147
95	61.1429 8002	58.1784 0294	55.4211 2744	50.4622 0054	46.1479 3265
96	61.5277 0299	58.5200 5235	55.7245 7031	50.7016 7541	46.3370 3455
97	61.9086 1682	58.8579 0096	56.0242 6698	50.9376 1124	46.5228 8408
98	62.2857 5923	59.1919 9106	56.3202 6368	51.1700 6034	46.7055 3718
99	62.6591 6755	59.5223 6446	56.6126 0610	51.3990 7422	46.8850 4882
100	63.0288 7877	59.8490 6251	56.9013 3936	51.6247 0367	47.0614 7304

PRESENT VALUE OF ANNUITY $[1 - (1 + i)^{-n}]/i$ (Continued)

Periods	Rate i				
n	.02 (2%)	.0225 (2¼%)	.025 (2½%)	.0275 (2¾%)	.03 (3%)
1	0.9803 9216	0.9779 9511	0.9756 0976	0.9732 3601	0.9708 7379
2	1.9415 6094	1.9344 6955	1.9274 2415	1.9204 2434	1.9134 6970
3	2.8838 8327	2.8698 9687	2.8560 2356	2.8422 6213	2.8286 1135
4	3.8077 2870	3.7847 4021	3.7619 7421	3.7394 2787	3.7170 9840
5	4.7134 5951	4.6794 5253	4.6458 2850	4.6125 8186	4.5797 0719
6	5.6014 3089	5.5544 7680	5.5081 2536	5.4623 6678	5.4171 9144
7	6.4719 9107	6.4102 4626	6.3493 9060	6.2894 0806	6.2302 8296
8	7.3254 8144	7.2471 8461	7.1701 3717	7.0943 1441	7.0196 9219
9	8.1622 3671	8.0657 0622	7.9708 6553	7.8776 7826	7.7861 0892
10	8.9825 8501	8.8662 1635	8.7520 6393	8.6400 7616	8.5302 0284
11	9.7868 4805	9.6491 1134	9.5142 0871	9.3820 6926	9.2526 2411
12	10.5753 4122	10.4147 7882	10.2577 6460	10.1042 0366	9.9540 0399
13	11.3483 7375	11.1635 9787	10.9831 8497	10.8070 1086	10.6349 5533
14	12.1062 4877	11.8959 3924	11.6909 1217	11.4910 0814	11.2960 7314
15	12.8492 6350	12.6121 6551	12.3813 7773	12.1566 9892	11.9379 3509
16	13.5777 0931	13.3126 3131	13.0550 0266	12.8045 7315	12.5611 0203
17	14.2918 7188	13.9976 8343	13.7121 9772	13.4351 0769	13.1661 1847
18	14.9920 3125	14.6676 6106	14.3533 6363	14.0487 6661	13.7535 1308
19	15.6784 6201	15.3228 9590	14.9788 9134	14.6460 0157	14.3237 9911
20	16.3514 3334	15.9637 **1237**	15.5891 6229	15.2272 5213	14.8774 7486
21	17.0112 0916	16.5904 **2775**	16.1845 4857	15.7929 4612	15.4150 2414
22	17.6580 4820	17.2033 5232	16.7654 1324	16.3434 9987	15.9369 1664
23	18.2922 0412	17.8027 8955	17.3321 1048	16.8793 1861	16.4436 0839
24	18.9139 2560	18.3890 3624	17.8849 8583	17.4007 9670	16.9355 4212
25	19.5234 5647	18.9623 8263	18.4243 7642	17.9083 1795	17.4131 4769
26	20.1210 3576	19.5231 1260	18.9596 1114	18.4022 5592	17.8768 4242
27	20.7068 9780	20.0715 0376	19.4640 1087	18.8829 7413	18.3270 3147
28	21.2812 7236	20.6078 2764	19.9648 8866	19.3508 2640	18.7641 0823
29	21.8443 8466	21.1323 4977	20.4535 4991	19.8061 5708	19.1884 5459
30	22.3964 5555	21.6453 2985	20.9302 9259	20.2493 0130	19.6004 4135
31	22.9377 0152	22.1470 2186	21.3954 0741	20.6685 8520	20.0004 2849
32	23.4683 3482	22.6376 7419	21.8491 7796	21.1003 2623	20.3887 6553
33	23.9885 6355	23.1175 2977	22.2918 8994	21.5088 3332	20.7657 9178
34	24.4985 9172	23.5868 2618	22.7237 8628	21.9064 0712	21.1318 3668
35	24.9986 1933	24.0457 9577	23.1451 5734	22.2933 4026	21.4872 2007
36	25.4888 4248	24.4946 6579	23.5562 5107	22.6699 1753	21.8322 5250
37	25.9694 5341	24.9336 5848	23.9573 1812	23.0364 1609	22.1672 3544
38	26.4406 4060	25.3629 9118	24.3486 0304	23.3931 0568	22.4924 6159
39	26.9025 8883	25.7828 7646	24.7303 4443	23.7402 4884	22.8082 1513
40	27.3554 7924	26.1935 2221	25.1027 7505	24.0781 0106	23.1147 7197
41	27.7994 8945	26.5951 3174	25.4661 2200	24.4069 1101	23.4123 9997
42	28.2347 9358	26.9879 0390	25.8206 0683	24.7269 2069	23.7013 5920
43	28.6615 6233	27.3720 3316	26.1664 4569	25.0383 6563	23.9819 0213
44	29.0799 6307	27.7477 0969	26.5038 4945	25.3414 7507	24.2542 7392
45	29.4901 5987	28.1151 1950	26.8330 2386	25.6364 7209	24.5187 1254
46	29.8923 1360	28.4744 4450	27.1541 6962	25.9235 7381	24.7754 4907
47	30.2865 8196	28.8258 6259	27.4674 8255	26.2029 9154	25.0247 0783
48	30.6731 1957	29.1695 4777	27.7731 5371	26.4749 3094	25.2667 0664
49	31.0520 7801	29.5056 7019	28.0713 6947	26.7395 9215	25.5016 5693
50	31.4236 0589	29.8343 9627	28.3623 1168	26.9971 6998	25.7297 6401

PRESENT VALUE OF ANNUITY $[1 - (1 + i)^{-n}]/i$ (Continued)

Periods	Rate i				
n	.02 (2%)	.0225 (2¼%)	.025 (2½%)	.0275 (2¾%)	.03 (3%)
50	31.4236 0589	29.8343 9627	28.3623 1168	26.9971 6998	25.7297 6401
51	31.7878 4892	30.1558 8877	28.6461 5774	27.2478 5400	25.9512 2719
52	32.1449 4992	30.4703 0687	28.9230 8072	27.4918 2871	26.1662 3999
53	32.4950 4894	30.7778 0623	29.1932 4948	27.7292 7368	26.3749 9028
54	32.8382 8327	31.0785 3910	29.4568 2876	27.9603 6368	26.5776 6047
55	33.1747 8752	31.3726 5438	29.7139 7928	28.1852 6879	26.7744 2764
56	33.5046 9365	31.6602 9768	29.9648 5784	28.4041 5454	26.9654 6373
57	33.8281 3103	31.9416 1142	30.2096 1740	28.6171 8203	27.1509 3566
58	34.1452 2650	32.2167 3489	30.4484 0722	28.8245 0806	27.3310 0549
59	34.4561 0441	32.4858 0429	30.6813 7290	29.0262 8522	27.5058 3058
60	34.7608 8668	32.7489 5285	30.9086 5649	29.2226 6201	27.6755 6367
61	35.0596 9282	33.0063 1086	31.1303 9657	29.4137 8293	27.8403 5307
62	35.3526 4002	33.2580 0573	31.3467 2836	29.5997 8879	28.0003 4279
63	35.6398 4316	33.5041 6208	31.5577 8377	29.7808 1634	28.1556 7261
64	35.9214 1486	33.7449 0179	31.7636 9148	29.9569 9887	28.3064 7826
65	36.1974 6555	33.9803 4405	31.9645 7705	30.1284 6605	28.4528 9152
66	36.4681 0348	34.2106 0543	32.1605 6298	30.2953 4409	28.5950 4031
67	36.7334 3478	34.4357 9993	32.3517 6876	30.4577 5581	28.7330 4884
68	36.9935 6351	34.6560 3905	32.5383 1099	30.6158 2074	28.8670 3771
69	37.2485 9168	34.8714 3183	32.7203 0340	30.7696 5522	28.9971 2399
70	37.4986 1929	35.0820 8492	32.8978 5698	30.9193 7247	29.1234 2135
71	37.7437 4441	35.2881 0261	33.0710 7998	31.0651 8270	29.2460 4015
72	37.9840 6314	35.4895 8691	33.2400 7803	31.2068 9314	29.3650 8752
73	38.2196 6975	35.6866 3756	33.4049 5417	31.3449 0816	29.4806 6750
74	38.4506 5662	35.8793 5214	33.5658 0895	31.4792 2936	29.5928 8107
75	38.6771 1433	36.0678 2605	33.7227 4044	31.6099 5558	29.7018 2628
76	38.8991 3170	36.2521 5262	33.8758 4433	31.7371 8304	29.8075 9833
77	39.1167 9578	36.4324 2310	34.0252 1398	31.8610 0540	29.9102 8964
78	39.3301 9194	36.6087 2675	34.1709 4047	31.9815 1377	30.0099 8994
79	39.5394 0386	36.7811 5085	34.3131 1265	32.0987 9685	30.1067 8635
80	39.7445 1359	36.9497 8079	34.4518 1722	32.2129 4098	30.2007 6345
81	39.9456 0156	37.1147 0004	34.5871 3875	32.3240 3015	30.2920 0335
82	40.1427 4663	37.2759 9026	34.7191 5976	32.4321 4613	30.3805 8577
83	40.3360 2611	37.4337 3130	34.8479 6074	32.5373 6850	30.4665 8813
84	40.5255 1579	37.5880 0127	34.9736 2023	32.6397 7469	30.5500 8556
85	40.7112 8999	37.7388 7655	35.0962 1486	32.7394 4009	30.6311 5103
86	40.8934 2156	37.8864 3183	35.2158 1938	32.8364 3804	30.7098 5537
87	41.0719 8192	38.0307 4018	35.3325 0671	32.9308 3994	30.7862 6735
88	41.2470 4110	38.1718 7304	35.4463 4801	33.0227 1527	30.8604 5374
89	41.4186 6774	38.3099 0028	35.5574 1269	33.1121 3165	30.9324 7936
90	41.5869 2916	38.4448 9025	35.6657 6848	33.1991 5489	31.0024 0714
91	41.7518 9133	38.5769 0978	35.7714 8144	33.2838 4905	31.0702 9820
92	41.9136 1895	38.7060 2423	35.8746 1604	33.3662 7644	31.1362 1184
93	42.0721 7545	38.8322 9754	35.9752 3516	33.4464 9776	31.2002 0567
94	42.2276 2299	38.9557 9221	36.0734 0016	33.5245 7202	31.2623 3560
95	42.3800 2254	39.0765 6940	36.1691 7089	33.6005 5671	31.3226 5592
96	42.5294 3386	39.1946 8890	36.2626 0574	33.6745 0775	31.3812 1934
97	42.6759 1555	39.3102 0920	36.3537 6170	33.7464 7956	31.4380 7703
98	42.8195 2505	39.4231 8748	36.4426 9434	33.8165 2512	31.4932 7867
99	42.9603 1867	39.5336 7968	36.5294 5790	33.8846 9598	31.5468 7250
100	43.0983 5164	39.6417 4052	36.6141 0526	33.9510 4232	31.5989 0534

PRESENT VALUE OF ANNUITY $[1 - (1 + i)^{-n}]/i$ (Continued)

Periods	Rate i				
n	.035 ($3\frac{1}{2}\%$)	.04 (4%)	.045 ($4\frac{1}{2}\%$)	.05 (5%)	.055 ($5\frac{1}{2}\%$)
1	0.9661 8357	0.9615 3846	0.9569 3780	0.9523 8095	0.9478 6730
2	1.8996 9428	1.8860 9467	1.8726 6775	1.8594 1043	1.8463 1971
3	2.8016 3698	2.7750 9103	2.7489 6435	2.7232 4803	2.6979 3338
4	3.6730 7921	3.6298 9522	3.5875 2570	3.5459 5050	3.5051 5012
5	4.5150 5238	4.4518 2233	4.3899 7674	4.3294 7667	4.2702 8448
6	5.3285 5302	5.2421 3686	5.1578 7248	5.0756 9207	4.9955 3031
7	6.1145 4398	6.0020 5467	5.8927 0094	5.7863 7340	5.6829 6712
8	6.8739 5554	6.7327 4487	6.5958 8607	6.4632 1276	6.3345 6599
9	7.6076 8651	7.4353 3161	7.2687 9050	7.1078 2168	6.9521 9525
10	8.3166 0532	8.1108 9578	7.9127 1818	7.7217 3493	7.5376 2583
11	9.0015 5104	8.7604 7671	8.5289 1692	8.3064 1422	8.0925 3633
12	9.6633 3433	9.3850 7376	9.1185 8078	8.8632 5164	8.6185 1785
13	10.3027 3849	9.9856 4785	9.6828 5242	9.3935 7299	9.1170 7853
14	10.9205 2028	10.5631 2293	10.2228 2528	9.8986 4094	9.5896 4790
15	11.5174 1090	11.1183 8743	10.7395 4573	10.3796 5804	10.0375 8094
16	12.0941 1681	11.6522 9561	11.2340 1505	10.8377 6956	10.4621 6203
17	12.6513 2059	12.1656 6885	11.7071 9143	11.2740 6625	10.8646 0856
18	13.1896 8173	12.6592 9697	12.1599 9180	11.6895 8690	11.2460 7447
19	13.7098 3742	13.1339 3940	12.5932 9359	12.0853 2086	11.6076 5352
20	14.2124 0330	13.5903 2634	13.0079 3645	12.4622 1034	11.9503 8248
21	14.6979 7420	14.0291 5995	13.4047 2388	12.8211 5271	12.2752 4406
22	15.1671 2484	14.4511 1533	13.7844 2476	13.1630 0258	12.5831 6973
23	15.6204 1047	14.8568 4167	14.1477 7489	13.4885 7388	12.8750 4239
24	16.0583 6760	15.2469 6314	14.4954 7837	13.7986 4179	13.1516 9895
25	16.4815 1459	15.6220 7994	14.8282 0896	14.0939 4457	13.4139 3266
26	16.8903 5226	15.9827 6918	15.1466 1145	14.3751 8530	13.6624 9541
27	17.2853 6451	16.3295 8575	15.4513 0282	14.6430 3362	13.8980 9991
28	17.6670 1885	16.6630 6322	15.7428 7351	14.8981 2726	14.1214 2172
29	18.0357 6700	16.9837 1463	16.0218 8853	15.1410 7358	14.3331 0116
30	18.3920 4541	17.2920 3330	16.2888 8854	15.3724 5103	14.5337 4517
31	18.7362 7576	17.5884 9356	16.5443 9095	15.5928 1050	14.7239 2907
32	19.0688 6547	17.8735 5150	16.7888 9086	15.8026 7667	14.9041 9817
33	19.3902 0818	18.1476 4567	17.0228 6207	16.0025 4921	15.0750 6936
34	19.7006 8423	18.4111 9776	17.2467 5796	16.1929 0401	15.2370 3257
35	20.0006 6110	18.6646 1323	17.4610 1240	16.3741 9429	15.3905 5220
36	20.2904 9381	18.9082 8195	17.6660 4058	16.5468 5171	15.5360 6843
37	20.5705 2542	19.1425 7880	17.8622 3979	16.7112 8734	15.6739 9851
38	20.8410 8736	19.3678 6423	18.0499 9023	16.8678 9271	15.8047 3793
39	21.1024 9987	19.5844 8484	18.2296 5572	17.0170 4067	15.9286 6154
40	21.3550 7234	19.7927 7388	18.4015 8442	17.1590 8635	16.0461 2469
41	21.5991 0371	19.9930 5181	18.5661 0949	17.2943 6796	16.1574 6416
42	21.8348 8281	20.1856 2674	18.7235 4975	17.4232 0758	16.2629 9920
43	22.0626 8870	20.3707 9494	18.8742 1029	17.5459 1198	16.3630 3242
44	22.2827 9102	20.5488 4129	19.0183 8305	17.6627 7331	16.4578 5063
45	22.4954 5026	20.7200 3970	19.1563 4742	17.7740 6982	16.5477 2572
46	22.7009 1813	20.8846 5356	19.2883 7074	17.8800 6650	16.6329 1537
47	22.8994 3780	21.0429 3612	19.4147 0884	17.9810 1571	16.7136 6386
48	23.0912 4425	21.1951 3088	19.5356 0654	18.0771 5782	16.7902 0271
49	23.2765 6450	21.3414 7200	19.6512 9813	18.1687 2173	16.8627 5139
50	23.4556 1787	21.4821 8462	19.7620 0778	18.2559 2546	16.9315 1790

PRESENT VALUE OF ANNUITY $[1 - (1 + i)^{-n}]/i$ (Continued)

Periods	Rate i				
n	.06 (6%)	.065 (6½%)	.07 (7%)	.075 (7½%)	.08 (8%)
1	0.9433 9623	0.9389 6714	0.9345 7944	0.9302 3256	0.9259 2593
2	1.8333 9267	1.8206 2642	1.8080 1817	1.7955 6517	1.7832 6475
3	2.6730 1195	2.6484 7551	2.6243 1604	2.6005 2574	2.5770 9699
4	3.4651 0561	3.4257 9860	3.3872 1126	3.3493 2627	3.3121 2684
5	4.2123 6379	4.1556 7944	4.1001 9744	4.0458 8490	3.9927 1004
6	4.9173 2433	4.8410 1356	4.7665 3966	4.6938 4642	4.6228 7966
7	5.5823 8144	5.4845 1977	5.3892 8940	5.2966 0132	5.2063 7006
8	6.2097 9381	6.0887 5096	5.9712 9851	5.8573 0355	5.7466 3894
9	6.8016 9227	6.6561 0419	6.5152 3225	6.3788 8703	6.2468 8791
10	7.3600 8705	7.1888 3022	7.0235 8154	6.8640 8096	6.7100 8140
11	7.8868 7458	7.6890 4246	7.4986 7434	7.3154 2415	7.1389 6426
12	8.3838 4394	8.1587 2532	7.9426 8630	7.7352 7827	7.5360 7802
13	8.8526 8296	8.5997 4208	8.3576 5074	8.1258 4026	7.9037 7594
14	9.2949 8393	9.0138 4233	8.7454 6799	8.4891 5373	8.2442 3698
15	9.7122 4899	9.4026 6885	9.1079 1401	8.8271 1975	8.5594 7869
16	10.1058 9527	9.7677 6418	9.4466 4860	9.1415 0674	8.8513 6916
17	10.4772 5969	10.1105 7670	9.7632 2299	9.4339 5976	9.1216 3811
18	10.8276 0348	10.4324 6638	10.0590 8691	9.7060 0908	9.3718 8714
19	11.1581 1649	10.7347 1022	10.3355 9524	9.9590 7821	9.6035 9920
20	11.4699 2122	11.0185 0725	10.5940 1425	10.1944 9136	9.8181 4741
21	11.7640 7662	11.2849 8333	10.8355 2733	10.4134 8033	10.0168 0316
22	12.0415 8172	11.5351 9562	11.0612 4050	10.6171 9101	10.2007 4366
23	12.3033 7898	11.7701 3673	11.2721 8738	10.8066 8931	10.3710 5895
24	12.5503 5753	11.9907 3871	11.4693 3400	10.9829 6680	10.5287 5828
25	12.7833 5616	12.1978 7673	11.6535 8318	11.1469 4586	10.6747 7619
26	13.0031 6619	12.3923 7251	11.8257 7867	11.2994 8452	10.8099 7795
27	13.2105 3414	12.5749 9766	11.9867 0904	11.4413 8095	10.9351 6477
28	13.4061 6428	12.7464 7668	12.1371 1125	11.5733 7763	11.0510 7849
29	13.5907 2102	12.9074 8984	12.2776 7407	11.6961 6524	11.1584 0601
30	13.7648 3115	13.0586 7591	12.4090 4118	11.8103 8627	11.2577 8334
31	13.9290 8599	13.2006 3465	12.5318 1419	11.9166 3839	11.3497 9939
32	14.0840 4339	13.3339 2925	12.6465 5532	12.0154 7757	11.4349 9944
33	14.2302 2961	13.4590 8850	12.7537 9002	12.1074 2099	11.5138 8837
34	14.3681 4114	13.5766 0892	12.8540 0936	12.1929 4976	11.5869 3367
35	14.4982 4636	13.6869 5673	12.9476 7230	12.2725 1141	11.6545 6822
36	14.6209 8713	13.7905 6970	13.0352 0776	12.3465 2224	11.7171 9279
37	14.7367 8031	13.8878 5887	13.1170 1660	12.4153 6952	11.7751 7851
38	14.8460 1916	13.9792 1021	13.1934 7345	12.4794 1351	11.8288 6899
39	14.9490 7468	14.0649 8611	13.2649 2846	12.5389 8931	11.8785 8240
40	15.0462 9687	14.1455 2687	13.3317 0884	12.5944 0866	11.9246 1333
41	15.1380 1592	14.2211 5199	13.3941 2041	12.6459 6155	11.9672 3457
42	15.2245 4332	14.2921 6149	13.4524 4898	12.6939 1772	12.0066 9867
43	15.3061 7294	14.3588 3708	13.5069 6167	12.7385 2811	12.0432 3951
44	15.3831 8202	14.4214 4327	13.5579 0810	12.7800 2615	12.0770 7362
45	15.4558 3209	14.4802 2842	13.6055 2159	12.8186 2898	12.1084 0150
46	15.5243 6990	14.5354 2575	13.6500 2018	12.8545 3858	12.1374 0880
47	15.5890 2821	14.5872 5422	13.6916 0764	12.8879 4287	12.1642 6741
48	15.6500 2661	14.6359 1946	13.7304 7443	12.9190 1662	12.1891 3649
49	15.7075 7227	14.6816 1451	13.7667 9853	12.9479 2244	12.2121 6341
50	15.7618 6064	14.7245 2067	13.8007 4629	12.9748 1157	12.2334 8464

ANNUITY WHOSE PRESENT VALUE IS 1

$$\frac{1}{a_{\overline{n}|}} = a_{\overline{n}|}^{-1} = \frac{i}{1 - (1+i)^{-n}} = \frac{i}{1 - v^n} = s_{\overline{n}|}^{-1} + i$$

Periods	Rate i				
n	.0025 ($\frac{1}{4}\%$)	.004167 ($\frac{1}{12}\%$)	.005 ($\frac{1}{2}\%$)	.005833 ($\frac{7}{12}\%$)	.0075 ($\frac{3}{4}\%$)
1	1.0025 0000	1.0041 6667	1.0050 0000	1.0058 3333	1.0075 0000
2	0.5018 7578	0.5031 2717	0.5037 5312	0.5043 7924	0.5056 3200
3	.3350 0139	.3361 1496	.3366 7221	.3372 2976	.3383 4579
4	.2515 6445	.2526 0958	.2531 3279	.2536 5644	.2547 0501
5	.2015 0250	.2025 0693	.2030 0997	.2035 1357	.2045 2242
6	.1681 2803	.1691 0564	.1695 9546	.1700 8594	.1710 6891
7	.1442 8928	.1452 4800	.1457 2854	.1462 0086	.1471 7488
8	.1264 1035	.1273 5512	.1278 2886	.1283 0352	.1292 5552
9	.1125 0462	.1134 3876	.1139 0736	.1143 7698	.1153 1929
10	.1013 8015	.1023 0596	.1027 7057	.1032 3632	.1041 7123
11	.0922 7840	.0931 9757	.0936 5903	.0941 2175	.0950 5094
12	.0846 9370	.0856 0748	.0860 6643	.0865 2675	.0874 5148
13	.0782 7595	.0791 8532	.0796 4224	.0801 0064	.0810 2188
14	.0727 7510	.0736 8082	.0741 3609	.0745 9295	.0755 1146
15	.0680 0777	.0689 1045	.0693 6436	.0698 2000	.0707 3639
16	.0638 3642	.0647 3655	.0651 8937	.0656 4401	.0665 5879
17	.0601 5587	.0610 5387	.0615 0579	.0619 5966	.0628 7321
18	.0568 8433	.0577 8053	.0582 3173	.0586 8499	.0595 9766
19	.0539 5722	.0548 5191	.0553 0253	.0557 5532	.0566 6740
20	.0513 2288	.0522 1630	.0526 6645	.0531 1889	.0540 3063
21	.0489 3947	.0498 3183	.0502 8163	.0507 3383	.0516 4543
22	.0467 7278	.0476 6427	.0481 1380	.0485 6585	.0494 7748
23	.0447 9455	.0456 8531	.0461 3465	.0465 8663	.0474 9846
24	.0429 8121	.0438 7139	.0443 2061	.0447 7258	.0456 8474
25	.0413 1298	.0422 0270	.0426 5186	.0431 0388	.0440 1650
26	.0397 7312	.0406 6247	.0411 1163	.0415 6376	.0424 7693
27	.0383 4736	.0392 3645	.0396 8565	.0401 3793	.0410 5176
28	.0370 2347	.0379 1239	.0383 6167	.0388 1415	.0397 2871
29	.0357 9093	.0366 7974	.0371 2914	.0375 8186	.0384 9723
30	.0346 4059	.0355 2936	.0359 7892	.0364 3191	.0373 4816
31	.0335 6449	.0344 5330	.0349 0304	.0353 5633	.0362 7352
32	.0325 5569	.0334 4458	.0338 9453	.0343 4815	.0352 6634
33	.0316 0806	.0324 9708	.0329 4727	.0334 0124	.0343 2048
34	.0307 1620	.0316 0540	.0320 5586	.0325 1020	.0334 3053
35	.0298 7533	.0307 6476	.0312 1550	.0316 7024	.0325 9170
36	.0290 8121	.0299 7090	.0304 2194	.0308 7710	.0317 9973
37	.0283 3004	.0292 2003	.0296 7139	.0301 2698	.0310 5082
38	.0276 1843	.0285 0875	.0289 6045	.0294 1649	.0303 4157
39	.0269 4335	.0278 3402	.0282 8607	.0287 4258	.0296 6893
40	.0263 0204	.0271 9310	.0276 4552	.0281 0251	.0290 3016
41	.0256 9204	.0265 8352	.0270 3631	.0274 9379	.0284 2276
42	.0251 1112	.0260 0303	.0264 5622	.0269 1420	.0278 4452
43	.0245 5724	.0254 4961	.0259 0320	.0263 6170	.0272 9338
44	.0240 2855	.0249 2141	.0253 7541	.0258 3443	.0267 6751
45	.0235 2339	.0244 1675	.0248 7117	.0253 3073	.0262 6521
46	.0230 4022	.0239 3409	.0243 8894	.0248 4905	.0257 8495
47	.0225 7762	.0234 7204	.0239 2733	.0243 8798	.0253 2532
48	.0221 3433	.0230 2929	.0234 8503	.0239 4624	.0248 8504
49	.0217 0915	.0226 0468	.0230 6087	.0235 2265	.0244 6292
50	.0213 0099	.0221 9711	.0226 5376	.0231 1612	.0240 5787

ANNUITY WHOSE PRESENT VALUE IS 1

$$a_{\overline{n}|}^{-1} = i/(1 - v^n) = s_{\overline{n}|}^{-1} + i \text{ (Continued)}$$

Periods	Rate i				
n	.0025 ($\frac{1}{4}\%$)	.004167 ($\frac{5}{12}\%$)	.005 ($\frac{1}{2}\%$)	.005833 ($\frac{7}{12}\%$)	.0075 ($\frac{3}{4}\%$)
50	.0213 0099	.0221 9711	.0226 5376	.0231 1612	.0240 5787
51	.0209 0886	.0218 0557	.0222 6269	.0227 2563	.0236 6888
52	.0205 3184	.0214 2916	.0218 8675	.0223 5027	.0232 9503
53	.0201 6906	.0210 6700	.0215 2507	.0219 8919	.0229 3546
54	.0198 1974	.0207 1830	.0211 7686	.0216 4157	.0225 8938
55	.0194 8314	.0203 8234	.0208 4139	.0213 0671	.0222 5605
56	.0191 5858	.0200 5843	.0205 1797	.0209 8390	.0219 3478
57	.0188 4542	.0197 4593	.0202 0598	.0206 7251	.0216 2496
58	.0185 4308	.0194 4426	.0199 0481	.0203 7196	.0213 2597
59	.0182 5101	.0191 5287	.0196 1392	.0200 8170	.0210 3727
60	.0179 6869	.0188 7123	.0193 3280	.0198 0120	.0207 5836
61	.0176 9564	.0185 9888	.0190 6096	.0195 2999	.0204 8873
62	.0174 3142	.0183 3536	.0187 9796	.0192 6762	.0202 2795
63	.0171 7561	.0180 8025	.0185 4337	.0190 1366	.0199 7560
64	.0169 2780	.0178 3315	.0182 9681	.0187 6773	.0197 3127
65	.0166 8764	.0175 9371	.0180 5789	.0185 2946	.0194 9460
66	.0164 5476	.0173 6156	.0178 2627	.0182 9848	.0192 6524
67	.0162 2886	.0171 3639	.0176 0163	.0180 7449	.0190 4286
68	.0160 0961	.0169 1788	.0173 8366	.0178 5716	.0188 2716
69	.0157 9674	.0167 0574	.0171 7206	.0176 4622	.0186 1785
70	.0155 8996	.0164 9971	.0169 6657	.0174 4138	.0184 1464
71	.0153 8902	.0162 9952	.0167 6693	.0172 4239	.0182 1728
72	.0151 9368	.0161 0493	.0165 7289	.0170 4901	.0180 2554
73	.0150 0370	.0159 1572	.0163 8422	.0168 6100	.0178 3917
74	.0148 1887	.0157 3165	.0162 0070	.0166 7814	.0176 5796
75	.0146 3898	.0155 5253	.0160 2214	.0165 0024	.0174 8170
76	.0144 6385	.0153 7816	.0158 4832	.0163 2709	.0173 1020
77	.0142 9327	.0152 0836	.0156 7908	.0161 5851	.0171 4328
78	.0141 2708	.0150 4295	.0155 1423	.0159 9432	.0169 8074
79	.0139 6511	.0148 8177	.0153 5360	.0158 3436	.0168 2244
80	.0138 0721	.0147 2464	.0151 9704	.0156 7847	.0166 6821
81	.0136 5321	.0145 7144	.0150 4439	.0155 2650	.0165 1790
82	.0135 0298	.0144 2200	.0148 9552	.0153 7830	.0163 7136
83	.0133 5639	.0142 7620	.0147 5028	.0152 3373	.0162 2847
84	.0132 1330	.0141 3391	.0146 0855	.0150 9268	.0160 8908
85	.0130 7359	.0139 9500	.0144 7021	.0149 5501	.0159 5308
86	.0129 3714	.0138 5935	.0143 3513	.0148 2060	.0158 2034
87	.0128 0384	.0137 2685	.0142 0320	.0146 8935	.0156 9076
88	.0126 7357	.0135 9740	.0140 7431	.0145 6115	.0155 6423
89	.0125 4625	.0134 7088	.0139 4837	.0144 3588	.0154 4064
90	.0124 2177	.0133 4721	.0138 2527	.0143 1347	.0153 1989
91	.0123 0004	.0132 2629	.0137 0493	.0141 9380	.0152 0190
92	.0121 8096	.0131 0803	.0135 8724	.0140 7679	.0150 8657
93	.0120 6446	.0129 9234	.0134 7213	.0139 6236	.0149 7382
94	.0119 5044	.0128 7915	.0133 5950	.0138 5042	.0148 6356
95	.0118 3884	.0127 6836	.0132 4930	.0137 4090	.0147 5571
96	.0117 2957	.0126 5992	.0131 4143	.0136 3372	.0146 5020
97	.0116 2257	.0125 5374	.0130 3583	.0135 2880	.0145 4696
98	.0115 1776	.0124 4976	.0129 3242	.0134 2608	.0144 4592
99	.0114 1508	.0123 4790	.0128 3115	.0133 2549	.0143 4701
100	.0113 1446	.0122 4811	.0127 3194	.0132 2696	.0142 5017

ANNUITY WHOSE PRESENT VALUE IS 1

$$a_{\overline{n}|}^{-1} = i/(1 - v^n) = s_{\overline{n}|}^{-1} + i \text{ (Continued)}$$

Periods	Rate i				
n	.01 (1%)	.01125 (1⅛%)	.0125 (1¼%)	.015 (1½%)	.0175 (1¾%)
1	1.0100 0000	1.0112 5000	1.0125 0000	1.0150 0000	1.0175 0000
2	0.5075 1244	0.5084 5323	0.5093 9441	0.5112 7792	0.5131 6295
3	.3400 2211	.3408 6130	.3417 0117	.3433 8296	.3450 6746
4	.2562 8109	.2570 7058	.2578 6102	.2594 4479	.2610 3237
5	.2060 3980	.2068 0034	.2075 6211	.2090 8932	.2106 2142
6	.1725 4837	.1732 9034	.1740 3381	.1755 2521	.1770 2256
7	.1486 2828	.1493 5762	.1500 8872	.1515 5616	.1530 3059
8	.1306 9029	.1314 1071	.1321 3314	.1335 8402	.1350 4292
9	.1167 4036	.1174 5432	.1181 7055	.1196 0982	.1210 5813
10	.1055 8208	.1062 9131	.1070 0307	.1084 3418	.1098 7534
11	.0964 5408	.0971 5984	.0978 6839	.0992 9384	.1007 3038
12	.0888 4879	.0895 5203	.0902 5831	.0916 7999	.0931 1377
13	.0824 1482	.0831 1626	.0838 2100	.0852 4036	.0866 7283
14	.0769 0117	.0776 0138	.0783 0515	.0797 2332	.0811 5562
15	.0721 2378	.0728 2321	.0735 2646	.0749 4436	.0763 7739
16	.0679 4460	.0686 4363	.0693 4672	.0707 6508	.0721 9958
17	.0642 5806	.0649 5698	.0656 6023	.0670 7966	.0685 1623
18	.0609 8205	.0616 8113	.0623 8479	.0638 0578	.0652 4492
19	.0580 5175	.0587 5120	.0594 5548	.0608 7847	.0623 2061
20	.0554 1531	.0561 1531	.0568 2039	.0582 4574	.0596 9122
21	.0530 3075	.0537 3145	.0544 3749	.0558 6550	.0573 1464
22	.0508 6372	.0515 6525	.0522 7238	.0537 0332	.0551 5638
23	.0488 8584	.0495 8833	.0502 9666	.0517 3075	.0531 8796
24	.0470 7347	.0477 7701	.0484 8665	.0499 2410	.0513 8565
25	.0454 0675	.0461 1144	.0468 2247	.0482 6345	.0497 2952
26	.0438 6888	.0445 7479	.0452 8729	.0467 3196	.0482 0269
27	.0424 4553	.0431 5273	.0438 6677	.0453 1527	.0467 9079
28	.0411 2444	.0418 3299	.0425 4863	.0440 0108	.0454 8151
29	.0398 9502	.0406 0498	.0413 2228	.0427 7878	.0442 6424
30	.0387 4811	.0394 5953	.0401 7854	.0416 3919	.0431 2975
31	.0376 7573	.0383 8866	.0391 0942	.0405 7430	.0420 7005
32	.0366 7089	.0373 8535	.0381 0791	.0395 7710	.0410 7812
33	.0357 2744	.0364 4349	.0371 6786	.0386 4144	.0401 4779
34	.0348 3997	.0355 5763	.0362 8387	.0377 6189	.0392 7363
35	.0340 0368	.0347 2299	.0354 5111	.0369 3363	.0384 5082
36	.0332 1431	.0339 3529	.0346 6533	.0361 5240	.0376 7507
37	.0324 6805	.0331 9072	.0339 2270	.0354 1437	.0369 4257
38	.0317 6150	.0324 8589	.0332 1983	.0347 1613	.0362 4990
39	.0310 9160	.0318 1773	.0325 5365	.0340 5463	.0355 9399
40	.0304 5560	.0311 8349	.0319 2141	.0334 2710	.0349 7209
41	.0298 5102	.0305 8069	.0313 2063	.0328 3106	.0343 8170
42	.0292 7563	.0300 0709	.0307 4906	.0322 6426	.0338 2057
43	.0287 2737	.0294 6064	.0302 0466	.0317 2465	.0332 8666
44	.0282 0441	.0289 3949	.0296 8557	.0312 1038	.0327 7810
45	.0277 0505	.0284 4197	.0291 9012	.0307 1976	.0322 9321
46	.0272 2775	.0279 6652	.0287 1675	.0302 5125	.0318 3043
47	.0267 7111	.0275 1173	.0282 6406	.0298 0342	.0313 8836
48	.0263 3384	.0270 7632	.0278 3075	.0293 7500	.0309 6569
49	.0259 1474	.0266 5910	.0274 1563	.0289 6478	.0305 6124
50	.0255 1273	.0262 5898	.0270 1763	.0285 7168	.0301 7391

ANNUITY WHOSE PRESENT VALUE IS 1
$$a_{\overline{n}|}^{-1} = i/(1 - v^n) = s_{\overline{n}|}^{-1} + i \text{ (Continued)}$$

Periods	Rate i				
n	.01 (1 %)	.01125 (1⅛ %)	.0125 (1¼ %)	.015 (1½ %)	.0175 (1¾ %)
50	.0255 1273	.0262 5898	.0270 1763	.0285 7168	.0301 7391
51	.0251 2680	.0258 7494	.0266 3571	.0281 9469	.0298 0269
52	.0247 5603	.0255 0606	.0262 6897	.0278 3287	.0294 4665
53	.0243 9956	.0251 5149	.0259 1653	.0274 8537	.0291 0492
54	.0240 5658	.0248 1043	.0255 7760	.0271 5138	.0287 7672
55	.0237 2637	.0244 8213	.0252 5145	.0268 3018	.0284 6129
56	.0234 0824	.0241 6592	.0249 3739	.0265 2106	.0281 5795
57	.0231 0156	.0238 6116	.0246 3478	.0262 2341	.0278 6606
58	.0228 0573	.0235 6726	.0243 4303	.0259 3661	.0275 8503
59	.0225 2020	.0232 8366	.0240 6158	.0256 6012	.0273 1430
60	.0222 4445	.0230 0985	.0237 8993	.0253 9343	.0270 5336
61	.0219 7800	.0227 4534	.0235 2758	.0251 3604	.0268 0172
62	.0217 2041	.0224 8969	.0232 7410	.0248 8751	.0265 5892
63	.0214 7125	.0222 4247	.0230 2904	.0246 4741	.0263 2455
64	.0212 3013	.0220 0329	.0227 9203	.0244 1534	.0260 9821
65	.0209 9667	.0217 7178	.0225 6268	.0241 9094	.0258 7952
66	.0207 7052	.0215 4758	.0223 4065	.0239 7386	.0256 6813
67	.0205 5136	.0213 3037	.0221 2560	.0237 6376	.0254 6372
68	.0203 3889	.0211 1985	.0219 1724	.0235 6033	.0252 6597
69	.0201 3280	.0209 1571	.0217 1527	.0233 6329	.0250 7459
70	.0199 3282	.0207 1769	.0215 1941	.0231 7235	.0248 8930
71	.0197 3870	.0205 2552	.0213 2941	.0229 8727	.0247 0985
72	.0195 5019	.0203 3896	.0211 4501	.0228 0779	.0245 3600
73	.0193 6706	.0201 5779	.0209 6600	.0226 3368	.0243 6750
74	.0191 8910	.0199 8177	.0207 9215	.0224 6473	.0242 0413
75	.0190 1609	.0198 1072	.0206 2325	.0223 0072	.0240 4570
76	.0188 4784	.0196 4442	.0204 5910	.0221 4146	.0238 9200
77	.0186 8416	.0194 8269	.0202 9953	.0219 8676	.0237 4285
78	.0185 2488	.0193 2536	.0201 4436	.0218 3645	.0235 9806
79	.0183 6983	.0191 7226	.0199 9341	.0216 9036	.0234 5748
80	.0182 1885	.0190 2323	.0198 4652	.0215 4832	.0233 2093
81	.0180 7179	.0188 7812	.0197 0356	.0214 1019	.0231 8828
82	.0179 2851	.0187 3678	.0195 6437	.0212 7583	.0230 5936
83	.0177 8887	.0185 9908	.0194 2881	.0211 4509	.0229 3406
84	.0176 5273	.0184 6489	.0192 9675	.0210 1784	.0228 1223
85	.0175 1998	.0183 3409	.0191 6808	.0208 9396	.0226 9375
86	.0173 9050	.0182 0654	.0190 4267	.0207 7333	.0225 7850
87	.0172 6418	.0180 8215	.0189 2041	.0206 5584	.0224 6636
88	.0171 4089	.0179 6081	.0188 0119	.0205 4138	.0223 5724
89	.0170 2056	.0178 4240	.0186 8491	.0204 2984	.0222 5102
90	.0169 0306	.0177 2684	.0185 7146	.0203 2113	.0221 4760
91	.0167 8832	.0176 1403	.0184 6076	.0202 1516	.0220 4690
92	.0166 7624	.0175 0387	.0183 5272	.0201 1182	.0219 4882
93	.0165 6673	.0173 9629	.0182 4724	.0200 1104	.0218 5327
94	.0164 5971	.0172 9119	.0181 4425	.0199 1273	.0217 6017
95	.0163 5511	.0171 8851	.0180 4366	.0198 1681	.0216 6944
96	.0162 5284	.0170 8816	.0179 4541	.0197 2321	.0215 8101
97	.0161 5284	.0169 9007	.0178 4941	.0196 3186	.0214 9480
98	.0160 5503	.0168 9418	.0177 5560	.0195 4268	.0214 1074
99	.0159 5936	.0168 0041	.0176 6391	.0194 5560	.0213 2876
100	.0158 6574	.0167 0870	.0175 7428	.0193 7057	.0212 4880

Financial Tables

ANNUITY WHOSE PRESENT VALUE IS 1

$$a_{\overline{n}|}^{-1} = i/(1 - v^n) = s_{\overline{n}|}^{-1} + i \text{ (Continued)}$$

Periods	Rate i				
n	.02 (2%)	.0225 (2¼%)	.025 (2½)%	.0275 (2¾%)	.03 (3%)
1	1.0200 0000	1.0225 0000	1.0250 0000	1.0275 0000	1.0300 0000
2	0.5150 4950	0.5169 3758	0.5188 2716	0.5207 1825	0.5226 1084
3	.3467 5467	.3484 4458	.3501 3717	.3518 3243	.3535 3036
4	.2626 2375	.2642 1893	.2658 1788	.2674 2059	.2690 2705
5	.2121 5839	.2137 0021	.2152 4686	.2167 9832	.2183 5457
6	.1785 2581	.1800 3496	.1815 4997	.1830 7083	.1845 9750
7	.1545 1196	.1560 0025	.1574 9543	.1589 9747	.1605 0635
8	.1365 0980	.1379 8462	.1394 6735	.1409 5795	.1424 5639
9	.1225 1544	.1239 8170	.1254 5689	.1269 4095	.1284 3386
10	.1113 2653	.1127 8768	.1142 5876	.1157 3972	.1172 3051
11	.1021 7794	.1036 3649	.1051 0596	.1065 8629	.1080 7745
12	.0945 5960	.0960 1740	.0974 8713	.0989 6871	.1004 6209
13	.0881 1835	.0895 7686	.0910 4827	.0925 3252	.0940 2954
14	.0826 0197	.0840 6230	.0855 3652	.0870 2457	.0885 2634
15	.0778 2547	.0792 8852	.0807 6646	.0822 5917	.0837 6658
16	.0736 5013	.0751 1663	.0765 9899	.0780 9710	.0796 1085
17	.0699 6984	.0714 4039	.0729 2777	.0744 3186	.0759 5253
18	.0667 0210	.0681 7720	.0696 7008	.0711 8063	.0727 0870
19	.0637 8177	.0652 6182	.0667 6062	.0682 7802	.0698 1388
20	.0611 5672	.0626 4207	.0641 4713	.0656 7173	.0672 1571
21	.0587 8477	.0602 7572	.0617 8733	.0633 1941	.0648 7178
22	.0566 3140	.0581 2821	.0596 4661	.0611 8640	.0627 4739
23	.0546 6810	.0561 7097	.0576 9638	.0592 4410	.0608 1390
24	.0528 7110	.0543 8023	.0559 1282	.0574 6863	.0590 4742
25	.0512 2044	.0527 3599	.0542 7592	.0558 3997	.0574 2787
26	.0496 9923	.0512 2134	.0527 6875	.0543 4116	.0559 3829
27	.0482 9309	.0498 2188	.0513 7687	.0529 5776	.0545 6421
28	.0469 8967	.0485 2525	.0500 8793	.0516 7738	.0532 9323
29	.0457 7836	.0473 2081	.0488 9127	.0504 8935	.0521 1467
30	.0446 4992	.0461 9934	.0477 7764	.0493 8442	.0510 1926
31	.0435 9635	.0451 5280	.0467 3900	.0483 5453	.0499 9893
32	.0426 1061	.0441 7415	.0457 6831	.0473 9263	.0490 4662
33	.0416 8653	.0432 5722	.0448 5988	.0464 9253	.0481 5612
34	.0408 1867	.0423 9655	.0440 0675	.0456 4875	.0473 2196
35	.0400 0221	.0415 8731	.0432 0558	.0448 5645	.0465 3929
36	.0392 3285	.0408 2522	.0424 5158	.0441 1132	.0458 0379
37	.0385 0678	.0401 0643	.0417 4090	.0434 0953	.0451 1162
38	.0378 2057	.0394 2753	.0410 7012	.0427 4764	.0444 5934
39	.0371 7114	.0387 8543	.0404 3615	.0421 2256	.0438 4385
40	.0365 5575	.0381 7738	.0398 3623	.0415 3151	.0432 6238
41	.0359 7188	.0376 0087	.0392 6786	.0409 7200	.0427 1241
42	.0354 1729	.0370 5364	.0387 2876	.0404 4175	.0421 9167
43	.0348 8993	.0365 3364	.0382 1688	.0399 3871	.0416 9811
44	.0343 8794	.0360 3901	.0377 3037	.0394 6100	.0412 2985
45	.0339 0962	.0355 6805	.0372 6751	.0390 0693	.0407 8518
46	.0334 5342	.0351 1921	.0368 2676	.0385 7493	.0403 6254
47	.0330 1792	.0346 9107	.0364 0669	.0381 6358	.0399 6051
48	.0326 0184	.0342 8233	.0360 0599	.0377 7158	.0395 7777
49	.0322 0396	.0338 9179	.0356 2348	.0373 9773	.0392 1314
50	.0318 2321	.0335 1836	.0352 5806	.0370 4092	.0388 6549

ANNUITY WHOSE PRESENT VALUE IS 1

$$a_{\overline{n}|}^{-1} = i/(1 - v^n) = s_{\overline{n}|}^{-1} + i \text{ (Continued)}$$

Periods			Rate i		
n	.02 (2%)	.0225 (2¼%)	.025 (2½%)	.0275 (2¾%)	03 (3%)
50	.0318 2321	.0335 1836	.0352 5806	.0370 4092	.0388 6549
51	.0314 5856	.0331 6102	.0349 0870	.0367 0014	.0385 3382
52	.0311 0909	.0328 1884	.0345 7446	.0363 7444	.0382 1718
53	.0307 7392	.0324 9094	.0342 5449	.0360 6297	.0379 1471
54	.0304 5226	.0321 7654	.0339 4799	.0357 6491	.0376 2558
55	.0301 4337	.0318 7489	.0336 5419	.0354 7953	.0373 4907
56	.0298 4656	.0315 8530	.0333 7243	.0352 0612	.0370 8447
57	.0295 6120	.0313 0712	.0331 0204	.0349 4404	.0368 3114
58	.0292 8667	.0310 3977	.0328 4244	.0346 9270	.0365 8848
59	.0290 2243	.0307 8268	.0325 9307	.0344 5153	.0363 5593
60	.0287 6797	.0305 3533	.0323 5340	.0342 2002	.0361 3296
61	.0285 2278	.0302 9724	.0321 2294	.0339 9767	.0359 1908
62	.0282 8643	.0300 6795	.0319 0126	.0337 8402	.0357 1385
63	.0280 5848	.0298 4704	.0316 8790	.0335 7866	.0355 1682
64	.0278 3855	.0296 3411	.0314 8249	.0333 8118	.0353 2760
65	.0276 2624	.0294 2878	.0312 8463	.0331 9120	.0351 4581
66	.0274 2122	.0292 3070	.0310 9398	.0330 0837	.0349 7110
67	.0272 2316	.0290 3955	.0309 1021	.0328 3236	.0348 0313
68	.0270 3173	.0288 5500	.0307 3300	.0326 6285	.0346 4159
69	.0268 4665	.0286 7677	.0305 6206	.0324 9955	.0344 8618
70	.0266 6765	.0285 0458	.0303 9712	.0323 4218	.0343 3663
71	.0264 9446	.0283 3816	.0302 3790	.0321 9048	.0341 9266
72	.0263 2683	.0281 7728	.0300 8417	.0320 4420	.0340 5404
73	.0261 6454	.0280 2169	.0299 3568	.0319 0311	.0339 2053
74	.0260 0736	.0278 7118	.0297 9222	.0317 6698	.0337 9191
75	.0258 5508	.0277 2554	.0296 5358	.0316 3560	.0336 6796
76	.0257 0751	.0275 8457	.0295 1956	.0315 0878	.0335 4849
77	.0255 6447	.0274 4808	.0293 8997	.0313 8633	.0334 3331
78	.0254 2576	.0273 1589	.0292 6463	.0312 6806	.0333 2224
79	.0252 9123	.0271 8784	.0291 4338	.0311 5382	.0332 1510
80	.0251 6071	.0270 6376	.0290 2605	.0310 4342	.0331 1175
81	.0250 3405	.0269 4350	.0289 1248	.0309 3674	.0330 1201
82	.0249 1110	.0268 2692	.0288 0254	.0308 3361	.0329 1576
83	.0247 9173	.0267 1387	.0286 9608	.0307 3389	.0328 2284
84	.0246 7581	.0266 0423	.0285 9298	.0306 3747	.0327 3313
85	.0245 6321	.0264 9787	.0284 9310	.0305 4420	.0326 4650
86	.0244 5381	.0263 9467	.0283 9633	.0304 5397	.0325 6284
87	.0243 4750	.0262 9452	.0283 0255	.0303 6667	.0324 8202
88	.0242 4416	.0261 9730	.0282 1165	.0302 8219	.0324 0393
89	.0241 4370	.0261 0291	.0281 2353	.0302 0041	.0323 2848
90	.0240 4602	.0260 1126	.0280 3809	.0301 2125	.0322 5556
91	.0239 5101	.0259 2224	.0279 5523	.0300 4460	.0321 8508
92	.0238 5859	.0258 3577	.0278 7486	.0299 7038	.0321 1694
93	.0237 6868	.0257 5176	.0277 9690	.0298 9850	.0320 5107
94	.0236 8118	.0256 7012	.0277 2126	.0298 2887	.0319 8737
95	.0235 9602	.0255 9078	.0276 4786	.0297 6141	.0319 2577
96	.0235 1313	.0255 1366	.0275 7662	.0296 9605	.0318 6619
97	.0234 3242	.0254 3868	.0275 0747	.0296 3272	.0318 0856
98	.0233 5383	.0253 6578	.0274 4034	.0295 7134	.0317 5281
99	.0232 7729	.0252 9489	.0273 7517	.0295 1185	.0316 9886
100	.0232 0274	.0252 2594	.0273 1188	.0294 5418	.0316 4667

ANNUITY WHOSE PRESENT VALUE IS 1

$$a_{\overline{n}|}^{-1} = i/(1 - v^n) = s_{\overline{n}|}^{-1} + i \text{ (Continued)}$$

Periods			Rate i		
n	.035 (3½%)	.04 (4%)	.045 (4½%)	.05 (5%)	.055 (5½%)
1	1.0350 0000	1.0400 0000	1.0450 0000	1.0500 0000	1.0550 0000
2	0.5264 0049	0.5301 9608	0.5339 9756	0.5378 0488	0.5416 1800
3	.3569 3418	.3603 4854	.3637 7336	.3672 0856	.3706 5407
4	.2722 5114	.2754 9005	.2787 4365	.2820 1183	.2852 9449
5	.2214 8137	.2246 2711	.2277 9164	.2309 7480	.2341 7644
6	.1876 6821	.1907 6190	.1938 7839	.1970 1747	.2001 7895
7	.1635 4449	.1666 0961	.1697 0147	.1728 1982	.1759 6442
8	.1454 7665	.1485 2783	.1516 0965	.1547 2181	.1578 6401
9	.1314 4601	.1344 9299	.1375 7447	.1406 9008	.1438 3946
10	.1202 4137	.1232 9094	.1263 7882	.1295 0457	.1326 6777
11	.1110 9197	.1141 4904	.1172 4818	.1203 8889	.1235 7065
12	.1034 8395	.1065 5217	.1096 6619	.1128 2541	.1160 2923
13	.0970 6157	.1001 4373	.1032 7535	.1064 5577	.1096 8426
14	.0915 7073	.0946 6897	.0978 2032	.1010 2397	.1042 7912
15	.0868 2507	.0899 4110	.0931 1381	.0963 4229	.0996 2560
16	.0826 8483	.0858 2000	.0890 1537	.0922 6991	.0955 8254
17	.0790 4313	.0821 9852	.0854 1758	.0886 9914	.0920 4197
18	.0758 1684	.0789 9333	.0822 3690	.0855 4622	.0889 1992
19	.0729 4033	.0761 3862	.0794 0734	.0827 4501	.0861 5006
20	.0703 6108	.0735 8175	.0768 7614	.0802 4259	.0836 7933
21	.0680 3659	.0712 8011	.0746 0057	.0779 9611	.0814 6478
22	.0659 3207	.0691 9881	.0725 4565	.0759 7051	.0794 7123
23	.0640 1880	.0673 0906	.0706 8249	.0741 3682	.0776 6965
24	.0622 7283	.0655 8683	.0689 8703	.0724 7090	.0760 3580
25	.0606 7404	.0640 1196	.0674 3903	.0709 5246	.0745 4935
26	.0592 0540	.0625 6738	.0660 2137	.0695 6432	.0731 9307
27	.0578 5241	.0612 3854	.0647 1946	.0682 9186	.0719 5228
28	.0566 0265	.0600 1298	.0635 2081	.0671 2253	.0708 1440
29	.0554 4538	.0588 7993	.0624 1461	.0660 4551	.0697 6857
30	.0543 7133	.0578 3010	.0613 9154	.0650 5144	.0688 0539
31	.0533 7240	.0568 5535	.0604 4345	.0641 3212	.0679 1665
32	.0524 4150	.0559 4859	.0595 6320	.0632 8042	.0670 9519
33	.0515 7242	.0551 0357	.0587 4453	.0624 9004	.0663 3469
34	.0507 5966	.0543 1477	.0579 8191	.0617 5545	.0656 2958
35	.0499 9835	.0535 7732	.0572 7045	.0610 7171	.0649 7493
36	.0492 8416	.0528 8688	.0566 0578	.0604 3446	.0643 6635
37	.0486 1325	.0522 3957	.0559 8402	.0598 3979	.0637 9993
38	.0479 8214	.0516 3192	.0554 0169	.0592 8423	.0632 7217
39	.0473 8775	.0510 6083	.0548 5567	.0587 6462	.0627 7991
40	.0468 2728	.0505 2349	.0543 4315	.0582 7816	.0623 2034
41	.0462 9822	.0500 1738	.0538 6158	.0578 2229	.0618 9090
42	.0457 9828	.0495 4020	.0534 0868	.0573 9471	.0614 8927
43	.0453 2539	.0490 8989	.0529 8235	.0569 9333	.0611 1337
44	.0448 7768	.0486 6454	.0525 8071	.0566 1625	.0607 6128
45	.0444 5343	.0482 6246	.0522 0202	.0562 6173	.0604 3127
46	.0440 5108	.0478 8205	.0518 4471	.0559 2820	.0601 2175
47	.0436 6919	.0475 2189	.0515 0734	.0556 1421	.0598 3129
48	.0433 0646	.0471 8065	.0511 8858	.0553 1843	.0595 5854
49	.0429 6167	.0468 5712	.0508 8722	.0550 3965	.0593 0230
50	.0426 3371	.0465 5020	.0506 0215	.0547 7674	.0590 6145

ANNUITY WHOSE PRESENT VALUE IS 1

$$a_{\overline{n}|}^{-1} = i/(1 - v^n) = s_{\overline{n}|}^{-1} + i \text{ (Continued)}$$

Periods	Rate i				
n	.06 (6%)	.065 (6½%)	.07 (7%)	.075 (7½%)	.08 (8%)
1	1.0600 0000	1.0650 0000	1.0700 0000	1.0750 0000	1.0800 0000
2	0.5454 3689	0.5492 6150	0.5530 9179	0.5569 2771	0.5607 6923
3	.3741 0981	.3775 7570	.3810 5167	.3845 3763	.3880 3351
4	.2885 9149	.2919 0274	.2952 2812	.2985 6751	.3019 2080
5	.2373 9640	.2406 3454	.2438 9069	.2471 6472	.2504 5645
6	.2033 6263	.2065 6831	.2097 9580	.2130 4489	.2163 1539
7	.1791 3502	.1823 3137	.1855 5322	.1888 0032	.1920 7240
8	.1610 3594	.1642 3730	.1674 6776	.1707 2702	.1740 1476
9	.1470 2224	.1502 3803	.1534 8647	.1567 6716	.1600 7971
10	.1358 6796	.1391 0469	.1423 7750	.1456 8593	.1490 2949
11	.1267 9294	.1300 5521	.1333 5690	.1366 9747	.1400 7634
12	.1192 7703	.1225 6817	.1259 0199	.1292 7783	.1326 9502
13	.1129 6011	.1162 8256	.1196 5085	.1230 6420	.1265 2181
14	.1075 8491	.1109 4048	.1143 4494	.1177 9737	.1212 9685
15	.1029 6276	.1063 5278	.1097 9462	.1132 8724	.1168 2954
16	.0989 5214	.1023 7757	.1058 5765	.1093 9116	.1129 7687
17	.0954 4480	.0989 0633	.1024 2519	.1060 0003	.1096 2943
18	.0923 5654	.0958 5461	.0994 1260	.1030 2896	.1067 0210
19	.0896 2086	.0931 5575	.0967 5301	.1004 1090	.1041 2763
20	.0871 8456	.0907 5640	.0943 9293	.0980 9219	.1018 5221
21	.0850 0455	.0886 1333	.0922 8900	.0960 2937	.0998 3225
22	.0830 4557	.0866 9120	.0904 0577	.0941 8687	.0980 3207
23	.0812 7848	.0849 6078	.0887 1393	.0925 3528	.0964 2217
24	.0796 7900	.0833 9770	.0871 8902	.0910 5008	.0949 7796
25	.0782 2672	.0819 8148	.0858 1052	.0897 1067	.0936 7878
26	.0769 0435	.0806 9480	.0845 6103	.0884 9961	.0925 0713
27	.0756 9717	.0795 2288	.0834 2573	.0874 0204	.0914 4810
28	.0745 9255	.0784 5305	.0823 9193	.0864 0520	.0904 8891
29	.0735 7961	.0774 7440	.0814 4865	.0854 9811	.0896 1854
30	.0726 4891	.0765 7744	.0805 8640	.0846 7124	.0888 2743
31	.0717 9222	.0757 5393	.0797 9691	.0839 1628	.0881 0728
32	.0710 0234	.0749 9665	.0790 7292	.0832 2599	.0874 5081
33	.0702 7293	.0742 9924	.0784 0807	.0825 9397	.0868 5163
34	.0695 9843	.0736 5610	.0777 9674	.0820 1461	.0863 0411
35	.0689 7386	.0730 6226	.0772 3396	.0814 8291	.0858 0326
36	.0683 9483	.0725 1332	.0767 1531	.0809 9447	.0853 4467
37	.0678 5743	.0720 0534	.0762 3685	.0805 4533	.0849 2440
38	.0673 5812	.0715 3480	.0757 9505	.0801 3197	.0845 3894
39	.0668 9377	.0710 9854	.0753 8676	.0797 5124	.0841 8513
40	.0664 6154	.0706 9373	.0750 0914	.0794 0031	.0838 6016
41	.0660 5886	.0703 1779	.0746 5962	.0790 7663	.0835 6149
42	.0656 8342	.0699 6842	.0743 3591	.0787 7789	.0832 8684
43	.0653 3312	.0696 4352	.0740 3590	.0785 0201	.0830 3414
44	.0650 0606	.0693 4119	.0737 5769	.0782 4710	.0828 0152
45	.0647 0050	.0690 5968	.0734 9957	.0780 1146	.0825 8728
46	.0644 1485	.0687 9743	.0732 5996	.0777 9354	.0823 8991
47	.0641 4768	.0685 5300	.0730 3744	.0775 9190	.0822 0799
48	.0638 9765	.0683 2505	.0728 3070	.0774 0527	.0820 4027
49	.0636 6356	.0681 1240	.0726 3853	.0772 3247	.0818 8557
50	.0634 4429	.0679 1393	.0724 5985	.0770 7241	.0817 4286

COMPOUND AMOUNT OF 1 FOR FRACTIONAL PERIODS, $(1 + i)^{\frac{1}{p}}$

p	$i = \frac{1}{4}\%$	$\frac{3}{8}$	$\frac{1}{2}$	$\frac{5}{8}$	$\frac{3}{4}$
2	1.0012 492	1.0020 812	1.0024 969	1.0029 124	1.0037 430
3	1.0008 326	1.0013 870	1.0016 639	1.0019 407	1.0024 938
4	1.0006 244	1.0010 400	1.0012 477	1.0014 552	1.0018 697
6	1.0004 162	1.0006 932	1.0008 316	1.0009 699	1.0012 461
12	1.0002 089	1.0003 466	1.0004 157	1.0004 848	1.0006 229
13	1.0001 921	1.0003 199	1.0003 837	1.0004 475	1.0005 749
26	1.0000 960	1.0001 599	1.0001 919	1.0002 237	1.0002 874
52	1.0000 480	1.0000 800	1.0000 959	1.0001 119	1.0001 437
365	1.0000 068	1.0000 114	1.0000 137	1.0000 159	1.0000 205

p	1	$1\frac{1}{8}$	$1\frac{1}{4}$	$1\frac{1}{2}$	$1\frac{3}{4}$
2	1.0049 876	1.0056 093	1.0062 306	1.0074 721	1.0087 121
3	1.0033 223	1.0037 360	1.0041 494	1.0049 752	1.0057 996
4	1.0024 907	1.0028 008	1.0031 105	1.0037 291	1.0043 466
6	1.0016 598	1.0018 663	1.0020 726	1.0024 845	1.0028 956
12	1.0008 295	1.0009 327	1.0010 357	1.0012 415	1.0014 468
13	1.0007 657	1.0008 609	1.0009 560	1.0011 459	1.0013 354
26	1.0003 828	1.0004 304	1.0004 779	1.0005 728	1.0006 675
52	1.0001 914	1.0002 152	1.0002 389	1.0002 864	1.0003 337
365	1.0000 273	1.0000 307	1.0000 340	1.0000 408	1.0000 475

p	2	$2\frac{1}{4}$	$2\frac{1}{2}$	$2\frac{3}{4}$	3
2	1.0099 505	1.0111 874	1.0124 228	1.0136 568	1.0148 892
3	1.0066 227	1.0074 444	1.0082 648	1.0090 839	1.0099 016
4	1.0049 629	1.0055 782	1.0061 922	1.0068 052	1.0074 171
6	1.0033 059	1.0037 153	1.0041 239	1.0045 317	1.0049 386
12	1.0016 516	1.0018 559	1.0020 598	1.0022 633	1.0024 663
13	1.0015 244	1.0017 130	1.0019 012	1.0020 890	1.0022 763
26	1.0007 619	1.0008 562	1.0009 502	1.0010 440	1.0011 375
52	1.0003 809	1.0004 280	1.0004 750	1.0005 218	1.0005 686
365	1.0000 543	1.0000 610	1.0000 676	1.0000 743	1.0000 810

p	$3\frac{1}{2}$	4	$4\frac{1}{2}$	5	$5\frac{1}{2}$
2	1.0173 495	1.0198 039	1.0222 524	1.0246 951	1.0271 319
3	1.0115 331	1.0131 594	1.0147 805	1.0163 964	1.0180 071
4	1.0086 374	1.0098 534	1.0110 650	1.0122 722	1.0134 752
6	1.0057 500	1.0065 582	1.0073 631	1.0081 649	1.0089 634
12	1.0028 709	1.0032 737	1.0036 748	1.0040 741	1.0044 717
13	1.0026 498	1.0030 215	1.0033 916	1.0037 601	1.0041 270
26	1.0013 240	1.0015 096	1.0016 944	1.0018 783	1.0020 614
52	1.0006 618	1.0007 545	1.0008 468	1.0009 387	1.0010 302
365	1.0000 942	1.0001 075	1.0001 206	1.0001 337	1.0001 467

p	6	$6\frac{1}{2}$	7	$7\frac{1}{2}$	8
2	1.0295 630	1.0319 884	1.0344 080	1.0368 221	1.0392 305
3	1.0196 128	1.0212 135	1.0228 091	1.0243 998	1.0259 856
4	1.0146 738	1.0158 683	1.0170 585	1.0182 446	1.0194 265
6	1.0097 588	1.0105 511	1.0113 403	1.0121 264	1.0129 095
12	1.0048 676	1.0052 617	1.0056 541	1.0060 449	1.0064 340
13	1.0044 923	1.0048 560	1.0052 181	1.0055 786	1.0059 376
26	1.0022 436	1.0024 250	1.0026 056	1.0027 854	1.0029 644
52	1.0011 212	1.0012 118	1.0013 020	1.0013 918	1.0014 811
365	1.0001 596	1.0001 726	1.0001 854	1.0001 982	1.0002 109

NOMINAL RATES CONVERTIBLE p TIMES PER YEAR
EQUIVALENT TO EFFECTIVE RATE i GIVEN IN HEADING,

$$j_p = p[(1 + i)^{\frac{1}{p}} - 1]$$

p	¼	⅜	½	⅝	¾
¼	.0025 094	.0041 928	.0050 376	.0058 846	.0075 848
½	.0025 032	.0041 754	.0050 125	.0058 504	.0075 281
2	.0024 984	.0041 623	.0049 938	.0058 249	.0074 860
4	.0024 977	.0041 602	.0049 907	.0058 206	.0074 790
6	.0024 974	.0041 595	.0049 896	.0058 192	.0074 767
12	.0024 971	.0041 587	.0049 886	.0058 178	.0074 743
13	.0024 971	.0041 587	.0049 885	.0058 177	.0074 742
52	.0024 969	.0041 582	.0049 878	.0058 167	.0074 725
365	.0024 969	.0041 580	.0049 876	.0058 164	.0074 721
∞	.0024 969	.0041 580	.0049 875	.0058 164	.0074 720

p	1	1⅛	1¼	1½	1¾
¼	.0101 510	.0114 413	.0127 363	.0153 409	.0179 648
½	.0100 590	.0113 133	.0125 781	.0151 125	.0176 531
2	.0099 751	.0112 185	.0124 612	.0149 442	.0174 241
4	.0099 627	.0112 029	.0124 418	.0149 164	.0173 863
6	.0099 586	.0111 976	.0124 354	.0149 071	.0173 737
12	.0099 545	.0111 924	.0124 290	.0148 979	.0173 612
13	.0099 541	.0111 920	.0124 285	.0148 971	.0173 602
52	.0099 513	.0111 884	.0124 240	.0148 907	.0173 515
365	.0099 505	.0111 874	.0124 227	.0148 889	.0173 490
∞	.0099 503	.0111 872	.0124 225	.0148 886	.0173 486

p	2	2¼	2½	2¾	3
¼	.0206 080	.0232 708	.0259 532	.0286 553	.0313 772
½	.0202 000	.0227 531	.0253 125	.0278 781	.0304 500
2	.0199 010	.0223 748	.0248 457	.0273 135	.0297 783
4	.0198 517	.0223 126	.0247 690	.0272 209	.0296 683
6	.0198 353	.0222 919	.0247 435	.0271 901	.0296 317
12	.0198 190	.0222 713	.0247 180	.0271 594	.0295 952
13	.0198 177	.0222 697	.0247 161	.0271 570	.0295 924
52	.0198 064	.0222 554	.0246 985	.0271 358	.0295 672
365	.0198 032	.0222 513	.0246 934	.0271 297	.0295 600
∞	.0198 026	.0222 506	.0246 926	.0271 287	.0295 588

p	3½	4	4½	5	5½
¼	.0368 808	.0424 647	.0481 297	.0538 766	.0597 062
½	.0356 125	.0408 000	.0460 125	.0512 500	.0565 125
2	.0346 990	.0396 078	.0445 048	.0493 902	.0542 639
4	.0345 498	.0394 136	.0442 600	.0490 889	.0539 007
6	.0345 002	.0393 492	.0441 787	.0489 891	.0537 804
12	.0344 508	.0392 849	.0440 977	.0488 895	.0536 604
13	.0344 470	.0392 799	.0440 915	.0488 818	.0536 512
52	.0344 128	.0392 355	.0440 355	.0488 131	.0535 683
365	.0344 031	.0392 228	.0440 195	.0487 934	.0535 447
∞	.0344 014	.0392 207	.0440 169	.0487 902	.0535 408

p	6	6½	7	7½	8
¼	.0656 193	.0716 166	.0776 990	.0838 673	.0901 223
½	.0618 000	.0671 125	.0724 500	.0778 125	.0832 000
2	.0591 260	.0639 767	.0688 161	.0736 441	.0784 610
4	.0586 954	.0634 731	.0682 341	.0729 784	.0777 062
6	.0585 528	.0633 064	.0680 416	.0727 583	.0774 567
12	.0584 106	.0631 403	.0678 497	.0725 390	.0772 084
13	.0583 997	.0631 276	.0678 350	.0725 222	.0771 893
52	.0583 016	.0630 129	.0677 027	.0723 710	.0770 180
365	.0582 736	.0629 802	.0676 649	.0723 278	.0769 692
∞	.0582 689	.0629 748	.0676 586	.0723 207	.0769 610

AMOUNT FOR YEAR OF p DEPOSITS OF $1/p,p$ TIMES PER YEAR, i/j_p

p	$\tfrac14$	$\tfrac38$	$\tfrac12$	$\tfrac58$	$\tfrac34$
$\tfrac14$	0.9962 5	0.9937 717	0.9925 312	0.9912 924	0.9888 201
$\tfrac12$	0.9974 8	0.9979 210	0.9975 062	0.9970 918	0.9962 640
2	1.0006 246	1.0010 406	1.0012 484	1.0014 562	1.0018 715
4	1.0009 370	1.0015 611	1.0018 730	1.0021 848	1.0028 081
6	1.0010 412	1.0017 347	1.0020 813	1.0024 278	1.0031 205
12	1.0011 453	1.0019 083	1.0022 896	1.0026 708	1.0034 329
13	1.0011 533	1.0019 216	1.0023 056	1.0026 895	1.0034 569
52	1.0012 254	1.0020 418	1.0024 498	1.0028 577	1.0036 732
365	1.0012 461	1.0020 762	1.0024 911	1.0029 058	1.0037 351
∞	1.0012 495	1.0020 819	1.0024 979	1.0029 138	1.0037 453

p	1	$1\tfrac18$	$1\tfrac14$	$1\tfrac12$	$1\tfrac34$
$\tfrac14$	0.9851 244	0.9832 823	0.9814 441	0.9777 791	0.9741 295
$\tfrac12$	0.9950 249	0.9944 065	0.9937 888	0.9925 558	0.9913 259
2	1.0024 938	1.0028 046	1.0031 153	1.0037 360	1.0043 618
4	1.0037 422	1.0042 089	1.0046 754	1.0056 076	1.0065 388
6	1.0041 586	1.0046 773	1.0051 958	1.0062 319	1.0072 671
12	1.0045 751	1.0051 458	1.0057 163	1.0068 565	1.0079 957
13	1.0046 071	1.0051 819	1.0057 564	1.0069 046	1.0080 518
52	1.0048 956	1.0055 063	1.0061 169	1.0073 372	1'0085 564
365	1.0049 780	1.0055 991	1.0062 199	1.0074 608	1.0087 007
∞	1.0049 917	1.0056 145	1.0062 371	1.0074 814	1.0087 247

p	2	$2\tfrac14$	$2\tfrac12$	$2\tfrac34$	3
$\tfrac14$	0.9704 950	0.9668 757	0.9632 715	0.9596 824	0.9561 082
$\tfrac12$	0.9900 990	0.9888 752	0.9876 543	0.9864 365	0.9852 217
2	1.0049 752	1.0055 937	1.0062 114	1.0068 284	1.0074 446
4	1.0074 686	1.0083 984	1.0093 268	1.0102 542	1.0111 807
6	1.0083 013	1.0093 344	1.0103 667	1.0113 979	1.0124 282
12	1.0091 339	1.0102 711	1.0114 072	1.0125 424	1.0136 766
13	1.0091 980	1.0103 431	1.0114 873	1.0126 305	1.0137 727
52	1.0097 747	1.0109 919	1.0122 082	1.0134 234	1.0146 376
365	1.0099 396	1.0111 775	1.0124 143	1.0136 502	1.0148 850
∞	1.0099 670	1.0112 083	1 0124 486	1.0136 878	1.0149 261

p	$3\tfrac12$	4	$4\tfrac12$	5	$5\tfrac12$
$\tfrac14$	0.9490 046	0.9419 6	0.9349 7	0.9280 5	0.9211 8
$\tfrac12$	0.9828 010	0.9803 922	0.9779 951	0.9756 098	0.9732 360
2	1.0086 748	1.0099 020	1.0111 262	1.0123 475	1.0135 660
4	1.0130 309	1.0148 774	1.0167 203	1.0185 594	1.0203 950
6	1.0144 858	1.0165 396	1.0185 895	1.0206 357	1.0226 781
12	1.0159 420	1.0182 035	1.0204 611	1.0227 148	1.0249 647
13	1.0160 541	1.0183 316	1.0206 051	1.0228 748	1.0251 407
52	1.0170 632	1.0194 847	1.0219 623	1.0243 160	1.0267 259
365	1.0173 517	1.0198 145	1.0222 733	1.0247 282	1.0271 793
∞	1.0173 997	1.0198 693	1.0223 349	1.0247 967	1.0272 546

p	6	$6\tfrac12$	7	$7\tfrac12$	8
$\tfrac14$	0.9143 7	0.9076 1	0.9009 1	0.8942 7	0.8876 8
$\tfrac12$	0.9708 738	0.9685 230	0.9661 836	0.9638 554	0.9615 385
2	1.0147 815	1.0159 942	1.0172 040	1.0184 110	1.0196 152
4	1.0222 269	1.0240 552	1.0258 800	1.0277 013	1.0295 190
6	1.0247 168	1.0267 517	1.0287 830	1.0308 106	1.0328 346
12	1.0272 107	1.0294 529	1.0316 914	1.0339 262	1.0361 572
13	1.0274 027	1.0296 609	1.0319 154	1.0341 661	1.0364 131
52	1.0291 319	1.0315 340	1.0339 324	1.0363 270	1.0387 179
365	1.0296 265	1.0320 699	1.0345 095	1.0369 453	1.0393 774
∞	1.0297 087	1.0321 589	1.0346 053	1.0370 480	1.0394 870

COMMISSIONERS 1941 STANDARD ORDINARY MORTALITY TABLE*

x	l_x	d_x	p_x	$\overset{\circ}{e}_x$	x	l_x	d_x	p_x	$\overset{\circ}{e}_x$
0	1 023 102	23 102	.977 42	62.33	**50**	810 900	9 990	.987 68	21.37
1	1 000 000	5 770	.994 23	62.76	51	800 910	10 628	.986 73	20.64
2	994 230	4 116	.995 86	62.12	52	790 282	11 301	.985 70	19.91
3	990 114	3 347	.996 62	61.37	53	778 981	12 020	.984 57	19.19
4	986 767	2 950	.997 01	60.58	54	766 961	12 770	.983 35	18.48
5	983 817	2 715	.997 24	59.76	**55**	754 191	13 560	.982 02	17.78
6	981 102	2 561	.997 39	58.92	56	740 631	14 390	.980 57	17.10
7	978 541	2 417	.997 53	58.08	57	726 241	15 251	.979 00	16.43
8	976 124	2 255	.997 69	57.22	58	710 990	16 147	.977 29	15.77
9	973 869	2 065	.997 88	56.35	59	694 843	17 072	.975 43	15.13
10	971 804	1 914	.998 03	55.47	**60**	677 771	18 022	.973 41	14.50
11	969 890	1 852	.998 09	54.58	61	659 749	18 988	.971 22	13.88
12	968 038	1 859	.998 08	53.68	62	640 761	19 979	.968 82	13.27
13	966 179	1 913	.998 02	52.78	63	620 782	20 958	.966 24	12.69
14	964 266	1 996	.997 93	51.89	64	599 824	21 942	.963 42	12.11
15	962 270	2 069	.997 85	50.99	**65**	577 882	22 907	.960 36	11.55
16	960 201	2 103	.997 81	50.10	66	554 975	23 842	.957 04	11.01
17	958 098	2 156	.997 75	49.21	67	531 133	24 730	.953 44	10.48
18	955 942	2 199	.997 70	48.32	68	506 403	25 553	.949 54	9.97
19	953 743	2 260	.997 63	47.43	69	480 850	26 302	.945 30	9.47
20	951 483	2 312	.997 57	46.54	**70**	454 548	26 955	.940 70	8.99
21	949 171	2 382	.997 49	45.66	71	427 593	27 481	.935 73	8.52
22	946 789	2 452	.997 41	44.77	72	400 112	27 872	.930 34	8.08
23	944 337	2 531	.997 32	43.88	73	372 240	28 104	.924 50	7.64
24	941 806	2 609	.997 23	43.00	74	344 136	28 154	.918 19	7.23
25	939 197	2 705	.997 12	42.12	**75**	315 982	28 009	.911 36	6.82
26	936 492	2 800	.997 01	41.24	76	287 973	27 651	.903 98	6.44
27	933 692	2 904	.996 89	40.36	77	260 322	27 071	.896 01	6.07
28	930 788	3 025	.996 75	39.49	78	233 251	26 262	.887 41	5.72
29	927 763	3 154	.996 60	38.61	79	206 989	25 224	.878 14	5.38
30	924 609	3 292	.996 44	37.74	**80**	181 765	23 966	.868 15	5.06
31	921 317	3 437	.996 27	36.88	81	157 799	22 502	.857 40	4.75
32	917 880	3 598	.996 08	36.01	82	135 297	20 857	.845 84	4.46
33	914 282	3 767	.995 88	35.15	83	114 440	19 062	.833 43	4.18
34	910 515	3 961	.995 65	34.29	84	95 378	17 157	.820 12	3.91
35	906 554	4 161	.995 41	33.44	**85**	78 221	15 185	.805 87	3.66
36	902 393	4 386	.995 14	32.59	86	63 036	13 198	.790 63	3.42
37	898 007	4 625	.994 85	31.75	87	49 838	11 245	.774 37	3.19
38	893 382	4 878	.994 54	30.91	88	38 593	9 378	.757 00	2.98
39	888 504	5 162	.994 19	30.08	89	29 215	7 638	.738 56	2.77
40	883 342	5 459	.993 82	29.25	**90**	21 577	6 063	.719 01	2.58
41	877 883	5 785	.993 41	28.43	91	15 514	4 681	.698 27	2.39
42	872 098	6 131	.992 97	27.62	92	10 833	3 506	.676 36	2.21
43	865 967	6 503	.992 49	26.81	93	7 327	2 540	.653 34	2.03
44	859 464	6 910	.991 96	26.01	94	4 787	1 776	.629 00	1.84
45	852 554	7 340	.991 39	25.21	**95**	3 011	1 193	.603 79	1.63
46	845 214	7 801	.990 77	24.43	96	1 818	813	.552 81	1.37
47	837 413	8 299	.990 09	23.65	97	1 005	551	.451 74	1.08
48	829 114	8 822	.989 36	22.88	98	454	329	.275 33	.78
49	820 292	9 392	.988 55	22.12	99	125	125	.000 00	.50

* Reproduced by permission of the Actuarial Society of America.

COMMUTATION COLUMNS 2 1/2%
Commissioners 1941 Standard Ordinary Mortality Table*

x	D_x	N_x	C_x	M_x	$1 + a_x$	A_x
0	1 023 102.00	31 374 230	22 538.536 6	257 876.88	30.665 8	0.252 054
1	975 609.76	30 351 128	5 491.969 1	235 338.35	31.109 9	.241 222
2	946 322.43	29 375 518	3 822.115 2	229 846.38	31.041 8	.242 884
3	919 419.28	28 429 196	3 032.216 8	226 024.26	30.920 8	.245 834
4	893 962.20	27 509 776	2 607.370 2	222 992.05	30.772 9	.249 442
5	869 550.88	26 615 814	2 341.136 0	220 384.68	30.608 7	.253 447
6	846 001.18	25 746 263	2 154.480 3	218 043.54	30.432 9	.257 734
7	823 212.53	24 900 262	1 983.744 5	215 889.06	30.247 7	.262 252
8	801 150.42	24 077 050	1 805.642 5	213 905.32	30.053 1	.266 998
9	779 804.53	23 275 899	1 613.174 7	212 099.67	29.848 4	.271 991
10	759 171.73	22 496 095	1 458.745 1	210 486.50	29.632 4	.277 258
11	739 196.60	21 736 923	1 377.065 5	209 027.75	29.406 1	.282 777
12	719 790.36	20 997 726	1 348.556 5	207 650.69	29.172 0	.288 488
13	700 885.94	20 277 936	1 353.882 1	206 302.13	28.931 9	.294 345
14	682 437.28	19 577 050	1 378.169 3	204 948.25	28.687 0	.300 318
15	664 414.29	18 894 613	1 393.730 0	203 570.08	28.438 0	.306 390
16	646 815.33	18 230 198	1 382.081 2	202 176.35	28.184 5	.312 572
17	629 657.27	17 583 383	1 382.353 7	200 794.27	27.925 3	.318 895
18	612 917.42	16 953 726	1 375.535 5	199 411.91	27.660 7	.325 349
19	596 592.68	16 340 808	1 379.212 3	198 036.38	27.390 2	.331 946
20	580 662.42	15 744 216	1 376.533 1	196 657.17	27.114 2	.338 677
21	565 123.40	15 163 553	1 383.619 6	195 280.63	26.832 3	.345 554
22	549 956.28	14 598 430	1 389.541 6	193 897 01	25.544 7	.352 568
23	535 153.17	14 048 474	1 399.327 5	192 507.47	26.251 3	.359 724
24	520 701.32	13 513 320	1 407.270 0	191 108.14	25.952 2	.367 021
25	506 594.02	12 992 619	1 423.464 9	189 700.88	25.647 0	.374 463
26	492 814.61	12 486 025	1 437.519 2	188 277.41	25.336 2	.382 045
27	479 357.22	11 993 210	1 454.549 1	186 839.89	25.019 4	.389 772
28	466 211.03	11 513 853	1 478.200 3	185 385.34	24.696 7	.397 643
29	453 361.83	11 047 642	1 503.646 4	183 907.14	24.368 3	.405 652
30	440 800.58	10 594 280	1 531.158 0	182 403.50	24.034 2	.413 800
31	428 518.18	10 153 480	1 559.609 4	180 872.34	23.694 4	.422 088
32	416 506.91	9 724 962	1 592.845 3	179 312.73	23 348 9	.430 516
33	404 755.37	9 308 455	1 626.987 4	177 719.88	22.997 7	.439 080
34	393 256.29	8 903 699	1 669.050 8	176 092.90	22.641 0	.447 781
35	381 995.63	8 510 443	1 710.561 0	174 423.84	22.278 9	.456 612
36	370 968.10	8 128 447	1 759.080 1	172 713.28	21.911 4	.465 574
37	360 161.02	7 757 479	1 809.692 8	170 954.20	21.538 9	.474 660
38	349 566.90	7 397 318	1 862.134 5	169 144.51	21.161 4	.483 869
39	339 178.75	7 047 751	1 922.486 9	167 282.38	20.778 9	.493 198
40	328 983.61	6 708 573	1 983.511 0	165 359.89	20.391 8	.502 639
41	318 976.11	6 379 589	2 050.694 7	163 376.38	20.000 2	.512 190
42	309 145.51	6 060 613	2 120.338 1	161 325.68	19.604 4	.521 844
43	299 485.04	5 751 467	2 194.136 7	159 205.35	19.204 5	.531 597
44	289 986.39	5 451 982	2 274.595 1	157 011.21	18.800 8	.541 443
45	280 638.95	5 161 996	2 357.209 9	154 736.61	18.393 7	.551 373
46	271 436.89	4 881 357	2 444.154 2	152 379.40	17.983 4	.561 381
47	262 372.33	4 609 920	2 536.765 0	149 935.25	17.570 1	.571 460
48	253 436.24	4 347 548	2 630.859 4	147 398.48	17.154 4	.581 600
49	244 624.00	4 094 112	2 732.529 2	144 767 62	16.736 3	.591 796
50	235 925.04	3 849 488	2 835.622 1	142 035.10	16.316 6	.602 035

* Reproduced by permission of the Actuarial Society of America.

COMMUTATION COLUMNS 2 1/2% (Continued)
Commissioners 1941 Standard Ordinary Mortality Table*

x	D_x	N_x	C_x	M_x	$1 + a_x$	A_x
51	227 335.15	3 613 563	2 943.137 4	139 199.47	15.895 3	.612 310
52	218 847.25	3 386 227	3 053.177 2	136 256.34	15.473 0	.622 609
53	210 456.33	3 167 380	3 168.222 9	133 203.16	15.050 1	.632 925
54	202 155.03	2 956 924	3 283.812 1	130 034.94	14.627 0	.643 244
55	193 940.61	2 754 769	3 401.913 1	126 751.12	14.204 2	.653 556
56	185 808.43	2 560 828	3 522.090 1	123 349.21	13.782 1	.663 852
57	177 754.43	2 375 020	3 641.783 5	119 827.12	13 361 2	.674 116
58	169 777.17	2 197 265	3 761.696 8	116 185.34	12.942 1	.684 340
59	161 874.57	2 027 488	3 880.185 4	112 423.64	12.525 1	.694 511
60	154 046.23	1 865 614	3 996.199 9	108 543.46	12.110 7	.704 616
61	146 292.80	1 711 567	4 107.708 0	104 547.26	11.699 6	.714 644
62	138 616.97	1 565 275	4 216.676 0	100 439.55	11.292 1	.724 583
63	131 019.40	1 426 658	4 315.413 8	96 222.87	10.888 9	.734 417
64	123 508.39	1 295 638	4 407.831 2	91 907.46	10.490 3	.744 139
65	116 088.15	1 172 130	4 489.449 7	87 499.63	10.096 9	.753 734
66	108 767.29	1 056 042	4 558.728 2	83 010.18	9.709 2	.763 191
67	101 555.70	947 274.4	4 613.189 3	78 451.45	9.327 6	.772 497
68	94 465.545	845 718.7	4 650.452 1	73 838.26	8.952 7	.781 642
69	87 511.050	751 253.1	4 670.014 3	69 187.81	8.584 7	.790 618
70	80 706.625	663 742.1	4 669.226 0	64 517.79	8.224 1	.799 411
71	74 068.942	583 035.4	4 644.235 4	59 848.57	7.871 5	.808 012
72	67 618.148	508 966.5	4 595.428 1	55 204.33	7.527 1	.816 413
73	61 373.498	441 348.3	4 520.662 7	50 608.90	7.191 2	.824 605
74	55 355.921	379 974.8	4 418.249 2	46 088.24	6.864 2	.832 580
75	49 587.526	324 618.9	4 288.286 9	41 669.99	6.546 4	.840 332
76	44 089.787	275 031.4	4 130.220 2	37 381.70	6.238 0	.847 854
77	38 884.206	230 941.6	3 944.961 8	33 251.48	5.939 2	.855 141
78	33 990.850	192 057.4	3 733.725 8	29 306.52	5.650 3	.862 189
79	29 428.077	158 066.6	3 498.684 1	25 572.80	5.371 3	.868 993
80	25 211.636	128 638.5	3 243.115 8	22 074.11	5.102 3	.875 553
81	21 353.602	103 426.8	2 970.736 8	18 831.00	4.843 5	.881 865
82	17 862.047	82 073.24	2 686.402 0	15 860.26	4.594 8	.887 931
83	14 739.984	64 211.19	2 395.321 2	13 173.86	4.356 3	.893 750
84	11 985.151	49 471.21	2 103.356 1	10 778.54	4.127 7	.899 324
85	9 589.474 6	37 486.06	1 816.194 6	8 675.180	3.909 1	.904 656
86	7 539.390 5	27 896.58	1 540.039 4	6 858.986	3.700 1	.909 753
87	5 815.463 2	20 357.19	1 280.145 4	5 318.946	3.500 5	.914 621
88	4 393.477 3	14 541.73	1 041.564 6	038.801	3.309 8	.919 272
89	3 244.754 6	10 148.25	827.621 52	2 997.236	3.127 6	.923 717
90	2 337.992 9	6 903.496	640.937 68	2 169.615	2.952 7	.927 982
91	1 640.030 9	4 565.503	482.773 06	1 528.677	2.783 8	.932 103
92	1 117.257 1	2 925.472	352.770 63	1 045.904	2.618 4	.936 136
93	737.236 29	1 808.215	249.339 10	693.133 5	2.452 7	.940 178
94	469.915 86	1 070.979	170.088 82	443.794 4	2.279 1	.944 413
95	288.365 67	601.062 8	111.467 79	273.705 6	2.084 4	.949 162
96	169.864 58	312.697 2	74.109 795	162.237 8	1.840 9	.955 101
97	91.611 740	142.832 6	49.001 885	88.128 0	1.559 1	.961 973
98	40.375 419	51.220 9	28.545 208	39.126 1	1.268 6	.969 058
99	10.845 444	10.845 4	10.580 921	10.580 9	1.000 0	.975 610

* Reproduced by permission of the Actuarial Society of America.

COMMISSIONERS 1958 STANDARD ORDINARY MORTALITY TABLE*

Age, x	Number Living l_x	Number Dying d_x	Deaths per 1,000	Age, x	Number Living l_x	Number Dying d_x	Deaths per 1,000
0	10,000,000	70,800	7.08	**50**	8,762,306	72,902	8.32
1	9,929,200	17,475	1.76	51	8,689,404	79,160	9.11
2	9,911,725	15,066	1.52	52	8,610,244	85,758	9.96
3	9,896,659	14,449	1.46	53	8,524,486	92,832	10.89
4	9,882,210	13,835	1.40	54	8,431,654	100,337	11.90
5	9,868,375	13,322	1.35	**55**	8,331,317	108,307	13.00
6	9,855,053	12,812	1.30	56	8,223,010	116,849	14.21
7	9,842,241	12,401	1.26	57	8,106,161	125,970	15.54
8	9,829,840	12,091	1.23	58	7,980,191	135,663	17.00
9	9,817,749	11,879	1.21	59	7,844,528	145,830	18.59
10	9,805,870	11,865	1.21	**60**	7,698,698	156,592	20.34
11	9,794,005	12,047	1.23	61	7,542,106	167,736	22.24
12	9,781,958	12,325	1.26	62	7,374,370	179,271	24.31
13	9,769,633	12,896	1.32	63	7,195,099	191,174	26.57
14	9,756,737	13,562	1.39	64	7,003,925	203,394	29.04
15	9,743,175	14,225	1.46	**65**	6,800,531	215,917	31.75
16	9,728,950	14,983	1.54	66	6,584,614	228,749	34.74
17	9,713,967	15,737	1.62	67	6,355,865	241,777	38.04
18	9,698,230	16,390	1.69	68	6,114,088	254,835	41.68
19	9,681,840	16,846	1.74	69	5,859,253	267,241	45.61
20	9,664,994	17,300	1.79	**70**	5,592,012	278,426	49.79
21	9,647,694	17,655	1.83	71	5,313,586	287,731	54.15
22	9,630,039	17,912	1.86	72	5,025,855	294,766	58.65
23	9,612,127	18,167	1.89	73	4,731,089	299,289	63.26
24	9,593,960	18,324	1.91	74	4,431,800	301,894	68.12
25	9,575,636	18,481	1.93	**75**	4,129,906	303,011	73.37
26	9,557,155	18,732	1.96	76	3,826,895	303,014	79.18
27	9,538,423	18,981	1.99	77	3,523,881	301,997	85.70
28	9,519,442	19,324	2.03	78	3,221,884	299,829	93.06
29	9,500,118	19,760	2.08	79	2,922,055	295,683	101.19
30	9,480,358	20,193	2.13	**80**	2,626,372	238,848	109.98
31	9,460,165	20,718	2.19	81	2,337,524	278,983	119.35
32	9,439,447	21,239	2.25	82	2,058,541	265,902	129.17
33	9,418,208	21,850	2.32	83	1,792,639	249,858	139.38
34	9,396,358	22,551	2.40	84	1,542,781	231,433	150.01
35	9,373,807	23,528	2.51	**85**	1,311,348	211,311	161.14
36	9,350,279	24,685	2.64	86	1,100,037	190,108	172.82
37	9,325,594	26,112	2.80	87	909,929	168,455	185.13
38	9,299,482	27,991	3.01	88	741,474	146,997	198.25
39	9,271,491	30,132	3.25	89	594,477	126,303	212.46
40	9,241,359	32,622	3.53	**90**	468,174	106,809	228.14
41	9,208,737	35,362	3.84	91	361,365	88,813	245.77
42	9,173,375	38,253	4.17	92	272,552	72,480	265.93
43	9,135,122	41,382	4.53	93	200,072	57,881	289.30
44	9,093,740	44,741	4.92	94	142,191	45,026	316.66
45	9,048,999	48,412	5.35	**95**	97,165	34,128	351.24
46	9,000,587	52,473	5.83	96	63,037	25,250	400.56
47	8,948,114	56,910	6.36	97	37,787	18,456	488.42
48	8,891,204	61,794	6.95	98	19,331	12,916	668.15
49	8,829,410	67,104	7.60	99	6,415	6,415	1,000.00

* Reproduced by permission of the Actuarial Society of America.

COMMUTATION COLUMNS 2 1/2%*
Commissioners 1958 Standard Ordinary Mortality Table

Age, x	D_x	N_x	C_x	M_x
0	10,000,000.0000	324,850,104.9680	69,073.1710	2,076,826.7172
1	9,687,024.4290	314,850,104.9680	16,632.9566	2,007,753.5462
2	9,434,122.5838	305,163,080.5390	13,990.2787	1,991,120.5896
3	9,190,031.7084	295,728,957.9552	13,090.0808	1,977,130.3109
4	8,952,794.4741	286,538,926.2468	12,228.1241	1,964,040.2301
5	8,722,205.5791	277,586,131.7727	11,487.5189	1,951,812.1060
6	8,497,981.3556	268,863,926.1936	10,778.2903	1,940,324.5871
7	8,279,935.2370	260,365,944.8380	10,178.0782	1,929,546.2968
8	8,067,807.4636	252,086,009.6010	9,681.6066	1,919,368.2186
9	7,861,350.0557	244,018,202.1374	9,279.8558	1,909,686.6120
10	7,660,329.9546	236,156,852.0817	9,042.8478	1,900,406.7562
11	7,464,449.7860	228,496,522.1271	8,957.6178	1,891,363.9084
12	7,273,432.4866	221,032,072.3411	8,940.8062	1,882,406.2906
13	7,087,090.8833	213,758,639.8545	9,126.8500	1,873,465.4844
14	6,905,108.1581	206,671,548.9712	9,364.0939	1,864,338.6344
15	6,727,326.7826	199,766,440.8131	9,582.3146	1,854,974.5405
16	6,553,663.2627	193,039,114.0305	9,846.7536	1,845,392.2259
17	6,383,971.1254	186,485,450.7678	10,090.0279	1,835,545.4723
18	6,218,174.4633	180,101,479.6424	10,252.3993	1,825,455.4444
19	6,056,259.3006	173,883,305.1791	10,280.6243	1,815,203.0451
20	5,898,264.9735	167,827,045.8785	10,300.1828	1,804,922.4208
21	5,744,104.7377	161,928,780.9050	10,255.1657	1,794,622.2380
22	5,593,749.4258	156,184,676.1673	10,150.6810	1,784,367.0723
23	5,447,165.8414	150,590,926.7415	10,044.0865	1,774,216.3913
24	5,304,263.9929	145,143,760.9001	9,883.7932	1,764,172.3048
25	5,165,007.9517	139,839,496.9072	9,725.3439	1,754,288.5116
26	5,029,306.7854	134,674,488.9555	9,617.0037	1,744,563.1677
27	4,897,023.7928	129,645,182.1701	9,507.1611	1,734,946.1640
28	4,768,076.9758	124,748,158.3773	9,442.8900	1,725,439.0029
29	4,642,339.5370	119,980,081.4015	9,420.4356	1,715,996.1129
30	4,519,691.3751	115,337,741.8645	9,392.0634	1,706,575.6773
31	4,400,062.8465	110,818,050.4894	9,401.2183	1,697,183.6139
32	4,283,343.0569	106,417,987.6429	9,402.5686	1,687,782.3956
33	4,169,468.7479	102,134,644.5860	9,437.1317	1,678,379.8270
34	4,058,337.1968	97,965,175.8381	9,502.3390	1,668,942.6953
35	3,949,851.0856	93,906,838.6413	9,672.2130	1,659,440.3563
36	3,843,840.9771	89,956,987.5557	9,900.3401	1,649,768.1433
37	3,740,188.4751	86,113,146.5786	10,217.2318	1,639,867.8032
38	3,638,747.0704	82,372,958.1035	10,685.3232	1,629,650.5714
39	3,539,311.8617	78,734,211.0331	11,222.0794	1,618,965.2482
40	3,441,765.0620	75,194,899.1714	11,853.1042	1,607,743.1688
41	3,345,966.5023	71,753,134.1094	12,535.2926	1,595,890.0646
42	3,251,822.2774	68,407,167.6071	13,229.3739	1,583,354.7720
43	3,159,280.1784	65,155,345.3297	13,962.4424	1,570,125.3981
44	3,068,262.0685	61,996,065.1513	14,727.5918	1,556,162.9557
45	2,978,698.8164	58,927,803.0828	15,547.3085	1,541,435.3639
46	2,890,500.3526	55,949,104.2664	16,440.4699	1,525,888.0554
47	2,803,559.9048	53,058,603.9138	17,395.7457	1,509,447.5855
48	2,717,784.6405	50,255,044.0090	18,427.9447	1,492,051.8398
49	2,633,069.2135	47,537,259.3685	19,523.3861	1,473,623.8951

* Reproduced by permission of the Actuarial Society of America.

COMMUTATION COLUMNS 2 1/2%* (Continued)
Commissioners 1958 Standard Ordinary Mortality Table

Age, x	D_x	N_x	C_x	M_x
50	2,549,324.6723	44,904,190.1550	20,692.9455	1,454,100.5090
51	2,466,453.0891	42,354,865.4827	21,921.2231	1,433,407.5635
52	2,384,374.4270	39,888,412.3936	23,169.1325	1,411,486.3404
53	2,303,049.8123	37,504,037.9666	24,468.5917	1,388,317.2079
54	2,222,409.2905	35,200,988.1543	25,801.7117	1,363,848.6162
55	2,142,402.4988	32,978,578.8638	27,171.9031	1,338,046.9045
56	2,062,976.8254	30,836,176.3650	28,599.9098	1,310,875.0014
57	1,984,060.3996	28,773,199.5396	30,080.3536	1,282,275.0916
58	1,905,588.3725	26,789,139.1400	31,604.8230	1,252,194.7380
59	1,827,505.7998	24,883,550.7675	33,144.7659	1,220,589.9150
60	1,749,787.7198	23,056,044.9677	34,722.7242	1,187,445.1491
61	1,672,387.2632	21,306,257.2479	36,286.6291	1,152,722.4249
62	1,595,310.6622	19,633,869.9847	37,836.1144	1,116,435.7958
63	1,518,564.5694	18,038,559.3225	39,364.2006	1,078,599.6814
64	1,442,162.1578	16,519,994.7531	40,858.9196	1,039,235.4808
65	1,366,128.5462	15,077,832.5953	42,316.6940	998,376.5612
66	1,290,491.6985	13,711,704.0491	43,738.1310	956,059.8672
67	1,215,278.1249	12,421,212.3506	45,101.6207	912,321.7362
68	1,140,535.6099	11,205,934.2257	46,378.0358	867,220.1155
69	1,066,339.5743	10,065,398.6158	47,449.5963	820,842.0797
70	992,881.7500	8,999,059.0415	48,229.7870	773,392.4834
71	920,435.3077	8,006,177.2915	48,625.9779	725,162.6964
72	849,359.6946	7,085,741.9838	48,599.8832	676,536.7185
73	780,043.7396	6,236,382.2892	48,142.0663	627,936.8353
74	712,876.2140	5,456,338.5496	47,376.6752	579,794.7690
75	648,112.3021	4,743,462.3356	46,392.1628	532,418.0938
76	585,912.5111	4,095,350.0335	45,261.0951	486,025.9310
77	526,360.8716	3,509,437.5224	44,008.9628	440,764.8359
78	469,513.8465	2,983,076.6508	42,627.3426	396,755.8731
79	415,434.9294	2,513,562.8043	41,012.5834	354,128.5305
80	364,289.7989	2,098,127.8749	39,087.3533	313,115.9471
81	316,317.3241	1,733,838.0760	36,831.6174	274,028.5938
82	271,770.6619	1,417,520.7519	34,248.4382	237,196.9764
83	230,893.6600	1,145,750.0900	31,397.0289	202,948.5382
84	193,865.0736	914,856.4300	28,372.4430	171,551.5093
85	160,764.2229	720,991.3564	25,273.7507	143,179.0663
86	131,569.3974	560,227.1335	22,183.1949	117,905.3156
87	106,177.1855	428,657.7361	19,177.1362	95,722.1207
88	84,410.3641	322,480.5506	16,326.1748	76,544.9845
89	66,025.3978	238,070.1865	13,685.6613	60,218.8097
90	50,729.3636	172,044.7887	11,291.0955	46,533.1484
91	38,200.9638	121,315.4251	9,159.6932	35,242.0529
92	28,109.5415	83,114.4613	7,292.8738	26,082.3597
93	20,131.0686	55,004.9198	5,681.8884	18,789.4859
94	13,958.1795	34,873.8512	4,312.1729	13,107.5975
95	9,305.5630	20,915.6717	3,188.7449	8,795.4246
96	5,889.8533	11,610.1087	2,301.6880	5,606.6797
97	3,444.5103	5,720.2554	1,641.3408	3,304.9917
98	1,719.1569	2,275.7451	1,120.6380	1,663.6509
99	556.5882	556.5882	543.0129	543.0129

* Reproduced by permission of the Actuarial Society of America.

MATHEMATICAL SYMBOLS AND ABBREVIATIONS

Symbols and Abbreviations of Commercial Arithmetic

#	Number (if written before a numeral); pounds (weight), lb. (if written after a numeral.)	Apr.	April	Dr.	Debit, debtor, doctor
		a/s	Account sales		
		Aug.	August	E	East
		av.	Average	ea.	Each
		avoir.	Avoirdupois	e.g.	(exempli gratia) for example
		bal.	Balance		
@	At, as "@ 5¢ per C," for "at 5 cents per hundred."	bbl. *or* brl.	Barrel	etc.	And so forth
				ex.	Example, exercise, express
		bk.	Bank, book		
		bl.	Bale	exch.	Exchange
		B/L	Bill of lading	exp.	Expense
%	Per cent; per hundred.	bu.	Bushel	F	Fahrenheit
		bx.	Box	Feb.	February
¢	Cents (placed after figures)	C	(centum) hundred	f.o.b.	Free on board
				Fri.	Friday
$	Dollars, (prefixed before figures).	cd.	Cord	frt.	Freight
		cg.	Centigram	ft. *or* f.	Foot
		ch.	Chain	gal.	Gallon
£	Pounds (British currency)	chg.	Charge	gi.	Gill
		c.i.f.	Carriage and insurance free.	gr.	Grain
✓	Check mark			gro.	Gross
&	And, as in "Smith, Jones & Co."	ck.	Check	gr. gro.	Great gross
		cm.	Centimeter	guar.	Guarantee
		cml.	Commercial	hf.	Half
c/o	Care of	Co.	Company, county	hhd.	Hogshead
A	Acre			hr.	Hour
a/c	Account	c.o.d.	Cash on delivery	i.e.	(id est) that is
acct.	Account	coll.	Collection	in.	Inch, inches
ad val	(ad valorem), according to value	com.	Commission	ins.	Insurance
		cr.	Credit, creditor, crate	*inst.*	(instant) the present month
A.M.	(ante meridiem) in the morning, between midnight and the following noon. 12:00 A.M. is noon, better 12:00 M, 12:01 A.M. is one minute after midnight.	cs.	Case	int.	Interest
or		c. *or*	Cent	inv.	Invoice
a.m.		ct.		inv'y	Inventory
		cu.	Cubic	Jan.	January
		cwt.	Hundredweight	kg.	Keg, kilogram
		d	Pence (British currency)	km.	Kilometer
				lb. lbs.	Pound, pounds
		da.	Day	lp	List price
		Dec.	December	ltd.	Limited
		dept.	Department	L.S.	(locus sigillis) place for the seal
		dft.	Draft		
amt.	Amount	disc.	Discount		
ans.	Answer	dm.	Decimeter	M	(mille) thousand; meridiem as in 12:00 M
ap	Apothecaries' weight or measure	do.	Ditto		
		doz.	Dozen		
		dr.	Dram	m.	Mill, meter

MATHEMATICAL SYMBOLS AND ABBREVIATIONS (Continued)

Symbols and Abbreviations of Commercial Arithmetic

Mar.	March	P.M.	(post meridiem)	Sat.	Saturday
mdse.	Merchandise	*or*	in the after-	sec.	Second
mi.	Mile	p.m.	noon, between	sec'y	Secretary
min.	Minute		noon and the	Sept.	September
mm.	Millimeter		following mid-	set.	Settlement
mo.	Month		night. 12:00	sig.	Signed, signa-
Mon.	Monday		P.M. is mid-		ture
mortg.	Mortgage		night, 12:01	sq.	Square
N, NE,	North, North-		P.M. is one	stk.	Stock
NW,	east, North-		minute after	Sun.	Sunday
etc.	west, etc.		noon.	T.	Ton
no. *or*	Number	pp.	Pages	temp.	Temperature
numb.		pr.	Pair	Thu.	Thursday
Nov.	November	*prox.*	(proximo) in the	treas.	Treasurer,
Oct.	October		following		treasury
O.K.	Correct		month	Tues.	Tuesday
oz.	Ounce	pt.	Pint, point	*ult.*	(ultimo) in the
p.	Page	pwt.	Pennyweight		last month
par.	Paragraph	(*or*		*via*	By way of
pay't	Payment	dwt.)		viz.	(videlicet)
pc.	Piece	qr.	Quire		namely
pd.	Paid	qt.	Quart	vol.	Volume
per	By, by the, as in	rd.	Rod, road	W	West
	"per C," "per	rec'd	Received	Wed.	Wednesday
	M," "per doz."	rec't	Receipt	wk.	Week
pfd.	Preferred	rm.	Ream	wt.	Weight
pk.	Peck, pecks	S, SE,	South, South-	yd.	Yard
pkg.	Package	SW,	east, South-	yr.	Year
		etc.	west, etc.		

Symbols Belonging to Plane Geometry

In blackboard presentation combined with oral discussion a variety of informal abbreviations is acceptable. But in written reports it is best to use only standard abbreviations, preferably those which are found on a typewriter. Avoid characters not sufficiently distinctive as to remain legible and unambiguous when written hurriedly. When used as nouns, the plural may be indicated by adding "s": when used as relations the copula "is" and preposition "to" may be deleted.

A°	*Angle* associated with the point or vector A. Use "rt°" for "right angle," and "st°" for "straight angle." Avoid ∠ which resembles symbol for "less than." Use "arc" rather than "⌒" to avoid confusion with bar for "line segment."
∠	Angle
∡	Angles

MATHEMATICAL SYMBOLS AND ABBREVIATIONS (Continued)

⊙   Circle. ⊙ A(B) designates the circle with center A passing through B. ⊙ (AB) has AB as diameter, and ⊙ (ABC) circumscribes △ABC. ⊙A, r has center A, radius r.

Ⓢ   Circles.

A : B(S)   Collinear. The line AB passes through the point S. Use $\overline{AB}$(S) for "S lies between A and B."

≅   Congruent. (Same shape and same size).

A : B(S,r)   Point of division. "S divides AB in the ratio AS : BS = r." Use (S, −) for internal division, and (S, +) for external division.

=   Equal, equivalent. The quantity measured may be indicated in parenthesis at the right of the statement, as "(area)," "(vol.)," "(angle)." Avoid pictogram ⌢⌣.

$\overline{\wedge}$ Perspective. See ABC : DEF(S) below.

$\wedge$ Projective. See ABC : : DEF below.

a/b   Fraction (with numerator a, denominator b). Same meaning as quotient "a ÷ b" (with dividend a, divisor b) and ratio a : b (with antecedent a, consequent b).

$\dot\sim$ Homothetic (Similar and perspective). "ABC $\dot\sim$ DEF" indicates that corresponding lines, such as BC and EF, are parallel. Use "$\dot\sim$ (S, r)" for "the homothecy with center S and ratio r."

AB   Line, segment, vector. When further distinctions are desired, use $\overline{AB}$ (or AB) for the length of the line segment (distance between A and B), use $\overrightarrow{AB}$ for the vector (displacement from A toward B), and use A : B for the infinite line (determined by the two points).

‖   Parallel.

▱   Parallelogram (vertices are named in counterclockwise order).

⊥   Perpendicular.

ABC : : DEF   Projective (related by a sequence of perspectivities). Same meaning as pictogram "$\wedge$."

ABC : DEF(S)   Perspective. The lines A : D and B : E and C : F are concurrent at the point S (center of perspectivity). Same meaning as pictogram "$\overline{\wedge}$."

QED   End of proof.

QEF   End of construction.

R   Cross ratio, anharmonic ratio R(AC, BD) = AB · CD/ AD · CB. R = −1 means "harmonic" and may be used for collinear points (range), concurrent lines (pencil), or cyclic quadrangle. R(CA, BD) = 1/R(AC, BD) = R(AC, DB). Also R(AB, CD) = 1 − R(AC, BD).

∼   Similar. △ABC ∼ △DEF means that A corresponds to D, B to E, and C to F, respectively.

□   Square. Use "rect" for "rectangle," "quad" for

MATHEMATICAL SYMBOLS AND ABBREVIATIONS (Continued)

	"quadrilateral" (or quadrangle), and "trap" for "trapezoid" rather than pictograms.
ABC $\doteqdot$ DEF(r = 1)	Displaced by translation. (The triangles are congruent and similarly placed).
$\triangle$	Triangle. Use "isos" for "isosceles triangle" (naming vertex opposite base first).
B̌	Vertex. In using triliteral symbol ABC, A is on the initial side, B is the vertex, C is on the terminal side. The vertex may be marked with a caret "AB̌C" or by superscript position "A^BC."

General Mathematical Symbols and Abbreviations

"Bold-face" or gothic type—To indicate vectors corresponding italic type indicates magnitude of the vector. In manuscript and at the blackboard, bold-faced type is variously indicated by wavy underscoring, or enclosure in a circle, or even by wavy overscoring. Some persons use German type.

Half-spaces—In writing numbers with many recorded digits, half-spaces (rather than commas or other marks) may well be used to separate convenient groups of digits. Thus $\pi = 3.14159\ 26536 -$.

Superscripts—To indicate: **1.** powers, as in x^2, $(a - x)^n$, etc. In modern practice $a^0 = 1$ always by definition (except for $a = 0$). Also in ∞', ∞^2, etc., indicating number of degrees of freedom. Wherever the context restricts the value of a to non-negative (real) values and n to positive integers, $a^{1/n}$ means the non-negative (real) nth root of a. For complex numbers, x^y is defined as $e^{y\ (\log x)}$, where the principal value of $\log x$ is to be taken. In tables 0.0^5314 may be used to indicate 0.00000314. Note special use of $\sin^n x$ for $(\sin x)^n$ except for $n = -1$, also for $\cos^n x$, etc. **2.** symbolic powers, or order of iteration, as in T^n or in D^n $(= d^n/dx^n)$, or in inverse functions as in $\sin^{-1}$, $\cos^{-1}$, $\sinh^{-1}$, etc. **3.** order of differentiation, as in y' ("y prime"), y'' ("y second," or "y double prime"), $\cdots$, $y^{(N)}$, $\cdots$ **4.** feet and inches, as in $3'4''$. **5.** degrees, minutes, seconds, as in $34°5'17''$. Do not omit ° for common angles. Write $0°$, $30°$, $45°$, $60°$, etc., not 0, 30, 45, 60, etc. Do not use superscript, ^{r}, for radians. Write $180° = \pi$ rad, but write $\cos (\pi/3)$ for $\cos 60°$. **6.** days, hours, minutes, seconds, as in $10^d3^h27^m5.3^s$. **7.** degrees of temperature as in $104°$. Where C (for Centigrade) or F (for Fahrenheit) is given, recent usage approves the omission of the °, thus $100C = 212F$, and $-40C = -40F$. **8.** For use with integral sign $\int$, and with vertical bar $|$, see these symbols. **9.** Vertex, as in A^BC.

Dot-accents—To indicate derivatives with respect to time, (Newton's notation), as in $\dot{x}$ for x-component of velocity, and $\ddot{x}$ for x-component of acceleration.

Subscripts—To indicate: **1.** position in a sequence, set, or matrix, as in a_1, a_2, a_3, $\cdots a_n$, $\cdots$, or $a_0x^n + a_1x^{n-1} + \cdots + a_rx^{n-r} + \cdots a_n$ or in $\begin{pmatrix} a_{11}a_{12}a_{13} \\ a_{21}a_{22}a_{23} \end{pmatrix}$. **2.** general distinguishing mark. Two subscripts may be written adjacently without commas as a_{11} and to be read "a sub one one," not "a sub eleven." A subscript is sometimes enclosed in parentheses as in $F_{(0)1}$ where such distinction seems demanded. For special uses see associated symbols.

MATHEMATICAL SYMBOLS AND ABBREVIATIONS (Continued)

Juxtaposition—To indicate: **1.** the algebraic product, as in $2bxy$. **2.** the logical product as in AB where A and B are given classes, and in symbolic logic. Also written with centrally placed dot as $A \cdot B$. **3.** the group product, as in ST (the result of performing first S, then T, or in aH, the co-set consisting for given a of all operations ah, where h is in H. **4.** general operational or functional combination as in dy/dx, $\sin x$, $\log x$, $\max y$, $\lim x_n$, etc. **5.** sequence of points or other elements determining a geometric figure, as line AB, parallelogram $ABCD$, angle ABC, etc. **6.** sum of products (in tensor notation) when index appears as subscript for one factor and superscript for another. Thus $a_i x^i$ means $\Sigma a_i x^i$, in tensor notation.

( )—Parentheses ("round brackets") to indicate: **1.** aggregation, as in $(a + b) \cdot (a - b) = a^2 - b^2$. **2.** argument of function, as in $f(x)$, $g(x,y)$, etc. **3.** sequence or set, as in $a = (a_i)$, $x = (x_{ij})$, (x,y,z), etc. **4.** matrix, as in $\begin{pmatrix} a_{11}a_{12}a_{13} \\ a_{21}a_{22}a_{23} \end{pmatrix}$ also written as $\begin{Vmatrix} a_{11}a_{12}a_{13} \\ a_{21}a_{22}a_{23} \end{Vmatrix}$. **5.** permutation (or substitution) in group theory as in $\begin{pmatrix} a_1 a_2 a_3 \\ b_1 b_2 b_3 \end{pmatrix}$ where a_i is replaced by $b_i (i = 1,2,3)$. **6.** binomial coefficient, as in $\binom{n}{r} = n!/[r!(n - r)!]$. This is also designated by $C_{n,r}$ or $_nC_r$. For n,r, positive integers, $\binom{-n}{r} = (-1)^r \binom{n + r - 1}{r}$, $\binom{n}{-r} = 0$, by definition. **7.** cycle or cylic permutation (in group theory) as in (a_1, a_2, a_3) for $\begin{pmatrix} a_1 a_2 a_3 \\ a_2 a_3 a_1 \end{pmatrix}$. **8.** greatest common divisor, as in $(30,42) = 6$, $(7,5) = 1$. **9.** inner product as in $(ab) = \Sigma_i a_i b_i$. **10.** segment or open interval, as in (a,b), for system of values of x, where $a < x < b$.

Superscript $^{(\ )}$—To indicate: **1.** general index as distinguished from exponent. **2.** index of order of derivative as in y, y', $\cdots$, $y^{(n)}$, $\cdots$. **3.** "factorial," as in $x^{(r)} = x(x - 1) \cdots (x - r + 1)$. By definition $x^{(-r)} = 1/[(x + 1) \cdot (x + 2) \cdots (x + r)]$.

[ ]—Brackets ("square brackets"), to indicate: **1.** aggregation. **2.** argument of function as with ( ). **3.** greatest integer in, as $[2] = 2$, $[-7/3] = -3$. **4.** inner product (for coefficients in normal equations in the method of least squares), as in $[aa]$, $[XY]$, etc. **5.** outer product of vectors. Other notations are $V\ \boldsymbol{ab}$ and $\boldsymbol{a} \times \boldsymbol{b}$. **6.** divided difference (in formal interpolation). $[x_i] = y_i$, $[x_i, x_{i+1}] = (y_{i+1} - y_i)/(x_{i+1} - x_i)$, $\cdots$ $[x_i, x_{i+1}, \cdots, x_{i+r}] = ([x_{i+1}, \cdots, x_{i+r}] - [x_i, \cdots, x_{i+r-1}])/(x_{i+r} - x_i)$. **7.** range of points (in projective geometry) as in $[P]$. **8.** base (basis) of Abelian group, as in $[a,b, \cdots, k]$. **9.** module or ideal, as $[2] = [0, \pm 2, \pm 4, \cdots, \pm 2n, \cdots]$. **10.** Christoffel symbol, as in $\begin{bmatrix} mn \\ p \end{bmatrix} = \frac{1}{2}\left(\frac{\partial g_{pm}}{\partial x^n} + \frac{\partial g_{pn}}{\partial x^m} = \frac{\partial g_{mn}}{\partial x^p} \right)$. **11.** closed interval, as in $[a,b]$ for system of values of x where $a \leqq x \leqq b$.

Subscript note. The use of adjacent subscripts, rather than of indices placed directly below is recommended on account of its availability for running text, and its economy of space and of expense in type setting. Thus use $\sum_i$ rather than $\sum_i$, $\int_a^b$ rather than $\int_a^b$, etc.

MATHEMATICAL SYMBOLS AND ABBREVIATIONS (Continued)

{ }—Braces ("curly brackets") to indicate: **1.**: aggregation, as in $\{(x-a)(x-b)\}^2$. **2.** class of (in theory of aggregates), where the general element only is mentioned, as in $\{a_i\} = [a_1, a_2, a_3]$, $(i = 1,2,3)$. **3.** Christoffel symbol, as in $\left\{ \begin{matrix} m & n \\ & p \end{matrix} \right\} = g^{rp} \left[\begin{matrix} m & n \\ & p \end{matrix} \right]$. **4.** the members in a uniquely determined set, as in $\{x_1, x_2, \cdots x_n\}$.

< >—Angle brackets to indicate: **1.** aggregation. **2.** closed interval as with [ ]. **3.** Angle between as in $A \cdot B = AB \cos <A, B>$. Use sparingly because of ambiguity with signs of inequality.

| |—Vertical bars, to indicate: **1.** absolute value (modulus of complex number). as $|a + ib|^2 = a^2 + b^2$. **2.** magnitude of (for vectors) as $a = |a|$. **3.** determinant, as in $\begin{vmatrix} a & b \\ c & d \end{vmatrix} = ad - bc$. The use of the notation $|a_{ij}|$ for the determinant of the matrix (a_{ij}), is common but is ambiguous. The notation det (a_{ij}) may be used for this determinant.

‖ ‖—Double bars, to indicate: **1.** matrix as in $\begin{Vmatrix} a_{11}a_{12}a_{13} \\ a_{21}a_{22}a_{23} \end{Vmatrix}$ or in $\|a_{ij}\|$. **2.** generalized length (for metrical spaces), as in $\|f\|^2 = \int f^2(x)dx$. **3.** To indicate the length of a vector, as in $\|X\|$.

(], [).—For intervals, as (a,b], for system of values of x for which $a < x \leq b$, and [a,b), for system of values of x for which $a \leq x < b$. Similarly $(a,b >$, and $< a,b)$ are sometimes used for these respectively.

⟨ ⟩—Brackets ("bent brackets"), to indicate an ordered set of objects, as in $\langle x, y, z \rangle$.

⊢—Is deducible from.

⊨—Is valid, or is a tautology (in logic), as in $\models A$ (A is valid).

∪—(is) the union, or sum or join (of), as in $A \cup B$.

∩—(is) the intersection, or product (of), as in $A \cap B$.

⊃—**1.** contains (or containing) as proper sub-class. **2.** implies (or implying).

⊇—contains (or containing) as sub-class. (Some writers use, ⊃, for this.)

⊂—(is) contained as proper sub-class within.

⊆—(is) contained as sub-class within. (Some writers use, ⊂, for this.)

≡—**1.** (is) identical with. $\equiv_x$ indicates (is) identical with for all values of x for which both members are defined. **2.** (is) congruent to (with respect to indicated modulus) as in $a \equiv b \pmod{m}$. **3.** (is) equivalent to (in formal logic).

=—(is) equal (to).

∧—and (in logic).

∨—or (in logic), as in $p \vee q$ (p or q), and/or

⊻—exclusive or, as in $p \veebar q$ (p or q, but not both).

<—(is) less than.

>—(is greater than. Use "less than" preferably as in "$a < x < b$" rather than "$b > x > a$" since former corresponds to order of real numbers on x-axis.

≦ *or* ≤—(is) less than or equal to. Sometimes read (in the case of real numbers) as "(is) not greater than."

≧ *or* ≥—(is) greater than or equal to. Sometimes read (in the case of real numbers) as "(is) not less than."

MATHEMATICAL SYMBOLS AND ABBREVIATIONS (Continued)

$\not\equiv$—**1.** (is) not identically equal (to). (Not "identically unequal to"), is unequal to for at least one value. **2.** (is) not congruent (to).

$\neq$—(is) not equal (to).

$\lesseqgtr$—**1.** (is) not equal (to), (for real quantities). **2.** (Sometimes when explained by context) less than or greater than respectively.

$\sim$—**1.** (is) formally, asymptotically, or approximately equal to. (The context should make the meaning specific.) Do not use $\doteq$ for "approximately equal to." **2.** (is) similar (to). **3.** not (in some works on formal logic). **4.** used to indicate the equivalence of two matrices.

Use "iff" for "if and only if." Alternately $``^{(n)}$ as" (read "as" may be used for "necessary and sufficient."

$\rightarrow$—**1.** approaches (as a limit), as in $\lim_{x \to a} f(x) = b$, $f(x) \to b$, as $x \to a$, etc. (Do not use $\doteq$). Not usually employed with long expressions. **2.** leads to, validates, implies (in logic). **3.** corresponds to. **4.** "if . . . , then . . . " relation (in logic).

$\leftrightarrow$—**1.** mutually implies (in logic). **2.** in one-to-one correspondence with, corresponds reciprocally to. **3.** if and only if, also iff.

$\downarrow$—decreases monotonically to a limit.

$\uparrow$—increases monotonically to a limit.

Superscript $\rightarrow$—directed line as $\overrightarrow{AB}$.

$|$—Vertical bar, to indicate: **1.** value at, as in $f(x)|_a = f(a)$, or $f(x)|_{x=a} = f(a)$. **2.** value between as in $f(x)|_a^b = f(b) - f(a)$. **3.** is a divisor of, divides (in number theory) as $3|6$, $3/6$ for "3 divides 6" or use solidus $6/3$ to indicate that this quotient is an integer, or $(x - a)|(x^2 - a^2)$. **4.** inner product (with parentheses) as $(a|b) = \Sigma_i a_i b_i$.

$\backslash$ or $/$—Stroke, mark of cancellation as in $3x = \overset{2}{\cancel{6}}$, $x + 3 = \overset{4}{\cancel{7}}$.

$/$—Solidus, or oblique rule, to indicate: **1.** actual or symbolic division, as in $3/7$, $(x - a)/(x - b)$, d/dx, dy/dx, d^2y/dx^2. Do not write ambiguously $a - b/c - d$, but $(a - b)/(c - d)$ or $a - (b/c) - d$, as may be intended. Do not write a/bc but $(a/b)c$ or $a/(bc)$ as intended. Write a proportion as $a/b = c/d$ not $a:b::c:d$. Where A, B, C, D designate displayed expressions, write the proportion as $\frac{A}{B} = \frac{C}{D}$. In commercial typing in place of $8\frac{5}{12}$, it is usual to write 8-5/12. The solidus form a/b, adapted to running text should be used where conveniently possible, rather than the displayed form $\frac{a}{b}$. **2.** quotient or factor group (in group theory) as G/H, (where H is a normal subgroup of G). **3.** per, as in ft/sec. **4.** discount symbol, as in Cash 6, 4/5, 2/30, n/90 indicating 6% discount for immediate payment, 4% discount if paid within 5 days, 2% discount if paid within 30 days, no discount thereafter, but face amount of bill is due (net) not later than the 90th day. **5.** shilling, (in British currency) as 3/6d, or 10/ $-$.

Superscript $\overline{}$—Vinculum. This may be regarded as obsolescent for general use as a mark of aggregation due to its unsuitability for monotype setting. In conjunction with the radical sign it is widely used, but may often be avoided. There is little logical or historical basis for using $\sqrt{2}$ rather than

MATHEMATICAL SYMBOLS AND ABBREVIATIONS (Continued)

$\sqrt{2}$. For a longer expression, one may write $\sqrt{(x^2 + a^2)}$ rather than $\sqrt{x^2 + a^2}$. Instead of $\sqrt{x - a}\,(x - b)$, one might write $(x - b)\sqrt{(x - a)}$.
In geometry, the vinculum may be used for line segments as in $\overline{AB}$.

Superscript $\overline{}$—Bar. To indicate: **1.** complex conjugate of, as $\bar{z}$. This is somewhat inconvenient for "upper extended" letters and capitals as, $\bar{b}$, $\bar{h}$, $\bar{X}$, etc. Also indicated by *conj*, as *conj* $(x + iy) = x - iy$ or by use of a "star" as in z^*. **2.** arithmetic mean value of, as in $\bar{x}$, $= \sum_i x_i / n$. **3.** closure of (in topology), as in $\bar{E}$ (the closure of E). **4.** "least upper," as in $\overline{\lim}$, and $\bar{B}$ for least upper limit and least upper bound, respectively. See "sup." **5.** repeating decimal, as in $1.\overline{14} = 1.141414 \cdots$.

Subscript $\underline{}$—To indicate: **1.** italics (in manuscript). **2.** "greatest lower," as in $\underline{\lim}$, and $\underline{B}$, for greatest lower limit, and greatest lower bound respectively. See "inf."

$\underline{}$—horizontal rule, sign of division, as in $\dfrac{x - a}{x + a}$. Ordinarily the solidus form, adapted to running text, is preferred, as in $(x - a)/(x + a)$. When numerator and denominator are both complicated, the displayed form using horizontal rule may be avoided by writing "A/B, where $A = \cdots$, and $B = \cdots$."

$-$ (centrally placed)—Minus sign. To indicate: **1.** subtraction as in $7 - 2 = 5$, $a^2 - b^2 = (a - b)(a + b)$. **2.** overestimate, as in $3.5-$. **3.** approach through negative values as in $-\infty$ and -0. **4.** region where variable indicated by context is negative (in graphs). **5.** logical difference (in theory of classes). **6.** in $(-)^n$, the sign expressed by $(-1)^n$.

(on line)—**1.** decimal point. In the decimal representation of a number between 0 and 1, the cipher, 0, should (except in tables) appear before the $\cdot$ decimal point. Thus 0.314 not $.314$. Notation by powers of 10, ("scientific notation") is recommended, especially when recording approximate values; thus to four significant figures, 3.140×10^9 and 3.140×10^{-6}. **2.** (sometimes used in quoting bond prices) as in 95.17 for $95\frac{17}{32}$. **3.** (sometimes used in recording mental age) as in 12.3 for 12 yr. 3 mo. **4.** (in symbolic logic) as mark of punctuation separating terms, also as, "and."

:—Colon. To indicate: **1.** hours, in recording time, as in 4:10 p.m. **2.** ratio (an obsolescent form) as in $a\!:\!b$. The form a/b is preferred. **3.** (in symbolic logic) as mark of punctuation separating groups of terms, as in $p \cdot p \supset q \supset\!\cdot q$. **4.** Indicates infinite line $A\!:\!B$, collinearity $A\!:\!B(S)$, and perspectivity. **5.** such that (in logic). $\cdot$ (centrally placed)—**1.** mark of algebraic multiplication, particularly where mere juxtaposition would be ambiguous, as in $\overline{AB} \cdot \overline{CD}$. **2.** (for vectors), the mark of inner or dot multiplication as in $\boldsymbol{a} \cdot \boldsymbol{b} = ab \cos < ab$. Other notations are (ab) and $S\,ab$.

$\cdot$ (placed above line)—to indicate repeating decimal, used in pairs, as in $1.\dot{7}3\dot{5} = 1.735735735 \cdots$.

$\cdots$ (preferably centrally placed)—"three dots" meaning "and so forth," or "and so forth up to." Particularly when the reader knows what has been omitted, as in the sequence of natural integers, etc. as in $1, 2 \cdots, n, \cdots$; or $a_0, a_1, \cdots, a_n, \cdots$, or $1, \cdots, m$.

MATHEMATICAL SYMBOLS AND ABBREVIATIONS (Continued)

∴—hence, therefore. Inverted ∵ since.

:., ::, ::., etc.—(in symbolic logic), marks of punctuation stronger than and :

„—ditto.

∘ (centrally placed)—indicates (in classes or sets) the composite of functions, as in $g{\circ}f$.

+ plus sign. To indicate: **1.** addition, as in $2 + 3$, $a + b$, 10^{a+1}. **2.** under-estimate, as in $3.5+$. **3.** continued fraction as in $a_0 + \dfrac{1}{a_1+} \ \dfrac{1}{a_2+} \ \cdots$ for

$a_0 + \dfrac{1}{a_1 + \dfrac{1}{a_2+}}$. **4.** approach through positive values as in $+\infty$, and in $+0$

5. region where variable indicated by the context is positive, (in graphs). **6.** logical addition (in theory of classes). **7.** " . . or . . or both," (in formal logic). Note: In writing series indicate sign before and after dots of omission, as $a_0 + a_1 + \cdots + a_n$, or $1 - \dfrac{1}{2} + \dfrac{1}{3} + \cdots + (-1)^{n-1}\dfrac{1}{n}$.

8. in abstract group theory a group or co-set may be expressed as the sum of its elements.

⊕—denoting a logical operation of summation between elements of a set, such as the sum of vectors.

±—**1.** "plus or minus." The repeated appearance of $\pm$ as in $\pm a \pm b \pm c$ is ambiguous. In many cases the sign $\pm$ before a term which appears repeatedly is intended to indicate the systematic use of the positive determination or of the negative determination throughout. Thus one may write $(a \pm b)^3 = a^3 \pm 3a^2b + 3ab^2 \pm b^3$. Where the context restricts the value of a to non-negative (real) values, $\sqrt{a}$ means the non-negative (real) square root of a. Hence when both signs are desired, write $\pm$ before the radical. For roots of a quadratic equation $ax^2 + bx + c = 0$, use $\pm$ as in $\dfrac{-b \pm \sqrt{b^2 - 4ac}}{2a}$. **2.** (in theory of observation), "with a probable error of." As in 17.2 ± 0.5 cm.

∓—"minus or plus respectively." Used in context where $\pm$ has appeared previously, as in $a^3 \pm b^3 = (a \pm b)(a^2 \mp ab + b^2)$. Here upper signs are to be taken throughout, or else lower signs. The notation $\pm a \mp b \pm c$ is ambiguous, meaning perhaps one of the four values $\pm(a - b) \pm c$, or one of the two values $\pm(a - b + c)$.

×—**1.** times, (sign of algebraic multiplication). Used chiefly in arithmetic, as in $2 \times 2 = 4$, 7.3×10^4. **2.** (for vectors) the sign of outer or cross multiplication. **3.** (for classes) the Cartesian product. Thus $A \times B$ is the class of all ordered pairs (a,b) where a is an element of A, and b of B.

⊗—denoting a logical operation of multiplication between elements of a set, such as the product of vectors.

÷—sign of division. Used chiefly in arithmetic. Should be replaced by solidus, /, where convenient.

$\sqrt{}$ $\sqrt[n]{}$—square root of, nth root of. (See discussion under "superscript," and under "vinculum"). By custom, for a positive, $\sqrt{(-a)}$ means usually $i\sqrt{a}$, rather than $-i\sqrt{a}$, but the latter unambiguous forms are preferred.

!—"factorial," as in $3! = 1 \cdot 2 \cdot 3 = 6$. $0! = 1$, (by definition). The ele-

MATHEMATICAL SYMBOLS AND ABBREVIATIONS (Continued)

mentary arithmetic definition of factorial n, may be replaced in favor of the definition as a special case of the Gamma function $\Gamma(x)$. For $-1 < n$, $n! = \Gamma(n+1), = \int_0^\infty x^n e^{-x} dx$. For n a large natural number, Stirling's asymptotic formula (extended) yields $n! \sim \sqrt{2n\pi}\,(n/e)^n \left(1 + \dfrac{1}{12n} + \dfrac{1}{288n^2} - \dfrac{139}{51840n^3} - \cdots\right)$. Note: Do not use the obsolescent form $\lfloor n$ for $n!$

$\int, \int_a^b, \int_a^x, \int\int, \int_c$ —Integral signs. (use preferably bold-face type)

$\int_a^b \int_c^d f(x,y)dxdy$ denotes $\int_a^b \left(\int_c^d f(x,y)dx\right)dy, = \int_a^b dy \int_c^d dx f(x,y)$.

$\mathscr{S}$ —curvilinear integral over closed path free from singularities. (Use preferably bold-face type.)

§—section, or article.

℟ or ¶—paragraph.

$\propto$ —varies as. Instead of $y \propto x$ one may write $y = kx$, k being the constant factor of proportionality.

∇ —nabla—To indicate: **1.** linear vector operator $\left(\dfrac{\partial}{\partial x}, \dfrac{\partial}{\partial y}, \dfrac{\partial}{\partial z}\right)$ as used also in divergence, gradient, and curl (or rotation). **2.** backward difference (in interpolation theory) $\nabla a_n = a_n - a_{n-1}$.

∇^2 —Laplace operator. Sometimes written Δ.

$\Box$ —Four dimensional differential operator of D'Alembert and Poincare [= point carré].

$°, ', '', ''', \cdots, (N) \cdots$, (superscript)—superscript numbers. See "superscripts."

∞ —infinity. Use $+\infty$ or $-\infty$ respectively, where direction of approach along real numbers is to be indicated. Otherwise use ∞ rather than $\pm\infty$. Note: "$n \to \infty$," may be read "as n increases without bound." $\text{Lim } f(x) = \infty$ means "$\text{Lim } 1/f(x) = 0$," so that whenever one variable "becomes infinite" the meaning is that its reciprocal "becomes zero."

$\in$ —(is) a member (of), as in $x \in A$. Several objects can be denoted as members in a set A by $x_1, x_2, \cdots x_n \in A$.

$\notin$ —(is) not a member (of).

$\mathscr{P}$ —denotes a power set, as in $\mathscr{P}(A)$ which denotes the set of all subsets of a set A.

$\aleph$ —Aleph (initial Hebrew letter) transfinite cardinal number, in particular that of all real numbers. $\aleph_0$ (aleph null) first transfinite cardinal. Use of Hebrew letters for transfinite numerals is recommended: "aleph" (omit the null) for the cardinal of the set of integers; $\beth$ "beth" for the cardinal of the continuum (number of points on a line); and $\gimel$ "gimel" for the cardinal of functions of a real variable.

$\mathfrak{F}$ —the Farey series. $\mathfrak{F}_n$ denotes the Farey series of order n.

α —Alpha. To indicate: **1.** (in analytic geometry of 3 dimensions), direction angle with X-axis. **2.** angular acceleration. **3.** (in statistics) $\alpha_0 = 1$, $\alpha_1 = 0$, $\alpha_2 = 1$, $\alpha_3 = \mu_3/\sigma^3$, $\alpha_4 = \mu_4/\sigma^4 = \mu_4/\mu_2^2$. **4.** (in mathematical astronomy), right ascension (also indicated by R.A.) **5.** angle of triangle

MATHEMATICAL SYMBOLS AND ABBREVIATIONS (Continued)

at A, opposite side a. **6.** root of algebraic equation as in $a(x - \alpha)(x - \beta)(x - \gamma) = 0$.

B—(Greek Beta)—$B(m,n) = \Gamma(m)\Gamma(n)/\Gamma(m + n)$, (Eulerian Beta-function).

β—Beta. To indicate: **1.** (in analytic geometry of 3 dimensions), direction angle with Y-axis. **2.** (in statistics), $\beta_1 = \alpha_3{}^2 = \mu_3{}^2/\mu_2{}^3$, $\beta_2 = \alpha_4 = \mu_4/\mu_2{}^2$. **3.** angle of triangle at B, opposite side b. **4.** root of algebraic equation. See α.

Γ—$\Gamma(x)$ Gamma-function. See "!" Among numerous definitions equivalent for positive real values of x, are the two following: (i) $\Gamma(x) = \lim_{n \to \infty}$

$$\frac{1 \cdot 2 \cdots n}{x(x + 1) \cdots (x + n - 1)} n^{x-1}, x > 0. \quad \text{(ii) } \Gamma(x) = \int_0^\infty e^{-t} t^{x-1} dt, R(x) > 0.$$

γ—Gamma. To indicate: **1.** (in analytic geometry of 3 dimensions) direction angle with Z-axis. **2.** Euler or Mascheroni constant. (Also indicated by C.) $\gamma = \lim_{n \to \infty} \left(\frac{1}{1} + \frac{1}{2} + \cdots + \frac{1}{n} - \log n \right) = 0.57721 \quad 56649 \quad 01532$ 86060 65120 $\cdots$ **3.** angle of triangle at C, opposite side c. **4.** radius of geodesic curvature. **5.** universal constant of gravitation $= 6.670 \times 10^{-8}$ cm^3/(gm. sec^2). **6.** root of algebraic equation, see α.

Δ—Delta. To indicate: **1.** triangle (in plane geometry). (For right triangle, write rtΔ, not $\angle$). Also area of triangle. **2.** increment, as in Δx, Δf, $f(x + \Delta x)$, etc. **3.** forward difference (interpolation theory). $\Delta a_n = a_{n+1} - a_n$. **4.** Laplacian operator $\frac{\partial^2}{\partial x^2} + \frac{\partial^2}{\partial y^2}$, or $\frac{\partial^2}{\partial x^2} + \frac{\partial^2}{\partial y^2} + \frac{\partial^2}{\partial z^2}$, also designated by ∇^2. **5.** selected square root of the discriminant of a given polynomial, as in $\Delta^2 = b^2 - 4ac$ for the polynomial $ax^2 + bx + c$. **6.** triangular number, (of form $(n^2 - n)/2$). **7.** Legendre's radical, $\Delta(\varphi)^2 = 1 - k^2 \sin^2 \varphi$.

δ—Delta. To indicate: **1.** positive constant dependent upon ϵ that may be chosen initially as near to zero as desired. (In theory of limits, of continuity, etc.) **2.** variation of. **3.** (in interpolational theory) central difference $\delta y_{c+i+\frac{1}{2}} = y_{c+i+1} - y_{c+i}$. **4.** (in mathematical astronomy) apparent declination. **5.** number of double points, or nodes (Plücker number). **6.** (in statistics) deviation. **7.** force of interest, $e^\delta = 1 + i$, (in mathematics of finance). **8.** Kronecker Delta, $\delta_{ij} = 0$ for $i \neq j$, $= 1$ for $i = j$. In tensor notation, also $\delta_i{}^j$. One has $\delta_{ij} = \begin{pmatrix} o \\ i - j \end{pmatrix}$ or $C_{0, i-i}$. **9.** unit elongation (in strength of materials).

∂—curly d. To indicate: **1.** partial differentiation as in $\partial f(x,y)/\partial x$. **2.** The Jacobian operator, as in $\partial(u,v,w)/\partial(x,y,z)$. This is variously represented, sometimes as $J\left(\dfrac{u,v,w}{x,y,z}\right)$ etc. **3.** a specified square root of the discriminant D. (also sometimes as Δ.)

ϵ—Epsilon. To indicate: **1.** positive constant, that may be chosen initially independently as near to zero as desired. (In theory of limits, of continuity etc.) **2.** primitive root of unity. **3.** (is) member of, (relation of element to containing class). **4.** eccentricity of conic section, usually better designated by e. **5.** (in mathematical astronomy) obliquity of ecliptic. **6.** an ϵ-number is a transfinite ordinal or a certain limiting type. Note: Do not use ϵ or ε for Napierian base except in engineering. See e.

MATHEMATICAL SYMBOLS AND ABBREVIATIONS (Continued)

∍—(Inverted Epsilon). Such that.

∉—(is not a member of.)

ζ—Zeta. To indicate: **1.** Riemann Zeta-function $\zeta(s) = \Sigma_{n=1}^{\infty} n^{-s}$ (for $s > 1$). **2.** (in statistics) a test of linearity. $\zeta = \eta^2 - r^2$.

η—Eta. To indicate: **1.** general variable or unknown constant, analogous to y as in case of moving system of coordinates, etc. Used in ordered set (ξ, η, ζ). **2.** a confocal coordinate. See ξ. **3.** (in statistics), correlation ratio. **4.** order-type of the aggregate of all rational numbers.

Θ—Theta. To indicate: **1.** Theta-function. See ϑ. **2.** absolute temperature (where t is used for time).

θ—Theta. To indicate: **1.** general angular displacement (in trigonometry and analytic geometry). **2.** (in plane polar coordinates (r cis θ)) angle from initial ray to radius vector, $x = r \cos \theta$, $y = r \sin \theta$. **3.** (in cylindrical coordinates ($r\ \theta\ z$)) angle from initial radial half-plane to radial half-plane containing radius vector. **4.** (in spherical coordinates (r, θ, φ)) co-latitude (measured from zenith) and (in astronomy) zenith distance. This notation is traditional in mathematical physics. In texts on analytic geometry, usage varies, θ being employed frequently for the longitude. See φ. **5.** Theta-function. See ϑ. **6.** (in formal theory of operations) a displacement operator. **7.** ordinary temperature (when t is used for time).

ϑ—Theta-function. Definitions and notations vary widely. For elliptic Theta-functions the notation given here is that followed by Whittaker and Watson. Here θ_i designates the value of $\vartheta_i(o,q)$, $\vartheta_i{'}$, the value of $d\vartheta_i(z,q)/dz$. ($i = 1,2,3,4$). These are defined by $\vartheta_1(z,q) = 2q^{\frac{1}{4}} \sin Z - 2q^{\frac{9}{4}} \sin 3z + 2q^{2\frac{5}{4}} \sin 5z - \cdots$ $\vartheta_2(z,q) = 2q^{\frac{1}{4}} \sin z + 2q^{\frac{9}{4}} \sin 3z + 2q^{2\frac{5}{4}} \sin 5z + \cdots$ $\vartheta_3(z,q) = 1 + 2q \cos 2z + 2q^4 \cos 4z + 2q^9 \cos 6z + \cdots$ $\vartheta_4(z,q) = 1 - 2q \cos 2z + 2q^4 \cos 4z - 2q^9 \cos 6z + \cdots$

ι—Iota, number of inflexions (a Plücker number).

ⁱ—inverted Iota, (in formal logic) the unique element fulfilling description stated.

κ—Kappa, number of cusps. (A Plücker number).

Λ—Lambda, sometimes used for null-class.

λ—Lambda. To indicate: **1.** general linear parameter (e.g., in a pencil), as in $F + \lambda G$. **2.** running index, as in $x_\lambda (\lambda = 1, 2, \cdots)$. **3.** longitude (in mathematical astronomy). **4.** characteristic value (as in λ_i) in theory of linear differential equations of second order, linear integral equations, etc. **5.** order-type of the aggregate of all real numbers. **6.** In solid analytic geometry (λ, μ, ν) are direction cosines.

μ—Mu. To indicate: **1.** running index, usually used with λ, as in $x_\lambda y_\mu$. **2.** general linear parameter, when used with λ, as in $\lambda F + \mu G$. **3.** (in statistics) moment, about the arithmetic mean, as in $\mu_k = \Sigma_i f_i (x_i - \bar{x})^k$, $\mu_2 = \sigma^2 =$ variance. **4.** μ_x, force of mortality $= -d(\log_e l_x)/dx$. **5.** (in number theory) inversion function of Moebius and Mertens. **6.** Various physical constants such as permeability, reduced mass. **7.** Integrating factor which converts integrable expression into exact differential form.

ν—Nu. To indicate: **1.** running index, usually with λ and μ. **2.** (in statistics) moment about arbitrary origin A (in "short method") as in $\nu_k = \Sigma_i f_i (x_i - A)^k$. **3.** Frequency.

ξ—Xi. To indicate: **1.** general variable, or unknown constant analogous to

MATHEMATICAL SYMBOLS AND ABBREVIATIONS (Continued)

x, as in moving systems of coordinates, etc. **2.** a confocal coordinate as in
(i) confocal ellipses and hyperbolas, $\dfrac{x^2}{a^2 - \lambda} + \dfrac{y^2}{b^2 - \lambda} = 1$, $-\infty < \xi < b^2 <$

$\eta < a^2$. (ii) confocal ellipsoids and hyperboloids of revolution, $\dfrac{x^2}{a^2 - \lambda} +$

$\dfrac{y^2 + z^2}{b^2 - \lambda} = 1$, $-\infty < \xi < b^2 < \eta < a^2$. (iii) confocal parabolas, $y^2 + 2\lambda$.

$(x - \lambda) = 0$, $-\infty < \xi < 0 < \eta < +\infty$. (iv) confocal paraboloids of revolution, $y^2 + z^2 + 2\lambda(x - \lambda) = 0$, $-\infty < \xi < 0 < \eta < +\infty$. (v) confocal

ellipsoids and hyperboloids, $\dfrac{x^2}{a^2 - \lambda} + \dfrac{y^2}{b^2 - \lambda} + \dfrac{z^2}{c^2 - \lambda} = 1$, $-\infty < \xi <$

$c^2 < \eta < b^2 < \zeta < a^2$. (vi) confocal paraboloids, $\dfrac{x^2}{a^2 - \lambda} + \dfrac{y^2}{b^2 - \lambda} = 2z - \lambda$,

$-\infty < \xi < b^2 < \eta < a^2 < \zeta < +\infty$. ($\xi$, η, ζ), Xi, eta, zeta, are used as
alternates for rectangular coordinates (x, y, z).

Π, $\Pi_i \Pi_{i-m}^n$, $\Pi_{(R)}$ or $\underset{(R)}{\Pi}$—1. product of terms with index i, or j, etc. ranging from

m to n, or over R. Do not use Π, $\overset{n}{\underset{i=m}{\Pi}}$, etc. (Bold-faced type preferred.)

2. (in some formal logical treatments) "for every."

Π_{ij}, Π_{ijk}, $\cdots$ —$\Pi_i \Pi_j$, $\Pi_i \Pi_j \Pi_k$, etc.

π—Pi. **1.** the ratio of the length of circumference of a circle, to the diameter.
$\pi = 3.14159\ 26535\ 89793\ 23846 \cdots$ **2.** general notation for plane,
projectivity, projective, period, etc.

ρ—Rho. **1.** radius of geodesic curvature. **2.** proportionality factor, as in
$\rho X_i = \Sigma_j a_{ij} x_j$.

$\sum$, $\sum_i$, $\sum_{i-m}^n$, $\sum_{(R)}$ or $\underset{(R)}{\sum}$—Sigma. **1.** summation, sum of terms of index i,

or j, etc., ranging from m to n, or over range R. Do not use $\sum_i$, $\overset{n}{\underset{i=m}{\sum}}$, etc.

(bold-faced type preferred). **2.** (on some formal logical treatments) "for
at least one." **3.** (in number theory) $\Sigma_{d/n}$ summation extended over all
divisors of n. **4.** (in mathematical astronomy) Σ-pt is the intersection of the
meridian with the equator.

Σ_{ij}, $\Sigma_{ijk} \cdots$ —$\Sigma_i \Sigma_j$, $\Sigma_i \Sigma_j \Sigma_k$, etc.

σ—Sigma. To indicate: **1.** radius of torsion. **2.** (in statistics) standard
deviation $\sigma^2 N = \Sigma_i (x_i - \bar{x})^2 f_i$. **3.** (in number theory), $\sigma_k(n) =$ sum of
kth powers of divisors of n. **4.** any one of several analogous Sigma-functions. The simplest elliptic Sigma-function $\sigma(x)$ is related to the Weierstrassian $\wp$ function by $\wp u = -d^2 \log \sigma u / du^2$. One has $\sigma u = u \Big\{ 1 - \dfrac{g_2}{2} \dfrac{u^4}{5!}$

$- 6 g_3 \dfrac{u^6}{7!} - \dfrac{9}{4} g_2^2 \dfrac{u^8}{9!} - 18 g_2 g_3 \dfrac{u^{10}}{11!} - \cdots \Big\}$ **5.** proportionality factor, usually

used with ρ.

τ—Tau. To indicate: **1.** number of bitangents (a Plücker number). **2.** time
(when t is used for temperature). **3.** torsion (of curve in space).

Υ—Upsilon. (In mathematical astronomy) vernal equinox.

ϕ—Phi. **1.** Used to indicate the Golden Ratio or Section, $\phi = 1.61803\ 39887$
$49894 \cdots$. **2.** Used to denote Euler's function, where $\phi(m)$ is the number

MATHEMATICAL SYMBOLS AND ABBREVIATIONS (Continued)

of positive integers not greater than and prime to m.   **3.** The null (or empty) set containing no elements.

φ—Phi. To indicate: **1.** general functional symbol, especially for polynomials. **2.** (in spherical coordinates, (r,θ,φ), longitude from x to y in right-handed system. In some astronomical work the z-axis points to the zenith, θ is the zenith-distance, and φ is the latitude. In some works on analytic geometry the roles of θ and φ are interchanged, although the system given is traditional mathematical physics. $x = r \sin \theta \cos \varphi$, $y = r \sin \theta \sin \varphi$, $z = r \cos \theta$. **3.** (in geocentric coordinates, (r,φ,λ), φ = latitude (not co-latitude as with spherical coordinates). **4.** (in plane polar coordinates (r,φ).) Used chiefly as specialized case of spherical coordinates $(r,\pi/2,\varphi)$. See θ. **5.** inclination of plane curve, $\tan \varphi = dy/dx = m$. **6.** (in number theory.) Euler's function or indicatrix. $\varphi(n)$ is the number of positive integers not exceeding n and prime to n. **7.** $\varphi_i(x)$, characteristic function, see λ_i. **8.** argument in Legendre's elliptic integrals. $E(k,\varphi) = \int_0^\varphi \Delta(\varphi)d\varphi$, $F(k,\varphi) = \int_0^\varphi d\varphi/\Delta(\varphi)$. **9.** the normal probability function of Laplace and Gauss in the form $\varphi(t) = \dfrac{1}{\sqrt{2\pi}}e^{\frac{-t^2}{2}}$. **10.** $\varphi_n(x)$, sometimes used for Bernoulli polynomial. See $B_n(x)$.

χ—Chi. (In statistical theory) χ^2 is a measure of goodness of fit, devised by Karl Pearson. $\chi^2 = \Sigma(f_i - Np_i)^2/(Np_i)$ for N items, with p_i the probability of appearances and f_i the frequency for items in an ith class.

ψ—Psi. To indicate: **1.** general functional symbol (usually with φ). **2.** angle from radius vector to tangent of plane curve. **3.** (with geocentric coordinates in mathematical astronomy), co-latitude. See φ.

Ω—Omega. To indicate: **1.** a certain annihilator in the theory of binary concomitants. **2.** (with subscript) transfinite ordinals of certain minimal type. **3.** (in geometry of the triangle) Ω,Ω', the Brocard points.

ω—Omega. To indicate: **1.** angular velocity. **2.** first transfinite ordinal, order-type of the aggregate of all natural numbers. **3.** imaginary cube root of unity, related to i, by $\omega = (-1 + i\sqrt{3})/2$. **4.** ω_1, ω_2, ω_3, half-periods of Weierstrassian $\wp$-function. **5.** (in geometry of the triangle) Brocard angle. $\cot \omega = \cot A + \cot B + \cot C$.

A—**1.** A vertex, and the associated angle of $\triangle ABC$. See α. **2.** A_{ij}, algebraic complement of a_{ij} in determinant, D. $A_{ij} = dD/da_{ij}$. **3.** (in astronomy) azimuth. **4.** (in astronomy) astronomical unit, mean geocentric distance to the sun. **5.** acres. **6.** area.

$\mathring{A}$—ångstrom.

$\mathbf{V}_x$—For every x.

AM—arithmetic mean. See also superscript $^{-}$.

Ans.—answer.

AP—arithmetic progression.

Ax—axiom.

a—**1.** (in elementary algebra) initial term in arithmetic or geometric progression. **2.** (with subscript) coefficient in Fourier series, $(a_0/2) + \Sigma_{n=1}^\infty(a_n \cos nx + b_n \sin nx)$. **3.** (with two indices) element in matrix or determinant, as in $\begin{pmatrix} a_{11}\ a_{12}\ a_{13} \\ a_{21}\ a_{22}\ a_{23} \end{pmatrix}$ or $\begin{vmatrix} a_{11}\ a_{12} \\ a_{21}\ a_{22} \end{vmatrix}$. **4.** (in elementary geometry) apothegm. **5.** (in

MATHEMATICAL SYMBOLS AND ABBREVIATIONS (Continued)

geometry or triangle) first side-line, also length of first side of the triangle. **6.** (in elementary analytic geometry) x-intercept. **7.** (in elementary analytic geometry) semi-major axis of ellipse or semi-transverse axis of hyperbola, etc. Thus latus rectum of central conic is $2p = 2b^2/a$, eccentricity $e = c/a$. For central conics and quadrics the a is sometimes associated with x, as in $(x^2/a^2) + (y^2/b^2) = 1$, even when a may be less than b, or as in $-(x^2/a^2) + (y^2/b^2) = 1$, where a is the semi-conjugate axis.

abs—absolute value of.

acc—acceleration.

am—amplitude function. $\varphi = \mathrm{am}\ u$, where $u = F = \int_0^\varphi d\varphi/\Delta(\varphi)$.

amp—amplitude of vibration.

antilog—antilogarithm.

approx—approximate(ly).

arc (in "arc sin" etc.)—inverse. Also written $\sin^{-1}$ etc. Do not use "arc" for inverse of hyperbolic functions. Write $\sinh^{-1}$, etc.

arg—argument. Angle in polar coordinates r cis θ, and in complex number. $re^{i\theta}$ for r and θ real. Better than "arc" and more legible than superscript -1 to indicate inverse hyperbolic functions, though "$\sinh^{-1} x$" is often used.

av—average.

B—**1.** (With subscripts) Bernoulli numbers and polynomials. To indicate what usage among many is being followed in any given case, authors would do well to list the values of the first few Bernoulli numbers as for example, $B_1 = \frac{1}{2}$, $B_2 = \frac{1}{6}$, $B_3 = 0$, $B_4 = -\frac{1}{30}$, etc. The Bernoulli polynomials, are defined as $B_n(x) = \Sigma_{r=0}^n \binom{n}{r} B_r x^{n-r}$, and satisfy $B_n(x + 1) - B_n(x) = nx^{n-1}$ with the choice of notation for Bernoulli numbers given above. (Also designated by $\varphi_n(x)$.) See page 380 for a second definition of Bernoulli numbers. **2.** bound (general symbol). $\bar{B}$, $\underline{B}$ designate least upper and greatest lower bound respectively. Preferred notations are "sup" and "inf" respectively. **3.** a vertex and the associated angle of $\triangle ABC$. See β. **4.** (in elementary solid geometry), area of base of a solid.

b—**1.** (in elementary geometry) length of base of plane figure. b,b', parallel bases of trapezoid. **2.** (in elementary analytic geometry) y-intercept. **3.** (in elementary analytic geometry) semi-axis. See a. **4.** (in geometry of the triangle) second side-line, also length of second side of the triangle.

bei(z)—Thomson-Bessel function, $\mathrm{bei}(z) = \dfrac{(\frac{1}{2}z)^2}{(2!)^2} - \dfrac{(\frac{1}{2}z)_6}{(6!)^2} + \dfrac{(\frac{1}{2}z)^{10}}{(10!)^2} - \cdots$

$\quad$ ber(z) $\pm i$ bei(z) $= J_0(zi\sqrt{\ } \pm i) = I_0(z\sqrt{\ } \pm i)$.

ber(z)—Thomson-Bessel function.   (See bei(z).) $\mathrm{ber}(z) = 1 - \dfrac{(\frac{1}{2}z)^4}{(4!)^2} + \dfrac{(\frac{1}{2}z)^8}{(8!)^2} - \cdots$

(B)-space—A Banach space.

B_m^s—An s-dimensional Betti group modulo m (m prime).

B_0^s—An s-dimensional Betti group relative to the group of integers.

C—**1.** arbitrary constant of integration. **2.** (in elementary geometry) circumference of circle; also, circle. **3.** general symbol for curve. **4.** (with subscripts) combination, as in $C_{n,r}$ or $_nC_r$, the number of combinations of n things taken r at a time (without repetitions). The form $_nC_r$ or even ^nC_r is

MATHEMATICAL SYMBOLS AND ABBREVIATIONS (Continued)

widely used but the notation $C_{n,r}$ or $C(n,r)$ or $\binom{n}{r}$ is to be preferred. **5.** Roman numeral for "hundred." **6.** Euler or Mascheroni constant. Also designated by γ. (See γ.) **7.** (chiefly as subscript) contour of integration. **8.** Centigrade, degree Centigrade, as $-52C$.

C_{I}—(in topology) class of spaces satisfying first axiom of countability, or property of satisfying first axiom of countability.

C_{II}—Same as above for second axiom of countability.

$\underline{C}$—(underlined) the set of complex numbers.

$\underset{\sim}{C}$—(wavy underline) indicates congruence of two n-square matrices.

Ci—cosine integral function, $Ci(x) = \int_{\infty}^{x} (\cos u/u)du$.

c—**1.** (in geometry of triangle) third side-line, also length of third side of triangle. **2.** (in elementary analytic geometry), z-intercept. **3.** (in elementary analytic geometry) semi-axis. (See a.)

cis—cis $\theta = \cos \theta + i \sin \theta = e^{i\theta} = exp(i\theta)$. Used to distinguish polar coordinates r cis θ from rectangular coordinates. Using Gaussian coordinates, r cis $\theta = x + iy$. In de Moivres' formula cis$^n \theta =$ cis $n\theta$.

cn—cosine amplitude function. (Jacobian elliptic function.)

colog—cologarithm, $= \log$ of reciprocal $=$ negative of log (especially with base 10).

conj—(complex) conjugate (of). See superscript —.

cos—cosine $=$ sine of the complementary angle.

cos^{-1}—inverse cosine (of). Also written arc cos. $\theta = \cos^{-1} x$ means $\cos \theta = x$. Arc cos x (with capital A) indicates principal value, $0 < \theta < \pi$.

cosh—hyperbolic cosine (of). Do not write Cos nor $\mathfrak{Cof}$ (in German letters).

cosh^{-1}—inverse hyperbolic cosine of. Also written as arg cosh.

covers—coversed sine or coversine.

csc—cosecant (of). Reciprocal of sine.

csc^{-1}—inverse cosecant (of). Also written arc csc.

ctn also cot—cotangent (of). Reciprocal of tangent.

ctn^{-1}—inverse cotangent (of). Also written as cot^{-1}, arc cot, or arc ctn.

ctnh—hyperbolic cotangent (of). Also written as coth.

ctnh^{-1}—inverse hyperbolic cotangent of. Also written as arg coth or arg ctnh.

cu—cubic. In arithmetic "cubic feet" is written "cu ft" but "ft^3" is better.

cum—cumulative.

D—**1.** differential operator, as in $Dy = y'$, $d_x f(x,y) = \partial f/\partial x$. **2.** Roman numeral for "five hundred." **3.** general symbol for denominator, or for determinant. **4.** discriminant of binary form, or of polynomial. **5.** (in statistical theory), (with subscripts 0, 1, $\cdots$, 10), decile marks. **6.** $D(a_1, a_1, \cdots, a_n)$ sometimes designates the Vandermonde determinant.

$$\begin{vmatrix} 1a_1 & \cdots & a_1{}^{n-1} \\ \cdots & \cdots & \cdots \\ 1a_n & \cdots & a_n{}^{n-1} \end{vmatrix}$$

Def—definition.

Dem—demonstration, proof.

d—**1.** (in elementary algebra), common difference in arithmetic progression. **2.** differential operator, as in d^2y/dx^2. **3.** (in elementary geometry) diameter. **4.** (as superscript) days, as in $2^d3^h17^m$. **5.** (British currency) pence.

MATHEMATICAL SYMBOLS AND ABBREVIATIONS (Continued)

deg—degree, degrees. In navigation use 3 digits measured clockwise from north, so that 090 is due east. In trigonometry use cis θ to indicate direction measured counterclockwise from the positive x-axis, so that cis 90 is the direction of the positive y-axis.

det—determinant of, as in det (a_{ii}).

div—divergence of, also indicated by $\nabla\cdot$ (with nabla and dot).

dn—dn(z), a Jacobian elliptic function.

∃—(there) exists.

∃|—there exist uniquely.

E—**1.** E,F,G fundamental differential quantities of first order for surfaces. **2.** $E(k,\varphi)$, Legendre's normal elliptic integral, of the second kind, $E = E(k,\varphi)$ $\int_0^\varphi \Delta(\varphi)d\varphi$. **3.** east. **4.** (in Euler's polyhedral formula) number of edges of polyhedron. **5.** displacement operator, $E(f(x)) = f(x + 1)$. **6.** (in mathematical astronomy) equation of time.

Ei—exponential integral function $Ei(x) = \int_{-\infty}^x \frac{e^v dv}{v}$.

Eq—equation.

Ex—exercise.

e—**1.** base of natural (or Napierian) logarithms. In place of e^4 one may write exp A. $e = 2.71828\ 18284\ 59045\ 23536\ \cdots \log_{10} e = M = 0.43429\ 44819$ $03251\ 82765\ \cdots \log_e 10 = 1/M = 2.30258\ 50929\ 94045\ 68402$. In some engineering work, where e is used otherwise, the base of natural logarithms is designated by ϵ. **2.** eccentricity of a conic. **3.** $e_1 = \wp(\omega_1)$, $e_2 = \wp(\omega_2)$, $e_3 = \wp(\omega_3)$, for Weierstrassian elliptic functions. **4.** (in mathematical astronomy) eccentricity of earth's orbit. **5.** (in elementary solid geometry) length of lateral edge (of right pyramid, prism, etc.).

eq—equivalent to.

erf—error function, $\text{erf}(x) = \frac{2}{\sqrt{\pi}} \int_0^x e^{-v^2} dv$.

erfc—complementary function to error function, $\text{erfc}(x) = 1 - \text{erf}(x) = \frac{2}{\sqrt{\pi}} \int_x^\infty e^{-v^2} dv$.

exp—exponential function of, as in $\exp(a^2 + b^2)$ for $e^{a^2+b^2}$. One could also write this "e^u where $u = a^2 + b^2$."

exsec—Exsecant

F—Force.

F—**1.** general symbol for function or functional. **2.** the second fundamental differential quantity of first order for surfaces. See E. **3.** (in Euler's polyhedral formula) number of faces of polyhedron. **4.** $F(k,\varphi)$, Legendre's normal elliptic integral of the first kind, $F = F(k,\varphi) \int_0^\varphi d\varphi/\Delta(\varphi)$. See Δ and E. φ is here the amplitude of F, $\varphi = $ am F. **5.** $F(a, b; c: x)$, hypergeometric function. **6.** Fahrenheit, degree Fahrenheit, as in 70F. **7.** falsity (in logic).

FS—Fourier series.

Fig.—figure.

Fr—frontier set of.

f—**1.** general symbol for function or functional. **2.** f_i, frequency of X_i in

MATHEMATICAL SYMBOLS AND ABBREVIATIONS (Continued)

univariate table. **3.** frequency of vibration. **4.** feet as in f/s, feet per second. Preferable ft/sec.

ft—feet. See also f and $'$.

G—**1.** general symbol for group. **2.** the third fundamental differential quantity of first order for surfaces. **3.** $G(x_1, \cdots, x_n; \xi_1, \cdots, \xi_n)$ Green's function for two points in n-space. **4.** (constant) linear group of points on an algebraic curve. See g. **5.** gravitational constant.

G.C.T.—Greenwich civil time.

GCD—greatest common divisor.

GCS—greatest common subgroup.

GF—Galois field, as in $GF(p^n)$.

GM—geometric mean.

GP—geometric progression.

g—**1.** general function symbol, used with f. **2.** (terrestrial) gravitational attraction. **3.** (variable) linear group of points on an algebraic curve. See G. **4.** g_i, frequency of y_i in bivariate table. **5.** general coefficient in tensor, as in $g_{ij}^k x^i y^i z_k$.

gd—Gudermannian. $e^u = \tan\left(\dfrac{\pi}{4} + \dfrac{1}{2}\,\mathrm{gd}\,u\right)$. If $\theta = \mathrm{gd}\,u$ then

$$\begin{aligned} \sin\theta &= \tanh u, & \cos\theta &= \operatorname{sech} u \\ \tan\theta &= \sinh u, & \cot\theta &= \operatorname{csch} u \\ \sec\theta &= \cosh u, & \csc\theta &= \coth u \end{aligned}$$

and corresponds to flipping the trigonometric hexagon on an axis perpendicular to cos-sec diagonal. Every vertex of the hexagon is the product of its adjacent vertices, (exhibiting 6 products, and 12 quotients, such as $\tan/\sec = \sin$) opposite vertices are reciprocals, and in each shaded sector the Pythagorean identity holds. These identities also hold for hyperbolic functions except that Pythagorean sum is at right (so that $\tanh^2 + \operatorname{sech}^2 = 1$).

—— grad—gradient of. Also written ∇.

H—**1.** general symbol for subgroup, as in G/H, particularly for normal (or self-conjugate) subgroup. **2.** Hessian, as $H(f) = \det\dfrac{\partial^2 f}{\partial x_i \partial x_j}$. **3.** $H_n(x)$, nth Hermite polynomial, $H_n(x) = e^{x^2} D^n e^{-x^2}$. **4.** $H(P_1, P_3; P_2, P_4)$ is the proposition that P_1 and P_3 separate harmonically P_2 and P_4. **5.** orthocenter of triangle where altitudes meet. **6.** $H(q_1, \cdots, q_n, t, p_1, \cdots, p_n)$ Hamiltonian function (in mathematical physics). **7.** mean curvature of surface, $H = EG - F^2$. **8.** (in mathematical astronomy) hour-angle. Also designated by t. **9.** Hilbert space, also $\mathfrak{H}$.

$\mathfrak{H}$—Hilbert space.

HCF—highest common factor.

MATHEMATICAL SYMBOLS AND ABBREVIATIONS (Continued)

HM—harmonic mean.

HP—(in elementary algebra) harmonic progression.

Hyp.—hypothesis.

h—**1.** (in interpolation theory), distance, between uniformly spaced ordinates. **2.** class interval, in x. **3.** increment of x. Also Δx. **4.** (as superscript) hours as in $8^h 15^m$. **5.** (terminal) hyperbolic, as in sinh, tanh^{-1}, etc. **6.** altitude ("height").

hav—haversine (of). hav $x = (\text{vers } x)/2 = (1 - \cos x)/2$.

I—**1.** general symbol for interval, and for definite integral. **2.** Roman numeral for "one." Write IV not IIII, IX not VIIII. **3.** $I(\ )$, imaginary part of, also designated by $\mathfrak{I}(\ )$, or Im$(\ )$. **4.** $I_n(z)$, the Bessel function "of imaginary argument," $I_n(z) = \sum_{m=0}^{\infty} \dfrac{(\frac{1}{2})z^{n+2m}}{m!\Gamma(n+m+1)}$. **5.** (in geometry) of triangle) in center where angle bisectors meet. **6.** sometimes used for the identity as an operation in a group.

$\mathfrak{I}$—(Black letter) imaginary part of. See I.

Im—imaginary part of. See I.

i—**1.** running index, as in a_i, $i = 1, \cdots, n$. **2.** one of the two imaginary square roots of -1. (In electrical engineering, when it is used for the current, j is used for this imaginary unit.)

i—i, j, k, unit vectors in a right-handed rectangular system. $i \times j = k$, $j \times k = i$, $k \times i = j$.

inf.—("infimum") greatest lower bound.

J—**1.** Jacobian as in $J\left(\dfrac{u,v,w}{x,y,z,}\right)$, also designated by $\partial(u,v,w)/\partial(x,y,z)$. **2.** $J_n(z)$, Bessel coefficient of order n. **3.** Jacobian curve. **4.** Jacobian group of points in a linear series of groups of points on an algebraic curve.

j—**1.** running index, with i. **2.** (sometimes in electrical engineering) $\sqrt{(-1)}$. See i.

j—a unit vector. See i.

K—**1.** specific curvature of surface. **2.** kernel of integral equation, as in $u(x) = f(x) + \lambda \int_a^b \tilde{K}(x,t)u(t)dt$. K_n, the nth iterated kernel is then defined recursively by $K_1 \equiv K$, $K_n(x,y) = \int_a^b K_{n-1}(x,t)K(t,y)dt$. Also designated by $K^{(n)}$. **3.** K, iK', periods for Jacobian elliptic functions. **4.** Symmedian (Lemoine) center of triangle. **5.** $K_n(z)$, the Bessel function ("second solution") $\lim\limits_{\nu \to n} \dfrac{(-1)^n}{2}\left[\dfrac{I_{-\nu}(z) - I_\nu(z)}{\nu - n}\right]$

k—**1.** proportionality factor for variation. Do not use $y \propto x$. **2.** running index, used with h. **3.** k,k', modulus and complementary modulus respectively of Jacobian elliptic functions. **4.** class interval, in y. **5.** increment in y. Also Δy.

k—a unit vector. See i.

kei, ker—Bessel functions defined as real for real z and satisfying, ker$(z) + i$ kei$(z) = K_0(z\sqrt{\ } \pm i)$.

L—**1.** general symbol for linear function. **2.** general symbol for linear system, or linear space. **3.** limit, as in $\underset{n \to \infty}{L}\ e^{-n} = 0$. See "lim." **4.** Roman nu-

MATHEMATICAL SYMBOLS AND ABBREVIATIONS (Continued)

meral for "fifty." **5.** length. Also designated by l. **6.** first fundamental differential quantity of second order for surfaces. **7.** Lexis ratio, $\sigma/\sqrt{pq/s}$, for sets of s objects each. **8.** $L_n(x)$, nth Laguerre polynomial, $L_n(x)e^{-x}n! = D^n(e^{-x}x^n)$.

LCD—lowest common denominator.

LCM—lowest (or least) common multiple.

l—**1.** running index. **2.** (in elementary algebra) last term (of arithmetic or geometric progression). **3.** $l = \cos\alpha$, directional cosine, (with x-axis). **4.** length. Also designated by L.

lat.—latitude.

li—logarithmic integral or integral logarithm function, $li(x) = \displaystyle\int_0^x du/\log u$.

lim—limit ( ), $\overline{\lim}$, least upper limit, $\underline{\lim}$, greatest lower limit.

ln—(Sometimes) natural logarithm of.

log—logarithm (of). In theoretical work, the natural base, e, is understood; in numerical computation with tables, the base 10 is understood unless otherwise specified. Some writers use "ln" for natural logarithm of. Where ambiguity is otherwise likely, indicate the base, thus $\log_b x$, $\log_{10} x$, $\log_b x$.

long—longitude.

M—**1.** Roman numeral, thousand. **2.** arithmetic mean. Also designated by superscript bar, as X, or by AM. **3.** centroid (in geometry of triangle) where medians meet. **4.** second fundamental differential quantity of second order for surfaces.

M.D.—mean deviation.

Md—median.

Mm—mid-mean, arithmetic mean of data in range Q_1 to Q_3.

Mo—mode.

m—**1.** general symbol for natural number, or integer, usually used with n. **2.** slope of line, dy/dx. **3.** $m = \cos\beta$, directional cosine (with y-axis). **4.** m_a, m_b, m_c, median lines, lengths of medians of triangle. **5.** (as subscript) meridian measurement. **6.** class of an algebraic plane curve (a Plücker number). **7.** (superscript) minutes, as in $10^d13^h5^m$. **8.** meters.

max—maximum (of).

meas—measure (of).

mi—miles.

min—**1.** minimum (of). **2.** minutes. **3.** mi. n. = nautical miles (at equator each minute of longitude corresponds to one nautical mile).

mod—**1.** modulus (of), as in $\mathrm{mod}(re^{i\theta}) = r$. **2.** modulo as in $7 \equiv -3(\mathrm{mod}\ 5)$.

N—**1.** third fundamental differential quantity of second order for surfaces. **2.** north. **3.** total frequency in a statistical distribution.

n—**1.** general symbol for natural number or integer. **2.** $n = \cos\gamma$, directional cosine (with z-axis). **3.** order or degree of plane algebraic curve (a Plücker number). **4.** (in elementary algebra) number of terms in finite progression. **5.** (sometimes) total frequency. See N. **6.** outward normal to surface, as in $\cos(\theta, n)$.

O—**1.** origin of coordinates. **2.** circumcenter of triangle where the perpendicular bisectors of the sides meet. **3.** of comparable order with, as $\Sigma_{n=0}^N n = O(N)^2$.

o—of inferior order to, as $\log n = o(n)$.

MATHEMATICAL SYMBOLS AND ABBREVIATIONS (Continued)

ord—order.

P—**1.** general symbol for polynomial, in particular the interpolational polynomial. **2.** product moment. Also expressed by p. **3.** general symbol for point. The common notation indicating the coordinate system used as $P(x,y,z)$, $P(r,\theta,\varphi)$, etc., is not recommended. **4.** general probability distribution function, in particular any one of Pearson's standard types, or Poisson's forms. **5.** $P_n(x)$, Legendre polynomial, $2^n n! P_n(x) = D^n(x^2 - 1)^n$. **6.** total force due to pressure. **7.** function, as in $Pdx + Qdy$, and in $y' + P(x)y = Q(x)$. **8.** $P_{n,r}$ or $_nP_r$, or $P(n,r)$, number of permutations of n distinct things taken r at a time (without repetitions), $n!/(n - r)!$. **9.** general potential due to finite number of particles. In Newtonian case $P = \Sigma_i m_i/r_i$. See U and W. **10.** horizontal parallax. **11.** north celestial pole.

PE—probable error. See $\pm$.

$P(E)$—Probability of E.

$P(E \wedge F)$—Probability of both E and F.

$P(E \backslash F)$—Probability of E, given F.

$P(E \veebar F)$—Probability of E or F, but not both.

$P(E \vee F)$—Probability of E or F or both.

Post.—postulate.

Prob.—**1.** problem. **2.** probability.

Prop.—proposition.

PS—power series.

Pt.—point.

$\wp$—Weierstrassian elliptic function.

p—**1.** general symbol for prime number. **2.** semi-latus rectum. **3.** probability ratio. **4.** genus (or deficiency) of a plane algebraic curve (a Plücker number). **5.** perpendicular distance from origin to given line or plane. **6.** p_n, numerator of nth convergent of continued fraction $a_0 + \dfrac{1}{a_1 +}\dfrac{1}{a_2 +}$ $\cdots$ $(p_{-1} = 0,\ p_0 = 1)$, $p_1 = a_0$, $p_{n+1} = a_n p_n + p_{n-1}$. **7.** p_{12}, p_{13}, p_{14}, p_{23}, p_{24}, p_{34}, line coordinates (point system). **8.** sometimes "per," as in "rpm," revolutions per minute. This use is not recommended. **9.** perimeter. Use s for semiperimeter. **10.** $p(n)$, total number of partitions of n. **11.** p_i, impulse component. **12.** the genus of an orientable surface.

p—page. pp—pages.

pos.—positive.

Q—**1.** general symbol for quadratic form or quadratic manifold. **2.** Q_1, Q_3 first and third quartile marks. (Q_2 is the median, Md.) **3.** function, as in $Pdx + Qdy$, and in $y' + P(x)y = Q(x)$. **4.** $Q(P_1, P_2, P_3; P_4, P_5, P_6)$, quadrangular set of six points.

Q—(underlined) the set of rational numbers.

Q^+—(underlined) the set of positive rational numbers.

QD—quartile deviation.

Q.E.D.—("Quod erat demonstrandum") which was to be proved.

Q.E.F.—("Quod erat faciendum") which was to be constructed.

q—**1.** complementary probability, $q = 1 - p$. **2.** q_n, denominator of nth convergent of continued fraction, $a_0 + \dfrac{1}{a_1 +}\ \dfrac{1}{a_2 +}$ $\cdots$ $(q_0 = 0)$, $q_1 = 1$, $q_{n+1} = a_n q_n + q_{n-1}$. **3.** q_{12}, q_{13}, q_{14}, q_{23}, q_{24}, q_{34}, line coordinates (plane sys-

MATHEMATICAL SYMBOLS AND ABBREVIATIONS (Continued)

tem).   **4.** q_1, q_2, quartile distances from the median.   **5.** q_i, force component.
6. the number of cross-caps on a non-orientable surface.

R—**1.** general symbol for remainder. $R_n(x)$, remainder after n terms in power-series in x.   **2.** radius, in particular circumradius of triangle.   **3.** real part of.   Also indicated by **IR** (Black letter), and Re.   **4.** general symbol for range of variable, as in $\int_{(R)}$.

$\underline{R}$—(underlined) the set of real numbers.

$\underline{R}^+$—(underlined) the set of positive real numbers.

IR—(Black letter) real value of.   See R.

R. A.—right ascension.   Also designated by α.

R_m^*—An s-dimensional Betti number modulo m (m prime).

R_0^*—An s-dimensional Betti number relative to the group of integers.

Re—real value of.   See R.

RMS—root-mean-square. $\sqrt{(\Sigma_{i=1}^n x^2/n)}$.

r—**1.** general running index, as in rth term.   **2.** radius (see R), in particular in radius of triangle.   **3.** coefficient of linear correlation, correlation coefficient.   **4.** (in elementary algebra) common ratio between successive terms in a geometric progression.   **5.** distance, in polar and in spherical coordinates; projected distances in cylindrical coordinates.   **6.** (sometimes) revolutions, as in $r.p.m.$ (revolutions per minute).   **7.** (sometimes) (superscript) radians, as in $2\pi^{(r)}$.   (This usage is not recommended.)   **8.** the number of boundary curves on a surface.

rad—**1.** radius.   **2.** radians.   Where no units are indicated angles are measured in radians, sin 30 means "sine of 30 radians," not sin 30°.   Do not write sin a^r or sin $a^{(r)}$ for sin a (where a is measured in radians), since superscript r is sometimes interpreted as "revolutions."

rot—rotation or curl of vector.   Also designated by $\nabla \times$ (nabla and cross).

S—**1.** general symbol for space, as S_n, space of n dimension.   See L.   **2.** general symbol for sum, as in S_n, sum of first n terms of given sequence or series.   See s.   **3.** south.   **4.** standard error of estimate.   **5.** radius of spherical curvature of curve.   **6.** a set (any collection of distinguishable objects).

∂S—Boundary of a set S.

Si—1st sine-integral function $Si(x) = \int_0^x (\sin u/u)du$.   See si.

S.T.—sidereal time.

s—**1.** general running index.   Used with r.   **2.** general symbol for sum, as in s_n sum of first n terms of sequence or series.   See S.   **3.** (in elementary algebra), sum of arithmetic or of geometric progression.   **4.** $s_k(n)$, sum of kth powers of first n natural numbers.   **5.** s_k, sum of the kth powers of the roots of an algebraic equation.   **6.** arc length.   **7.** slant height.   **8.** (usually as superscript) seconds.   **9.** semi-interquartile range.   **10.** semi-perimeter of triangle, $s = (a + b + c)/2$.   **11.** (sometimes) number of individuals in sample.   **12.** root-mean-square deviation about arbitrarily assumed origin, (in "short method").

sec—secant (of).   Reciprocal of cosine.

$\sec^{-1}$—inverse secant (of).   Also designated by arc sec.

sech—hyperbolic secant (of).   Do not use Sec or $\mathfrak{Sec}$ (in German letters).

sech^{-1}—inverse hyperbolic secant of.   Also written as arg sech.

MATHEMATICAL SYMBOLS AND ABBREVIATIONS (Continued)

si—2nd sine-integral function, $\beta_i(x) = \int_{\infty}^{x} (\sin u/u)du$. See Si.

sgn—(signum) sign (of), more generally for z complex, sign $z = z/|z|$.

Use $\sigma_1 = \begin{pmatrix} + & + \\ - & - \end{pmatrix}$ for the signum of the sine (in the corresponding quadrant).

Use $\sigma_2 = \begin{pmatrix} - & + \\ - & + \end{pmatrix}$ for the signum of the cosine.

and $\sigma_3 = \begin{pmatrix} - & + \\ + & - \end{pmatrix}$ for the signum of the tangent.

Thus $d(\text{arc sin } x)/dx = \sigma_2/\sqrt{1 - x^2}$;
$d(\text{arc cos } x)/dx = -\sigma_1/\sqrt{1 - x^2}$
and $\sigma_1/\sigma_2 = \sigma_1\sigma_2 = \sigma_3$.

sin—sine (of). Do not use Sin. In general triangle $\sin A = a/d$ where d is circumdiameter. Identity $d = a/\sin A = b/\sin B = c/\sin C$ is the "law of sines."

$\sin^{-1}$—inverse sine (of). Also designated arc sin.

sinh—hyperbolic sine (of).

$\sinh^{-1}$—inverse hyperbolic sine of—also written as arg sinh.

sk—skewness of frequency distribution.

sn—(Jacobian elliptic function), sine amplitude.

sq—square.

sup—(supremum) least upper bound. Sometimes designated by L.U.B., or l.u.b.

T—**1.** total time, (as in time of flight of projectile). **2.** clock time. **3.** general symbol for transformation, T^n, nth iterate of T. **4.** tons. **5.** (in logic), true or truth. **6.** absolute temperature.

Th—theorem.

t—**1.** general variable or parameter. **2.** time. (In navigation) use 4 digits 0230 for 2:30 a.m., and 1430 for 2:30 p.m. See τ. See "dot accent." **3.** ordinary temperature. See T, τ, θ.

tan—tangent (of).

$\tan^{-1}$—inverse tangent (of). Also designated by arc tan.

tanh—hyperbolic tangent (of). Do not use Tan or $\mathfrak{Tan}$ (in German letters).

$\tanh^{-1}$—inverse hyperbolic tangent (of). Do not use arc tanh. Also written as arg tanh.

T_0-space—A topological space such that for distinct x and y there is either a neighborhood of x not containing y or a neighborhood of y not containing x.

T_1-space—A topological space such that for distinct x and y there is a neighborhood of x not containing y.

T_2-space—A Hausdorff topological space.

T_3-space—A T_2-space which is regular.

T_4-space—A T_2-space which is normal.

U-general (line surface or volume) potential. In Newtonian case, $U = \int_{(L)} \frac{\mu dL}{r}$, or $\int_{(S)} \frac{\mu dS}{r}$, or $\int_{(V)} \frac{\mu dV}{r}$. See P and W.

u—**1.** general variable, especially dependent variable or real part thereof. See w. **2.** u_n, Lucas' function $u_n = (\alpha^n - \beta^n)/(\alpha - \beta)$, α, β, roots of given quadratic.

V—**1.** Roman numeral, five. **2.** (in Euler's polyhedral formula) number of

MATHEMATICAL SYMBOLS AND ABBREVIATIONS (Continued)

vertices. **3.** general harmonic function. **4.** volume. **5.** coefficient of variation.

v—(linear) velocity.

v—**1.** general variable, especial dependent variable, used with u, or coefficient of pure imaginary part thereof. See w. **2.** v_n, Lucas' function $\alpha^n + \beta^n$, α, β, roots of given quadratic. See u_n. **3.** speed.

vers—versed sine or versine.

W—**1.** west. **2.** general potential of double layer. In Newtonian case,

$$W = \int_{(S)} v \frac{\partial}{\partial n}\left(\frac{1}{r}\right) dS, = -\int_{(S)} \frac{v}{r^2} \cos (r,n)\, dS. \text{ See } P \text{ and } U.$$ **3.** Wronskian,

$$W = \begin{vmatrix} y_1 \, y_1{}' & \cdots & y_1{}^{(n-1)} \\ \cdots & \cdots & \cdots \\ y_n \, y_n{}' & \cdots & y_n{}^{(n-1)} \end{vmatrix}.$$

4. total weight. Also designated by Wt. **5.** work (or energy). Also designated by Wk.

Wt.—weight. See W.

w—**1.** general symbol for variable, particularly dependent variable. Used with u and v as in $J\left(\dfrac{u,v,w}{x,y,z}\right)$, etc. **2.** dependent complex variable, $w = u + iv$, or $w(z) = u(x,y) + iv(x,y)$ where $z = x + iy$, x,y,u,v, real.

X—**1.** Roman numeral, ten; as in XCIII, etc. **2.** X_i, original numerical data for x-variates, (previous to change of origin or scale). **3.** general symbol for variable point, particularly on x-axis. **4.** function, as in $Xdx + Ydy + Zdz$ or $\dfrac{dx}{X} = \dfrac{dy}{Y} = \dfrac{dz}{Z}$.

x—**1.** general symbol for independent variable or unknown. **2.** first rectangular coordinate. In space a right-handed coordinate system such as indicated by

$$\begin{matrix} Z \\ | \\ \diagup O \text{—} Y \\ X \diagup \end{matrix} \quad \text{or} \quad \begin{matrix} Y \\ | \\ \diagup O \text{—} X \\ Z \diagup \end{matrix} \text{ is recommended. The former with } OZ$$

directed to the zenith is more common. **3.** real part of independent complex variable $z = x + iy$.

Y—**1.** Y_i, original numerical data for y-variates (previous to change of origin or scale). **2.** function as in $Xdx + Ydy + Zdz$, or $\dfrac{dx}{X} = \dfrac{dy}{Y} = \dfrac{dz}{Z}$.

y—**1.** general symbol for dependent (real) variable. **2.** general symbol for second independent variable, r unknown. **3.** second rectangular coordinate. See x. **4.** pure imaginary coefficient, in independent complex variable, $z = x + iy$.

Z—zenith.

$\underline{Z}$—(underlined) the set of integers.

$\underline{Z}^+$—(underlined) the set of positive integers.

Z.T.—zone time.

z—**1.** independent complex variable, $z = x + iy$. **2.** general symbol for third independent variable or unknown. **3.** third rectangular coordinate. See x. **4.** axial coordinate in cylindrical coordinates (r, θ, z). **5.** zenith distance, $(90^0 - h)$. **6.** Fisher's z statistic.

MATHEMATICAL SYMBOLS AND ABBREVIATIONS (Continued)

Selected Symbols Used in Financial and Actuarial Theory

α—net premium in first policy year.

β—net premium in each policy year after the first.

δ—force of interest (and of discount) $e^\delta = 1 + i$.

ω—terminal recorded age in mortality table, "limiting" age.

A_x—commutation symbol, present value of net single premium for whole life policy on (x), $= M_x/D_x$.

$a_{\overline{n}|i}$—present value of annuity for unit periodic payment, $= (1 - v^n)/i$.

$a_{\overline{n}|i}^{(p)}$—present value of an annuity of 1 per annum at interest rate i, payable p times a year (in installments of $1/p$ each).

a_x—commutation symbol, present value of (ordinary) whole life annuity on (x) of unit annual payment.

$a_x^{(m)}$—present value of whole life annuity on (x), of unit annual payment, payable m times a year.

$n|a_x$—present value of whole life annuity, on (x), deferred n years for unit annual payment.

$a_{x\overline{n}|}$—present value of temporary life annuity, on (x), for n years, for unit annual payment.

$a_{\infty i}$—present value of perpetuity at rate of interest, i.

$a_{\infty i}$—present value of perpetuity due at rate of interest, i.

a_x—commutation symbol present value of whole life annuity due, on (x), of unit annual payment.

$a_{\overline{n}|i}$—present value of an annuity due, for unit periodic payments at interest rate i.

B—book value.

B_k—book value, after k years.

C—**1.** original cost. **2.** capitalized cost.

C_x—commutation symbol, $= v^{x+1}d_x$.

c_x—natural premium at age x, $= C_x/D_x$.

D—total simple discount.

D_b—total bank discount.

D_c—cash discount, where for example, "terms 4/10, 2/30, n/90" designates 4% discount for payment within 10 days, 2% thereafter but within 30 days, payable net in 90 days.

D_t—trade discount.

D_x—commutation symbol, $= v^x l_x$.

d—rate of simple discount, $= 1 - v = (1 + i)^{-1} = i/(1 + i)$.

d_x—number dying between ages x and $x + 1$, according to mortality table (for 100,000 alive at age 10).

E—present value of expectation.

$_nE_x$—present value of an n-year pure endowment to (x), $= v^n l_{x+n}/l_x$.

e_x—curtate expectation of life for (x), $= (l_x + \cdots + l_\omega)/l_x$.

$\overset{o}{e}_x$—complete expectation of life, for (x), $= e_x + \frac{1}{2}$.

F—**1.** net-cost-rate factor. **2.** face value of bond.

I—total interest (ordinary simple).

I'—total interest (exact, simple).

i—rate of interest (effective).

MATHEMATICAL SYMBOLS AND ABBREVIATIONS (Continued)

$j_{(p)}$—nominal rate of interest convertible p times a year corresponding to effective annual rate i, $= p[(1 + i)^{1/p} - 1]$.

k_x—valuation symbol, $= C_x/D_{x+1}$.

$_nk_x$—valuation symbol, $= (M_x - M_{x+n})/D_{x+n}$, $[_1k_x = k_x]$, accumulated cost of insurance.

L—**1.** list price (for trade discount). **2.** salvage value.

l_x—number living at age x according to mortality table.

N_x—("open bar N"), commutation symbol, $= D_x + D_{x+1} + \cdots + D\omega$.

n—number of conversion periods (for compound interest).

P—principal.

P_b—bank proceeds.

P_x—net annual premium for ordinary whole life policy, on (x), for unit annual payment $= A_x/(1 + a_x)$.

$_rP_x$—net annual premium for r-payment life policy, $= M_x/(\mathsf{N}_x - \mathsf{N}_{x+r})$.

p—**1.** probability of success. **2.** interest period/payment interval.

p_x—probability of living for another year for a person of age x (according to mortality table).

$_np_x$—probability that a person aged x will live n years, $= l_{x+n}/l_x$.

p_{xy}—the probability that (x) and (y) will survive jointly for one year.

$_np_{xy}$—the probability that (x) and (y) will survive jointly for n years.

q—probability of failure, $= 1 - p$.

q_x—probability of dying within a year for a person of age x (according to mortality table).

$|_nq_x$—probability that (x) will die within n years.

$_n|q_x$—the probability that (x) will die between ages $x + n$ and $x + n + 1$.

R—**1.** periodic payment or "rent." **2.** replacement cost. **3.** repair charge (annual).

S—amount.

S—**1.** scrap value. **2.** amount of sinking fund. **3.** subscription price. **4.** amount (at simple interest).

s—amount (at compound interest) for unit principal $= (1 + i)^n$.

$s_{\overline{n}|i}$—amount of annuity for unit periodic payment, $= [(1 + i)^n - 1]/i$.

$s_{\infty i}$—amount of perpetuity at interest rate i.

s_∞—amount of perpetuity due.

$s_{\overline{n}|i}$—amount of an annuity due, for unit periodic payments.

$s_{\overline{n}|i}^{(p)}$—amount at end of n years of annuity of 1 per annum at interest rate i, payable p times a year (in installments of $1/p$ each).

u_x—valuation symbol, $= D_x/D_{x+1}$.

$_nu_x$—valuation symbol, $(\mathsf{N}_x - \mathsf{N}_{x+n})/D_{x+n}$, $[_1u_x = u_x]$, accumulated value of individual survivors payments.

V—purchase price (of bond).

$_tV_x$—terminal reserve of tth policy year on policy on (x) of unit annual payment.

v—present value (at compound interest) for unit principal, $= (1 + i)^{-1}$.

W—wearing value, $=$ original cost minus scrap value.

x—age of insured (to nearest year).

(x)—a person aged x (for use with mortality table).

$x]$—where $[x] + t$ indicates a life, now aged $x + t$, who was accepted for insurance t years ago at age x.

GREEK ALPHABET

Greek letter	Greek name	English equivalent	Greek letter	Greek name	English equivalent
A α	Alpha	a	N ν	Nu	n
B β	Beta	b	Ξ ξ	Xi	x
Γ γ	Gamma	g	O o	Omicron	ŏ
Δ δ	Delta	d	Π π	Pi	p
E ε	Epsilon	ĕ	P ρ	Rho	r
Z ζ	Zeta	z	Σ σ s	Sigma	s
H η	Eta	ē	T τ	Tau	t
Θ θ ϑ	Theta	th	Υ υ	Upsilon	u
I ι	Iota	i	Φ φ φ	Phi	ph
K κ	Kappa	k	X χ	Chi	ch
Λ λ	Lambda	l	Ψ ψ	Psi	ps
M μ	Mu	m	Ω ω	Omega	ō

INDEX

B

C

F

G

H

I

N

T

U